Modern refrigeration and air conditioning

Modern refrigeration and air conditioning

theory, practice of refrigeration and air conditioning systems

by

ANDREW D. ALTHOUSE, B.S. (M.E.), M.A.

Technical-Vocational Education Consultant
Life Member, American Society of
Heating, Refrigerating, and Air-Conditioning Engineers

CARL H. TURNQUIST, B.S., (M.E.), M.A.

Director of Vocational Education
Detroit, Michigan Public Schools
Associate Member, American Society of
Heating, Refrigerating, and Air-Conditioning Engineers
Member, Refrigeration Service Engineers Society

ALFRED F. BRACCIANO, B.S., M.Ed., Ed. Sp.

Director of Technical and Vocational Education
Warren, Michigan Consolidated Schools
Member, Refrigeration Service Engineers Society

Homewood, Illinois
THE GOODHEART-WILLCOX COMPANY, INC.
Publishers

4

INTRODUCTION

MODERN REFRIGERATION and AIR CONDITIONING covers the practical application of refrigeration in all of its branches -- Domestic, Commercial, Air Conditioning, Heat Pumps, Automotive Air Conditioners, Thermoelectric, Special Devices and Applications.

MODERN REFRIGERATION and AIR CONDITIONING teaches the fundamental principles of refrigeration and air conditioning. It acquaints the serviceman with the function of various mechanisms and their components. It provides the foundation on which a sound, thorough knowledge of refrigeration and air conditioning is based.

Beginners and apprentices will find MODERN REFRIGERATION and AIR CONDITIONING a real aid to getting started and pursuing a pleasant and profitable career. Experienced servicemen will find it a valuable guide and reference.

Andrew D. Althouse

Carl H. Turnquist

Alfred F. Bracciano

ACKNOWLEDGMENTS

The production of a book of this nature would not be possible without the cooperation of the Refrigeration and Air Conditioning Industry. In preparing the manuscript for MODERN REFRIGERATION and AIR CONDITIONING, the industry has been most cooperative. The authors acknowledge the cooperation of these companies with great appreciation:

A C and R Components, Inc., Abrax Instrument Corp., Acme Electric Corp., Aeroquip Corp., Aerovox Corp., Air Filter Corp., Airo Supply Co., Inc., Airserco Mfg. Co., Airtemp Div. of Chrysler Corp., Alco Valve Co., Allied Chemical Corp. General Chemical Div., Allied Chemical Corp. Industrial Chemicals Div., Allin Mfg., Inc., Alnor Instrument Co. Illinois Testing Laboratories, Inc., Amana Refrigeration, Inc. Subsidiary of Raytheon Co., American Automatic Ice Machine Co., American Brass Co., American Motors Corp., American Society of Heating, Refrigerating and Air Conditioning Engineers, Inc. (ASHRAE), American Standard Air Conditioning Div. of American Radiator and Standard Sanitary Corp., American-Standard Controls Div., Amprobe Instrument Div. Soss Mfg. Co., Anemostat Products Div., Ansul Co., Armstrong Cork Co., Arrow Louver and Damper Corp., Automatic Switch Co., Bacharach Industrial Instrument Co. Sub. of American Bosch Arma Corp., Bally Case and Cooler, Inc., Baltimore Aircoil Co., Inc., Bell and Gossett ITT, Bendix Corp. Friez Instrument Div., Bernzomatic Corp., Bohn Aluminum and Brass Co., Bristol Co., Buick Motor Div. General Motors Corp., Cadillac Motor Car Div. General Motors Corp., Carrier Air Conditioning Co., Century Electric Co., Chicago Valve Plate and Seal Co., Chrysler Corp., Cleveland Sales Co., Cleveland Twist Drill Co., Climatic Air Sales, Inc., Connor Engineering Corp., Continental Air Filters, Inc., Controls Co. of America, Controls and Instruments Div. ITT, Copeland Refrigeration Corp., Cutler-Hammer, Inc., Danfoss Inc., DoALL Co., Dodge Div. Chrysler Corp., Dole Refrigerating Co., Dunham-Bush Inc., E. I. duPont de Nemours and Co., Inc., Duro Metal Products Co., F. W. Dwyer Mfg. Co., Inc., Ebco Mfg. Co., Edison Electric Institute, Electro-Air Cleaner Co., Inc., Electromode Div. of Friden Inc., Electronics Corp. of America, Emerson Electric Co., Esco Cabinet Co., Essex Wire Corp., Excelsior Steel Furnace Co., Fabcel Div. of Fabreeka Products Co., Farr Co., Fedders Corp., Filtrine Mfg. Co., Flexonics Div. of Calumet and Hecla, Inc., Flo-Con Div. of Refrigerating Specialties Co., Ford Motor Co., Franklin Appliance Div. of Studebaker Corp., Frigidaire Div. of General Motors Corp., Frigiking Co. Div. of Cummins Engine Co., Inc., Fulton Cryogenics, Inc., Fusite Corp., G and L Adhesives Corp., Gates Rubber Co., General Electric Co., General Radio Co., Gibson Refrigerator Sales Hupp Corp., Greenfield Tap and Die Corp., Halstead and Mitchell Co., Handy and Harman, Hansen Mfg. Co., Harrison Radiator Div. of General Motors Corp., H-B Instrument Co., Henry Valve Co., Honeywell, Hotpoint Div. of General Electric Co., Howe Corp., Imperial-Eastman Corp., International Harvester Co., Jarrow Products, Inc., Johnson Service Co., Johnston Refrigeration Service, Joseph Kaye and Co., Inc., Kaiser Aluminum and Chemical Corp., Kelvinator Div. of American Motors Corp., Kent-Moore Corp., Kerotest Mfg. Co., Koch Refrigerators, Inc., Kold Hold Div. of Tranter Mfg., Inc., Kramer Trenton Co., Lehigh Mfg. Co., Lennox Industries Inc., Linde Div. of Union Carbide Corp., Madden Brass Products Co., Div. of Robinair Mfg. Corp., Marsh Instrument Co., Marshalltown Mfg., Inc., Materials Electronic Products Corp., Maurey Mfg. Corp., Maxitrol Co., Mechanical Refrigeration Enterprises, Mine Safety Appliances Co., Minnesota Mining and Mfg. Co. Electrical Products Div., John E. Mitchell Co., Monarch Mfg. Works, Inc., Montgomery Ward and Co., Mueller Brass Co., Mueller Climatrol Div. of Worthington Air Conditioning Co., McCall Refrigerator Corp., McCord Corp., McCray Corp., McDonnell and Miller, Inc., McIntire Co. Sub. of Superior Valve and Fittings Co., McQuay Inc., National Cooler Corp., National Cylinder Gas Div. of Chemetron Corp., Nicholson File Co., Norge Div. of Borg-Warner Corp., Owens-Corning Fiberglas Corp., Packless Metal Hose Co., Paragon Electric Co., Inc., Peerless of America, Inc., Penn Controls Inc., Pennsalt Chemicals Corp., Philco Corp. Sub. of Ford Motor Co., Polymer Corp., Pontiac Motor Div. of General Motors Corp., Ranco Inc., Recold Div. of Borg-Warner Corp., Refrigerating Specialties Co., Refrigeration Engineering Inc., Refrigeration Service Engineers Society (RSES), Remington Air Conditioning Div. of Singer Co., Republic Steel Corp., Resistoflex Corp., Ridge Tool Co., Robertshaw Controls Co. Milford Div., Robinair Mfg. Corp., Ross-Temp Inc., Rotary Seal Div. of Muskegon Piston Ring Co., Rubatex Corp., Schaefer Brush Mfg. Co., Inc., Scotsman-Queen Products Div. of King-Seeley Thermos Co., Scovill Schrader Div. of Automotive Products, Sears, Roebuck and Co., Simpson Electric Co., Snap-On Tools Corp., Sporlan Valve Co., Standard Refrigeration Co., Stevens Appliance Truck Co., Stewart-Warner Corp. Heating and Air Conditioning Div., Sunstrand Hydraulic Div. of Sunstrand Corp., Superior Valve and Fittings Co., Sweden Freezer Mfg. Co., Taylor Instrument Companies, Tecumseh Products Co., Temprite Products Corp., Tenney Engineering Inc., Texas Instruments Inc., Thermal Industries of Florida, Inc., Therm-O-Disc, Inc., Tork Time Controls Inc., Torrington Mfg. Co., Tubing Appliance Co., Inc., Turbo Refrigerating Co., H. W. Tuttle and Co., Tyler Refrigeration Div. of Clark Equipment Co., United States Air Conditioning Corp., Wabash Corp., Wagner Electric Corp., Warren Co., Inc., Watsco, Inc., Webster Electric Co., Westinghouse Electric Corp. Air Conditioning-Sturtevant Div., Whirlpool Corp., White-Rodgers Div. of Emerson Electric, Williamson Co., Wilson Refrigeration, Inc., York Corp Sub. of Borg-Warner Corp.

CONTENTS

Chapter 1

FUNDAMENTALS OF REFRIGERATION

In studying refrigeration, it is important to master the fundamental principles explained in this chapter.

Much of this basic material will be a review of physics and chemistry for those who have studied these subjects. In addition, however, some engineering principles and formulas have been included. The principles and formulas have been simplified, and are introduced by practical applications.

1-1 Development of Refrigeration

Refrigeration, the industry of preserving food by cold, first became of commercial importance during the 18th century. Ice which formed on the surface of lakes and ponds was cut and stored in insulated storerooms to be used during the summer. This practice was expanded by shipping ice from the colder climates to the hotter zones. The use of natural ice made necessary the building of insulated containers or iceboxes for use in stores, restaurants, homes, etc. These first appeared on a large scale during the 19th century.

Ice was first made artificially about 1820 on an experimental basis, but it was not until 1834 that artificial ice manufacturing was perfected. Jacob Perkins, an American engineer, was the inventor of the apparatus used, which was the forerunner of our modern compression systems. In 1855 a German engineer produced the first absorption type of refrigerating mechanism, although Michael Faraday discovered the principles of absorption type refrigeration in 1824.

The production of artificial ice made very little progress until shortly after 1890. During 1890 a shortage of natural ice gave impetus to the mechanical ice-making industry. Since that time, the growth of mechanical refrigeration in the United States has been phenomenal.

Mechanical domestic refrigeration first made its appearance about 1910. J. M. Larsen produced a manually operated household machine in 1913. It was not until 1918 that the first automatic refrigerator was made available on the American market (Kelvinator). The Kelvinator Company sold its first machine in 1918 and sold a total of sixty-seven machines that year. Between 1918 and 1920 two hundred units were sold.

The General Electric Monitor Top appeared in 1926 after eleven years of experimenting. The Monitor Top was the first of the "sealed" or hermetic automatic refrigeration units.

Beginning with 1920, domestic refrigeration became one of our important industries. The Electrolux, which was an automatic domestic absorption unit, appeared on the American market in 1927. The use of automatic refrigeration units for comfort cooling, air conditioning, appeared on the market in 1927.

By 1940 practically all domestic units were of the hermetic type, while commercially, units of thousands of tons of refrigeration capacity were successfully made and used.

The preservation of food for extended periods of time by fast freezing was developed about 1923. This was the origin of the modern frozen foods industry.

The use of mechanical refrigerating mechanisms in connection with home and building heating plants during the 1920's, was the beginning of our modern air conditioning business.

From a very small and slow start in the 1930's, air conditioning of automobiles has grown to over 1,600,000 units a year.

1-2 Scope of Mechanical Refrigeration

Mechanical refrigeration is used for domestic refrigeration, commercial refrigeration, air conditioning (comfort cooling), dehumidifying, food freezing, cooling in manufacturing processes, and numerous other applications.

1-3 How a Mechanical Refrigerator Works

In order to understand the operation of the mechanical refrigerator, it is important to understand the physical and thermal properties of mechanisms and substances used to extract heat. A brief study of the elementary physics involved is provided in this chapter, in order that all explanations may be made clear.

The operation of a modern mechanical refrigerator (removing heat from inside the refrigerator) might be compared to removing water from inside a leaking canoe. In removing water from the canoe a sponge is used to sop up the water. The sponge is held over the side, squeezed, and the water is deposited overboard. The operation may be repeated as often as is necessary. In this operation water is transferred from inside the canoe back into the lake.

In a refrigerator heat is transferred instead of water. Heat leaks into a refrigerator through the insulation and enters when the door is opened. Inside the refrigerator heat is absorbed, "sopped up," by the liquid refrigerant in the cooling unit (evaporator) as indicated in Fig. 1-1. The refrigerant in absorbing heat changes from a liquid to a gas. After the refrigerant has absorbed heat and turned to a gas, it is pumped outside the refrigerator. It is then compressed and the heat is "squeezed" out by being subjected to high pressure and cooled in a condenser. The refrigerant continues to flow through the refrigerating cycle absorbing heat inside the refrigerator and releasing it outside the refrigerator until the desired refrigerating temperature is reached and the action stops. Heat is not destroyed to make the refrigerator cold, it is simply removed from the refrigerated space and released outside the cabinet.

The paragraphs in this chapter which follow will give you the foundation needed to understand and describe the heat removal operation in a more technical way.

In arithmetic problems which follow these basic signs are used:

+   means plus or add

-     means minus or subtract

x   means multiply or times

( )   means brackets, do the arithmetic inside the brackets first.

=   means equals

$(4)^2$ means the number inside of the brackets is multiplied by itself the number of times indicated (squared). The indicator number is called the exponent. Example - 4^2 means 4 x 4 = 16.

Service managers of refrigerator companies prefer service and installation mechanics who are well grounded in the essential principles of physics as it pertains to refrigeration.

1-4 Heat and Heat Flow

Heat is molecular motion. All substances are made up of tiny molecules which are in a state of rapid motion. As the temperature of a substance is increased the motion increases and as the temperature decreases, the molecular motion decreases.

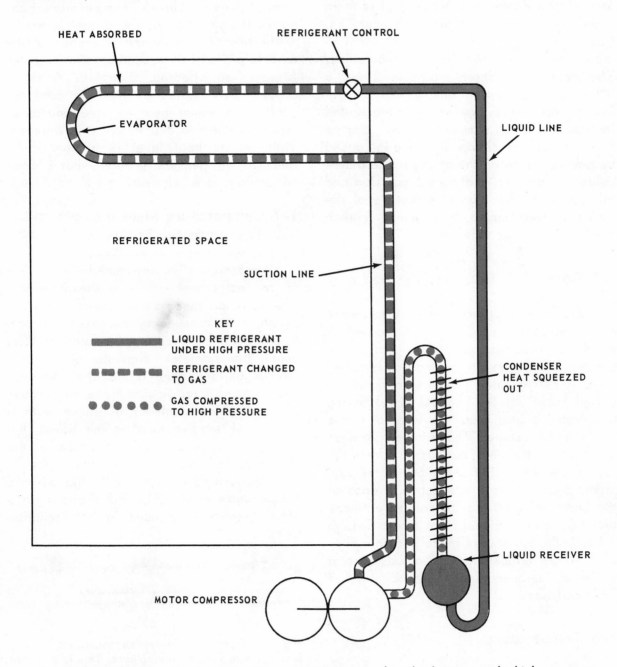

HEAT ABSORBED **REFRIGERANT CONTROL**

EVAPORATOR

LIQUID LINE

REFRIGERATED SPACE

SUCTION LINE

KEY

LIQUID REFRIGERANT UNDER HIGH PRESSURE

REFRIGERANT CHANGED TO GAS

GAS COMPRESSED TO HIGH PRESSURE

CONDENSER HEAT SQUEEZED OUT

LIQUID RECEIVER

MOTOR COMPRESSOR

Fig. 1-1. An elementary mechanical refrigerator. In operation liquid refrigerant under high pressure (solid red) flows from the liquid receiver to the refrigerant control valve and into the evaporator coil. Here the pressure is greatly reduced and the liquid refrigerant boils and absorbs heat from the evaporator coil. The refrigerant is now a gas (broken red) and it is drawn back to the compressor and compressed to a high pressure (red dots). Its temperature is greatly increased and in the condensor the heat is transferred to the surrounding air and the refrigerant is cooled and becomes a liquid again. It flows back into the liquid receiver from which its cooling cycle is repeated.

If all heat is extracted (absolute zero) from a substance, the molecular motion will cease completely.

Heat always flows from a warm substance to a cooler substance; that is from higher temperatures to lower temperatures. Faster moving molecules impart some of their energy to slower moving molecules. Therefore, the faster molecule slows a little and the slower one moves a little faster. Sometimes, however, the molecules instead of moving slower or faster, change their shape. The change in shape is caused by one or more of the atoms in the molecules shifting to a different position and this shift in the atomic structure of the molecule may cause it to change from a gas to a liquid, or vice versa.

1-5 Cold

Cold is a relative term used to denote a low temperature. Cold is not something which is produced, but rather heat is extracted and the resulting condition is called cold. A refrigerator produces a condition called "cold" by the process of extracting or removing heat from the interior of the refrigerator cabinet. The refrigerator does not destroy the heat, but rather pumps the heat from the inside of the box to the outside. Heat and cold are opposite ends of the same thing. It may be pointed out here that heat cannot travel from a cold body to a hot body, but always travels from a body of a higher temperature to a substance at a lower temperature. (Second law of Thermodynamics.)

1-6 Temperature

Temperature may be defined as the heat intensity or heat level of a substance. Temperature alone does not give the amount of heat in a substance, but it is an indication of the degree of warmth, or how hot the body is.

The molecular theory of heat states that temperature is an indication of the speed of motion of the molecule. It is important not to use the words heat and temperature carelessly. Temperature measures the speed of motion of one molecule, while heat is the speed of motion of the molecule PLUS the number of molecules (weight) so affected. Example: A small copper dish heated to 1340 F. does not contain as much heat as five pounds of copper heated to 300 F. but it is warmer. That is, its heat level is higher or its intensity of heat is greater, but it does not contain as much heat.

1-7 Temperature Measurement and Thermometer Scales

Temperature is measured by the use of an instrument called a thermometer. The common thermometer measures temperature by measuring the expansion of a liquid such as mercury or alcohol. The usual thermometer consists of a glass tube of uniform bore, a bulb at the bottom, and a quantity of liquid. Since glass does not expand or contract as much with a change of temperature as the liquid, the liquid will rise and fall in the tube, as the temperature changes. The glass tube is then calibrated or marked to the desired temperature scale. Fig. 1-2 shows a glass stem thermometer used in refrigeration work.

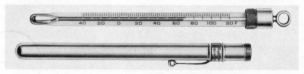

Fig. 1-2. Stem type refrigeration thermometer (68 deg. reading) with pocket carrying case. This is a Fahrenheit Thermometer. (Taylor Inst. Co.)

The methods and scales used to measure temperatures have been arbitrarily chosen by scientists, and the following standards have been established. The common Britsh and American scales are the Fahrenheit scale (F) and the Fahrenheit absolute scale (F_A), while the metric system uses the Centigrade (C) and Centigrade absolute scales (C_A). The Fahrenheit scale is the one most used in the refrigeration industry.

Some thermometers operate on the basis of the expansion and contraction of metals with a change in temperature.

Other thermometers have been developed which indicate temperature by measurement of the very small electric current generated in a thermocouple. These thermometers are mostly used in the measurement of high temperatures above the range of a glass stem thermometer. These instruments are called Pyrometers.

The Fahrenheit scale is so fixed that it divides the temperature difference between the freezing temperature of water and the boiling temperature of water into 180 equal divisions and sets the freezing temperature of water at 32 divisions above the zero on the scale. Therefore, water freezes (ice melts) at 32 F. and water boils at 212 F. (180 F. + 32 F.) assuming standard atmospheric pressures.

The Centigrade scale has coarser divisions than the Fahrenheit scale and the zero (0) of this scale is set at the melting temperature of ice. The boiling point of water is fixed 100 divisions above that point or at 100 C. assuming standard atmospheric pressure.

In the German language the word for Centigrade is Celsius. Some english speaking countries also use the word Celsius.

A comparison of the Fahrenheit thermometer scale and the Centigrade scale is shown in Fig. 1-3.

You may wonder why the melting temperature of ice and the boiling temperature of water were taken as standards. These conditions were chosen because water has a very constant freezing and boiling point temperature, and water is a common substance.

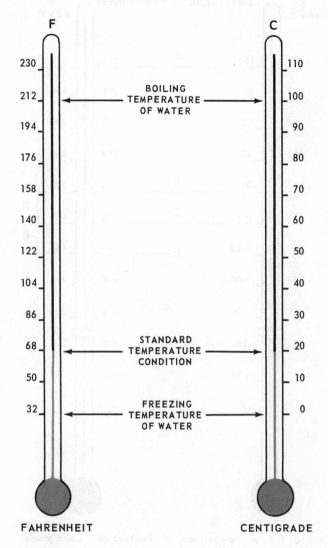

Fig. 1-3. A comparison of Fahrenheit and Centigrade thermometer scales.

1-8 Absolute Temperature Scales, Rankin, Kelvin

There are two absolute temperature scales used in connection with very low temperature work such as Cryogenics, see Par. 1-49.

These two scales are the Fahrenheit Absolute Scale (F_A) and the Centigrade Absolute Scale (C_A).

The Absolute Zero Fahrenheit (F_A) Scale uses the same divisions as the Fahrenheit Scale, however, the zero for this scale is located 460 deg. below zero Fahrenheit.

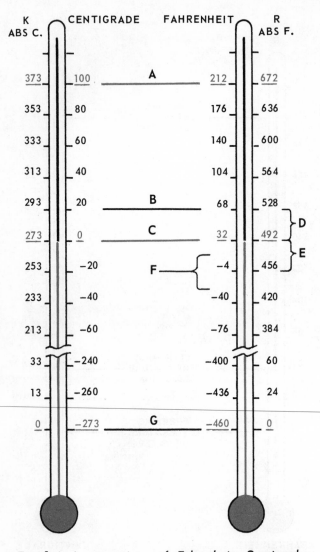

Fig. 1-4. A comparison of Fahrenheit, Centigrade, Rankin and Kelvin thermometer scales. A—Boiling temperature of water. B—Standard conditions temperature. C—Freezing temperature of water. D—Range of refrigerating temperatures for food. E—Range of evaporator temperatures for food. F—Range of frozen food cabinet temperatures. G—Absolute 0.

Problem: What is the freezing point and boiling point of water using the Rankin Scale?

Solution: To calculate the freezing point: Water freezes at 32 F.

The Rankin Scale zero is 460 degrees below zero F.

R temperature at which water will freeze is 460 + 32 = 492 R.

The freezing temperature of water may be expressed as 492 R.

To calculate the boiling point: Water boils at 212 degrees above zero F.

The boiling point on the Rankin Scale will be: 460 + 212 = 672 R.

The boiling temperature of water may be expressed as 672 R.

Problem: What is the temperature at which water freezes and boils using the Kelvin Scale?

Solution: To calculate the freezing point: Water freezes at zero degrees Centigrade. The Kelvin Scale zero is 273 degrees below zero Centigrade.

The freezing temperature of water is therefore 273 degrees above zero Kelvin or 273 degrees Kelvin.

Freezing temperature may be expressed as 273 K.

To calculate the boiling point: Water boils at 100 degrees above zero Centigrade.

The boiling point of water on the Kelvin Scale will be: 100 + 273 = 373 K. Boiling point may be expressed as 373 K.

1-9 Temperature Conversion

It is sometimes necessary to convert a temperature registered in Fahrenheit degrees to Centigrade degrees, or conversely. For this purpose formulas have been developed, based upon the fact that the Fahrenheit zero is located at 32 F. degrees below the Centigrade zero and the distance between the freezing point of water and the boiling point of water is 180

The Absolute Zero Centigrade Scale uses the same divisions as the Centigrade Scale which places the zero for the scale 273 deg. below zero Centigrade.

The Absolute Fahrenheit Scale is called the Rankin Scale (R).

The Absolute Centigrade Scale is called the Kelvin Scale (K).

Fig. 1-4 shows a comparison of the Fahrenheit, Centigrade, Rankin, and Kelvin thermometer scales.

degrees on the Fahrenheit scale and 100 degrees on the Centigrade scale.

To convert Centigrade degrees into Fahrenheit degrees:

$$\text{Temp. F.} = \left(\frac{180}{100} \times \text{Temp. C.}\right) + 32 \text{ or}$$

$$\text{F.} = \left(\frac{9}{5} \text{ C.}\right) + 32$$

Example: Convert 75 C. into F. degrees.

$$\text{F.} = \left(\frac{9}{5} \times 75\right) + 32 = 135 + 32 = 167 \text{ F.}$$

To convert Fahrenheit degrees into Centigrade degrees:

$$\text{Temp. C.} = \frac{100}{180} \times (\text{Temp. F.} - 32) \text{ or}$$

$$\text{C.} = \frac{5}{9} \times (\text{F.} - 32)$$

Example: Convert 212 F. into C. degrees:

$$\text{C.} = \frac{5}{9} \times (212 - 32) = \frac{5}{9} \times (180) = 100 \text{ C.}$$

F. = temp. degrees Fahrenheit
C. = temp. degrees Centigrade.

1-10 How Cold Preserves Food

As the molecules move slower, there is an important effect on the bacteria that are present in most foods. Cold, or low temperature, slows up the growth of these bacteria and foods do not spoil as fast. Slowing the movement or cooling of the molecules tends to make all organisms more sluggish. Spoiling of food is actually the growth of bacteria in the food. If the bacteria can be kept from increasing, the food will be edible for a longer period of time. Since most foods have a considerable water content, the food must be kept just above freezing temperatures (32 F.).

If food is frozen slowly at or near the freezing temperature of water, the ice crystals formed are large and their growth ruptures the food tissues. When the food melts or defrosts, it spoils rapidly and its appearance and taste are ruined.

Fast freezing at very low temperatures (0 to -15 F.) forms small crystals and the

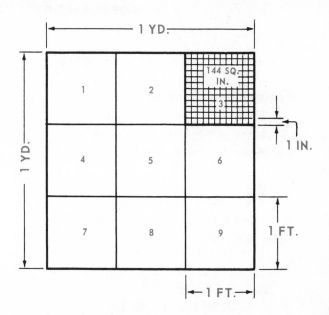

Fig. 1-5. The relation of standard areas. 144 square inches are equal to 1 square foot. 9 square feet are equal to 1 square yard.

food tissues are not injured. Food freezers are maintained at or below 0 F., and food placed in them is frozen very quickly.

It is well to keep in mind during the ensuing chapters that the average correct refrigerating temperature for domestic refrigerators is between 35 F. and 45 F. and to make ice, a temperature lower than 32 F. is needed.

1-11 Dimensions

All measurement of dimensions in this text are based on the English units such as inches, feet and yards. You must be able to accurately measure cabinet sizes and volumes. You must be able to measure tubing sizes, pistons, cylinders, journal sizes and the like, to very accurate dimensions.

12 inches	(in.) = 1 foot (ft.)
3 feet	(ft.) = 1 yard (yd.)
5280 feet	(ft.) = 1 mile (mi.)
6080 feet	(ft.) = 1 nautical (mi.)

Two dimensional space (area) is also measured in inch and foot units; that is, a square inch or a square foot. One square inch is a square with a 1 inch measurement on each side, as shown in Fig. 1-5.

144 square inches (sq. in.) = 1 square foot (sq. ft.)

9 square feet (sq. ft.) = 1 square yard (sq. yd.)

Fig. 1-6 shows a circle. To determine the area of a circle, the following formula is used:

$$A = \pi r^2$$
$$\pi = 3.1416$$

r = radius of the circle in inches.

The solution to the problem shown in Fig. 1-6 is as follows:

The area of a circle (A) equals πr^2

$$A = 3.1416 \times 1.2^2$$
$$= 3.1416 \times 1.2 \times 1.2$$
$$= 3.1416 \times 1.44$$
$$= 4.52 + \text{ square inches}$$

In the above formula the radius of the circle equals one-half the diameter $(\frac{D}{2})$.

The formula $\frac{D^2}{4}$ may be used instead of r^2 if desired $\left(\frac{D^2}{2} = \frac{D}{2} \times \frac{D}{2} = \frac{D^2}{4}\right)$.

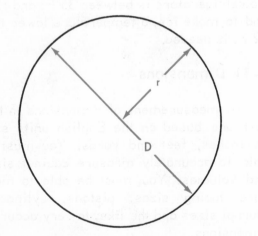

Fig. 1-6. The area of a circle is equal to πr^2. The value of π = 3.1416. The diameter (D) of the circle is 2.4 in. The radius (r) is 1.2 in. r^2 = r x r = radius x radius.

Three dimensional space (volume) is also measured in English units. All substances must be of three dimensions. These measurements are the cubic inch, the cubic foot, and the cubic yard, as shown in Fig. 1-7. One cubic inch (cu. in.) is a cube, 1 inch (in.) on each dimension.

1728 cubic inches (cu. in.) = 1 cubic foot (cu. ft.)

27 cubic feet (cu. ft.) = 1 cubic yard (cu. yd.)

Fig. 1-8 illustrates a cylinder.

To determine the volume of a cylinder the following formula is used:

$$V = A \times L$$

A = Area of cylinder cross section in inches.

L = Length of the cylinder in inches.

The volume of the cylinder shown in Fig. 1-8 would be calculated as follows:

$$V = A \times L$$
$$A = \pi r^2 \text{ or } 3.1416 \times 1 \text{ (radius} = 1 \text{ in.,}$$
$$1^2 = 1 \times 1 = 1)$$
$$= 3.1416 \text{ sq. in.}$$
$$L = 2 \text{ in.}$$
$$V = 3.1416 \times 2 = 6.2832 \text{ cu. in.}$$

Test Your Knowledge

1. How many square inches are there in four square feet? Ans. 576.
2. How many square feet are equal to 1440 square inches? Ans. 10.
3. How many square yards are equal to 1296 square inches? · Ans. 1.
4. How many cubic inches are there in 10 cubic feet? Ans. 17280.
5. How many cubic feet are equal to 6 cubic yards? Ans. 162.
6. What is the area of a circle 4 inches in diameter? Ans. 12.57 sq. in.
7. What is the volume of a cylinder 4 inches in diameter and 6 inches long? Ans. 75.42 cubic inches.

1-12 Weight and Mass

The English units for weight are the ounce, the pound, and the ton.

16 ounces (oz.) = 1 pound (lb.)

2000 pounds (lb.) = 1 ton (ton)

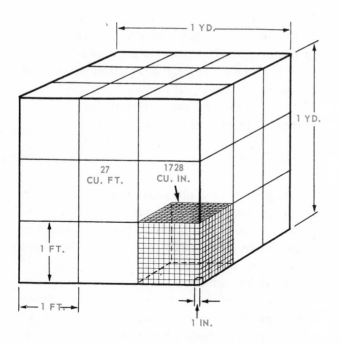

Fig. 1-7. *The relation of standard volumes. 1728 cubic inches equal to 1 cubic foot. 27 cubic feet equal to 1 cubic yard.*

The weight of a substance is due to the earth's attraction on the substance (gravity). The only condition in which a substance has

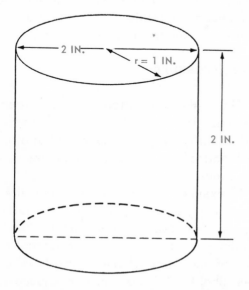

Fig. 1-8. *The volume of a cylinder is equal to the area of the end multiplied by the length. Cylinder dimensions are usually expressed in inches and decimals of an inch such as 1.250 in. and not 1 1/4 in.*

no weight is when it is falling in a vacuum under the influence of gravity. At all other times it has weight.

An object orbiting the earth, at a speed which keeps it in orbit, is considered to be weightless since it is actually falling, but its speed is such that it remains away from contact with the earth.

Mass is a property of all matter, for everything has mass. Gas has mass, water has mass, and metals have mass. The mass is an indication of the number of molecules present in a unit quantity of a substance.

The gravity pull on an object will give the object a falling acceleration at 32.2 feet per second per second.

Perhaps this statement may be better explained by using a mathematical formula. The distance that an object will fall in a given time is expressed by the formula; distance (s) equals the acceleration (a) multiplied by the time (t) squared. The time (t) is expressed in seconds. To determine the distance that an object will fall in four (4) seconds, use the following formula.

$$s = at^2$$
$$s = 32.2 \times 16 = 515.2 \text{ ft.}$$

Weight divided by acceleration due to gravity is mass. The unit of mass is the slug.

$$\text{Mass} = \frac{w}{g} = \text{slugs}$$

w = weight of substance
g = 32.2 feet per second per second

Example: What is the mass of a 10 lb. substance?

Solution: Mass is $= \frac{w}{g} = \frac{10}{32.2} = .3106$ slugs.

It is important to know this slug value because all force obeys the following rule:
Force = Mass x acceleration
Force = Slugs x 32.2

Force is expressed in pounds, acceleration is expressed in feet per second per second.

1-13 Solids

Substances exist in three physical forms. The solid, the liquid, and the gaseous. These three physical forms are shown in Fig. 1-9. Water, for example, may exist in any one of the above physical forms. If it is ice, it is a solid. If it is water, it is a liquid. As a water vapor (steam), it is a gas. Three different methods are used to express physical properties of substances or materials corresponding to the state of the substance.

A solid is any physical substance which retains a certain shape unsupported. It is made of untold billions of molecules, all exactly the same size, weight, and shape that stay in the same relative place to each other and at the same time are in a condition of rapid vibration. The rate of vibration will depend upon the temperature. The lower the temperature, the slower the molecules vibrate; the higher the temperature, the faster the molecules vibrate.

The molecules are strongly attracted to each other and considerable force is necessary to separate them.

A solid must be supported or it will fall vertically. The force supporting a solid is always upward. As shown in Fig. 1-9A.

1-14 Liquids

A liquid is any physical substance which will assume the shape of its container, as shown in Fig. 1-9B, but which has the molecules strongly attracted to each other. You might imagine that the molecules are swimming among their fellow molecules but never leaving them. As the temperature rises, the molecules swim faster and vice versa.

There is another pressure condition which involves liquids. Refer to Fig. 1-9D. In this illustration, a fluid is contained in a closed space. A piston having a cross sectional area of one square inch is fitted into a cylinder connected to the container.

The container is completely filled with fluid and a pressure of 100 lbs. is applied to the piston. The pressure gauges indicate that the pressure is transmitted equally in all directions and all pressure gauges read 100 psi (pounds per square inch). This principle is called Pascal's Law.

1-15 Gases

A gas is any physical substance which must be contained in a sealed container or it will soon dissipate. These molecules have little attraction for each other and travel in a straight line (fly) and will ricochet or rebound from each other, from other molecules of any substance, or from the container walls. They have little or no attraction for each other nor for any other substance. The pressures shown in the gas-filled balloon in Fig. 1-9C illustrate how gases behave.

Any particular substance can be made to exist in any of these three forms; that is, it may exist as a solid, a liquid, or a gas. Any molecule can be made to vibrate, swim, or fly depending on two things: temperature and pressure. To understand this change of state, one must study temperature and pressure relationships.

1-16 Pressure

Since the operation of a refrigerator depends mainly on pressure differences in the system, a basic understanding of pressure and of the laws of pressures is very important.

Pressure is defined as the weight or force per unit area, and it is usually expressed in pounds per square inch or pounds per square foot. The normal pressure of the atmosphere at sea level averages about 14.7 pounds per square inch. (Note: There are 144 square inches in 1 square foot; therefore to get the pressure per square foot, 14.7 must be multiplied by 144.)

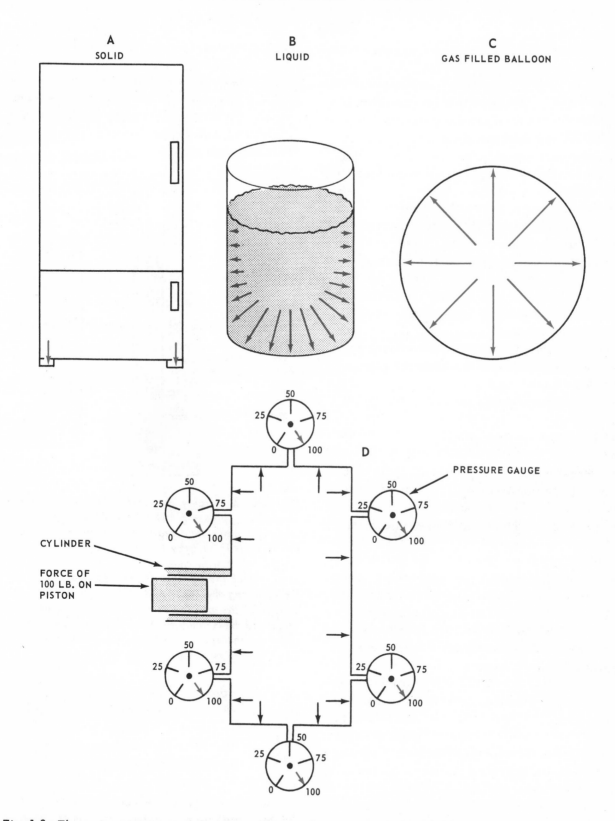

Fig. 1-9. *The various ways materials exert pressure. The arrows in color represent the direction and the relative amount of the pressures. Note that: (A) a solid must be supported from falling. The liquid (B) always is the shape of its container. A gas (C) fills its container and would escape if not sealed tight. An enclosed liquid under pressure (D) exerts pressure equally in all directions (Pascal's Law).*

Substances always exert pressure on the surfaces supporting them. A refrigerator (a solid) exerts a pressure on its legs because if they were removed the box would fall; a liquid always exerts a pressure on the sides and bottom of its container, such as a bottle; and a gas always exerts a pressure on all the surfaces of its container, such as a balloon. Fig. 1-9C illustrates these types of pressures.

If a solid weight of one pound were made with its bottom surface area one inch square, it would exert a pressure of one pound per square inch upon a flat surface.

A liquid in a container maintains an increasing pressure on the sides and bottom as the liquid depth increases. Gases, however, do not always exert a constant pressure on the container because the pressure is determined by the temperature and the quantity of the gas in the container.

1-17 Pressures, Gauge and Absolute

Pressures are expressed in pounds per unit of area or in inches of static pressure of liquids. The most popular pressure indicating instruments (gauges) register in pounds per square inch ABOVE the atmospheric pressure (psig) or (psi). The pressure of zero pounds per square inch gauge is equal to the atmospheric pressure, approximately 14.7 pounds per square inch; (15 pounds per square inch is usually used for computation purposes). Pressures below atmospheric pressure are termed partial vacuums. A perfect vacuum may be described as 0 pounds per square inch absolute (0 psia). Therefore, the absolute pressure scale has its zero at a pressure which cannot be further reduced. Pressure may also be indicated in inches of mercury ("Hg) or feet or inches of water column and may be either above atmospheric pressure or absolute pressure depending on the construction of the gauge. Mercury is usually used for measuring pressures below atmospheric pressure.

The barometer, as shown in Fig. 1-10, is an example of a mercury gauge. With a vacuum in one end of the tube, the atmospheric pressure will support a mercury column 29.92 in. in height at sea level under standard conditions.

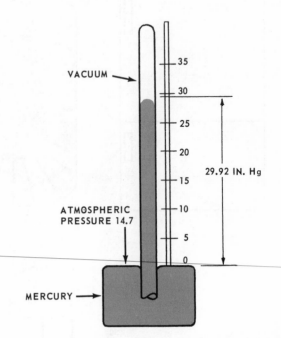

Fig. 1-10. A mercury barometer used for measuring atmospheric pressure. The mercury barometer consists of a glass tube sealed at one end and open at the other. It is made by turning the tube upside down and filling it with mercury. Place a finger over the open end of the mercury filled tube and turn it upright placing the lower end of the tube beneath the surface of the mercury in the container. Remove the finger and the mercury will drop to a level corresponding to the atmospheric pressure. The glass tube should be about 34 in. in length.

For most pressure and volume computations it is necessary to use absolute pressures, (psia).

Example: What is the absolute pressure when a pressure gauge shows a reading of 21 psi?

Solution: Absolute pressure equals gauge pressure (psig) plus atmospheric pressure.

psig + 15 = psia
21 + 15 = 36 psia

It is possible to measure air pressure and amount of vacuum using a column of water. A column of water would be about 34 feet in height to equal a 29.92 inch column of mercury. This is because mercury is much heavier than water.

In refrigeration and air conditioning work, the service engineer is often testing pressures and vacuums in the same system. Also, under certain conditions of operation, a part of the system may be under considerable pressure and during another part of the operating cycle it may be under a high vacuum.

Pressure gauges are made which will measure both pressures above atmospheric pressure and pressures below atmospheric. These gauges are called compound gauges. Fig. 1-11 illustrates a compound gauge used in refrigeration work.

Water columns are often used for measuring small pressures above or below atmospheric pressure such as pressures in air ducts, gas lines, and the like. These pressure measuring devices are called manometers and they are calibrated in inches of water column. A common type of manometer is shown in Fig. 1-12.

In some large refrigerating machines pressure gauges are calibrated in atmospheres. One atmosphere corresponds to 15 pounds per sq. in. (psig), two atmospheres 30 psig, three atmospheres to 45 psig and so on. Fig. 1-13 shows a table comparing various pressure scales.

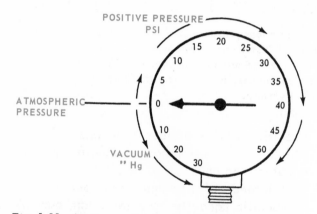

Fig. 1-11. *A compound gauge used for measuring pressures. Note that 0 on this scale is atmospheric pressure. Pressures above atmospheric pressure are measured in pounds per square inch (psi) and pressures below atmospheric are measured in inches of mercury ("Hg.)*

1-18 Density

Comparative weights of solids and liquids may be expressed by either density or specific gravity. Density is defined as the weight per unit volume.

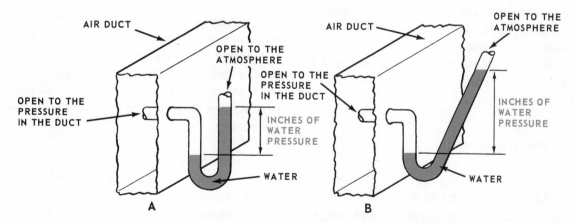

Fig. 1-12. *A. A water manometer used to measure slight pressures in air ducts, gas lines, and the like. The pressure is indicated in inches of water and is measured by the difference in level between the surface of the water in the two branches of the tube. In order to make these manometers more sensitive to pressure measurement the end open to the atmosphere is often placed at a low angle as shown at B. These are called slant gauges and are in common use. A red dye placed in the water makes the gauges easier to read.*

	POUNDS PER SQUARE INCH		ATMOSPHERES	INCHES MERCURY VACUUM
	ABSOLUTE psia	GAUGE psig or psi	At.	"Hg.
Positive Pressure	105	90	6	
	90	75	5	
	75	60	4	
	60	45	3	
	45	30	2	
	30	15	1	
Atmospheric Pressure	15	0	0	0
Negative Pressure or Vacuum	10	−5		10
	5	−10		20
	0	−15	−1	30

Fig. 1-13. A table showing a comparison of the various pressure scales. The pressures most used by the refrigeration service and installation engineers are: psia-pounds per square inch absolute, psi-pounds per square inch gauge, and "Hg-inches of mercury column. Note it is correct to indicate psig as psi. Numbers in red indicate a perfect vacuum.

Comparative densities of gases are expressed by specific volumes. Specific volume is the volume of one pound of a gas at standard conditions. Standard conditions are considered to be 68 F. and 29.92 inches of mercury column pressure.

The volume of one pound of air at standard conditions is 12.388 cubic feet. As a comparison, one pound of hydrogen occupies 178.9 cubic feet and one pound of ammonia (R-717) occupies 21 cubic feet, while carbon dioxide (R-744) only occupies 8.15 cubic feet. If one pound of a gas occupies a greater space than air, we think of it as being a light gas while if it occupies less space than air it is classified as a heavy gas.

1-19 Specific Gravity

Specific gravity (sp. gr.) is defined as the ratio of the weight of a certain volume of a substance as compared to the weight of an equal volume of water.

Water is considered to have a specific gravity of one.

Objects which float on water have a specific gravity of less than one. Objects which sink in water have a specific gravity greater than one.

Mixtures of salt and water (brine) have a specific gravity greater than one. A calcium chloride brine adjusted to freeze at 0 F. will have a specific gravity of 1.18. See Chapter 27 for a table of brine densities and freezing temperatures.

1-20 Force

Force is a word used to denote total pressure or influence to cause motion or movement. To determine the total force on the head of a piston of 10 square inches in area, and under a pressure of 25 pounds per square inch, you may use the following formula:

F = A x P

F = total force

A = area of the piston head (which is 10 sq. in.)

P = pressure (which is 25 pounds per sq. in.)

To solve the above problem:

F = 10 x 25

F = 250 pounds

1-21 Work and Energy

ENERGY is described as THE CAPACITY TO DO WORK. WORK is defined as FORCE MULTIPLIED BY THE DISTANCE THROUGH WHICH IT TRAVELS. The unit of work is called the foot-pound. One foot-pound is the amount of work done in lifting a one pound weight a vertical distance of one foot. Work is sometimes expressed in inch-pounds. In this case, the distance through which the force acts is measured in inches.

Example: Calculate the work done in foot-pounds when lifting a weight of 2000 pounds a vertical distance of 10 feet.

Work = Force x Distance

= 2000 x 10 = 20,000 foot-pounds

or expressed in inch units.

2000 x 10 x 12 = 240,000 inch-pounds

Energy is the ability to do work. The electric motor supplies the energy to drive the refrigerator compressor.

1-22 Power

POWER IS DEFINED AS THE TIME RATE OF DOING WORK. The common unit of mechanical power is the horsepower (hp) and is the equivalent of 33,000 foot-pounds of work per minute. If in the above problem the 2000-pound weight is lifted 10 feet in 2 minutes, the power required would be:

$$\text{Horsepower} = \frac{\text{weight x distance}}{\text{time x 33,000}}$$

$$\text{Horsepower} = \frac{2000 \times 10}{2 \times 33,000} = \frac{20,000}{66,000} = .3 \text{ hp}$$

1-23 British Thermal Unit

In Paragraphs 1-4 and 1-6 the difference between heat and temperature was explained. A thermometer may be used to measure temperature. Heat must be calculated. There is no instrument for measuring the amount of heat in an object.

The unit of heat is the British thermal unit (Btu). A Btu is defined as the amount of heat required to raise the temperature of 1 pound of water, 1 degree Fahrenheit, as shown in Fig. 1-14.

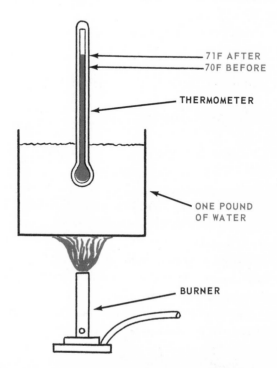

71F AFTER
70F BEFORE

THERMOMETER

ONE POUND OF WATER

BURNER

Fig. 1-14. In this experiment one pound of water at 70 F. is placed in a position to be heated. Note the thermometer reading. The burner is lighted and the thermometer reading watched. At 71 F. the burner is turned off. One Btu of heat has been added to the water.

Conversely, if a substance is cooled, heat (Btu's) is removed.

Example: How much heat will be required to raise the temperature of 62.4 lbs. (1 cu. ft.) of water from 40 F. to 80 F.?

Btu = Wt. x degree change

= 62.4 x 40

= 2496 Btu

Example: How much heat must be removed to cool 50 lbs. of water from 80 F. to 35 F.?

Btu = Wt. x degree change

= 50 x 45

= 2250 Btu

1-24 Therm

A therm is 100,000 Btu. It is used in heating calculations which involve large heat loads. To determine the therm load for a heating installation, divide the total Btu by 100,000.

Example: The total head load for an apartment building is 5,050,000 Btu's. What is the load in therms?

Solution: 5,050,000 divided by 100,000

or: $\dfrac{5,050,000}{100,000} = 50.5$ therms

1-25 Sensible Heat

If a substance is heated (heat added) and the temperature rises as the heat is added, the increase in heat is called sensible heat. Likewise heat may be removed from a substance (heat subtracted) and if the temperature falls the heat removed is again sensible heat. Therefore, we call that heat which causes a change in temperature in a substance sensible heat.

1-26 Specific Heat

The specific heat of a substance is the amount of heat required, or released, to change the temperature of one pound of the substance one degree Fahrenheit.

The sensible heat required to cause a temperature change in substances varies with the kind of substance and the amount of the substance. The specific heat of water is 1.0. Different substances require different amounts of heat per unit quantity to effect these changes of temperature.

The specific heat of several common substances is shown in Fig. 1-15.

Paragraph 1-23 shows how to calculate the heat (Btu) added or removed from water.

To determine the amount of heat necessary to cause a desired change of temperature in a substance multiply the weight of the substance by the specific heat and by

Material	Specific Heat (Btu/lb./deg. F.)
Wood	.327
Water	1.
Ice	.504
Iron	.129
Mercury	.0333
Alcohol	.615
Copper	.095
Sulphur	.177
Glass	.187
Graphite	.200
Brick	.200
Glycerine	.576
R-717 (Liquid ammonia at 40 F.)	1.1
R-744 (Carbon dioxide at 40 F.)	.6
R-502	.255
Salt Brine 20%	.85
R-12	.213
R-22	.26

The above values may be used for computations which involve no "change of state." If a change of state is involved the specific heat for each state of the substance must be used.

Fig. 1-15. A table of the specific heat values for some common substances.

the temperature change, provided there is no change of state.

In order to calculate the amount of heat added or removed from substances, the following formula should be used.

Amount of heat added or removed in Btu = Wt. of substance x sp. ht. x temperature change in degrees F., or Btu = Wt. x sp. ht. x F. change.

Example: How many Btu must be removed to cool 40 lbs. of 20% salt brine (see Fig. 1-15) from 60 F. to 20 F.?

Solution:

Btu = Wt. x sp. ht. x F. change

Btu = 40 x .85 x 40

Btu = 1380

1-27 Latent Heat

A physical phenomenon of all pure substances is their ability to change their state, such as solid to liquid and liquid to gas. These changes of state occur at the same temperature and pressure combinations for any given substance. It takes addition of heat or the removal of heat to produce these phenomena. We call heat which brings about a CHANGE OF STATE, WITH NO CHANGE IN TEMPERATURE, LATENT (hidden) HEAT.

It may be noted in Fig. 1-16 that although considerable heat (144 Btu) was added between points A and B, the temperature did not change. This heat was required to change the ice to water. This heat is called latent heat of fusion during a cooling operation or latent heat of melting during a heating operation. Likewise, between points C and D, 970 Btu were added and the temperature did not change. This heat was required to change the water to steam. This heat is called latent heat of vaporization.

change the substance from the solid state to the liquid is called the latent heat of melting or fusion.

The heat required to change the liquid to a vapor is called latent heat of vaporization.

If heat is being removed from the substance (cooled-meaning that energy is subtracted), the heat removed to condense the vapor to a liquid is still the heat of vaporization but in this case it is called the latent heat of condensation. As the liquid is cooled to change the substance from a liquid to a solid state, this heat is again called the heat of fusion or freezing. Fig. 1-17 shows the latent heat for water and several common refrigerants.

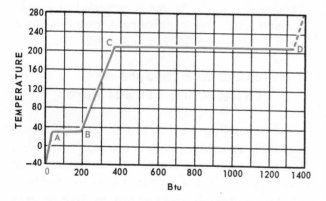

Fig. 1-16. A temperature-heat diagram for one pound of water at atmospheric pressure, heated from -40 F. through complete vaporization.
From 0 to A 36.3 Btu were added to heat the ice from -40 F. to 32 F.
From A to B 144 Btu were added to melt the ice. Note that the temperature did not change.
From B to C 180 Btu were added to heat the water from 32 F. to 212 F.
From C to D 970 Btu were added to vaporize the water. Note that the temperature did not change.

Material	Freezing or Melting Btu/lb.	Latent Heat of Vaporization or Condensation Btu/lb.
Water	144	970.4 at 212 F.
R-717 (Ammonia).		565.0 at 5 F.
R-502		68.96 at 5 F.
R-40 (Methyl chloride) . . .		178.5 at 5 F.
R-12		68.2 at 5 F.
R-22		93.2 at 5 F.

Fig. 1-17. A table of the latent heat of vaporization value of water and some common refrigerants. The latent heat of fusion is only given for water as the refrigerants do not freeze at temperatures commonly handled by the refrigeration service engineer.

There are two latent heats for each substance, solid to liquid heat (melting and freezing) and liquid to gaseous (vaporizing and condensing). If heat is being added to a substance, the heat required to

The explanation for the change of state is that as the molecules move under a certain pressure their motion will increase to a certain speed but then if further heat is added each molecule undergoes a peculiar change. This change takes place within the molecule. It is believed that there is a shift of atoms within the molecule. It is estimated that one or more of the atoms change their position from the outer face of the molecule to the inside or the reverse. There are other theories, all of them based on molecular motion and magnetic attraction. The heat energy needed to make this change is tremendous. It takes as much heat to change one pound of ice to one pound of water as it does to raise the temperature of that same one pound of water from 32 F. to 176 F.

The difference between sensible heat and latent heat should be kept very clearly in mind because all of the basic operations of the compression refrigeration cycle are based upon these two heats, SENSIBLE and LATENT.

1-28 Application of Latent Heat

In refrigeration work, the physics of latent heat is of special importance because it is this heat which produces the constant cold or freezing temperatures. When ice melts, its temperature remains constant; nevertheless it absorbs a considerable amount of heat changing from ice to water. The heat absorbing quality (latent heat of fusion) of melting ice was the source of refrigeration in the iceboxes used many years ago. It is still the cooling medium when ice cubes or crushed ice are used to cool beverages.

When a substance passes from a liquid to a gas as in a mechanical refrigerator, its heat absorption is very high, and advantage is taken of this fact in the operation of the refrigerator.

The temperature level at which a substance changes its state depends on the pressure. The higher the pressure, the higher the temperature needed to make the change of state take place. Also, if the pressure is lowered, the temperature at which the change of state will take place will also be lowered. For example, water will turn to steam at 212 F. at 14.7 psia, 300 F. at 67 psia, 400 F. at 247 psia, 40 F. at .12 psia.

If a low pressure is produced over a liquid it will boil at a lower temperature and if the gas resulting from this boiling is then compressed it will condense to a liquid at a higher temperature.

Every substance has a different latent heat value to bring about a change of state for both solid-liquid and liquid-gaseous states. Latent heats for water and the more common refrigerants are shown in Fig. 1-17. See Chapter 9 for information concerning refrigerants.

In a modern refrigerator, freezer or air conditioner, liquid refrigerant is piped under pressure into the evaporator coil. In the evaporating coil the pressure is greatly reduced and the refrigerant boils (changes to a gas) and absorbs considerable heat from the coil. This produces a low temperature and cools the evaporating coil. This refrigerant gas is pumped out of the coil and again compressed. It then flows into the condenser which is located outside of the refrigerator where the heat that it absorbed in the evaporator coil is released "squeezed out" to the surrounding atmosphere and the refrigerant returns to a liquid again and the cycle is repeated.

1-29 Effect of Pressure on Evaporating Temperatures

The boiling temperature for any liquid depends upon the pressure under which the liquid is placed. Water normally boils at 212 F., but if the pressure on the surface of the water is increased to 100 pounds per square inch gauge, the boiling-point will be raised to 338 F. If instead of increasing the pressure it is decreased to an absolute pressure of 3 pounds per square inch, (24 in. Hg. vacuum) the water will boil at 142 F. as shown in Fig. 1-18.

It is the effect of reduced pressure on the boiling temperature of certain liquids that makes the operation of the mechanical and absorption refrigerator possible. As an illustration of this, the refrigerant R-12 boils at -21.7 F. under atmospheric pressure while at 10 inches of vacuum the boiling temperature is -38.5 F. See Fig. 9-6 for a graph of the temperature characteristics of R-12.

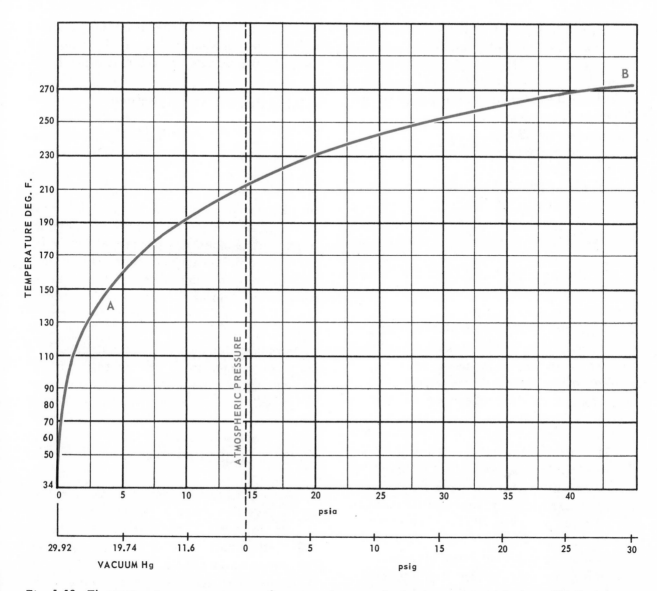

Fig. 1-18. The temperature pressure curve for water. At atmospheric pressure water boils at 212 F. At point (A) which is at a pressure of 24" Hg water boils at 142 F. Increasing the pressure above atmospheric increases the boiling temperature. At point B, which is at a pressure of 30 psi, the boiling temperature is 272 F.

1-30 Refrigeration Effect of Ice

Ice is still an important item in the refrigeration industry.

As stated before, ice changes to water at 32 F. at atmospheric pressure. Changing ice to water at 32 F., the heat absorption is 144 British thermal units per pound.

The heat absorption ability of ice, when changing from a temperature below 32 F. to 32 F., is .504 British thermal units per pound per degree change in temperature.

The specific heat of ice = .504 Btu per pound.

The latent heat of fusion (melting) of ice = 144 Btu per pound.

The specific heat of water = 1 Btu per pound.

Example: How many Btu will 25 pounds of ice at 5 F. absorb in changing to water at 40 F.?

From ice at 5 F. to ice at 32 F.

Wt. of ice x sp. ht. of ice x temp. change
25 x .504 x (32 -5) or
25 x .504 x 27 = 340.2 Btu
From ice to water at 32 F.
Wt. of ice x latent heat of fusion of ice
25 x 144 = 3600. Btu
From water at 32 F. to water at 40 F.
Wt. of water x sp. ht. of water x temp.
change
25 x 1 x (40 -32) or
25 x 1 x 8 = 200. Btu
    340.2
   3600.0
    200.0
Total 4140.2 Btu

1-31 "Ton" of Refrigeration Effect

The common unit used to measure refrigeration effect is the "ton." This is the amount of heat absorbed in melting one ton (2000 lbs.) of ice in twenty-four hours.

The Btu equivalent of 1 ton of refrigeration is 288,000 Btu. This may be calculated by multiplying the weight of ice by the latent heat of fusion (melting) of ice.

2000 lbs x 144 = 288,000 Btu

A refrigerating or air conditioning mechanism capable of absorbing heat will be rated in tons by its heat absorbing ability in Btu divided by 288,000.

$$T = \frac{HA}{288,000} = \text{Tons of Refrigeration Effect}$$

T = Tons of Refrigeration Effect
HA = Heat absorbing ability

Example: The heat absorbing ability of a refrigerator unit is rated at 1,440,000 Btu per 24 hours. What is its ton rating?

$$\text{Solution: } T = \frac{1,440,000}{288,000} = 5 \text{ tons of refrigeration effect.}$$

SAMPLE PROBLEMS: What will be the TON Rating of a refrigerating mechanism capable of absorbing 1,728,000 Btu in 24 hours? Answer: 6 Tons.

What is the Btu heat absorbing capacity of a 1/2 ton refrigerating system? Answer: 144,000 Btu per day or 6,000 Btu per hour.

1-32 Ambient Temperature

The term ambient temperature is used to denote the temperature of the air surrounding a motor, a control mechanism, or other device. As an example, a motor may be guaranteed to deliver its full horsepower under operating conditions when its temperature does not exceed 40 C. (72 F.) over the ambient temperature. This means that the temperature of the motor must not be warmer than 72 F. over the surrounding air if the motor is to maintain its operating efficiency.

Ambient temperature is not usually a constant temperature but it may change day-by-day and hour-by-hour depending on usage of the space, sunshine, and many other factors.

1-33 Heat of Compression

As a gas is compressed its temperature is raised. The gaseous refrigerant returning to the compressor from the cooling coil will probably be at or slightly below the room temperature. This same gas, as it leaves the compressor and enters the condenser will be at a much higher temperature. Little or no heat has been added. However, the total heat of the gas is now squeezed into a much smaller space and a much higher temperature results. This is called "heat of compression," although, technically, no heat has been added. The compression of gaseous refrigerant in a refrigerator compressor is considered to be near a state of adiabatic compression. See Par. 1-54 for a definition of Adiabatic Compression. The fact that the compressed gas in the condenser is now at a temperature higher than the temperature of the surrounding air, the heat will be rapidly transferred to the surrounding air. See Second Law of Thermodynamics, Chapter 27.

1-34 Energy Conversion Units

In refrigeration work, three common forms of energy must be considered: mechanical, electrical and heat.

The study of refrigeration deals mainly with heat energy, but it must be understood that the heat energy is usually produced by utilizing a combination of electrical and mechanical energy. There is a relation that exists between these three forms of energy. In an electric refrigerating unit, electrical energy flows into an electric motor and this electrical energy is turned into mechanical energy. This mechanical energy is used to turn a compressor, and the compressor in turn compresses the gas to a high temperature. Energy conversion units are expressed as follows:

778 foot-pounds = 1 British thermal unit (Btu)

1 hp = 2545.6 Btu/hr.
1 hp = 746 watts
1 Btu/hr. = .000393 hp
1 Btu/hr. = .293 watts
1 watt = .00134 hp
1 watt = 3.41 Btu/hr.

These conversion units will be used in Chapter 16 in calculating loads and determining the capacity of equipment required for specific refrigeration applications.

1-35 The Function of a Refrigerator

The basic purpose of a refrigeration system is to remove heat from one space and deposit it into another space. Confusion often occurs when an explanation of refrigeration is given on the basis of heat transfer. One is tempted to think in terms of refrigeration as "cold" and "hot." However, cold is a relative term which describes a lack of heat. Thus to produce "cold," heat must be removed. This heat removal is accomplished in refrigeration through the use of refrigerants. These refrigerants are fluids which have the ability of boiling at a low temperature while under a low pressure. The refrigerant in the cooling compartment (evaporator coil) absorbs the heat from the food which is placed in the refrigerator, thereby lowering the temperature of the food. The refrigerant is now in a gaseous state because it has absorbed heat from the food and has evaporated. This evaporated refrigerant gives up its heat outside of the box by means of a condensing unit.

The condensing unit consists of a compressor and a condensing coil. The compressor compresses the vaporized refrigerant back to a high pressure and high temperature and passes it into the condensing coil where its heat is given up in much the same way that the water in the cooling system of a car gives up its heat to the air as the water passes through the car radiator tubes.

1-36 Elementary Refrigerator

In Fig. 1-19, refrigerant cylinder A is shown with the valve closed. The pressure, the temperature (inside and out), the number of molecules leaving the gaseous state, the number diving back into the liquid and the liquid molecules flying out of the liquid into the gaseous state are equal. All conditions are balanced.

On cylinder B, the valve has been opened slightly and some of the gas is escaping. The results are twofold. The pressure over the liquid refrigerant in the cylinder is reduced. This will cause more of the liquid to change to a gas. In changing from a liquid to a gas, heat is absorbed and the liquid refrigerant will be cooled. The temperature of the refrigerant and cylinder is now 50 F. Some heat from the surrounding area, which is at 70 F., will now flow into the cylinder and into the refrigerant.

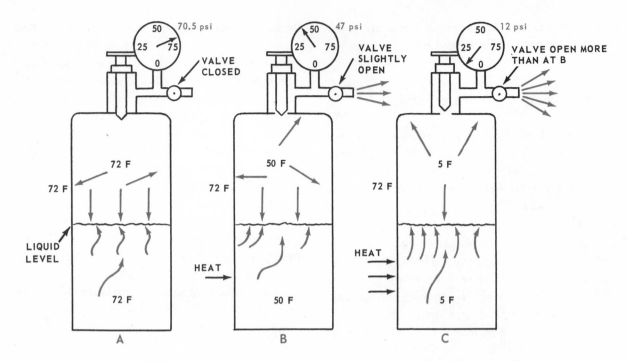

Fig. 1-19. *The cooling effect of different pressures operating on the surface of liquid refrigerant R-12. A-Shows a cylinder of refrigerant with the valve closed. The refrigerant is in a state of equilibrium. The refrigerant and the cylinder are both at room temperature. The pressure in the cylinder is 70.5 psi. B-Shows a cylinder of refrigerant with the valve slightly opened and refrigerant gas beginning to leave the cylinder. In order to maintain an equilibrium between the gas leaving the liquid and the internal gas pressure the liquid absorbs heat from the cylinder and the surrounding air. This has caused the temperature to drop to 50 F. The pressure in the cylinder is 47 psi. C-Shows the cylinder of refrigerant with the valve open wider. Refrigerant gas is flowing rapidly from the cylinder. A large amount of heat will be absorbed since the pressure on the surface of the liquid is not great enough to retard the vaporization of the refrigerant. The rapid absorption of heat has reduced the refrigerant and cylinder temperature to 5 F. This results in a rapid absorption of heat from the surrounding space. The pressure in the cylinder is 12 psi.*

On cylinder C, the valve has been opened more than at B with the result that refrigerant gas flows out more rapidly. This results in still a lower pressure on the liquid refrigerant and a more rapid evaporation of the refrigerant. This increase in the rate of evaporation lowers the temperature of the refrigerant and the cylinder still more with the result that the 72 F. air surrounding the cylinder will more rapidly give up its heat to the colder cylinder.

On cylinder A, we have a state of equilibrium with all temperatures and pressures in balance.

On cylinder B, we have a slight unbalance due to the gas escaping through the valve. If this condition were to continue for a considerable time, a condition of balance would again prevail but in this case its balance would not be a static one as in A; rather a balance between the rate of heat flow into the cylinder, the evaporation of refrigerant and the flow of refrigerant gas out of the cylinder valve. In this condition of balance, the refrigerant is cooling the cylinder and its surroundings.

On cylinder C, we have a greater unbalance than at cylinder B with the result that the cylinder pressure and temperature will be lowered still farther.

As long as the valve is open and gas molecules can escape, the temperature will be lower because more liquid molecules are becoming gas molecules, than gas molecules are returning into the liquid. This gas bombardment is called vapor pressure. If this vapor pressure can be reduced, the temperature of the liquid can be reduced since evaporation will be increased.

If the gas molecules can be removed fast enough by any means such as suction from a compressor, a chemical to absorb the molecules, or other means, a low enough vapor pressure may be produced to create refrigerant boiling temperatures which are at the refrigerating level.

The operation of the mechanical refrigerator is based on the heat absorption property of a fluid passing from the liquid to the gaseous state. If one were to put a cylinder of refrigerant into an icebox and vent the gas to the outside, we would have a heat absorber in the box, as shown in Fig. 1-20. The liquid can boil only at its

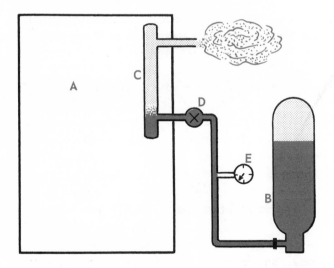

Fig. 1-20. An elementary refrigerator using R-12 but not recondensing the vaporized refrigerant. A-Refrigerated space. B-Cylinder of liquid refrigerant. C-Evaporator. D-Control valve. E-Pressure gauge.

evaporation temperature, say 20 F., and this liquid will be at this temperature until it has completely evaporated. If one tried to raise its temperature by adding heat, the only result would be a more rapid evaporation of the liquid into a gas, pro-

vided the pressure remained constant. Being at this low temperature there is, of course, a transfer of heat to it from the surrounding objects. This heat helps the evaporating and the heat is carried away in the vapor passing off. Thus, the fluid changing its state to gas gets the energy (or heat) for doing this from the objects surrounding it, and that heat is removed with the vapor to the outside of the box.

This type of refrigerator works nicely, but it is an expensive method because the refrigerant fluid is lost. There are some mobile refrigerating units (trucks) which use this method. The refrigerant used is usually liquid nitrogen which is relatively inexpensive. It is called chemical refrigeration.

In the mechanical refrigerator this escaping vapor is captured, compressed, and cooled to a liquid state again so that it can be used over and over, as shown in Fig. 1-21.

To follow through the refrigerant cycle in this refrigerator mechanism, begin with the refrigerant in the tank B. The refrigerant used in this illustration is R-12.

The refrigerant at B is under a pressure corresponding to the room temperature of 72 F. For R-12 this pressure will be approximately 71 psi. At the refrigerant control, C, this pressure is reduced to provide low pressure, low temperature evaporation in the evaporating (cooling) coil. Since the refrigerant temperature is to be held at 35 F. the pressure in the evaporating coil must be held at or below 30 psi. It is the purpose of the refrigerant control to allow refrigerant to flow from the storage tank (high side) into the evaporator coil (low side) while at the same time maintaining the pressure difference between the high-pressure side (high side) and the low-pressure side (low side). In the evaporator, D, the liquid refrigerant is now under a much reduced pressure and it will evaporate or boil very rapidly thus cooling the evaporator coil. The compressor, E,

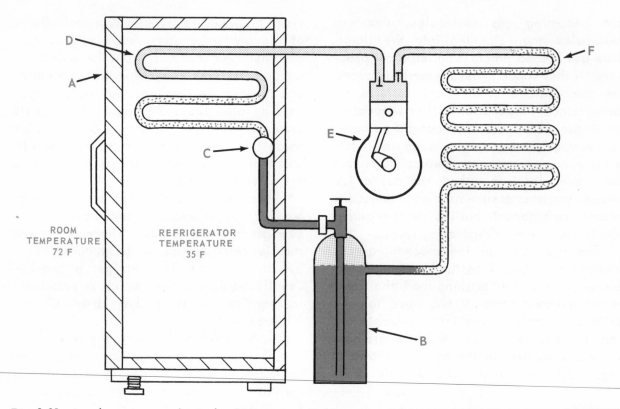

Fig. 1-21. An elementary mechanical refrigerator. A-Refrigerator. B-Liquid refrigerant receiver. C-Refrigerant control. D-Evaporator. E-Motor driven compressor. F-Condenser. In this refrigerator the refrigerant is not allowed to escape but is recycled as necessary to obtain the desired temperatures.

draws (sucks) the evaporated refrigerant gas from the evaporator coil and compresses it back to the high side pressure. From the compressor the high temperature (see heat of compression, Par. 1-33) high-pressure gaseous refrigerant flows into the condenser coils F. The temperature of the gas as it enters these coils will be several degrees warmer than the room temperature. This results in a very rapid transfer of the heat from the condenser coils to the surrounding air. The gas as it flows through the condenser is cooled and loses its heat of evaporation and returns to the liquid state again. As a liquid it flows from the condenser coils back into the liquid refrigerant storage at B. This refrigeration cycle is repeated over and over until the desired temperature is reached and a thermostat breaks the circuit to the driving motor and the compressor stops.

The temperature at which a refrigerator cooling unit is kept depends on the pressure at which the refrigerant is evaporated, while the amount of heat removed depends entirely on the amount of refrigerant changed into a gas.

1-37 Heat Transfer

There are three methods by which heat may be transferred from one body to another. These methods are radiation, conduction, and convection. Some systems of heat transfer make use of a combination of these three methods.

1-38 Radiation

The earth receives its heat from the sun by radiation. The heat rays from the sun are turned into heat as they strike an object which will absorb some or all of the heat rays (opaque or translucent material). The rays heat the air very little as they pass through it and they heat a glass windowpane a very minimum as they pass through it. Heat rays generate more heat on striking dark-colored objects than when striking light-colored and polished surfaces.

Any heated surface loses heat to cooler surrounding space or surfaces through radiation. Likewise a cold surface will absorb radiated heat which may strike it.

Some space heating systems depend on radiated heat in ceilings, walls or floors to heat a space or room.

1-39 Conduction

Conduction is the flow of heat from one part of a substance to another part of the same substance, or from one substance to another substance in direct contact with it. A piece of iron with one end placed in a fire will soon become warm from end to end. This is an example of the transfer of heat by conduction. The heat travels through the iron using the iron as the conducting medium.

Substances differ in their ability to conduct heat. In general, substances which are good conductors of electricity are also good conductors of heat.

Substances which are poor conductors of heat are called heat insulators. Such substances are used to insulate refrigerators, homes, and any structure whose temperature is to be controlled regardless of its surrounding (ambient) temperature.

1-40 Convection

Convection is the moving of heat from one place to another by heating a substance (fluid) such as air or water and circulating the substance from a heat source to the area to be heated. The same method may be used to cool a space by picking up unwanted heat and discharging it outside of the space.

A common example of this is the movement of heat-laden air from a furnace into the rooms of a house where it releases its heat and then returns through the cold air duct to receive another supply of heat from the furnace.

1-41 Control of Heat Flow

The flow of heat by each method can be controlled. That is, the transfer of heat by each of the methods can be aided or restricted according to the particular need.

Radiation, or rather the transfer of heat by radiation, may be aided by making the radiating surfaces of a material, or of a color known to be a good radiator of heat, and by making the receiving surfaces of a material or color known to be a good absorber (or poor reflector) of radiated heat. Conversely, it may be impeded by reversing this application. Dark materials or colors absorb and radiate readily. Light-colored or shiny materials have the opposite properties.

Conduction may be aided by providing large conducting surfaces and good conducting materials, such as copper, aluminum, and iron. Cork, wood, mineral wool, and many other similar materials are poor conductors of heat. Poor conductors of heat are often referred to as heat insulators (insulation).

Convection may be aided by speeding the flow of the conveying medium; for example, forced-air circulation heating systems. Conversely, it can be impeded by retarding the flow of circulation.

1-42 Ice and Salt Mixtures

Refrigerating by ice will not provide refrigeration temperatures below 32 F. Therefore, to obtain lower temperatures required in some instances, ice and salt mixtures are used. These mixtures, ice and salt (sodium chloride - NaCl) and ice and calcium chloride (CaCl) lower the melting temperature of ice. That is, an ice and salt mixture may be made which will melt at 0 F. The reason that the ice and salt mixture produces lower temperatures is that the salt causes the ice to melt faster and this forced absorption of heat causes the lower temperature which results from the mixture. See Chapter 27, for a table of ice and salt mixtures, and their corresponding temperatures.

1-43 Brine and "Sweet Water"

Salt (NaCl) or calcium chloride (CaCl) added to water raises the temperature at which water will boil and lowers the temperature at which it will freeze. Some refrigeration and air conditioning applications require that the water be kept from freezing at temperatures considerably below the freezing temperature of 32 degrees. Also some heating and air conditioning applications require that water at atmospheric pressure be kept from boiling at temperatures above 212 degrees. See Chapter 27 for tables of brine solutions and their characteristics.

There are some refrigerating and air conditioning installations which use tap water without the addition of any salt or other substance. Such water is referred to as "sweet water" as compared to brine.

1-44 Dry Ice

Solid carbon dioxide (CO_2) is sometimes used for refrigeration. It is a white crystalline substance formed by allowing liquid carbon dioxide to escape into a snow chamber. The heat for vaporizing the liquid is drawn from the interior of the chamber so that a very low temperature, -109 F. is formed, with the result that quantities of the carbon dioxide solidify. This solid is pressed into various shapes and sizes and sold for refrigeration purposes under such names as dry ice, zero ice, etc. It

remains at a temperature of -109 F. while in a solid state at atmospheric pressure, and sublimes, that is, it goes directly from the solid to the vapor state without becoming a liquid. It has some desirable characteristics in that it does not wet the surfaces that it touches, and the gas given off is a preservative. The very low temperature maintained permits handling frozen foods without an expensive insulated container. It is used a great deal by ice cream vendors and delivery trucks.

The latent heat of sublimation is 248 Btu per pound.

The heat absorbed by the vapor in passing from -109 F. to 32 F. is approximately 27 Btu per pound. This added to the latent heat of sublimation makes a total heat-absorbing capacity of 275 Btu per pound. This is a greater heat-absorbing value than for water ice. Dry ice is generally more expensive per pound than water ice.

1-45 Critical Temperature

The critical temperature of a substance is the maximum temperature at which the substance may be liquefied, regardless of the pressure applied upon it. Refer to Chapter 27, for a list of critical temperatures for common refrigerants. The condensing temperature for all refrigerants must be kept below the critical temperature for the refrigerant used; otherwise the refrigerator would not operate. Carbon dioxide (R-744) has a critical temperature of 87.8 F. This refrigerant cannot be used in air-cooled condensers because the condensing temperature would usually be above this temperature.

1-46 Critical Pressure

The critical pressure of a substance is the pressure at or above which the substance will remain a liquid and it cannot be turned into a gas by the addition of heat.

1-47 Enthalpy

Enthalpy, for practical purposes, is the total amount of heat in one pound of a substance calculated from an accepted temperature base. The temperature of 32 F. is the accepted base for water and water vapor calculations. For refrigerant calculations the accepted base is -40 F.

Example: What is the enthalpy of 1 lb. of water at 212 F. assuming 0 enthalpy at 32 F.?
Solution:
Enthalpy at 32 F. = 0.
Heat to raise the temperature of 1 lb. of water from 32 F. to 212 F. = 212 - 32 = 180 Btu.
This is one Btu per pound of water per degree F.
Total heat at 212 F. = 180 Btu.
Example: What is the enthalpy of 10 lbs. of steam at 212 F.?
Solution:
Enthalpy at 32 F. = 0.
Enthalpy of water at 212 F. = 180 Btu
Enthalpy of steam at 212 F. = 970 Btu
Total heat of 1 lb. of steam
                    at 212 F. = 1150 Btu
Total heat of 10 lbs. of steam at 212 F. will be 1150 x 10 = 11,500 Btu.
The latent heat of vaporization of water at atmospheric pressure is 970 Btu/lb., as shown in Par. 1-27.
Practical applications of this procedure are used in Chapter 16.

1-48 Entropy

Entropy is the heat available measured in Btu per pound degree change for a substance.
Entropy calculations are made from generally accepted temperature bases. For heating and steam power using water as the medium, the accepted base is 32 F. For domestic, and most commercial refrigeration calculations, the base is -40 F. For research and very low temperature work, a base of a lower temperature may be selected.
Entropy is generally used only in engineering calculations. Entropy tables have been worked out and are contained in most engineering handbooks.

1-49 Cryogenics

The term cryogenics is used to describe the use of, or the creating of, temperatures in the range of -250 F. to absolute zero. The term is also applied to the low temperature liquefication of gases, handling and storage, insulation of containers, instrumentation, and techniques used in such work.
The present extensive use of liquid helium and liquid hydrogen has increased the common use of the term cryogenics. Fig. 1-22 shows the boiling temperature

BOILING TEMPERATURE AT ATMOSPHERIC PRESSURE

FLUID	FAHREN-HEIT	RANKIN	CENTI-GRADE	KELVIN
	F	R (Absolute F Scale)	C	K (Absolute C Scale)
Water	212	672	100	373
R-12 Refrigerant	-22	438	-30	243
R-22 Refrigerant	-41	419	-43	230
R-290 Refrigerant Propane	-44	416	-44	229
R-744 Refrigerant Carbon Dioxide	-109	351	-78	195
R-1150 Refrigerant Ethylene	-135	325	-93	180
Beginning of the Cryogenic Range	-250	210	-157	116
Methane	-258	202	-161	112
Oxygen	-297	163	-183	90
Air	-313	147	-192	81
Nitrogen	-320	140	-196	77
Neon	-411	49	-246	27
Hydrogen	-423	37	-253	20
Helium	-452	8	-270	3
Absolute Zero	-460	0	-273	0

Fig. 1-22. Boiling temperatures of some common refrigerants and some other fluids at atmospheric pressure. Note the difference between the boiling points of some commonly used refrigerants and the boiling points of the fluids in the cryogenic range.

1-50 Boyle's Law

Boyle's Law expresses a very interesting relation between the pressure and volume of a gas. It may be stated as follows:

"The volume of a gas varies inversely as the pressure, provided the temperature remains constant."

This means that if a certain quantity of gas has its pressure doubled, the volume becomes one-half that of the original. Or, if the volume is doubled, the gas has its pressure reduced by one-half. If a perfect gas is considered, Boyle's Law may be expressed as a formula:

Pressure x Volume = A constant number.

This being true, one can say that when either the pressure or the volume is changed, the corresponding pressure or volume is changed in the opposite direction. Therefore, Old Pressure x Old Volume = the New Pressure x the New Volume, Expressed in letter form:

$P_o \times V_o = P_n \times V_n$

P_o = Old Absolute Pressure
P_n = New Absolute Pressure
V_o = Old Volume
V_n = New Volume

Note this formula will hold true only if the pressures are expressed as absolute pressures (psia).

Example: What will be the new volume, of 5 cubic feet of gas at 20 psig if it is compressed to 60 psig, providing the temperature remains constant?

Consider atmospheric pressure = 15 psi

$P_o \times V_o = P_n \times V_n$

P_o = 20 psig atmospheric pressure
= (20 + 15) = 35 psia
P_n = 60 psig + atmospheric pressure =
(60 + 15) = 75 psia

$P_o \times V_o = P_n \times V_n$, substituting the preceding values in this formula
35 x 5 = 75 x Vn or

$$\frac{35 \times 5}{75} = V_n$$

$$V_n = \frac{35}{15}$$

= 2.33 cu. ft. at 60 psig

1-51 Charles' Law

Gases behave consistently with temperature changes. This is stated in Charles' Law. "At a constant pressure the volume of a confined gas varies directly as the absolute temperature; and at a constant volume, the pressure varies directly as the absolute temperature." This is sometimes known as Gay-Lussacs law of gasses. Absolute pressures must always be used in the equations. In the equation form:
At constant volume

The Old Pressure x the New Absolute Temperature = the New Pressure x the Old Absolute Temperature

$P_o \times T_n = P_n \times T_o$
T = Absolute Temperature
P_o = Absolute Pressure
At constant pressure

The Old Volume x the New Absolute Temperature = the New Volume x the Old Absolute Temperature

$V_o \times T_n = V_n \times T_o$

Example: A 5 cubic feet volume of gas at 37 F. is raised to 90 F. at constant pressure. What is the new volume?

Solution:
$V_o \times T_n = V_n \times T_o$
5 x (90 + 460) = Vn x (37 +460)
5 x 550 = Vn x 497
$$\frac{5 \times 550}{497} = \frac{2750}{497} = V_n$$
Vn = 5.54 cubic feet.

Example: What is the pressure of a quantity of confined gas when raised to 60 F. if its original pressure was 35 pounds per square inch gauge and temperature 40 F., at a constant volume?

Solution: Note absolute temperatures and pressures must be used.

$$Po \times Tn = Pn \times To$$
$$(35 + 15)(60 + 460) = Pn \times (40 + 460)$$
$$50 \times 520 = Pn \times 500$$

$$\frac{50 \times 520}{500} = Pn$$

$$Pn = \frac{520}{10} = 52 \text{ psia}$$

$$Psig = 52 - 15 = 37$$

1-52 Gas Law

Boyle's Law and Charles' Law may be combined to solve true gas problems and the formula is as follows:

$$\frac{Po \times Vo}{To} = \frac{Pn \times Vn}{Tn}$$

To = Old temperature
Tn = New temperature
Po, Vo, and To represent original conditions.
Pn, Vn, and Tn represent new conditions. Absolute values for temperatures and pressure must be used in this equation. A more concrete equation is: PV = WRT. Where P = Pressure in Pounds Per Square Foot abs.

V = Volume in Cubic Feet
R = Gas Constant
W = Weight of Gas in Pounds
T = Absolute Temperature F.

This equation is useful for many pressure-volume problems and its use is easily followed.

R = Gas constant and it must be known for the gas under consideration. Fig. 1-23 lists the value of R for several common gases.

1-53 Dalton's Law

Dalton's Law of partial pressures is the foundation of the principle of operation of

Material	Specific Heat		
	CP	CV	R
Air	.24	.17	53.34
R-717 (Ammonia)	.51	.35	123.24
R-744 (Carbon Dioxide)	.22	.17	38.82
Ether	.48	.45	23.11
Oxygen	.22	.16	48.55
Alcohol	.45	.40	41.55
Water Vapor	.480	.37	83.23

Fig. 1-23. A table of gas values (constants) for some common substances.

one of the absorption type refrigerators. The law may be stated as follows:

"The total pressure of a confined mixture of gases is the sum of the partial pressures of each of the gases in the mixture." The total pressure of the air in a compressed air cylinder is the sum of the oxygen gas, the nitrogen gas, the carbon dioxide gas, and the water vapor pressure.

The law further explains that each gas behaves as if it occupies the space ALONE. This behavior also explains why water will evaporate from a floor after a scrubbing. The water vapor pressure is so low in the air that the water will turn to water vapor (very slowly of course) at temperatures of 70 F. down to freezing.

1-54 Adiabatic Expansion and Contraction

The term adiabatic refers to the process whereby a gas expands or contracts without any transfer of heat into it or from it during the expansion or compression.

Adiabatic expansion and compression of gases would occur if the gas was placed in a perfectly insulated cylinder with a frictionless piston so that heat could not enter the gas during expansion or escape during compression.

During the adiabatic expansion of ideal gases, the work performed, compression and expansion, is obtained FROM THE GAS.

Thus, during expansion, the pressure and temperature of the ideal gas decreases. Also, when work is done on a gas as it is adiabatically compressed, the heat generated is not lost, but increases the temperature and consequently the pressure of the confined gas.

1-55 Isothermal Expansion and Contraction

An isothermal condition is the expansion or contraction of a gas which occurs without a change in temperature (Boyle's Law, Par. 1-50). This condition can occur either during the expansion or the compression of a gas.

During the expansion of a gas, the gas is cooled and therefore the heat necessary to keep the gas at a constant temperature must be obtained from an outside source. The heat obtained from the outside source must be exactly equal to that given up by the gas during its expansion, in order to keep the temperature constant.

Similarly, during the isothermal compression of a gas, heat must be removed from the gas in an amount equal to the heat energy of compression in order to maintain a constant temperature. Regardless of whether the compressor is air-cooled or water-cooled, the heat removed must be equal to the heat input done by the work of compressing the gas.

1-56 Standard Atmosphere

The pressure, temperature and relative humidity of the atmosphere is continually changing. For air conditioning calculations it is agreed to use pressures, temperatures and humidity values known as the Standard Atmosphere. These values are:

Pressure = 29.92 in. Hg. = 14.7 psia
                     = 0 psig
Temperature = 59 F. = 15 C.
Humidity = 50%

These values are in common use and are the basis for air computations in this and other textbooks.

It should be noted that the pressure of 29.92 in. Hg. is for sea level. For calculations concerning air at elevations, greatly above sea level, correction factors may be applied.

The pressure of the atmosphere drops approximately 1 in. Hg. or 1/2 lb./sq. in. for each 1000 feet of elevation. At 5280 feet (1 mile) above sea level the atmospheric pressure is 12.02 psi.

The barometer reading multiplied by .49 will give the psi.

Example: What will be the approximate elevation of point X which has a barometer reading of 25 in. Hg.?

Solution:
Standard atmospheric pressure 29.92 in. Hg.
Barometer reading at Point X = 25 in. Hg.
Barometric difference between sea level and point X = Standard atmospheric pressure less 25 in. or 29.92 - 25 = 4.92 in. Hg. The pressure difference in psi between sea level and point X will be:

4.92 in. Hg. difference multiplied by .49
4.92 × .49 = 2.41 psi
converting psi to elevation:
1/2 psi difference = 1000 feet elevation.
2.41 divided by psi difference for

$$1000 \text{ ft.} = \frac{2.41}{.5} = 4.8$$

4.8 × 1000 = 4800 feet elevation.

Also it should be noted that as the elevation above sea level increases, the the boiling temperature of water decreases. The temperature at which water boils drops approximately one degree F. for each 550 feet of increase in elevation above sea level.

Example: What is the approximate boiling temperature of water at 3000 feet above sea level?

Solution: Temperature drops one degree for each 550 feet of elevation $\frac{3000}{550} = 5.45$ degrees drop.

Boiling temperature of water at sea level = 212°.

Boiling temperature at 3000 ft. = 212° -5.45° = 206.55°.

1-57 Humidity

The word humidity as used on connection with refrigeration, air conditioning and weather information refers to water vapor or moisture contained in the air. Air absorbs moisture (water vapor) the amount depending on the pressure and temperature of the air. The higher the temperature of the air, the more moisture it can absorb. The higher the pressure of the air, the smaller the amount of moisture it can absorb. The amount of moisture carried in a sample of air, compared to the total amount which it can absorb at the stated pressure and temperature, is called relative humidity. See Chapter 19.

1-58 Relative Humidity

As previously explained, relative humidity is the percentage of moisture contained in a sample of air compared to the maximum amount of moisture which it is capable of holding at the stated temperature and pressure. See Chapter 27 for tables of moisture holding ability for air at various temperatures and pressures.

1-59 Saturated Vapor

The term "saturated vapor" identifies a condition of balance on an enclosed quantity of a vaporized fluid in which liquid will be condensed out if the temperature is lowered or the pressure increased. There is usually some of the substance in liquid form present when the vapor is saturated. This implies that all of the substance has been vaporized that can be vaporized under the present conditions of pressure and temperature.

1-60 Humidity Measurement (Hygrometer)

Relative humidity is measured by a hygrometer. A hygrometer consists of two identical thermometers. The bulb of one is uncovered and dry, (dry bulb). The bulb of the other thermometer is covered with a wick and it is kept moist, (wet bulb). The two thermometers will not read alike. The bulb of the wet bulb thermometer will be cooled slightly by the evaporation of the moisture from the wick surrounding the bulb. Consequently, this thermometer will read lower than the dry bulb thermometer.

The lower the humidity the more rapidly the moisture on the wet bulb will evaporate and this rapid evaporation will cool the wet bulb to a much lower temperature than the dry bulb.

If the humidity is high, approaching 100%, the difference between the dry bulb temperature and the wet bulb temperature will be very slight, one degree or less.

To determine the relative humidity, the operator records the difference between the dry bulb and wet bulb temperatures and refers to established tables which indicate the relative humidity for the air being tested. See Chapters 19 and 27. An instrument for measuring relative humidity using a wet and a dry bulb thermometer is called a psychrometer.

Hygrometers using moisture absorbing wood, hair and other substances are being used, however the wet and dry bulb thermometer (psychrometer) is simple, reliable and easy to operate.

1-61 Temperature Humidity index

The term "temperature humidity index" (THI) is a number which aims to establish the degree of discomfort of the average individual due to the ambient temperature and the relative humidity.

It is indicated by a number. The THI is calculated by a mathematical formula as follows: THI = .4 of the sum of the wet and dry bulb temperature plus 15.

Example No. 1. On a certain day the wet bulb temperature was 70 degrees and the dry bulb temperature was 80 degrees.

$$\begin{aligned} \text{The THI} &= .4 \times (70 + 80) + 15 \\ &= .4 \times (150) + 15 \\ &= 60 + 15 \\ &= 75 \end{aligned}$$

From this it may be seen that the relative humidity as indicated by the wet bulb temperature is quite important in establishing the temperature humidity index.

Example No. 2. On a certain day the dry bulb temperature was 80 degrees and the wet bulb temperature was 75 degrees.

$$\begin{aligned} \text{The THI} &= .4 \times (80 + 75) + 15 \\ &= .4 \times (155) + 15 \\ &= 62 + 15 \\ &= 77 \end{aligned}$$

In example No. 1, the relative humidity was 61% and in example No. 2 it was 79%. The dry bulb or ambient temperature was the same on both days, however, the THI is two points higher on the second day due to the higher humidity.

1-62 Degree Days

Degree days is a term used to indicate the heating or cooling needed for any certain day.

It is calculated from a temperature of 65 degrees. (It should be noted that the standard conditions temperature is 68 degrees.) The degree day is computed by taking the mean of the highest temperature and the lowest temperature for a day and subtracting it from 65.

Example: The lowest recorded temperature for a certain day was 28 F. (degrees)

The highest recorded temperature for the same day was 36 F. (degrees)

The mean temperature for the day was

$$\frac{28 + 36}{2} = 32 \text{ degrees}$$

$65 - 32 = 33$ degree days.

Degree days may be added by weeks, months or for a season to give a comparison of the heating needs for different years.

1-63 Review, Abbreviations, Symbols

Btu = British thermal unit

Btuh = British thermal units per hour

F. = Degrees Fahrenheit

C. = Degrees Centigrade

F_A = Degrees Fahrenheit Absolute

C_A = Degrees Centigrade Absolute

R^o = Degrees Rankin = degrees absolute F.

K^o = Degrees Kelvin = degrees absolute C.

p = pounds = lbs.

psi = pounds per square inch = lbs. per sq. in.

i = inches = in.

f = foot or feet = ft.

si = square inch = sq. in.

sf = square feet or foot = sq. ft.

r = radius of circle

π = 3.1416 (a constant use in determining the area of a circle)

pcf = pounds per cubic foot = lbs. per cu. ft.

Hg = inches of mercury vacuum

sp.gr. = specific gravity

sp.ht. = specific heat

hp = horsepower

W. = Watts

ft.lb. = foot-pounds

ton = ton of refrigeration effect

lb./cft. = pounds per cubic foot

psig = pounds per square inch gauge

psi = pounds per square inch = lbs. per sq. in.

psia = pounds per square inch absolute
= pounds per square inch gauge plus atmospheric pressure of 14.7 lbs. or 15 lbs. per sq. in.

Po = Old absolute pressure
Pn = New absolute pressure
Vo = Old Volume
Vn = New Volume
To = Old absolute temperature
Tn = New absolute temperature
∞ = Infinity

1-64 Evaporator - Cooling Coil

In this text the word evaporator is used to indicate the coil or surface in which liquid refrigerant boils or evaporates and picks up heat. In some trade literature the word cooling coil is used to indicate the area in which cooling takes place. The correct technical terminology is evaporator coil.

1-65 Vapor - Gas

In this text the word vapor is used to indicate refrigerant which has become heated, usually in the evaporator and has changed to a vapor or gaseous state. In some trade and service literature refrigerant in this state is called a gas. However, the correct technical terminology is vapor. Accordingly, the word vapor is used in this text.

1-66 Test Your Knowledge, Chapter 1

1. What is the absolute pressure equivalent in pounds per square inch of 8 inches of mercury vacuum?

2. What is the gas space in the cylinder of of a compressor if it has a 2-inch bore and a 3-inch stroke?

3. If 100 cubic inches of a gas at 15 pounds per square inch gauge were compressed to 20 cubic inches, what is the gauge pressure if the temperature remains constant?

4. If 100 cubic inches of gas under constant pressure were changed from 40 F. to 290 F., what is the new volume?

5. How many Btu's will be required to change 5 pounds of ice at 32 F. into water at 82 F.?

6. How many pounds of R-12 must be evaporated at 5 F. to change 50 pounds of water from 72 F. to ice at 5 F. if the container for the water is made of copper and weighs 3 pounds?

7. If 2 cubic feet of gas at 90 F. and under a pressure of 15 pounds per square inch gauge is changed to 4 cubic feet at 40 F., what is the new gauge pressure?

8. What is the pressure difference in pounds per square inch between 6 inches of mercury vacuum and 8 pounds per square inch gauge?

9. If a 15 pound weight is placed on an area 2 by 3 inches, what is the unit pressure in pounds per square inch absolute?

10. If the head pressure is 85 pounds per square inch gauge, what is the total force on one face of a circular disk 5 inches in diameter?

11. What is the average temperature desired in a domestic cabinet?

12. What determines the temperature at which a refrigerant will vaporize?

13. Express standard atmospheric pressure in pounds per square foot.

14. Should refrigerants be operated at temperatures above or below their critical temperature?

15. What is dry ice?

16. Should dry ice ever be put in a sealed container? Why?

17. What is the relative heat absorbing value of 1 pound of dry ice as com-

pared to 1 pound of water ice?

18. Does color affect the amount of heat absorbed by a surface by radiation? How?

19. Name a condition which illustrates the principle of convection.

20. Which material conducts heat the fastest, glass or copper?

21. Convert 78 F. to C.

22. Convert 20 C. to F.

23. Convert 5 F. to C.

24. Convert 432 F. to C.

25. Convert 14 F_A to C_A.

26. What is the equivalent of 20 kilowatts in:

A. British thermal units?

B. Foot-pounds?

27. What is the new volume of 50 cubic feet of gas if the pressure changes from 35 pounds per square inch gauge to 85 pounds per square inch gauge?

28. How many British thermal units must be extracted to cool 10 pounds of iron from 70 F. to 10 F.?

29. How many British thermal units must be removed from a cooling unit to cool it from 85 F. to 15 F., if it contains 10 pounds of copper and 20 pounds of glycerine?

30. Calculate the number of British thermal units required to convert 1 pound of ice at 0 F. to steam at 212 F.

Chapter 2

REFRIGERATION TOOLS
AND MATERIALS

The refrigeration serviceman's job consists mainly of performing rather basic mechanical operations using common tools and materials. There are three basic principles which should guide the serviceman:

1. Know what needs to be done.
2. Select the proper tools and materials.
3. Keep all refrigeration mechanisms clean and dry.

This chapter is carefully planned to give the refrigeration and air conditioning serviceman the necessary basic knowledge concerning tools and materials used in this industry. In addition, directions are given concerning the selection of proper tools and materials and the correct and safe handling of tools used in the many types of refrigeration work.

2-1 Tubing

Most tubing used in refrigeration and air conditioning is made of copper. However, some aluminum and steel tubing is being used. Instructions in th[...] pter will deal principally w[...]ng. All tubing to b[...]ng and refri[...]essed [...]side [...]s to [...] in

[...]ates [...]r air con[...]on and that it has

been processed to give the desired characteristics. ACR tubing is charged with gaseous nitrogen to keep out air and eliminate oxidation when soldering and silver brazing fittings to the tubing. This tubing should have the ends plugged immediately after cutting a length from the piece.

Another type of copper tubing used in heating and plumbing is called nominal size tubing.

Copper tubing is available in both soft and hard types. Both hard and soft copper tubing is available in two wall thicknesses, K and L. Most ACR tubing used at present is the L thickness.

2-2 Soft Copper Tubing

Soft copper tubing is used in domestic, also in some commercial refrigeration and air conditioning work. It is annealed to make the tubing flexible and easy to bend and flare. Since this tubing is easily bent, the tubing must be supported by clamps or suitable brackets when used. Soft copper tubing is most often used in connection with flared fittings (SAE) and soft soldered fittings. This tubing is sold in rolls of 25, 50 and 100 foot lengths. The most commonly used sizes are 3/16, 1/4, 5/16, 3/8, 7/16, 1/2, 9/16, 5/8 and 3/4 in. outside diameter (OD). The wall thickness is usually specified in thousandths of an inch.

Fig. 2-1 is a table of common copper tube diameters and thicknesses. Soft copper tubing may become hardened by repeated bending or hammering. This is called work hardening. The tubing may be softened some if it is heated to a blue surface color and allowed to cool slowly at room temperature. This treatment is called annealing.

2-3 Hard Drawn Copper Tubing

Hard drawn copper tubing is used extensively in commercial refrigeration and air conditioning applications. Due to its hardness and stiffness, it needs a minimum of clamps or supports, particularly in the larger diameters. This tubing should not be bent. Use straight lengths and fittings to form the necessary tubing design.

Hard drawn tubing should be used with silver brazed fittings. Soft solder should not be used. Fig. 2-1 shows a table of copper tube diameters and thicknesses. It may be noted that the diameters and thicknesses are the same for both soft and hard drawn ACR copper tubing.

Hard drawn copper tubing is supplied in 20 foot lengths.

2-4 Steel Tubing

Some thin-wall steel tubing is used in refrigeration and air conditioning work.

OUTSIDE DIAMETER	WALL THICKNESS
1/4	.030
3/8	.035
1/2	.040
5/8	.042
3/4	.045
1	.050
1 1/4	.055

Fig. 2-1. A table of copper tube Outside Diameter (OD) sizes and Wall Thicknesses for tubing used in refrigeration work. This tubing is identified as ACR tubing since it is manufactured particularly for air conditioning and refrigeration work. Both the soft and hard drawn sizes conform to the measurements listed in this table. The OD size for this tubing is the actual outside diameter of the tube.

NOMINAL SIZE INCHES	TYPE	OD INCHES		WALL THICKNESS INCHES
1/4	K	0.375	3/8	0.035
	L	0.375	3/8	0.030
3/8	K	0.500	1/2	0.049
	L	0.500	1/2	0.035
1/2	K	0.625	5/8	0.049
	L	0.625	5/8	0.040
5/8	K	0.750	3/4	0.049
	L	0.750	3/4	0.042
3/4	K	0.875	7/8	0.065
	L	0.875	7/8	0.045
1	K	1.125	1 1/4	0.065
	L	1.125	1 1/4	0.050
1 1/4	K	1.375	1 1/4	0.065
	L	1.375	1 1/4	0.055
	M	1.375	1 1/4	0.040

Fig. 2-2. Nominal size copper tubing. Not ordinarily used in connection with refrigerants. It should be noted that OD sizes indicated by dimensions are not the actual tube sizes. Type K—Heavy wall. Available in hard and soft temper. Type L—Medium wall. Available in hard and soft temper. Type M—Light wall. Available in hard temper only. Type K is used where corrosion conditions are severe. Type L is used where conditions may be considered normal. Type M is used for drainage and other nonpressure applications and other services less severe than those for which types K and L are recommended.

The sizes are practically the same as for copper tubing used in refrigeration work. Connections may be made on steel tubing by using either flared fittings or silver brazed connections. Copper or brass tubing should not be used in connection with R-717 (ammonia refrigerant); steel tubing should be used.

2-5 Nominal Size Copper Tubing

We have in common use a size of copper tubing used on water lines, drains, etc., but never used in connection with refrigerants. This is called nominal size copper tubing. It is available in both soft and hard drawn grades. Fig. 2-2 gives a table of commonly used sizes and wall thicknesses in this tubing.

2-6 Cutting Tubing

To cut tubing a hacksaw or a tube cutter may be used. The tube cutter should be used on the annealed copper tubing while the hacksaw is usually used for cutting hard copper tubing. Fig. 2-3 illustrates a wheel type tube cutter. After the tubing

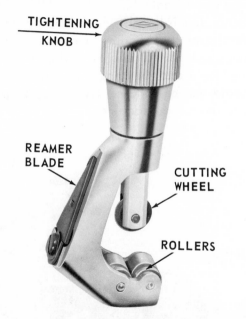

Fig. 2-3. *A copper tube cutter. This type of cutter is usually used on soft copper tubing. Note the attached reamer which is used to remove burrs from the inside of the tube after cutting. The grooves in the rollers allow the cutter to be used to remove a flare from a tube with little tubing waste.*
(Imperial-Eastman Corp.)

has been cut, its ends must be scraped or reamed with a pointed tool to remove any sharp burrs in the end of the tubing. Most tube cutters have such a tool built into them for this purpose. If a saw is to be used, a wave set blade of 32 teeth per inch is preferable. It is important that no filings or chips of any kind be allowed to

enter the tubing. In cutting tubing with a hacksaw, hold the tubing in such a manner that chips will not fall into the section that is to be used. Fig. 2-4 illustrates a sawing fixture.

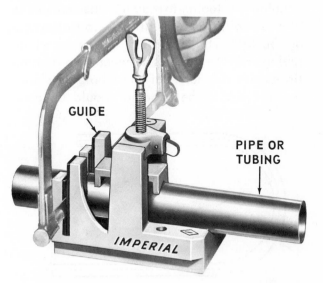

Fig. 2-4. *A sawing fixture used to insure square and accurate cuts when cutting tubing with the use of a hand hacksaw. This is the recommended method for cutting hard drawn and steel tubing.*

If soft tubing is used, pinching the tube eliminates the danger of chips entering the tubing that is not to be used. It also seals the tubing against moisture and protects it for further use. If hard copper tubing is being used, the tubing ends should be capped or plugged.

To provide a full-wall thickness at the end of the tubing, many servicemen file the end of the tubing with a smooth or medium cut mill file. The tubing should be straight to eliminate an off-center flare.

2-7 Bending Tubing

It takes considerable practice to become competent in bending tubing. For the smaller size tubing used in domestic models, it is not necessary to use special tools to do the bending. However, a much neater job and a much more satisfactory one is obtainable by using special tools. As mentioned before, the tubing should be bent so that it does not apply any strain on the fittings after it has been installed. The tubing, at the bend, should not be reduced in cross-sectional area. Be very careful when bending the tubing to maintain the roundness of the tubing and not allow it to flatten out or buckle. The minimum radius in which tubing may be bent is between five and ten times the diameter of the tubing as shown in Fig. 2-5. Tube bending should be done

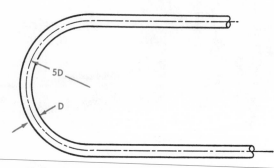

Fig. 2-5. The minimum safe bending radius for bending tubing. D is the diameter of the tube being bent.

quite slowly and carefully. It is always wise to bend the tubing into as large a radius as possible because this reduces the amount of flattening of the tubing to a minimum, and it is also easier to bend a large radius. Do not try to make the complete bend in one operation, but bend the tubing gradually so that it will not rupture by too sudden a stress. An inexpensive coil spring bending tool as illustrated in Fig. 2-6 may be easily carried in a kit. These are available in all sizes and are made for both external and internal use. The internal spring is for use near the ends of the tubing

or flared tubing, while the external is best used in the middle of long lengths of tubing. A 1/4 inch OD tube bending spring may be used as an internal spring for 1/2 inch OD tubing.

When tubing is bent with a bending spring, it tends to bind on the tubing. It may be easily removed by twisting the spring to cause the external spring to expand or to cause the internal spring to contract. If a bend is to be made near a flare and an external spring is to be used, bend the tubing first. An internal spring can be used either before or after the flaring operation.

Some special tools which have been used to facilitate the bending operations are a round block or a short-section of large piping for hand bending. To obtain very accurate work, bending tools may be purchased from manufacturers.

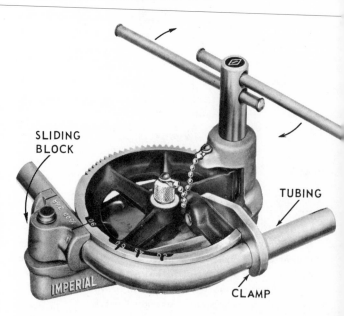

SLIDING BLOCK

TUBING

CLAMP

IMPERIAL

Fig. 2-7. A tube bending tool designed to produce accurate bends and prevent buckling of the tube while bending.

Fig. 2-7 shows a convenient tool used for bending tubing. A lever-type bender for accurate bending to within 1/32 in. for soft or hard tubing is shown in Fig. 2-8. It can be purchased in six different sizes to

IMPERIAL

Fig. 2-6. A tube bending spring which may be fitted either outside or inside a copper tube while bending the tube. The bending spring reduces the danger of a tube being flattened while being bent.

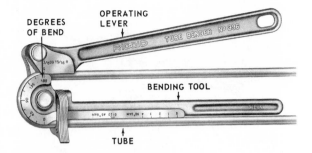

Fig. 2-8. A lever type tube bending tool. Bends to a required number of degrees are possible with this tool. Tubing is stretched slightly in length during a bend. The amount of the stretch (gain) is indicated on the bending tool. (Ridge Tool Co.)

match the diameter of the tube to be bent. Always use a bending tool when bending hard drawn or steel tubing.

Fig. 2-9 shows some practice bends on tubing.

2-8 Connecting Tubing

Since tubing walls are too thin for threading, other methods of joining tubing to tubing and to fittings must be used. The common methods are flared connection, soldered connection and silver brazed connection.

2-9 Flaring Tubing

A good flare is very important if a solid, strong, leakproof joint is to be made at the flared connection. Tubing flares are made with special flaring tools. Some flares are made which have a single thickness of the tube forming the flare, other flares are made which provide a double thickness of metal in the flare surface. Double thickness or "double flares" as they are called are used mostly on commercial applications and on automobile air conditioning installations. Double flares are stronger and usually cause less trouble if properly made. Fig. 2-10 illustrates how a flare is used to form a leakproof joint between a tube and a fitting.

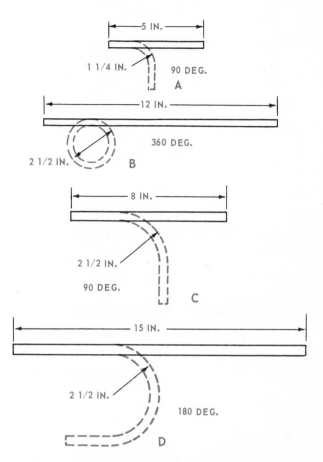

Fig. 2-9. Some practice bends on tubing. A-90 deg. bend on 1/4 in. tubing. B-360 deg. bend on 1/4 in. tubing. C-90 deg. bend on 1/2 in. tubing. D-180 deg. bend on 1/2 in. tubing.

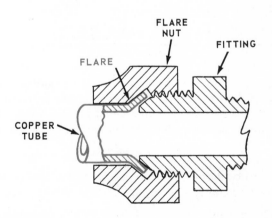

Fig. 2-10. A cross section of a flared fitting. Note that the seal is made by the flare nut surface pressing the flare against the mating surface of the fitting. All of the mating surfaces are accurately machined.

2-10 Single Thickness Flare

Before starting a flare, the end of the tube should be carefully prepared for flaring. The end must be straight and square with the tube and the burr from the cutting operation removed by reaming. Fig. 2-11 illustrates the steps necessary to prepare a tube for flaring. First, use

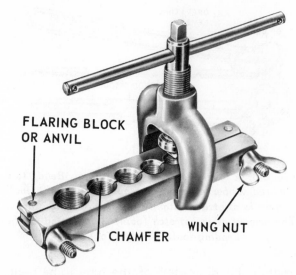

Fig. 2-12. *This illustrates a popular style flaring tool used for making single thickness flares on refrigeration tubing. The flaring block is split making it easy to insert and clamp the tubing in place for flaring. Note the 45 deg. chamfer in the block which gives the flare its correct shape.*
(Duro Metal Products Co.)

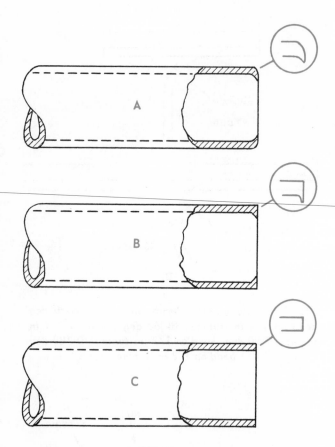

Fig. 2-11. *The end of the tube must be carefully prepared before flaring. A-Shows the tube after being cut. B-Shows the tube after being squared with a file. C-Shows the tube filed, reamed and ready for flaring.*

a smooth cut file to square the end of the tube. Use great care that no filings enter the tubing. Next, use a burring reamer to remove the slight burr which remains after the cutoff operation.

A single thickness flare may be made with a flaring tool as shown in Fig. 2-12.

To produce a flare of the correct dimensions using a chamfered flaring block, proceed as follows:

Insert the tube in the flaring tool so that it extends above the surface of the block as shown in Fig. 2-13A. This is to allow sufficient metal to form a full flare. If the tube extends above the block more than the amount indicated, the flare will be too large in diameter and the flare nut will not fit over it. If the tube does not extend above the block, the flare will be too small and it may be squeezed out of the fitting as the flare nut is tightened. Fig. 2-13B shows a completed flare as it is formed in the flaring tool.

To form the flare, first put a drop of refrigerant oil on the flaring tool spinner where it contacts the tubing. Tighten the spinner one-half turn and back it off one-quarter turn. Advance it three-quarters of a turn and again back it off one-quarter turn. Repeat the forward movement and backing off until the flare is formed.

Some serviceman make the flare using one continuous motion of the flaring cone; that is, without a back-and-forth motion. It

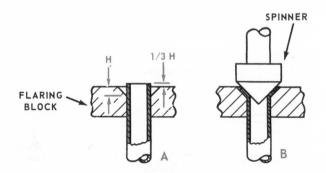

SPINNER

H   1/3 H

FLARING
BLOCK

A   B

Fig. 2-13. The tubing to be flared should extend a small amount above the flaring block to allow sufficient metal to form a satisfactory flare. The amount to allow is approximately one-third of the height of the flare. A-The proper position of the tube in the flaring tool before flaring. B-A completed flare.

is believed by some that the continuous turning of the cone, without back turning, may work harden the tubing and make it more susceptible to splitting.

Some servicemen prefer to use a flare which is not completely formed, about

seven-eighths complete, and depend on tightening the flare nut on the flare to complete it.

Under no circumstances tighten up the spinning tool too much because this will thin the wall of the tubing at the flare and weaken it considerably.

A word to the beginner--always place the flare nut on the tube in the proper position before the flare is made because it cannot, in most cases, be installed on the tube after it has been flared.

2-11 Double Thickness Flare

Double thickness flares are formed with tools made for this purpose. Fig. 2-14 illustrates a cross section through a simple block-and-punch type of tool used to make

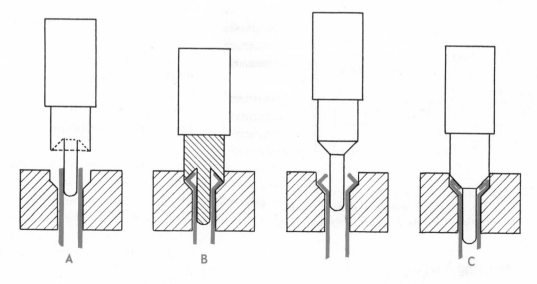

A   B   C

Fig. 2-14. A cross section showing a simple block and punch tool for forming double flares on copper tubing. A-The tube is clamped in the body of the flaring block. B-The first (female) punch bends the end of the tube inward. C-The second (male) punch folds the end of the tube downward to form a double thickness and expand the flare into final form.

a double flare. The appearance of the double flare is shown in the final operation in this figure. Some flaring tools are fitted with adapters which makes it possible to form either single or double flares with the same tool. Fig. 2-15 shows such a tool.

Fig. 2-15. A flaring tool which, with necessary adapters, is capable of producing either single or double flares. (Imperial-Eastman Corp.)

Fig. 2-16 shows the step-by-step procedure in making a double flare.

Double thickness flares are recommended for only the larger size tubing (5/16 in. and over) and are not easily formed on smaller tubing. The double flare makes a stronger joint than a single flare.

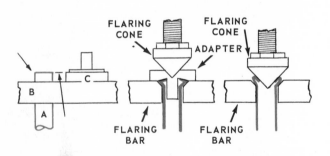

Fig. 2-16. This shows the correct procedure for forming a double flare using the adapters with a combination single flare - double flare, flaring tool.

2-12 Annealing Tubing

If a flare splits when being made, it may be due to the age of the tubing. Old tubing becomes brittle after a certain period of use and cannot be flared satisfactorily. A remedy is to anneal the tubing by heating to a dull cherry red or blue color and allowing it to cool in air or water. Pounding, rough handling, or bending the tubing tends to harden it. Hard drawn tubing cannot be bent or flared unless annealed.

2-13 Swaging Copper Tubing

Swaging permits two pieces of soft copper tubing of the same diameter to be joined together without the use of fittings as shown in Fig. 2-17.

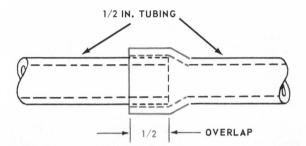

Fig. 2-17. Two pieces of soft copper tubing are shown swaged and ready for soldering or brazing to make a joint connecting the two pieces of tubing. Note that both pieces of the tubing are of the same diameter.

The process of swaging copper tubing is often used as it is more convenient to solder one joint than to make two joints when using couplings.

The length of engagement of the two pieces of tubing is important. A general rule is to make the length of engagement equal to the outside diameter (OD) of the tubing.

There are two types of swaging tools available: the punch type and the screw type. In both cases different sizes are available for use with the various sizes of copper tubing. The screw type swaging tool is used in the same manner as the flaring tool.

When using the punch type swaging tool, the copper tubing is inserted into the correct hole size in the anvil block and then a corresponding punch is inserted into the copper tubing and hammered down until the punch has entered the tubing the desired distance. Fig. 2-18 shows a punch type swaging tool.

Many prefer to use streamlined fittings when joining two pieces of tubing of the same diameter as it saves the time required to swage the one tube.

Fig. 2-18. A punch type swaging tool complete with various size punches and anvil for swaging tubing from one-quarter to one-half inch in diameter.

2-14 Tube Constrictor

There are many cases where a serviceman needs to make a soldered or brazed joint between two tubes; one tube which fits rather loosely inside the other. Good practice demands that the tubes be as close as .003 in. to each other. Fig. 2-19 shows a special tool used to constrict the outer tube until it fits the OD of the inner tube. Using this tool the serviceman can easily solder or braze the joint without danger of leaks or of flux getting into the system.

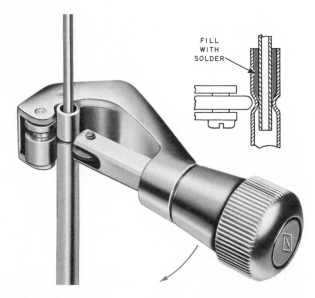

Fig. 2-19. A combination tube cutter and constrictor. A different wheel is used for cutting than the one used for constricting The insert shows two tubes joined by soldering or brazing. The outer oversize tube has been constricted before soldering.
(Imperial-Eastman Corp.)

2-15 Tubing Fittings

There are many different fitting designs on the market, but the accepted standard for refrigeration fittings is a forged fitting using either pipe thread or Society of Automotive Engineers (SAE) National Fine Thread. The fittings are usually drop-forged brass and are accurately machined to form the NF threads, the NP threads, the hexagonal shapes for wrench attachment and the 45 degree flare for fitting against the tubing flare. These threaded fittings must be carefully handled to prevent injury. Fig. 2-20 illustrates some of the common flared type fittings used in refrigeration work.

Fig. 2-20. This figure illustrates some of the more common flared type fittings used in refrigeration and air conditioning work. A-Flared Tee fitting, flare x flare x flare. B-Flared Union coupling flare x flare. C-Flared Half Union coupling flare x m p t D-Flared Union 90 deg. Elbow flare x flare. E-Flare Nut.
(Mueller Brass Co.)

All fitting sizes are based on the tubing size to which the fittings are attached. A 1/4 in. flare unit which fastens 1/4 in. tubing to a flared fitting has 7/16 NF threads and a 3/4 in. size wrench opening is used to turn it. Wherever annealed copper tubing is attached to a fitting, the flared type of seal is generally used.

REFRIGERATION FITTINGS (FLARED TYPE)
Sizes are based on the Outside Diameter of the Tubing

Name and Description	1/4	5/16	3/8	7/16	1/2	5/8
Nut Forged	X	X	X	X	X	X
Union (Threads same size)	X	X	X	X	X	X
Half Union (1/8 Pipe)	X	X				
Half Union (1/4 Pipe)	X	X	X	X		
Half Union (3/8 Pipe)					X	
Half Union (1/2 Pipe)						X
Elbow	X	X	X	X	X	X
Elbow (One 1/8 Pipe)	X	X				
Elbow (One 1/4 Pipe)	X	X	X	X		
Elbow (One 3/8 Pipe)					X	
Elbow (One 1/2 Pipe)						X
Tee (Threads same size)	X	X	X	X	X	X
Tee (One 1/8 Pipe)	X	X				
Tee (One 1/4 Pipe)			X	X		
Tee (One 3/8 Pipe)					X	
Tee (One 1/2 Pipe)						X
Cross	X	X	X	X	X	X
Flared Tube Sealing Plug	X	X	X	X	X	X
Flared Tube Sealing Cap		X	X	X	X	X
Flared Tube Copper Seal Cap . .	X	X	X	X	X	X
Union (Reducing)	5/16-1/4	3/8-1/4	1/2-1/4	1/2-3/8		
Elbow (Reducing)	5/16-1/4	3/8-1/4	1/2-1/4	1/2-3/8	5/8-1/2	
Tee (Reducing)	5/16-1/4	3/8-1/4	1/2-1/4	1/2-3/8	5/8-1/2	

Fig. 2-21. A table of some of the more popular flared type copper tube fittings which are commonly used by the refrigeration and air conditioning service engineer.

Fig. 2-21 shows a table of common flared fitting sizes. Modern standards often call for a soldered or brazed connection between the fitting and tubing, as shown in Fig. 2-22.

The correct method of installing tubing is to install it in such a way that there is no extra strain on the tubing when job is completed. Horizontal loops may be used to keep vibration from crystallizing the copper which might cause it to crack or break. Some tubing fittings have pipe threads on one end. Pipe threads taper 1/16 in. in diameter for every inch in length. Fig. 2-23 illustrates some common soldered or brazed tube fittings, often referred to as sweat fittings.

2-16 Soft Soldering

Soldering is a regular service operation. It is only after diligent study and application of soldering theory and practice that real soldering results may be obtained.

Soldering is applying a molten metal to metals that have been heated but are not molten. It is an adhesion process. Solder flows into the pores of the metals being joined, and as the solder solidifies, a good bond is obtained.

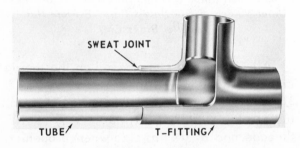

SWEAT JOINT

TUBE — T-FITTING

Fig. 2-22. Figure illustrating cross section through a tee fitting brazed to a hard ACR tube.

Brass parts, copper tubing, fittings, and containers, such as the cooling unit of the refrigerator, are easily soldered and this facilitates the work of the serviceman.

Fundamentally, in order to solder, (1) the surfaces to be soldered must be very clean; (2) a good clean flux must be used; (3) and a source of heat of sufficient quantity must be on hand. Flux does not clean the metal. It keeps the metal clean once it has been cleaned by filing, scraping, using steel wool, wire brushes, etc. The parts must have all the grease, dirt and oxides removed from the surfaces being soldered.

A 50 percent tin and 50 percent lead solder is usually satisfactory for soft soldering, except on cooling coils and their

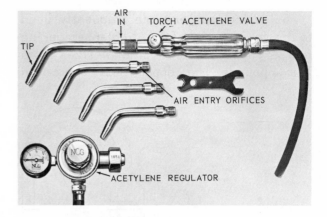

Fig. 2-24. An air-acetylene torch which may be used for both soldering and brazing tubing. These torches use the small portable Prest-O-Lite acetylene cylinders. The flame is very clean and hot and the torch is easy to use. (National Cylinder Gas Co.)

Fig. 2-23. Some common soldered or brazed copper tube fittings. A-Coupling with rolled stop, sweat x sweat. B-Tee, sweat x sweat x sweat. C-90 deg. elbow, sweat x sweat. D-Adapter, sweat x male pipe thread m.p.t.

connections. Solders containing as much as 95 percent tin are now being recommended for refrigeration work on cooling coils subjected to temperatures below 30 deg. F.

A portable torch, Fig. 2-24, is a practical tool to use for heating surfaces to be soldered. The gas that is recommended for this type of torch is acetylene. The flux recommended for this type of work is one which has no corrosive properties. A satis-

factory flux may be made of alcohol and rosin. Acid flux should not be used because it tends to corrode the fittings and makes them unsightly and difficult to work on later.

An important fundamental of good soldering is that the metal being joined must be hot enough to melt the solder. This is the only way the solder will go into the pores of the metal. The heat should be applied to the metal to be soldered; then touch the solder to the metal. If the parts to be soldered are of the correct temperature, have been cleaned and fluxed, the solder will flow over the surface quickly. Do not heat the solder with the torch.

When joining tubing and tubing fittings by soldering, you must clean the exterior thoroughly. Rolls of abrasive paper or cloth are a good cleaning means. Internal and external brushes are also used considerably. Fig. 2-25 illustrates a tube soldering unit that can be connected to a R-12 cylinder or compressed air line and used to check for leaks. Never use oxygen when testing for leaks. Any oil in contact with oxygen under pressure will form an explosive mixture.

When soldering tubing, certain definite steps should be followed in a definite order. Fig. 2-26 illustrates the correct procedure.

Soldering coppers are frequently used to perform some of the lighter soldering tasks. These coppers come in sizes from 1 to 4 pounds. The copper must have a thin

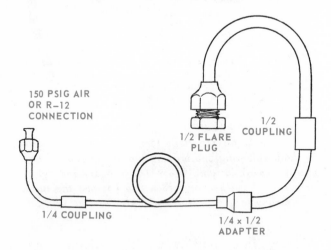

150 PSIG AIR OR R–12 CONNECTION

1/2 FLARE PLUG

1/2 COUPLING

1/4 COUPLING

1/4 x 1/2 ADAPTER

Fig. 2-25. A practice piece used to develop skill in copper tube soldering. The completed assembly should be pressurized as indicated and all of the joints tested for leaks using soapsuds.

coating of solder on the surface of the point. This "tinning" of the copper is accomplished as follows:

1. Remove the oxide from the point with a smooth file or sandpaper.
2. Heat the copper.
3. Sand the point of the copper.
4. Immerse the point in flux.
5. Rub the point of the copper in solder placed in the hollow of a sal ammoniac block (a flux).

Wire solder is usually the most convenient to use because of the difficulty of getting at the soldering surfaces, and the ease of application of the wire solder. To clean the surfaces previous to the soldering, a dry abrasive should be used, such as sandpaper. Do not use emery cloth or emery paper on the surface under any conditions. Emery cloth often contains oil which applied on tubing will make soldering difficult. In addition, the abrasive or emery cloth is usually silicon carbide which is a very hard abrasive and if any grains of

this abrasive were to enter the refrigerating mechanism they might do great damage to the compressor and other parts. While soldering, a helpful procedure is to "wipe" the surfaces after putting some solder on them; use a cloth, a brush, or the solder wire itself. This action will remove any dirt and will help tin the surfaces.

2-17 Silver Brazing

One of the best methods of connecting parts together in a leakproof manner and to provide maximum strength is to silver braze the joints. These joints are very strong and will stand up under the most extreme temperature conditions. Silver soldering, or silver brazing as it is more correctly called, can be easily done if the correct procedure is followed:

A. Clean the joints mechanically.
B. Fit the joint closely and support the joint.
C. Apply the flux which is recommended for the silver brazing alloy. Follow the manufacturer's instructions.
D. Heat evenly to recommended temperature.
E. Apply the silver brazing alloy as directed.
F. Cool the joint properly.
G. Clean the joint properly and thoroughly.

An oxyacetylene torch is an excellent heat source for silver brazing. There are various silver alloys on the market. Most of these have a 35 to 45 percent silver content. This material usually melts at 1120 F. and flows at 1145 F. Contact your local welding supply house for suitable silver brazing supplies.

CAUTION: Carefully check the specifications of the silver brazing alloy used. If it contains any amount of cadmium be SURE that the work space is well ventilated and that none of the fumes are inhaled or come in contact with the eyes or skin. Cadmium fumes are very poisonous.

Step 1. Cut tube to length and remove burr with file or scraper.

Step 2. Clean outside of tube with sandpaper or sandcloth.

Step 3. Clean inside of fitting with wire brush, sandcloth or sandpaper.

Step 4. Apply flux thoroughly to inside of fitting.

Step 5. Apply flux thoroughly to outside of tube—assemble tube and fitting.

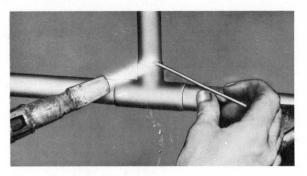

Step 6. Apply heat with torch. When solder melts upon contact with heated fitting, the proper temperature for soldering has been reached. Remove flame and feed solder to the joint at one or two points until a ring of solder appears at the end of the fitting.

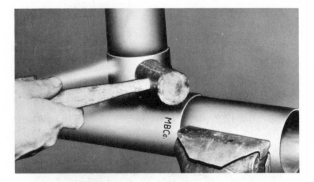

Step 7. Tap larger sized fittings with mallet while soldering, to break surface tension and to distribute solder evenly in joint.

Fig. 2-26. Recommended step-by-step procedures to be followed when soldering tubing.
(Mueller Brass Co.)

The part to be brazed must be made to fit accurately and must be cleaned. Any external surface should be cleaned to remove dirt. A fine grade of steel wool is considered good. Internal circular surfaces can be cleaned with clean wire brushes or steel wool rolled on a rod or by using a clean drill.

The parts must have contacting surfaces of sufficient size, such as a tube sliding into a fitting (not a drive fit), Fig. 2-27. The contacting surfaces need not be very large (three times thinnest section). If the parts are dented or are out of round, these faults must be corrected before the brazing is done. It is important to support the parts

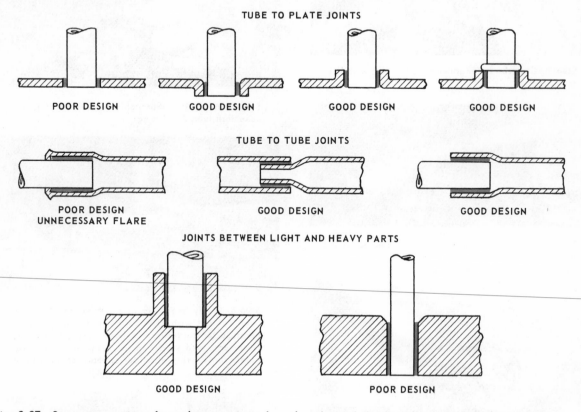

TUBE TO PLATE JOINTS

POOR DESIGN   GOOD DESIGN   GOOD DESIGN   GOOD DESIGN

TUBE TO TUBE JOINTS

POOR DESIGN UNNECESSARY FLARE   GOOD DESIGN   GOOD DESIGN

JOINTS BETWEEN LIGHT AND HEAVY PARTS

GOOD DESIGN   POOR DESIGN

Fig. 2-27. Some suggestions for making joints to be silver brazed. In this illustration the actual thickness of the silver brazing is exaggerated to show its application. (Handy and Harman)

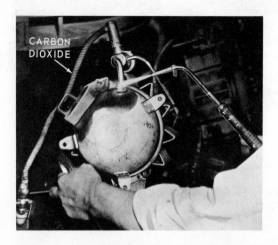

CARBON DIOXIDE

Fig. 2-28. A fitting being silver brazed to a compressor dome. Note the tube carrying carbon dioxide through the fitting and into the compressor during the silver brazing operation.

securely during the operation so no movement will take place.

It is also important to make sure that no flux enters the system during the brazing operation as it cannot be easily removed. This overfluxing can be avoided by applying the flux to the surface that is to slide into the part. The excess flux will then stay on the outside.

Heating of the joint must be carefully done. Carbon dioxide or nitrogen should be circulated through the refrigerator system during any soldering operation on a complete mechanism to prevent an explosion, as shown in Fig. 2-28. CAUTION: NEVER USE A REFRIGERANT OR COMPRESSED AIR. The flux behavior is a good indication of the temperature of the joint as the heating progresses. Keep the joint covered with the flame all during the operation to prevent air getting to the joint. The flux will dry out; the moisture (water) will boil off at 212 F.; then the flux will turn milky in color. Next it will bubble at about 600 F., following this it will turn into a clear liquid at about 1100 F. This temperature is just short of the brazing temperature. The silver alloy itself melts at 1120 F. and flows at 1145 F. A torch tip several sizes larger than the tip used for soft soldering should be used. Be sure to heat BOTH pieces which are to have the silver alloy adhere to them. An excellent indicator of the proper temperature for silver brazing is when the secondary flame begins to turn green as it passes the circular tubing.

In silver brazing the torch is never held steady in one spot, but must be moved around the brazed area. Never concentrate the heat in one area but keep the torch moving. Many servicemen prefer to move the torch in a figure eight motion. Larger torch tip sizes are recommended to allow a soft large quantity of heat without excess pressure or "blow." A slight feather on the inner cone is recommended. See Fig. 2-29.

Fig. 2-29. Silver brazing a copper tubing connection. Note the large soft flame used. See text for suggestions on flame adjustments. (Handy and Harman)

2-18 Cleaning the Brazed Joint

It is necessary to thoroughly wash with water and scrub the outside of the completed silver brazed joint. Any flux left on the metals will tend to corrode them and the residue flux may also temporarily stop a leak which will show up later.

The joint may be cooled quickly or slowly. Cooling with water is permissible. This water may be used to wash the joint at the same time. Visual inspection of the joint will quickly reveal any places where the silver alloy did not adhere. It is advisable to watch for this adherence and make any corrections during the brazing operation.

2-19 Pipe Fittings and Sizes

Air conditioning and refrigeration installations use pipe fittings and pipe threads extensively. American Standard Taper Pipe Threads (ASA) are specially formed V-threads made on a conical spiral that permits the threads to bind against each other. If the threads were not tapered, a gasket or a machined shoulder would be necessary to provide a leakproof joint.

Besides being tapered (or in a conical spiral), pipe threads are different from Fine-thread series (NF) and the Coarse-thread series (NC). NF and NC sizes are based on the maximum diameter or outside diameter, whereas pipe thread sizes are based on flow diameter, or the diameter of the hole in the pipe (inside diameter or ID). For example, a 1/4 pipe has close to a 1/4 hole; and when the pipe has a 1/8 in. wall thickness, the OD of the pipe will be 1/2 in. (1/8 plus 1/4 hole plus 1/8). The external threads are cut on the pipe with a pipe die which is turned by a standard die stock, a ratchet die stock or power driven die stock. The pipe thread taps (for cutting the female or internal threads) are turned with a tap wrench. A pipe tap is shown in Fig. 2-30.

Fig. 2-30. A pipe tap. Note the taper. (Greenfield Tap and Die Corp.)

Pipe fittings are made with the threads already tapped. The most common fittings are the coupling, the reducing coupling, the union, the nipple, the 90 deg. elbow, the reducing elbow, the 45 deg. elbow and the street ell.

The threads are made self-sealing by the pressing of the sharp V-threads together as they are threaded. Various compounds are available to help seal these threads; white lead, red lead and litharge. Litharge is formed by mixing red lead with glycerine to form a thick paste. This, brushed on pipe threads before assembly, will make a strong leakproof joint.

Special thread cutting compound should be used when cutting pipe threads. The taps and dies must be kept in excellent condition.

2-20 Repairing Threads

Occasionally the threads of a fitting or fixture, especially pipe threads, may become worn to such an extent that they will not remain leakproof. A very convenient and rapid remedy for this condition is to coat the threads with solder and then remove the excess solder by sharply rapping the fitting while it is still warm. The threads will then be coated with a thin film of solder which will usually remedy the trouble.

2-21 Epoxy Bonding

The epoxy resins have good adhesion qualities when used with steel, copper, wood, and many types of plastics. Epoxy adhesives are available from many manu-facturers or refrigeration supply wholesalers. The most desirable type of adhesive is the two-part system. This consists of an epoxy resin and a hardener. Combinations of these two will harden at room temperature as opposed to the one-part adhesive which must be heated in order to cause it to harden.

The two-part system, consists of two jars or tubes of a paste-like substance which are of contrasting colors.

In repairing objects with epoxy cement it is necessary to first determine whether a patch is necessary or whether the hole can be repaired by placing the mixed epoxy over the hole or leak. Small leaks or holes of up to 1/16 in. in diameter can often be successfully sealed by placing the mixed epoxy over the leak and allowing it to cure. The same procedure is recommended for tubing cracks. For larger holes, a patch of the same type of material is recommended. The basic step procedure for the use of epoxy resin is as follows:

The two parts of epoxy compounds are mixed together (equal parts of each) until all color streaks have been eliminated and the substance has a consistant color.

The refrigeration serviceman is cautioned to purchase the epoxy compound from a refrigeration wholesaler because some epoxies available elsewhere are not compatible with R-12 and R-22. Furthermore, the shelf life of most epoxy resins is approximately six months.

The serviceman should be careful when using epoxy compounds because they contain chemicals which may irritate the skin. Prolonged contact with the skin should be avoided. In case of contact, remove the epoxy and clean the skin with rubbing alcohol followed by a thorough washing with soap and water.

The procedure for using epoxy compounds is as follows:

1. Clean the surface or surfaces which are to be bonded by sanding with coarse sandpaper or steel wool.

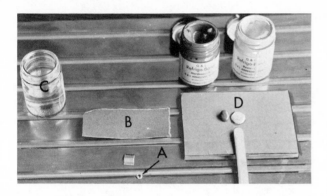

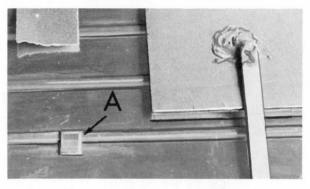

Fig. 2-31. *Refrigeration leak undergoing repairs with the use of epoxy compounds. A-The leak to be repaired. B-Sandpaper. C-Cleaning solvent. D-Epoxy compounds ready for mixing on piece of cardboard. (G & L Adhesives Corp.)*

Fig. 2-32. *Completed patch using the epoxy compound to join the patch material to the injured part. A-The completed patch.*

2. Clean surface with recommended solvents such as toluene, acetone or a similar industrial solvent.

3. Mix epoxy on a clean surface such as a piece of cardboard as shown in Fig. 2-31.

4. Apply the epoxy mixture to the surface if it is a small hole or apply to mating surfaces if a patch is to be used as shown in Fig. 2-32. Epoxy compounds should be used immediately after mixing as the hardener starts the chemical hardening, or setting, immediately.

2-22 Hand Tools

The refrigeration and air conditioning service engineer performs his work chiefly with the use of hand tools. To be successful he must select good tools, take good care of them and be skilled in their use. Most service failures can be traced to poor workmanship which means poor hand tool skills.

Practically all common small tools are used on refrigerating units. This includes brushes, chisels, hacksaws, hammers, mallets, punches, rules, stamps, vises, etc.

The refrigerating mechanism, in comparison to an automobile engine, is relatively light duty. It can easily be damaged by abuse. Therefore, when you work on these mechansims, it is necessary to be careful to avoid damaging the units.

The following paragraphs provide useful suggestions for the selection, care and use of hand tools.

2-23 Wrenches

Most refrigeration and air conditioning installation and service work necessitates the use of various types of wrenches. A loose or worn wrench may slip and spoil the corners on nuts making proper servicing impossible without replacing the nut. Many nuts and parts used in servicing work are copper or brass and therefore rather soft. Never use pliers on parts that require a wrench.

A serviceman needs wrenches of several types and sizes. Wrenches obtained should be made of good alloy steel, properly heat treated, and accurately machined and ground to fit the assembly devices. The wrench must fit the nut or bolt head accurately, and it must fit as much of the hexagon as possible. For these reasons, the wrench types are listed in their order of preference:

1. Socket Wrenches.
2. Box Wrenches.
3. Open End Wrenches.
4. Adjustable Wrenches.

Fig. 2-33 shows an assortment of basic hand tools needed by the serviceman.

2-24 Socket Wrenches

If the nut or bolt head does not have any obstructions over it, the six or twelve

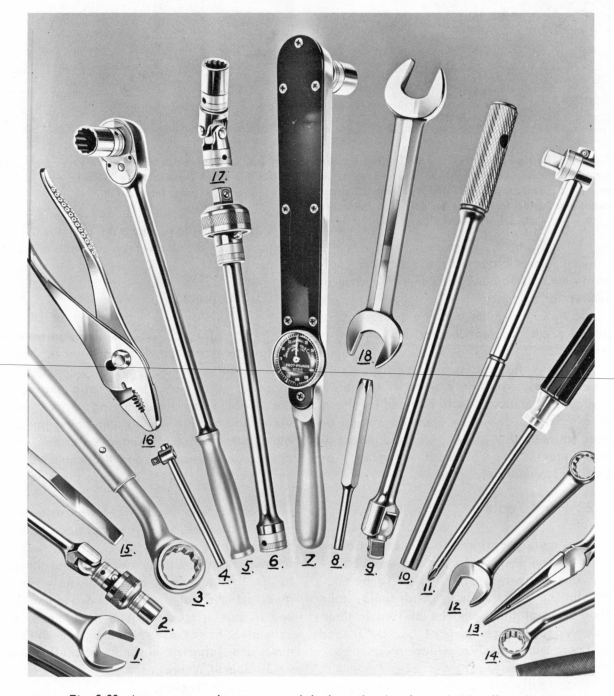

Fig. 2-33. An assortment showing some of the basic hand tools needed by all mechanics.
(Snap-On Tools Corp.)

point socket is the best wrench to use. These sockets are usually made of chromium-vanadium steel and are turned by handles that have a 1/4, 3/8, or 1/2 in. square drive, Fig. 2-34. The handles come in a variety of designs: Swivel handles, T-handles, Ratchet handles, Speed handles, Torque handles, etc.

Socket wrenches are more usable if they are double broached (12 point). This type socket is easier to use if the handle must be operated in a small or restricted space.

2-25 Box Wrenches

When the nuts or bolt heads are in close quarters and you cannot use the socket wrench, the box wrench is satisfactory. Box wrenches are usually 12 point and provide a powerful noninjuring grip, Fig. 2-35.

Box wrenches may be either straight, offset or double offset. Most box wrenches are double end. Both ends may be of the same size with one end offset, or they may be of the same pattern and different sizes. The refrigeration service engineer will find that for standard bolts and nuts the table in Fig. 2-36 will give the size of the wrench across the flats for the sizes of bolts and nuts in most common use.

The size of the wrench opening across the flats is marked at each wrench opening.

Box wrenches having flat and 15 deg. handles are necessary for a complete tool kit.

2-26 Flare Nut Wrenches

Flare nuts used on SAE flared connections require special wrenches. Since the nut is on a fitting connected to tubing, the common box wrench cannot be used.

Fig. 2-35. An alloy steel box wrench. This wrench is a 12 point wrench or double hex. Next to the socket wrench, box wrenches are the safest type of wrench to use as they are less likely to slip off the nut as compared to open end type wrenches.

NOMINAL BOLT SIZE	HEAD AND NUT WIDTH ACROSS FLATS
1/4	7/16
5/16	1/2
3/8	9/16
7/16	5/8
1/2	3/4
9/16	13/16
5/8	7/8
3/4	1

Fig. 2-36. Table of wrench openings for standard bolt heads and nuts.

Special flare nut wrenches have been developed for this purpose. These wrenches are made with an opening which permits the box end to be fitted over the tubing as shown in Fig. 2-37. Since the flare nut wrench is often used in very limited space, special wrenches have been devised to aid

Fig. 2-34. Typical socket wrenches and handles.

Fig. 2-37. Flare nut wrench used when turning SAE flare nuts. Note the slot in the end which allows the wrench to be fitted over tubing.
(Duro Metal Products Co.)

the serviceman in quickly turning the nuts. Fig. 2-38 illustrates a ratchet type flare nut wrench. A strong, easy to operate opening type flare nut wrench is shown in Fig. 2-39.

2-27 Open End Wrenches

These wrenches can slide on the nut or bolt head from the side and are used in close quarters and on unions and the like where the socket wrench and the box wrench cannot be placed on the assembly device.

End wrenches should not be used when the jaws are spread or when there are burrs. It is also recommended that end wrenches used in servicing work have a thick jaw, otherwise they will have a tendency to bite into the soft brass parts. Some popular sizes for wrenches are: 1/2 in. across flats for 5/16 in. NC and NF cap screws which are commonly used on compressors and expansion valves, etc. The 7/16 in. across flat wrenches for 1/4 in. screws and bolts are often needed. The 3/4 in. across flats are used for 1/4 in. flare nuts which use 7/16 in. 20 NF threads. The 1 in. across flat end wrenches fit the 1/2 in. flare nuts which use 3/4 in. 16 NF threads. A typical open end wrench, number 18, is shown in the assortment making up Fig. 2-33.

2-28 Adjustable Wrenches

Wrenches with an adjustable opening between the jaws are necessary in the tool kit because of the odd size nuts and bolts found in this work. Adjustable wrenches must be kept in good repair. If the wrench does not fit tightly, its use may result in a ruined wrench, bruised hands, and a ruined nut or bolt head.

Fig. 2-40 illustrates a popular type of adjustable wrench.

It is important to use wrenches in such a way that they fit completely on the nut or bolt. One should always pull on a wrench

Fig. 2-38. Ratchet type flare nut wrench which is especially useful when the space for movement of the handle is limited. (Tubing Appliance Co.)

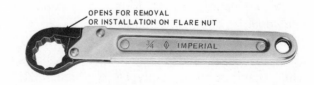

Fig. 2-39. A special type of flare nut wrench. This wrench opens to pass over the tubing and closes on the flare nut to give positive contact with the flare nut surfaces. (Imperial Eastman Corp.)

Fig. 2-40. Adjustable wrench. It is recommended that when using this type of wrench that the handle should be pulled in the direction shown by the arrow. (Snap-On Tools Corp.)

Fig. 2-41. Refrigeration service valve wrench. Note fixed end for "cracking" purposes and "ratchet" opening for rapid valve operation. The end openings are 1/4 in. and small right hand opening is 3/16 in.

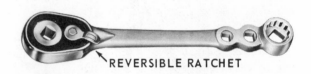

Fig. 2-42. Reversible ratchet wrench opening or closing. The fixed end has openings for three different size valve stems. (Duro Metal Products Co.)

rather than push on it, otherwise sudden loosening may cause serious injury to the hand.

2-29 Service Valve Wrench

The service valve stems are usually constructed with a square end milled on the valve shaft and require a special wrench to manipulate them. This tool usually has a ratchet and a fixed end for this kind of work. It may be mentioned here that, when "cracking" valves, the fixed end only should be used. By "cracking" is meant, the slight opening required to cause the valve needle or plunger to leave its seat but not allow any appreciable flow of refrigerant or gas. This is to give the serviceman rapid control of the slight opening and closing of a valve. When opening and closing valves through any appreciable distance, the ratchet end may be used. Fig. 2-41 illustrates a service valve wrench.

Some service valve wrenches have a reversible ratchet which enables the operator to reverse the turning without removing the wrench from the stem. Fig. 2-42 illustrates such a wrench.

2-30 Service Valve Wrench Adapters

Many manufacturers use valve stems other than the 1/4 in. square. Some valve stems are constructed in such a manner that the milled end is inside the valve body, necessitating a socket wrench to manipulate it. To accommodate these valves, adapters are available in various sizes. The male, or drive, part of the socket is usually 1/4 in. square although there are a few which use a larger drive (9/32 in.). The socket, or opening which fits the valve stem, comes in five sizes: 3/16 in., 7/32 in., 1/4 in., 5/16 in. and 3/8 in. These sockets are usually made with eight points to simplify their use. Most valve stems have internal packing gland nuts, and special sockets must be used on these. It is de-

sirable to obtain these special sockets with ball bearing grippers to prevent losing them when working in difficult positions. Fig. 2-43 illustrates a set of these special sockets. The set also includes necessary sockets for packing gland fittings.

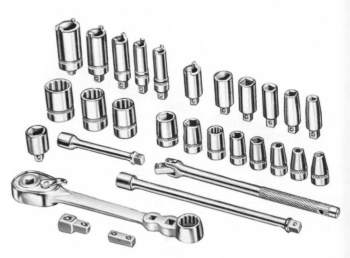

Fig. 2-43. Special service valve set. The top row illustrates packing gland sockets and valve stem sockets. The middle row shows a variety of 6 point and 12 point sockets.

2-31 Torque Wrenches

All materials are elastic. Even cast iron and hardened steels used in the construction of compressors are elastic to a degree. In tightening bolts, nuts, and other attachments on compressor parts and assemblies, it is important that the degree of tightness be measured in order not to distort or cause a misalignment of parts. To measure the degree of tightness, a torque wrench is used, Fig. 2-44.

Torque wrenches are usually wrench handles only and are made to receive sockets of various sizes. The handle is equipped with a graduated dial or pointer which is calibrated in foot pounds or inch pounds. To use a torque wrench, the operator fits the socket to the nut, then draws up the tightness until the wrench indicator shows the tightness prescribed. Service manuals list the recommended torque (twist) for various parts and fittings to give a snug fit and still not cause excessive distortion.

Torque is calculated by multiplying the length of the handle in feet by the pull in pounds applied to the handle (foot pounds). Inch pounds is calculated by multiplying the length of the handle in inches by the pull on the handle in pounds.

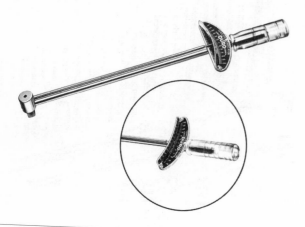

Fig. 2-44. Torque wrench used to measure the degree of tightness of nuts and screws. This handle is made to be used with standard sockets.

2-32 Instruments and Gauges

The refrigeration service engineer must use instruments and gauges in order to determine the condition (pressure and tem-

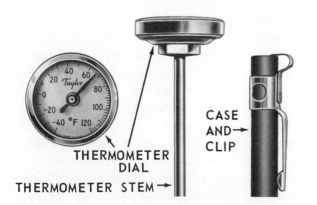

Fig. 2-45. Dial stem thermometer. This thermometer is calibrated in 2 degree increments from -40 F. to +120 F. This is the range most used in refrigeration and air conditioning work.
(Taylor Instrument Co.)

perature) within the operating mechanism. The most common instruments are thermometers, micrometers, pressure gauges and vacuum gauges. In later chapters such special instruments as recording thermometers, hygrometers, ammeters, voltmeters, ohmmeters and others will be shown and described.

All such use requires that the instruments be kept in good condition and carefully handled in order to maintain their accuracy. If in doubt concerning the accuracy of an instrument, it should be sent to an instrument repair concern for testing and calibration.

2-33 Thermometers

The thermometer is used to check cooling unit temperature, refrigerator cabinet temperature, and condensing unit temperature. To determine whether the thermometer is accurate, an ice and water bath may be used. When inserted into this solution the thermometer should check within 1 F. of 32 F.

Many types and sizes of thermometers have been developed for the refrigeration service and installation man. A popular type has the glass stem mounted in a metal case and is fitted with a pocket clip, as shown in Fig. 1-2.

Glass stem thermometers usually read from -30 F. to 120 F. in 2 deg. increments. The tube may contain either mercury or a red fluid. The mercury-filled thermometer is faster, but it is more difficult to read. Some thermometers have a special magnifying front built into the glass to enlarge the liquid line to aid in reading.

Dial-stem thermometers are also popular and easy to use. A typical dial-stem thermometer is shown in Fig. 2-45.

Dial thermometers are also used extensively. They may be operated either by a bimetal strip or by a bellows charged with a volatile fluid. Some of the dial thermometers have a remote sensitive bulb connected to the bellows by means of a capillary tube, as shown in Fig. 2-46.

The temperature range for this instrument is from -40 to 120 F. at 2 deg. increments. A caution to be observed when

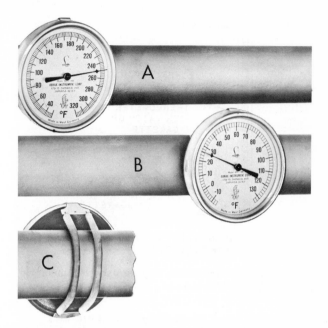

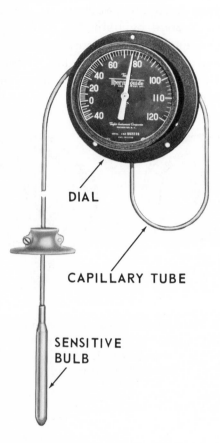

DIAL

CAPILLARY TUBE

SENSITIVE BULB

Fig. 2-46. Dial type thermometer with a remote temperature sensing bulb. The range for this instrument is from -40 F. to +120 F.

using any kind of thermometer is to never expose the thermometer to temperatures beyond the limits of the scale; to do so may ruin the instrument.

Dial thermometers for use on pipes are very useful. Fig. 2-47 illustrates two of these thermometers and shows how the instrument may be clamped to pipes or tubes to check temperatures.

Occasionally, the fluid in the liquid column of the thermometer may separate. To make the column solid again try cooling

Fig. 2-47. Dial type thermometer. These dial thermometers may be easily clamped to pipes to indicate the temperature of the pipe. A-Shows a calibration from 40 F. to 320 F. by 2 degree increments. B-Shows a calibration from -10 F. to 130 F. by 2 degree increments. C-Shows the spring arrangement for attaching the thermometer to a pipe.

the bulb with a small quantity of liquid R-12 sprayed on it. The column will shrink into the bulb, and when it reexpands, the break should have disappeared. Caution: If the mercury is frozen into a solid the thermometer will break.

Another way to connect the column when a break occurs is to heat the thermometer as shown in Fig. 2-48.

2-34 Gauges

Since pressure gauges are used by the serviceman to determine what is happening inside the system, it is obvious that these gauges must indicate correctly. This necessitates obtaining accurate gauges and periodic recalibrating of the gauges to reset them to their original accuracy. The two gauges most used are the HIGH PRESSURE GAUGE used on the high side of the system and the COMPOUND GAUGE used on the low side of the system.

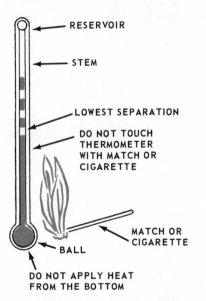

RESERVOIR

STEM

LOWEST SEPARATION

DO NOT TOUCH
THERMOMETER
WITH MATCH OR
CIGARETTE

MATCH OR
CIGARETTE

BALL

DO NOT APPLY HEAT
FROM THE BOTTOM

Fig. 2-48. A method which may be used to connect a break in the liquid column of a glass stem thermometer.

(White-Rodgers Electric Co.)

The high pressure gauge (A) has a single continuous scale usually reaching from 0 to 300. The compound gauge (B) measures pressures both above atmospheric and below atmospheric. These two gauges are calibrated quite differently. See Fig. 2-49, A and B.

There are a large number of different dial calibrations on the market, Fig. 2-50.

The high-pressure gauge scale is usually in either 2 lb. or 5 lb. graduations, while the compound gauge scale is either in a 1, 2 or 5 in. graduation below atmospheric pressure and as above for pressures above atmospheric. Some gauges use a retarder to permit accurate readings in the usual operating range by using an extra spring at pressures above normal. These gauges are easily recognized by the change in graduations at the higher readings of the positive pressure scale.

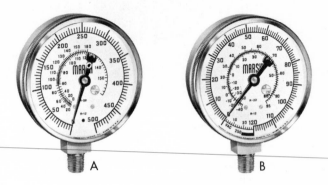

Fig. 2-49. Refrigeration gauges. A-High-pressure gauge. B-Compound gauge which measures pressures from 120 to 250 psi.
(Marsh Instrument Co.)

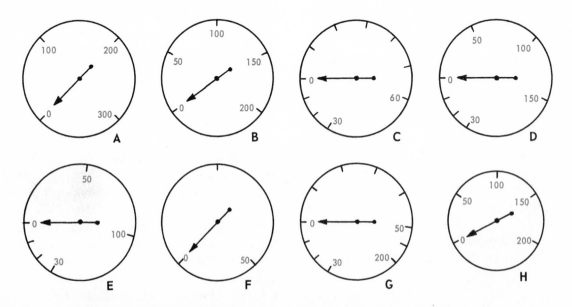

Fig. 2-50. Drawing illustrating some of the common pressure gauge dials. A, B, F and H are pressure gauges. C, D, E and G are compound gauges.

The gauges are constructed using a Bourdon tube as the operating element. The Bourdon tube is a flattened copper tube sealed at one end, curved and soldered to the gauge fitting at the other end, Fig. 2-51. A pressure rise in the Bourdon

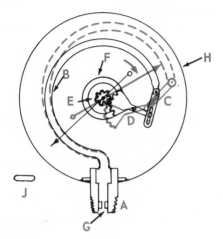

Fig. 2-51. Internal construction of a pressure gauge. A-Adapter fitting, usually an 1/8 in. pipe thread. B-Bourdon tube. C-Link. D-Gear sector. E-Pointer shaft gear. F-Calibrating spring. G-Restricter. H-Case. J-Cross section of the Bourdon tube. The red line indicates how the pressure in the Bourdon tube causes it to straighten and operate the gauge.

tube will cause it to tend to straighten out. This movement will pull on the link, which will turn the gear sector counterclockwise and the pointer shaft will then turn clockwise to move the needle.

Instruments have been designed to calibrate gauges accurately. Any shop that uses a large number of gauges or is remotely situated should have one of these instruments on hand for calibration. These instruments are usually built on the basis of dead weights for calibration above atmospheric pressure and a mercury column indicator for pressures below atmospheric, or vacuum.

The high-pressure gauges have a range as shown, of 0-300 psig pressure, but this does not protect the gauges from being harmed at lower pressures. A rapidly fluctuating pressure at any pressure will soon harm the gauge. A sudden release of 300 psig into the gauge will also injure it. The most popular gauges have a 2 1/2 in. dial and use a 1/8 in. pipe, male thread. However, many have 1/8 in. pipe female thread. A serviceman should use another fitting 1/8 in. pipe male by 1/8 in. female to protect the gauge threads. The compound gauge especially should be protected from any abuses and sharp pressure fluctuations. These gauges should be calibrated at least once every month. By calibration is meant that they should be checked on a machine using a master gauge. They must be checked over their full range or scale.

The compound gauge may be obtained in various calibration ranges such as 30 in. Vac-0-60 psig, 30 in. Vac-0-90 psig and 30 in. Vac-0-120 psig. Compound gauges should never be used on the high-pressure side of a system. When using a compound gauge on machines, in which the high pressure may back up through the compressor or balance through the refrigerant control while the compressor is stopped, a 30 in. Vac-0-200 psi gauge should be used.

One company is now marketing a special compound gauge, Fig. 2-52, which, in addition to the usual pressure calibration, 30 in. Vac-0-psi, has three additional scales which give the evaporating temperature corresponding to the various pressures for such

QUICK COUPLER

Fig. 2-52. Compound refrigeration gauge which shows the evaporating temperature for R-12 and R-22 corresponding to the gauge pressure. The gauge reads from 30 in.-0-120 psig. (Madden Brass)

refrigerants as R-12 and R-22. This extra scale makes it unnecessary to refer to pressure temperature curves or tables for common refrigerants in order to check operating pressures.

2-35 Rules

A 9 in. or 12 in. steel ruler is frequently needed when overhauling units or installing them. The ruler should be calibrated in 1/32 in., and if possible, should be of stainless steel to avoid rusting. The numerals and graduations should be clearly visible. Installation men will find a 6 ft. flexible steel tape of value when laying out a job.

2-36 Micrometers

It is often part of the refrigeration serviceman's job to inspect, check sizes, dimensions, and make accurate measurements to a few thousandths of an inch. The common micrometer is the tool most used for this purpose. Fig. 2-53 illustrates a high quality micrometer caliper. The following points may help the beginner learn to read a micrometer:

1. If the micrometer being used is one inch, the divisions 0, 1, 2 are tenths of an inch.
2. The four divisions between the tenths markers are 1/40 in. or .025 (twenty five thousandths of an inch).
3. The thimble, (right hand end of the micrometer), carries the spindle and is threaded into the micrometer body on a 40 threads per inch screw. One turn of the thimble moves the spindle 25 thousandths (.025) of an inch.
4. There are 25 graduations on the thimble. Turning the thimble one graduation moves the spindle 1/1000 (.001) of an inch.
5. The micrometer as shown reads .200 inches. The inserts showing portions of the micrometer would read as shown in the preceding figure.

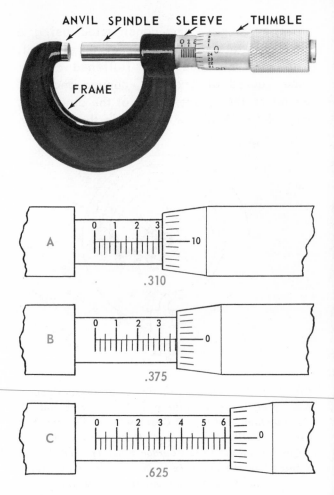

Fig. 2-53. Micrometer caliper. The reading as the micrometer is shown indicates a measurement of .200 in. Drawing: A-Shows a measurement of .310 in. B-Shows a measurement of .375 in. C-Shows a measurement of .625 in.

It should be noted that this is a one inch micrometer and it has a range of 0 to 1 in. A two inch micrometer has a range of 1 to 2 in. A three inch micrometer has a range of 2 to 3 in.

2-37 Brushes

Work must be kept clean to obtain good results. For many jobs brushes are useful for cleaning tools.

For cleaning copper and steel surfaces for welding or brazing, a clean steel wire brush is an excellent tool. These brushes may be obtained in a variety of shapes and sizes. The brush should have fine steel wire bristles, thickly set, and should have a comfortable handle. Special cylindrical brushes are available in all sizes for cleaning external and internal surfaces of tubing and fittings prior to soldering and brazing. See Fig. 2-54.

Fig. 2-54. Wire brush used for cleaning tubing preparatory to soldering or brazing.
(Schaefer Brush Mfg. Co.)

Paint brushes are needed to apply paint or to use with cleaning solvents. If used for painting, the brushes should be of good quality. The brushes must be thoroughly cleaned after being used, and they should be wrapped in wax paper and labeled before storing. When used with cleaning solvent, the brush handle should be drilled and the brush hung over the cleaning tank.

File brushes and file cards are necessary as file teeth become filled with metal, and unless the clogging material is removed, the files become useless. Do not use a file card for any purpose other than cleaning a file as the bristles may become clogged with foreign matter.

2-38 Cold Chisels

In a refrigeration shop, a cold chisel sometimes comes in handy for use on odd jobs. As an example, you may find the assembly devices on cooling coils corroded, and a chisel may be needed to remove the nut or screw. A 3/4 in. flat cold chisel is a popular size. Be sure to keep the hammering end of the chisel free from mushrooming. Pieces may fly from a mushroomed head causing injuries.

2-39 Files

For cleaning of metal surfaces and various filing jobs files of various sizes and types are necessary.

Files are classified according to tooth size, shape, and the number of directions the teeth are cut on the file. Files are either single cut or double cut. Fig. 2-55.

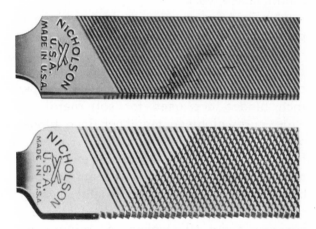
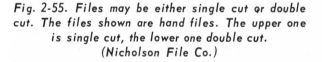

Fig. 2-55. Files may be either single cut or double cut. The files shown are hand files. The upper one is single cut, the lower one double cut.
(Nicholson File Co.)

Single cut files are used for finishing surfaces, and double cut files are used for fast metal removal.

Files come in different lengths: 4, 6, 8, 10, 12 in., etc., and the coarseness of the teeth is proportional to the length. The size of the teeth on files varies from dead smooth, smooth, second cut, bastard, to coarse. A second cut 6 in. file has smaller teeth than a second cut 12 in. file.

Files come in a variety of shapes: rectangular, half round, round, triangular, square, wedge shape, etc.

One oddity in files is that there are three types of rectangular cross section files; (1) hand, (2) flat, and (3) mill.

The mill file has only single cut teeth. The hand and flat files have double cut teeth. But the hand file has one edge that has no teeth, called a safe edge, and the edges of the file are straight edges. The flat file has teeth on all four surfaces and edges which are curved.

It is important to use file handles on files to avoid hand injury.

2-40 Hacksaws

A hand hacksaw is a popular tool for cutting tubing and for other installation and maintenance work.

A rigid frame using a 10 in. blade is popular for this work.

Fig. 2-56 illustrates a suitable saw. Blades are available having different numbers of teeth per inch. Fourteen teeth per inch blades are used for soft metal and wide cuts; eighteen teeth per inch blades are used for medium soft metals; twenty-four teeth per inch blades are used for general work; and thirty-two teeth per inch blades are used for thin metal, tubing, and/or hard metal. You should stroke a hacksaw about 60 strokes per minute and always lift the blade slightly on the back stroke.

With most blades, the teeth are hardened while the back of the blade is soft and flexible. The blades are usually tungsten steel alloy, although high quality blades may be tungsten or molybdenum steel alloy. Fig. 2-57 illustrates a saw blade to be used in a hand saw, and shows how blades are marked.

Special hacksaw frames are available for working in small holes. There is also a stub hacksaw blade and an adapter drive to fit electric drills.

2-41 Hammers

A hammer is a necessity in the refrigeration shop. A 12 or 16 ounce ball peen hammer is a useful size. It is important that the hammer head is firmly fastened to the handle and that the handle is in good condition. In use the hammer handle should be grasped about two-thirds of the way along the handle from the head.

2-42 Mallets

In refrigeration and air conditioning service work, the mallet is frequently needed to drive parts into place or to separate parts without injury to the surfaces. To do this driving, a 1 1/2 lb. to 2 lb. mallet is desirable. A rawhide, rubber, wood, or lead mallet should be used.

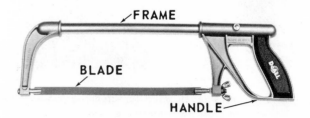

Fig. 2-56. A hand hacksaw must have a rigid frame in order to hold the blade in proper tension. (DoALL Co.)

2-43 Punches

The center punch is used to locate positions to drill. Remember that the center punch mark must be large enough to hold the point of the drill. Center punches may also be used to make alignment marks on refrigeration parts before dismantling.

These tools are usually of carefully heat-treated chrome-alloy steel. The cutting edge must be hard, while the pounding end must be tough and shatterproof. Always grind away any mushroom head that forms. A fairly heavy 6 in. punch will be the most satisfactory.

Drift punches and pin punches are used to remove retainer pins and keys. The blunt end is called the bill. Punches are measured by overall length and by diameter of the stock. Chrome-vanadium steel punches come in sizes, 3/32 to 5/16 in.

2-44 Pliers

Pliers are universal tools. Many different types are available.

Gas pliers: These pliers are slip joint

combination pliers, and are handy for general use. They should not be used on nuts, bolts, or fittings, as they might slip and injure the device.

Cutting Pliers: These pliers come into good use when working on the wiring of the refrigerator. The type called the lineman's pliers is a powerful cutting and gripping tool. Another type called diagonal pliers is used to cut in close quarters.

Nut pliers: On some jobs a pair of nut pliers can be used to good advantage. Nut pliers have parallel jaws, and on some there is adjustable cam action that locks the jaws on the object.

In general, it is not considered good practice to use pliers to hold bolts or nuts, but on a job such as holding the head of a bolt while turning the nut with a wrench, the use of nut pliers is permissible.

Slim nose pliers and duckbill pliers are frequently used in hard-to-reach places.

Round nose pliers are used to shape wire into loops and to bend sheet metal edges.

Pliers are made of alloy steel, usually with manganese, although some are chrome-vanadium steel. Top quality pliers are usually drop forged.

2-45 Screwdrivers

Screwdrivers are extensively used in refrigeration service work; for installation, and for shop work. A complete set of screwdrivers will be found highly desirable. The length of a screwdriver is measured as the length of the blade, not including the handle. The recommended sizes for the average shop should include 2 1/2, 4, 6 and 8 in. sizes.

There are several types of screwdrivers. There is the straight blade, or regular screwdriver, and also the Phillips type, in which a recessed cross in the head of the screw forms a socket for a mating point on the screwdriver. Phillips screwdrivers are available in four sizes: The 3 in. size for No. 4 and smaller screws, the 4 in. size for No. 5 to No. 9 screws, the 5 in. size for No. 10 to No. 16 screws, and the 8 in. size for No. 18 and larger screws.

The size of the screw end of the screwdriver is important. The screwdriver bit should fit the screw slot snugly and the blade should be wide enough to fill the screw slot end to end.

Stubby screwdrivers are available for working in small spaces. Screwdrivers may be equipped with a screw grasping clip to aid in starting a screw. Better quality screwdrivers have strong handles firmly bonded to the blade. Plastic handles are popular.

An offset screwdriver is necessary in refrigeration work as there are many places where it is the only type that can be used.

A hammer should never be used to pound on a screwdriver. If a screwdriver is needed for heavy service, one with a solid steel handle should be obtained.

2-46 Stamps

It is good practice for the refrigeration serviceman to stamp his name and the date on units sold or serviced. This often eliminates arguments. Many companies have a code system whereby only their own employees are able to interpret the information stamped on the unit. This stamping is done with hardened steel stamps, obtainable in a variety of sizes, letters, figures, or symbols. One-eighth inch letters are a popular size. These stamps are not suitable for use on hardened materials such as tools, etc.

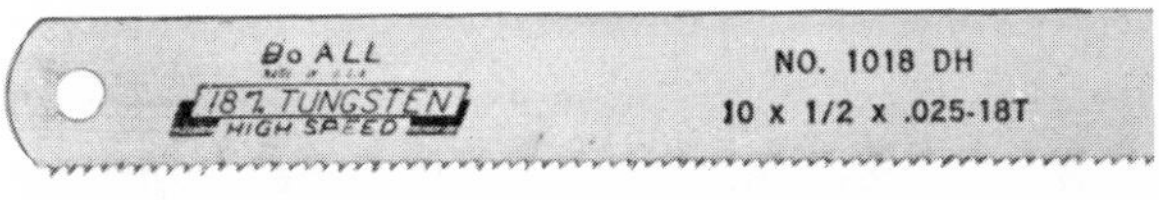

Fig. 2-57. Hand hacksaw blade. This is a tungsten alloy blade. The markings 10 x 1/2 x .025 - 18 T indicates that it is 10 in. in length, 1/2 in. wide, .025 in. thick and that it has 18 teeth per inch.

2-47 Vises

Sturdy machinist's vises are quite necessary in the shop. The vise is particularly convenient for holding parts for drilling, filing, or assembly.

A pipe vise is also a useful shop tool. Always remember to use soft jaws when working on a part which must not be marred.

It is advisable to have in the shop a vise large enough to hold most compressor bodies. A vise that is useful in a large shop installation, is a special pipe vise that has a hacksaw blade slot for accurate cutting of copper pipe.

2-48 Drills

Drills are frequently used for installation and repair work. Drills are available for drilling metal, wood, plastics, and masonry. These drills may be turned by drill presses, electric hand drills and hand braces. Drills for drilling metal come in three different set sizes; namely, number sizes, letter sizes, and fractional sizes. These drills are usually of the straight shank type, meaning that the drill has a straight round section to be gripped by a three-jaw chuck. The size and kind of drill is stamped on the shank. See Fig. 2-58. These drills may be either high

Fig. 2-58. Straight shank twist drill for drilling in metal. (Cleveland Twist Drill Co.)

carbon steel (least expensive) or high speed drills (alloy steel) (HSS). The number sizes 1 to 80 vary in size from .2280 in. to .0135 in. The higher the number, the smaller the drill. Letter size drills are a series of drill sizes over 1/4 in. diam-

eter and they vary from .234 for the A drill to .413 for the Z drill. Fractional size drills vary from 1/16 in. to 1 in. by 1/64 of an inch. See Chapter 27, for tables of the various drill diameters.

Drills are revolved on the basis of cutting speed; the smaller the drill the faster it is turned. Most drills have two cutting edges called lips. The cutting edges must be sharp, and must have clearance and a rake angle, Fig. 2-59.

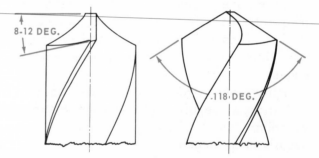

Fig. 2-59. A correctly ground twist drill point. The clearance angle shown is the angle used for mild steel and cast iron.

Drills are provided with flutes which remove chips from the hole. Most flutes are spiralled at an angle which automatically provides a rake angle for the cutting edges.

Always be sure the drill is cutting when it is being used. If the cutting edges are just rubbing against the stock they will quickly heat up and the hardness of the drill will be destroyed. To insure that the drill forms the correct size hole, both cutting lips must be exactly the same length and angle, Fig. 2-60. If one lip is longer, the hole being drilled will be oversize; and if one lip has a smaller angle, it will do all the cutting and will soon become dull.

Various devices may be used to turn drills. Hand powered drills include the hand drill, breast drill and the automatic or push drill. These tools must have a chuck that will hold the drill true. Power drills include: electric hand drill, breast electric, and the air-powered drills.

You should always wear safety goggles when drilling, either with a drill press or with portable drills. Electric drills should be grounded for safety, i.e., the frame of the drill should be electrically connected to a good ground (water pipe or a conduit).

2-49 Taps

Many assembly devices require the use of machine screws or cap screws threaded into tapped holes.

For making internal threads in a hole, a tap is used. Taps are made of hard steel or hard steel alloy. Taps are accurately made with clearance pockets provided for chips; the threads are made with small clearance to provide good cutting.

There are separate taps for each size or diameter thread and also for each kind of thread such as National Fine (NF), National Coarse (NC), or American Standard Taper Pipe Thread (ASA). Three types of taps are obtainable for each size,

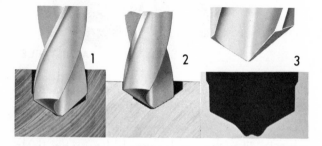

Fig. 2-60. This illustration shows the results which will be obtained if a drill is incorrectly sharpened. 1-Lips are equal in length but at different angles. 2-Lips are at equal angles but are of different lengths. 3-Lips are at different angles and at different lengths.

the taper tap, plug tap, and bottoming tap. The most common tap is the plug type. See Fig. 2-61.

The shank of the tap is ground to square shape at the end, and a tap wrench is used to turn the tap. Power tools may also be used to drive taps; however a special tap driving accessory must be used.

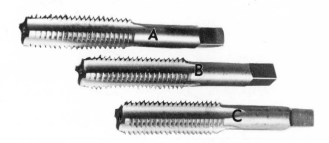

Fig. 2-61. Set of taps for cutting 1/2 in. NC threads. A-Illustrates the taper tap. B-Illustrates the plug tap. C-Illustrates the bottoming tap.

Because tapping is basically a cutting operation, the general rules for cutting metals apply to tapping. Most taps have four cutting edges for each thread. These cutting edges must be sharp. They must have a ground cutting face, and they must have cutting clearance. A coolant and lubricant must be used for tapping most metals.

It is particularly important that the hole being tapped be the correct size. If the hole is oversize, the threads will not be full size; and if the hole is undersize, the top must cut too much metal and will probably break, Fig. 2-62.

Taper taps are used for starting a cut and for tapping thin pieces in which the tapped hole goes all the way through. Plug taps are used to do most of the cutting in blind holes, while bottoming taps are used to cut full thread to the bottom of a blind hole.

2-50 Dies

Dies are used to cut threads on round stock. They make external threads that match the threads cut by the tap. Because

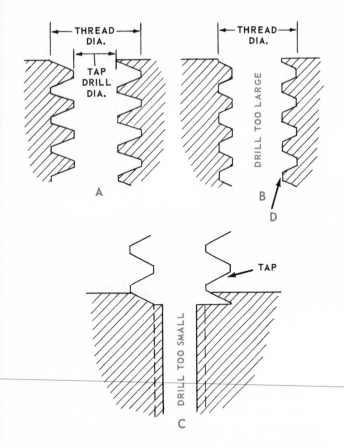

few thousandths of an inch) might break the die. If the stock is undersize the threads will not be full.

Always use 1/4 to 1/2 turn and then reverse the turning of the diestock when cutting threads with both the tap and the die.

Adjust the die to full open position to first cut the threads and then adjust the die to cut deeper until the thread just matches the tapped thread.

Taps and dies may also be used to clean threads that are corroded or damaged.

Always use a special thread cutting lubricant when doing any kind of threading except when threading cast iron.

2-51 Tap Drill Sizes

The correct size hole must be drilled in the metal before tapping. The proper size drill must be used. If the drill is too large, the threads will not be full size. If the drill is too small, the tap will be damaged as it attempts to cut too much

Fig. 2-62. Illustrated are some points to be observed when tapping threads in metal. A-A correctly formed thread. B-The tap drill was too large. C-The tap drill was too small. The tap is likely to be broken. D-The threads are not fully formed.

a tap is nonadjustable, dies are usually made adjustable to permit careful fitting of the threads. The dies are turned by a diestock which is a special tool to hold the die and turn it, Fig. 2-63.

There are dies for each type of thread and each size. Because they are cutting tools like taps, they too, must be made of tool steel; and they must be carefully shaped to cut the threads correctly.

To cut threads straight on a piece of round stock, special precautions should be taken to start the thread correctly. Guides are available that mount in the diestock and closely fit the round stock being threaded. See Fig. 2-64.

The size of round stock must be accurate. Oversize stock (even if it is only a

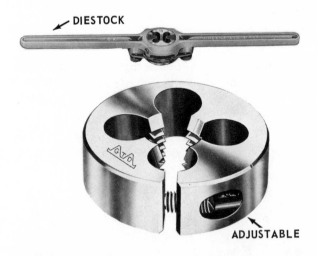

Fig. 2-63. An adjustable die and the die installed in the diestock. (Greenfield Tap and Die Corp.)

metal. The tap drill should be just a little larger in diameter than the root diameter of the threads for which it is drilling the hole. Generally speaking, threads 75 percent of full size are considered satis-

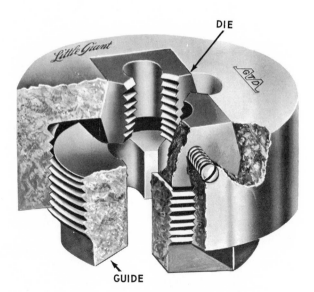

DIE

GUIDE

Fig. 2-64. Section through a threading die showing a guide in place.

factory. Always refer to tap-drill size tables for the correct size drill.

For most refrigeration and air conditioning work, the tap drill table, Fig. 2-65, will be satisfactory.

2-52 Refrigeration Supplies

Space limitations prevent us from giving specifications for all refrigeration supplies. However, a few of the basic items will be named and some information given concerning their specifications, handling and use.

2-53 Valves

Most systems that contain fluids use valves to either manually or automatically control the flow of the fluids. Automatic valves are operated by liquid level changes, pressure changes, or temperature changes. Examples of these are the low side float valve, the automatic expansion valve, and the solenoid valve.

The serviceman must also be familiar with manual valves installed in refrigerating systems. These valves enable the serviceman to separate the various parts of the system, one from the other, and to install gauges, charge, or discharge a system.

There are several kinds of manual or hand valves in use. These valves may have handwheels on the stems, but most of them are made in such a way that a valve wrench is needed to turn them. The valve stems are made of steel or brass. The body of the valve is usually made of drop forged

TAP	TAP DRILL	TAP	TAP DRILL
4/36	No. 43	14-20	No. 9
	No. 44		No. 10
	No. 45		No. 11
4-40	3/32	14-24	No. 6
	No. 43		No. 7
	No. 44		No. 8
4-48	No. 41	1/4-20	No. 5
	No. 42		No. 6
5-40	No. 37		13/64
	No. 38		No. 7
	No. 39		No. 8
5-44	No. 36	1/4-28	7/32
	No. 37		No. 3
	No. 38	5/16-18	17/64
6-32	No. 33		G
	No. 34		F
	7/64	5/64-24	J
	No. 36		I
6-40	No. 32	3/8-16	O
	No. 33		5/16
8-32	No. 29	3/8-24	R
8-36	No. 28		Q
	No. 29	7/16-14	3/8
10-24	No. 24		U
	No. 25	7/16-20	25/64
	No. 26		W
10-32	No. 19	1/2-13	27/64
	No. 20	1/2-20	29/64
	No. 21	9/16-12	31/64
	No. 22	9/16-18	33/64
12-24	No. 15	5/8-11	17/32
	No. 16	5/8-18	37/64
	No. 17	3/4-10	21/32
12-28	3/16	3/4-16	11/16
	No. 13		
	No. 14		
	No. 15		

Fig. 2-65. Table of tap drill sizes recommended for common tapping operations. Note that for certain sizes the tap drill may be a number drill, a letter drill or a fractional size drill.

brass. Packing is installed around the valve stem, and an adjusting nut is used to keep the joint from leaking.

Valves in use are the one-way valve and the two-way valve. The one-way valve is closed by turning the valve stem all the way in (to the right or all the way clockwise). The two-way valve usually closes or shuts off the refrigerant flow in the system when the stem is turned all the way in; while it shuts off the charging, discharging or gauge opening when the valve stem is turned all the way out or all the way counterclockwise. The valve is open both ways if the stem is turned to be part way between all the way out or all the way in, Fig. 2-66.

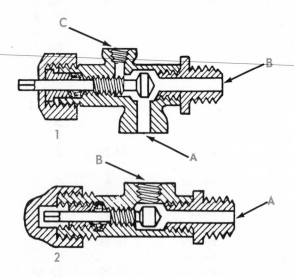

Fig. 2-66. Two typical service valve designs: 1. Two way valve. A-Opening to the compressor. B-Opening to the refrigerant line. C-Service gauge opening. 2. One way valve. A-Opening to the liquid line. B-Opening to the liquid receiver.

The tubing, or pipe, is fastened to valves by flare connection or by soldering. The valve may be attached to the refrigerating mechanism by either pipe threads or by bolted flanges.

It is good practice to open any valve by first just "cracking" it, i.e., opening it 1/16 to 1/8 turn. This slow opening pre-

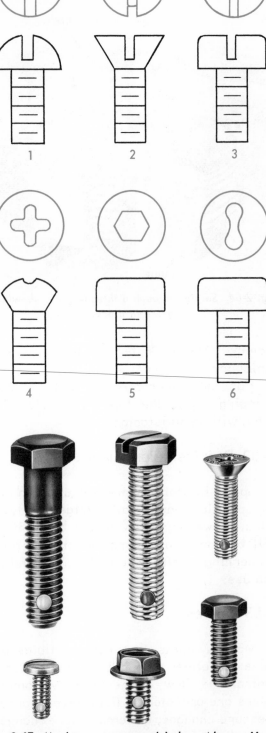

Fig. 2-67. Machine screws and bolts. Above. Variety of machine screw heads. 1-Round head. 2-Countersunk head. 3-Fillister head. 4-Phillips head. 5-Allen head. 6-Clutch head. Below. Screws with nylon inserts which lock the nut or screw in place. This eliminates the use of cotter pins and the screws do not loosen under vibration. (Republic Steel)

vents a shock pressure rush, which may injure mechanisms or flush oil in abnormal amounts.

2-54 Fastening Devices

Many items are made in one piece today that were considered impossible to fabricate a short time ago. However, many mechanisms must still be made of several pieces and then assembled. Also, if there is motion in the mechanism, such as a piston in a cylinder, the apparatus must be made of two or more pieces.

Many clever ways have been developed to fasten multiple pieces together. In woodwork--pegs, glue, nails, screws, have all been used. In metal work--soldering, brazing, welding, crimping, rivets, bolts, machine screws, pins, spring fasteners, force fits have all been used with success.

The assembly devices used depend to a considerable extent on the kind and condition of the metal, and second on how frequently the pieces must be dismantled.

MACHINE SCREW NUMBER	DIAMETER IN.	THREADS PER INCH	
		COARSE	FINE
2	.086	56	64
3	.099	48	56
4	.112	40	48
5	.125	40	44
6	.138	32	40
8	.164	32	36
10	.190	24	32
12	.216	24	28
1/4	.250	20	28
5/16	.3125	18	24
3/8	.375	16	24

Fig. 2-68. Table of common machine screw sizes.

If the parts are to be put together permanently, riveting, welding, soldering, and brazing are popular assembly devices.

If the parts must be dismantled occasionally, assembly devices are used that can be easily removed without injuring the parts. Nuts and bolts, cap screws, machine screws, and set screws are used for this purpose. Fig. 2-67 illustrates an assortment of fastening devices.

2-55 Machine Screws

Many small parts are assembled using specially threaded devices called machine screws. Machine screws may be made of steel, stainless steel, brass, Monel Metal, etc. They are available in a variety of head shapes, such as round head, countersunk or flat head, fillister head, etc. Various methods have been used to turn these screws, such as the regular flat blade screwdriver, the allen hex drive, the Phillips cross type screwdriver, etc., Fig. 2-67.

Machine screws come in various diameters; eight in the number sizes, three in the fraction sizes. Each size may have either fine or coarse threads; the larger the number, the larger the diameter. A table of machine screw sizes and threads is given in Fig. 2-68.

2-56 Abrasives

Surfaces are cleaned, smoothed or made to accurate size with abrasives. Abrasives are grinding particles attached to paper or cloth by glue or other adhesive. Various abrasive materials are used. Sandpaper was the only abrasive for many years, and it is still excellent for wood finishing or where a dry surface is wanted. Emery, aluminum oxide, and silicon carbide are abrasive materials commonly used today.

Emery cloth is available in different grades. These grades are 0000 (finest), 000 (extra fine), 00 (very fine), 0 (fine), 1/2 (medium fine), and 1 (medium).

Silicon carbide abrasives are available as follows: 500 (finest), 360 (very fine), 320 (fine), 220 (medium fine), and 180 (medium).

Aluminum oxides are available as follows: 320 (extra fine), 240 (fine), 150 (medium fine), and 100 (medium).

These abrasives come in 9 in. x 11 in. sheets or in rolls usually 1 inch wide.

When using sheet abrasives, the paper or cloth should be backed by a block made of wood, metal, felt or rubber. Special sanding blocks are also available.

2-57 Gaskets

Most mating surfaces are rough, to at least a minor degree, and to make a leak-proof joint it is necessary to use gaskets between the surfaces. Gaskets are relatively soft and resilient.

Gaskets are used to seal joints between assembled parts to keep the refrigerant from leaking out, to prevent oil leakage, and to keep air from leaking into the system. Gaskets are used between the valve plate and the compressor body, and between the valve plate and the compressor head. Gaskets are also used on the crankcase and at the crankshaft seal.

Metal gaskets are commonly used. Lead is popular because it is soft and non-corrosive. Aluminum has also been used. Composition gaskets made of plastic impregnated paper are also popular.

Gaskets must not restrict the openings. They must not lose their compressibility, and replacement gaskets must not be thicker than the original gaskets.

Surfaces that contact the gasket must be kept free of burrs, bruises, and foreign matter.

2-58 Cleaning Solvents

Before any refrigeration mechanism is repaired, it must be thoroughly cleaned. Also, this same mechanism must be cleaned after it has been repaired. Many methods have been used to clean mechanisms. Some do not do a thorough job; some are dangerous. A cleaning method must be able to remove oil, grease and sludge. It must not injure the parts and it must not be injurious to the user. In refrigeration and air conditioning applications, the cleaning method must remove moisture, or at least not add moisture.

There are several cleaning methods:

1. Steam Cleaning: If the parts are exposed to hot water or steam, the grease will usually become fluid and float off the surface. However, steam and hot water will burn the serviceman if carelessly used.

2. Caustic Solution Cleaning: When an alkaline cleaner is dissolved in hot water, the mixture will remove grease and oil. This solution must be carefully used or you may suffer burns or injured eyes.

3. Oleum or Mineral Spirits: A petroleum product that is popular for cleaning, is a petroleum derivative that has a flash point of approximately 140 F. (kerosene has a flash point of 130 F.). It cleans well and leaves a smudge-free surface. However, there is a fire hazard involved with this fluid. For this reason it should always be used in small amounts. It should be used in self-closing tanks, and the tank should be exhaust ventilated (have a hood and an explosion-proof exhaust fan).

4. Carbon Tetrachloride: This is a heavy fluid that cleans grease, oils, sludge, etc., and it also absorbs some moisture. However, carbon tetrachloride is dangerous to use. The effect of carbon tetrachloride is accumulative and it may be absorbed either through the lungs or the skin. Breathing even small concentrations of the fumes will eventually make one ill and may even cause death. If used, be sure that excellent ventilation is provided.

5. Never use gasoline for cleaning. It has a low flash point, and its fumes are heavy and may travel far to ignition sources.

6. Alcohol is a good cleaning fluid. However, it is both flammable and toxic. Special precautions must be taken when using it.

7. Vapor degreasing is a system whereby a cleansing fluid is placed in a tank; the fluid is warmed so that the upper part of the tank is filled with the vapors of the

cleaner. Any parts suspended in this cleaning vapor are quickly and thoroughly cleaned. Such a tank must be specially vented.

8. There are several patented cleansing fluids available. When these are used you should read and carefully follow manufacturer's instructions.

Refer to Chapter 27, for more information on cleaning.

2-59 Refrigeration Oil

In the mechanical refrigerator the moving parts must be lubricated with oil in order to have long life and provide efficient performance.

Refrigerant oil is specially prepared mineral oil. Refining precautions are taken to remove excessive wax, moisture, sulphur and other impurities. Most refrigerant oils have a foaming inhibitor added.

Be sure to use oils that have a low enough pour point so there will be no wax separation at the low temperature to cause refrigerant control clogging.

Refrigerant oils are available in several viscosities. Viscosity is the time in seconds it takes for a definite quantity of the oil to flow through a certain size opening at 100 degrees F. (Saybolt). The lower the viscosity number, the thinner the oil. The six standard viscosities are 75-85, 95-105, 150-162, 192-208, 300-324, and 485-515.

The Freon group of refrigerants use the thicker oils such as 300-324 and occasionally 485-515 (air conditioning).

R-40 uses the 300-324 group; while the 95-105 group is for low temperature use.

Food freezer and frozen food units need oils that have extra low pour points, and a low wax content.

Hermetic system oils must be of the best quality obtainable. These oils must have a minimum of foreign matter, moisture, and wax. The oil must not have any hydro-carbons that may precipitate on the compressor valves or other parts. The

viscosity of the oil must be accurately determined for the temperature ranges to which the refrigerator may be exposed. The oils must have a very low temperature pour point and a very low wax separation point. The accepted method to test an oil for moisture content is the Dielectric Test. This test imposes a 25,000-volt electric pressure on electrodes immersed in an oil sample. If any current flows there is moisture present in the oil and the oil is unfit for refrigeration use. It is highly important that this oil be kept in sealed containers, that it be transferred in chemically clean containers and lines, and that it not be left exposed to the air as it will absorb moisture. Never refill a refrigerator with used oil. Always use new oil.

Refrigeration oil may be obtained in one gallon cans, five gallon cans, and in barrels. The price varies somewhat with the grades. A low pour point oil is more expensive than one having a higher pour point value. The pour point of any oil is the temperature at which it starts to flow. For domestic machines with refrigerant temperatures as low as 0 F. to 5 F., a pour point of -20 F. is desirable. Always seal an oil container after having drawn some oil from it.

See Chapter 27, for tables of oil characteristics for use with each refrigerant and with the different types of compressors.

2-60 Refrigerants

The refrigeration service engineer is required to handle and charge refrigerants into refrigerating mechanisms. Various refrigerants are named and their physical characteristics are carefully described in Chapter 9. Chapter 1 contains information common to all refrigerants and safety in handling which is of special value to the beginning serviceman.

Refrigerants must be kept DRY and CLEAN. Remember that all exposed surfaces absorb moisture if left in the open. If a compressor is torn down, overhauled and reassembled it must not be immediately charged with refrigerant. It must first be dehydrated. See Chapter 12 for detailed instructions concerning compressor overhaul and dehydrating.

Refrigerants are stored and handled by the serviceman using portable refrigerant cylinders. Refrigerants are identified by a cylinder color code. See Chapter 9 for a table of color codes for common refrigerants.

Cylinders for various refrigerants must not be interchanged.

2-61 Refrigerant Cylinders

Refrigerant cylinders are made of steel. They are usually of one-piece construction with one opening for the service valve. The larger cylinders usually have a fuse plug threaded into the concave bottom as a protection against overheating or excessive pressures.

The refrigerant cylinders should be stamped with an ICC stamp (Interstate Commerce Commission) and should also be dated. The cylinder should not be used when the date on the cylinder is more than six years old. Refrigerant manufacturers request that all cylinders be returned to them each six months or more often in order that the valve fittings and the complete cylinder may be carefully checked. This service helps to assure safe cylinders.

The serviceman's cylinders are usually 10 lb. or 25 lb. refrigerant capacity and are usually equipped with a 1/4 in. male flared fitting.

A refrigerant service cylinder with carrying handle, may also serve as a stand for direct liquid charging if the cylinder is turned upside down. These cylinders have a protective ring around the valve. All of the cylinders shown in Fig. 2-69, except G, have either fusible plugs or pressure-relief safety valves.

The larger type refrigerant cylinders are usually of the standard type which have a screw or protective cap and have 1/4 in. male flare connections.

A new liquid-vapor valve is available on standard size cylinders. This valve, Fig. 9-19, enables the serviceman to charge a system in the usual manner from a standard valve fitting either as a vapor or as a liquid without inverting the cylinder. This is accomplished by the addition of a second handwheel, attached to the side of the valve. This handwheel is connected to a tube which extends to the bottom of the cylinder and delivers liquid refrigerant when required. By leaving the liquid valve closed and turning the vapor wheel valve, the serviceman may obtain vaporized refrigerant from the cylinder.

It is economical to purchase refrigerants in 100 and 150 lb. cylinders. The transferring of refrigerant from the large cylinder to the smaller service cylinder should be carefully performed and a record kept of the quantity of refrigerant removed. To the total figure add three percent to account for gas losses. A charging cylinder should be thoroughly rinsed out periodically using R-11 or a moisture absorbent clean-

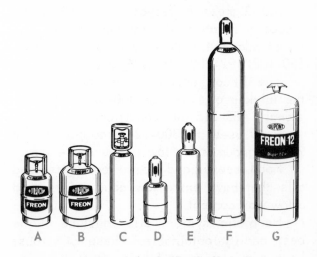

Fig. 2-69. *Some common refrigerant cylinders. A-through E-are service cylinders. F-is a supply cylinder. G-shows a "throw away" container.*
(E. I. duPont de Nemours)

ing fluid, as the impurities getting into the refrigerants may be corrosive to the refrigerating system.

CAUTION: Never completely fill a refrigerant cylinder with liquid refrigerant. If a cylinder is completely filled, there is no space for expansion. Liquid refrigerant expands with an increase in temperature. A cylinder completely filled with cold or cool refrigerant would burst if allowed to warm up. Always allow space for expansion. To be sure, shake the cylinder endwise. If there is some unfilled space the liquid refrigerant will be heard as it sloshes from end to end. A completely filled cylinder will make no sound. The safe limit is 85 percent full.

The cylinder valves should receive the same care as the service valves of a refrigerator. The valve is a packed, one-way valve; the packing nut should be kept tight unless using the valve. The opening should be sealed with a plug when not in use.

Service tanks should be weighed before and after filling. In this way the amount of refrigerant in the cylinder may be readily determined. When charging a cylinder, the service cylinder should be placed on accurate scales and only the specified weight of refrigerant charged into it.

Many popular refrigerants are available in small quantities, usually up to 10 lbs., in "throw away" cans. These containers are easy to handle and they eliminate the problem of refilling as they are purchased filled and are thrown away when empty.

2-62 Portable Charging Cylinders

The development of the capillary tube type refrigeration system has necessitated the careful measurement of the amount of refrigerant which may be charged into a system. Modern refrigeration requirements often call for a specific number of ounces by weight of the refrigerant as opposed to a pounds designation. The serviceman should always refer to the manufacturer's specifications for the amount of refrigerant to be charged into a system. With the use of the portable charging cylinder, precise measurements of refrigerants are possible. Fig. 2-70 illustrates a portable charging cylinder.

For servicing the smaller domestic refrigerator, portable charging cylinders are available in 3 different sizes: 2 1/2 pound, 6 pound, and 10 pound.

The portable charging cylinder may be obtained for use with any three of the following refrigerants: R-12, R-22, R-114, and R-502. The charging cylinder is equipped with the selected refrigerant scales, a pressure-temperature gauge, a purge-relief valve and a temperature compensation calibrator. For charging the large commercial units, large panel-mounted cylinders are available in several sizes ranging in capacity from 17 to 137 pounds.

2-63 How to Use a Portable Charging Cylinder

The portable charging cylinder is used as follows: The cylinder is filled with the required refrigerant by the serviceman who turns the external cylindrical dial to correspond to the type of refrigerant used. He then adjusts the scale to compensate for volume changes due to the ambient temperature. At the top of the charging cylinder is a pressure gauge indicating the internal pressure of the charging cylinder. Because of temperature-pressure relationships, temperature determines pressure and pressure in turn determines volume.

Turn the calibrated plastic shroud which surrounds the charging cylinder to the proper volume-pressure chart which corresponds to the indicated pressure on the charging cylinder gauge. The amount of refrigerant needed in the unit is determined from the identification tag or other sources. The serviceman will set the upper indicator arrow at the amount of refrigerant in the cylinder and the arrow at the lower level indicating the amount which will remain in the cylinder after the unit has been charged. If the charging cylinder being used is not equipped with indicator arrows, the serviceman should record the amount of refrigerant in the cylinder at

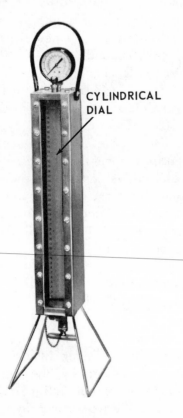

CYLINDRICAL DIAL

Fig. 2-70. *Portable charging cylinder (transparent tube) for accurately recharging a system. This charging cylinder has a 2 1/2 lb. capacity.* (Airserco Mfg. Co.)

the beginning of charging and anticipate the amount that will remain after charging. The serviceman is then ready to accurately charge the system to plus or minus 1/8 of an ounce.

2-64 A Review of Safety in Handling Refrigeration Supplies and Equipment

1. Tubing should be bent in as large a radius as possible.
2. There are certain hazards when using epoxy bonding materials. They may irritate the skin of the user.
3. "Mushroom" heads should be removed from chisels and punches as these parts may fly when struck with the hammer and may cause serious injury to the operator.
4. Files should never be used without handles as the tang may injure the hands.
5. Wear goggles when drilling. Sometimes chips may fly and the eyes should always be protected.
6. Emery cloth should not be used to clean tubing preparatory to soldering. It may leave an oily deposit on the tubing. The grit is hard and would cause considerable damage if allowed to enter the refrigerating mechanism.
7. In testing for leaks in tubing circuits, use carbon dioxide or nitrogen. Never use oxygen. It may cause an explosion.
8. If carbon tetrachloride is used for cleaning, provide adequate ventilation; avoid prolonged skin contact.
9. Silver brazing materials sometimes contain cadmium. Fumes from heated cadmium are very poisonous. Be sure that the work space is well ventilated. If at all possible, use silver brazing alloys which DO NOT contain cadmium.
10. It is recommended that refrigerant cylinders never be filled above 85 percent of their capacity. If over filled, the hydrostatic pressure may cause them to burst.
11. Wrenches used on refrigeration line fittings should always fit the nuts well. Poorly fitting wrenches will ruin nuts and bolt heads.
12. Always "crack" service valves and cylinder valves before opening. This gives positive control of the flow of gases.
13. Moisture is always a hazard to refrigerating mechanisms. Keep everything connected with refrigerating mechanisms thoroughly dry.

2-65 Test Your Knowledge, Chapter 2

1. List the fittings to be used when connecting a compound gauge with 1/8 in. pipe male thread to a service valve having 1/4 in. pipe female thread.
2. When cutting tubing with a hacksaw, what two precautions must be taken?
3. What are the SAE thread specifications of 1/4, 3/8 and 1/2 in. tube flare nuts?
4. What is the thickness of refrigeration tubing? What is the inside diameter of 1/4 in. tubing?
5. What causes copper tubing to harden?
6. Why do some servicemen file the end of copper tubing?
7. How may an external bending spring be easily removed from the tubing after bending?
8. Is it sufficient to clean metal for soldering with flux? Why?
9. When soldering, how hot must the metal being soldered be?
10. Why must a soldered joint be cleaned after soldering?
11. How may one tell when the correct silver brazing temperature is reached?
12. What type of wrench should be used on a valve stem?
13. Should one push or pull a wrench?
14. Describe an easy way to check the accuracy of a thermometer.
15. What is the purpose of a compound gauge?
16. Why must refrigerant oil be practically wax free?
17. What is a very important precaution one must take when filling refrigerant cylinders?
18. What is a double cut file?
19. Name the tools shown in Fig. 2-33.
20. Why are torque wrenches used?

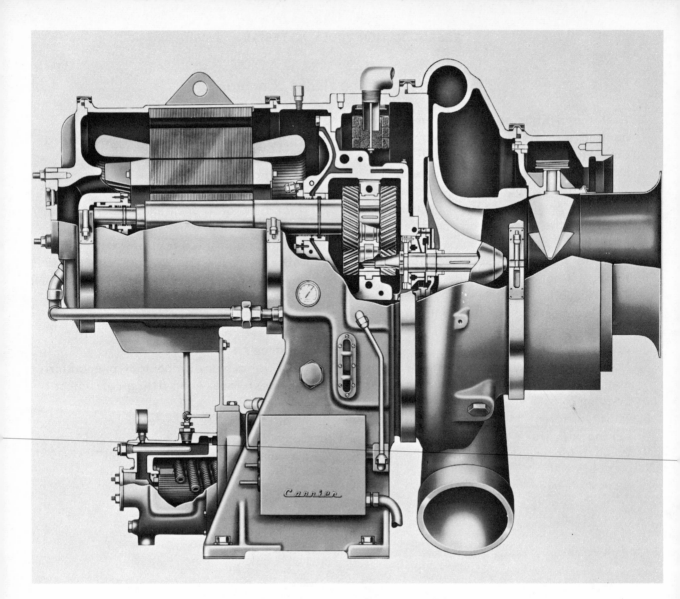

Cross section of a single stage hermetic centrifugal compressor.

Chapter 3

BASIC REFRIGERATION SYSTEMS

In this chapter basic refrigeration systems will be described and illustrated.

There are several ways refrigeration systems may by classified: by type of refrigerant control, type of motor control, compression system, absorption systems, etc. In this chapter, no classification system will be followed. Similar systems will be grouped together.

With each Basic Refrigeration System discussed, we will:

1. Name the system.
2. Show a schematic diagram of the system.
3. Explain how the system works.
4. Describe the operating characteristics.
5. Name some common applications.
6. Explain the motor characteristics and motor control required.
7. Give some service notes.

It is important that you become familiar with the fundamental principles of operation of the common systems as described in this chapter.

The illustrations are not intended to show parts and applications of actual units. Instead, the aim is to explain the fundamentals of construction and operation applicable to all units. Details and actual applications will be shown and described in detail in later chapters.

3-1 ICE REFRIGERATION

Ice (frozen water) was for years the only refrigerating means available. It is still used in many refrigerating applications.

The usual ice refrigerator consists of an insulated cabinet equipped with a tray or tank at the top, for holding blocks or pieces of ice. See Fig. 3-1. Shelves for food are located below the ice compartment. Cold air flows downward from the ice compartment and cools the food on the shelves below. Air returns from the bottom of the cabinet, up the sides and back of the cabinet, which are warmer, flows over the ice, and again flows down over the shelves to be cooled. Ice refrigeration has one advantage in particular. The interior of the cabinet is maintained at fairly high relative humidity, which means that food stored in this type refrigerator does not dry out rapidly.

Until the development of the mechanical refrigerator, ice refrigeration was quite universally used. In the early days, ice was harvested during the winter months from the surface of ponds and lakes, and stored in insulated ice houses for use throughout the year. Since that time, artificial ice has been manufactured for use in household and commercial refrigerators. Temperatures inside an ice refrigerator are controlled by the flow of cooled air over the ice and through the cabinet. Temperatures will usually range between 40 and 50 deg. F.

When it is necessary to use ice for cooling temperatures below 32 degrees, ice and salt mixtures may be used. Temperatures down to zero may be easily obtained with ice and salt mixtures. See chapter 27 for a table of ice and salt mixtures.

Fig. 3-1. Ice refrigerator.

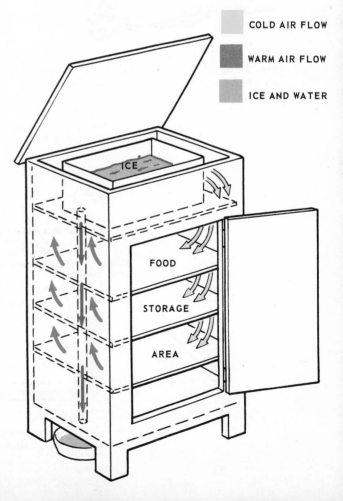

COLD AIR FLOW

WARM AIR FLOW

ICE AND WATER

ICE

FOOD

STORAGE

AREA

3-2 WATER EVAPORATIVE REFRIGERATION

Heat is absorbed when a fluid evaporates. Evaporation of water is an example. This explains why we perspire. Evaporation of moisture from the skin surface helps to keep us cool. Another common application of this principle is the "desert bag" used to keep drinking water cool. This bag, Fig. 3-2A, consists of a tightly woven fabric bag filled with drink-

ing water. The bag is not waterproof, consequently some water seeps through and the surface of the bag remains moist. Under desert conditions, which are usually both hot and dry, moisture on the surface of the bag evaporates rapidly. A large part of the heat necessary to cause this evaporation comes from the bag and the water which it contains. This removal of heat cools the drinking water, inside the canvas, keeping it at a temperature several degrees below the temperature of the surrounding air.

Another common application of water evaporation refrigeration is the method of making artificial snow for ski slopes. This device (snow machine) consists of a water nozzle into which a high pressure jet of air is inserted. Water flows from the nozzle, as shown in Fig. 3-2B, and the air under high pressure flowing out with the water, causes the water to break up into tiny droplets (almost a fog). If the surrounding air temperature is near freezing or below freezing, the droplets of water tend to evaporate from their surfaces and rapidly cool to the point that tiny drops of ice are formed. In using this method, artificial snow is made when the temperature of the surrounding air is 32 deg. F. or lower.

However, if the relative humidity is low, artificial snow can be made when the temperature is as high as 34 F. This is because of the rapid evaporation and evaporative cooling which is caused by the low relative humidity.

Evaporative condensers are often used in connection with air conditioners. The evaporation of water helps cool the refrigerating mechanism condenser.

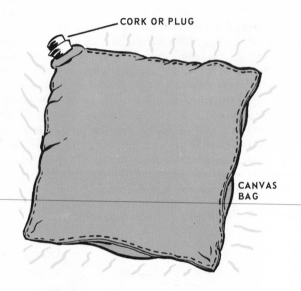

CORK OR PLUG

CANVAS BAG

Fig. 3-2A. The "desert bag" is an example of cooling by evaporative refrigeration.

Fig. 3-2B. Water – compressed air nozzle, used for making artificial snow.

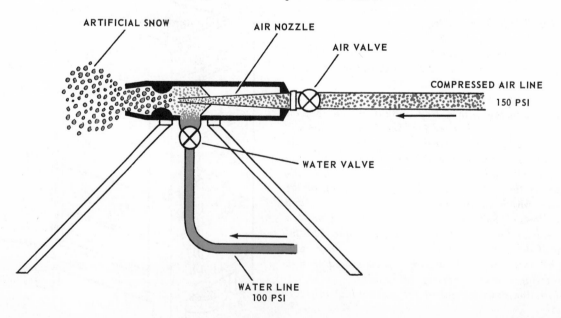

ARTIFICIAL SNOW

AIR NOZZLE

AIR VALVE

COMPRESSED AIR LINE
150 PSI

WATER VALVE

WATER LINE
100 PSI

3-3 COMPRESSION SYSTEM USING CAPILLARY TUBE REFRIGERANT CONTROL

The "capillary tube" system, Fig. 3-3, is one of the most popular compression type systems. The compressor is shown in the base of the cabinet. The liquid refrigerant flows from the condenser up through the liquid line to the filter (this may be both a filter and a drier). From the filter the refrigerant flows through the capillary tube refrigerant control into the evaporator. The pressure of the liquid refrigerant as it enters the capillary tube at the filter end, is at a high pressure (high-pressure side). The pressure in the evaporator is at a low pressure. The design of the capillary tube is such that it maintains a pressure difference while the compressor is operating. The compressor maintains a low pressure in the evaporator coil, and the refrigerant boils rapidly absorbing heat from the evaporator coils. The vaporized refrigerant is drawn through the suction line back to the compressor, where it is compressed to a high pressure and discharged into the condensing coil, where it is cooled, returns to a liquid, and flows into the liquid line. This operation continues until the thermal element has been cooled to a preset low temperature. When the desired low temperature is reached the thermal element operates the motor control mechanism and the power is disconnected from the motor and the refrigeration cycle is stopped. It will remain stopped until the thermal element warms up and signals the motor control to again operate the compressor. It should be noted that the running of the compressor causes refrigeration to take place.

This type of refrigerating cycle is quite satisfactory for most refrigerating applications where the number of degrees of temperature fluctuation (2 to 5 F.) provides satisfactory refrigeration.

This cycle is commonly used in household refrigerators, freezers, air conditioners and many small commercial applications.

On the off cycle the capillary tube allows the pressures to balance between the high and low sides so it is not usually necessary to provide a driving motor with a high starting torque.

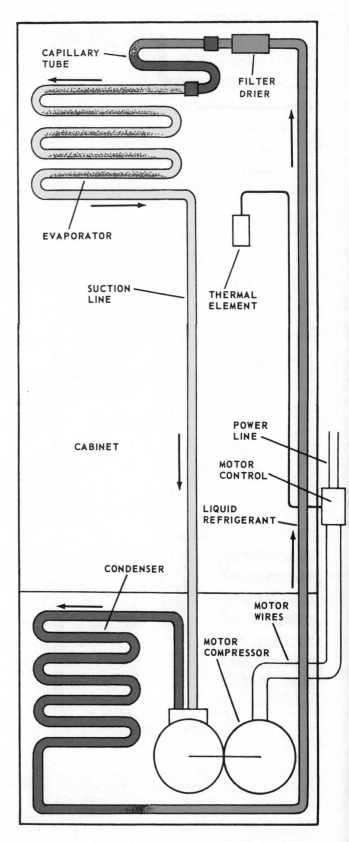

Fig. 3-3. Compression system using capillary tube type refrigerant control. Red indicates liquid refrigerant under high pressure, yellow low pressure vapor, and blue high pressure vapor.

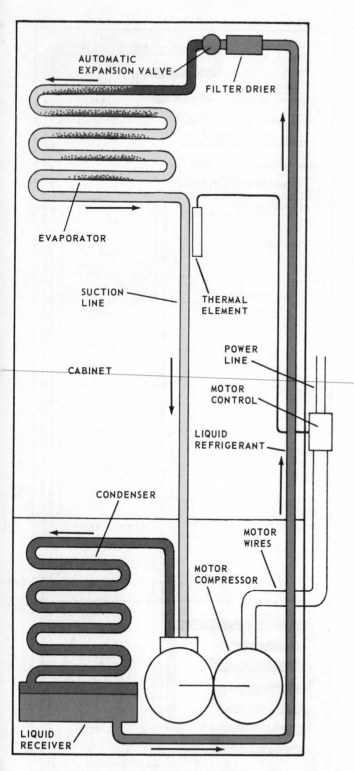

3-4 A COMPRESSION SYSTEM USING AN AUTOMATIC EXPANSION VALVE REFRIGERANT CONTROL (AEV)

The operation of an automatic (AEV) expansion valve refrigerant control refrigerating mechanism is illustrated in Fig. 3-4.

The compressor, motor and condenser (condensing unit) are in the base of the cabinet. Liquid refrigerant flows from the liquid receiver through the liquid line, through the filter to the automatic expansion valve. The automatic expansion valve is so designed that no liquid refrigerant will flow through it, unless the pressure in the evaporator coil is reduced by the running of the compressor. As the compressor runs and liquid refrigerant flows through the automatic expansion valve, it is sprayed into the evaporator coils where due to the low pressure, it boils rapidly and absorbs heat from the coil. This vaporized refrigerant is drawn back to the compressor through the suction line. In the compressor, it is compressed back to the high side pressure. As it flows through the condenser it is cooled, gives up the heat that it absorbed in the evaporator, returns to a liquid, and flows into the liquid receiver ready to repeat the cycle. The motor control thermal element is clamped to the end of the evaporator coil, at the beginning of the suction line. After the evaporator coil is cooled to its proper temperature, the control bulb pressure causes the motor control to turn off the current to the driving motor, and the compressor is stopped.

The operating characteristics of this system are quite satisfactory. The refrigerant oil is circulated without trouble. The temperature control limits can also be kept quite close.

This type of refrigeration cycle was quite popular in some of the older types of domestic refrigerators, and it is still used extensively in small commercial applications.

Due to the fact that the pressures do not balance on the off cycle, it is necessary to provide a compressor driving motor which will start under load.

If the needle or seat in the expansion valve is faulty and refrigerant leaks through the valve on the off cycle, liquid refrigerant may flow into the suction line. When the compressor starts, this will be indicated by frosting of the suction line. If the trouble is severe, it may result in liquid refrigerant entering the compressor through the suction line. This may cause the compressor to knock severely.

Fig. 3-4. Compression system using automatic expansion valve refrigerant control (AEV). Red indicates liquid refrigerant under high pressure, green low pressure liquid, yellow low pressure vapor, blue high pressure vapor.

3-5 A COMPRESSION SYSTEM USING A THERMOSTATICALLY CONTROLLED EXPANSION VALVE (TEV)

Principle of the thermostatically controlled expansion valve (TEV) refrigeration cycle is shown in Fig. 3-5.

In this system, the liquid refrigerant flows from the liquid receiver through the liquid line to the filter-drier, and to the thermostatic expansion valve. The operation of the thermostatic expansion valve is controlled both by the temperature of the TEV control bulb, and the pressure in the evaporator. There must be a low pressure in the evaporator, and the temperature of the TEV control bulb must be above the desired temperature, before it will open. The amount of opening will be governed by the temperature of the evaporator coil. If the coil is quite warm, (considerable refrigeration effect needed) the needle will open quite wide allowing a rapid flow of refrigerant into the evaporator, and in this way hasten the cooling effect. As the temperature of the evaporator lowers, the TEV needle valve will reduce the flow of refrigerant.

The vaporized refrigerant from the evaporator is drawn back into the compressor, where it is compressed back to the high side pressure. As it flows through the condenser it gives up the heat which was absorbed in the evaporator, and is cooled. The refrigerant is condensed to a liquid, and flows back into the liquid receiver, and the refrigerating cycle is repeated.

When the evaporator coil reaches the desired temperature, the motor control bulb will cause the motor control to turn off the current to the motor, and the compressor will be stopped. When this happens, the TEV needle valve will close, and no more refrigerant will flow through it, until the compressor again lowers the pressure in the evaporator coil.

This system is used on large commercial, and on many air conditioning applications.

Since the pressures do not balance on the off cycle, it is necessary to provide a compressor driving motor which will start under load.

The refrigerant orifice in the TEV control remains closed, unless the evaporator is under reduced pressure, and the temperature is above normal. A leaking valve will be indicated by a frosted suction line.

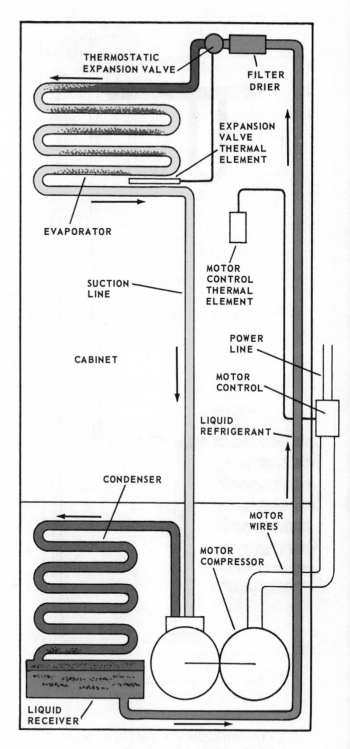

Fig. 3-5. Compression system using thermostatically controlled expansion valve (TEV). The red line indicates liquid refrigerant under high pressure, green line low pressure liquid, yellow line low pressure vapor, and blue line high pressure vapor.

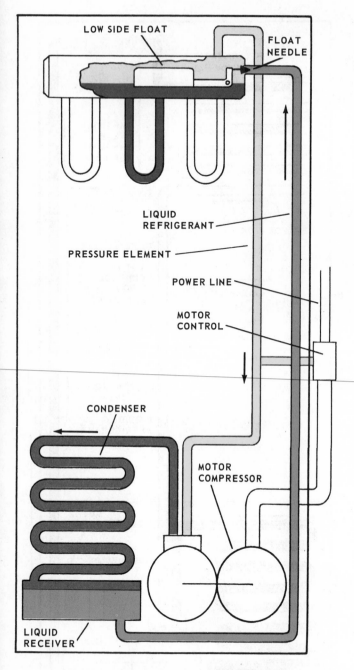

LOW SIDE FLOAT

FLOAT NEEDLE

LIQUID REFRIGERANT

PRESSURE ELEMENT

POWER LINE

MOTOR CONTROL

CONDENSER

MOTOR COMPRESSOR

LIQUID RECEIVER

Fig. 3-6. Compression system using a low side float refrigerant control.

3-6 A COMPRESSION SYSTEM USING A LOW SIDE FLOAT REFRIGERANT CONTROL

The "low side float" refrigerant control system was very popular in many of the early refrigerating mechanisms. This system is known as a flooded system.

Fig. 3-6 shows a schematic diagram of this sys-

tem. The red line indicates high pressure liquid refrigerant in the liquid receiver and in the liquid line. Green indicates low pressure liquid in the low side float tank, yellow low pressure vapor, blue high pressure vapor. The liquid refrigerant flows from the liquid receiver through the liquid line, up to the low side float needle. The evaporator in this mechanism consists of a finned tank (evaporator) which contains a float and needle arrangement, this maintains a constant level of liquid refrigerant under a low side pressure. This refrigerant, since it is a liquid on the low side, is at low temperature. The cold liquid refrigerant will absorb considerable heat on the off cycle.

Vaporized refrigerant is drawn through the suction line to the compressor, where it is compressed to a high pressure and discharged into the condensing coil, there it is cooled, returns to a liquid, and flows into the liquid receiver. This operation continues until the desired low temperature is reached.

The pressure on the low side in a flooded system, such as this, will vary with the temperature. The higher the temperature the higher the low side pressure. This system may use a pressure motor control, as in Fig. 3-6.

A spring loaded pressure sensitive device on the suction line, or on the evaporator, is made to actuate a motor control switch. As the motor drives the compressor, the pressure and temperature in the low side float tank will be reduced. At a given pressure setting, the motor will be disconnected from the line, and the compressor will stop.

The cycle will be repeated, as soon as the pressure in the low side tank reaches a level corresponding to the refrigerant temperature at which the motor-compressor is to cut in again.

The cabinet temperature may be controlled using a temperature control switch. In this case, the temperature sensitive element, may be clamped to the fins on the low side evaporator coil.

This refrigerating cycle is often used on drinking fountains, and other installations, where a constant temperature is desired.

Since the pressures do not balance on the off cycle, it is necessary to use a motor which will start under a load.

This system requires a rather large refrigerant charge, as there is liquid refrigerant in both the liquid receiver and in the low side float tank.

All flooded systems such as these, are quite efficient since cold liquid refrigerant wets the evaporator coil surfaces providing excellent heat transfer. These systems are easy to service.

The float needle and seat must be kept in good condition in order to avoid possible flooding of the low side.

3-7 A COMPRESSION SYSTEM USING A HIGH SIDE FLOAT REFRIGERANT CONTROL

This high side float system is also known as a flooded system, as the evaporator coils are always wet with liquid refrigerant.

A schematic diagram of this system is shown in Fig. 3-7. Red indicates high pressure liquid refrigerant in the lower part of the condenser, in the high side float valve, and in the line up to the weight valve. Green indicates low pressure liquid, yellow low pressure vapor, blue high pressure vapor.

In operation, as the compressor runs, liquid refrigerant flows from the liquid line into the high side float mechanism. As soon as enough liquid refrigerant has entered the high side float mechanism, it will raise the float ball, and refrigerant will begin to flow through the control to the evaporator coil. Since the evaporator coil is under low pressure, the tube connecting the high side float and the evaporator coil, should be insulated. This connection may be a capillary tube. If it is not a capillary tube, it should have a weight valve at the evaporator coil, otherwise the refrigerant may start to boil in the connecting tube. The weight valve should be just heavy enough to supply slight pressure on the refrigerant in the connecting tube. Fig. 3-7 shows a weight valve in the connecting line.

Refrigerant entering the evaporator coil is under low pressure. It will rapidly evaporate (boil) and absorb heat from the coil. The vapor then flows through the suction line to the compressor, where it is compressed to the high side pressure. In the condenser coil heat absorbed in the evaporator, is removed and the refrigerant is returned to the liquid state. It flows into the high side float mechanism where the cycle is repeated.

Either a temperature, or a pressure motor control, may be used on this refrigeration cycle. Fig. 3-7 shows a temperature motor control located in the refrigerated space.

This system is most used on commercial applications where high operating efficiency is desired.

This system is easy to service; however, amount of refrigerant charged into the system must be very accurately measured.

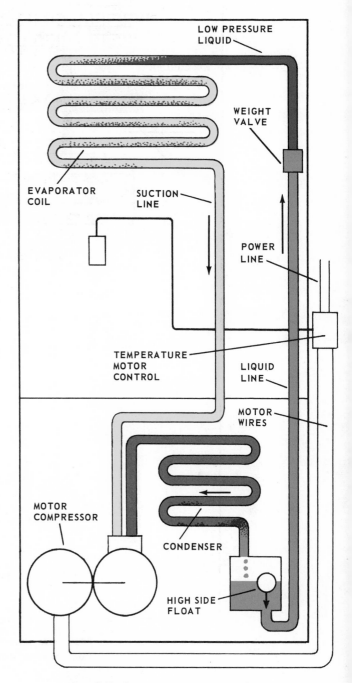

Fig. 3-7. Compression system using high side float refrigerant control.

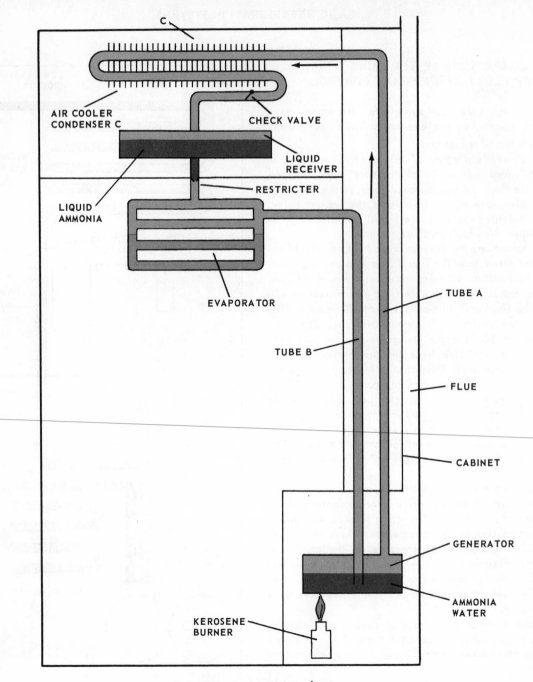

Fig. 3-8A. Intermittent absorption system, generating cycle.

3-8 AN INTERMITTENT ABSORPTION SYSTEM

The intermittent cycle absorption refrigerating system may use various sources of power for its operation. The most popular of the refrigerators using this system have been kerosene fired. Kerosene fired absorption refrigerators are especially popular in areas where electric power is not available.

Figs. 3-8A and 3-8B show a schematic diagram of a kerosene fired intermittent cycle absorption refrig-

erator. The generator is charged with water and ammonia.

In operation, Fig. 3-8A, the kerosene burner tank is filled with just enough kerosene for one cycle of operation. This usually is once per day. The burner is filled and lighted. The heat from the burner heats the fluid in the generator, and the ammonia is driven off through tube (A), up to the condenser (C), where the ammonia gas is cooled and condensed to liquid ammonia and flows into the receiver. During this part

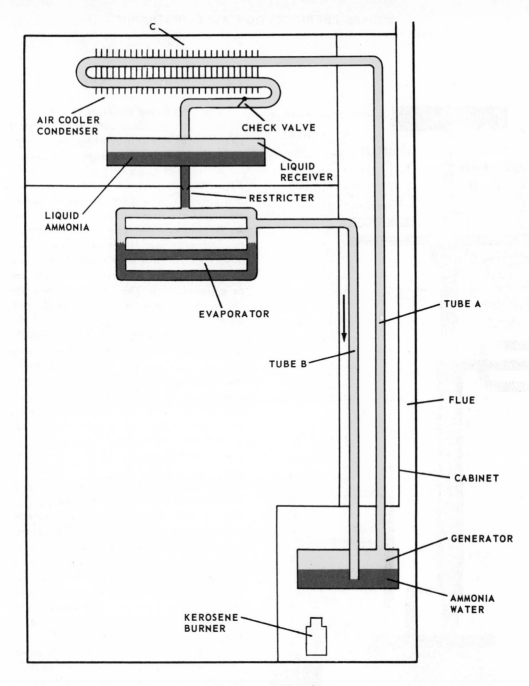

Fig. 3-8B. Intermittent absorption, system, cooling cycle.

of the cycle (generating) little or no refrigeration is taking place. As soon as the kerosene has all been burned (usually from 20 to 40 minutes), the generating cycle ends. The pressure in the system drops, the liquid ammonia flows into the evaporator coil, and begins to evaporate and cool the coil, Fig. 3-8B. The evaporated ammonia flows back through tube B, and is again absorbed by the water in the generator. Refrigeration continues, usually until the next firing of the kerosene burner.

This type refrigerating system is quite simple.

The piping is welded steel, since the pressures on the generating cycle are quite high. The refrigerating ability of this refrigerator mechanism is quite good.

This system may be used for both domestic and commercial applications. Servicing these refrigerators is quite simple. The burner must be kept in good condition and the flues kept clean. Some of these refrigerators use a water cooled condenser. In such applications the water tank must be kept filled or the water flow regulated. The cabinets are usually quite heavily insulated.

3-9 A CONTINUOUS CYCLE ABSORPTION SYSTEM

The continuous cycle absorption system generally uses gas or electricity as the heat source. The operation of this refrigerating mechanism depends on Dalton's Law. See Paragraph 1-53, page 37.

A schematic drawing of this cycle is shown in Fig. 3-9. The generator contains a solution of water and ammonia. Heat from the gas flame heats the solution, and the ammonia is driven out and up tube A. As it flows into the separator, any water vapor present is condensed, and flows back through tube B into the absorber. The ammonia vapor flows up through tube C to the condenser, where it is cooled and condensed to a liquid (red). The liquid ammonia flows into the evaporator. The evaporator, tube D, and part of the absorber, contain hydrogen. Pressure throughout the system is approximately 200 psi. From Dalton's Law, we learn that in a mixture of gases, each gas develops its own vapor pressure, so in this refrigerator the ammonia in the areas which include hydrogen, will evaporate and try to develop an ammonia vapor pressure of 200 psi. Since the hydrogen represents a large part of the gas in the area, the ammonia keeps on boiling or vaporizing at its own low pressure, and absorbing heat. The vaporized ammonia and hydrogen from the evaporator are at a low temperature. By gravity these vapors flow down through tube D back to the absorber. In the absorber, the water is relatively cool. It again absorbs the ammonia vapor, and returns the cool water and ammonia solution back to the generator. The hydrogen which flows down to the absorber with the ammonia is not absorbed by the water, and is returned through the heat exchanger back to the evaporator. This cycle operates continuously as long as refrigeration is needed. A thermostat which controls the burner is used to regulate the refrigerated space temperature.

Since the refrigerant used is ammonia, it is capable of producing quite low temperatures. Most of the automatic refrigerators require electrical devices, so both gas and electricity must be supplied. The cooling effect is from the heat generated by burning gas in the generator. With the exception of the thermostatic controls, there are no moving parts in the refrigerating mechanism.

This refrigerating device is widely used in domestic refrigerators, and it also has been developed for use in year around air conditioning of both homes and larger buildings.

Since there are no moving parts in these refrigerating mechanisms, the service is usually quite simple. The burner and stack must be kept clean. The refrigerator should be carefully leveled before being placed in operation.

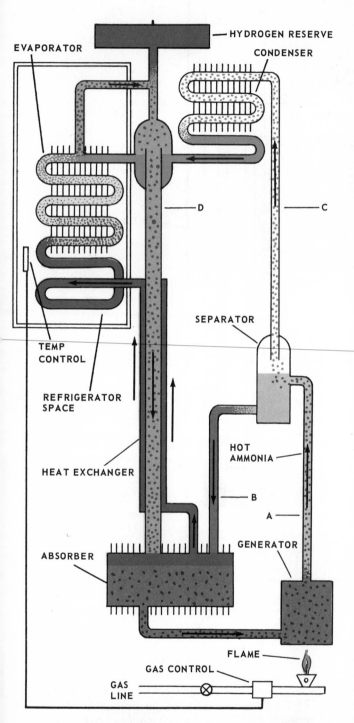

Fig. 3-9. Continuous cycle absorption system. Liquid ammonia shown in red, hydrogen in green.

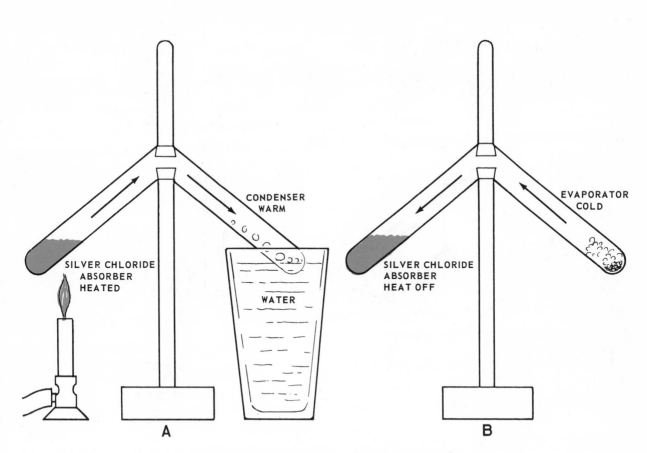

Fig. 3-10. Solid absorbent refrigerator principle.

3-10 SOLID ABSORBENT REFRIGERATION

Various kinds of solid absorbent refrigerators have been developed; however all have depended on the original Faraday experiment. Faraday's experiment is described as follows:

"Michael Faraday, in 1824, performed a series of experiments to liquefy certain "fixed" gases -- gases which certain scientists believed could exist only in vapor form. Among them was ammonia, for it had always been regarded as a "fixed" gas. Faraday knew that silver chloride, a white powder, had the peculiar property of absorbing large quantities of ammonia vapor. He exposed silver chloride to dry ammonia vapor. When the powder had absorbed all of the vapor it would take, he sealed the ammonia-silver chloride compound in a test tube which was bent to form an inverted "V." (See Fig. 3-10A.) He then heated the end of the tube containing the powder, and at the same time cooled the opposite end of the tube with water. The heat released ammonia vapor and drops of color-less liquid soon began to appear in the cool end of the tube. The liquid which was produced was liquid ammonia.

Faraday continued the heating process until suffi-cient liquid ammonia had been produced for his pur-pose. When this was accomplished, he extinguished the flame under the powder, removed the cooling water, and proceeded to observe the characteristics of the newly discovered substance.

A few moments after the flame had been extin-guished, Faraday began to note a most unusual oc-currence. The liquid ammonia, instead of remaining quietly in the sealed test tube, began to bubble and then to boil violently, Fig. 3-10B. The liquid was rapidly changing back into a vapor, and the vapor was being reabsorbed by the powder. Upon touching the end of the tube containing the boiling liquid, Faraday was astonished to find it intensely cold. Ammonia, in changing from liquid to vapor form, extracted heat. It took this heat from the nearest thing at hand, which was the test tube itself."

Many refrigerating cycles have been developed which use this principle; however these are not in common use at the present time.

Cooling mechanisms using this principle have been developed, which use water as the refrigerant, and lithium bromide or lithium chloride as the absorbent.

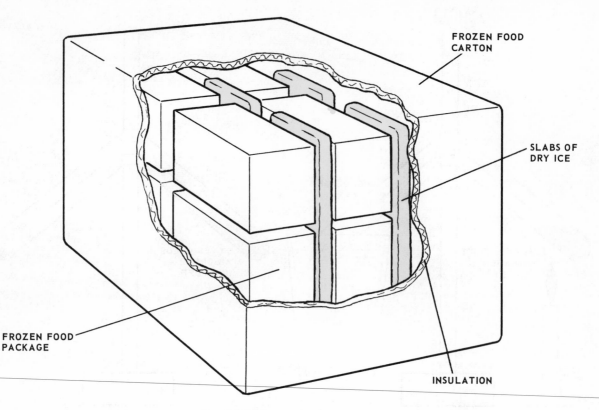

FROZEN FOOD
CARTON

SLABS OF
DRY ICE

FROZEN FOOD
PACKAGE

INSULATION

Fig. 3-11. Dry ice refrigeration.

3-11 DRY ICE REFRIGERATION

Dry ice is solid carbon dioxide. Dry ice may be pressed into various sizes and shapes, blocks or slabs. It changes directly from a solid to a vapor, and does not go through the liquid state. It is said to sublime. At atmospheric pressure its subliming temperature is −109 deg. F.

Dry ice is usually packed in frozen food cartons either beside or on top of the food packages. Carbon dioxide, as it changes to a vapor, keeps the food frozen. The dry vapor tends to replace the atmospheric air in the carton which also helps to preserve the food.

Fig. 3-11 illustrates a common method of using dry ice as a frozen food refrigerating device.

Dry ice is usually stored in heavily insulated cabinets. It should never be handled with the bare hands. Always wear heavy gloves.

3-12 COMPOUND REFRIGERATING SYSTEMS

In compound refrigerating systems, two or more compressors are connected in series, as shown in Fig. 3-12. In this illustration compressor No. 1, discharges into the intake side of compressor No. 2.

Compressor No. 2, discharges into the condenser, and liquid refrigerant flows to the evaporator. There are intercoolers between each of the compressors.

The advantage of such a compound system is to increase the capacity when pulling down to a temperature that is lower than is available from one compressor.

Compound systems require intercoolers between compressors Nos. 1 and 2. The refrigerant vapor is not condensed between the stages, but its temperature is decreased and its pressure increased. This type of installation requires an oil separator between the second stage and the condenser. A single-temperature motor control operates all motors, and a thermostatic expansion valve controls the liquid refrigerant flow into the evaporator.

Since the pressures do not balance on the off cycle, motors capable of starting under load are required.

Compound installations usually operate under rather heavy service requirements. The condensers and refrigerant must be kept clean, and the compressor valves must be kept in good condition.

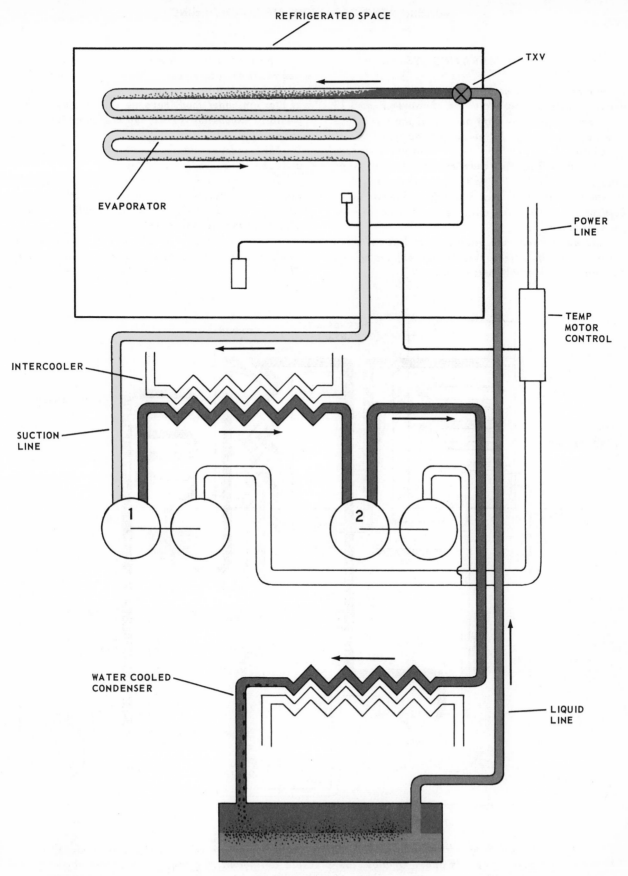

REFRIGERATED SPACE

TXV

POWER LINE

TEMP MOTOR CONTROL

EVAPORATOR

INTERCOOLER

SUCTION LINE

1

2

WATER COOLED CONDENSER

LIQUID LINE

Fig. 3-12. Compound refrigerating systems.

97

3-13 CASCADE REFRIGERATING SYSTEM

In a cascade refrigerating system two or more condensing units are connected as shown in Fig. 3-13. The condensing units both operate at the same time. The condensing unit A (the one on the right) has its evaporator A (heat absorbing part) arranged to cool the condenser B for the condensing unit B. The evaporator for the condensing unit B is arranged to supply the cooling effect desired. The refrigerant control for both of the condensing units is by thermostatic expansion valve (TEV).

Cascade systems are often used in industrial processes where it is necessary to cool objects to temperatures considerably below zero.

The control for both motors is connected to motor control temperature sensing bulb on evaporator B.

Motors used on cascade systems must be capable of starting under load, because with the use of thermostatic expansion valves, the pressures do not balance on the "off" cycle.

The condenser-evaporator is usually of the shell-and-tube flooded evaporator type.

Since these systems operate at very low temperatures, the refrigerant used must be dry otherwise any moisture would condense in the needle-seat of the TEV and stop the flow of refrigerant.

Oil separators must be installed in the compressor-condenser lines on both of these condensing units. The refrigerant must be kept clean and dry.

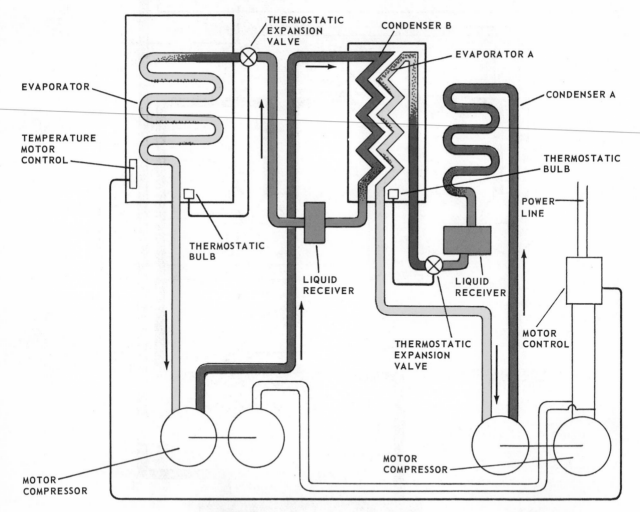

Fig. 3-13. Cascade refrigerating system. Lines shown in red are carrying liquid refrigerant. High pressure vapor is shown in blue, low pressure refrigerant in green, low pressure vapor in yellow.

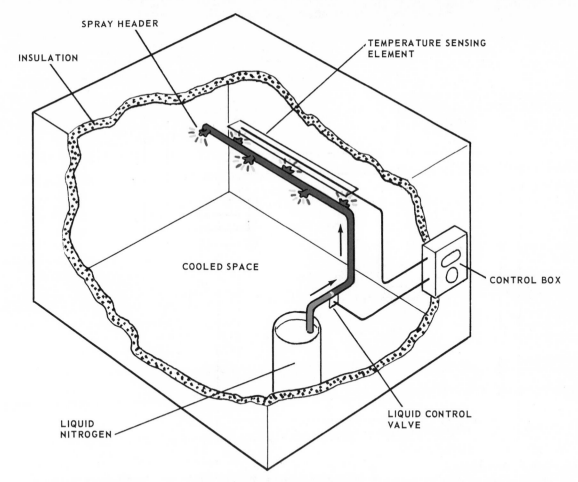

INSULATION

SPRAY HEADER

TEMPERATURE SENSING ELEMENT

COOLED SPACE

CONTROL BOX

LIQUID CONTROL VALVE

LIQUID NITROGEN

Fig. 3-14. Expendable refrigerant cooling system. Red indicates liquid refrigerant (nitrogen), and green low pressure liquid refrigerant.

3-14 EXPENDABLE REFRIGERANT COOLING SYSTEM

This system is sometimes called chemical refrigeration.

This is an increasingly popular type of refrigerating mechanism being used on trucks and other vehicles, in the transportation and storage of chilled and frozen foods. The mechanism is quite simple. It consists basically of a heavily insulated space, which is cooled either by being surrounded by tubes carrying evaporating liquid nitrogen, or by spraying liquid nitrogen directly into the space to be cooled. Fig. 3-14 illustrates the latter type of system. The liquid nitrogen (red) is supplied from a cylinder located within the refrigerated space. Green indicates low-pressure liquid refrigerant. The liquid nitrogen is kept under a pressure of approximately 200 psi.

A temperature sensing element, control box, and liquid control valve, control the flow of liquid nitrogen from the nozzles, and maintain the desired temperatures within the refrigerated space.

Although the liquid nitrogen is kept under pres-

sure and the cylinder is insulated, the heat leaking into the cylinder may cause the vapor pressure to rise above the automatic pressure release setting. Cold nitrogen vapor. released by the automatic pressure release valve, is discharged into the refrigerated space, or into the refrigerating tubes, depending on the system being used.

Liquid nitrogen vaporizes (boils) at a temperature of −320 F. at atmospheric pressure, as shown in Fig. 1-22. This type of system is excellent for use in shipping frozen foods, as the temperatures may be maintained as low as desired, usually about −20 F.

With extensive use of oxygen in steel making, liquid nitrogen has become a by-product which is relatively inexpensive and quite readily available.

Due to the simple construction of this refrigerating equipment, little attention is needed other than to replace or recharge the nitrogen storage cylinder. An advantage of this system is its ability to operate without any connection to a power source.

Safety devices are incorporated in spaces refrigerated by liquid nitrogen. The safety devices shut off the flow of nitrogen upon opening a door to the refrigated space.

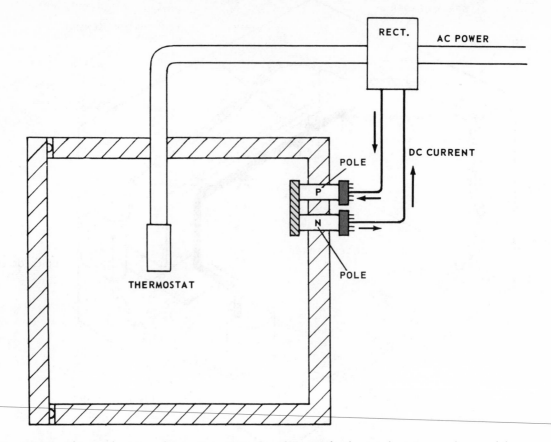

RECT.

AC POWER

POLE

P

N

DC CURRENT

POLE

THERMOSTAT

Fig. 3-15A. Thermoelectric refrigeration. Diagram of a simple thermoelectric couple, used for refrigerating an insulated space. Heat absorbed by the thermoelectric couple is released to the outside by fins attached to the heat radiating surface.

3-15 THERMOELECTRIC REFRIGERATION

The physical principle (Peltier effect) upon which thermoelectric refrigeration is based, has been known since 1834. In this system of transferring heat energy from one place to another, electrons are used instead of a refrigerant. Fig. 3-15A illustrates a simple thermoelectric couple capable of moving heat from the inside of an insulated space, and carrying it by means of electrons, to a heat exchanger on the outside of the refrigerated space. Fins are often used to increase the heat flow on the cooling coil, and on the outside of the heat exchanger, to move the heat to the surrounding air.

The effectiveness of the thermoelectric couple depends on the difference in the energy level of the two semiconductors P and N. Note that the P and N do not refer to the positive and negative polarity of an electrical circuit, but to the use of the two semiconductors.

The science of semiconductor electronics has given us some metallic alloys and oxides, which vary greatly in energy levels. The electrical qualities of semiconductors lie between those of insulators and conductors. The choice of materials for the semiconductors P and N, determines the efficiency of the device.

Since the materials P and N, are not good conductors of electricity, they are made quite large in cross section in order to reduce the electrical resistance, and lessen the heat generated by the current flowing through them.

Fig. 3-15A shows what is called a thermoelectric

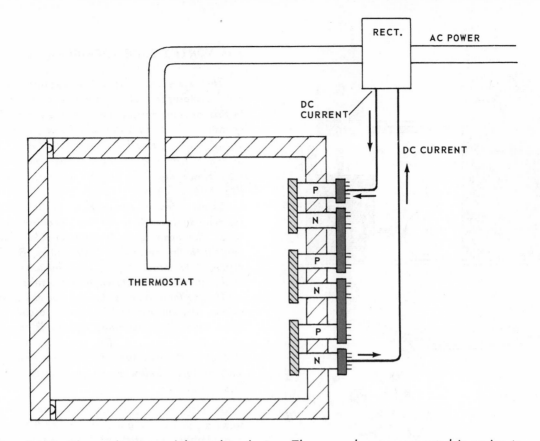

Fig. 3-15B. Thermoelectric module cooling device. Three couples are connected in series to increase the heat absorbing effect. Note that the thermostat controlling the module is connected in the alternating current circuit.

couple. Not much heat can be transferred by a single couple. In order to increase the cooling effect, several couples may be connected in series as shown in Fig. 3-15B. Several couples connected together in series are called a module. Groups of modules may be connected together in parallel, to increase the capacity still further. (See Chapter 7 for series-parallel connections.)

A thermostat located in the refrigerated space, controls the current flow through the transformer-rectifier which supplies a controlled DC current to the modules, and in this way, controls the temperature inside the refrigerator.

There are no moving parts in this refrigerator. Aside from the construction of the modules, the construction is quite simple. The thermal efficiency of the system is low. That is, the amount of refrigerating effect obtained for a given amount of electrical energy spent, is less than with a conventional compressor type refrigeration system.

It should be noted that by reversing the direction of the flow of current through a thermoelectric device, the hot and cold surfaces will be reversed. The same device can be used for either heating or cooling an insulated space, by controlling the direction of flow of the current. A larger application of this thermoelectric device has been in the air conditioning of nuclear submarines. The device is used for both heating and cooling the submarine. It is also used extensively to control temperatures in electronic equipment (computers, aero space devices, etc.).

Refer to Chapter 18, for further technical information concerning thermoelectric refrigeration and air conditioning devices.

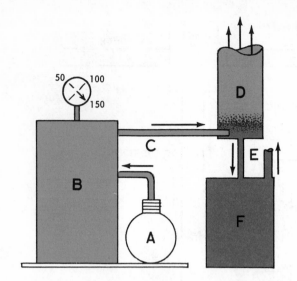

3-16 VORTEX TUBE REFRIGERATION

The vortex tube is an interesting device which uses compressed air to produce a low temperature. In this device, compressed air is directed tangentially into a tube or cylinder, closed at one end and open at the other. A small diameter tube leaves the center of the closed end of the cylinder, and through this tube flows the cold air. Its operation is shown in Fig. 3-16.

Compressed air source B, is connected to the vortex tube device. There are three openings to the vortex tube. The opening C, is a jet nozzle which is connected to the compressed air source B. This jet is arranged to inject the air into the tube at a tangent to the outside circumference of the tube.

Due to the design of the jet and the high pressure of the air, the air swirls rapidly around inside the large tube. Both openings D, and E, are at or near atmospheric pressure. The temperature of the air as it leaves through tube E, will be greatly reduced. Temperatures below zero, are easily obtained with this device.

It is particularly useful in applications where both fresh air and cooling are desired at the same time. A considerable quantity of high-pressure compressed air must be readily available.

A typical application is in the cooling of suits for industrial workmen such as miners.

Applications of this kind are usually designed to accommodate a particular job, and therefore operate continuously without any type of thermostatic control.

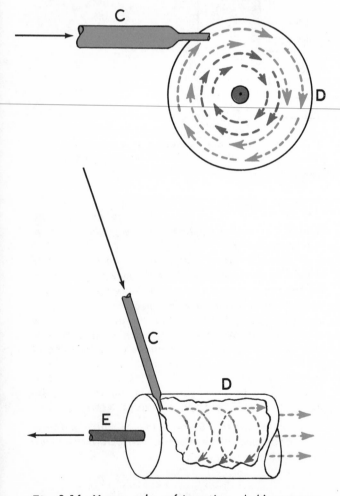

Fig. 3-16. Vortex tube refrigeration. A-Air compressor, B-Compressed air storage tank, C-Compressed air nozzle. Cold air is produced at E, and flows into space F, which is to be cooled. Warm air is expelled through large tube D.

3-17 STEAM JET REFRIGERATION

Steam jet refrigeration is really a type of water evaporative refrigeration.

Water is used as the refrigerant. The principle of operation is based on the fact that water will boil or vaporize rapidly, at a relatively low temperature, 40 to 50 deg. F., if the absolute pressure on the surface is reduced sufficiently. See Fig. 1-18. Under a vacuum of 29.74 in. Hg. water will theoretically boil at 32 deg. F. At 29.67 in. Hg. water boils at 40 deg. F.

The table, Fig. 3-17A, shows the boiling temperature of water corresponding to various absolute pressures.

A steam jet is shown in Fig. 3-17B. An ejector, sucks or draws water vapor from the surface of the water in the evaporator, causing the pressure in the evaporator to drop. It is the job of the ejector, to reduce the pressure in the evaporator to a point at which the water will vaporize at the desired temperature. In vaporizing, it absorbs heat and cools the remainder of the water in the evaporator.

The steam pressure at the ejector nozzle should be about 150 psia. The pressure in the condenser, not shown in the illustration, will also be low.

The evaporation of the water in the evaporator, reduces the temperature of the water in the evaporator. This cold water, 40 to 70 deg. F., is circulated by means of pumps, to the area to be cooled.

Due to the requirements for a large supply of steam under a fairly high pressure, and for a large supply of water for cooling the condenser, these systems are usually of considerable capacity . . . 100 tons and over.

Steam jet systems are used extensively in air conditioning, and for cooling of water used in certain chemical plants for gas absorption. The cooling temperatures provided by the steam jet mechanism are usually between 40 and 70 deg. F. Temperatures below 40 deg. F. are impractical due to the danger of freezing.

psia	Boiling Temp. °F.	psia	Boiling Temp. °F.
.1	35	5.	162
.2	53	6.	170
.3	64	7.	177
.4	73	8.	183
.5	80	9.	188
.6	85	10.	193
.7	90	11.	198
.8	94	12.	202
.9	98	13.	206
1.	102	14.	209
2.	126	14.7	212
3.	141	15.	213
4.	153	20.	228

Fig. 3-17A. Table showing the boiling temperature of water at various pressures. Note that the pressures are in pounds per square inch absolute (psia). Atmopheric pressure is 14.7 psia.

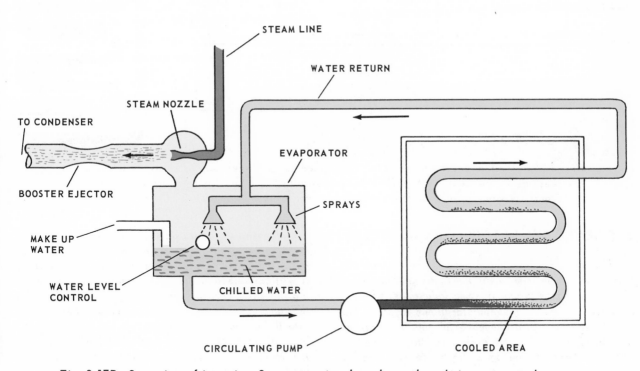

Fig. 3-17B. Steam jet refrigeration. Steam escaping through nozzle and ejector causes low pressure condition over surface of water in evaporator. Low pressure on surface of water causes it to evaporate rapidly, absorbing heat and reducing temperature of water in evaporator. Chilled water may be circulated where needed for cooling purposes.

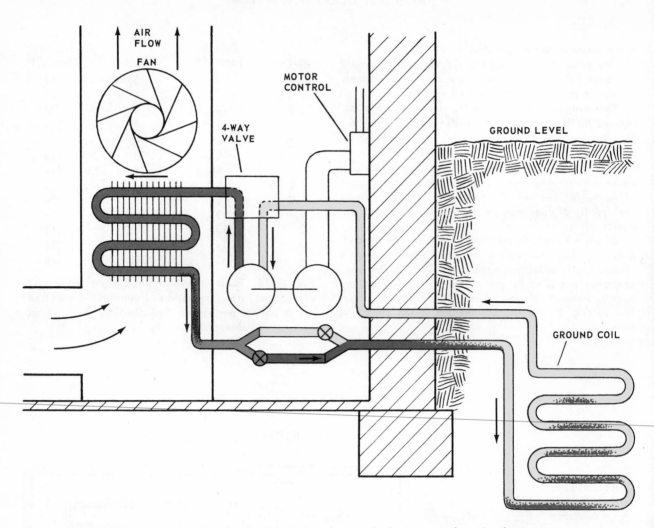

MOTOR
CONTROL

4-WAY
VALVE

GROUND LEVEL

GROUND COIL

Fig. 3-18A. Heat pump, heating cycle. Red indicates high pressure liquid refrigerant, green low pressure liquid refrigerant, yellow low pressure vapor, blue high pressure vapor. Note the four-way valve which controls the direction of flow of the refrigerant in the system.

3-18 HEAT PUMP – HEATING, COOLING CYCLES

The refrigerating and air conditioning industry has accepted the term "heat pump" to mean a mechanism used in homes and in some industries, whereby heat is absorbed in an evaporator in one location, and is released through a condenser in another location. By means of valves, the system can be changed so that the evaporator becomes the condenser, and the condenser becomes the evaporator (heat flow is reversed). Fig. 3-18A illustrates a typical heat pump installation. The evaporator in this case consists of many feet of tubing (coil) buried in the ground.

In operation, liquid refrigerant flows through a refrigerant control and into the ground coil. Since the refrigerant in the ground coil is under low pressure, it will boil, absorbing heat from the ground surrounding the coil. The vaporized refrigerant is drawn into the compressor, where it is compressed and discharged into the condenser, which in this case, is the heating coil for the heating system. The condenser cools the vaporized refrigerant, and it returns as a liquid, to the refrigerant control to repeat the cycle of absorbing heat from the ground, and giving up heat to the building to warm it. The same mechanism may be used to cool the building in summer by reversing the

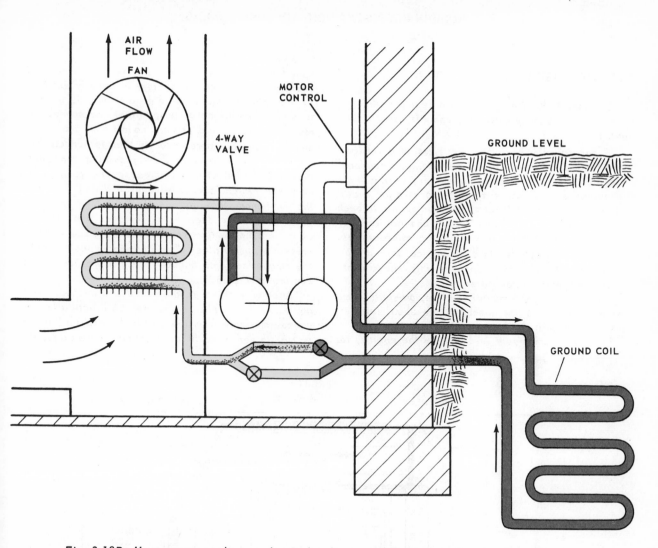

Fig. 3-18B. Heat pump, cooling cycle. Red indicates high pressure liquid refrigerant, green low pressure liquid refrigerant, yellow low pressure vapor, blue high pressure vapor. Note the four-way valve which controls the direction of flow of the refrigerant in the system.

cycle and moving heat from the building to the outdoors. In this case, the condensing coil serves as the evaporator, and the ground coil becomes the condenser. The ground absorbs the heat from the vaporized refrigerant. Fig. 3-18B illustrates the heat pump with the valves set for cooling the building.

The four-way valve is electrically controlled by the thermostat. If heat is called for, the valve will allow fluid flow as indicated in Fig. 3-18A. If cooling is needed, the flow will be as shown in Fig. 3-18B. In each case, the compressor is turning in the same direction, and the suction side and discharge side of the compressor are always the same. The cycle change is accomplished entirely by the operation of the four-

way valve.

Heat pump installations are ideal for locations where the heating load in winter is almost the same as the cooling load in summer.

Many heat pump installations operate on an "air to air" basis; that is, both the condenser and the evaporator are in the air. Air to air installations are most satisfactory, when the ambient air temperature in the winter remains above or only occasionally below the freezing temperature. Heat pump installations are most efficient if a spring or flowing well with water at about 50 deg. F. is available for use as the evaporator heat source or as the condenser cooling medium.

3-19 AUTOMOBILE AIR CONDITIONING

Air conditioning an automobile requires the use of many pieces of refrigerating and air conditioning equipment.

In general, the equipment consists of a refrigerating compressor driven by the car engine, a condenser located ahead of the car radiator, a liquid line to the refrigerant control, an evaporator located in a coil conveniently located to circulate cooled air through the car, and the necessary piping and controls, to make the system operate at satisfactory temperatures.

Fig. 3-19, illustrates in diagramatical form a typical automobile air conditioner. In this illustration, the various parts are identified.

Air conditioning a moving vehicle, presents some problems which do not appear in the usual refrigeration or air conditioning installation.

Since the compressor is driven by the engine, its speed will change as the car speed changes. The cooling capacity of the system is usually sufficient to take care of the cooling load under the most unfavorable conditions of temperature and speed. As a result, under normal driving conditions, the system has considerably more capacity than is needed. This problem is usually solved by providing a magnetic clutch in the hub of the compressor drive pulley. This magnetic clutch is controlled by a thermostat. When the car temperature has been brought down to the desired level, the thermostat releases the magnetic clutch on the compressor drive pulley, and the compressor stops turning. When cooling is again needed, the magnetic clutch engages the compressor and the cooling begins again.

Another problem is presented in air conditioning an automobile. The evaporator coil naturally condenses moisture from the air. If the coil temperature is maintained at or below freezing temperature, this

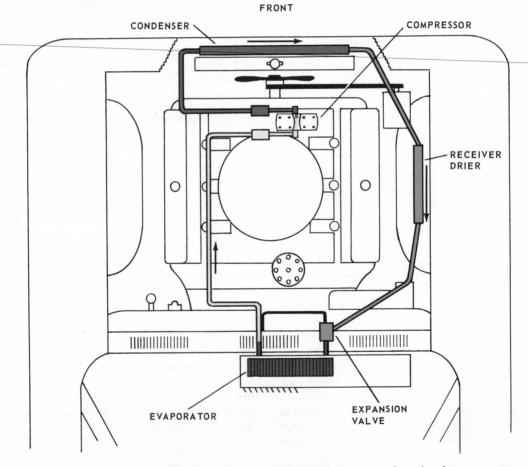

Fig. 3-19. Automobile air conditioner. Red indicates high pressure liquid refrigerant, green low pressure liquid refrigerant, yellow low pressure vapor, blue high pressure vapor. The compressor is driven by a belt from the engine. The condenser coil is located ahead of the car radiator, the evaporator is located in the passenger compartment.

moisture will freeze and adhere to the coil. Soon the evaporator coil will be completely frozen over, and no air can circulate through it. This problem is solved by placing a suction throttling valve in the suction line. This valve maintains pressure in the evaporator coil slightly above the pressure at which the temperature of the boiling refrigerant in the evaporator, will cause the moisture to freeze to the coil surface.

See Chapter 25 for full details concerning automobile air conditioning.

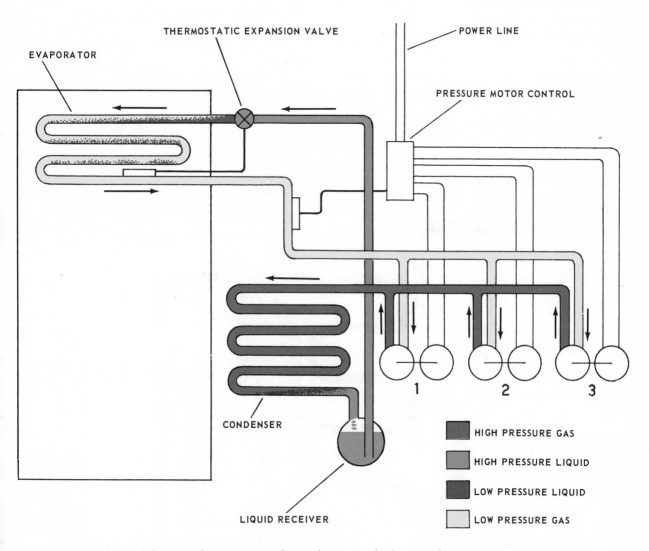

Fig. 3-20. Modulating refrigeration cycle mechanism, which uses three motor-compressors. A pressure motor control is arranged to operate one or more compressors as needed. Red indicates high pressure liquid refrigerant, green low pressure liquid refrigerant, yellow low pressure vapor, blue high pressure vapor.

3-20 MODULATING REFRIGERATION CYCLE

In most refrigeration installations, the cooling or refrigerating capacity of the installation is sufficient to maintain the desired temperature under the heaviest anticipated load. The desired temperature is maintained by the motor control which starts the motor-compressor when cooling, or heat removal, is required and shuts it off as soon as the desired temperature is reached. If the heat load is light, the single unit may be considerably oversize for the job. The operating expense is greater than it would be if the machine capacity more nearly matched the load.

A modulating (varying capacity) system has been developed to more nearly fit the machine capacity to the load. This is done by using two or more compressors connected in parallel. Each compressor is operated by a motor control. In operation; as the heat load increases, and temperature rises, one compressor will run. If the temperature continues to rise, the second compressor will also operate. Additional compressors may cut in until enough capacity is obtained. Fig. 3-20 illustrates a typical cycle diagram for a modulated installation. This installation has three compressors. The motor control is a pressure control

connected to the suction line. The motor control contains a special switching device, which rotates the service of the various compressors, so each compressor will be used about the same amount of time.

The modulating cycle maintains uniform temperature and operates quite economically.

The system may be operated with any conventional refrigerant control; however, the thermostatic expansion valve, as shown in Fig. 3-20, is commonly used.

The same condenser coil and liquid receiver may be used by all the compressors, or separate ones may be used. The same evaporator coil arrangement is connected to all of the compressors.

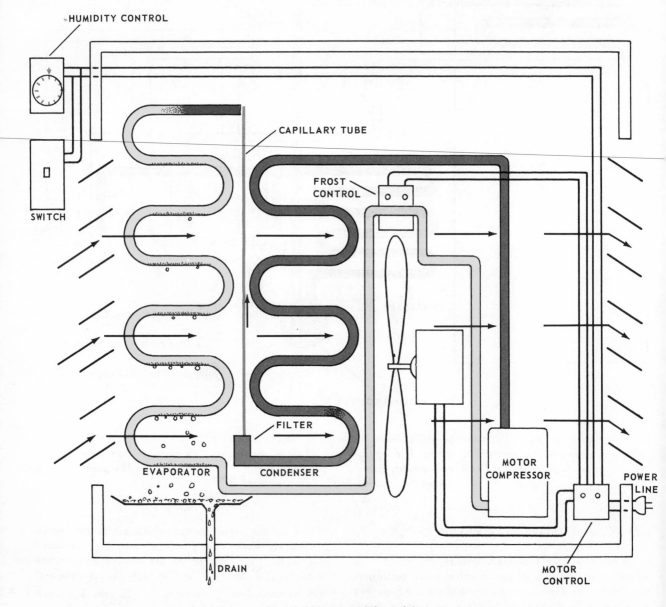

Fig. 3-21. Room dehumidifier.

3-21 DEHUMIDIFIER

Compressor type room dehumidifier. A typical dehumidifier consists of a hermetic compressor, condenser, and evaporator using a capillary tube type refrigerant control. See Fig. 3-21. In the schematic diagram, red indicates high pressure liquid, green low pressure liquid, yellow low pressure vapor, blue high pressure vapor.

Liquid refrigerant collects in the lower coils of the condenser and flows through the filter into the capillary tube, then into the evaporator which is under low pressure. In the evaporator, the liquid refrigerant boils rapidly and picks up heat from the evaporator surface. A motor driven fan forces a considerable amount of air through the evaporator coils. Because of the low temperature of the coils, the moisture carried in the air is condensed on the evaporator surfaces. The moisture flows to the bottom of the evaporator coil, and drips into the condensate trough. Air flowing through the evaporator coils is both cooled and dehumidified. Cooled air is then drawn through the condenser coils, where it cools the condenser and again picks up heat, so the air leaving the dehumidifier is about the same temperature as it was when it entered.

Low pressure vapor is drawn from the evaporator through the suction line to the compressor. It is again compressed to the high side pressure and is forced into the condenser, where it is cooled, becomes a liquid, and the cycle is repeated.

In addition to an on-and-off switch, dehumidifiers usually have two other controls. One is a humidity control which permits the dehumidifier to operate until the desired relative humidity is reached, then shuts the machine off. The other is a frost control element placed in the suction line between the evaporator and the compressor, which stops the motor compressor at high enough temperature so the evaporator coil will not freeze over and stop the flow of air through it.

In the drawing, arrows in black show the direction of flow of air through the dehumidifier.

3-22 WINDOW TYPE ROOM AIR CONDITIONER

The usual window type air conditioner consists of a hermetic compressor, condenser and evaporator using a capillary tube refrigerant control.

In the schematic diagram, red indicates high pressure liquid refrigerant, green low pressure liquid refrigerant, yellow low pressure vapor, blue high pres-

Fig. 3-22. Room air conditioner.

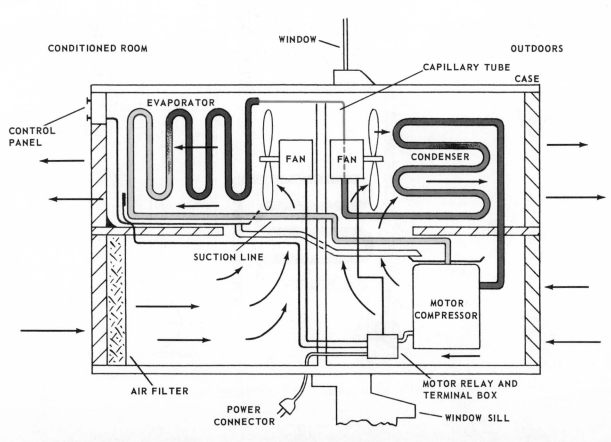

sure vapor. See Fig. 3-22.

Liquid refrigerant collects in the lower coils of the condenser and flows through the capillary tube refrigerant control into the evaporator coil. When the unit is in operation, this is under low pressure. The liquid refrigerant rapidly boils and picks up heat from the evaporator surface. A motor-driven fan draws air from inside the room, through a filter and forces it over the evaporator coils where it is cooled and circulated back into the room. Red arrows show the air flow pattern. Low pressure vapor is drawn from the evaporator through the suction line back to the compressor where it is compressed to the high side pressure, and forced into the condenser where it is cooled and condensed to a liquid. The cycle is then repeated. An adjustable thermostat mounted on the control panel, with an on-and-off switch, provides the necessary control.

The compressor and condenser are mounted in such a way, the fan in the compressor-condenser compartment draws outdoor air in, circulates it over the condenser coil and discharges it outside. Air flowing through the evaporator coils is cooled and to some extent dehumidified. Moisture which collects on the evaporator coils is collected in a drip pan under the coils. In some machines it flows into a pan in the compressor compartment, where in evaporating, it aids in cooling the compressor and condenser.

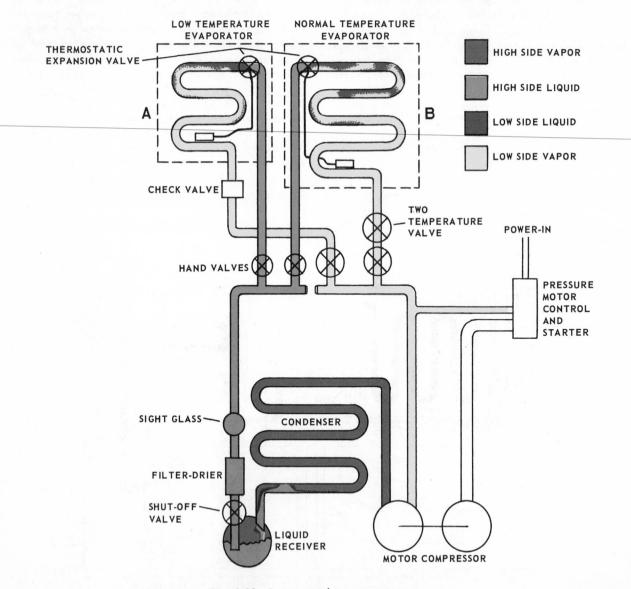

Fig. 3-23. System with two evaporators.

3-23 MULTIPLE EVAPORATOR SYSTEM

Some commercial refrigerating systems have one condensing unit connected to two or more evaporators. Liquid refrigerant (red) flows through the thermostatic expansion valves to the evaporator coils. The evaporators may have the same evaporator temperature, or they may evaporate the refrigerant at different temperatures. If the evaporator temperatures are the same, the system usually uses low side floats or thermostatic expansion valves as the refrigerant controls. If two or more evaporating temperatures are desired, i.e., a frozen foods temperature, and a water cooling temperature, a device must be used to keep one of the evaporators at a higher low side pressure. In the schematic, Fig. 3-23, a two-temperature valve in the

suction line keeps the low side pressure in COIL B above the pressure of the colder evaporator, COIL A. The evaporator temperature is governed by the evaporating pressure. The lower the pressure the lower the temperature.

A check valve in the suction line of the colder evaporator prevents the warmer higher pressure low-side vapor from moving into the colder evaporator during the off part of the cycle.

Note the filter-drier on the liquid line. This device keeps the refrigerant clean and dry. A liquid indicator (sight glass) is frequently included in the liquid line, so the serviceman may check to see if there is enough refrigerant in the system (bubbles will indicate a refrigerant shortage).

Multiple evaporator refrigeration systems are commonly used in commercial systems.

3-24 ICE CUBE MAKER

Ice cube makers use a variety of refrigerating devices. A unit of simple design is shown in Fig. 3-24.

Referring to the schematic, the operation is explained as follows: The motor compressor and condenser are usually located in the bottom of the cube maker. Liquid refrigerant flows from the bottom of the

Fig. 3-24. Ice cube maker.

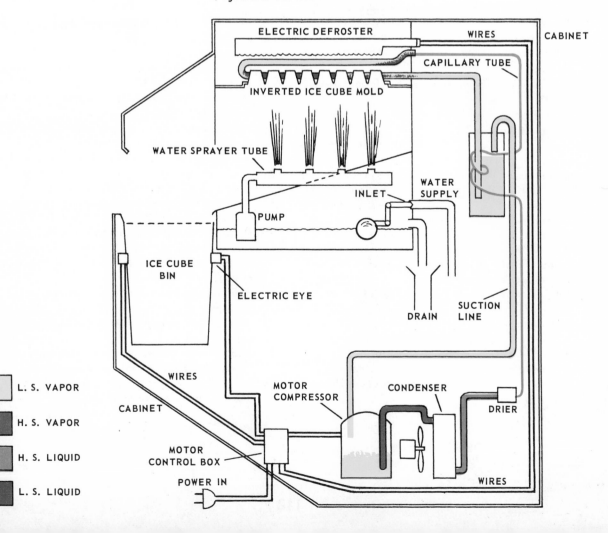

condenser up through a filter-drier, through a capillary tube into the evaporator coil which surrounds inverted ice cube molds. From the evaporator coil, the refrigerant vapor flows into an accumulator which has a coil from the liquid refrigerant line in it, or around it. This serves as a heat exchanger. The refrigerant vapor is then drawn back to the compressor, where it is compressed back to the high side pressure and is forced into the condenser. From here the cycle is repeated.

The mechanism which makes and handles the ice is also shown in the drawing. Note that the ice cube molds are inverted. Cold water is sprayed into these inverted molds. Since the temperature of the molds is very cold, the water striking the molds freezes to the surface of the mold and gradually builds up in size until complete ice cubes are formed. Then the refrigerating cycle is stopped. An electric heating unit heats the ice cube molds and the cubes fall out and slide down the chute into the ice cube bin.

3-25 TEST YOUR KNOWLEDGE – CHAPTER 3

1. What were some advantages of the old icebox type of refrigeration?
2. What is the principle upon which the "desert bag" water cooling device operates?
3. What are some of the advantages of the capillary tube type refrigerant control?
4. What causes the needle valve to open in an automatic expansion valve refrigerant control?
5. What causes the needle to open in the thermostatically controlled expansion valve?
6. What controls the cabinet temperature on a system which uses a thermostatically controlled expansion valve?
7. What substances are most used in absorption type refrigerators?
8. What did Faraday discover in his famous experiment?
9. What is the chief advantage of a compound refrigerating system?
10. What is the chief characteristic of a cascade refrigerating system?
11. In a thermoelectrical refrigeration system, how is heat carried out of the space to be refrigerated?
12. What is the chief advantage of vortex tube refrigeration?
13. Where is steam jet refrigeration most used?
14. What is the most common heat pump application?
15. In automobile air conditioning, how is the compressor usually driven?
16. How is modulation in refrigeration effect accomplished?
17. What purpose does the evaporator serve in a dehumidifier?
18. What is the basic principle of operation of a room air conditioner installed in a window opening?
19. Why is it sometimes necessary to use a multiple evaporator system?
20. What is the basic principle of operation of most ice cube makers?
21. What are some of the advantages of the low side float type of refrigerant control?
22. Is the amount of refrigerant charged into the system very important in a high side float type refrigerating mechanism?
23. What principle is used in the continuous type absorption refrigerator?
24. Where is "expendable refrigerant" cooling most used?
25. What is the chief disadvantage of thermoelectrical refrigeration?
26. In automobile air conditioning, why is it necessary to use a magnetic clutch on the compressor of the drive pulley?
27. What are some of the advantages of dry ice refrigeration?
28. What controls the magnetic clutch in the hub of the compressor drive pulley as used on an automobile air conditioning system?
29. Will a dehumidifier, operating in a room, change the temperature within the room?
30. What is the advantage in using a modulating refrigeration system?
31. In a heat pump installation, is the direction of flow of refrigerant vapor reversed through the compressor when the cycle is reversed from heating to cooling?
32. What is a common application of the vortex tube cooling system?
33. In what kind of refrigerating mechanism are semiconductors used?
34. What is the refrigerant most commonly used in "expendable refrigerant" cooling systems?
35. In "cascade" systems, are the operating temperatures usually above or below 0 F.?

Chapter 4

COMPRESSION SYSTEMS

Introduction

The compression system is the basis of operation of the refrigeration units described in this chapter. A thorough knowledge of the compression cycle is necessary to properly diagnose mechanical difficulties. Various types of compression systems are presented to enable the serviceman to become familiar with the basic characteristics. The basic mechanism consists of the following: compressor, means to drive the compressor, (motor), condenser, refrigerant control, evaporator (cooling coil) and a device to provide automatic cycling and temperature control.

With these components the refrigerant may be used repeatedly without having to replace it.

Liquid refrigerant absorbs heat in the evaporator and becomes a vapor. Refrigerant vapor is sometimes called a gas by servicemen, also some service literature refers to refrigerant vapor as a "gas." The student should remember that the words vapor or gas may be used interchangeably.

4-1 Laws of Refrigeration

All refrigerating mechanisms are designed and built around these basic thermal laws:

1. Fluids absorb heat while changing from a liquid state to a vapor state, and give up heat in changing from a vapor to a liquid.

2. The temperature at which a change of state occurs is constant during the change, but this temperature will vary with the pressure.

3. Heat will flow only from a body at a higher temperature to a body at a lower temperature. -- (Hot to cold.)

4. In selecting metallic parts of the cooling and condensing units, metals are selected which have a high heat conductivity.

5. Heat energy and other forms of energy and other forms of energy are mutually convertible.

4-2 Compression Cycle

All refrigeration compression systems use a refrigerant sealed in an airtight and leakproof mechanism. The system repeats over and over the freezing and cooling operations. The process of repetition of a similar order of operations is called a cycle. All refrigerators operate on cycles.

In mechanical refrigeration two different cycles are used. One cycle uses a mechanical compressor to compress the vapors. This is called a COMPRESSION CYCLE. The other is the ABSORPTION SYSTEM, which works on the principle of temperature and pressure changes resulting from heat applications. The operation of the absorption system is explained in Chapter 17.

The compression cycle is given this name because it is the compression of the refrigerant from a vapor to a liquid by the compressor which permits transfer of the heat energy. The refrigerant absorbs heat in one place and releases it in another. In other words, the compressor is used to put the heat-laden vaporized refrigerant in such a condition that it may dissipate the heat energy it absorbed when it was vaporized at a low pressure. Because the compression machine transfers heat from one place to another, it may also be called a heat engine or a heat pump.

A refrigerating apparatus consists principally of a high pressure side and a low pressure side, Fig. 4-1.

temperature difference and to get the temperature differences there must be a high pressure side (dissipators) and a low pressure side (absorbers).

4-3 Operation of Compression Cycle

Basically (Fig. 4-2), the liquid evaporates in the evaporator unit (1) under a low pressure. The pressure will vary in popular refrigerators between 29 in. of

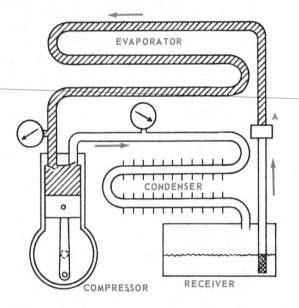

Fig. 4-1. A compression cycle showing the two pressure conditions. The low pressure side extends from the refrigerant control A to the compressor inlet valve. The high pressure side extends from the exhaust side of the compressor to the refrigerant control A.

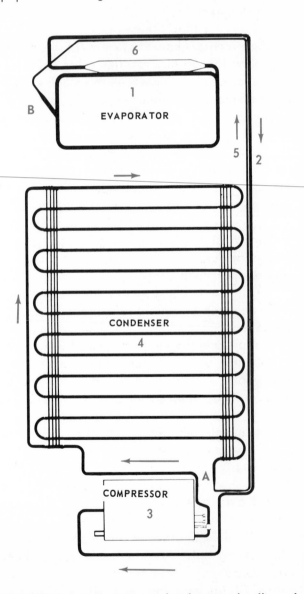

Fig. 4-2. A compression cycle showing the flow of refrigerant. 1-Evaporator. 2-Suction line. 3-Compressor. 4-Condenser. 5-Capillary tube, A to B. 6-Accumulator.   (Hotpoint Co.)

In operation the apparatus transfers heat from one place to another place, i.e., from the inside of a refrigerator to the outside air, or from the water of a water cooler to the outside air.

This action may be compared to a sponge picking up water in one place and releasing it in another by squeezing it. To have a transfer of heat there must be a vacuum and 13 lbs. of pressure depending on the refrigerant used and the low temperature required. This allows the evaporation (absorbing of latent heat) to take place at a low temperature; because, as the pressure decreases, the boiling or evaporating temperature also falls. This heat-laden vapor then passes through the suction line (2) to the compressor (3) which compresses and discharges it into the condenser (4) where it cools and gives up its latent heat by evaporation under a high pressure. Then it converts to a liquid and collects in the liquid receiver tank. The liquid line (5) carries the liquid refrigerant to a restriction where the pressure is reduced. The refrigerant then enters the evaporator where it evaporates and absorbs heat (1) and the suction line (2) carries the vapor back to the condensing unit. In a refrigeration cycle, the following parts are necessary:

Compressor -- driven by a motor. High Pressure Side: Condenser -- heat dissipator, Liquid receiver -- storage tank, Liquid line -- liquid refrigerant carrier, Refrigerant control--pressure reducer-restrictor. Low Pressure Side: Evaporator unit -- heat absorber, Suction line -- vapor refrigerant carrier.

A thermostat controlling the motor is used to obtain automatic operation.

4-4 Typical Compression Cycle

The cycle operates as follows: The vapors are compressed in the compressor and passed to the condenser. During compression the pressure increases (due to Boyle's Law, Par. 1-50), and the temperature increases (explained by Charles' Law, Par. 1-51), until the vapor temperature is greater than the temperature of the condenser cooling medium (air or water). Heat will then flow from the condenser to the cooling medium, allowing the vaporized refrigerant to return to the liquid state.

Because pressure is the sum of the bombarding molecules, and because temperature is the speed of molecular motion, it is necessary to speed up the molecules to raise their temperature to a level where they can give up heat to surrounding cooling surfaces (air or water).

When the compressor starts, it moves molecules from the low pressure side to the high pressure side without much difficulty and the molecules are not increased much in speed, as shown in Fig. 4-3, Detail A. These molecules are moved into the condenser through opening 1, from the compressor. The temperatures are the same (70 deg. F.) inside and out.

As the compressor continues to run, more and more vapor molecules are moved into the condenser 2. With each successive stroke, the pressure increases as there are more molecules hitting the sides of the container. The compressor piston pushing the molecules against the higher pressure hits the vapor molecules harder raising their speed (temperature).

The pressure and temperature continues to rise until the molecules are traveling at such a high speed that their temperature (ambient temperature) is higher than the surrounding container. This higher temperature, as shown in Fig. 4-3, Detail B, causes a flow of heat to the surrounding metal and air. Heat is being removed from the vaporized refrigerant as shown at 3. This process continues until all of the vapor molecules are compressed together, and until enough heat is removed to cause some of the vapor molecules to become liquid molecules as shown at 4.

The temperature and pressure will continue to rise until a condition is reached where as many vapor molecules are condensed into a liquid as the compressor can pump into the condenser, Fig. 4-3, Detail C. This provides a state of balance. Heat is being radiated at 6 and liquid refrigerant is forming at 7. If anything causes this balance to change the condensing pressure

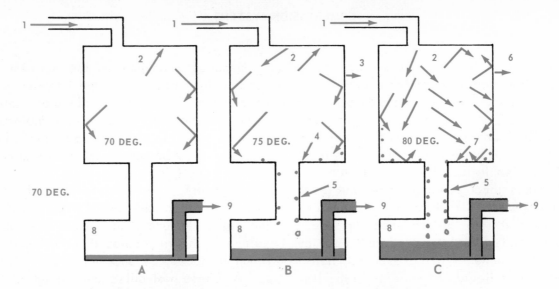

Fig. 4-3. Behavior of a refrigerant as it changes from a vapor to a liquid in the condenser.
A–1. Vapor under pressure from the compressor. A–2. Condenser.
B–3. Heat radiating from the condenser (small amount). B–4. Vapor loosing heat and condensing to a liquid.
C–5. Condensed refrigerant droplets (large amount). C–6. Heat radiating from the condenser A. C–7. Condensed refrigerant flowing into the liquid receiver. C–8. Liquid receiver. C–9. Refrigerant liquid line.

and temperature will adjust accordingly. For example, if the room were to get warmer, the heat, pressure and temperature will rise again until just as many vapor molecules are condensing as are being pumped into the condenser.

After condensing (liquefying) the liquid refrigerant is stored in the liquid receiver 8 until needed. From the liquid receiver it passes through the high pressure liquid line 9 to the refrigerant control, which may be either an expansion valve (dry system), float needle valve (flooded system), or to the capillary tube, where the pressure is reduced sufficiently to allow an evaporization of liquid at a temperature of 5 to 10 deg. F. In evaporating the liquid in the evaporator unit, considerable heat is absorbed and refrigeration furnished. After expansion and evaporation in the evaporator, or cooling unit, the vapor travels back to the low side of the compressor through the suction line. It passes through the intake valve of the compressor into the cylinder. Here it is compressed and discharged through the exhaust valve into the high pressure side condenser where the heat absorbed in the evaporator unit is released. This release of heat causes the refrigerant to recondense to a liquid, and it is stored in readiness for a repetition of the cycle just described.

4-5 Types of Compressors

There are several different kinds of compressors:
1. Piston-cylinder type (Reciprocating).
2. Rotating pump type (Rotary).
3. Centrifugal type.
4. Gear type.
5. Diaphragm type.

4-6 Reciprocating Compressor

The reciprocating type compressor has long been used to pump gases and vapors of all types. It is easy to construct, easy to service and has excellent wearing qualities. Its parts must be fitted with close tolerance. It has a high pumping efficiency.

The compressor basically consists of a cylinder with a piston inside which fits closely. Fig. 4-4, shows the principle of operation of a reciprocating compressor. When the piston (B) moves downward, a vacuum is produced in the chamber. Vapor pressure at (C) will rush into the chamber. When the piston (B) moves upward, the vapor will be pressed closer together. When its pressure is greater than the pressure at (D), the vapor will flow out the opening. Flapper or reed valves prevent the vapor from returning or backing up.

Because the temperatures in a refrigerating unit rarely exceed 175 deg. F., small clearances may be used between moving parts of the unit. Clearances of .0001 in. are common. The clearance is so small that some manufacturers do not use piston rings on their pistons. The piston com-

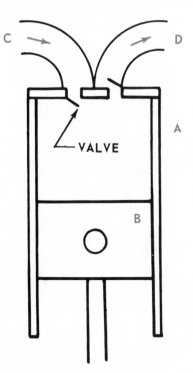

Fig. 4-4. Basic construction of a reciprocating compressor. A-Cylinder. B-Piston. C-Intake port from suction line. D-Exhaust port to condenser.

presses the vapor admitted into the cylinder chamber into the high pressure side. The piston is designed to come as close as possible to the cylinder head without touching it in order to press practically

all the gas into the high pressure side. The clearance between the piston and the cylinder head, when the piston is at upper dead center, is approximately .010 in. to .020 in. The maximum lift allowed the reed valves without permitting them to become noisy is approximately .010 in. for both the intake and exhaust valves.

The parts are usually bolted together and sealed by means of either paper or lead gaskets. The special paper gaskets must be dehydrated (completely freed from moisture) before use. The oil used varies with the refrigerants but dehydrated mineral oil is satisfactory for most of them.

4-7 Reciprocating Compressor Construction

The reciprocating or piston type compressor is the type most commonly used. Referring to Fig. 4-5, it may be seen that this compressor consists of a cylinder, crankshaft, piston, connecting rod, cylinder head, intake and exhaust valves, servicing valves, flywheel, crankshaft seal, gaskets, and oil. It is a very efficient type of compressor. Its construction resembles in many ways that of the automobile engine. The cylinders and cylinder heads are made of high grade cast iron, or cast steel, and pistons are made of similar materials. Aluminum may be used for some parts; however, caution must be used. Aluminum may be corroded by some refrigerants. The connecting rods and crankshaft are usually drop forged steel, although some of them are made of cast iron. Bronze connecting rods have been used.

4-8 Types of Crankshafts Used on Reciprocating Compressors

There are three common types of shafts used in refrigerator compressor design:
  A. Crank throw.
  B. Eccentric.
  C. Scotch yoke.

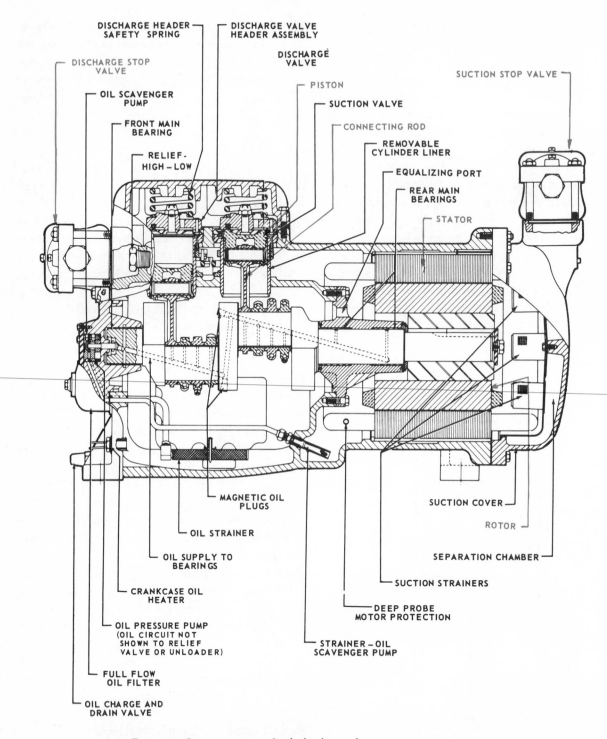

DISCHARGE HEADER
SAFETY SPRING

DISCHARGE VALVE
HEADER ASSEMBLY

DISCHARGE
VALVE

DISCHARGE STOP
VALVE

SUCTION STOP VALVE

PISTON

OIL SCAVENGER
PUMP

SUCTION VALVE

FRONT MAIN
BEARING

CONNECTING ROD

REMOVABLE
CYLINDER LINER

RELIEF –
HIGH – LOW

EQUALIZING PORT

REAR MAIN
BEARINGS

STATOR

MAGNETIC OIL
PLUGS

OIL STRAINER

SUCTION COVER

OIL SUPPLY TO
BEARINGS

ROTOR

CRANKCASE OIL
HEATER

SEPARATION CHAMBER

SUCTION STRAINERS

OIL PRESSURE PUMP
(OIL CIRCUIT NOT
SHOWN TO RELIEF
VALVE OR UNLOADER)

DEEP PROBE
MOTOR PROTECTION

STRAINER – OIL
SCAVENGER PUMP

FULL FLOW
OIL FILTER

OIL CHARGE AND
DRAIN VALVE

Fig. 4-5. Cross section of a bolted type hermetic motor-compressor.
(Air Temp Div., Chrysler Corp.)

The most common one is the crank throw type, Fig. 4-6. This crankshaft is usually made of steel and case-hardened. Fig. 4-7, shows an eccentric type of crank-shaft, in which the eccentrics and connecting rods are made of cast iron. Basically, an eccentric consists of a cast iron disk placed off-center on the crankshaft. An

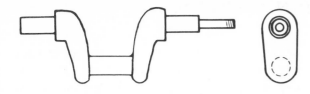

Fig. 4-6. Forged crank "throw" type crankshaft.

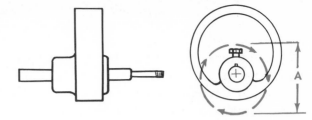

Fig. 4-7. An eccentric type crankshaft. Note that the eccentric is attached with a key and a setscrew. A indicates the piston stroke.

eccentric type crankshaft is permissible in a refrigerating compressor because of the low bearing loads encountered. A sectional view of a two-cylinder compressor using an eccentric crankshaft is shown in Fig. 4-8. Some flywheels are unbalanced and are so placed on the crankshaft that the flywheel unbalance neutralizes the unbalance of the crankshaft.

In some compressors, the crankshaft and connecting rod unit is replaced with a

Fig. 4-8. Sectional view of a small open type two cylinder refrigerator compressor. Note the use of an eccentric type crankshaft.

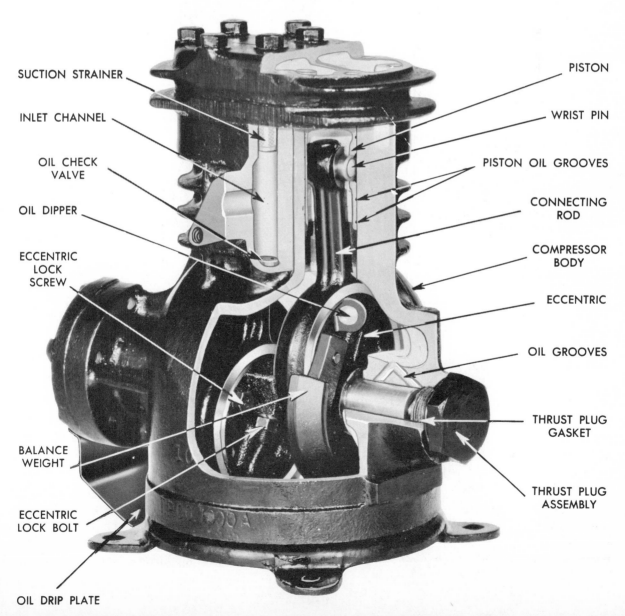

SUCTION STRAINER

INLET CHANNEL

OIL CHECK VALVE

OIL DIPPER

ECCENTRIC LOCK SCREW

BALANCE WEIGHT

ECCENTRIC LOCK BOLT

OIL DRIP PLATE

PISTON

WRIST PIN

PISTON OIL GROOVES

CONNECTING ROD

COMPRESSOR BODY

ECCENTRIC

OIL GROOVES

THRUST PLUG GASKET

THRUST PLUG ASSEMBLY

Scotch yoke mechanism. In this mechanism the piston is not fitted with an articulating connecting rod; instead the piston extends to the crankshaft and is connected to it by means of a sliding member which attaches to both the piston and the crankshaft, Fig. 4-9. This mechanism is used .on several small high-speed direct drive hermetic compressors.

brass tube soldered to a ring of bronze and graphite at one end and to a flange at the other. The flange is fastened to the crankcase with a gasket between the two. A spring presses the ring mounted on the other end of the bellows against a shoulder on the crankshaft. The two surfaces are perfectly smooth, and under a 35-45 lb. spring pressure, if lubricated with a little

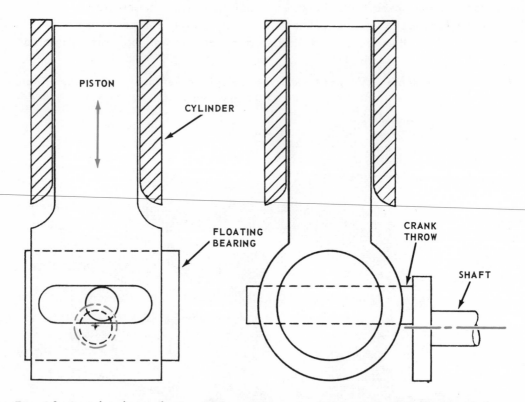

PISTON

CYLINDER

FLOATING BEARING

CRANK THROW

SHAFT

Fig. 4-9. Scotch yoke mechanism. Note no connecting rod is used. The piston extends to the yoke mechanism and the compressor cylinder serves as a guide.

4-9 Stationary Seal (Sylphon Seal)

A leakproof joint or seal must be maintained where the crankshaft comes through the crankcase to connect to the flywheel. This seal must hold under all pressure conditions, and must withstand pressures whether the crankshaft is stationary or revolving. See Fig. 4-10.

The seal (typical) consists essentially of a bellows and revolving sealing surface. The bellows consists of a corrugated thin

compressor oil, will stand most of the pressures encountered in a normal system. This seal is called a stationary bellows seal. Seals of this kind have been known to stay in service many years and still give good service, Fig. 4-10. In another type of seal the gasket and bellows are attached to the crankshaft. As the crankshaft revolves, the ring on the bellows rubs against a flat, smooth disk mounted on the crankcase.

Many modern compressors use a syn-

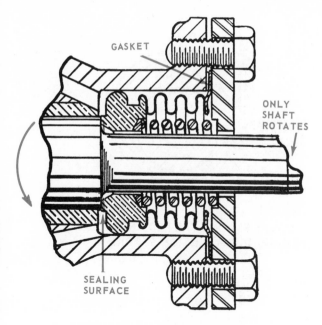

Fig. 4-10. Crankshaft seal.

thetic rubber seal, this is simple yet satisfactory. Teflon is often used as seal material on the crankshaft seal for compressors used on automobile air conditioning compressors.

4-10 Compressor Valves

The compressor valves are usually made of thin steel disks. These disks seat against shoulders constructed in the valve plate. Some designs use springs to keep the valve in place, Detail A, Fig. 4-11, while others use the pressure differences and the weight of the disk, Detail B, Fig. 4-11.

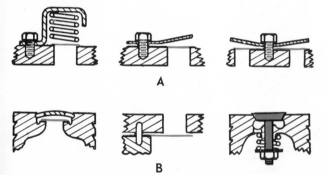

Fig. 4-11. Some typical compressor valve designs.

4-11 Flywheel

On open type systems, the motor is separate from the compressor. A V-belt is used as a means of transmitting motion from the motor to the compressor.

Flywheels on open systems are usually made of cast iron with grooved periphery to fit the V-belt, and are fastened to the crankshaft by means of a tapered shaft, a woodruff key, and a lock nut. Some flywheels are fabricated from stamped steel parts with the spokes formed into fan blades to aid in cooling the compressor.

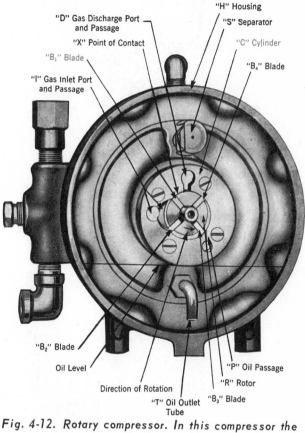

Fig. 4-12. Rotary compressor. In this compressor the blades or vanes rotate with the shaft.

4-12 Rotary Compressor

In a rotary type compressor, the pumping effect which takes low-temperature, low-pressure vapor and converts it into

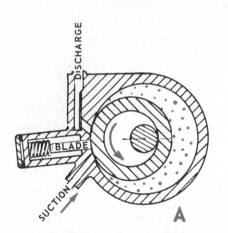

**CYLINDER FULL OF GAS
AT START OF COMPRESSION**

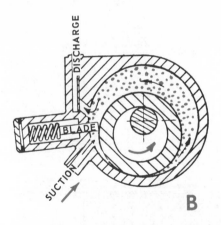

**COMPRESSION STARTED AND
BEGINNING OF SUCTION STROKE**

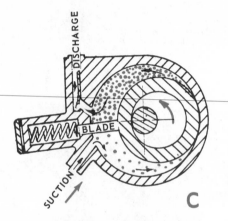

**DISCHARGE AND SUCTION
STROKES HALF COMPLETED**

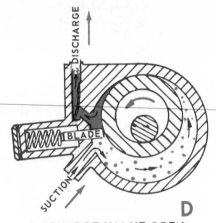

**DISCHARGE VALVE OPEN
ON COMPRESSION STROKE**

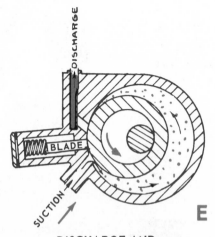

**DISCHARGE AND
SUCTION STROKES COMPLETED**

*Fig. 4-13. Rotary compressor. In this compressor the blade or vane is stationary. A ro-
tating eccentric creates the pumping action.   (Norge Sales Corp.)*

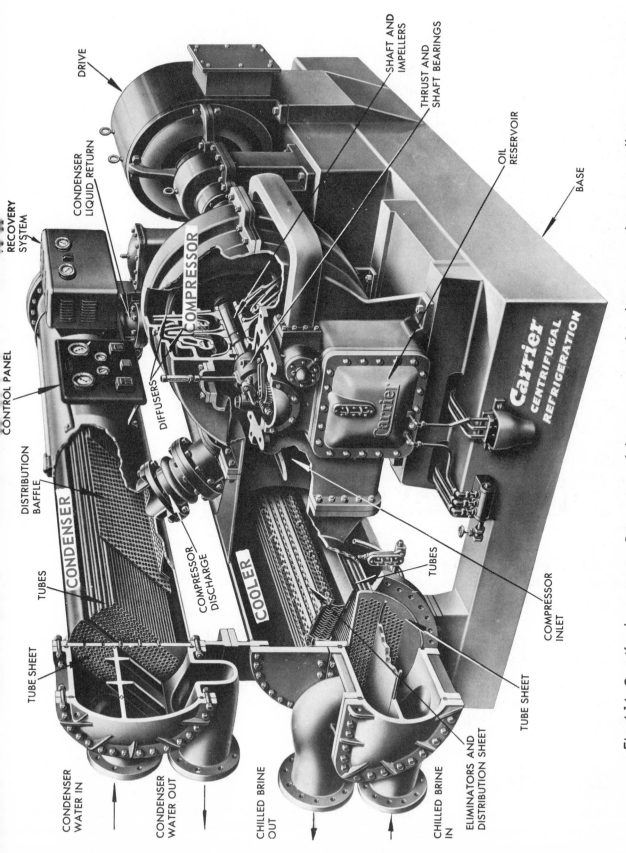

DRIVE

SHAFT AND IMPELLERS

THRUST AND SHAFT BEARINGS

CONDENSER LIQUID RETURN

RECOVERY SYSTEM

OIL RESERVOIR

BASE

CONTROL PANEL

COMPRESSOR

DIFFUSERS

DISTRIBUTION BAFFLE

CONDENSER

TUBES

COMPRESSOR DISCHARGE

COOLER

TUBE SHEET

TUBES

COMPRESSOR INLET

TUBE SHEET

CONDENSER WATER IN

CONDENSER WATER OUT

CHILLED BRINE OUT

CHILLED BRINE IN

ELIMINATORS AND DISTRIBUTION SHEET

Fig. 4-14. Centrifugal compressor. Compressors of this type are used in large air conditioning installations.

high temperature vapor is produced by rotary motion. This type compressor is illustrated in Fig. 4-12. There are two principal types of rotary compressors; one uses sealing blades that rotate with the shaft, and the other has a stationary blade. The blade has a rubbing contact against the rotating shaft, Fig. 4-13.

In the rotating blade type, Fig. 4-12, low-pressure vapor is imprisoned between two blades as the blades rub against the wall of the cylinder due to centrifugal force. When the rotor revolves (counter-clockwise in this case) the low-pressure vapor is gradually compressed into a high-temperature, high-pressure condition. As the vapor, occupying very little space, comes opposite the opening (D), it passes into the high-pressure dome because it cannot go through the point of contact between the rotor and the housing, labeled "X." The small clearance at this point (.0001 in.) plus the presence of lubricating oil makes the joint pressure tight. The vapor cannot back up because of the rotating blade following it. Note that this compressor uses no eccentric, and that the housing is mounted off-center enough to allow the rotor to almost rub against the housing at a point between the intake and exhaust ports.

In a stationary blade type compressor the shaft rotates in a chamber so the eccentric on the shaft or the enlargement

of the shaft constantly rubs against the outer wall of the chamber. As the rotor turns around in this chamber, the blade imprisons quantities of gas which are compressed into small space, building up the pressure and temperature and finally forcing the gas into the high pressure side of the system.

In rotary compressors check valves are sometimes used to prevent the high-pressure vapor from flowing back into the evaporator coil.

4-13 Centrifugal Compressor

The centrifugal type compressor is used extensively in large air conditioning installations. This compressor operates on the principle of increasing the pressure by rapidly revolving circular impellers connected in multiple stages. Several of these impellers are mounted in series in one housing, and are usually directly driven by a motor or steam turbine. See Fig. 4-14. Refrigerants used with this type compressor have the ability to function with but little pressure difference between the high pressure and low pressure sides. Refrigerants such as water, methyl formate, R-11, etc., are frequently used in this type of installation. Many recent centrifugal compressors have a self-contained control panel, as shown in Fig. 4-15.

4-14 Gear and Diaphragm Type Compressors

The gear type compressor is a type that was tried but found to be impractical due to the fine tolerances needed to maintain pumping efficiency. This compressor used two spiral gears; a drive gear meshed with another gear. As the gears revolved the vapor was carried around the periphery of the gears between the teeth. As the gears meshed the vapor was forced out of the space between the teeth and out the exhaust port.

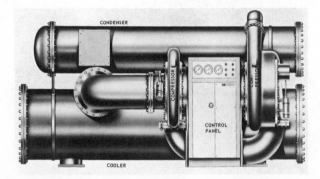

Fig. 4-15. Centrifugal compressor. (Air Temp Div., Chrysler Corp.)

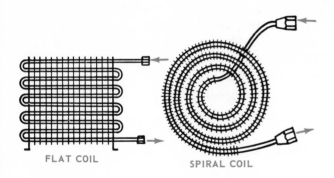

FLAT COIL   SPIRAL COIL

Fig. 4-16. *Two air-cooled condensers.*

The diaphragm type compressor is another type not commonly used at present. In this type, a crank or a cam operates a diaphragm. When the diaphragm is moved out, the space is filled with low-pressure vapor. As it closes, the vapor is forced into the condenser.

4-15 The Condenser

The condenser is usually made of copper or steel tubing with fins attached which assist in rapid radiation of heat, Fig. 4-16. For domestic use the condenser is usually air-cooled by natural convection (natural flow). Air surrounding the con-

denser will be warmer than the air in the room. This warm air will rise and cooler air will flow in to take its place. Some condensing units use a motor driven fan to force air over the condenser tubing, and to increase the air cooling effect on the condenser.

There are several types of condensers in present day use. The smaller refrigerators use what is called a natural convection air-cooled, (sometimes called a static) condenser. This may consist of two plates of metal with refrigerant passages stamped in them or of tubing with or without fins. The condensers are cooled by air passing over the surfaces by natural convection, Fig. 4-17. A firm shroud is usually placed around the condenser to improve the airflow (provide chimney effect). As the unit size increases, the natural convection condenser becomes bulky and cumbersome. A forced convection condenser is then used. This condenser, Fig. 4-18, uses a fan, fan motor, finned tubing, and a shroud around the fan and the condenser to improve the air circulation. Many of the condensers are made of copper, but both steel and aluminum tubing have been used successfully. Fins attached to the tubes in-

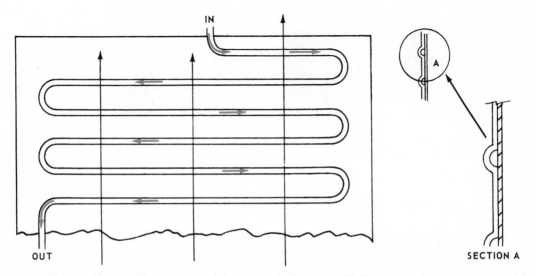

IN

OUT   SECTION A

Fig. 4-17. Air-cooled condenser. The air surrounding the condenser will flow upward as it is warmed by heat from the condenser. The red arrows indicate the direction of the fluid flow in the condenser. The black arrows indicate airflow over the surface of the condenser.

crease the surface area and assist in cooling. Lint and dust on condensers which will act as insulation and interfere with proper cooling, must be removed regularly.

Water-cooled condensers are commonly used on commercial installations.

receiver. When the mechanism is taken apart for servicing the refrigerant is pumped into and stored in the liquid receiver.

Liquid receivers are commonly made of drawn steel shells welded together.

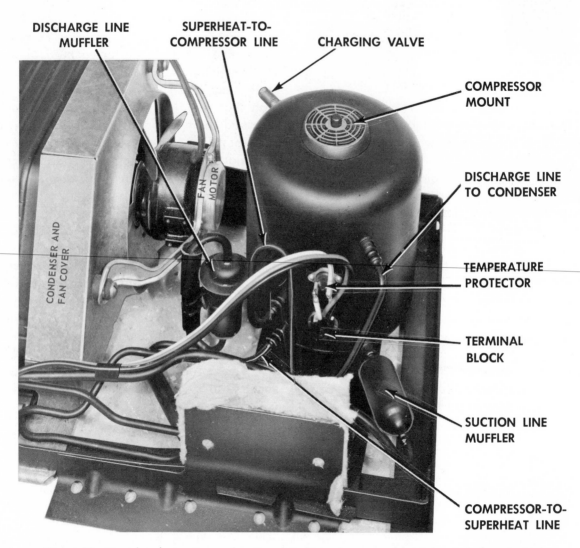

DISCHARGE LINE MUFFLER

SUPERHEAT-TO-COMPRESSOR LINE

CHARGING VALVE

COMPRESSOR MOUNT

FAN MOTOR

CONDENSER AND FAN COVER

DISCHARGE LINE TO CONDENSER

TEMPERATURE PROTECTOR

TERMINAL BLOCK

SUCTION LINE MUFFLER

COMPRESSOR-TO-SUPERHEAT LINE

Fig. 4-18. Complete hermetic condensing unit. Note the motor driven fan and shroud which directs the cooling air through the condenser coils. (Frigidaire Div., General Motors Corp.)

4-16 The Liquid Receiver

The liquid receiver, Fig. 4-19, is a storage tank for liquid refrigerant installed in the system for servicing and other purposes. If there is an excess of liquid refrigerant, this is stored in the liquid

Occasionally you may find a liquid receiver made of a cast material or built into the condenser; that is, the bottom tubes of the condenser form the liquid receiver. Most liquid receivers are furnished with service valves. Screen of fine copper mesh is usually found in the outlets of the liquid

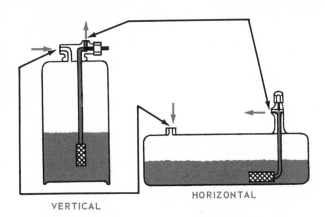

Fig. 4-19. *Two common types of liquid receivers; vertical and horizontal. The compressor discharge service valve serves as a shut-off valve between the compressor and the liquid receiver.*

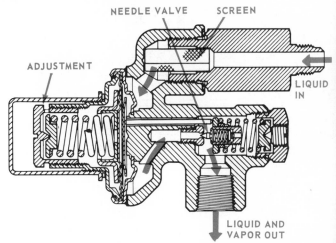

Fig. 4-20. *Automatic expansion valve. This valve controls the flow of liquid refrigerant into the evaporator coil, and maintains a constant low pressure in the evaporator. (American Standard, Controls Div.)*

receivers to prevent particles of foreign substances from entering the refrigerant control valves.

Liquid receivers are used on most systems with the float type or the expansion valve refrigerant control. Capillary tube systems, because all the liquid refrigerant is stored in the evaporator unit during the off part of the cycle, do not use a liquid receiver. The greater use of hermetic systems and capillary tube refrigerant controls has eliminated much of the need for liquid receivers in domestic systems.

4-17 Evaporator or Cooling Unit

After the refrigerant passes through the condenser and a liquid receiver if the system uses one, the liquid passes through the liquid line (high pressure) to the evaporator unit where it is reduced to a low evaporating pressure by means of an automatic expansion valve, as shown in Fig. 4-20, (dry system), float needle valve as used in the low side float, Fig. 4-21,

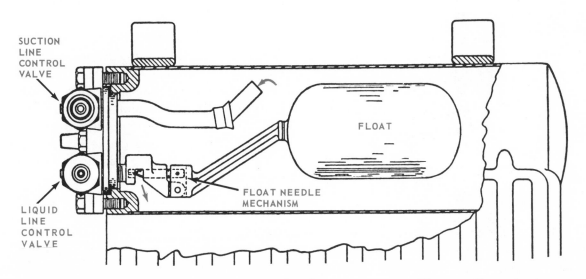

Fig. 4-21. *Low-side float refrigerant control and evaporator unit: Float needle mechanism, Suction line control valve, Liquid line control valve.*

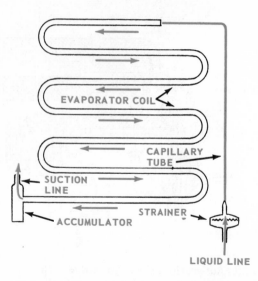

Fig. 4-22. *Capillary tube refrigerant control. A strainer is located in the liquid line at the entrance to the capillary tube. Note the accumulator or surge header. This serves as a receiver for any liquid refrigerant which remains on the low pressure side.*

(flooded system), or capillary tube, Fig. 4-22. The low pressure results in a low boiling or evaporating temperature for the refrigerant with the result that it evaporates and absorbs considerable heat. This heat is obtained from inside the box or area to be cooled.

The evaporated refrigerant now passes through the return or low pressure tube (suction line), which is usually larger than the liquid line, back to the inlet of the compressor.

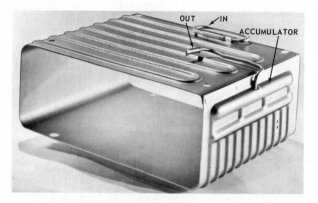

Fig. 4-23. *Shell type evaporator coil used with capillary tube, or high side float type refrigerant control.* (Houdaille-Hersey)

All of the connections, whether mechanical, soldered, or brazed, must be carefully made to eliminate all possibility of leakage.

Evaporator units are made in four different styles:
1. Shell type -- Fig. 4-23.
2. Shelf type -- freezers -- Fig. 4-24.
3. Wall type--freezer chest--Fig. 4-25.
4. Fin tube type with forced circulation -- Fig. 4-26.

There are five principal types of refrigerant controls:
1. Automatic expansion valve. (Dry System.)
2. Thermostatic expansion valve. (Dry System.)
3. Capillary tube. (Flooded System.)
4. Low side float. (Flooded System.)
5. High side float. (Flooded System.)

The five refrigerant controls are divided into two distinct areas: Dry and Flooded, dependent upon their conditions of operation.

If an expansion valve is used, the evaporating unit consists of a coil of tubing. The thermostatic expansion valve is popular in commercial refrigeration as it can be used in multiple systems, is adjustable, and takes up very little space.

When a low side float control is used, the evaporator unit consists of a tank out of which runs short lengths of tubing. The tank contains the float mechanism as illustrated in Fig. 4-21. Note that the mechanism holding the float, called a header, is bolted to the evaporator coil and also that shut-off valves are normally used on the float chambers. Lead gaskets are usually used whenever a joint needs to be sealed, because it has low moisture retention.

If there is a high side float or capillary refrigerant control, the evaporator unit may be either a cast tank or a series of coils which will provide an evaporating surface for the refrigerant, or a shell type aluminum plate coil. Fig. 4-23 illustrates an evaporator coil which has the refriger-

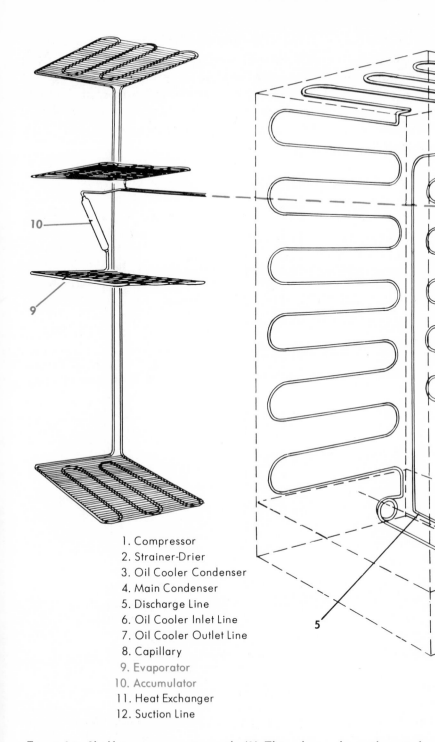

1. Compressor
2. Strainer-Drier
3. Oil Cooler Condenser
4. Main Condenser
5. Discharge Line
6. Oil Cooler Inlet Line
7. Oil Cooler Outlet Line
8. Capillary
9. Evaporator
10. Accumulator
11. Heat Exchanger
12. Suction Line

Fig. 4-24. Shelf type evaporator coil. (9) This shows the coil as it forms the shelf in an upright freezer. (10) An accumulator is located at the outlet of the evaporator coil between the coil and the compressor. This serves as a small reservoir for any refrigerant over the quantity required to serve the evaporator coils.

ant passages formed as part of the coil.

The "no frost" freezer, refrigerator and cabinet use a fan in combination with the evaporator coil. Fig. 4-27 illustrates a finned evaporator coil which uses a fan to circulate the air and increase the efficiency of the coil. Most manufacturers use some type of shroud to direct the air over the coil, as shown in Fig. 4-26. On the defrost cycle, the frost which has accumulated on the coils melts and the water is channeled to an evaporization pan over the condenser.

4-18 The Automatic Expansion Valve

In the dry system previously mentioned the refrigerant, when passing from the liquid line to the evaporator, is controlled by an automatic expansion valve (AEV). As

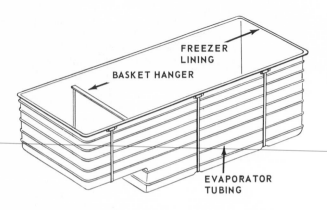

Fig. 4-25. Wall type evaporator coil. Note that the evaporator coils are attached to the lining of the freezer cabinet. This arrangement provides a smooth inside surface with uniform cooling throughout the cabinet.

the pressure decreases on the low side, the expansion valve opens and refrigerant escapes into the evaporating coils where it absorbs heat while evaporating on the low pressure side. The valve maintains a constant pressure in the evaporating coil when the system is running. This system operates independently of the amount of refrigerant in the system.

The expansion valve is, therefore, one of the division points between the high and low pressure sides of the system. See Chapter 6 for a detailed explanation of expansion valves.

The automatic expansion valve has an adjustment which may be manually regulated to give the evaporator coil the desired amount of refrigerant, as shown in Fig.

4-20. Turning the adjustment to the right, clockwise, will increase the rate of flow. The rate of flow of refrigerant through the automatic expansion valve is controlled by the pressure in the evaporator. It should be noted that no refrigerant will flow

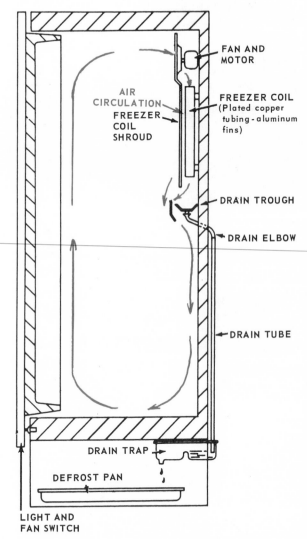

Fig. 4-26. Forced circulation evaporator coil as used in upright freezer cabinet. A door switch on the fan stops the fan when the cabinet door is opened. (Gibson Refrigerator Sales Corp., Hupp Corp.)

through the automatic expansion valve, unless the compressor is running and the evaporator and the connecting tubing are under a low pressure.

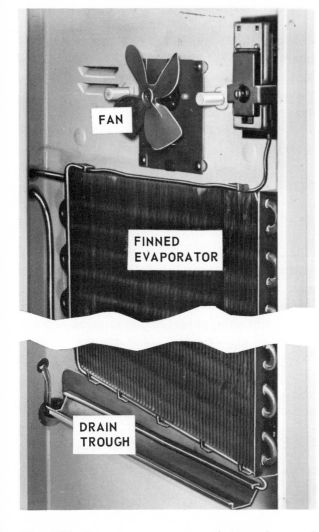

Fig. 4-27. Fan type evaporator coil. Note the trough to collect and carry away moisture which collects on the evaporator coil.
(Kelvinator Div. - American Motors Corp.)

4-19 The Thermostatic Expansion Valve

Many units, especially commercial ones, are equipped with an expansion valve called a thermostatic expansion valve (TEV), Fig. 4-28. This valve has a sensitive bulb located at the outlet of the evaporator unit. When this bulb is cooled, the contraction of the fluid in it causes the diaphragm or bellows to contract.

This diaphragm or bellows is connected to the expansion valve needle and will tend to close it. This addition of a thermo-sensitive mechanism to the valve enables the evaporator coil to fill more quickly and permits more efficient cooling. The thermostatic expansion valve operates to keep the cooling coil full of liquid refrigerant when the system is running. See Chapter 6 for a more detailed explanation of its function. As the evaporator coil becomes colder the TEV reduces the rate of flow of refrigerant into the coil. No refrigerant will flow through the TEV unless the compressor is running and the evaporator and the outlet tubing are under a low pressure.

4-20 Capillary Tube or Choke Tube

Another method of throttling the high-pressure liquid to a low evaporating pressure, is to use a long length of small diameter tubing. This tube reduces the pressure, due to the resistance to flow of refrigerant through the length of the small tubing. The tube is usually about 1/8 in. in outside diameter. It may have a variety of inside diameters. The tube is placed between the liquid line and the evaporating

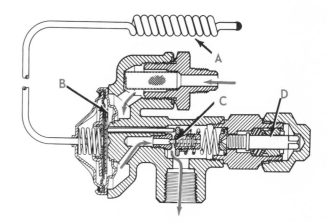

Fig. 4-28. Thermostatic expansion valve. The red arrows indicate the direction of the refrigerant flow. A-Temperature control bulb. B-Control diaphram. C-Control needle. D-Needle adjustment.
(American Standard, Controls Div.)

Fig. 4-29. Capillary tube refrigerant control.
(Wabash Corp.)

ADAPTOR
FITTINGS

COMPRESSION
NUTS

coil, Fig. 4-22. The inside diameter varies, depending upon the refrigerant, the capacity of the unit, and the length of the line. The Rice Company, originators of the capillary tube refrigerant control, built a conventional refrigerator using this tube. See Fig. 4-29.

The capillary tube operates on the principle of restriction. It operates on the pressure differences between the high pressure side and the low pressure side. A tube is chosen that will allow just enough liquid through it to make up for the amount that is vaporized in the evaporator unit as the compressor operates. It thus reduces the liquid refrigerant from its high pressure to the evaporating pressure. Actually there is no change to the liquid except a slight drop in pressure for about the first two-thirds of the length of the capillary tube. Then the liquid starts to change to vapor and by the time the refrigerant reaches the end of the tube about 10 to 20 percent of it has vaporized. The increased volume of the vapor causes most of the pressure drop to occur in the latter end of the tube. Because there is no shut-off valve, the pressures equalize as the liquid refrigerant in the condenser moves into the cooling coil during the off part of the cycle. This equalizing of pressure permits easier starting of the compressor. It also means that the system must not have an overcharge of refrigerant as the extra refrigerant would tend to fill the evaporator unit too full. This would be indicated by a severe frosting of the suction line when the motor starts.

4-21 Low Pressure Side Float Control

Another type of refrigeration cycle is the flooded system. This differs from the dry system in that the evaporating coil is flooded with refrigerant and the amount of the refrigerant is controlled by a float valve. It functions as follows: as heat is absorbed by the refrigerant in the evaporator unit, it evaporates and the liquid level falls, which causes a lowering of the float. As the float lowers, it opens the needle valve connected to it, which allows more liquid to enter from the high pressure liquid line taking the place of the evaporated liquid. The unit which is simple has one disadvantage -- it requires more refrigerant than the dry system. Fig. 4-30 illustrates the exterior appearance and the interior construction of a flooded evaporating unit using a low side float. The motor control is operated the same as in the direct expansion system, but may use either a temperature or pressure motor control switch.

Take particular note of the lever mechanism and the oil layer over the refrigerant. This float control operates by maintaining a constant level of liquid refrigerant in the low pressure side.

The oil is normally returned through a small opening at a predetermined level in the suction return tubing of the float. Because of the small diameter of the hole, if the unit is not level, the oil will not return to the compressor and "oil binding" will result. In effect, the oil forms a layer on the surface of the refrigerant liquid and prevents the refrigerant from evaporating at a rapid rate.

4-22 High Pressure Side Float Control

This system uses a float located in the liquid receiver tank, or in an auxilliary chamber in the high pressure side. It oper-

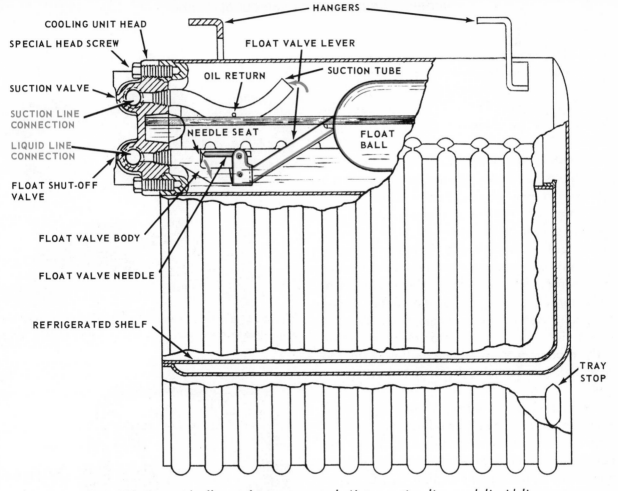

Fig. 4-30. Low side float refrigerant control. Note suction line, and liquid line connections. The float and needle mechanism maintain constant level of liquid refrigerant in the evaporator.

ates as follows: when enough liquefied refrigerant has collected in the float chamber, the float will rise enough to open the needle valve and admit the liquid into the low pressure side or evaporating unit. The

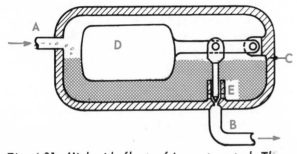

Fig. 4-31. High side float refrigerant control. The red arrows show the direction of flow of refrigerant through the control. A-Liquid refrigerant line. B-Liquid line to evaporation. C-Liquid refrigerant level. D-Float. E-Float needle.

float controls the level of liquid refrigerant on the high pressure side. The amount of refrigerant in the system must be carefully regulated to allow the evaporator unit to receive the correct amount of refrigerant, and to operate correctly. Any extra refrigerant in the system will be stored in the evaporating coil. Any leak of refrigerant will cause a lack of refrigerant in the evaporating coil. Fig. 4-31 illustrates a high side float mechanism. The high side float refrigerant control is described in detail in Chapter 6.

4-23 Open Unit Motors

The driving mechanism or the source of power for refrigeration units is usually an electric motor. Small gasoline engines have also been used for this purpose. Electric motors used are of a sturdy construction and are designed to furnish high starting power. To insure quietness, the motors are mounted on rubber or springs, Fig. 4-32.

Electric motors are made in two general types. Open or conventional units have an open motor which uses a belt to drive the compressor. The motors usually have bearings that need oiling once or twice a year, but some motors have a sintered (porous) oil bearing that is lubricated at the factory for the life of the motor. The serviceman should check the motor carefully and determine whether there is provision for oiling. The motor must be carefully mounted to align the pulley with the flywheel and to have the proper belt tightness.

The position of open unit motors is adjustable to facilitate belt adjustment. Motor size varies from 1/8 hp to 1/3 hp for domestic refrigeration, with the 1/8 hp and 1/6 hp motors predominating. Chapter 7 explains the construction of these motors in greater detail.

4-24 Motors (Hermetic Units)

The hermetic motor drives the compressor directly. The motors are mounted under the same sealed dome as the compressor. Hermetic motors usually run at 3450 rpm. These are of the two pole design and are oiled by the same oil as the compressor. Because arcing would deteriorate the oil and the refrigerant, these motors do not use brushes or open points inside the dome. Fig. 4-33, shows the parts of a motor used in a hermetic refrigeration compressor. The motor control devices are mounted on the outside of the dome. Hermetically sealed compressor motors have the windings coated to prevent deterioration by the refrigerant. Fig. 4-34, shows a typical hermetic compressor and motor. Refrigerant oil settles to the bot-

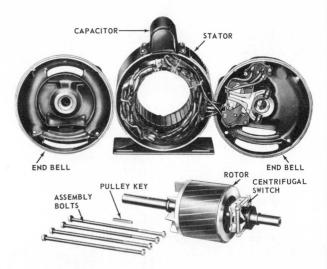

Fig. 4-32. Electric motor of capacitor type used on open type compressor. (Emerson Electric Mfg. Co.)

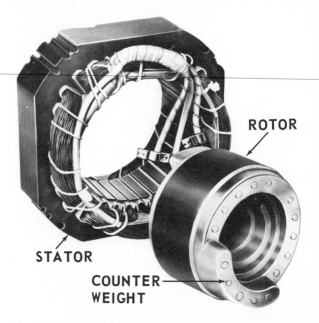

Fig. 4-33. Hermetic unit motor stator and rotor. The rotor is mounted directly on to the compressor crankshaft. Note the counterweight which balances the weight of the crank, connecting rod and piston.

tom of the mechanism. The various parts are lubricated by this oil which is pumped and distributed to all wearing surfaces.

4-25 Motor Controls

Practically all automatic electric refrigerators are designed to have excess capacity and, therefore, under normal usage need not run all of the time. In the older styles of refrigerators, the compressor ran approximately one hour and then was idle for about two hours if the running temperatures were normal. This cycling time has been gradually reduced until at present, the mechanism runs approximately five to ten minutes and remains idle ten to twenty minutes. The total running time per day remains approximately the same; and under normal running temperature conditions, it is 8 to 10 hours out of 24.

There are two principal types of motor controls used to turn the motors on and off in order to obtain correct refrigeration. Many older domestic units and many commercial units use a pressure type of motor control designed to shut off the electrical power when the low side pressure of the system, corresponding to the temperature desired, indicates that the cabinet is cool enough. It then turns the current on when the pressure has risen to a predetermined pressure corresponding to the allowable temperature rise in the box. This pressure

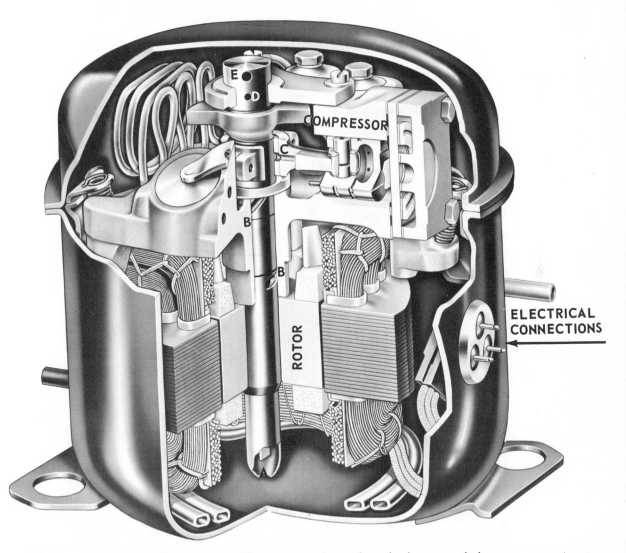

Fig. 4-34. Hermetically sealed compressor. The motor is located at the bottom and the compressor is at the top. A-Oil entrance. B-Oil channel to main bearing. C-Oil hole to connecting rod and piston. D-Oil hole to upper bearing. E-Oil slinger hole from which oil is thrown over all surfaces for cooling purposes. (Tecumseh Products Co.)

control was used with the low side float systems or multiple systems.

Today, the more popular type of motor control is the thermostatic control which turns the motor off when the evaporating unit gets sufficiently cool, and turns it on again when the evaporating coil has warmed up 8-10 deg. F.

The thermostatic control, Fig. 4-35, consists of a bulb connected by a capillary tube to a diaphragm or bellows. This element is charged with a volatile fluid which will build up pressure when the bulb becomes warmer and will decrease in pressure when the bulb gets cooler.

As the bulb pressure increases, the diaphragm moves out. Since the diaphragm is connected to a toggle or snap action switch, it will turn this switch on (close the circuit). Then as the bulb cools and the diaphragm or bellows moves in, the toggle switch will snap open. These controls have adjustments that permit variations in operating temperatures. Many of these controls have a manual switch to permit shutting off or turning on the refrigerator as desired. They also may include an overload protector which will open the switch if the unit draws too much electricity (current). An adjustable knob en-

ables the owner to change the thermostat operating temperatures to meet different operating conditions. These thermostats may also be connected to timers used to automatically defrost the evaporator coil.

You should keep in mind the fact that the pressure of the refrigerant in the system varies with the temperature; therefore, temperature may be indicated by pressure. This permits the use of pressures to control temperatures. See Chapter 8 for more details on controls.

4-26 Refrigerant Lines

Copper tubing is commonly used to carry the liquid refrigerant from the condenser to the evaporator unit, and also to carry the refrigerant vapor from the evaporator unit back to the compressor. Tubing made of steel is often used in domestic units. These lines are mounted in back of the refrigerator cabinet or are hidden behind the breaker strip at the refrigerator door jamb (frame). The lines are attached by soldering or brazing. It is important that these lines be kept from being pinched or from being buckled. They must also be supported to prevent wearing or breaking due to vibration.

Refrigerant lines in commercial units are usually connected with flared fittings.

4-27 Service Valves

All open units have some means to enable the serviceman to mount gauges on the system or to check pressures and to put in or take out refrigerant or oil. Some of the older units had as many as five valves.

The more recent domestic models do not have service valves and the serviceman must use a saddle or "tap a line." See Chapter 12. Two typical service valves are shown in Fig. 4-36. A is a low side or suction-service valve. B is a high side or pressure-service valve.

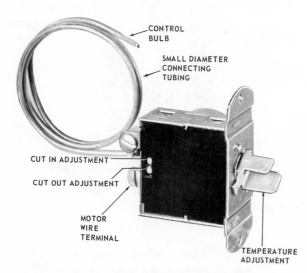

CONTROL BULB

SMALL DIAMETER CONNECTING TUBING

CUT IN ADJUSTMENT

CUT OUT ADJUSTMENT

MOTOR WIRE TERMINAL

TEMPERATURE ADJUSTMENT

Fig. 4-35. Temperature motor control.
(Cutler-Hammer, Inc.)

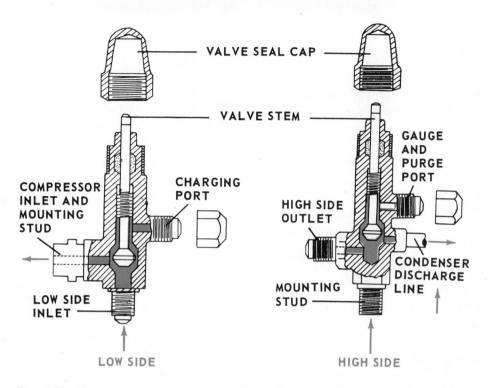

VALVE SEAL CAP

VALVE STEM

GAUGE AND PURGE PORT

COMPRESSOR INLET AND MOUNTING STUD

CHARGING PORT

HIGH SIDE OUTLET

CONDENSER DISCHARGE LINE

LOW SIDE INLET

MOUNTING STUD

LOW SIDE

HIGH SIDE

Fig. 4-36. Two common compressor service valves. Note low side or suction service valve and high side or pressure service valve. Both of these valves are "double seating." When the valve stem is turned all the way out the service port opening is closed. When the stem is turned all the way in the outlet is closed.
(Gibson Refrigerator Sales Corp., Hupp Corp.)

4-28 Safety Notes and Summary

The term "safety" as applied to any phase of refrigeration or air conditioning activity may have three different applications. It may pertain to:

A. Safety to the operator.
B. Safety or correct handling of tools and equipment to avoid any damage or abuse of the equipment.
C. Safety to the produce, foods or occupants of refrigerated or air conditioned space.

In this chapter the student is expected to develop an understanding of the construction and operation of the many mechanisms used in this industry and to respect their accurate design and sensitive adjustment. As an installing or service technician he should always handle the parts with care, keep every dismantled part clean and dry. He should study and understand the theory of operation of the various parts and carefully study the manufacturers' installation and service procedures to make sure that every assembly and adjustment is correctly done.

There are many compression cycle designs. All must have a compressor, a means to drive this compressor, a condenser, a refrigerant control, an evaporator (cooling) unit, and a means to turn the motor on and off automatically. The refrigeration system can be broken down into two types:

A. Open type.
B. Hermetic or sealed type.

Both A and B may use any of the compressor designs mentioned in this chapter.

4-29 Test Your Knowledge, Chapter 4

1. How many laws of refrigeration are considered in refrigeration work?
2. Name the eight important parts found in all compression cycle refrigerators.

3. Name the main parts commonly located in the low pressure side.
4. Name the main parts commonly located in the high pressure side.
5. Name four types of compressors.
6. What kind of condensing units do not use a crankshaft seal?
7. Why does a gas rise in temperature as it is being compressed?
8. Why are check valves used in the suction line on some rotary compressors?
9. Why should condensers be cleaned occasionally?
10. What name is applied to the type of evaporator coil that uses an expansion valve?
11. What control determines the refrigerator cabinet temperature?
12. Name five types of refrigerant controls.
13. What advantage does an eccentric crankshaft have over a crank throw type?
14. How much clearance is allowed between the piston and the cylinder on small compressors?
15. What is the size of the compression chamber when the piston is upper dead center?
16. How much lift is allowed the intake and exhaust valves?
17. The low side float maintains a constant _____ on the low side.
18. The automatic expansion valve maintains a constant _____ on the low side when the unit is running.
19. The high side float maintains a constant _____.
20. What is the purpose of the crankshaft seal?
21. Another word for "evaporation" of a liquid is _____.
22. Of what material are the refrigerant lines made?
23. How does a capillary tube reduce the pressure?
24. When does the condensing pressure stop rising?
25. What basic conditions are necessary to produce refrigeration?
26. What type of service valve must be used on a hermetic unit?
27. Name the two types of refrigeration systems?

Chapter 5

COMPRESSOR CONSTRUCTION

5-1 How a Compressor Works

In a refrigeration system, a compressor (gas pump), usually driven by an electric motor, is used to compress the gas molecules of the evaporated refrigerant until they reach a high temperature. The heated vapor, under high pressure, is then discharged into the condenser. The heat flows from the compressed vapor through

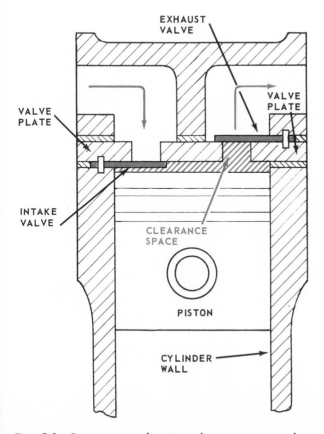

VALVE PLATE

INTAKE VALVE

EXHAUST VALVE

VALVE PLATE

CLEARANCE SPACE

PISTON

CYLINDER WALL

Fig. 5-1. Compressor showing clearance space between head of piston and cylinder head.

the metal walls of the condenser into the cooling medium (air or water) which surrounds the condenser.

If the system is to work efficiently, the compressor must operate with very little loss due to leakage or friction.

5-2 Types of Compressors

Three types of compressors which are used successfully at the present time are:
1. Reciprocating compressor.
2. Rotary compressor.
3. Centrifugal compressor.

The reciprocating type compressor is most commonly used. Its simplicity of manufacture, durability, and ease of maintenance make it a popular choice. The rotary compressor can be used with fair efficiency at high speeds, but close manufacturing tolerances are required. The centrifugal compressor is used chiefly in large (100 hp and more), commercial applications.

5-3 Compressor Efficiency

In operating a compressor, if any of the pumped vapor leaks back into the compressor on the suction stroke, energy is wasted. Likewise, if energy is used to overcome friction or inertia of the parts, the compressor will lose efficiency. All compressors have some frictional losses.

Volumetric efficiency of a compressor is the volume of gas pumped, divided by the calculated volume. If the compressor is designed to pump 10 cu. in. of vapor each revolution or stroke (this is called the piston displacement) but it pumps only 6 cu. in., the volumetric efficiency of the pump is 60 percent (6/10).

For efficient operation, the volumetric efficiency must be as high as possible. Several factors affect the volumetric efficiency. First, if the head pressure or the pressure the compressor must pump against increases, the amount pumped per stroke will decrease. Second, if the low side pressure decreases, it is more difficult for the vapors to fill the cylinder, and the amount pumped per stroke will decrease. Third, if the clearance pocket is enlarged, the amount pumped per stroke will decrease. The clearance pocket is the space left in the cylinder when the roller or piston is at the end of its pumping stroke, as shown in Fig. 5-1.

5-4 Reciprocating Compressor

The piston-cylinder type of compressor is a reciprocating compressor. To recip-

rocate means to move to and fro, or back and forth in a straight line. To compress the charge of vapor in a reciprocating-type compressor, a plunger or piston is moved in a cylinder and the vapor is compressed and moved through the opening provided. As the piston moves out of the cylinder, a void (or partial vacuum) is created. A new charge of vapor rushes into this space, and it in turn is compressed and moved into the condenser. Because the original source of pumping energy is usually an electric motor which has rotary motion only, a mechanism must be made to change the rotary motion to reciprocating motion. This change is usually accomplished by means of a crank and a rod connecting the crank to the piston. The complete mechanism is housed in a leakproof container called a crankcase. A typical reciprocating compressor is shown in Fig. 5-2.

The most common way to classify reciprocating compressors is by the number of cylinders. Many refrigeration compressors are of the single or one cylinder type,

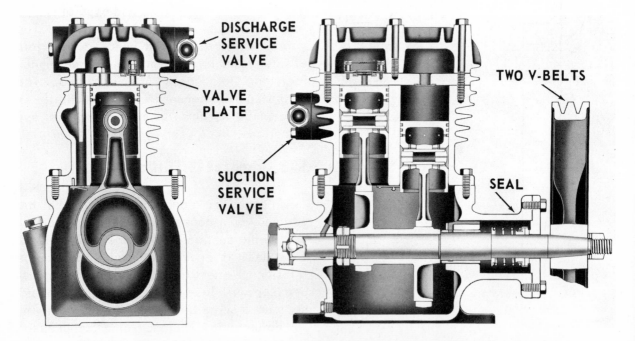

Fig. 5-2. *Typical large capacity two cylinder reciprocating compressor. Note that this compressor uses an eccentric type crankshaft, and the pistons are fitted with rings.*

but two cylinder models are in use in many hermetic systems. They run smoothly and are compact. For large commercial installations, compressors are made with three, four, five, six, seven, or more cylinders.

The cylinder arrangement is another method of classifying compressors; vertical single, horizontal single, 45 deg. single (inclined), vertical two cylinder, V-type two cylinder, W-type three cylinder, radial three cylinder, vertical four cylinder, V-type four cylinder, etc., have all been used.

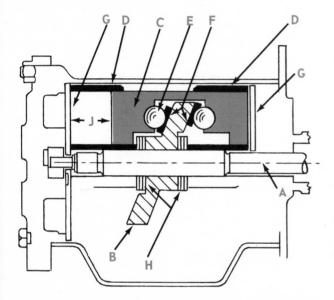

Fig. 5-3. Cross section through a "swash" plate type of reciprocating compressor. A-Drive shaft. B-Swash plate. C-Piston. D-Cylinder wall. E-Drive ball. F-Ball shoe. G-Valve plate (valve not shown). H-Thrust bearing. J-Piston stroke. As the driveshaft and swash plate revolve the piston is moved back and forth in the cylinder.

A popular type of reciprocating compressor used on many automobile air conditioning systems is known as a "swash" plate or "wobble" plate compressor. No crankshaft or connecting rod is used in this type of compressor. The cylinder and pistons are mounted as shown in Fig. 5-3. As the shaft revolves the swash plate causes the pistons to reciprocate in the cylinders. Usually the swash plate com-

pressor has three or more cylinders arranged in a circle around the drive shaft. Since the compressor is double acting, that is, compression takes place at each end of the stroke, a three cylinder compressor will give a pumping action corresponding to a six cylinder conventional compressor of the same cylinder and stroke dimensions. This type compressor has also been built as a single acting compressor. A five cylinder model has been used in automotive systems.

5-5 Cylinder Construction

Compressor cylinders are usually made of cast iron. The cast iron must be dense enough to prevent the seepage of refrigerant through it. A small amount of nickel is usually added to get this required density. The castings must be thoroughly aged before machining, to prevent warpage after the finishing operations. Smaller compressors usually have fins cast integrally with the cylinders to provide better cooling. The larger compressors may have water jackets surrounding the cylinders to cool the compressor. Some compressors are built with cylinder liners which may be replaced if worn.

In most cases the crankcase is part of the same casting as the cylinder. This practice cuts down the number of the joints and the possibility of leaks. It also permits close alignment between the crankshaft main bearings and the cylinder.

Assembly devices that thread into the cylinder usually have national coarse threads due to their greater strength in cast iron.

The cylinder bore in which the piston travels must be made extremely accurate. This is usually made by first boring, and then finishing by honing and lapping. Some companies lap the piston and the cylinder together to form a matched set. Some of the small cylinders (1 in. in diameter, approximately) have tolerances, that is, accuracy of bore diameter, varying between one ten thousandth (.0001) and one hundred thousandth of an inch (.00001).

5-6 Piston Construction

The pistons are usually made of cast iron and are accurately machined and ground on their outer surface to fit the cylinders. The piston must have holes drilled and reamed to take the piston pin. This pin is used to attach the connecting rod to the piston.

The smaller pistons have oil grooves around the periphery (outside) of the piston while larger pistons (over 1 1/2 in.) may have grooves machined in them and fitted with piston rings, as shown in Fig. 5-4.

specting and repairing a compressor it is important to rigidly follow the manufacturer's specifications.

Piston rings are usually made of cast iron although some bronze rings have been used. The rings should be fitted to the groove as closely as possible and still allow movement. A 45 deg. tapered or angled ring gap is used to permit the ring to exert a pressure against the cylinder wall. This gap should be approximately .001 for each inch of diameter of the piston. Two types of rings are used on the larger pistons; compression rings and oil rings.

Piston pins are made of hardened high carbon steel. They are hollow to reduce weight and are accurately ground to be perfectly straight. Piston pins are usually

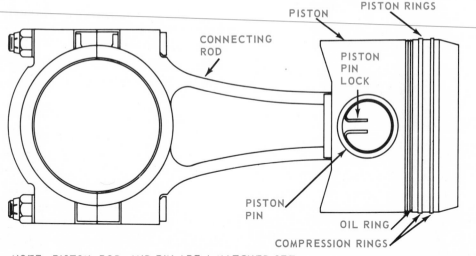

NOTE: PISTON, ROD, AND PIN ARE A MATCHED SET.

Fig. 5-4. Compressor piston and connecting rod assembly. (Airtemp Div., Chrysler Corp.)

Since piston and cylinder temperatures seldom exceed 200 deg. F., excessive expansion caused by heat is not a problem. The parts may be fitted with very little clearance. Approximately .0002 in. should be allowed for each inch diameter of the piston. However, the larger pistons which use piston rings usually are fitted with a little more than this clearance. When in-

of the full floating type, which means that the piston pin is free to turn in both the connecting rod bushing or the piston boss bushings. It is possible to have the intake valve mounted in the top of the piston. This valve construction enables the piston movement to help open and close the valve, but it makes a more costly repair if the valve assembly needs overhaul.

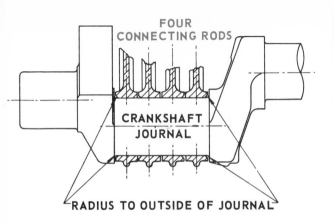

FOUR
CONNECTING RODS

CRANKSHAFT
JOURNAL

RADIUS TO OUTSIDE OF JOURNAL

Fig. 5-5. Four connecting rods mounted on one crank journal. This arrangement could be used on a four cylinder V-type compressor.
(Airtemp Div., Chrysler Corp.)

5-7 Connecting Rod Construction

The connecting rod is used to attach the piston to the crankshaft. These rods are sometimes made of drop forged steel, and sometimes of cast iron or cast steel. The type that is used with the crank throw type crankshaft has a split lower end that clamps around the crankshaft journal. This bearing must be fitted to a clearance of approximately .001 in.; it is therefore important that the bolts be carefully tightened (torqued). Fig. 5-5 shows four connecting rods mounted on one crankshaft journal.

Fig. 5-6. Piston and connecting rod assembly.
(General Electric Co.)

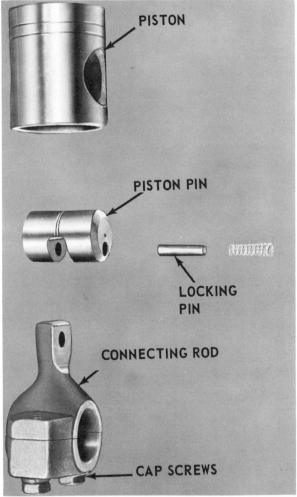

PISTON

PISTON PIN

LOCKING
PIN

CONNECTING ROD

CAP SCREWS

Fig. 5-7. Piston and connecting rod assembly dismantled. This is the same assembly as shown in Fig. 5-6. Note the small pin which locks the connecting rod to the large piston pin, and the two cap screws used to attach the cap to the crankshaft end of the connecting rod.

This arrangement could be used in a four cylinder V-type compressor or radial compressor.

The eccentric type connecting rod usually has cast iron as the bearing surface. The crank throw end is a solid ring and must be mounted on the eccentric before the crankshaft proper is assembled to the eccentric.

A small piston and connecting rod assembly, such as used in a hermetic unit, is shown in Fig. 5-6. The connecting rod is attached rigidly to a large piston pin by means of a locking pin and spring. The unit dismantled is shown in Fig. 5-7.

The principle of another type of piston device, called the Scotch yoke, is shown in Fig. 5-8. In this device no connecting rod is used. The piston is longer than the cylinder, and at the crank end a special bearing device enables the crank to revolve in a slot arrangement causing the piston to move back and forth. This arrangement is used extensively in small high-speed compressors.

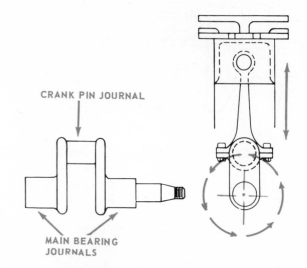

Fig. 5-9. Crank throw type crankshaft. As the crankshaft rotates, the piston reciprocates. The piston pin oscillates as it reciprocates with the piston. The lower end of the connecting rod rotates with the crankshaft.

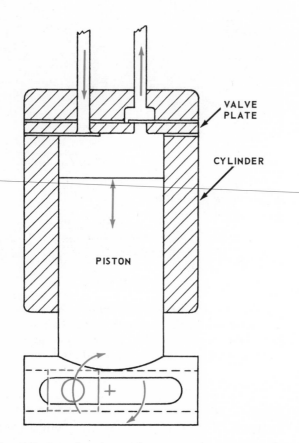

Fig. 5-8. Scotch yoke mechanism used to connect the piston to the crankshaft. No connecting rod is used.

5-8 Crankshaft Construction

The crank is a rotating lever. It can be used to produce torque on a shaft, and it is used to change rotary motion to reciprocating motion when used with a connecting rod, as shown in Fig. 5-9. This type of crankshaft is usually made of drop forged medium carbon steel or cast steel. The main parts of the crankshaft are the main bearing journals (two or more), connecting rod bearing journals, end play bearing or device, crankshaft seal shaft or shoulder and flywheel holding device. The wearing surfaces of the crankshaft are usually case hardened. The bearings or bushings in which the crankshaft journals turn are usually made of some copper alloy (bronze) or lead alloy (babbitt). The accurately ground case-hardened journals must fit in the bearings with clearances of approximately .001 in. Many of the crankshaft journals are also specially treated (lubrite by Parker is one) as a safety precaution against bearing failure in case of a temporary shortage of lubricant. It is common practice to fasten the flywheel to the crankshaft with a standard taper, a woodruff key and a nut-lock washer combination. You must be cautious when working on crankshaft threads to be sure they are not damaged, as this might necessitate replacing the complete crankshaft.

Another type of crankshaft mechanism is the eccentric, as shown in Fig. 5-10. The crankshaft consists of a steel shaft on which is mounted a cast iron eccentric (an

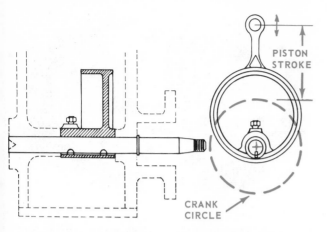

Fig. 5-10. Eccentric type crank mechanism.

off-center mounted disk). This type shaft provides a large wearing surface for the connecting rod; it can be well balanced and is smooth running. The shaft has the usual two main bearing journals, crankshaft seal device and provision for mounting the fly-

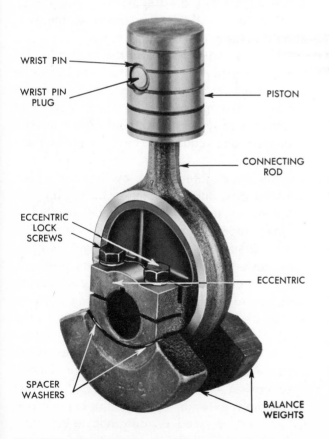

Fig. 5-11. Eccentric crankshaft assembly. Note the lock screws and the balance weights.

WRIST PIN

WRIST PIN PLUG

PISTON

CONNECTING ROD

ECCENTRIC LOCK SCREWS

ECCENTRIC

SPACER WASHERS

BALANCE WEIGHTS

wheel. The eccentric is attached to the shaft by means of a key and setscrews, as shown in Fig. 5-11.

5-9 Valve Construction

The valve assembly consists of a valve plate, an intake valve, an exhaust valve, and the retainers for the valves. See Fig. 5-12.

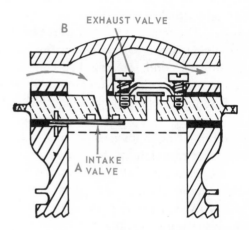

Fig. 5-12. Typical compressor valve plate. A-Intake valve. B-Exhaust valve. Heavy springs on the exhaust valve cage protect the compressor in case of severe oil pumping.

Valve plates are commonly made of cast iron, but the trend is toward using hardened steel valve plates as they are thinner and have longer wearing valve seats. The valves proper are usually made of spring steel (reeds) accurately ground. The intake valve is usually kept in place by small pins and the clamping action between the compressor head and valve plate. The exhaust valve may also be clamped in the same manner. Some may be held in place by small machine screws with a spring and a cage. This latter mechanism permits a wider exhaust valve opening if the compressor should pump oil. Fig. 5-13 shows a typical valve plate assembly.

The valve disks or reeds must be perfectly flat. Differences of only .0001 in. or .0002 in. will cause valves to leak. There is no practical way to repair the disks or reeds, so they must be replaced if leaking. The valve seat can be repaired by first grinding the plate on a surface grinder or on a surface plate by hand, and then lapping the plate with the finest lapping powder obtainable.

Of the two valves (intake and exhaust), the intake valve ordinarily gives the least trouble as it is constantly lubricated by retained oil in the cool refrigerant vapors and it operates at a relatively cool temperature. The exhaust valve must be fitted with special care as it operates at high temperatures and it must be leakproof against a relatively high-pressure difference. Because of the high vapor velocities and the high temperatures, there is a tendency for the heavy ends of the hydrocarbon oils to settle on the valve and valve seat as carbon. Moisture tends to accelerate this deposit and also aids corrosion.

The valves open approximately .010 in. If the movement is more than this amount, a valve noise develops. If the movement is too little, not enough vapor can enter the cylinder in the case of the intake valve, or leave the cylinder from the exhaust valve.

5-10 Crankshaft Seal Construction

The type of refrigerating system that uses an external motor (open type) to drive the compressor must have a leakproof joint where the crankshaft comes out of the crankcase of the compressor. This joint requires careful designing as it is a place where the shaft rotates part of the time and is idle part of the time. The joint must also be leakproof as the pressures may vary in the crankcase from a vacuum to pressures as high as the condensing pressure in the system.

The contact surfaces (the rubbing surfaces) are usually made with one face hardened tool steel and the other of some bearing metal such as bronze or carbon. The surfaces must be as straight and as smooth as it is possible to make them. At

Fig. 5-13. *Typical refrigerant compressor valve plate construction. Note the wire lock used in the two exhaust valve screws. (A) is the inlet port. Note the extension to prevent oil from entering the intake.*

present they are honed and lapped. They are inspected optically to flatness accuracies of nearly .000001 in. in tolerance. Fig. 5-14 shows a crankshaft seal used on a pressure lubricated system.

For long satisfactory service, the seal should be constantly lubricated.

The spring loading of the seal must be carefully calculated. Too much spring force will cause too rapid wear. If the spring force is not enough, excessive crankcase pressures may force the seal ring from the shoulder and cause at least a temporary leak.

The corrugated brass cylinder to which the seal ring and the gasket clamp ring are mounted is usually called a bellows. The bellows must be made of noncrystallizing metal (nonwork hardening). Some companies have used a double thickness bellows, while others have used a small coil spring wrapped around the main spring wire to eliminate critical vibration periods in the seal (chattering).

Modern conventional refrigerator compressors usually use a synthetic rubber seal gasket (such as neoprene) where the crankshaft extends through the crankcase. Compressors used on automobile air conditioning systems use a synthetic rubber gasketed crankshaft seal. Teflon is also

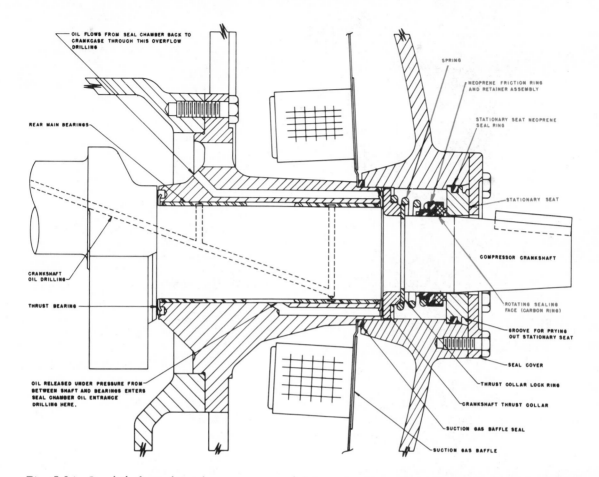

OIL FLOWS FROM SEAL CHAMBER BACK TO CRANKCASE THROUGH THIS OVERFLOW DRILLING

SPRING

NEOPRENE FRICTION RING AND RETAINER ASSEMBLY

STATIONARY SEAT NEOPRENE SEAL RING

REAR MAIN BEARINGS

STATIONARY SEAT

COMPRESSOR CRANKSHAFT

CRANKSHAFT OIL DRILLING

THRUST BEARING

ROTATING SEALING FACE (CARBON RING)

GROOVE FOR PRYING OUT STATIONARY SEAT

SEAL COVER

THRUST COLLAR LOCK RING

OIL RELEASED UNDER PRESSURE FROM BETWEEN SHAFT AND BEARINGS ENTERS SEAL CHAMBER OIL ENTRANCE DRILLING HERE.

CRANKSHAFT THRUST COLLAR

SUCTION GAS BAFFLE SEAL

SUCTION GAS BAFFLE

Fig. 5-14. Crankshaft seal used on a pressure lubricated refrigeration compressor. A carbon ring serves as a part of the rotating seal surface. (Airtemp Div., Chrysler Corp.)

used for seals which must operate at a high temperature as in automobile air conditioning applications.

Fig. 5-15 shows the construction of four different types of crankshaft seals.

See Chapter 15 for some illustrations of replacement seals for commercial compressors.

5-11 Gaskets

When assembling a compressor, the joints that lead to the external surface of the compressor must be sealed. Gaskets are used for this purpose. These gaskets must be made of a material that will not react chemically with the oils or refrigerants used in the system. The material must be compressible without being deformed permanently. The material must not change its size as the temperature changes. It must have an expansion rate close to the coefficient of expansion of the compressor parts.

Gaskets made of cork, paper composition, asbestos, lead, rubber and aluminum have been used. Paper composition and lead are popular gasket making materials. Aluminum cannot be used with certain refrigerants as it decomposes. The most important gasket is the one between the cylinder and the valve plate. If this gasket is too thick, it will produce a clearance pocket that is too large and the compressor will lose volumetric efficiency. If the gasket is too thin, the piston may pound against the valve plate. If the holes in the gasket where the piston and cylinder contact the valve

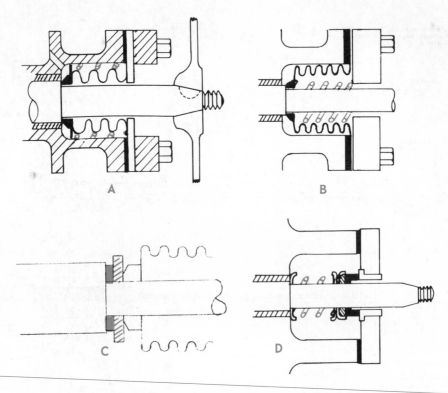

Fig. 5-15. Four common crankshaft seal designs: A-External spring-bellows. B-Internal spring-bellows. C-Replacement crankshaft seal shoulder. D-Synthetic rubber non-bellows.

plate are too large, an extra clearance pocket will be formed.

It is best to use gaskets supplied by the manufacturers of the equipment being used. It is especially important that replacement gaskets be in perfect condition when used on compressors that use water jackets for cooling.

Many gaskets fail because the surfaces they are clamped between are scored, warped or bruised in some manner. Be sure to check all surfaces for trueness and damage. If damaged, recondition the surfaces by filing, grinding or lapping.

5-12 Lubrication

Compressors are lubricated either by a splash system or by a pressure (force feed) system.

In the splash system, the crankcase is filled with the correct oil up to the bottom of the main bearings or to the middle of the crankshaft main bearings. Each time the crankshaft revolves, the crank throw or the eccentric dips into the oil and splashes or slings it around the inside of the compressor. Oil is thrown on cylinder walls, piston pin bushings and into small cavities where it drains into the main bearings. This is an excellent system for normal use in small compressors. Some compressor connecting rods have little dips or scoops attached to the lower ends to aid in picking up the oil and slinging it around to the other parts.

Generally speaking, the clearances between the moving parts is less in this type system. Noisy bearings will occur at smaller clearances in this system than in the pressure system.

The force feed or pressure system is a system which uses a small oil pump to force oil to the main bearings, lower connecting rod bearings, and in some cases, piston pins. This system is more expensive due to the cost of the pump and the cost of drilling the crankshaft and connecting rod. However, the compressor is better protected with oil at all times and it will run more quietly even though there are greater bearing clearances.

The oil pump is usually mounted on one end of the crankshaft which will be fitted with an eccentric in case a piston pump is used, a gear mounted in case a gear oil pump is used, or a rotor mounted in case a rotor pump is used. Whenever an oil pump is used, an overload relief valve must be built into the pump to protect against excessive oil pressures. Fig. 5-16

shows a pressure type lubrication system. The oil pump delivers oil under pressure to all bearing surfaces. A scavenger pump returns the oil from the crankcase to the oil tank. Larger compressors which use pressure lubrication sometimes use an oil pressure switch which will stop the unit if the oil pressure fails.

5-13 Compressor Drives (Open Type)

Compressors of the external drive type may be driven at a reduced speed or at motor speed. The larger compressors are usually driven at a reduced speed because

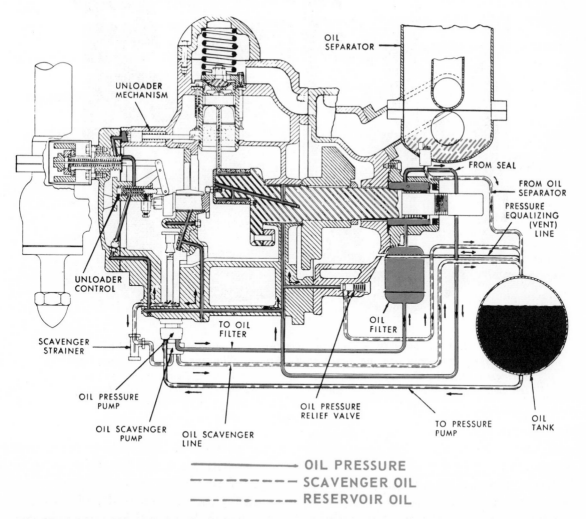

Fig. 5-16. Pressure lubricated refrigerator compressor which uses a multi-cylinder radial cylinder arrangement. A scavenger pump returns the oil from the crankcase back to the oil tank. The crankcase does not serve as an oil reservoir.

they are more efficient at the lower speed, and one compressor can be used for several different capacity applications by varying the speed. Bearing, valve, and piston life are increased by using reduced speeds. The

ple applications. The V-belts have been improved until they are approximately 98 percent efficient in power transmission. The slight loss is due to the flexing of the belt as it bends around the flywheel and

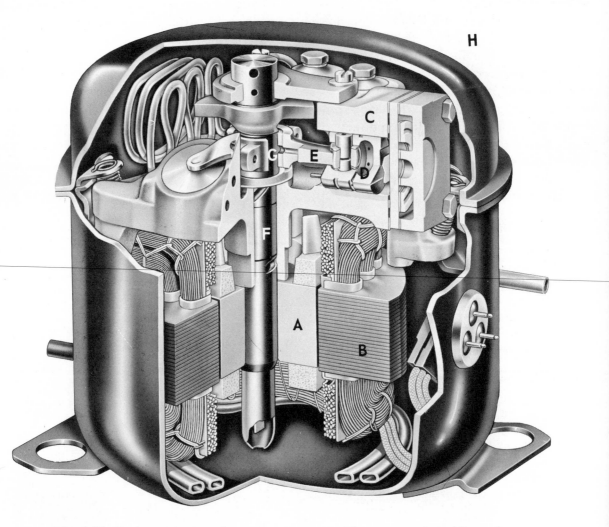

Fig. 5-17. Reciprocating type hermetic compressor. The cutaway dome shows the compressor at the top and the motor at the bottom. The assembly is mounted on springs inside the dome. A-Motor rotor. B-Motor stator. C-Compressor cylinder. D-Compressor pistons. E-Connecting rod. F-Crankshaft. G-Crank throw. H-Compressor shell. (Tecumseh Products Co.)

reduced speed drive also aids the motor and enables it to start more easily because of the lower starting torque required. The reduction in speed can be produced by using a belt drive, a gear drive or a fluid coupling.

V-belts may be used in single or multi-

motor pulley. An advantage of the V-belt is that it will work efficiently over a large range of tightness. However, the flywheel and pulley must be carefully aligned or excessive end loads will be put on the motor bushings and the compressor bearings. Misalignment can be produced by the shafts not being parallel to each other, or by having the motor pulley ahead or behind the flywheel line.

Compressor rpm can be determined by using this formula, if you know the motor speed, pulley size and flywheel size:

$$\text{Compressor rpm} = \frac{\text{motor rpm} \times \text{pulley diam.}}{\text{flywheel diam.}}$$

An accurate result may be obtained by measuring the pulley diameter and the flywheel diameter from the middle of the V-belt to the middle of the belt on the opposite side of the flywheel or pulley.

5-14 Compressor, Sealed Unit

A sealed refrigerant compressor is commonly known in the refrigeration industry as a "hermetic" motor-compressor.

The main difference between a hermetic compressor and an open type compressor is that in a hermetic compressor the motor is in the sealed housing with the compressor. The compressor is directly driven and therefore revolves at motor speed. Various cylinder arrangements have been used. One-cylinder models are popular for small units, while two-cylinder units are commonly used in larger units.

Details of construction and the design of the compressor are shown in Fig. 5-17.

There are three basic hermetic designs. One type puts the compressor and motor in a steel casing sometimes called a dome or "hat." The motor stator is sometimes pressed into one half of this dome and the compressor is bolted to the stator. This type is externally mounted on springs or rubber mounts to absorb vibrations. Another design has the motor and compressor assembly mounted on springs inside the dome or casing. The casing is usually made in two pieces and the joint is welded, as shown in Fig. 5-18. The third type uses the compressor body as the casing and extends the crankcase of the compressor to hold the motor. See Fig. 5-19. This type unit usually uses a bolted assembly

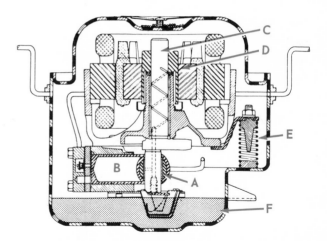

Fig. 5-18. Hermetic compressor using a Scotch yoke mechanism. A-Crank throw and Scotch yoke. B-Hollow piston. C-Combined motor shaft and crankshaft. D-Crankshaft thrust bearing. E-Internal mounting spring. F-Oil reservoir.

and is commonly called a "serviceable hermetic" because it can easily be dismantled and assembled.

A major engineering problem when designing hermetic units is the proper cooling of the electric motor. One method used to aid in cooling the motor is to press the stator into the dome to provide easy heat transfer from the motor windings to the

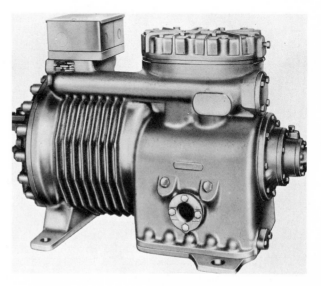

Fig. 5-19. A bolted type hermetic motor-compressor assembly. The motor is at the left and the compressor on the right. (Copeland Refrigeration Corp.)

casing. Another method is to pass the vapor returning from the evaporator around the motor windings before they are com-

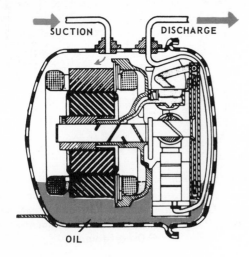

Fig. 5-20. A single cylinder hermetic compressor. The cool refrigerant vapor from the suction line flows over the motor windings to aid in cooling the motor. Note that this compressor uses a Scotch yoke piston crank mechanism and that the compressor is inverted.

pressed by the compressor. This relatively cool vapor removes much of the heat; however, it has a tendency to warm the returning vapor enough to reduce the volumetric efficiency of the compressor. Fig. 5-20 shows a motor compressor with suction vapor cooling the compressor.

An exploded view of a hermetic motor compressor that revolves at 3600 rpm is shown in Fig. 5-21. The two-pole motor drives a one-cylinder compressor by means of a Scotch yoke. This unit has an intake valve in the piston. It uses a pressure lubrication system. The pan at the left has an oil cooler V tube attached to it.

5-15 Mufflers

Most of the smaller hermetic units have sound deadening devices called mufflers on both the intake and the exhaust openings of the compressors. The mufflers eliminate the sharp gasping sound on the intake

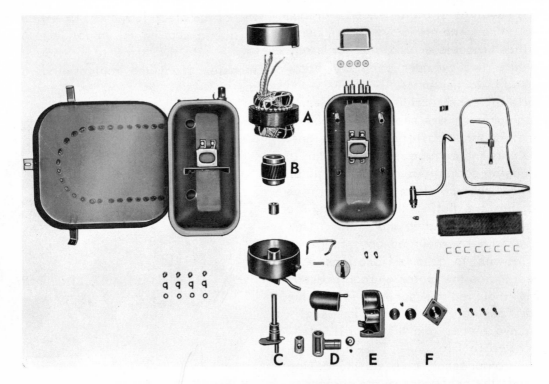

Fig. 5-21. Exploded view of a single cylinder 3600 rpm hermetic motor-compressor.
A-Stator. B-Rotor. C-Crankshaft. D-Piston. E-Cylinder. F-Valve plate.
(General Electric Co.)

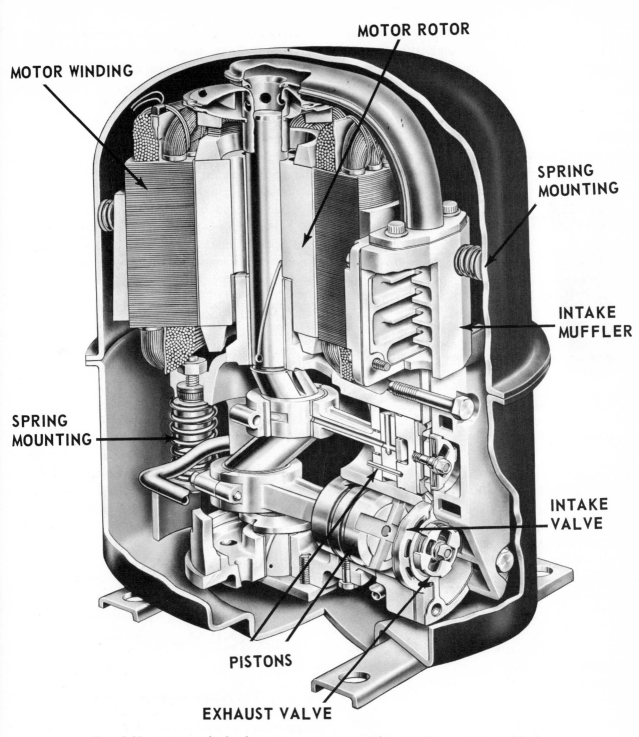

MOTOR ROTOR

MOTOR WINDING

SPRING MOUNTING

SPRING MOUNTING

INTAKE MUFFLER

INTAKE VALVE

PISTONS

EXHAUST VALVE

Fig. 5-22. A two cylinder hermetic compressor. This compressor is suitable for use either in a commercial application or as a part of a residence air conditioning system. Note the intake muffler.   (Tecumseh Products Co.)

stroke and the even sharper puff of the exhaust. These mufflers are small brazed cylinders with baffle plates mounted inside and based on Bernoulli's Theorem, the sudden increase in volume slows the velocity and reduces the annoying pumping sound. Fig. 5-22 shows a unit equipped with a suction "intake" muffler.

In one design, both suction and exhaust mufflers are connected directly to the compressor cylinder head as shown in Fig. 5-23.

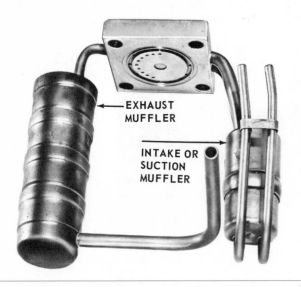

Fig. 5-23. *Compressor cylinder head. Mufflers are attached at both the suction and exhaust openings. A-Exhaust muffler. B-Intake or suction muffler.*

5-16 Compressor Cooling

The compressor is heated some by friction between the moving parts. It is also heated by compression which increases the temperature of the vapors as they are compressed and forced into the condenser. This heat must be removed in order to prevent excessive loss of efficiency of the pump and to maintain the lubricating qualities of the oil.

The oil that circulates in the compressor is an excellent remover of heat. It receives the heat from the friction surfaces and carries this heat to the outer surfaces of the unit.

To increase this heat removal, many compressors and many domes have metal fins on their outer surfaces. Some even use a motor driven fan to force air over the compressor to help remove the heat.

When a water-cooled condenser is used, water is often used to cool the compressor or dome. Cast-in water jackets are used on some open compressors while occasionally copper tubing is wound around the hermetic dome to carry coolant.

Hermetic units, with both the motor and compressor inside the dome, in most cases present a special cooling problem. The heat created by both the motor and the compressor must be removed. The motor is often cooled by passing the suction vapors and return oil over the motor windings. Some units circulate the oil through a cooling coil and this cooled oil helps cool the motor-compressor.

5-17 Rotary Compressors

Two types of rotary compressors which are used in the refrigeration field are:
1. Stationary blade type.
2. Rotary blade type.
These two types can also be classified by their cylinder design.

The stationary blade type could be called a concentric cylinder model, and the rotary blade type could be called an eccentric cylinder model. See Fig. 5-24.

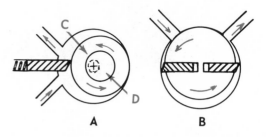

Fig. 5-24. *Two common types of rotary compressors. A-Stationary blade type. B-Rotary blade type. C-Rotary roller which is mounted on the eccentric D.*

The principle of operation of the stationary blade type is that the rotating cylinder is mounted on an eccentric shaft. This rotating roller is sealed at its ends by plates fastened to the ends of the cylinder. As the roller rotates, it leaves a space between the roller and the under part of the blade and the cylinder. This space is filled with the suction vapor from the evaporator coil. This filling action continues until the high part of the roller pushes the blade completely out of the space back into its slot. Then as the high part of the roller continues past the intake opening or port, this vapor charge is trapped in the cylinder

The rotating blade type of rotary compressor mounts the cylinder off center from the shaft in such a way that the shaft roller comes to within .00001 in. of the cylinder at a spot between the intake and exhaust ports. The roller usually has two or four slots in which are mounted two or four blades that rub against the inner surface of the cylinder, as shown in Fig. 5-25.

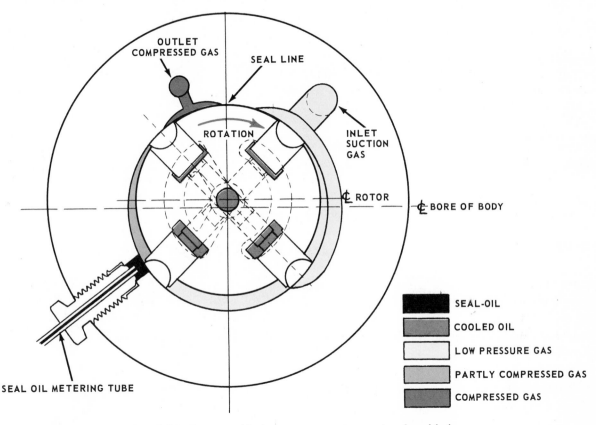

Fig. 5-25. *Rotating blade type compressor using four blades.*

cavity. The roller now squeezes this gas into a smaller and smaller space between the upper part of the blade, the cylinder and the roller. As may be noted, the compressor has almost a full revolution for its compression stroke and likewise for its intake stroke. All the parts must be fitted to extremely close tolerances and clearances. Any scores or clearances will allow the vapors to pass by the roller surface or roller ends and reduce the efficiency of the pump.

The ends of the blades must fit the length of the cylinder with clearances of approximately .0005 in. For pumping efficiency the blades must also have about this same clearance in their slots. Some compressors use two blades 180 deg. apart, as shown in Fig. 5-26.

As the roller rotates, a space is formed between the cylinder, the blade, the roller and the point of contact between the roller and the cylinder. This vapor charge is trapped into smaller and smaller spaces as the next blade moves past the contact point.

A check valve is always required with a rotary compressor. An exhaust valve, usually the reed type, is placed at the exhaust port of the compressor to keep the exhaust vapors from backing into the pump.

5-18 Rotary Cylinder Construction and Fitting

Rotary cylinders are usually made of cast iron. Each cylinder is accurately machine-honed, lapped on the inner surface, and on the ends. The cylinder contains intake and exhaust ports; some models have oil passages for lubrication. This cylinder is usually mounted on an end plate that is part of the main crankcase of the compressor and the refrigerant passages continue into this part. The exhaust valve reed is mounted on the exhaust port outlet of the compressor as close to the compression chamber as possible. Four or more bolts hold the cylinder to the main part of the compressor. There are also one or more steel dowel pins to help align the cylinder on the compressor. After the cylinder is mounted, in the rotating blade type, snugly on the back plate, the cylinder is moved by tapping it slightly until the cylinder binds on the roller. A light tap is then used to relieve the binding and the bolts are tightened to their proper torque.

In the stationary blade type compressor, the cylinder is mounted snugly, and then the shaft is turned and the cylinder is shifted until there is an equal amount of resistance for the complete revolution. Then the cylinder bolts are tightened (torqued).

5-19 Rotor Construction

In the rotating blade type compressor, the rotor is a fixed part of the shaft. Its length must be accurate to .0005 in. It cannot have any scores on the outer surface.

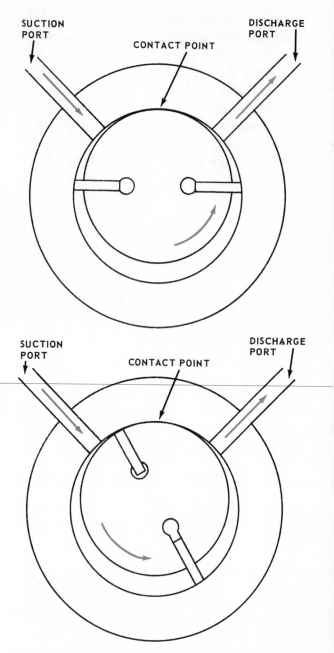

Fig. 5-26. Rotating blade type compressor using two blades. Note the direction of rotation of the blades and the direction of flow of the refrigerant vapor, as it is drawn from the suction line and compressed into the condenser.

Its slots must be free from burrs and they must be true. The blades are lapped to fit the width and length of the slots. Usually the slots are on a radius to the center of the shaft, but one company puts the slots at an angle to prevent the blades from touch-

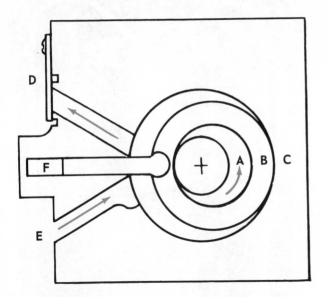

Fig. 5-27. Stationary blade compressor with blade attached to bushing mounted on revolving eccentric. A-Eccentric shaft. B-Bushing. C-Cylinder. D-Exhaust valve. E-Inlet port. F-Blade.

ing the cylinder until the compressor has almost reached its operating speed, thus reducing the starting load.

In the stationary blade type of compressor, the rotor is usually a roller that accurately fits the eccentric, which is a fixed part of the shaft. Some compressors have the blade attached to a bushing to provide a positive means to move the blade in and out of its slot and to provide a more positive leakproof joint between the eccentric and the blade. This construction, Fig. 5-27, puts extra wear on the eccentric surface and the inner surface of the bushing.

5-20 Blade Construction

The rotating blade type compressor usually has two to four blades. These blades may be made of either cast iron, steel, aluminum or carbon. One company made the blade in two pieces to enable the blade contact surface on the cylinder to be the full width of the blade at all times. The efficiency of the compressor depends to a great extent on the condition of the contact edge of the blade with the cylinder. Blades

must have perfectly smooth edges and their length must be the same as the cylinders. Aluminum and carbon blades are used to reduce blade clicking noises and to reduce chattering of the blades.

5-21 Crankshaft Construction

The crankshaft is usually of forged steel construction. It is made of medium carbon steel and the high wear surfaces are case hardened. It usually has two journals for the two main bearings although some have been built with only one main bearing.

On open type compressors the shaft also has the taper shoulder, a woodruff key slot, and the threads for the flywheel and retaining nut. End play of the shaft is usually absorbed by a shoulder on one main bearing journal, and by using the seal spring as an initial load device. It is important that the main bearing journals be straight and smooth. These journals must fit the bearings or bushings within .0005 in. and the shaft must be true throughout its length. V-blocks, a surface plate and a good quality height gauge may be used to check the journals and the shaft for roundness and alignment.

Some of the directly driven compressors have a fitting on the end of the shaft for the mounting of a flexible joint to permit small inaccuracies in motor and compressor alignment.

5-22 Valve Construction

The exhaust valve is usually made of high carbon alloy steel heat treated to give the properties of a flat spring. It is optically flat with no burrs on either surface. The valve seat is usually part of one of the plates that attaches on the end of the cylinder. The valve seat is usually made of the same material as the plate. It is designed to be as close to the inner surface of the plate as practical to keep the clearance pocket as small as possible. Some valve designs use small springs to help in closing the valve and to allow more lift to the valve during those moments that the unit may pump oil.

Intake valves are also usually of the reed type. They are usually held in place with small dowel pins.

Rotary compressors do not use an intake valve as such because of the self-trapping action of the blade or blades of the compressor. However, due to the pressure differences, compressor oil might be forced back into the suction line and into the evaporating coil unless a check valve is installed in the intake passages to keep this oil in the compressor. This check valve is usually a disk valve with a small spring loading. One compressor design uses a ball type check valve.

5-23 Crankshaft Seal Construction

Seals used on open type rotary compressors are similar to the seals used on reciprocating compressors. One design has the shaft seal on the high pressure side of the system. The shaft has a shoulder

Fig. 5-29. *Hermetic rotary compressor. This is a single, stationary blade type compressor.* (Frigidaire Div. - General Motors Corp.)

against which a synthetic rubber washer is impressed and a seal ring is inserted. This seal ring has a pin to keep it from turning on the shaft. Another construction mounts the bellows and ring on the shaft so the ring turns with it, and the matching face is the end of the main bearing.

5-24 Gaskets

Gaskets used on rotary compressors are made of the same materials as used for gaskets on reciprocating compressors. Thickness of the gaskets is not as important as in some reciprocating compressor gaskets, as none are used in critical places in the rotary compressor.

5-25 Lubricating Rotary Compressors

In a rotary compressor it is essential to have a constant film of oil present on the

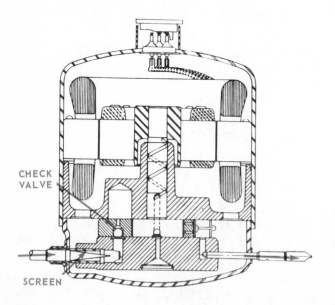

Fig. 5-28. *Hermetic rotary compressor showing an inlet screen and an inlet check valve.*

cylinder, roller, and blade surfaces. As a natural result of the operation of the compressor, the oil feeds through the main bearings into the cylinder. The cylinder is located so the oil level is approximately half way up the main bearings. In larger units and even in some of the smaller units, a forced feed lubrication system is used. Some of the units use a separate oil pump, but some take advantage of the pumping action of the blades moving in and out of their slots.

The lubricant must be carefully selected. It must be the special moisture free, wax free, unfoaming oil of the cor-rect viscosity for the refrigerant being used. There is a tendency for carbon to form around the exhaust valve if there are impurities in the oil.

5-26 Hermetic Rotary Compressors

Rotary compréssors are used extensively in hermetic units. Since the compressors are direct driven, the design must be adapted to the higher speed.

The design of a typical small sealed unit rotary compressor is shown in Fig. 5-28. Vapor enters through a screen, passes the check valve and is compressed

Fig. 5-30. Two-stage centrifugal compressor. 1-Second stage variable inlet guide vane. 2-First stage impeller. 3-Second stage impeller. 4-Water-cooled motor. 5-Base, oil tank, and lubricating oil pump assembly. 6-First stage guide vanes. 7-Labyrinth seal. 8-Crossover connection. 9-Guide vane actuator. 10-Volute casing. 11-Pressure lubricated sleeve bearing.
(Airtemp Div., Chrysler Corp.)

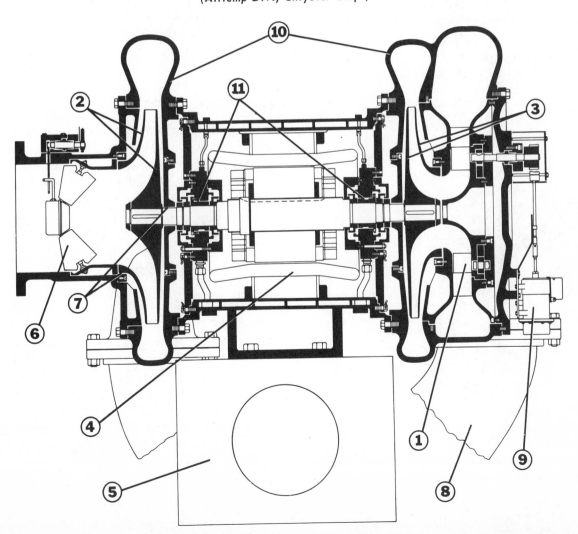

in the rotary compressor, passes the exhaust valve and exits to the condenser.

Fig. 5-29 shows a sealed unit motor-rotary compressor with a stationary blade compressor.

5-27 Centrifugal Compressors

Centrifugal compressors are used successfully in large refrigerating systems. In this type compressor, vapor moved rapidly in a circular path, tends to move outward. This action is called centrifugal force. Vapor is fed into a housing near the center of the compressor. A disk with radial blades (impellers) is rapidly turned in this housing, and the vapor is forced against the outer diameter of the housing. The pressure difference obtained is small so that several of these compressor wheels or impellers are put in series to create sufficient pressure differences and to produce a sufficient volume of vapor. There is considerable similarity in appearance between this type of compressor and a steam turbine or an axial flow air compressor for a gas turbine engine. The centrifugal compressor has the advantage of complete simplicity of operation. There are no valves or pistons and cylinders. The only wearing parts are the main bearings. Since the pumping efficiency of these compressors increases with speed, these units operate at quite high speeds. The impeller arrangement in a centrifugal compressor is shown in Fig. 5-30.

5-28 Stator Construction

The stator or casing of a centrifugal compressor is usually made of cast iron. It has a varying radius inside to adapt itself to the gas pickup of the impellers. The casing (cylinder) contains the main bearings, the oil pressure producing pump, and the intake and exhaust ports for the gases. It also holds the shaft seal where the shaft protrudes from the casing for the power drive attachment, if an external motor is used.

5-29 Rotor Construction

The rotor or impeller of the centrifugal compressor is keyed to the compressor shaft. It is made of cast iron or steel and is specially designed to move the vapors without exceeding gas velocity limits and without vapor trapping pockets. A typical rotor is shown in Fig. 5-31.

5-30 Review of Safety

Prior to running a compressor, make certain all nuts and bolts have been carefully torqued to the prescribed tension so that the part will not leak under high pressure. Always pull on a wrench (instead of push) to prevent possible slippage of the wrench which could cause rounded corners on nuts or bolts and possible injury to your hands. It is recommended that a hoist be used in lifting compressors which weigh over 60 lbs. Always use leg muscles when

INTAKE

EXHAUST

Fig. 5-31. Impeller (rotor) from a centrifugal compressor. (Part 3, shown in the drawing, Fig. 5-30.)

lifting objects; never use back muscles. Make certain that all connections are tightened prior to operating a compressor for efficiency check so that fittings will not separate under high pressures. Make certain no oil is spilled on the floor. Before operating open type compressors be sure the flywheel and pulley are in alignment.

5-31 Test Your Knowledge, Chapter 5

1. What is the purpose of a compressor?
2. What is gained by using a multiple cylinder reciprocating compressor?
3. What is a full floating piston pin?
4. Why must compressor valves be of light weight?
5. How is the crankshaft joint sealed where it leaves the compressor body?
6. Of what materials are compressor pistons made?
7. Why must the clearance pocket volume be kept as small as possible?
8. How are compressor cylinders cooled?
9. What is an internally sprung hermetic compressor?
10. How are hermetic motors usually cooled?
11. Is the stationary blade in a stationary blade rotary compressor really stationary?
12. How many intake strokes and exhaust strokes does the four-blade rotating blade type compressor have per each revolution?
13. Why are the main bearing clearances so closely controlled in a rotary compressor?
14. What is used in a rotary compressor in place of an intake valve?
15. How may the blades be used to help oil circulation in a rotary compressor?
16. Is it possible to have the crankshaft seal on the high pressure side of a rotary compressor?
17. Why are some rotary compressor blades made of carbon?
18. What would happen if the shaft of a compressor were bent?
19. Does a centrifugal compressor have exhaust valves?
20. Does a centrifugal compressor revolve at a higher or lower speed than a reciprocating compressor?
21. What is a connecting rod journal?
22. Explain what is meant by the term volumetric efficiency.
23. Should the crankshaft seal rubbing surfaces be lubricated?
24. Is it possible for large compressors to have two oil pumps?
25. Are some compressors water-cooled?

Chapter 6

REFRIGERANT CONTROLS

A refrigerating unit which operates automatically, must have a device which will reduce the high pressure liquid refrigerant to a low pressure liquid refrigerant in the correct quantities to keep the evaporator unit operating at maximum efficiency, without overloading the compressor. Mechanical or compression system refrigerators use five main types of refrigerant controls. These controls are often referred to in abbreviated terms. As an example, Automatic Expansion Valve is referred to as AEV or AXV. The following chart gives full names of the controls and accepted abbreviations:

FULL NAME OF CONTROL
(A) Automatic Expansion Valve
(B) Thermostatic Expansion Valve
(C) Low Pressure Side Float
(D) High Pressure Side Float
(E) Capillary Tube

The basic principle of these systems is described in Chapter 3.

6-1 Compression System Refrigerant Controls

Modern refrigeration systems are almost completely automatic in operation. Devices have been developed for controlling refrigerant flow into the evaporator and also for controlling the electrical motor which drives the mechanism.

The refrigerant controls may be divided into three principal classes:

1. Control based on pressure changes.
2. The control based on temperature changes.
3. Control based on volume or quantity changes. A combination of controls may also be used.

Automatic controls are required to maintain the temperature in the refrigerated space within specific limits. Automatic motor controls are explained in Chapter 7.

Some popular temperature ranges desired are:

1. For fresh food storage the temperatures are usually maintained at 35 45 deg. F.

ABBREVIATION
AEV - AXV
TEV - TXV
LSF
HSF
Cap. Tube

2. For frozen food storage, usual temperature is between -10 and 0 deg. F.
3. For comfort cooling the temperatures are usually maintained at 10 to 12 deg. F. below the ambient temperature.

6-2 Automatic Expansion Valve Principles

An automatic expansion valve (AEV) or pressure controlled expansion valve is a refrigerant control operated by the low side pressure of the system, its purpose is to throttle the liquid refrigerant in the liquid line down to a constant pressure on the low pressure side. The letters AEV are often used as the identifying initials for the valve. The valve may also be identified as an AXV valve.

The action of the valve is similar to a spray nozzle. While the compressor is running, the liquid refrigerant is sprayed into the evaporator unit tubing. Because the evaporator is never filled with liquid refrigerant, but rather a mist or fog, a system using an automatic expansion valve is sometimes called a "dry" system. Chapter 3 describes the basic prinicple of this type system.

6-3 Automatic Expansion Valve Design

The pressure method illustrated in Fig. 6-1, shows a flexible bellows connected to the linkage of a needle valve with evaporator pressure P_2 on the inside and with atmospheric or confined gas pressure P_1 on the outside. F_1 spring force tends to open the valve while spring force F_2 tends to close the valve. From the illustration, it may be seen that, as the pressure in the evaporator decreases, the differences in pressures will force the bellows toward the valve body. As it is attached to the needle, it will open the needle valve, and some liquid refrigerant will spray into the coil which, as it evaporates at the constant low pressure, keeps the evaporator and cabinet temperature within its design limits.

This opening of the expansion valve occurs only when the compressor is running because this is the only time the pressure is reduced which causes it to operate. The expansion valve cannot flood the low side when the compressor is running, because, as soon as the evaporating refrigerant liquid spray and vapor reaches the end of the evaporator tubing, the motor control (sensitive bulb) located there will cool and open the switch and stop the motor, and the low side pressure will then immediately build up enough to close the expansion valve.

These valves are adjustable to permit the opening of the needle valve over a varying range of pressures. Expansion valve adjustments must be made for varying altitudes as their operation is influenced by atmospheric pressure (P_1). An increase in altitude, which causes a decrease in atmospheric pressure, will require screwing in the adjusting screw to make up for the decreased atmospheric pressure. Also different refrigerants require different expansion valve settings because their evaporating pressures are different.

Automatic expansion valves are made in a variety of designs. The flexible member may be made either as a diaphragm or as a bellows, usually of phosphor bronze, and may be soldered or brazed to the valve body. The flexible elements must move in and out millions of times without loss of flexibility.

The body of the valve is usually drop forged brass although some are cast. These bodies must be seepage (leak) proof.

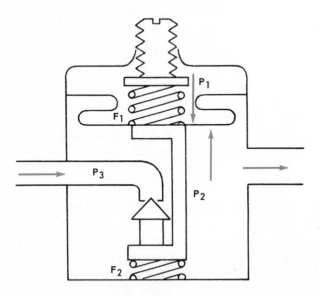

Fig. 6-1. Diagram of an automatic expansion valve showing the various pressures within the valve which cause it to operate. P_1–Atmospheric pressure. P_2–Suction or evaporator pressure. P_3–Liquid line pressure. F_1–Adjustable pressure spring. F_2–Nonadjustable spring.

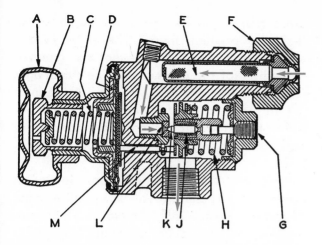

Fig. 6-2. *Diaphragm type automatic expansion valve.* *A—Rubber cap. B—Adjusting screw. C—Adjusting spring. D—Diaphragm. E—Screen. F—Inlet flare nut. G—Factory adjustment. H—Spring. J—Spring. K—Valve needle. L—Valve seat. M—Guide pin. Red arrows show the direction of flow of the refrigerant.* (American Standard Controls Div.)

The liquid inlet is either a soldered connection, a standard flange connection, or a pipe thread. A screen is usually located in this inlet, and it is designed for easy removal. This screen is made of brass wire of 60 to 100 mesh, (60 to 100 openings in one inch).

An AEV with the double spring arrangement on the needle to balance the forces

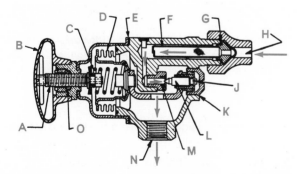

Fig. 6-3. *Bellows type automatic expansion valve.* *A—Adjusting screw. B—Rubber cap. C—Adjustment spring. D—Bellows. E—Gasket. F—Screen. G—Shipping plug. H—Liquid refrigerant inlet. J—Needle shoulder. K—Seating plug. L—Needle. M—Needle valve seat. N—Refrigerant outlet. O—Packing gland. Arrows show the direction of flow of refrigerant through the valve.*

and to give a smoother control of the flow of the refrigerant is shown in Fig. 6-2.

It is important to remember that the same weight of liquid refrigerant should flow by the expansion valve needle, as the weight of gas pumped by the compressor. In other words, this means the valve capacity should equal the pump capacity. One must be careful to use a one ton capacity valve with a one ton capacity condensing unit. An under capacity valve tends to starve an evaporator (not enough refrigerant can get through). An over-capacity valve will tend to allow too much refrigerant into the evaporator each time it opens (this causes sweat backs or frost backs down the suction line).

6-4 Bellows Type Automatic Expansion Valve

A bellows type automatic expansion valve is illustrated in Fig. 6-3. The body is made of special alloys. The valves usually have softer seats than the needles to eliminate as much as possible the wearing of a shoulder on the needle (usually Stellite needles and Monel metal seats). The spring (C) is attached at both ends. It can be adjusted for either pressure or tension, thus eliminating a spring inside the refrigerant space. The needle (L) is mounted in a ball and socket to insure full seating by allowing the needle to align with the seat (M). The bellows (D), made of special brass, is flexible and is soldered to both the body and the disk. This bellows is made of stock .005 to .010 in. thick. It is carefully made in a series of rolling operations. The liquid line is usually 1/4 in. outside diameter (OD) and is fastened to the valve (H) by a special nut permitting easy removal of the screen. Note how the external surface of the bellows is sealed at (O) and (B) to insure that moisture will not enter. If moisture enters it may freeze on the bellows and interfere with the accurate operation of the valve. The valves may be attached to

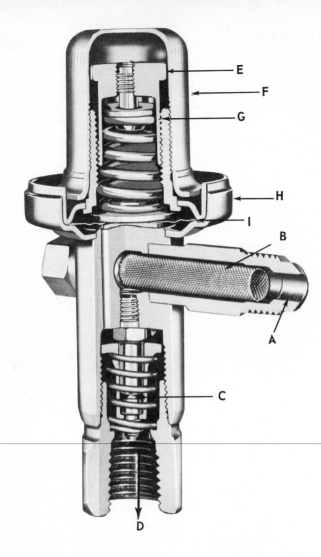

side. Metal guards are placed against the disks to protect them. The valve is designed with stops to prevent too great a movement of the diaphragm. The diaphragm is placed into the body recess; the cap is put in place, and the assembly is soldered. Note that the diaphragm has concentric corrugations (ripples) to improve its flexibility.

Fig. 6-4A shows an external view of an automatic expansion valve with the word IN marked on the inlet port to insure proper installation. Its capacity when used with R-12 refrigerant, is marked on the cap.

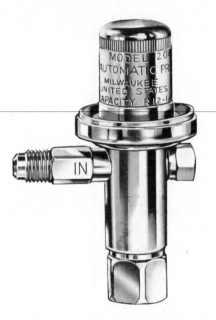

Fig. 6-4. Diaphragm type automatic expansion valve. A—Liquid refrigerant inlet. B—Screen. C—Refrigerant needle and seat. D—Refrigerant outlet to the evaporator. E—Valve adjustment. F—Bonnet. G—Adjustment spring. H—Valve housing. I—Control diaphragm.

Fig. 6-4A. External view of an automatic expansion valve. Note the refrigerant designation on the cap, and the word IN marked on the inlet to show the proper flow direction. (Controls Co. of America)

the evaporator cooling coil either by means of threaded fittings or by a two-bolt flange. Flanges sealed with lead gaskets are usually preferable.

The automatic expansion valve is used chiefly on domestic air conditioning units, vending machines, and as a replacement for capillary tubes.

6-5 Diaphragm Type Automatic Expansion Valve

A diaphragm type automatic expansion valve is illustrated in Fig. 6-4. Note that the diaphragm has two disks; one on each

Another diaphragm expansion valve design is shown in Fig. 6-5. The diaphragm movement is limited by the body and the cap. The diaphragm assembly is fastened to the body of the valve by threads. The cap or cover plate, protecting the pressure adjustment, is tightly fitted over the entire assembly. It slips off to make an adjustment on the valve. The diaphragm has a disk on its low pressure side. This disk presses on a pin that moves the ball valve away from the seat. When the low side pressure increases, the diaphragm moves against the adjustment springs, and this

not need great starting torque or power. Capillary tube systems have this property of balancing pressures during the off cycle.

Because automatic expansion valves do

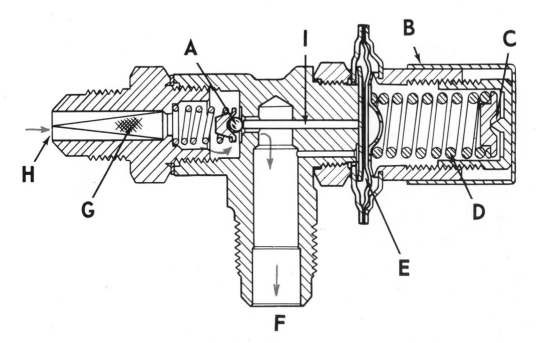

Fig. 6-5. Drawing which shows parts and operation of an automatic expansion valve. A—Valve (ball) and seat. B—Metal cap. C—Adjusting screw. D—Adjusting spring. E—Diaphragm. F—Outlet to evaporator (low pressure). G—Screen. H—Liquid refrigerant inlet (High pressure). I—Valve operating pin. Arrows indicate the direction of flow of refrigerant through the expansion valve.
(American – Standard Controls Div.)

allows the spring by the ball valve to push the ball valve against the seat. The inlet is a 1/4 in. male flare connection, and the outlet is a 3/8 in. male flare.

6-6 Bypass Automatic Expansion Valve

Many motor-compressor units are designed to start under a low load (torque) condition, such as when the low side and high side pressures are equal (balanced). The equal pressures allow the compressor to start without pushing against a pressure. The motor of the motor-compressor can therefore be less powerful, or, it does

seal the refrigerant orifice during the off part of the cycle, the pressures will not balance unless an opening is designed into the valve to permit the pressures to balance. A typical way to do this is to make a V-shaped slot in the valve seat as shown in Fig. 6-6. The bypass or bleeder openings are small enough to not interfere with the operation of the valve during the running part of the cycle. When using this type of expansion valve, the refrigerant charge must be of the correct amount and the evaporator outlet must have an accumulator; otherwise liquid refrigerant will travel down the suction line and cause sweating or frost on the suction line.

6-7 Adjusting Automatic Expansion Valve (AEV)

To cause a refrigerator to operate at a colder temperature, turn the expansion valve out (counterclockwise). This adjustment releases some of the spring pressure or force on the outside of the bellows and requires that a lower pressure be reached before the needle valve will open, to allow liquid refrigerant to flow into the evaporator. To raise the evaporator temperature, turn the adjusting screw in (clockwise) which will increase the spring pressure (force) on the outside of the bellows. The low side pressure must rise slightly to move the needle back against the seat. Since these coils operate at quite a constant pressure, a pressure type motor control cannot be used. A thermostatic motor control must be used when a AEV refrigerant control is used.

6-8 Servicing Automatic Expansion Valve

An automatic expansion valve is subject to the following troubles:
1. The screen may be partially clogged or clogged.
2. The needle and seat may leak.
3. The valve may be out of adjustment.
4. Moisture may have frozen at the orifice.

Chapter 12 explains how to install gauges and how to remove a part from a system.

The screen or filter in the liquid inlet may cause faulty refrigeration if it becomes partially or completely clogged. A completely clogged screen will stop the flow of refrigerant. The evaporator will defrost and the unit will run continuously. A partially clogged screen will cause a partially frosted evaporator. The frost will also appear on the valve close to the liquid line fitting. A leaking valve will cause sweating or frosting of the suction line.

The valve adjustment is easy to check using a compound gauge. See Chapters 12 and 15. Moisture acts like a clogged screen except the unit will start cooling after each

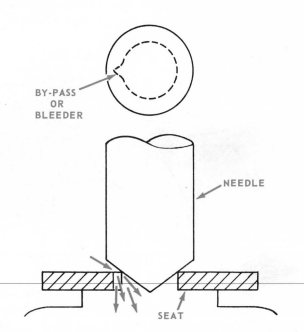

Fig. 6-6. The needle valve and seat used on a by-pass or "bleeder" type automatic expansion valve. On the off cycle the pressures will balance.

warm up (as moisture in the system melts allowing the refrigerant to flow again). Installing a drier in the liquid line will trap the moisture in the drier and remedy the problem.

6-9 Thermostatic Expansion Valve Principles

In the automatic expansion valve, as shown in Paragraphs 6-3; 6-4; and 6-5, the (AEV) rate of refrigerant flow through the valve and into the evaporator is controlled by the pressure in the evaporator coil.

In the thermostatic expansion valve the rate of flow of refrigerant through the valve and into the evaporator is controlled by both the pressure in the evaporator (low side) and the temperature of the evaporator coil outlet. The valve provides

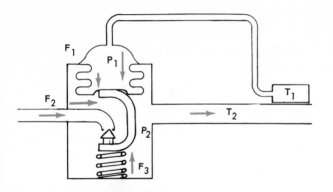

Fig. 6-7. *Diagram of a thermostatic expansion valve showing the various pressures and temperatures within in the valve which cause it to operate. F_1—Vapor pressure force tending to open the valve. F_2—Low side pressure force tending to close the valve. F_3—Spring force tending to close the valve. P_1—Control bulb pressure tending to open the valve. P_2—Suction pressure (low side) tending to close the valve. T_1—Control bulb temperature. T_2—Evaporator refrigerant temperature (low side). The valve opens when F_1 is greater than the combined force of F_2 and F_3. The valve closes when the combined F_1 and F_2 forces are greater than F_1.*

a rather high rate of flow if the evaporator is quite empty (warm) and slows up the flow as it fills (cools) with refrigerant.

The thermostatic expansion valve works on the pressure difference basis; that is, the accumulated pressure difference or force difference between the element bellows and the body sealing bellows as shown

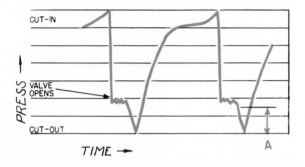

Fig. 6-8. *A thermostatic expansion valve low side pressure-time cycle diagram using a high superheat adjustment.*

    A. *The pressure drop on the low side between the opening of the valve and the cutout point.*

in Fig. 6-7. This valve is often referred to as a TEV or TXV. With the unit running, the refrigerant, (T_1) in the expansion valve thermostatic element is usually about 10 deg. F. warmer than the refrigerant in the evaporator (T_2) producing the different pressures and therefore the different forces. This means that the unit pressure in the element (P_1) is greater than the unit pressure (P_2) in the evaporator coil (both the system and the thermal element usually have the same refrigerant). This temperature difference is often described as the superheat of the bulb over the refrigerant temperature inside the coil. It should be noted that as the temperatures increase or decrease the pressures will increase or decrease accordingly.

When the compressor stops, the low side pressure and the element pressure tend to equalize. The total expansion valve internal force (F_2) plus (F_3) overpowers the element force (F_1), and the needle is forced firmly into the seat stopping the flow of refrigerant. The needle will stay closed until the element force builds up enough to overcome the low side force. This valve opening action can only happen when the unit is running. The closing of the valve while the compressor is idle prevents the flooding of the low side (if the valve is adjusted correctly).

With the adjustment turned to enable the needle to seat itself easier while the unit is running, the needle will close even though there is a greater temperature difference (about 15 deg. F. temperature difference) between the refrigerant in the coil and that in the bulb, as shown in Fig. 6-8. The evaporator coil refrigerant liquid will not reach the bulb location in this case, because the low pressure vapor only will be cold enough to reduce the element temperature and therefore the pressure to the closing point. The coil will be starved and the needle will shut off before the coil becomes full of liquid refrigerant droplets.

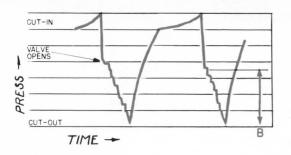

Fig. 6-9. A thermostatic expansion valve low side pressure-time cycle diagram using a low superheat adjustment.

B. The pressure drop on the low side between the opening of the valve and the cutout point.
Note: compare B with A, in Fig. 6-8, to understand how the superheat adjustment controls the evaporator (low side) pressure.

When the adjustment is turned in one or two revolutions to move the needle away from the seat, the temperature of the con-

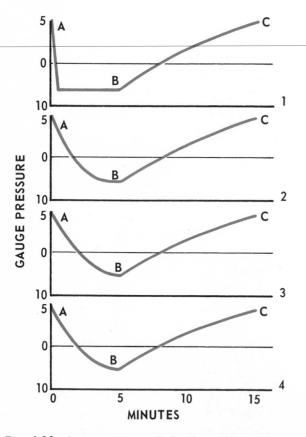

Fig. 6-10. A comparison of the low side pressure-time cycles for various refrigerant controls.
1. Automatic (pressure) expansion valve.
2. Low side float.
3. High side float.
4. Thermostatic expansion valve.

trol element refrigerant will become closer to the temperature of the evaporator coil refrigerant (5 to 7 deg. F.) as shown in Fig. 6-9. The coil must now become more than full of liquid refrigerant droplets to bring the temperature (pressure) difference down to this value. The coil will be completely flooded, and some liquid droplets may even go into the suction line causing a sweating or frosting of the suction line. This adjustment is sensitive and should never be turned more than one-quarter of a turn at a time.

Some thermostatic expansion valves use diaphragms instead of bellows. In this case, the valve is closed when the unit is idle by means of springs working in favor of the low side pressure pressing on one side and against the element pressure on the other side. Fig. 6-10 illustrates the low side pressure behavior during one cycle when the various refrigerant controls are used.

Chapter 3 describes the basic principles of a TEV system.

6-10 Thermostatic Expansion Valve Design

The thermostatic expansion valve is the leading multiple evaporator system refrigerant control. This control eliminates the trouble with oil binding experienced with some low side float installations, and also the presence of large quantities of liquid refrigerant in the evaporator.

The theory of the thermostatic expansion valve is as follows: a power element, consisting of a capillary tube, a bellows and thermostatic bulb apparatus-hermetically sealed, is mounted into a typical expansion valve. It controls the valve in a way which keeps the evaporator coil filled with refrigerant rather than maintaining a definite low side pressure as in the case with the automatic expansion valve. The thermal expansion valve does not regulate the low side pressure, but rather controls

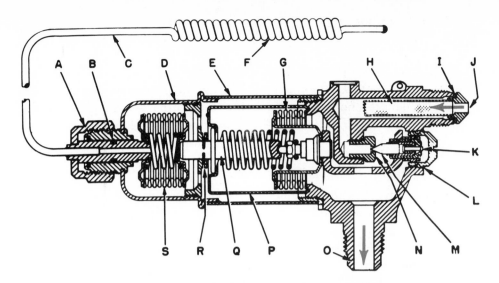

Fig. 6-11. Sectional view of a thermostatic expansion valve. A—Adjusting nut.
B—Seal ring. C—Capillary tube. D—Bellows housing. E—Housing spacer. F—Thermal bulb. G—Body bellows. H—Screen. I—Gasket. J—Refrigerant inlet. K—Needle pin. L—Sealed fitting. M—Needle. N—Seat. O—Evaporator coil connection. P—Inner spacer. Q—Spacer rod. R—Snap ring. S—Thermal bellows.
(American-Standard Controls Div.)

the filling of the evaporator with refrigerant. The pumping action of the compressor establishes the low side pressure. Fig. 6-11 illustrates a bellows type thermostatic expansion valve. This valve has an advantage over the low side float multiple system, in that several different temperatures may be obtained without using any other special device. This action may be accomplished by starving the coils in the cabinets desired to be kept at a warmer temperature.

The construction of this valve consists of a brass body into which the liquid line and evaporator coil are connected. The needle and seat are inside the body. The needle is joined to a flexible metal bellows or diaphragm. This bellows, in turn, is actuated by a nonheat conducting rod connected at the other end to a sealed bellows (power element), which is joined to the thermostatic bulb by means of a capillary tube. Fig. 6-12 shows the refrigerant behavior in the element. This thermostatic element is usually charged with the same refrigerant that is used in the system. Each manufacturer has a code for identifying the refrigerant with which the thermostatic element is charged. Some use letters such as S, M, F, etc., indicating

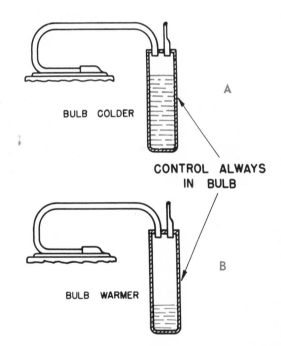

Fig. 6-12. Effect of temperature on the thermal element of a thermostatic expansion valve.

A. Control bulb is cold and a considerable quantity of control refrigerant is shown as a condensed liquid in the bulb.

B. Control bulb is warmer and the control refrigerant has evaporated and is exerting pressure in the expansion valve which causes it to admit more refrigerant into the evaporator coil.

Note that there is enough refrigerant in the control bulb to insure liquid refrigerant in the control bulb at all times.

sulphur dioxide (R-764), methyl chloride (R-40), or Freon 12 (R-12). Others use colors or numbers to denote charge. Some valves are marked with the refrigerant number. The valve is sealed to prevent moisture seeping into any part. A screen or strainer is always located between the liquid line connection and the orifice to keep dirt away from the needle and seat,

as shown in Fig. 6-13. Some air conditioning systems use as many as six of these thermostatic expansion valves on one evaporating coil.

Another type thermostatic expansion valve is shown in Fig. 6-13A. It is of the single diaphragm type. Rods carry the diaphragm action to the needle. The liquid inlet is on the left, and the evaporator coil

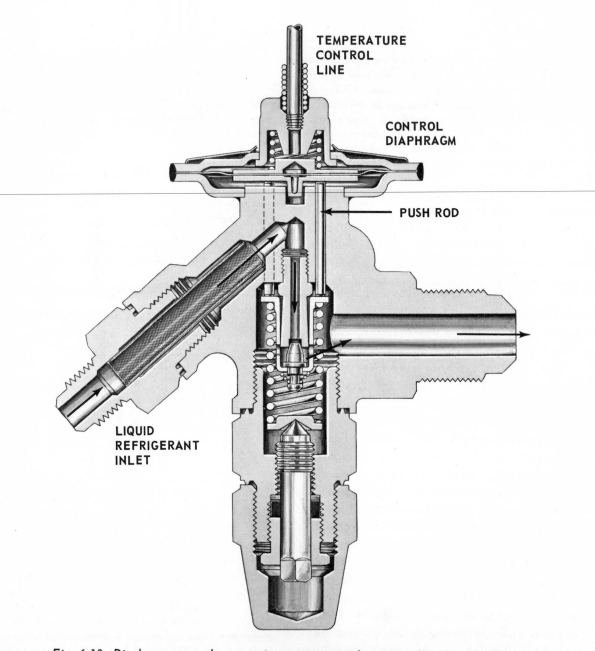

Fig. 6-13. Diaphragm type thermostatic expansion valve using flared inlet and outlet connections. (Controls Co. of America)

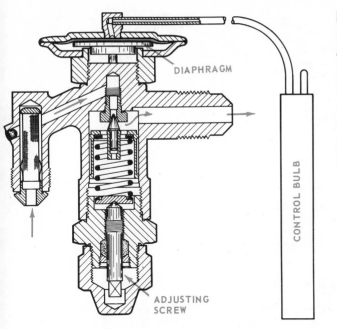

Fig. 6-13A. *Diaphragm type thermostatic expansion valve. The control bulb pressure operates on the top surface of the diaphragm. As the control bulb temperature increases, the pressure on the top of the diaphragm tends to open the valve allowing refrigerant to enter the evaporator coil. Note the screen at the liquid line and the direction of refrigerant flow through the valve.* (Sporlan Valve Co.)

begins to cool. As soon as the suction line, to which the power bulb is attached, becomes cooled sufficiently, the pressure in the bulb decreases, due to condensation of its refrigerant. This reduces the pressure against the diaphragm. The action causes a movement of the diaphragm, and the expansion valve is shut off, leaving the evaporator coil filled with liquid refrigerant and vapor. The refrigerating mechanism now

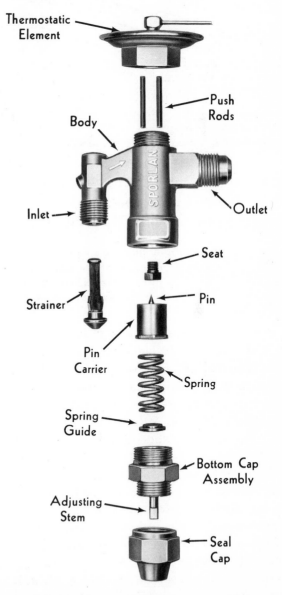

Fig. 6-14. *Parts of a thermostatic expansion valve similar to the valve shown in Fig. 6-13. In this valve the thermostatic element is threaded on the body of the valve.* (Sporlan Valve Co.)

connection is on the right. An exploded view of a similar valve is shown in Fig. 6-14. The pin or needle is made of Stellite, seat Monel metal, and body brass. Note that the inlet flare surface is mounted on the screen.

The proper installation of the thermostatic expansion valve is necessary to obtain satisfactory service. The bulb of the thermostatic expansion valve should be located at the outlet of the evaporator coil. The operation of the valve is simple. When the bulb warms, some of the refrigerant in the bulb vaporizes and builds up pressure in the power element by means of the capillary tube connection, and the diaphragm moves toward the body. This forces the needle to move away from the seat admitting liquid refrigerant into the evaporator coil. This action continues until the whole coil is cooled, and the suction line

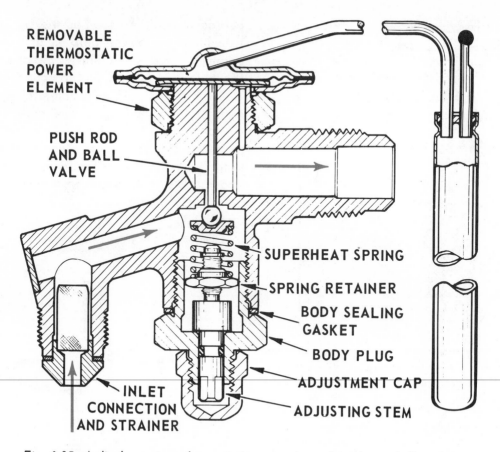

REMOVABLE THERMOSTATIC POWER ELEMENT

PUSH ROD AND BALL VALVE

SUPERHEAT SPRING

SPRING RETAINER

BODY SEALING GASKET

BODY PLUG

ADJUSTMENT CAP

ADJUSTING STEM

INLET CONNECTION AND STRAINER

Fig. 6-15. A diaphragm type thermostatic expansion valve. Note a ball is used as the valve in place of the usual needle. Direction of flow of refrigerant through the expansion valve is indicated by arrows.
(American - Standard Controls Div.)

lowers or decreases the low side pressure, since it continues to run until the pressure motor control or thermostatic motor control cuts out, at the desired temperature. When the condensing unit stops, the thermostatic expansion valve, if it were still open, would close because the low side pressure begins to build up. This closing action is important; otherwise the evaporator coil would become flooded with liquid refrigerant. Fig. 6-15 shows a diaphragm type valve with a ball type valve while Fig. 6-16 shows the external appearance of the same valve.

The needles are usually made of Stellite, Hastelloy, or stainless steel, while the seats are made of stainless steel, Monel or brass.

The needles are usually sharp pointed

OUTLET

INLET

SEALING CAP

Fig. 6-16. Exterior view of the thermostatic expansion valve shown in Fig. 6-15. The valve may be adjusted after removing the sealing cap.

cones but spherical valves (balls) and flat orifice closers may also be used.

The conical needle is popular for small capacity valves, while the ball bearing needle or the flat needle is used in larger valves. Fig. 6-17 illustrates a large capacity needle and seat.

Fig. 6-18. Thermostatic expansion valve with adjustment in the body of the valve.
(Alco Valve Co.)

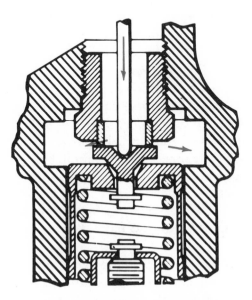

Fig. 6-17. Large capacity thermostatic valve orifice. Note that in this valve flat surfaces form both the valve and the valve seat. The arrows indicate the direction of flow of refrigerant through the valve seat mechanism.

Most of these valves are equipped with an adjustment. One of the adjustments is designed to move the power element against the expansion valve bellows. If it is turned out or counterclockwise, the power element will be moved away from the expansion valve bellows. This action will "starve" the evaporator coil or result in closing the needle before the coil becomes full of liquid refrigerant.

Turning the adjustment in or clockwise will increase the amount of refrigerant allowed to flow into the evaporator.

Another type valve has the adjusting screw in the body of the valve, Fig. 6-18. In this type the evaporator coil will receive more refrigerant if the adjusting screw is turned out, and the coil will be "starved"

if the adjusting screw is turned in.

There are four types of charges which are given the power element of the thermostatic expansion valve:
1. Normal charge.
2. Vapor (gas) charge.
3. Liquid charge.
4. Cross charge.

In the normal charged power element the quantity of refrigerant is sufficient so there is always some liquid refrigerant in the element regardless of its temperature.

In the gas charged element, little or no liquid refrigerant is present in the element. Its energy comes from changing of the refrigerant vapor pressure with temperature change. The liquid charged element contains 100 percent liquid at all times.

In the cross charged element a small quantity of liquid refrigerant is charged into the power unit; however, at the higher temperature all of the liquid will be evaporated and the power element will then respond the same as a gas charged unit.

6-11 Normal Power Element

The thermostatic element of the thermostatic expansion valve is accurately made. It is essential that the element be charged with the same refrigerant as is in the system. This enables the valve to maintain a constant superheat setting even though the low side pressures and temperatures change as shown in Fig. 6-19. The term "superheat" as used in this paragraph refers to the difference in temperature between the vapor in a saturated condition as compared to the temperature of the same vapor at a temperature above the saturated condition.

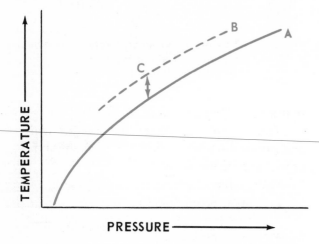

Fig. 6-19. Constant superheat setting of a thermostatic expansion valve. A—Vapor pressure curve of the refrigerant in the evaporator coil. B—Vapor pressure curve of the refrigerant in the bulb at the same moment. C—Superheat difference (normally 10 deg. F.).

One problem encountered with the thermostatic expansion valve is that with a normal refrigerant charge in the thermostatic power element (one half liquid and one half vapor) the element will overload the condensing unit when the refrigerating machine starts up after a long shut down period. For example, if a 1 hp unit has been idle for several days, and the cabinet, the evaporator coil, and the condensing unit are all at ambient temperature (room temperature) when the unit is started, the low side pressure will be very high. It will continue to be high as the cabinet slowly cools down. The reason for this long overload is

that the expansion valve will keep the evaporator full of liquid refrigerant whether the coil is at 75 or 0 deg. F. That is, if the evaporator refrigerant is at 75 or 85 deg. F. the expansion valve will open. This prolonged overload may cause the refrigerating unit to fail (motor burn-out, etc.).

Another problem encountered with the normal charged element is that the element may lose its sensitivity, if the liquid refrigerant collects at the bellows or diaphragm. For example, if the valve body is located in a sheltered spot on the coil, and the bellows or diaphragm end of the element becomes colder than the bulb, all of the liquid refrigerant will settle at the bellows or diaphragm. The bulb, being filled with gas cannot respond to coil temperature changes.

6-12 Gas Charged Power Element

One way to eliminate overloading of a condensing unit during a "pull-down" from warm conditions, is to use a thermal unit having a small charge of refrigerant. This charge is small enough so that at a certain predetermined temperature, all of the refrigerant in the bulb is in a vapor state, and the element pressure will not increase above this point. For example, if just enough refrigerant is put in the element to produce a maximum pressure of 40 psig regardless of how warm the bulb becomes, the element pressure will never exceed this pressure. When the low side pressure exceeds this pressure, the valve will not open, as shown in Fig. 6-20. With the vapor charged power element, there is greater tendency for the small amount of liquid in this type of element to collect at the bellows or diaphragm, and the valve to lose its sensitivity.

6-13 Liquid Charged Power Element

For installations where the body of the valve is exposed to colder temperature than the bulb, a liquid charged element has been developed. This element is completely filled with liquid refrigerant. Under no conditions can the sensitive bulb be emptied of liquid. This valve operates under hydraulic principles at its lower temperatures.

6-14 Cross Charged Power Element

The vapor charged element and the liquid charged element, are each designed for a temperature range of about 30 to 40 deg. F. This limitation means that different expansion valves must be used for air conditioning, normal refrigeration ranges and low temperature ranges. The serviceman must be sure to use the correct capacity valve, also one designed for the temperature range of the unit.

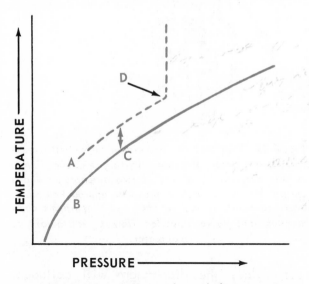

Fig. 6-20. Action of a gas charged thermostatic expansion valve thermal element. A—Maximum pressure in the thermostatic element. B—Path of the low side pressure and temperature as the unit "pulls-down." C—Path of thermal element pressure and temperature below maximum pressure setting until constant superheat setting has reached D.

A normal charged power element is in use which has a combination of volatiles (liquids and vapors) in the element. The mixture is carefully prepared to maintain a constant superheat over a much larger

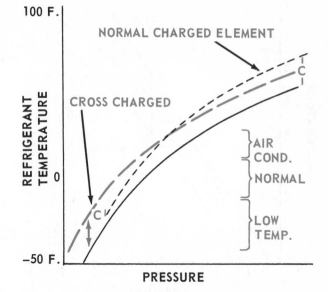

Fig. 6-21. Graph showing constant superheat of cross charged power element which is designed to be used for all 3 applications; low temperature, normal and air conditioning; as compared to a normal charged power element during wide temperature ranges. The red dotted line shows the degrees of superheat for a cross charged thermostatic power element, and the black dotted line shows the degrees of superheat for the normal charge. Notice how C, normal charge, changes as the temperature drops, and how C^1, cross charge, remains constant as the temperature drops.

range of temperature. Fig. 6-21 shows the difference in the superheat curve of the cross charged element as compared to a normal charged element.

Another type of liquid charged power element is one which contains a different liquid in the thermal element than that used in the system. The pressure-temperature curve of this refrigerant is such that the valve has high superheat when the coil is warm, and the low side pressures are high. Then as the coil cools and the low side pressure reduces, the superheat setting is reduced as shown in the graph, Fig. 6-22. This type of liquid charged element is used mostly in low temperature installations. The valves are usually liquid charged valves. You must be accurate in choosing the correct valve and the correct size valve for each installation.

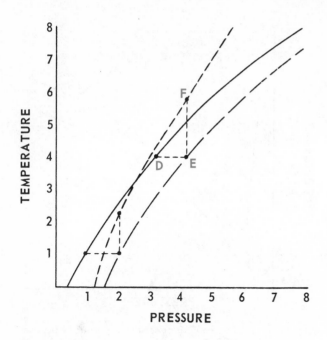

Fig. 6-22. *Graphical presentation of a cross charged element which is designed for application within a specific temperature range. It provides a rapid pull down and is used for normal refrigeration. Superheat setting at the top end is quite wide to prevent flooding of the unit. D—Given evaporator pressure and corresponding saturation temperature. E—Evaporator pressure plus the equivalent superheat spring pressure. F—Corresponding remote bulb and power assembly pressure. F-E—Superheat setting in degrees Fahrenheit for this evaporator pressure and particular superheat spring setting.*

6-15 Pressure Limiters

Another method used to prevent overloading the condensing unit is to put a collapsible element between the thermal element mechanism and the needle mechanism. This small sealed bellows is designed to collapse at a certain force. This may come from either the element pressure or the low side pressure. Therefore, if this collapsible element is designed to collapse at 40 psi of the diaphragm or bellows, the needle will close if the low side pressure ever exceeds this amount regardless of the element temperature or pressure. The operation is similar to that shown in Fig. 6-20. This type thermostatic expansion valve is shown in Fig. 6-23.

A gas charged collapsible element can also be used to provide a limit to the pressure which will open the valve. When the pressure in the low side exceeds a certain

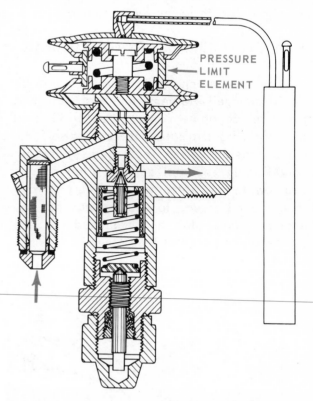

Fig. 6-23. *Thermostatic expansion valve with pressure limit element. Pressure limiting is accomplished in this element by means of two diaphragms and a spring. Whenever suction pressure approaches motor overload point, spring between two diaphragms compresses and valve throttles flow of refrigerant to evaporator.*

set value, the diaphragm will collapse. Fig. 6-24 illustrates such a TEV. The gas used is a noncondensable gas and obeys Charles' and Boyle's Laws only.

An example of how the pressure limiting device prevents a long running time at excessive low side pressures when the refrigerator is warm, is shown in Fig. 6-25. The cycle record shows a pressure drop from over 50 psi to 10 psi in just a few minutes. The unit then ran for two hours before a thermostat shut it off.

Another type of pressure limiter ther-

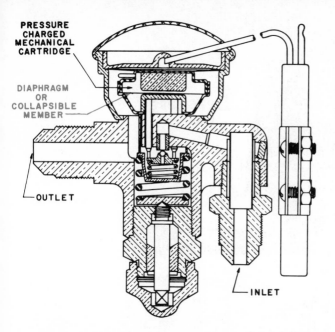

PRESSURE
CHARGED
MECHANICAL
CARTRIDGE

DIAPHRAGM
OR
COLLAPSIBLE
MEMBER

OUTLET

INLET

Fig. 6-24. A diaphragm type thermostatic expansion valve with collapsible element mounted between thermal element and valve. (Alco Valve Co.)

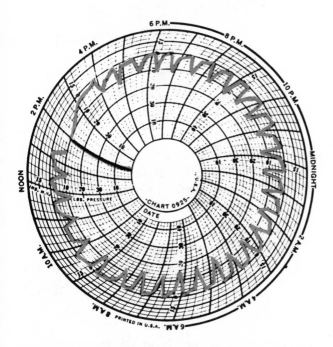

Fig. 6-25. A 24 hour record of the pressure-time relationship for food freezer as it is cycled beginning with warm condition at 2 P.M. The freezer is equipped with pressure limited thermostatic expansion valve and thermostatic motor control. Note quick reduction of pressure until valve opened at 10 P.M. (Sporlan Valve Co.)

mostatic expansion valve is shown in Fig. 6-26. This valve has an adjustable pressure limiter (A). Above a certain set pres-

sure setting at (A) the spring above the diaphragm will compress instead of the valve needle being opened. The liquid inlet is at (B) and the evaporator coil connection is at (C). The capillary tube and thermal bulb is not shown but the connection is at

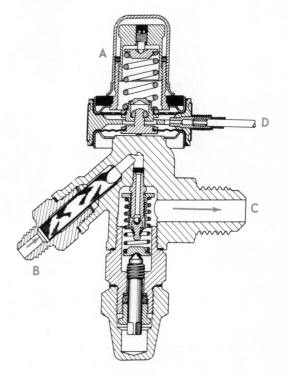

Fig. 6-26. Thermostatic expansion valve with adjustable pressure limiter device.
    A. Pressure limiter adjustment.
    B. Liquid refrigerant inlet.
    C. Evaporator coil connection.
    D. Thermal bulb connection.

(D). Another spring loaded pressure limiter is shown in Fig. 6-27. The pressure limiter assembly is shown in Fig. 6-28. It will stay as a rigid rod, and open and close the valve until the pressures in the low pressure side and in the thermal element are greater than the pressure of the spring.

6-16 Power Element Mounting

The location and the actual mounting of the power element bulb is very important. The bulb must be in good thermal contact

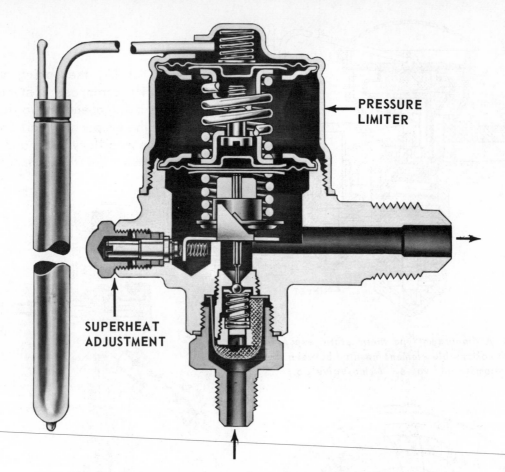

PRESSURE LIMITER

SUPERHEAT ADJUSTMENT

Fig. 6-27. Thermostatic expansion valve with spring loaded pressure limiter.
(American-Standard Controls Div.)

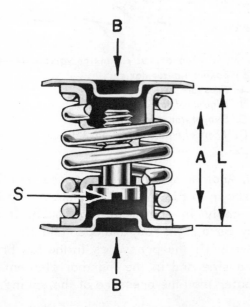

Fig. 6-28. Pressure limiter device used on thermostatic expansion valve shown in Fig. 6-27. Adjusting screw (S) is set to give length (L). When forces at (B) exceed forces (A) spring will be compressed and refrigerant orifice in expansion valve will close.
(American-Standard Controls Div.)

with the evaporator coil outlet as shown in Fig. 6-29. The bulb should be mounted on the top of the suction line so the liquid is close to the suction line. If it is necessary

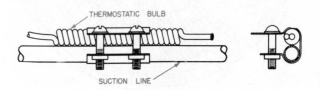

THERMOSTATIC BULB

SUCTION LINE

Fig. 6-29. Correct way to attach thermostatic expansion valve control bulb to suction line. Note that thermal bulb is best mounted in horizontal position and on top of suction line.

to mount the bulb on a vertical suction line, the capillary tube of the bulb should enter from the top of the bulb as shown in Fig. 6-24; never from the bottom. To keep the bulb from being affected by the air or liquid being cooled the bulb should be insulated. Special rubber forms are available to put around the bulb, or friction tape can be used to insulate the bulb so that only the suction line temperature will affect the bulb.

Metal straps, copper, and nonrusting machine screws are usually used to fasten the bulb to the suction line. The bulb must have excellent thermal contact with the suction line. The connection must be clean and tight. You should clean both the suction line and the bulb with steel wool before assembling.

6-17 Thermostatic Expansion Valve Capacities

One type of thermostatic expansion valve has one standard body, but it has an easily replaced needle and seat assembly. These assemblies come in a variety of sizes (orifice sizes). The larger the orifice size the more liquid refrigerant can be fed into the coil per unit of time.

The valves are rated in tons of refrigeration. However, the same orifice usually has three different tonnage capacities. This change in capacity is because the amount of liquid that will flow, depends on the difference between the high pressure on the condensing side and the low pressure, on the low pressure side. Therefore, if the valve is used on an R-12 system, a valve that has a 1/2 ton rating at a 13 psi on the low side pressure on a certain installation will have a 3/4 to 1 ton capacity at 5 in. vacuum on a frozen food unit and only a 1/3 ton capacity at a low side pressure of 40 psi. In the first case there is a 130-13 = 117 lb. pressure difference, assuming 130 psi head pressure. In the second case it is 130+2 1/2 (5 in. vacuum = 2 1/2 lbs.) = 132 1/2 psi pressure difference, and in the last case it is 130-40 = 90 psi pressure difference.

It is important to use a valve of the correct capacity. If the valve orifice is undersize, the coil will be starved regard-less of the superheat setting, and the full capacity of the coil cannot be obtained.

If the orifice is oversize, the valve will "hunt" or surge. When the valve opens, too much refrigerant will pass into the evaporator coil, and the coil will sweat or frost down into the suction line before the thermal element can close the valve. If you try to correct this condition by increasing the superheat setting, the coil will be starved much of the time, and full efficiency cannot be realized.

6-18 Special Thermostatic Expansion Valves

Many different thermostatic expansion valve designs are available.

One type valve combines a distributing tube or manifold in the body of the valve. See Fig. 6-30. This design is used to re-

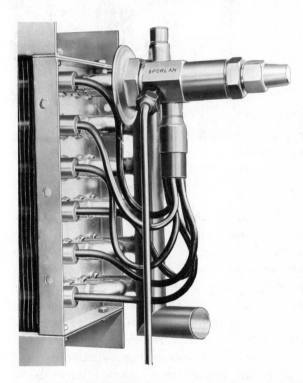

Fig. 6-30. Special thermostatic expansion valve for air conditioning applications. Refrigerant distribution tube or manifold is brazed onto outlet connection of valve. This valve uses an equalizer tube which connects to the suction line and enters under the valve diaphragm. (Sporlan Valve Co.)

duce the pressure drop in a large evaporating coil. It is popular for air conditioning applications. The design must be carefully engineered, as each tube must receive an equal amount of refrigerant.

Fig. 6-31 shows a valve with a multiple outlet, distributor, and an external equalizer.

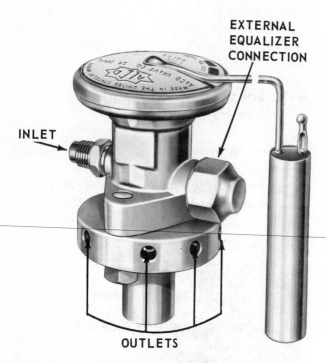

Fig. 6-31. *Thermostatic expansion valve having multiple outlets to evaporating coils. Valve is fitted with connection for an equalizer tube.*
(Alco Valve Co.)

Fig. 6-32 shows a thermostatic expansion valve installed in a normal situation with a 10 deg. F. superheat. It has been shown that when there is an appreciable pressure drop in the evaporator coil, the pressure on the inside of the valve body will be higher than the pressure of the boiling refrigerant near the bulb location. This action tends to starve the evaporator coil due to the higher than normal valve body pressure. See Fig. 6-33. Although the valve is adjusted for a 10 deg. F. superheat, the excessive pressure drop actually results in a 15 deg. F. superheat setting and a starved coil.

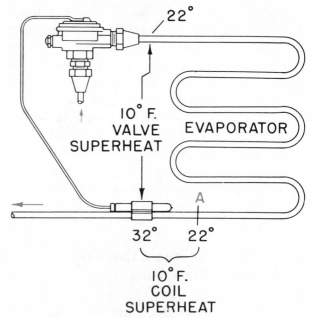

Fig. 6-32. *Normal 10 deg. F. superheat setting. Liquid refrigerant will reach point (A) before valve closes.*

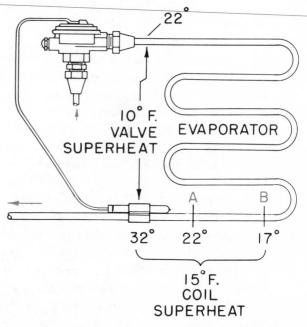

Fig. 6-33. *A "starved" evaporator coil due to pressure drop in evaporator. Liquid reaches point B at 17 deg. F. and vapor warms to 22 deg. F. at which time valve closes.*
(American-Standard Controls Div.)

If a small tube (1/4 in. OD) is connected to the suction line and then tapped into the expansion valve so the pressure under the

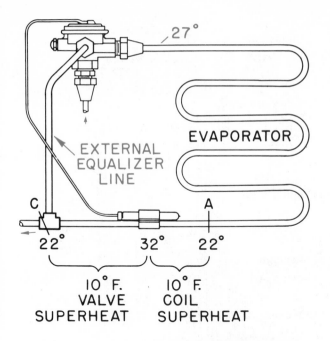

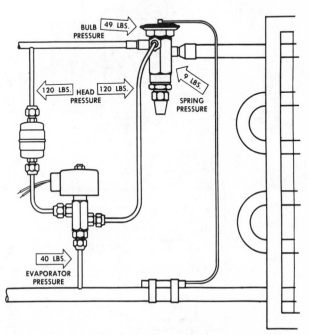

Fig. 6-34. An automatic expansion valve fitted with an equalizer tube. The equalizer tube connects the suction line pressure at the thermal bulb to the underside of the valve bellows or diaphragm (low pressure side). This assumes that the low side pressure operating the valve is the same as the pressure at the thermal bulb. This compensates for any pressure drop through the evaporator.

valve diaphragm is equal to the suction line pressure, as shown in Fig. 6-34, the valve will operate better.

The equalizer tube is connected to the low side pressure side of the bellows or diaphragm. Therefore, even though the low side pressure drop in the coil is high, the pressure operating the valve is the same as the pressure in the suction line at the thermal bulb setting.

It is recommended that this equalizer device be used if there is more than 4 psi existing between the inlet of the evaporator and the outlet.

Another problem encountered with the thermostatic expansion valve is its tendency to open intermittently during the off-cycle because of temperature fluctuations caused by opening and closing the cabinet. To prevent this, one may impose the high side pressure on the valve to force it

closed. A solenoid valve is used to control this pressure. A special solenoid valve connected into the equalizer tubing is shown in Fig. 6-35. The solenoid valve electrical circuit is opened as the motor-compressor circuit opens. The solenoid core falls and closes the equalizer tube to the suction line. The high pressure refrigerant enters

Fig. 6-35. Special solenoid valve used to keep the thermostatic expansion valve tightly closed on off cycle. With driving motor on off cycle, valve opens allowing high pressure to flow up equalizer tube and close valve.

the top of the solenoid valve and passes up the equalizer tube and forces the thermostatic diaphragm up, closing the valve. Fig. 6-36 shows a cross section of a special solenoid pilot control. This arrangement permits using a small solenoid valve to control large capacity systems.

A valve that has been made with an unusual adjustment is shown in Fig. 6-37. This valve uses a needle fastened to a disk and to a ball on a stem, so the same spring that pushes the diaphragm against the element pressure, will force the needle against its seat. The other end of the spring is encased in a washer that is positioned by the adjusting stem. When this adjusting stem is turned in or clockwise, it increases superheat setting or starves the coil. The outlet to the evaporator coil is not shown in the illustration.

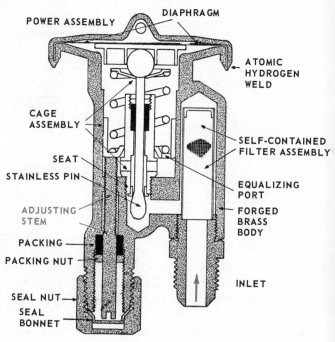

Fig. 6-37. *Thermostatic expansion valve with super-heat adjustment which adjusts spring pressure. When adjusting stem is screwed in, superheat difference will increase.*

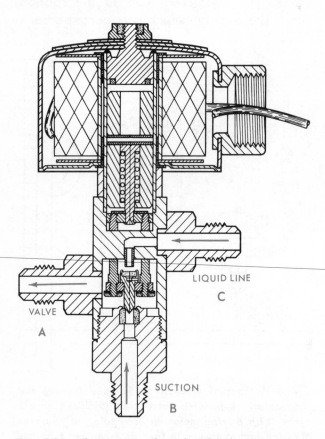

Fig. 6-36. *Three-way solenoid valve used to close thermostatic expansion valve during "off" part of cycle. When compressor is running, connections "suction" and "valve" are connected. When compressor is idle "liquid line" and valve are connected.*

A large capacity valve is shown in Fig. 6-38. It has flanged refrigerant line connections bolted together and gasketed. Instead of a needle and seat, it has a disk valve and seat (B). An equalizer tube connection is shown in the upper right part of the body (A).

When thermostatic expansion valves are used in low temperature installations, the pressures are too low to create enough force to efficiently open and close the valve.

A differential valve which operates on the difference in temperature at two coil positions solves this difficulty. Such a valve is shown in Fig. 6-39. The operating details of this valve are shown in Fig. 6-40. In operation the control bulb (A) will be attached to the suction line. The control bulb (C) will be attached to the evaporator coil. It should be noted that it is the difference in pressure between the two control bulb elements which operates the opening of this expansion valve refrigerant control needle.

6-19 Testing and Adjusting the Thermostatic Expansion Valve

Thermostatic expansion valves sometimes get out of adjustment, also a particular application may require a readjustment of this valve.

A simple method of testing thermostatic expansion valves in the shop as recom-

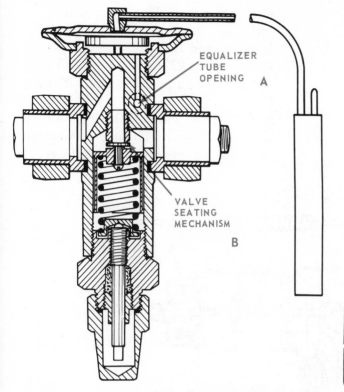

EQUALIZER
TUBE
OPENING
A

VALVE
SEATING
MECHANISM

B

Fig. 6-38. A large capacity thermostatic expansion valve which uses disk type valve and seat. This valve is fitted with an equalizer connection. Note: equalizer tube opening, and valve seating mechanism. (Sporlan Valve Co.)

should be accurate and should be in good condition so that the pointer does not have too much lost motion. A high pressure gauge is recommended in order to show the pressure on the inlet of the valve.

3. A small quantity of finely crushed ice is necessary, and one of the most convenient ways of handling this is to keep it in a thermos bottle with a large size neck. If such a container is completely filled with crushed ice, it will easily last for 24 hours. What-

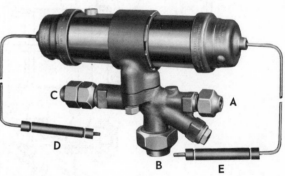

C

D

A

B

E

Fig. 6-39. Differential type thermostatic expansion valve. Note the two control bulbs. A—Refrigerant inlet, high side. B—Refrigerant outlet to the evaporator. C—Anti-surge adjustment. D—Superheat bulb. E—Evaporator coil bulb.

mended by the American Standard Controls Inc., is as follows:

A regular service kit containing the necessary equipment and set up required is shown in Fig. 6-41. The equipment required is as follows:

1. Service cylinder of R-12 or R-22. In the shop a supply of clean dry air at 75 to 100 lbs. pressure can be used in place of the service cylinder. The service cylinder is merely for purpose of supplying pressure, and for this reason the refrigerant used does not have to conform with the valve being tested. In other words, a cylinder of R-12 would be satisfactory for testing with R-22, R-40, or R-12 valves.

2. High pressure and low pressure gauges. The low pressure gauge

ever the container is, it should be completely filled with crushed ice. Do not attempt to make this test with the container full of water and a little crushed ice floating around on the top (32 deg. F., ice floats at the top, while 39 deg. F., water sinks to the bottom).

Proceed as follows to adjust the valve:
1. Connect the valve as shown. The adapter on the expansion valve outlet is to provide a small amount of leakage through the number 80 drill orifice opening. A 10 cu. in. tank is used to reduce pressure fluctuations.

2. Insert the bulb in the crushed ice and allow the bulb to cool.

3. Open the valve on the service drum and be sure the drum is warm enough to build up a pressure of at least 70 lbs. on the high pressure gauge connected in the line to the valve inlet.

4. The expansion valve can now be adjusted. The pressure on the outlet should equal the pressure for the re-

different for various refrigerants as follows:

R-12, Freon 12 . . . . 22 psig
R-22, Freon 22 . . . . 45 psig
R-500 . . . . 29 psig
R-502 . . . . 55 psig

When making the adjustment, be sure there is a small amount of leakage through the low pressure orifice.

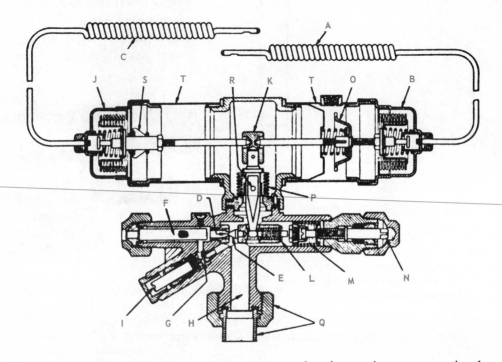

Fig. 6-40. Differential temperature expansion valve designed to meet needs of extremely low temperatures. A—Superheat bulb, B—Superheat power element, C—Evaporator bulb, D—Main valve orifice, E—Main valve needle, F—Strainer, G—Bypass valve orifice, H—Outlet passage, I—Bypass valve adjustment, J—Evaporator power element, K—Operating lever, L—Needle carrier assembly, M—"Anti-surge" spring, N—"Anti-surge" adjustment, O—Factory superheat adjustment, P—Sealing bellows, Q—Forged union connection, R—Operating lever fulcrum, S—Anti-chatter device, T—Stainless steel spacer.
(American-Standard Controls Div.)

frigerant at 22 deg. F. (32-10). The water and ice mixture is 32 deg. F. and the sensitive bulb is also 32 deg. F. If the superheat is to be 10 deg. F. then the temperature of the refrigerant will be 22 deg. F. and the pressure must be adjusted to match this 22 deg. F. temperature. The pressure on the outlet gauge should be

5. Tap the body of the valve lightly in order to determine if the valve is smooth in operation. The needle of the low pressure gauge should not jump more than one pound.

To test the needle for leaks, close the orifice to stop the leakage and determine if the expansion valve closes off tightly. With a good valve the pressure will increase a

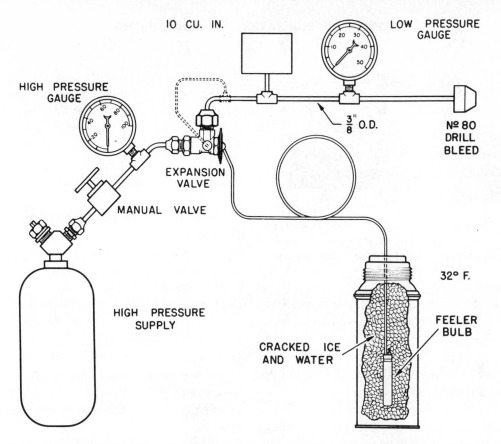

Fig. 6-41. Recommended setup for testing and adjusting thermostatic expansion valve. Note that liquid refrigerant is supplied from storage cylinder. Control bulb is immersed in vacuum bottle filled with cracked ice which gives a known low temperature of 32 deg. F. The bleed hole is made with a No. 80, .0135 in. diameter drill.

few pounds and then either stop or build up slowly. With a leaking valve, the pressure will build up rapidly until it equals the inlet pressure.

The power element may be tested by removing the power element bulb from the crushed ice and warming it up with your

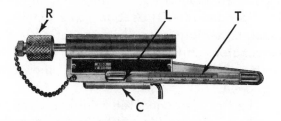

Fig. 6-42. An instrument used for testing and adjusting thermostatic expansion valves.

T. Accurate thermometer.

C. Clamp for holding the expansion valve control bulb.

R. Fitting for attaching a refrigerant cylinder.

L. Shallow trough for holding liquid refrigerant.

hand, or by putting it in water at about room temperature. The pressure should increase rapidly showing that the power element is operating.

Another method of checking and adjusting a thermostat is shown in Fig. 6-42. It consists of a clamp for the thermostat bulb, an accurate thermometer, and a small cavity for refrigerant. With this instrument mounted on the thermostat bulb and the cavity charged with liquid R-12, the small screw is for adjusting boiling pressure, and therefore the temperature of the R-12, the bulb temperature can be quickly and accurately lowered and raised, to ascertain the adjustment of the control, and to readjust it if necessary. Fig. 6-43 shows the instrument in use.

Note: With the new vapor charged expansion valves (charged with a small quantity of refrigerant) the amount of charge in the power element is limited, and the pres-

Fig. 6-43. Thermostatic expansion valve being tested. Note refrigerant cylinder, thermometer, low pressure gauge, high pressure gauge, and expansion valve being tested.

sure will not build up above the specified pressure. This pressure is always marked on the valve body and must be considered when testing vapor charged valves.

The body bellows is tested with high pressure showing on both gauges as outlined in the preceding paragraph. A leak is detected by using a leak detector to detect the escape of vapor. When making this test, it is important that the body of the valve has a fairly high pressure, and also that the gauge and other fittings are screwed up tight, to eliminate leakage at other points. Leakage can also be detected by use of oil or soap suds.

6-20 Servicing the Thermostatic Expansion Valve

Removing and replacing a TEV is explained in Chapters 12 and 15. Before replacing a TEV you must be sure it is the cause of the trouble. If the sympton or indication is a sweating or frosting suction line, check to see that the thermal element is tightly clamped to the suction line, that the bulb is in the correct position, that the bulb is not exposed to unusual temperature conditions (warm air, etc.), and that the valve capacity is not too great.

If the evaporator coil is starved, the trouble may be a clogged or partially clogged screen. The screen is easily removed, (see Chapter 15). It might also be an undersized TEV.

If the valve seat and needle or the power element seems to be at fault, replace with a TEV of the correct capacity and one designed for that temperature range and for the refrigerant in the system.

6-21 Low Side Float Principles

The low side float is an efficient, yet simple control. It operates on the principle of maintaining a constant liquid level in the evaporator coil. The system is an efficient heat transfer device, because of the ease of heat transfer from a solid to a liquid.

The float itself is a sealed ball or cylinder, or an open pan. It is connected by levers to a needle which closes an orifice when the level reaches the correct height, and opens the valve when some of the refrigerant evaporates and the liquid level drops.

Because the float will float in either oil or liquid refrigerant, special provisions must be made to return any excess oil to the compressor.

This system uses a liquid receiver and extra refrigerant in the system is stored in the liquid receiver.

The basic principles of the low side float system are explained in Chapter 3.

6-22 Low Side Float Design

The low side float was at one time a popular method of controlling the refrigerant flow and is still used to some extent. It consists simply of a float operating in the evaporator unit which controls the level of the liquid refrigerant, as shown in Fig. 6-44.

The float is connected to either a needle or a ball valve and is calibrated so that the valve will close when the float is at the proper level; that is, when there is a certain level of liquid refrigerant in the evaporator coil.

The suction tube on these evaporating units extends into the float chamber and

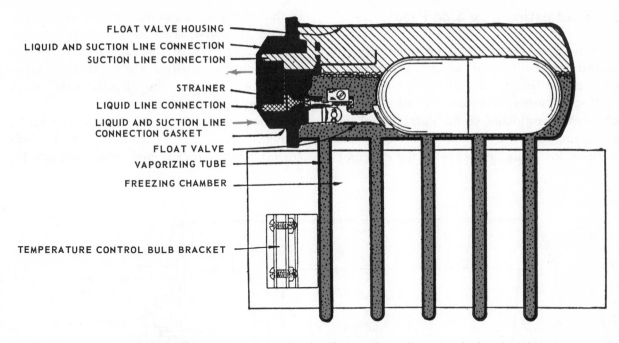

FLOAT VALVE HOUSING
LIQUID AND SUCTION LINE CONNECTION
SUCTION LINE CONNECTION
STRAINER
LIQUID LINE CONNECTION
LIQUID AND SUCTION LINE CONNECTION GASKET
FLOAT VALVE
VAPORIZING TUBE
FREEZING CHAMBER
TEMPERATURE CONTROL BULB BRACKET

Fig. 6-44. Low pressure side float refrigerant control. Float and needle controls level of liquid refrigerant in evaporator.

has its opening located near the top. This opening is protected from picking up liquid refrigerant by having a baffle plate located between it and the liquid. This baffle is necessary because the liquid, as it evaporates, sometimes agitates violently. If this baffle plate were not provided, the suction tube might receive liquid refrigerant in it when the compressor is running.

These cooling coils, (evaporators) are usually made of copper (tin-dipped). The float chamber has tubes running out of it and down, forming a box for the ice cube trays; the tubing then returns to the float chamber. The joints are sealed by copper hydrogen brazing or silver brazing. The float itself is usually a sealed brass ball connected to the needle by means of a brass lever. The needles used in early refrigerators were made of steel, but are now made of stainless steel or Stellite. The seats are built into the removable header and are made of brass or Monel metal. Five to seven cap screws hold the header in place. A lead gasket is usually used to seal the joint, because it is easily broken open, it

takes up little space, needs no cleaning upon removal, and it may be used again. Cap screws may be made of either Monel metal or may be cadmium plated steel to prevent rusting.

Fig. 6-45 illustrates the pan type or bucket type float. The float is made of brass and operates similar to the ball type float. The header on this type of float is usually welded into place. A removal cartridge type needle and seat assembly is therefore used. The pan type float is used because it insures a more positive oil return. This return is accomplished by extending the suction line into the bucket, since the oil collects in the open bucket as it settles out of the spray in the float chamber. One company used a wick to help remove the oil from the chamber into the bucket.

Low side float systems are used in large industrial systems and in some water cooled systems.

This type float control is also used for controlling water level in cooling towers and in evaporative condensers.

6-23 Adjusting Low Side Floats

Low side floats must be carefully adjusted or calibrated when assembled to control the liquid level at a certain definite setting in the cooling coil. If the float mechanism is adjusted so the refrigerant level is too low, it will result in a lower than normal low side pressure. If the refriger-

is that if they are not agitated or the action helped in some other way, the pressures may sometimes be reduced far below the refrigerant's boiling point at that temperature, before the liquid will start evaporating.

Many methods have been promoted to prevent this occurrence; these include sawed tubing, tacks, and other materials,

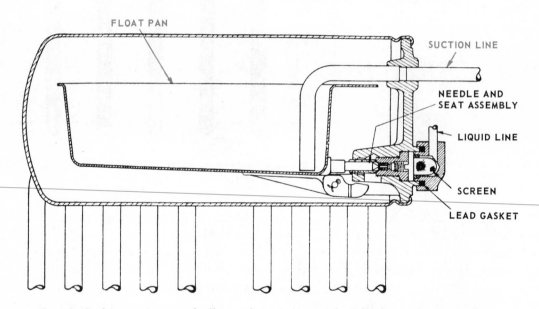

Fig. 6-45. Low pressure side float refrigerant control. A bucket or pan type float is used in this refrigerant level control. Note that suction line dips to bottom of open float in order to remove oil which might otherwise accumulate in open pan.

ant level is too low, an excess accumulation of oil will take place in the cooling coil. This may oil bind the refrigerant. If the float is calibrated so the refrigerant level is too high, this will result in liquid refrigerant entering the suction line, and a frosted suction line will result. This will increase the cost of operation of the machine.

The floats are adjustable either by bending the float arm or by a special adjusting screw on the mechanism. See Fig. 6-44. The float must be designed to allow for a certain oil layer and amount of refrigerant.

A peculiar phenomenon of refrigerants

which are placed in flooded cooling units. Some of these are still being used, but perhaps the best development along this line has been the use of special wood. This, when located in the liquid-filled tubes of the cooling unit, acts as a catalytic agent and causes the refrigerant to boil at the correct temperature. These substances are called ebulators.

6-24 Servicing the Low Side Float

The float control is practically trouble free, but occasionally the unit will stick either open or closed. A closed needle valve may be detected by a lack of refrigeration, or a high vacuum on the low pressure side. A leaky needle may be indicated by a continuous gurgling or hissing in the cooling unit after the compressor has stopped, an equalizing of the pressure gauges, and a frosted suction line. All float controls must be mounted level for efficient operation.

A leaky needle or seat will result in a sweating or frosting suction line.

6-25 High Pressure Side Float Principles

A high side float refrigerant control is somewhat similar to the low side float mechanism, except that it is located in the high pressure side. When the compressor is running, the refrigerant which is condensed in the condenser, flows directly to the high side float mechanism. No liquid receiver is used. As the liquid refrigerant level rises, the float opens a valve allowing the liquid refrigerant to flow into the evaporator coil. In this type of refrigerant control, the liquid refrigerant is stored in the evaporator coil, which makes the coil a flooded coil, and it is designed accordingly. As the liquid level falls in the float chamber, the float will move down and close the valve opening into the evaporator. In this way the pressure difference between the high side and the low side is maintained.

6-26 High Pressure Side Float Design

The high side float is located on the high pressure side of the system. This float maintains a constant level of liquid refrigerant on the high pressure side.

The floats are made of either copper or steel. In the hermetic or semihermetic units the steel type is usually used. These units cannot use a liquid receiver unless the float is located within it. These float controls do not have as much difficulty with oil binding as the low side float con-

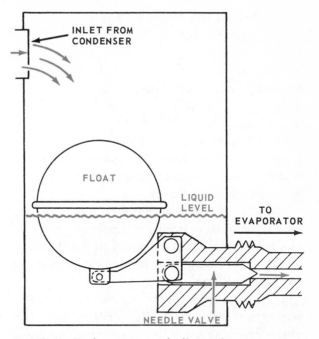

Fig. 6-46. *High pressure side float refrigerant control mechanism. Liquid refrigerant flowing in from condenser will cause float to raise and open needle valve allowing liquid refrigerant to flow into evaporator.*

trol, because at the higher pressure, the oil is dissolved more readily in the liquid refrigerant and circulates with it. However, the cooling coil used in connection with a high side float control must be equipped with a special oil return, or oil binding trouble will be encountered in it.

The high pressure side float is preferred to the low side float, in that it permits an evaporator coil design which utilizes all the coil space for useful refrigeration, rather than float chamber space.

The float must be a sealed ball. It may be connected directly to the needle, or operates the needle by a simple lever as shown in Fig. 6-46. The needles and seats are made of long wearing alloys such as stainless steel or hard surfaced alloys.

Some high side float systems use a weight check valve if the float chamber is located remote from the evaporator coil. Chapter 3 shows this type system.

Either a thermostatic or pressure motor control may be used with this refrigerant control.

6-27 Servicing High Pressure Side Floats

The float ball on high side floats may be constructed of either copper or steel. They must be strong as they are subject to crushing by the high side pressure. A crushed float will not rise with the liquid level and the evaporator coil will be evacuated. A stuck-closed valve may also cause an evacuated evaporator coil. Tapping briskly on the float chamber may free the valve, or if the float is made of steel, an electromagnet may be used to raise it. To operate correctly the high side float must be mounted level.

The amount of refrigerant in the system must be carefully controlled. Too much refrigerant will cause flooding back in the suction line and perhaps compressor damage. Too little refrigerant will lower the refrigerant level in the evaporator coil with consequent loss of refrigerating capacity. The frost line on the evaporator usually indicates the refrigerant level.

6-28 Capillary Tube Refrigerant Control Principles

The capillary tube is a popular type of refrigerant control. This control consists of a length of tubing with a small diameter, which acts as a constant throttle on the refrigerant. It was first used successfully in the late 1920's with the Rice domestic refrigerator using methyl chloride as the refrigerant. It is now being used by practically all manufacturers.

The amount of refrigerant in the system must be carefully calibrated, since all of the liquid refrigerant will move into the low side during the off-cycle and the pressures balance or equalize. Too much refrigerant will cause the unit to frost back on the low side. It must be used in conjunction with a thermostatic motor control.

There are several theories concerning the principle of operation of the capillary tube. The tube presents a fluid flow resistance, and the pressure decreases as the small liquid flow progresses through the tube until the liquid starts to evaporate in the tube. This vapor formation provides a sudden pressure and temperature drop in approximately the last one fourth of the length of the tube. It is cooled to evaporator temperature, and its pressure is reduced to evaporator pressure. This vapor formation in the capillary tube is called "vapor lock." The design of the capillary tube depends on four variables:

1. Tube length.
2. Inside diameter.
3. Tightness of tube windings.
4. Temperature of tubing.

There are several formulas for calculating capillary tube sizes and length, but the best system seems to be to use the original tube size and then change the windings, temperature, and the length of the tube until it functions correctly.

At one time the Frigidaire Standard line used a refrigerant control similar in action to the capillary tube control. It was called a "Restrictor" and consisted of a refrigerant passage formed by the threaded portion of a large diameter screw tightly enclosed in a threadless housing. This refrigerant control is illustrated in Fig. 6-47.

6-29 Capillary Tube Design

The capillary tube refrigerant control, Fig. 6-48, does not have any moving parts; therefore, it has several advantages. First, there are no parts to wear or stick; second, the pressures balance in the system when the unit stops. This condition places a minimum starting load on the motor.

The tube is made of seamless copper. It has a small and accurate inside diameter. It usually is equipped with a fine filter on its inlet, and it generally has a drier installed on its inlet to remove moisture from the refrigerant.

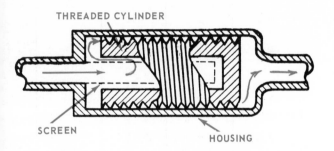

Fig. 6-47. Refrigerant "restriction" which operates similar to a capillary tube refrigerant control.

The capillary tube is usually coiled for most of its length. In Fig. 6-48, the coil of tubing is housed in the suction line enlargement. This arrangement permits the suction line vapor to cool the liquid refrigerant in the capillary tube.

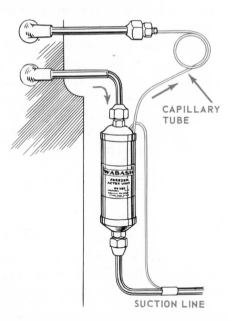

Fig. 6-48. Capillary tube suction line combination. In this device cool suction line vapor cools liquid refrigerant in capillary tube.
(Wabash Corp.)

6-30 Capillary Tube Capacities

The capillary tube refrigerant control is the simplest of all refrigerant controls. It consists of a length of accurately made seamless copper tubing. The inner diam-

eter must be very accurately controlled to provide sensitive pressure reduction. Some popular capillary tube sizes are shown in Fig. 6-49.

CAPILLARY TUBE DIAMETERS, OD AND ID

Outside Diameter	Inside Diameter
.083	.031
.094	.036
.109	.042
.114	.049
.120	.055
.130	.065

Fig. 6-49. A table of some common capillary tube diameters.

Tubing .114 OD by .049 ID is often used for the R-12 domestic unit. This is suitable for average temperatures and frozen food temperatures, dependent on the power of the unit and the use. Approximate sizes for capillary tube installations for R-12, are shown in Fig. 6-50.

6-31 Capillary Tube Fittings

The capillary tube is often silver brazed at both the condenser end and the evaporator coil end. The capillary tube may also be attached to the evaporator coil and condenser or drier with mechanical fittings that are leakproof and vibration-proof. Fig. 6-51 illustrates three popular ways to make these connections. Detail 1 shows the use of a special nut that squeezes against both the capillary tube and the fitting. Because the nose section is deformed as the nut is tightened, the nut should always be replaced when the capillary tube is serviced; Detail 2 shows the capillary tube silver brazed to a 1/4 OD soft copper tubing. The larger tube may then be connected to the system by the usual flared fitting. Detail 3 shows a larger tube silver brazed to the capillary tube.

HORSEPOWER	TEMP.	CAPILLARY TUBING ID						
		.031	.036	.040	.042	.049	.055	.065
1/8	H	1.1	2.2	3.5	4.5	9	15	
	M	4	8	13	16	32	56	
	L	9	18	29	36	72	126	
1/5	H						10	
	M	2.2	4.4	7.0	9	18	31	
	L	5.2	10.5	17	21	42	73	
1/4	H						5	
	M	1.1	2.2	3.5	4.5	9	15	
	H							7.5
1/3	M						9.5	
	L	1.75	3.5	5.6	7	14	2.5	

Fig. 6-50. Table of capillary tube sizes and applications. Temperatures are shown as high H, medium M or low L. Required length of tube in feet is indicated for each tube inside diameter (ID). Sizes are calculated for R-12 refrigerant.

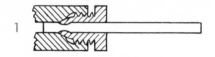

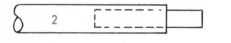

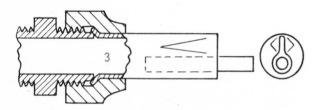

Fig. 6-51. Some approved capillary tube connections.
1. Special nut that squeezes against both the capillary tube and the fitting.
2. Capillary tube inserted and silver brazed into a 1/4 in. OD soft copper tube.
3. Capillary tube inserted into larger soft copper tube and larger tube is compressed to fit capillary tube and soldered to form a tight joint. Larger tube is then fitted into system with a flared fitting.

The larger tube connection is then made with a flared fitting. In most cases the capillary tube will be silver brazed into the system. However, mechanical connections may be substituted at the time of overhaul using special capillary tube fittings. See Fig. 6-52.

A capillary tube system which is easily adjusted and installed is shown in Fig. 6-53. This may be fitted to systems of low, medium, or high temperature, using either refrigerant R-12 or R-22. The tubing is of the same OD and ID for all systems, but the capacity is varied by putting various diameter wires of various lengths inside the tubing. A complete table of wire sizes and lengths recommended is furnished by the manufacturer.

6-32 Servicing Capillary Tubes

The major problem encountered with capillary tubes is the accumulation of wax or ice formation within the tube. These reduce the size of the ID and cause less refrigerant to reach the evaporator coil.

Fig. 6-52. Some capillary tube connections.
(Wabash Corp.)

This causes what is commonly called a "starved coil." As the wax accumulation increases, the amount of refrigeration will decrease. One method of removing the accumulation of wax, is to heat the capillary tube starting at the inlet of the tube and working the torch through the entire length of the capillary tube. However, caution must be exercised to be sure that the brazed joints at the inlet and outlet fittings are not loosened.

If this treatment proves ineffective, a capillary tube pressure plunger may be required. This pump will create pressures of approximately 14,000 psi causing the plugged capillary tube to be cleared. For more detailed information, see Chapter 12.

Moisture in the system may form ice in the capillary tube creating a blockage, and a lack of cooling in the evaporator. On each off cycle the moisture may melt, or may melt as the unit passes through the defrost cycle. If a drier is in the system, it should be replaced. If no drier is present, a liquid drier (mainly methanol - about 2 cc per lb. of refrigerant) may be used. CAUTION: the use of methanol usuallay invalidates the warranty of hermetic motor-compressor systems. This treatment does not remove the moisture; it merely acts as an "antifreeze" and keeps the moisture in circulation.

Fig. 6-54 (A) illustrates a system which has the proper length and diameter capillary tubing installed. Fig. 6-54 (B) illustrates an example of a capillary tube which produces too much resistance either because of its small ID or its excessive length.

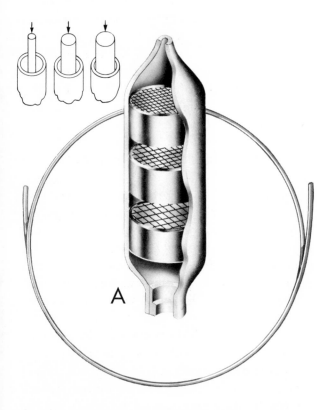

Fig. 6-53. Capillary tube. A single size tube may be used by inserting special calibrated wires in the tube to restrict the refrigerant flow. Tables supplied by the manufacturer give the necessary information concerning wire size to use with the desired refrigerant or refrigerating capacity. Note the provision for attaching the filter to various size copper tubes as shown at (A).   (Watsco Inc.)

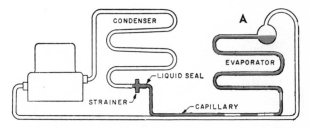

Capillary selected for capacity balance conditions. Liquid seal at capillary inlet but no excess liquid in condenser. Compressor discharge and suction pressures normal. Evaporator properly charged.

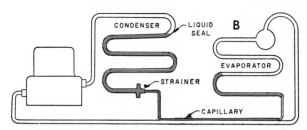

Too much capillary resistance—liquid refrigerant backs up in condenser and causes evaporator to be undercharged. Compressor discharge pressure may be abnormally high. Suction pressure below normal. Bottom of condenser subcooled.

Fig. 6-54. An illustration showing the effect of a correct and an incorrect capillary tube installation.
   A. Correct installation, operation normal.
   B. Incorrect capillary tube, too much resistance in the tube and the evaporator is "starved."

If a capillary tube installation is not working correctly, it should be replaced, along with the filter-drier, with correct size and length of new capillary tube.

6-33 Replacing Capillary Tube With Automatic Expansion Valve (AEV)

The automatic expansion valve is a good replacement for a capillary tube refrigerant control when a unit is being serviced in the field. These valves are adjustable, and are not as critical to the refrigerant charge as the capillary tube

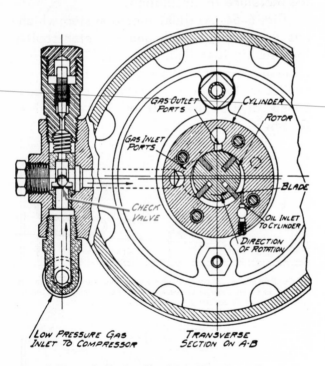

Fig. 6-55. A ball check valve is used on this rotary type compressor.

system. If an automatic expansion valve is used as a replacement in a hermetic system, one important precaution should be taken. When the motor is a low starting torque type, the head pressure must be reduced during the off-cycle. To accomplish this unloading, an AEV with a groove put in the valve seat to permit a small amount of refrigerant to "bleed" past the

valve needle during the off-cycle must be used. This "bleed" opening must be large enough to permit pressure balancing during the off-cycle, but must be small enough to permit control of the refrigerant when the system is at its lowest operating pressure.

6-34 Check Valves

Rotary and gear compressors are equipped with check valves in the suction line to prevent backing up of the high pressure vapor, and the refrigerant oil into the evaporator unit, Fig. 6-55. These check valves may use either a disk or a solid ball in their design.

They may also operate differently. Some use a spring to keep the valve against the seat; others are mounted so the weight of the valve keeps it against its seat. Many multiple systems use check valves to keep refrigerants from backing up into the suction lines of multiple systems.

6-35 Solenoid Valve Principles

In many refrigerating applications it is necessary to close off or open refrigerant circuits in order to accomplish the desired refrigerating effect. A solenoid valve is usually used for this purpose since it is easily installed, and the control is accomplished by simple electrical control circuits.

A solenoid valve consists of an electromagnet with a movable core or center.

The basic construction of an electrical solenoid valve includes an armature attached to the valve needle, which is sealed into the valve body, so the armature can raise and lower the valve needle. A coil is wound around the valve housing which contains the armature as shown in Fig. 6-56. As the coil is energized, the armature moves upward toward the center of the coil, opening the valve. When the circuit is opened the coil is de-energized and the weight of the armature forces the needle against the valve seat.

6-36 Types of Solenoid Valves

Three types of solenoid valves are in common use:

The 2-way valve which controls the flow of refrigerant through a single line.

The 3-way valve with an inlet which is common to either of two opposite openings, and controls refrigerant flow in two different lines.

The 4-way reversing valve used extensively on heat pumps.

Fig. 6-57 shows a 2-way solenoid valve which may be used in hot gas defrost systems or other similar applications. Solenoid valves may be activated by means of a thermostat used to control the temper-

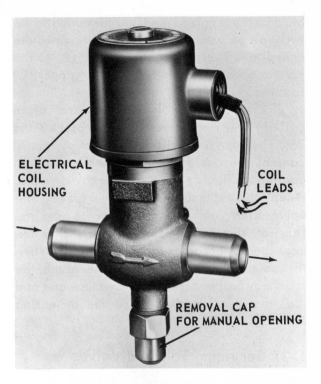

Fig. 6-57. A two-way solenoid valve. The coil leads will be connected into the control circuit. The direction of flow of refrigerant through the coil is indicated by the arrows. Note the cap which may be removed for manual operation of the valve.
(American-Standard Controls Div.)

ature of a room space at a desired level.

Three-way solenoid valves are used chiefly on commercial refrigeration units. They may be used to obtain two separate refrigerant circuits for defrosting, two temperature coils, etc.

A 3-way solenoid valve is shown in Fig. 6-36. In this valve the opening (A) is the common opening and is never closed. As the electromagnet is de-energized the weight of the solenoid plunger assembly plus the force of the upper spring holds the ball firmly against the upper seat closing port (B) to the common port. This action in turn forces the push spring, and creates a pressure against the lower ball, forcing it away from its seat. This action thereby opens port (C) with the common port. When the electrical circuit is closed because of the actuation device, the solenoid

Fig. 6-56. An exploded view of a two-way solenoid valve. Note that the armature is attached to the valve needle. Raising the armature opens the needle valve.
(Alco Valve Co.)

becomes energized and the piston with the two valves attached to it will move in the opposite direction, opening port (B) to the common port and thereby closing port (C) to the common port.

Four-way solenoid valves are often called reversing valves. See Chapters 3 and 26. They are used chiefly on heat pumps to control the cycle to give either heating or cooling as the requirements may demand. When the solenoid is de-energized, the valve stem closes several ports and the flow of the refrigerant is such that the heat pump becomes a cooling unit. When the solenoid valve becomes energized the four-way valve stem is drawn upward and the heat pump system becomes a heating unit.

6-37 Servicing Solenoid Valves

Solenoid valves involve both electrical problems and refrigerant troubles. If the electrical connections are dirty or loose, the coil may not create enough magnetism to raise the valve. Usually the valve should be mounted with the coil on top and with the valve level, or they may stick or chatter. Solenoid valves sometimes will develop a leaky needle and seat. In this case the valve must be replaced. It is important that the solenoid be of the proper voltage and amperage rating otherwise the coil may burn out. An example--a 12V valve connected to a 240V circuit. The serviceman must also be careful to place the solenoid right side up and in a vertical position, as shown in Fig. 6-57, otherwise it will not operate.

Chapter 15 describes how to remove a valve from the system.

6-38 Suction Pressure Valves

There are many systems that use bellows or diaphragm-operated pressure regulating valves on the low side of the system. Some operate from the cooling coil pressure and keep the pressure in the cooling coil constant. Some operate from the crankcase pressure and keep the compressor from being overloaded. Additional information on these valves may be obtained from Chapter 13.

6-39 Review of Safety

A basic safety rule in all cases when one works on a refrigerating unit is to be sure, by use of gauges and by temperature, that all liquid refrigerant is removed and that the pressure is atmospheric in that part of the system being taken apart.

When removing a valve from a system you should always use two wrenches to avoid twisting the valve or the tubing.

When testing a thermostatic expansion valve using a refrigerant cylinder, ventilate the work station carefully to avoid breathing the fumes.

Always wear goggles when working on a refrigerating system to protect your eyes from liquid refrigerant, in case a line breaks.

6-40 Test Your Knowledge, Chapter 6

1. What is meant by float calibration?
2. How many pressures or forces influence the needle movement of an automatic expansion valve needle?
3. Why are expansion valves made adjustable?
4. Which refrigerant controls can operate satisfactorily with a varying amount of refrigerant in the system?
5. What is thermostatic expansion valve superheat?
6. How much liquid refrigerant turns into vapor as the refrigerant passes by the needle valve?
7. What is meant by a gas charged power element as used in connection with a thermostatic expansion valve?
8. What mesh screens are used in refrigerant controls?

9. What is the most common expansion valve body material?

10. What may happen if the thermostatic expansion valve orifice is too large?

11. How is the liquid line usually attached to the expansion valve?

12. Why does the suction line extend down into the pan type float?

13. What is a cartridge needle?

14. How may low side floats be adjusted?

15. Of what materials are high side floats usually made?

16. What may cause a high side float to collapse?

17. In what position must a float be mounted?

18. What is the purpose of an automatic refrigerant control?

19. How does a capillary tube operate?

20. Does a capillary tube system have a liquid receiver?

21. What happens to the capacity of a capillary tube if the tube is lengthened?

22. Does a capillary tube need a filter or a screen at its inlet?

23. Is it possible to adjust the capacity of a capillary tube?

24. What type of system needs a check valve?

25. What energy opens a solenoid valve?

26. Why is a thermostatic expansion valve equalizer tube used?

27. What is the purpose of the gas-charged thermal element on a thermostatic expansion valve?

28. What may be the trouble if a capillary tube unit frosts down the suction line?

29. What is meant by a four-way solenoid valve?

30. What type of service requires the use of a four-way solenoid valve?

Chapter 7

ELECTRIC MOTORS

The compression type refrigerating system must have a power source or energy source to turn the compressor. Various energy sources have been used, such as steam engines, diesel engines, gasoline engines and electric motors. The electric motor is the most popular for the small and medium size units because it is simple, quiet, and it is easy to provide automatic control. The electric motor changes electrical energy into mechanical energy.

Electric motors are also used to drive other devices in refrigeration and air conditioning systems. Many troubles in refrigerating units may be electrical. It is therefore important that the refrigeration serviceman thoroughly understands electricity, magnetism, electric motors, and electrical circuits.

It should be noted that in this chapter power supply voltages are sometimes indicated as 115V and 230V and at other times 120V and 240V. The voltages supplied by the electric utility companies vary in different parts of the country. The students should be sure that they know the voltages supplied in their community and that the equipment used matches the voltages supplied.

7-1 Electric Motor Applications

Electric motors used for operating refrigerating systems may be classified as open motors or sealed-in (hermetic) motors. The open motor drives the compressor directly or by means of a belt. The sealed-in, or hermetic motor, is built or put inside the compressor dome and usually drives the compressor directly.

Electric motors are also often used to drive fans, condensate pumps, chilled water pumps, dampers, and many other devices.

The motor uses may be grouped as follows:

1. To drive compressors:
   A. Open type belt drive.
   B. Hermetic type direct drive.
2. To drive fans:
   A. Condenser fans.
   B. Evaporator fans.
3. To drive pumps:
   A. Condensate pumps.
   B. Chilled water pumps.
   C. Condenser water pumps.
4. To drive miscellaneous devices:
   A. Vending machines.
   B. Automatic ice cube makers.
   C. Ice making machine water pumps.

See paragraph 7-34 for a listing of the various types of electric motors used in refrigerating and air conditioning applications.

7-2 Basic Electricity

Electricity is a form of energy. You must understand basic electricity before you can understand motors; know how to use them, diagnose their troubles, install and repair them.

All materials are made up of molecules; all molecules are made up of atoms. Finally, all atoms are made of electrons, neutrons, and protons. Electrons are negative charges of electricity. Protons are positive charges of electricity. If an atom collects an extra electron for a moment, it is negatively charged. If an atom loses an electron, it is positively charged. The electrons travel from extra electron atoms to atoms with a lack of electrons.

Electricity is the flow of these electrons (or negative charges). The number of electrons that flow are called coulombs (it is calculated that 6,900,000,000,000 electrons equal one coulomb). One coulomb flowing for one second equals one ampere. The ampere is known as the quantity of electricity.

If there are too many protons, and electrons move to make up the difference, this movement or pressure to move is called voltage or pressure difference (potential difference). This attraction is also called electromotive force.

Electric current consists of electrons traveling in a conductor which may be a solid, liquid, or gas. Electrons are the revolving particles of an atom. They revolve around a center made of protons. Electrons are attracted by protons. Therefore, electrons will flow toward a substance that is short of electrons (has an excess of protons) as shown in Fig. 7-1.

Electricity can be created from energies such as heat energy, mechanical energy and others. Any method which produces an imbalance in the electrons or protons causes an electrical potential.

Electricity is related to magnetism. If a wire moves across a magnetic field, electricity is created in the wire. If electricity flows along a wire, magnetism is created around the wire. By correctly using the magnetism created by electricity, we can make an electric motor turn electrical energy into mechanical energy. An electromagnet may be made to operate valves, relays and other electrical devices.

Electrical engineers and scientists have established standard voltage systems for use in homes and industry. Most domestic systems operate at a 120 volt potential difference although in some areas the voltage difference may be 240 volts.

In the following paragraphs the necessary fundamentals of electricity and magnetism will be studied in order that the student may satisfactorily understand the construction and operation of electric motors of the types used in the various refrigerating and air conditioning applications.

7-3 Volts, Electrical Potential

The tendency for electricity to flow is called electromotive force and is abbreviated emf or E. The unit for emf is the volt. A common dry cell has an emf of 1 1/2 volts, a lead acid wet cell has an emf of 2.2 volts. Most household electrical circuits have an emf of 120 volts.

Voltage may be compared to the pressure of water in a water system. The higher the pressure of water in a pipe the faster the water will flow if a valve is opened. A high electrical pressure or voltage will cause a rapid current flow in an electrical circuit.

7-4 Amperes, Rate of Current Flow

The number of electrons flowing in the conductor is called coulombs. A coulomb is a quantity of electricity which passes a given point on a conductor in one second when the rate of current flow is constant at one ampere. If one coulomb flows along a conductor each second, this rate of flow is called one ampere and is the intensity of the electricity. Ampere flow is also known as current.

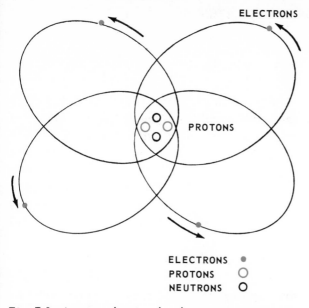

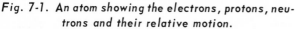

ELECTRONS •
PROTONS ○
NEUTRONS ○

Fig. 7-1. An atom showing the electrons, protons, neutrons and their relative motion.

7-5 Watts, Electrical Power

Electrical power is measured in watts and kilowatts. A kilowatt is 1,000 watts. In direct current circuits, the wattage may be obtained by multiplying the current in amperes by the voltage. In alternating current circuits, the wattage may not be exactly the products of the current multiplied by the voltage. This is because the current in an AC circuit may not be exactly in phase with the voltage. The current usually lags behind the voltage depending on the characteristics of the circuit. Therefore, the wattage or power of an AC circuit must be obtained by multiplying the product of the current times the voltage by the power factor. Special instruments are required for determining the power factor. In calculating electrical horsepower, 746 watts or 0.746 kw equal one horsepower.

7-6 Ohms, Electrical Resistance to Current Flow

The difficulty that electrons have while moving in a conductor is called resistance (R). Energy is wasted by this resistance. This is shown by the heating of the conductor as the electricity flows in it.

The unit for resistance is the ohm. If an emf of one volt is needed to cause a current intensity of one ampere to flow, the resistance of the conductor is one ohm.

Resistance in a conductor produces heat and increases the temperature of the conductor. The resistance will be reduced if the cross section of the conductor is increased. The resistance of the conductor will increase if the length of the conductor is increased.

7-7 Ohm's Law

The relationship between the volt, the ampere, and the ohm is known as Ohm's law. It has been found that if a wire one foot long will allow one ampere to flow with an emf of one volt, this same wire will allow two amperes to flow if the emf is two volts. Also, if the wire is two feet long only 1/2 an ampere will flow. Therefore, it is evident that emf is the product of the current intensity (amperes) multiplied by the resistance or:

emf = Intensity × Resistance

$$E = IR$$

and therefore $I = \dfrac{E}{R}$

or $\qquad R = \dfrac{E}{I}$

where E = Electromotive force in volts

I = Amperes; intensity in amperes

R = Resistance in ohm's

Fig. 7-2 shows the relationship of I, E, and R.

You may learn from this basic law that, if the resistance stays constant, the current can only be increased by increasing the voltage. Also, if the resistance becomes small in a circuit, the amperage will become high. For example, if a 1/3 hp motor draws 5 amperes at 120V, its resistance is as follows:

$$E = IR$$

$$\frac{120}{5} = R$$

$$24 = R$$

If a short should occur so that the resistance is reduced to 8 ohms the current will be increased to 15 amperes, as shown:

$$E = IR$$
$$120 = I \times 8$$
$$\frac{120}{8} = I$$
$$15 = I$$

If the fuse does not "blow," the motor windings will become too hot as they try to carry this excessive current, and the insulation on the wires will be destroyed and the motor will be ruined.

The formula also means that when $E = I \times R$, if one doubles the voltage in a circuit (the resistance remaining the same) the current flow will double and may cause trouble. An example would be to connect 240V power into a 120V circuit. Unless the fuses "blow," the circuit will be damaged.

If the resistance is increased (putting in a smaller wire or leaving a dirty or loose connection) and the voltage stays the same, the current flow will decrease, causing a loss of power.

7-8 Circuits

An electrical circuit is a complete path (or paths) for the electrons to follow. It might consist of a battery, two wires, and a lamp. When the wires are connected from the two lamp terminals to the two battery terminals, the lamp will light, indicating that current is flowing out of the battery along the other wire as shown in Fig. 7-3.

To have electrical flow, we must have a circuit. A circuit is an electrical flow that leaves an electrical source and returns to the same source. Continuity is the term applied to a completed, closed circuit path for electrical flow.

When the circuit is complete (there is a closed path for electron flow) it is called a closed circuit. It may be called a continuous circuit. Fig. 7-4 shows three types of circuit troubles. An open circuit is an interrupted circuit meaning one with an open switch or a broken wire. A short circuit is when the electrons have a short cut to follow to get back to their source. As an example, a small wire could be put

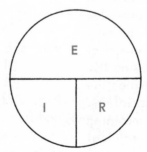

If solving for E, cover E and the circle shows $E = I \times R$ $E =$

If solving for R, cover R and the circle shows $R = \dfrac{E}{I}$ $R =$

If solving for I, cover I and the circle shows $I = \dfrac{E}{R}$ $I =$

Fig. 7-2. Ohms law equations shown in graphical form.

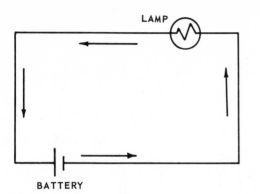

Fig. 7-3. Simple electrical circuit using a one cell battery, two wires or conductors and one lamp.

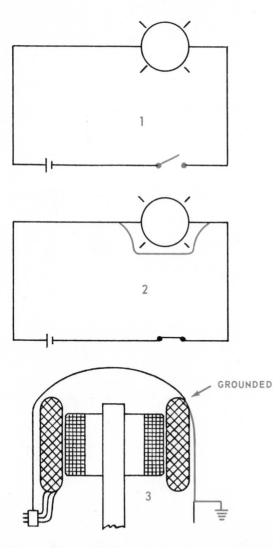

Fig. 7-4. Three common electrical circuit troubles: 1—Open circuit. This may be either an open switch as shown here or a broken conductor. 2—Shorted circuit. 3—Grounded circuit.

across the terminals of a lamp. Because most of the electrons flow along the path of least resistance, the wire will now carry most of them, and the light will go out. The amperage flow will greatly increase (because of a decrease in resistance), and usually trouble occurs. Another more common example of a short is the touching of two adjacent wires. A ground is a condition in which a wire touches some of the metal structure of the device. An example is a bare field winding wire touching the frame of the motor.

Electrical wiring diagrams use symbols for many of the electrical parts. A suggested standard of electrical symbols is shown in Fig. 7-5.

7-9 Types of Electric Current

There are two common types of electric current:
1. Direct current.
2. Alternating current.

Direct current flows continuously in the same direction. It is the type of current used in automobile lighting and other automotive applications. It is also used on cordless electric appliances such as toothbrushes, electric shavers and drills.

Alternating current flows back and forth in a circuit. It is the type of current available in most houses served by an electric utility. Direct current is needed for battery charging. A battery charger operating on alternating current must be equipped with a rectifier of some type to convert the alternating current to direct current.

7-10 Direct Current

Direct current is electric circuit flow in which the current flows continuously in one direction. It is the type of current that is produced by dry cells.

Direct current may be produced by using a direct current generator such as used on older automobiles and trucks.

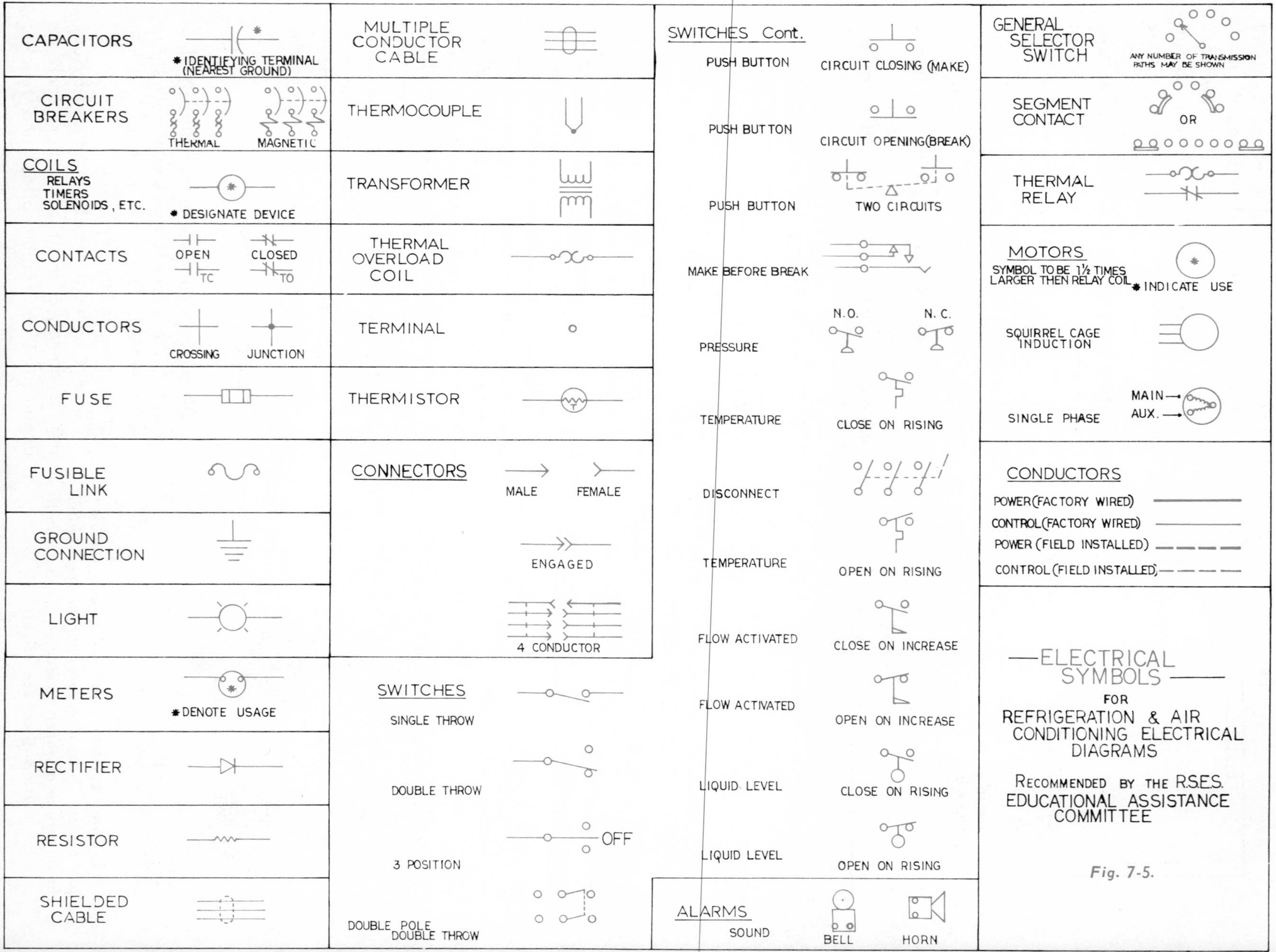

ELECTRICAL SYMBOLS

FOR

REFRIGERATION & AIR CONDITIONING ELECTRICAL DIAGRAMS

Recommended by the RSES. EDUCATIONAL ASSISTANCE COMMITTEE

Fig. 7-5.

CAPACITORS
* IDENTIFYING TERMINAL (NEAREST GROUND)

CIRCUIT BREAKERS

COILS
RELAYS, TIMERS, SOLENOIDS, ETC.
THERMAL
MAGNETIC
* DESIGNATE DEVICE

CONTACTS
OPEN
CLOSED
TC
TO

CONDUCTORS
CROSSING
JUNCTION

FUSE

FUSIBLE LINK

GROUND CONNECTION

LIGHT

METERS
* DENOTE USAGE

RECTIFIER

RESISTOR

SHIELDED CABLE

MULTIPLE CONDUCTOR CABLE

THERMOCOUPLE

TRANSFORMER

THERMAL OVERLOAD COIL

TERMINAL

THERMISTOR

CONNECTORS
MALE
FEMALE
ENGAGED
4 CONDUCTOR

SWITCHES
SINGLE THROW
DOUBLE THROW
3 POSITION
OFF
DOUBLE POLE DOUBLE THROW

SWITCHES Cont.

PUSH BUTTON — CIRCUIT CLOSING (MAKE)

PUSH BUTTON — CIRCUIT OPENING (BREAK)

PUSH BUTTON — TWO CIRCUITS

MAKE BEFORE BREAK

N.O.   N.C.
PRESSURE

TEMPERATURE — CLOSE ON RISING

DISCONNECT

TEMPERATURE — OPEN ON RISING

FLOW ACTIVATED — CLOSE ON INCREASE

FLOW ACTIVATED — OPEN ON INCREASE

LIQUID LEVEL — CLOSE ON RISING

LIQUID LEVEL — OPEN ON RISING

ALARMS
SOUND
BELL
HORN

GENERAL SELECTOR SWITCH
ANY NUMBER OF TRANSMISSION PATHS MAY BE SHOWN
OR

SEGMENT CONTACT

THERMAL RELAY

MOTORS
SYMBOL TO BE 1½ TIMES LARGER THEN RELAY COIL * INDICATE USE
SQUIRREL CAGE INDUCTION
SINGLE PHASE
MAIN →
AUX. →

CONDUCTORS
POWER (FACTORY WIRED)
CONTROL (FACTORY WIRED)
POWER (FIELD INSTALLED)
CONTROL (FIELD INSTALLED)

Most modern motor vehicle generators produce alternating current which is rectified to produce direct current for battery charging. Electricity is not stored in batteries as electrical energy, but rather the current charge in the storage cell causes a chemical action, which makes possible the withdrawal of current as the chemical action is reversed.

Some power companies still produce and sell direct current (DC), however its use is fast disappearing. At present, its chief uses are in electronics, elevator service, electric welding and a few other applications.

In the case of both elevator operation and electric welding, the direct current is usually generated at the site where it is to be used by an alternating current rectifier or on AC motor driving a DC generator.

With the development of new lightweight storage cells and rectifiers many small appliances are using "cordless" power. This is an application of DC. Motors in these appliances will usually operate on either AC or DC current. These are called universal motors.

7-11 Alternating Current

When the current first flows in one direction along a conductor and then reverses itself and flows in the opposite direction along the same wire, the current is said to alternate its direction of flow. It is then called alternating current AC.

7-12 Alternating Current Cycles

If electricity flows for one half second in one direction and then for one half second in the other direction, this is called one cycle. Most alternating current electricity is generated in 60 cycles, which means that in one second the electricity flows 60 times one way and 60

times the other, or for 1/120 of a second it flows in one direction and then for 1/120 of a second in the other direction. The current therefore makes a complete cycle in 1/60 of a second.

This reversal of the current flow can be shown by a graph, as shown in Fig. 7-6.

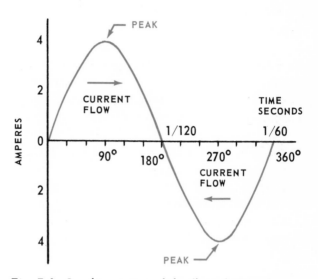

Fig. 7-6. Graphic picture of the flow of 60 cycle current. Peaks of the curve are those times when generating conductor is moving at right angles to magnetic lines of force.

This drawing shows a sine wave of 60 cycle alternating current. In some industries 180 cycle current is generated to operate hand tools such as wrenches, drills, screwdrivers and the like. These high cycle tools do not draw heavy currents and do not overheat if stalled.

7-13 Magnetism

The earth is a magnet. The operation of the magnetic compass depends on the fact that the north magnetic pole of the earth is near the north geographic pole. The compass needle is free to turn and "line up" with the earth's magnetic field.

All magnets have two poles; a north pole and a south pole. Like poles repel each other and unlike poles attract or pull toward each other.

There are lines of magnetic force connecting the north and south poles of a magnet. These lines of force are called flux. The space in which a magnetic force is operating is called a magnetic field. There is no insulation or substance through which magnetic flux cannot flow. It is not stopped by glass, mica, wood, air or any of the usual electrical insulating substances.

Some substances, particularly soft iron, are better conductors of magnetic flux than other substances. This is the reason that certain parts of electric motors and generators are made of soft iron.

Fig. 7-7 shows a magnet and its magnetic field. Permanent magnets are usually of hardened steel. Once they have been magnetized they remain magnetized. There are some patented alloys of iron, aluminum, nickel and cobalt which make strong and satisfactory permanent magnets.

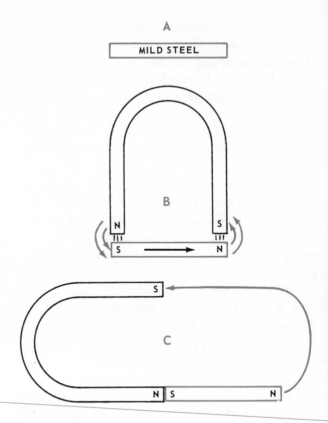

Fig. 7-8. Induced magnetism. A—Nonmagnetized soft iron bar. B—Bar shown at A has become a magnet by being placed in magnetic field. C—Bar A is again magnetized by being placed in magnetic field.

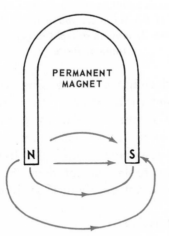

Fig. 7-7. Magnetic field surrounding a magnet. Note lines of force from N to S.

7-14 Induced Magnetism

A property of magnetism is that it may produce magnetism in some other metals near it, as shown in Fig. 7-8.

In this figure, the permanent magnet is surrounded by its magnetic field, but the mild steel piece has no magnetism. If the mild steel piece A is placed near the permanent magnet or is touching it, it too becomes a magnet as shown in B and C. Thus any material that is capable of being magnetized will become a magnet if it is placed in a magnetic field. This is called induced magnetism. It must be remembered that the power of a magnetic field decreases as the square of its distance from the source; that is, a magnetic field is four times stronger, 3 in. from a magnet than it is 6 in. from it. It is nine times stronger 1 in. from the magnet than it is 3 in. from it.

7-15 Electromagnets

If a current of electricity is passed through a conductor, the conductor will be surrounded by a magnetic field as shown in Fig. 7-9. If the current is turned off the magnetic field will end. If the conductor is wrapped around a piece of soft iron, which is a good magnetic conductor, and current is passed through it, the soft

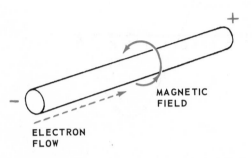

MAGNETIC FIELD

ELECTRON FLOW

Fig. 7-9. Experiment showing relationship between electron flow and magnetism. Each conductor carrying a current is surrounded by a circular magnetic field.

iron becomes a strong magnet. Turning off the current ends the magnetic effect. This magnetic effect is called electromagnetism. Magnets formed in this manner are called electromagnets. An electromagnet is shown in Fig. 7-10. The soft iron part is called the core and the current carrying conductor is called the winding.

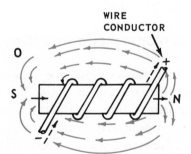

WIRE CONDUCTOR

O

S

N

Fig. 7-10. An electromagnet. If several turns of wire (conductors) are placed on a soft iron core, the individual circular magnetic fields are combined in the core to form one magnet.

The strength of an electromagnet is determined by the number of turns in the winding around the core and the number of amperes flowing through the wind-

ing. This strength is indicated by the term "ampere-turns" which is obtained by multiplying the number of turns in the winding by the amperes flowing through the winding.

Electromagnets are used in motors, in electrical relays, and many other electromagnetic applications.

7-16 Electrical Generator

If a conductor is moved across a magnetic field an electrical potential will be generated in the conductor. If the conductor is placed in a circuit so that the generated potential may cause current to flow, the magnetic field surrounding the conductor will oppose the movement of the conductor across the field. This is illustrated in Fig. 7-11.

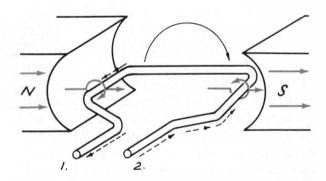

N

S

1.

2.

Fig. 7-11. Generation of current. The wire loop (1 and 2) is revolving clockwise. As wire near N pole cuts lines of flux, flux is bent clockwise around wire. As wire near S pole cuts flux lines, the lines bend around wire counterclockwise. Left hand rule then determines direction of electron travel (broken arrow lines). When the loop turns one half revolution or 180 deg. the wire (1) will now bend flux lines in opposite direction and produce current flowing in the opposite direction.

The current flow is zero at the start and the current builds to a peak (the wire is now perpendicular to the magnetic lines of force). Then the current goes back to zero as the conductor is moving parallel with the magnetic field. As the wire

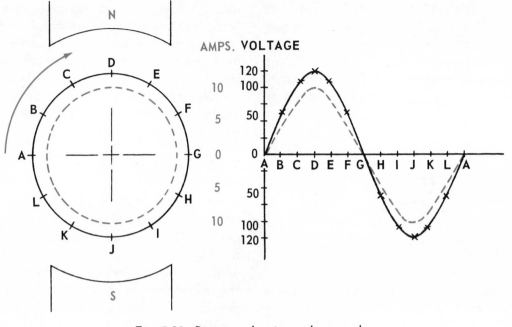

Fig. 7-12. Diagram showing voltage and current changes in an alternating circuit.

crosses the magnetic lines in the oppo-site direction, the current increases again, but in the opposite direction. At the end of a one-half turn, the current flow is again at 0. The cycle will now repeat itself.

Fig. 7-12 shows the voltage and current changes in an alternating circuit as the generator conductor (armature) revolves. Alternating current AC is the type of cur-rent that all generators produce, because the wires of the generator first cut the magnetic field in one direction and then in the other direction, thus producing an al-ternate (or opposite) flow for each revolu-tion as the conductors pass the magnetic poles. However, commutators and brushes on DC generators provide that the current leaving the generator is constantly flowing in the same direction.

It should be noted that as the current flows from the generator, a magnetic field surrounds the conductor in which the cur-rent is generated. This field is such that it opposes the movement of the conductor across the generator field. This is the reason that it takes power to drive a gen-erator which is producing a current. The greater the current produced, the greater the power required to drive the generator.

This principle is stated in Lenz's Law which may be stated as follows: "The mag-netic effect, surrounding the conductor in which a current is induced, opposes the movement by which the current is in-duced."

7-17 Electromagnetic Induction

Par. 7-14 shows how one magnet may cause another magnetic substance to be-come a magnet. Par. 7-15 illustrates how the flow of electricity may produce mag-netism. Electromagnetic induction uses both of these principles, and it is the ba-sis of operation of the induction motor which we will be studying in detail in this chapter, and which is used most for driv-ing refrigeration and air conditioning com-pressors.

The principle of electromagnetic in-duction is illustrated in Fig. 7-13. Coils A and B are separate.

The leads to coil A are connected to an alternating current supply as shown. Upon closing the switch (S) both the lights L$_A$ and L$_B$ will light. This is because the alternating field created around coil A induces a magnetic field around coil B. As the magnetic flux builds up and reverses,

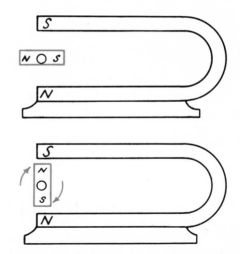

Fig. 7-14. Magnet mounted on an axis will turn when put in another magnetic field. Note direction of movement of pivoted magnet.

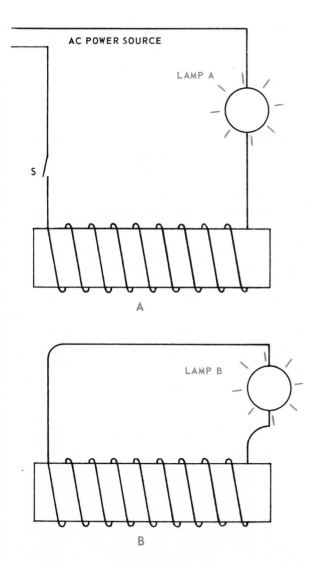

Fig. 7-13. Electromagnetic induction. Coils A and B are wound on a soft iron core. Coil A is connected through a switch to an alternating current supply. The lamp in the circuit is to control amount of current flowing through coil A. Coil B is wound on a core adjacent to coil A but not connected to coil A electrically. A low voltage lamp is connected to terminals of coil B. When switch to coil A is closed, both lights will light indicating that a current is being generated in coil B by electromagnetic induction.

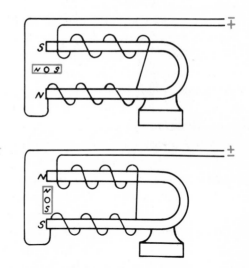

Fig. 7-15. By reversing flow of current through field (stator) winding, its magnetic polarity will be reversed. This will cause rotor magnet to turn on its axis.

the coils of wire around coil B have generated in them an emf. The building up and collapsing of the magnetic field produces the effect of the wires cutting across a magnetic field, which is the basic principle of the electric generator as explained in Par. 7-16.

This magnetic inducing or induction property is used in electric motors by making the rotor of mild steel. Magne-

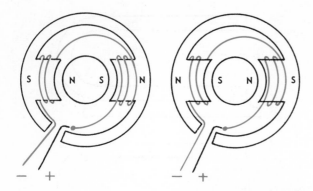

Fig. 7-16. Two pole stator motor. The rotor will make a one-half turn with each current cycle. It has more turns on field poles than running winding, consequently its magnetic effect builds up more slowly.

tism in the rotor may be made or induced by magnetism created in the stator magnets or field windings.

Induced magnetism is useful in electric motors. By putting electrical windings on the field poles, magnetism can be created or induced in the rotor. There is a slight time delay in this induction, and therefore, if the rotor has started to turn, it will continue to turn, because the field pole (stator) always has the opposite polarity. During the time the field pole changes its polarity, it induces an opposite pole in the stator. This repels the rotor pole toward the next stator pole, which has become an opposite pole in the meantime. The rotor must turn the full distance between the two poles before the induced magnetism can be changed or the motor will not keep running. It is important to remember that it takes time for the magnetism to build up to its full strength even though only 1/120 of a second is used to change the magnetism from full strength N to a full strength S pole.

7-18 The Elementary Electric Motor

Electrical energy can be changed to mechanical energy in an electric motor. This change is produced by changing the electrical energy into magnetism and mag-

netism may be used to cause motion. Because like poles repel (N repels N and S repels S), and because unlike poles attract (N attracts S and S attracts N), you can produce motion by putting one magnet on a shaft and mounting another in a fixed position as shown in Fig. 7-14.

The bar magnet on the shaft will turn until its S pole is near to the fixed N pole, and the shaft bar magnets N pole is near the fixed S pole. The fixed magnets which are stationary, are called the stator; the other magnets which rotate are called the rotor.

The rotor will now stay in the vertical position unless something is changed. If the magnetism of the stator, or of the rotor is now changed, the shaft will rotate another half turn.

The magnetism is changed by using electromagnets instead of permanent ones as shown in Fig. 7-15. Now, when the rotor reaches the vertical position, the alternating current reverses, due to its cycling, and the stator polarity reverses. The rotor S pole is now near the S pole of the stator, and they will repel each other. The rotor will now turn or revolve one half a revolution or 180 degrees. If the rotor turns a half revolution during one half of 60 cycles, then it turns a half turn during 1/120 of a second. It will then turn 60 revolutions per second or

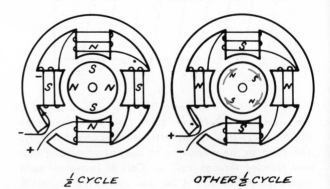

Fig. 7-17. Four pole stator. It produces one quarter turn of the armature as current completes one cycle in field windings.

60 x 60 seconds or 3600 revolutions in one minute. The two pole motor (3600 rpm) has become a popular hermetic motor for refrigerating and air conditioning units. Its construction is shown in Fig. 7-16.

If four poles are used in the stator, the motor will turn only 1800 revolutions per minute; that is, the rotor will only turn one fourth revolution in 1/120 of a second as shown in Fig. 7-17. Most open motors are of this design, and some hermetic motors also use the four pole principle.

The 3600 rpm and 1800 rpm speeds are called synchronous speeds. Under actual conditions the 3600 design usually operates at 3400 rpm while the 1800 design at 1750 rpm.

A typical electric motor is shown in Fig. 7-18. This motor is an open motor of the capacitor start type. It can be used to drive refrigeration compressors, pumps, and the like.

7-19 Inductance and Inductors

A magnet formed by winding a coil of wire on a soft iron core as shown in Fig. 7-10, will become magnetized if an electrical current is passed through the wire. The entire coil is surrounded and permeated by magnetic lines of force (flux). As the current is switched on to such a coil, the magnetism is not built up instantly. There is a delay of perhaps a few hundredths of a second during which time the current continues to increase until it reaches its full value depending on the resistance and voltage of the circuit. Likewise, when the switch is opened and the current is turned off, it does not instantly stop flowing. The magnetic lines build up as the switch is turned on or collapse as the switch is turned off, and there is a tendency to generate within the coils of wire an electromotive force which counteracts the change in the current flow. This counteracting force is

called counter electromotive force or counter emf. It acts much like a flywheel on a piece of machinery. The flywheel requires power to give it a rotating motion and likewise it gives up power if it is forced to stop.

Induced magnetism is useful in electric motors. By putting electrical windings on the field poles, magnetism can be created or induced in the rotor. There is a slight time delay in this induction, and therefore, if the rotor has once started to turn, the rotor will continue to turn, because the field pole (stator) always has the opposite polarity. During the time the field pole changes its polarity, it induces an opposite pole in the stator. This repels the rotor pole toward the next stator pole, which has become an opposite pole in the meantime. The rotor must turn the full distance between the two poles before the induced magnetism can be changed or the motor will not keep running. It is also important to remember that it takes only 1/120 of a second to change the magnetism from full strength N to a full strength S pole. This principle is used in the design of the split-phase motor. There are two windings in this motor; a starting winding and a running winding. The starting winding is a smaller diameter wire than the running winding, however it has a greater number of turns than the running winding. As a result, its magnetic inductance will be greater than for the running winding. This means that the starting winding is always behind the running winding in both building up and stopping its magnetic field. This type of inductance is generally known as self inductance. There is another type of inductance, known as mutual inductance. In this type of inductance the magnetic effect in one coil induces a flow of electricity and a magnetic field in another coil which is close to it. This principle is illustrated in Fig. 7-13. The principle of mutual induction is used in all induction type mo-

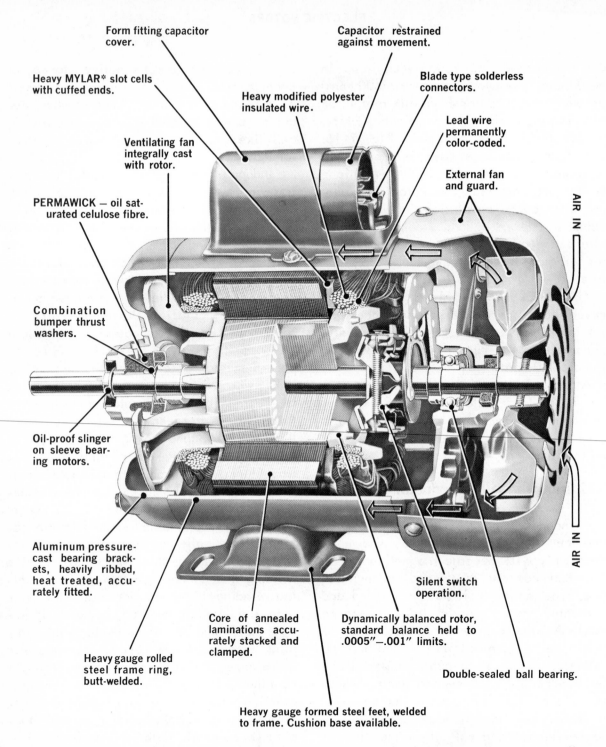

Form fitting capacitor cover.

Capacitor restrained against movement.

Heavy MYLAR* slot cells with cuffed ends.

Heavy modified polyester insulated wire.

Blade type solderless connectors.

Lead wire permanently color-coded.

Ventilating fan integrally cast with rotor.

External fan and guard.

PERMAWICK — oil saturated celulose fibre.

AIR IN

Combination bumper thrust washers.

Oil-proof slinger on sleeve bearing motors.

Aluminum pressure-cast bearing brackets, heavily ribbed, heat treated, accurately fitted.

AIR IN

Silent switch operation.

Heavy gauge rolled steel frame ring, butt-welded.

Core of annealed laminations accurately stacked and clamped.

Dynamically balanced rotor, standard balance held to .0005"—.001" limits.

Double-sealed ball bearing.

Heavy gauge formed steel feet, welded to frame. Cushion base available.

Fig. 7-18. Section through typical motor suitable for use on refrigeration and air conditioning installations. This illustration shows a sleeve bearing at shaft extension end and a ball bearing at other end. This is to illustrate possible bearing construction. (Century Electric Co.)

tors. In these motors, the magnetic effect of the current flowing in the field windings induces the current in conductors on the rotor. The magnetic effect of this induced rotor current causes the rotor to revolve. This characteristic of the flow of current, in an electromagnet, to resist the flow when the current is turned on and to resist the stopping of the flow when the current is turned off, depends on

214

Lenz's Law (see Par. 7-16) which states that the polarity of an induced voltage is such that it opposes the motion of the flux inducing it.

7-20 Electronics Terminology

Electronics may be defined as the art and science of electron flow through gases, vacuums, and semiconductors. Electronics was first developed with the discovery of vacuum tubes and gas filled tubes.

It was found that electrons would flow from a heated element in a tube to another element if a potential difference existed between the two elements. Fig. 7-19 shows a simple circuit of this type.

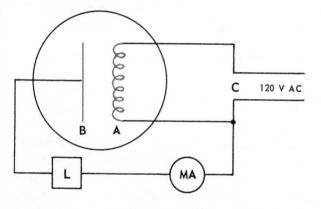

Fig. 7-19. Diagram of vacuum tube rectifier. Electrons will flow from heated element A to plate B. C shows power source which is 120V alternating current. L indicates direct current load. This might be a storage cell on charge. MA is a milliammeter which shows rate of DC flow.

The first radios used the vacuum tube to control and amplify the radio signals. These tubes were fragile and relatively large. The invention of the semiconductor has greatly enlarged the applications of electronics.

In the previous paragraphs in this chapter, the necessary fundamental circuit information pertaining to electric motors has been given in an elementary way. In the following ten paragraphs some elec-

tronics technical terminology will be explained. This includes such things as:

1. Capacitance.
2. Semiconductors.
3. Diodes.
4. Rectifiers.
5. Transistors.
6. Thermistors and Varistors.
7. Sensors.
8. Amplifiers.
9. Transducers.
10. Photoelectricity.

With the development of rather complicated automatic refrigerating and air conditioning appliances, we are making use of more and more electronic devices. It will be necessary for you to understand these devices in order to understand the circuits in which they are used.

7-21 Capacitance

Capacitance may be defined as a system of conductors and insulators which permit the storage of electricity. This ability is indicated by the letter C. In referring to the capacities of a series or group of capacitors, they are usually designated as C_1, C_2, C_3, etc.

The unit of capacity is the farad. The symbol for the farad is the small letter f. A farad may be defined as a charge of one coulomb on the capacitor surface with a potential difference of one volt between the plates. A farad is a rather large unit of capacity. Most capacitors (condensers) used in the refrigeration industry are rated in microfarads. A microfarad is one-millionth of a farad. The symbol for the microfarad is (μf). The Greek letter μ(mu) is used instead of the English m.

7-22 Semiconductors

Semiconductors are carefully created small wafers or capsules of metallic materials combined with insulating materials to produce a material classified as a

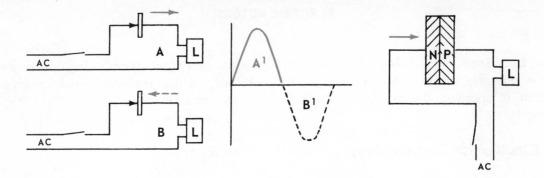

Fig. 7-20. *When alternating current is imposed on diode wafer it allows only current represented by that part of sine wave shown at* A[1] *to pass through, and will stop the other half cycle* B[1] *from passing through. This will provide an intermittent flow of direct current.*

semiconductor. The material has electrical properties somewhere between a conductor (metals) and insulators (nonmetals). These are called solid state semiconductors. These semiconductors are often made of germanium and silicon. These materials are "doped" in a very careful way with impurities. The "dope" changes the atom structure (crystal structure). Scientists have developed "doped" semiconductors which will provide a variety of desired electronic characteristics. Some are developed to provide thermoelectric effect and are used in thermoelectric refrigerators. See Par. 3-15.

7-23 Diodes

A solid state diode is a two-material solid material wafer or capsule which al-

lows electrons to flow through it in one direction only as shown in Fig. 7-20. The diode acts as an electron flow check valve.

Vacuum tubes can also serve as diodes as shown in Fig. 7-21. Electrons will flow from the pointed filament to the plate but during the other half cycle the electrons will not flow from the plate to the pointed filament.

7-24 Rectifiers

Rectifiers are electronic valves which permit the flow of electrons through them in one direction only. These devices rectify the alternating current to an output of direct current only. A simple rectifier therefore uses only one half of the sine wave. To use both halves of the sine wave and still produce only direct current one must use four diodes as shown in Fig. 7-22. A SCR is a silicon controlled rectifier.

Four vacuum tubes can be used in the same manner to produce a constant flow of DC.

7-25 Transistors

A transistor is a three layer sandwich of two different components which consist chiefly of germanium semiconductor material. Electrically the three wafers are connected as shown in Fig. 7-23.

The materials are labeled P for positive, meaning a lack of electons (it has "holes" ready to receive electrons), and N for negative, meaning the material has a

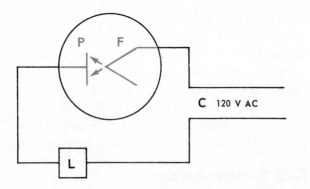

Fig. 7-21. *A diagram of a vacuum tube serving as an alternating current rectifier. Vacuum tube is serving as a diode. Note that electrons will flow only from pointed filament F to plate P. L indicates direct current load. This may be a storage battery being charged.*

surplus of electrons. Three wires connect to the transistor; one wire attaches to the base or middle wafer, one wire connects to one of the outer wafers which is called the emitter and the third wire is connected to the collector. The outer two

All three parts are semiconductors having added substances to give the desired characteristics. Fig. 7-23A shows in a schematic way, the basic construction of a transistor. The symbol for a transistor is shown in Fig. 7-23B.

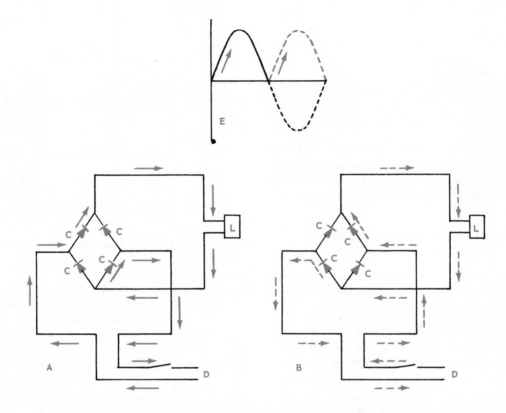

Fig. 7-22. Circuit for a full wave rectifier: A—Circuit for one-half of wave. B—Circuit for other half of wave. C—Four diodes needed. D—60 cycle AC power supply. E—Note how two halves of AC cycle have been caused to provide a DC current flowing in same direction. L—DC load.

wafers are of the same material and the base material (middle wafer) is a different material.

A small electron flow from the emitter to the base will control a large electron flow from the emitter to the collector. The device therefore acts as a valve and as a relay. An electron signal circuit emitter to base may control electron flow a thousand times larger than emitter to collector.

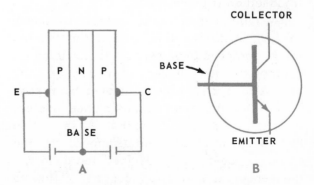

Fig. 7-23. Electrical symbol for a transistor.

A transistor connected as an amplifier is shown in Fig. 7-24. The low energy signal enters the circuit at the left. The signal is amplified by the action of the transistor and energy supplied by the batteries. The amplified signal (load) is shown leaving the circuit at the right.

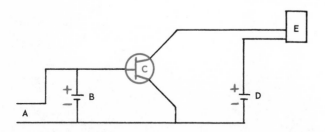

Fig. 7-24. Circuit diagram showing transistor used in amplifier circuit. A—Signal (current) to be amplified enters here. B—Battery. C—Transistor. D—Battery. E—Amplified current load.

7-26 Thermistors and Varistors

A thermistor is a solid state semiconductor which permits or allows more electrons to flow through it as the material's temperature increases. It can be used in place of a bimetel strip or in place of a temperature sensitive power element. It is used as a temperature safety device in electric motors, and to stop the electric power flow to a motor if the motor windings temperature increases to the danger point.

A varistor is a semiconductor which decreases in resistance as the voltage imposed on it increases.

A typical thermistor circuit is shown in Fig. 7-25. In this circuit the thermistor temperature sensor C is used to control the temperature of a room or conditioned space which is heated by means of a 120V AC electric resistance heater.

The temperature control A is set to the desired room temperature. If the room is below this desired temperature the sensor C will allow current to flow to transistors D and E where the current is

amplified and the thermal relay heater I will cause the contact points at J to close which brings the electric space heater K into operation.

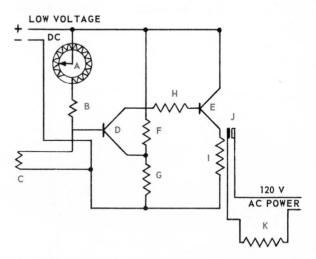

Fig. 7-25. Typical thermister circuit. A—Temperature control knob which controls variable resistance. B—Fixed resistance. C—Thermister temperature sensor. D and E—Transistors. F and G—Bias resistors. H—Current limiting resistor. I—Thermal relay heater. J—Thermal relay. K—120V AC electric space heater. This sensor will maintain temperature of heated space within close limits.

As soon as the desired temperature is reached the sensor C will cause the current to the heater coil to be switched off and the contact points at J will open and stop the flow of current to the space heater. These devices are very sensitive and will maintain the space temperature within a fraction of a degree variation.

7-27 Sensors

In electronic circuits the control signal is controlled by a sensor. This sensor is a solid state semiconductor material which controls electron flow as its temperature changes. A typical completely automatic automotive air conditioner uses three sensors in its circuitry; 1. outside (ambient) temperature, 2. in the car temperature, 3. in the air discharge duct temperature.

7-28 Amplifiers

An amplifier is an electronic device used to change a small current flow to a large current flow. Both the vacuum tube and the semiconductor type may be used. Some systems use a combination of tubes and solid state semiconductors. A typical amplifier circuit is shown in Fig. 7-26.

7-29 Transducers

The term transducer is used to identify a great variety of devices which are sensitive to changes in the intensity of some form of energy and which may respond by controlling the intensity of some other form of energy. Transducers may be operated by pressure, temperature, fluid flow, vibration, electrical potential and others. A small varying current flow through a transducer may be amplified by an amplifier and the amplified current may then operate an indicating instrument or a control circuit.

An application of a transducer is shown in Fig. 7-27. In this application a pressure transducer is connected to a pipe (A) which is carrying fluid under pressure. The transducer (B) will change pressure variation into electric current variation. In the amplifier (C) electric current variations are amplified and connected to (D), a relaying device which may translate what was a weak pipe pressure variation into a recorder, pressure gauge, signal light, oscilloscope or other signal indicating devices.

7-30 Photoelectricity

Photoelectricity is the property of certain substances to create differing amounts of electron flow depending on the light energy striking their surface.

A typical application is the photoelectric operation of store doors or the operation of an automatic ice cube maker.

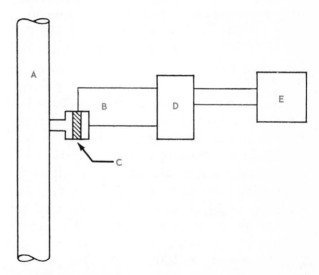

Fig. 7-27. A transducer application: A—Pipe carrying a fluid under pressure. B—Transducer. C—Crystal. D—Amplifier. E—Recording device which records or shows pressure condition in pipe (A). This may be a gauge, signal light, oscilloscope, a pressure recorder or any other pressure indicating device.

7-31 Electrical Power, Units, Sources and Distribution

Electrical power is measured in watts (w), kilowatts (kw), and megawatts (mw). A watt is the amount of electrical power produced by a current of one ampere flowing under a potential of one volt. A mw equals 1,000,000 watts.

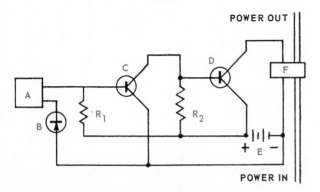

Fig. 7-26. Typical amplifier circuit. A—Sensor. B—Diode. C—Transistor. D—Transistor. E—Low voltage DC supply. F—Relay. R_1 and R_2—Voltage control resistors. This amplifier may be used to multiply weak signals making possible the control of more powerful circuits.

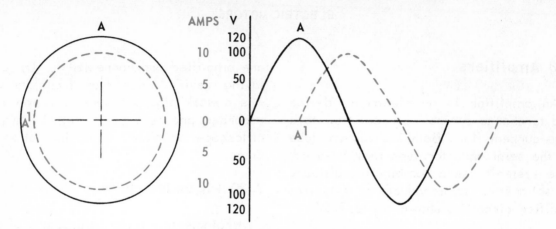

Fig. 7-28. Combined voltage and current curve. Current is maximum when voltage is changing fastest. This curve will only apply when the circuit is connected to motors or coils, or what is known as an inductive load.

Electrical power in watts is equal to the voltage multiplied by the current (amperage). This is true with DC circuits but may not be exactly true with AC circuits. This is because the voltage wave and the current wave in an AC circuit are not always together. This condition is shown in Fig. 7-28.

In AC circuits the power may be indicated by E multiplied by I_e in which case I_e = the I x power factor which may be determined by the use of instruments. The utility company is always in a position to determine the power factor for a circuit. Certain kinds of electrical loads tend to reduce the power factor while other kinds of electrical loads tend to improve it.

A kilowatt is 1000 watts. One horsepower is equal to 746 watts. Since power is voltage multiplied by amperage, a certain amount of electrical power may be supplied either by using a high voltage and low amperage or by using a low voltage and a high amperage.

Power (W) = (E) voltage x (I) amperage.

W = E x I

Example: 115V x 20 I = 2300 watts
    or   230V x 10 I = 2300 watts

In Par. 7-6, it was explained that resistance to electrical flow in a conductor produces heat. The heat produced is indicated by voltage drop in the circuit. It is indicated by I x R and is called IR drop. The amount of power loss to heat will be voltage drop I x R multiplied by the current or it may be indicated by I x R x I = I^2R. This is called I squared R loss or I^2R loss.

From this it may be seen that the power

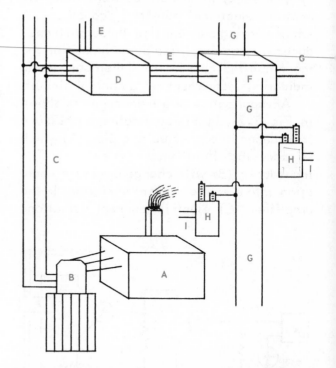

Fig. 7-29. Schematic diagram of a power generating and distribution system: A—Steam power generating plant. B—Step up transformer. Generated power is stepped up to 120,000V. C—120,000V transfer lines. D—Region transformer station. Power is stepped down to 40,000V. E—Sub-transmission line 40,000V. F—Area transformer station, voltage is stepped down to 13,200 or 4,800V. G—Primary distribution circuits. H—House or neighborhood transformers. I—Secondary circuit to homes, businesses and industry. 120, 240 or 440V.

220

loss in a circuit for a certain size of conductor may be decreased by increasing the voltage and lowering the current. This is the reason that cross country power lines always operate at high voltages.

The electric motors used in an air conditioning or refrigeration system must match (must be designed to be used with) the electric power furnished by the electric utility.

These motor properties must match the power source:

1. Voltage.
2. Cycle.
3. Phase.

The wires must be large enough to carry the full or maximum current that the motor will use.

The voltage may be:

1. 110V.
2. 115V.
3. 120V.

or

1. 208V.
2. 220V.
3. 230V.
4. 240V.
5. 277V.

The cycle may be:

1. 25.
2. 50.
3. 60.

The phase may be:

1. Single phase.
2. Two phase.
3. Three phase.

Some popular power electrical sources are:

115V, 60 cycle, single phase.
120V, 60 cycle, single phase.
208V, 60 cycle, single phase.
230V, 60 cycle, single phase.
240V, 60 cycle, single phase.
230V, 60 cycle, three phase.
240V, 60 cycle, three phase.
440V, 60 cycle, three phase.

In special cases current may even be two phase or four phase. The technology of electric power is rapidly changing. It may be that power sources will change in the future. Because the size of the motor depends on the voltage and the phase, the future may see 440 to 500 volt power sources at high cycles (120,300 and 500). The aircraft industry already uses motors of this type to save weight and space. In this design motors may be much smaller for the same horespower.

Carefully check the power source before purchasing or installing equipment. Check with the electrical utility before installing equipment of any sizeable horsepower. One of the concerns of the electrical utility is the flicker in lights, television sets, and radios when a motor-compressor starts. This flicker is especially critical if the motor-compressor starts more than four times in an hour. This flicker is worsened when power to motor is not strong enough (wires too small or too long).

Several types of transformers are used by electrical utilities to transform high voltage to electrical power that is satisfactory to the user. The systems used are dependent on whether the electrical power is mainly for residential, for industrial power, or for commercial lighting.

At the generating station the power is stepped up to a voltage considerably above the voltages used by appliances and motors for either domestic service or by industry. This current is usually sent across country over a high voltage transmission line at a voltage of 120,000 volts. A schematic diagram which illustrates the fundamentals of a power distributing system is shown in Fig. 7-29.

Step down transformer stations (region stations) are located along the high voltage transmission line in areas which are to be served with power. At these region stations, step down transformers step down the high voltage transmission line electricity to a voltage of 40,000 volts. This is carried to the communities to be served where it is again stepped down to 13,200 or

4,800 volts. This voltage may be safely handled with the usual utility linemen's equipment.

Electricity is carried to the customers by the primary distributing lines. At the customer's premises, the electricity is again stepped down to the voltage needed; 120, 240, or 440 volts, depending on the customer's needs.

7-32 Transformers

As indicated in Par. 7-31, alternating electrical current is generated and distributed at voltages greatly above the voltage used by the consumer.

Transformers are required to step down this voltage to the final voltage to be used by the consumer.

It should be noted that the final voltage delivered will depend on the nature of the customer's use for the current.

Common types of transformers are:
1. Delta type (from the Greek letter delta Δ).
   A. Open Delta.
   B. Closed Delta.
2. Y type (from the capital letter Y).

Fig. 7-30 shows a wiring diagram for the open delta type transformer. The closed delta type will be explained later.

The input voltage from the power station can be one of several voltages (usually 4200V), and the circuit is three phase (three hot wires). The open delta system is different from the closed delta system in that two connected transformers are used (1 and 2) instead of three. The power into the transformer windings is called the primary, the power out of the transformer windings is called the secondary, regardless of which of the two are of the higher voltage. The voltage of each secondary outlet is designed to be 240 volts (A to B or B to D). A ground wire is connected to the middle of secondary winding of 1. Therefore the voltage between D and C is 120 volts and B and C is 120 volts. A

special voltage is created between C and A. Because the secondary winding is all of 2 and then angles half way down the secondary winding of 1, the voltage between A and C (a geometric change of angle) is 208 volts. This 208V is popular where the main electrical load of a building is the lighting load. It is not a good motor voltage. Many motor-compressors are connected to this type circuit, however the motor must be designed to operate at this voltage or a line voltage transformer must be used. See Par. 7-33.

The electrical utility will inspect the circuitry on request and determine for the user if their lines or wires are large enough to carry a new electrical load to

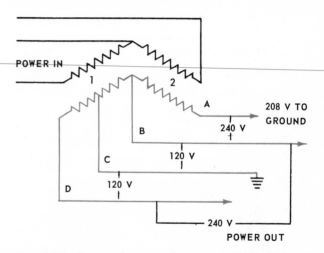

Fig. 7-30. Circuit diagram of open type "delta" transformer. Power may be obtained from four taps A, B, C and D as follows:

From: A to B 240 volts.
       A to C 208 volts.
       B to C 120 volts.
       C to D 120 volts.
       B to D 240 volts.

the building. However, the serviceman himself must check the wires inside the building. (The longer the length of wire, the larger the diameter must be to safely carry the current.) This inspection makes sure the correct voltages will be available at the maximum amperage load to the motor-compressor.

A dangerous condition exists if there is a voltage drop of over 5%, less than 95% of the desired voltage, at the motor-compressor. For example, if a 208V circuit, due to its length, wire size, and amperage load, has only (208V x 95% = 208V x .95 = 197.6 volts), it is at the very lowest usable voltage. If the voltage goes below this, the motor may work poorly or burn out.

A serious situation may occur if a 240 volt motor compressor is connected to a 208V line because (240 x 95%) = 240 x .95 = 228V. The 240V motor will operate poorly, the overload protection will operate, and the motor may fail.

A 230V motor will operate down to 218.5V (230 x 95% = 230V x .95 = 218.5V). Therefore a 208V circuit is dangerous.

A 220V motor will operate down to 209V (220V x 95% - 220V x .95 = 209V) and this motor may operate at 208 volts, but it is a borderline case and the efficiency will be low.

However, motors can use voltages over their voltage rating. In fact, a 208V motor connected to a 220V line will operate very well, will start faster, and will give more power to the compressor. A 10% over normal voltage will let a motor carry a 20% overload. However, a 208V motor on a 240V line will be much noisier, important in air conditioning.

A 220V motor operates very well on a 240V line. A 220V motor can operate on a 208V line, but it will have lower torque. These are single-phase motors. Motors with as much as 7 1/2 horsepower may be wired for single phase. When only single phase is available and more than 7 1/2 horsepower is needed, two or more motor-compressors should be used in the system.

A table of changes in a motor's operating characteristics, as the input voltage changes, is as follows:

A 230V motor compressor works with the same efficiency as a 115V motor compressor. The notion that a 230V motor uses less kilowatt hours to do the same amount of work is false. For example, a 115V motor uses 5 amperes to create 775 watts (115 x 5) = 775 watts or .775 kilowatts. The only advantage is that the 230V unit may use smaller size wires from the meter box to the unit.

Some motors are labeled 208-220V to to indicate that they may be used with either voltage. However, these motors are sensitive to voltages below 208V and voltages of 195V or lower must not be used.

For example in a home air conditioner, the power circuit is usually 230V, three wire. This means there is 230V between the two hot wires and there is 115V between the hot wire and the ground wire, as shown in Fig. 7-31. These voltages should

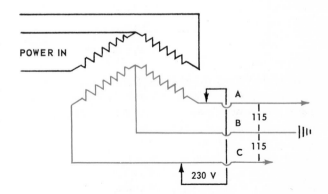

Fig. 7-31. Schematic circuit diagram of transformer. This is type transformer used to serve usual home. Note that 115 volts are available between both A and B, and B and C, B is a ground. Voltage of 230 is available between lines A and C.

be checked (verified) with a voltmeter. Do not trust a test light and guess at its bulb brilliance.

Another transformer design used by utilities is the Y type shown in Fig. 7-32.

INPUT VOLTAGE	CURRENT	TORQUE	TEMPERATURE	CYCLE SLIP	EFFICIENCY
+ 10%	– 7%	+ 21%	–3 deg. C. = (5.5 deg. F.)	17% decrease	1% increase
–10%	+11%	–15%	+7 deg. C. = (12.5 deg. F.)	23% increase	2% decrease

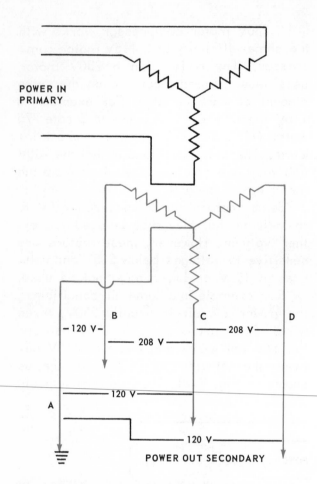

POWER IN
PRIMARY

B

C

D

— 120 V —

— 208 V —

— 208 V —

— 120 V —

A

— 120 V —

POWER OUT SECONDARY

Fig. 7-32. Y-type transformer. Note that center of Y is grounded in secondary circuit. The following voltages may be obtained from this transformer by connecting the following terminals:

> A and B – 120 volts.
> A and C – 120 volts.
> A and D – 120 volts.
> B and C – 208 volts.
> C and D – 208 volts.

This system uses three transformers, connected as shown. Note that a 208V circuit is also possible for this system. In fact, any two of the three wires produces 208V. This is made possible by the angle of the two secondary windings.

When studying a building wiring system to decide on the circuit necessary for a motor compressor, the wire sizes should be checked for capacity when all electrical appliances are on at the same time. Also, the average load per day should be checked. A recording ammeter may be

used for this purpose if the utility does not already have the data. A demand meter will usually be put in by the electrical utility if requested.

A voltage system which is recommended by some utilities is the 277-440V system. It is the least critical and therefore it is a good system for commercial-industrial use. This system is shown in Fig. 7-33. One difficulty with this system is that the motor may continue to run even though the motor wires are grounded. A grounded conductor or a motor in the circuit may act as a condenser, and the other motors may continue to operate (with a loss of power) even though one fuse is blown.

Utilities circuits may show as much as 212V at the meter on a 208V system, or as much as 250V on a 240V system. However, because an increase in voltage is as much a disadvantage to light bulb life as it is an advantage for a motor-compressor, the utilities keep their circuit voltages as close to the noted value as possible.

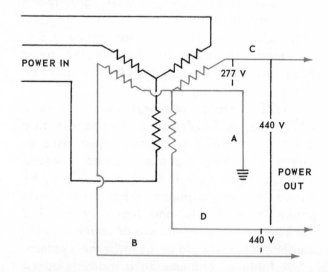

POWER IN

C

277 V

440 V

A

POWER
OUT

D

B

440 V

Fig. 7-33. Schematic of Y-type transformer. This is the type of transformer for industrial and commercial users. The following voltages are available from the transformer:

> Between: A and C – 277 volts.
> B and D – 440 volts.
> C and D – 440 volts.

The closed delta system is shown in Fig. 7-34. This system is sometimes found in large industries. The transformer is not grounded.

A three-phase motor will continue to run even though one fuse is blown (open). The faulty fuse can only be accurately located by using a voltmeter (it will show about a 50V difference between the open line and one of the other lines).

The 277V circuit is used for some units of 15,000 to 35,000 Btu/hour capacity. It may be obtained by an angular tap from a Y type transformer, when one lead is from any of the three legs and the other lead is from the center of the Y.

7-33 Line Voltage Transformer /0

Improper line voltage may lead to a "burn out" in refrigeration and air conditioning motors. Line voltages may vary as much as 5 to 10%. Equipment which is designed to operate on 115 volts plus or minus 10 volts may not operate well in areas where the voltage drops to 100 volts or lower. To overcome the problem of voltage fluctuation and also to provide for the use of equipment designed for 115 volts to be used on 240V lines, a line voltage

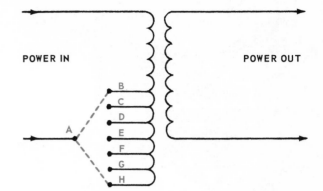

Fig. 7-35. *Wiring diagram of transformer designed to step up or step down voltages to provide correct voltage for driving motor. Connecting terminal A to B, C, or D will step up the power out voltage. Connecting terminal A to F, G, or H will step down power out voltage. Connecting A to E will not change voltage but will tend to stabilize it.*

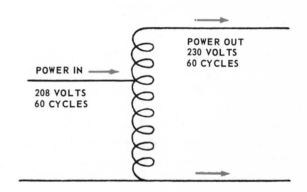

Fig. 7-36. *Wiring diagram of voltage transformer used to step up 208V to 230V.*

transformer may be used to provide the proper voltage service to the appliance. This transformer is designed to increase or decrease the input voltage to the motor as needed. Fig. 7-35 shows a basic wiring diagram of a "boost-and-buck" voltage transformer being used to correct the line voltage to 115 volts. Fig. 7-36 shows a wiring diagram of a single coil transformer designed to change a 208V circuit to 230 volts. A voltage of 208V is quite common in buildings in which the lighting load is the main electrical load. A line transformer will be required if 115 or 230V motors are to be used on

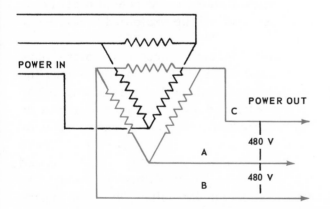

Fig. 7-34. *Diagram of closed delta type transformer. The following voltages are available from this transformer:*

    Between: A and B – 480 volts.
               A and C – 480 volts.

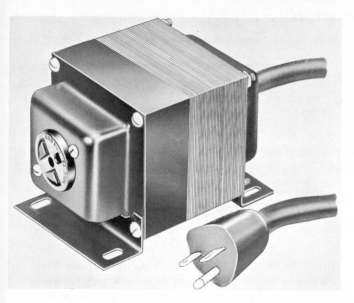

Fig. 7-37. Line transformer which may be used to transform 208V AC current to 230V AC current. (Acme Electric Corp.)

the 208V current supply. This is sometimes called an auto transformer. See Fig. 7-37.

A 115V transformer output can be produced through the use of various connections on the input side ranging from 95 to 260 volts. The serviceman must first determine the required voltage by referring to the motor name plate and specifications. A voltmeter is used to measure the voltage and amperage at the motor-compressor when the unit is running. A transformer is then selected which will carry the amperage and it is adjusted to raise (most common) or lower the voltage as needed. The transformer is connected in the circuit between the electrical service and the refrigerating unit. The serviceman should check the completed installation for both ampere flow and voltage. If these values are different than the motor ratings, further adjustments will be necessary.

7-34 Types of Electric Motors

Two types of current may be used to drive refrigerating equipment. These are alternating current (AC) and direct current (DC). Alternating current is the type

most commonly used although there are a few areas which still use direct current.

The alternating current motor types used to drive compressors are as follows:

1. Basic types:
   A. Single-phase motors.
   B. Two, three and four-phase motors (polyphase).
2. The open motor. These are used on open belt driven compressors:
   A. Repulsion-start induction type.
   B. Capacitor-start induction type.
   C. Capacitor-start, capacitor-run type.
   D. Capacitor-run motor.
   E. Induction polyphase type.
3. The hermetic motor. These are used on hermetic systems in which the motor and compressor are sealed in a common housing or dome:
   A. Capacitor-start induction type.
   B. Capacitor-start, capacitor-run type.
   C. Capacitor-run type.
   D. Induction two-phase and polyphase types.
4. The condenser and evaporator coil fan motor types:
   A. Split-phase type.
   B. Shaded-pole type.
   C. Capacitor type.

The types listed in red are in most common use and will be explained in some detail.

Repulsion-start induction motors have been used since 1918. These were used for the conventional belt-driven compressor in the 20's and 30's. One exception was an early Copeland unit, which used an induction motor on a belt-driven unit and used a centrifugal clutch pulley which allowed the motor to start without a load. The clutch engaged the pulley after the motor reached almost full speed.

The capacitor motor is now being used on most applications. It is the most popular motor used on single-phase hermetic machines.

226

Direct current motors are used in areas which are supplied with direct current only.

7-35 Open System Motors

There are two main types of motors used to drive open model compressors:
1. Repulsion start-induction run motor, as shown in Fig. 7-38.
2. Capacitor start-induction run motor, as shown in Fig. 7-39.

The motors are usually connected to the compressor by means of V-belts. The speed reduction is usually about three to one. This reduction means that the compressor flywheel diameter is three times larger than the motor pulley diameter.

7-36 Induction Motors

Induction motors have no windings on the armature or rotor. However, the rotor does have copper bars, or other conducting material, in its outer surface parallel to the motor shaft and in which a current of electricity is induced. The turning or torque is produced by induced magne-

Fig. 7-38. Section view of a repulsion-start induction 1/2 hp motor. Note that this motor has wound rotor and centrifugal mechanism which shorts rotor winding and raises brushes off commutator as soon as motor attains approximately 75% of running speed. A—Centrifugal mechanism. B—Commutator shorting segments. C—Brushes and brush holder. Wick oilers are used at bearings.
(Wagner Electric Corp.)

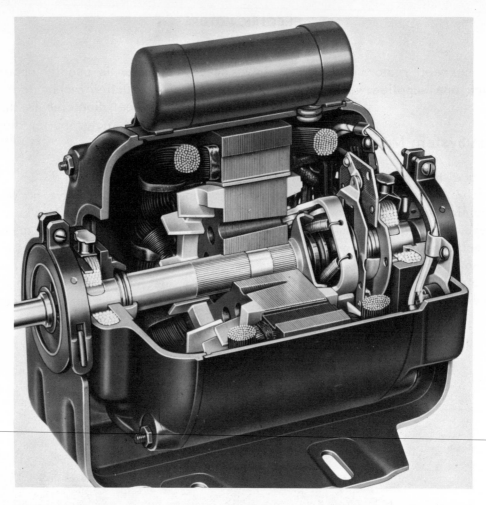

Fig. 7-39. *Capacitor-start induction motor. Motor has rubber mounts at each end which provide flexibility. Capacitor is mounted in housing on top of motor. Wick oiling is used.*

tism in these bars. One or more field windings are mounted in the stator. As the alternating current passes through these windings, it creates a changing magnetic field. This magnetism in turn passes through the rotor, inducing (building up) an electrical current in the rotor bars. This induced current creates an opposite magnetic field in the rotor. The opposing magnetism causes the rotor to revolve as it tries to keep up with the changing field polarities.

All motors used inside hermetic machines are induction motors and most of them use two field windings: (1) a starting winding, (2) a running winding. An external relay is used to disconnect the starting winding as soon as the motor reaches about 75 percent of its full speed.

Almost all motors are a form of an induction motor. The larger two and three-phase motors use a running winding only.

7-37 Split-Phase Induction Motors

This is the basic type motor used for most fractional horsepower appliance operation. It has the advantage of relatively low cost and the principle of operation is simple. It has two stator windings, a running winding and a starting winding.

The starting windings are made into two or four coils in series depending on the motor speed. These starting windings are usually positioned several degrees from the running windings. This positioning puts the starting windings several electrical degrees from the running windings.

A smaller wire is used in the starting winding, however it has more turns than the running winding. Due to the counter emf in the greater number of coils in the starting winding, the current will build up more slowly in this winding, consequently the magnetic effect of these windings will be retarded in relation to the running windings. This will cause a torque on the rotor which causes it to start turning. The starting windings are disconnected as soon as the motor reaches approximately 75 percent of its running speed.

This motor does not have windings on the rotor, however localized magnetism does build up in the rotor. Some rotors have heavy copper bars fitted into slots in the laminated iron of the rotor. The ends of these copper bars are braze welded to heavy copper rings at each end to complete the electrical circuit. This type of winding is often called squirrel-cage winding.

7-38 Repulsion-Start Induction Motor

The repulsion-start induction motors have long been popular where starting and stopping operation is needed, such as open unit refrigerators, washing machines, oil

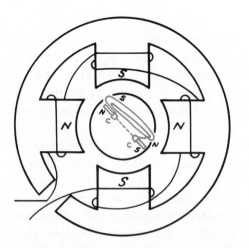

Fig. 7-40. *Diagrammatic sketch of repulsion-start, induction-run motor C commutator. Brushes that contact commutator are grounded and complete circuit between two commutator bars.*

burners, etc. However, this type motor has now been replaced by capacitor type motors in many cases. The repulsion-start induction motor is an induction motor with a special winding in the armature to give it a high starting torque. The motor starts as a repulsion motor using brushes in the armature winding circuit. As soon as it reaches a specified speed, the armature windings are shorted, the brushes are usually lifted from the commutator, and the motor operates as an induction motor, as shown in Fig. 7-40.

The brush-lifting motors usually have radial commutators. Some of the motors do not lift the brushes but simply short circuit the commutator. The motors which do not lift the brushes but simply short circuit the commutator usually have cylindrical commutators.

Refrigeration motors for open units usually need a high torque at starting speeds to overcome the inertia of the refrigeration units' parts and to compress the vapor from the low side pressure to the high side pressure.

Because the turning movement of a motor is the result of magnetism, it is necessary to add more magnets to increase the starting torque or increase the strength of the magnets.

The repulsion-start induction motor increases the starting torque by increasing the magnetic strength of the rotor magnets.

The rotor is wound with a number of separate coils of wire. The ends of these coils are fastened to commutator bars. There are the same number of brushes as field poles. The carbon brushes complete the circuit between commutator bars, and there is current flow in the rotor coils. Because this current flow creates magnetic poles, the brushes can be located so these magnets repulse the magnetism of the field poles and create torque. Due to the current going through the starting winding, the motor draws more current during starting.

When the motor reaches one-half to two-thirds of its standard rpm, a centrifugal weight moves and shorts out the bars of the commutator, short circuiting the current flow in the rotor windings. Many motors connect this centrifugal device to the brushes also, and the brushes are lifted from the commutator bars, at the same time the commutator bars are shorted, to reduce brush wear.

Due to possible arcing inside the motor as it starts, these motors are not suitable for hermetic compressors.

7-39 Capacitor Type Induction Motor

The open capacitor motor is a popular type of motor. The name comes from the use of a capacitor (a condenser) or the use of a combination condenser and transformer. Fig. 7-41 shows the most common type which becomes a two-phase motor when starting and reverts to single-phase when it has gained approximately 75 percent of its full speed. The capacitor is

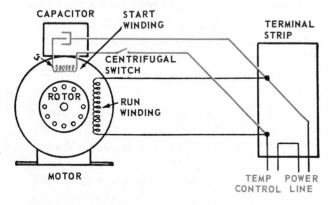

Fig. 7-41. Wiring diagram of capacitor-start induction motor. Note that capacitor is in series with starting field winding as motor starts. Centrifugal switch opens this winding as soon as motor reaches approximately 75 percent of full speed.
(Stewart-Warner Corp.)

used to change the phase angle of the current in the starting winding to produce two-phase electrical characteristics when starting.

The mechanical construction of the capacitor motor is quite similar to the repulsion start-induction motor; that is, the external appearance, the mountings, and the bearing design is the same both as to size and lubrication. However, instead of using a starting winding in the armature, the capacitor type has a condenser which is usually placed on top of the motor. The capacitor is connected to a centrifugal switch built into the motor and to a starting winding in the stator, as shown in the line diagram, Fig. 7-42.

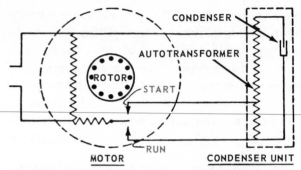

FOR COUNTERCLOCKWISE ROTATION CONNECT AS SHOWN

Fig. 7-42. Wiring diagram of combination capacitor and autotransformer motor. Note double-throw single-pole switch for changing transformer output when centrifugal switch moves from start to run.
(Norge Sales Corp.)

The operation of the mechanism is quite simple. When the motor starts, the centrifugal switch is closed, making the current pass through both the starting winding and the running winding. The starting winding is connected in series with a capacitor which puts the electrical surges in the starting winding out of step or out of phase with those of the running winding. The motor then acts as a temporary two-phase motor and has a very high starting torque. When the motor reaches about 75 percent of its rated speed, a centrifugal switch opens and disconnects the starting winding. The motor, however, continues to run, but now as an induction motor.

These motors are called capacitor-start induction-run motors. The capacitor is usually mounted in a steel cylinder which is placed on top of the motor. It has two terminals, one is connected to the centrifugal switch lead and one to the starting winding lead.

The least complicated method to produce greater torque is to change the single-phase motor into a two-phase motor during starting and/or running by using a capacitor. There are two types of capacitors:

1. Starting capacitor.
2. Running capacitor.

The dry type capacitor is usually used as a starting capacitor and has two sheets of conductor metal separated by an insulator, as shown in Fig. 7-43. When a condenser

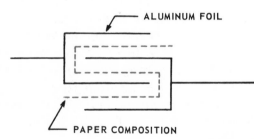

Fig. 7-43. Diagram of capacitor construction. Two layers of metal foil are separated by special insulating paper. The two sheets of foil are connected to two terminals of condenser. Capacitors used on motors are rolled or folded into compact package.

or capacitor is placed in an alternating current line, the capacitor is charged during the buildup of the voltage and current by the surge of power in the line. Then, during the decrease in current flow in the power line as the AC reverses, the capacitor discharges which causes another power surge in the motor starting windings as shown in Fig. 7-44.

The principle of the capacitor is that when the two plates are connected into a circuit, one plate becomes saturated with electrons while the other plate has its

electrons reduced. This other plate therefore has a surplus of protons, when the alternating current reverses the electrons discharge, sending an extra current flow through the starting winding.

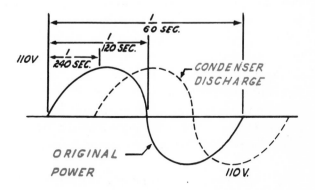

Fig. 7-44. Cycle diagram showing effect of capacitor in series with power flow in single-phase circuit.

The running capacitor operates on the same principle except it is always in operation when the motor is running. This capacitor is usually smaller in size and is designed and constructed to provide better heat removal. The insulation, plates and terminals are designed for durability and long life. Additional information may be found in Paragraph 27-17.

7-40 The Motor Structure

Before each type of motor is studied, it is necessary to know the physical make-up of the basic motor.

The two main parts of a motor are (1) the stator and (2) the rotor. The stator is also known as the frame. This frame is usually cylindrical in shape. The field poles with field windings on them are usually attached to this stator and are part of it. The identification plate is also mounted on the stator.

The rotor is the revolving or rotating part of the motor. It is sometimes called an armature. This rotor is mounted on a shaft. The shaft usually has two journal bearings, one at each end of the motor shaft.

The ends of the motor usually hold the bearings in which the rotor shaft journals are mounted and provide support for the rotor. These end bells or end plates are attached to the stator or frame. The end bells must be carefully lined up to the stator because the bearings must be accurate enough to provide and maintain .001 in. to .002 in. clearance between the field poles and the rotor. The motor bearings are also designed and built to give the proper amount of rotor end play. These bearings are commonly made of brass or bronze. In hermetic units, the compressor bearings may also serve as rotor bearings.

7-41 Starting and Running Windings

Most motors have two windings. These windings are mounted on the stator.

The running winding is the winding the electricity passes through when the motor is in operation. It is a heavier wire than the starting winding. It is installed in the motor in four coils, equally spaced in the 4-pole motor, 1750 rpm; or it is installed in two coils, equally spaced 2-pole motor, 3400 rpm. All motors have a main winding.

Starting winding is found in split-phase motors, and in capacitor motors of all types. It is a smaller diameter wire than the running winding. It, too, is mounted in the stator with the same number of coils as the running winding. The winding is of smaller diameter to allow room for a greater number of turns and therefore split the phase which creates off center magnetism.

Fig. 7-45 shows the electrical circuits of a split-phase electric motor during the time that the motor is starting. When the current goes into the R terminal (during one-half of the cycle) the electrons separate. Most will go through the running winding, while some will go through the starting winding. The magnetism builds up faster in the running winding; thus when the magnetism is created a few thousandths of a second later in the starting winding a turning force is given to the rotor.

When the current, during the other one-half cycle, enters terminal R, most will go through the running winding while some will go through the starting winding. This action reverses the polarity of the electromagnets and again there is the delay of

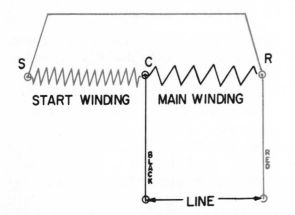

Fig. 7-45. The circuit diagram of an elementary split-phase motor. C is common terminal for both windings. C–R is main or running winding. C–S is starting winding. R is running winding terminal and S is starting winding terminal. Starting winding is usually opened as soon as motor reaches approximately 75 percent of its operating speed.

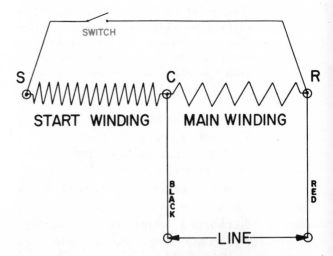

Fig. 7-46. Circuit diagram of split-phase motor using switch in starting winding circuit. Switch is closed as motor starts and will open when motor reaches approximately 75 percent of its running speed.
(Copeland Refrigeration Corp.)

magnetic buildup in the starting winding. The rotor is attracted and repulsed in the same direction of rotation as in the first half of the cycle.

To change the direction of rotation on some of these types of motors, disconnect the starting winding leads from the two terminals and reverse them. That is, put the old S connection (lead) on terminal R and put the old R connection (lead) on terminal S. Reversing the two main leads will not reverse the rotation of the motor.

If the starting winding is left in the circuit it may overheat. Therefore, a switch is mounted in the starting winding circuit which will open when the motor reaches 75 percent of its designed speed, as shown in Fig. 7-46.

7-42 Mechanical Construction of Open Motors

Conventional motors are all similar in design. The stator is made of mild steel rolled into a cylinder and the joint is welded. Aluminum may also be used. The inside of the stator is carefully machined in relation to the machined outside surface of the rotor. Field poles also made of mild steel are fastened to the stator frame by means of large countersunk machine screws, or they may be pressed into the stator.

Iron or aluminum end bells or end frames are carefully fitted to the stator by machine screws. Some have bolts which go the entire length of the stator and hold the two end bells against the stator. The machined face of the stator fits the end bells accurately and helps provide proper alignment. These end bells hold the rotor bearings, which may be either bronze bushings or ball bearings, in which the shaft revolves. The bronze bushings are usually lubricated with No. 30 SAE (300 viscosity) oil while the ball bearings usually have sealed lubrication.

One of the end bells also holds the brush mechanism or centrifugal switch

mechanism. The other end bell has a through bushing, and the rotor shaft extends through this bushing and becomes the pulley shaft. This shaft extension may also have a keyway machined in it, or a flat spot machined for an inch or two of its length. The pulley fits on this shaft extension. A key or setscrew prevents the pulley from slipping on the shaft.

7-43 Motor Connections

Except for reversible and some special motors, motors usually come with two or four leads used to connect the motor to one of two different voltages.

Either 115 or 230 volts (or other corresponding voltages) are equally good, providing the correct voltage is maintained at the motor terminals. These motors may be used on circuits having voltage of 105 to 125 or 210 to 250 volts.

Most electrical power companies are now providing 120V and 240V electrical power. These voltages are safe to use on motors labeled 110-220V or 115-230V.

It is recommended that, when possible, all motors be connected to 230V service. If the wires are of good size, this will result in more certainty of good voltage at the motor terminals, especially if the motor is heavily loaded.

Most repulsion-start induction motors use four motor leads. These leads are connected to field windings, two leads to a winding. The windings are connected in parallel if the voltage to be used is 115 volts. The leads are connected in series if the voltage to be used is 230 volts. Since the power is the product of the voltage multiplied by the amperage, the amperage flow for any specified power using 230 volts will be one-half of the current flow if using 115 volts.

Fan motors and the like are usually wired either for 115 or 230 volts only and therefore have only two leads connected to the field windings. You must be careful to avoid connecting a 115V motor to a 230V circuit. If this were done, the motor would overheat and "burn out." The maintenance of proper voltage at the motor terminals is absolutely necessary. The power that an alternating current motor will develop varies directly as the square of the voltage impressed at the motor terminals. Low voltage will result in a rapid dropping of the horsepower capacity of any motor.

Number 14 wires are of sufficient size to use with motors up to one-fourth hp if the wires are of reasonable length (under 50 feet). If the wires exceed 50 feet, number 12 wire should be used. Loose connections cause excessive voltage drop and are a fire hazard. All connections should be soldered or connected with Underwriters Approved mechanical clamps.

A 120V motor supplied with current at 100V will develop only about 75 percent as much power as it would if supplied with 115V current. Therefore to do the job and to develop its full hp, it must draw more current. This increase in current may overheat the "power in" leads and/or the motor windings and cause insulation failure. Fig. 7-47 shows a method of making connections for single-phase motors. Note how the direction of rotation may be changed. Special motors requiring other connections are shipped with diagrams and instructions showing proper connections.

A 120-230V motor is usually connected to a 120V line through an across-the-line starter. An across-the-line starter is a switch which opens or closes the circuit by interrupting or closing one wire in the circuit. This switch is usually operated by the cabinet temperature, although low side pressure may be used. The same motor control may be used to operate a 120-230V motor installed on either the 120V or 230V circuit.

The field winding leads come out of the motor frame through an insulated opening. The wire is usually protected with

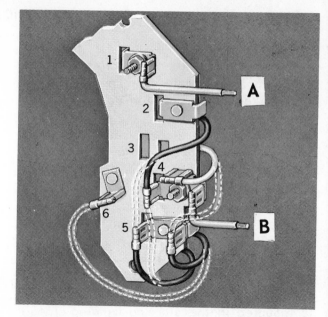

Fig. 7-47. An illustration which shows how motor leads may be made to give desired direction of rotation and connect motor to voltage supplied. Power in leads are shown at A and B. Wiring diagram inside motor cover plate indicates correct connection for each voltage and direction of rotation. Dotted lines show method of reversing.
(Century Electric Co.)

a rubber, fabric, or plastic grommet. A small metal box is usually mounted over the leads to provide a protected place to house the electrical connections.

7-44 Hermetic System Motors

Hermetic motors used today are the result of many years of development. Hermetic designs were developed to eliminate the belt and the compressor seal. When the motor and the compressor are placed inside a dome or housing, this is normally called a hermetic unit. A hermetic unit requires that the motor drive the compressor directly. This requires good electrical connections which must be made without danger of a leak and must have a motor with good power characteristics. Motors must be of the induction type. Motors using rotor windings requiring either brushes or slip rings are not usable. The development of the split-phase motor and the capacitor motor made the successful hermetic motor possible.

The original hermetic motors were four (4) pole motors which operate at approximately 1750 rpm.

To calculate the speed, the formula is:

$$N = \frac{120f}{P}$$ where N = rpm, f = frequency (cycle), P = number of poles

$$N = \frac{120 \times 60}{4} = 30 \times 60 = 1800 \text{ revolutions per minute (rpm)}$$

The 120 in the formula is the 60 seconds per minute x 2 (the magnetism or polarity changes 2 times per cycle).

This speed of 1800 is the synchronous speed, meaning the rotor is in perfect time with the frequency changes (an ideal no load condition: no rotor gap, perfect magnets, no rotor weight, etc.). Actually the motor does not reach this speed. Instead it operates at 1725 to 1750 rpm.

Four-pole motors are still used, however two-pole motors are becoming very popular.

Using the above formula, the speed of a 2-pole motor will be:

$$N = \frac{120 \times f}{P}$$

$$N = \frac{120 \times 60}{2} = 60 \times 60 = 3600 \text{ rpm}$$ synchronous speed or about 3400 rpm actual speed. The reason the motor is almost twice as fast is that the motor rotor has to travel one-half revolution during one-half cycle instead of one-fourth revolution as with the 4-pole motor. These 2-pole motors are about two-thirds the size of the 4-pole motors of the same power.

Hermetic motors present some problems not present with open motors:

1. Special cooling provisions must be made.
2. Wiring insulation must be resistant to chemicals in the refrigerant and the oil, particularly in the presence of moisture.
3. Manufacturing standards must provide exact alignment of the stator, rotor and compressor.

4. Electrical connections through the sealing dome must be electrically perfect and leakproof.

The motors may be cooled by several methods. One successful method is to press the stator into the dome and then put cooling fins on the dome. Another method uses a water coil to cool the motor windings while the unit is running. Some designs pass partly cooled condenser refrigerant around the motor housing to help cool the electric motor. Many models flow the return cool suction line vapor and oil over the motor windings.

Motor windings (wires) have presented many electrical and mechanical problems to the refrigeration engineer. These windings must be compact, be easily cleaned and dried, chemically inert, and must stand considerable overloads without shorting or grounding. Several companies have developed special synthetic wire coatings, (usually synthetic enamels), which have good

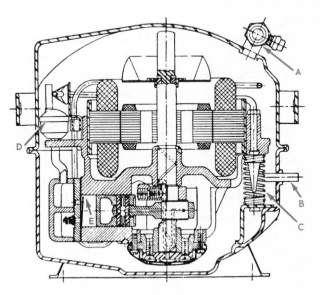

Fig. 7-48. Hermetic motor compressor unit. Note that reciprocating compressor cylinder is attached to and becomes a part of motor frame:

A—Suction service valve.
B—Discharge line.
C—Mounting spring.
D—Intake muffler.
E—Intake valve.

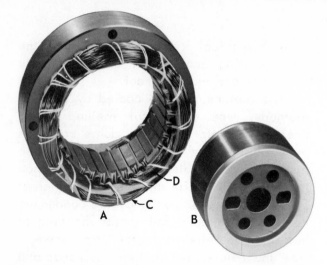

Fig. 7-49. Rotor and stator from a 1/4 hp split-phase hermetic motor:
  A—Stator.
  B—Rotor.
  C—Running winding.
  D—Starting winding.
          (Wagner Electric Corp.)

insulating qualities and are safe to use with most of the popular refrigerants.

One of the important alignment problems is to produce an equal and absolutely minimum air gap between the rotor and the stator of the motor. An appreciable gap between these two decreases the motor efficiency, and any unequal air gap is likely to produce a motor hum that can be loud enough to create noise complaints. Note in particular that many motor compressors are mounted on springs inside the dome.

The alignment of the electric motor parts and the compressor is usually done by using a common surface on the motor stator to which the compressor body is bolted. The aligning dowel pins or shoulders must be accurately matched to produce maximum accuracy, quietness and operating efficiency.

Fig. 7-48 shows a hermetic motor-compressor unit. The stator and rotor of a hermetic motor are shown in Fig. 7-49.

Most of the service connections for checking pressures, purging, etc., are mounted on the compressor dome. The connections usually require the use of a valve adapter set or a Schrader valve may be used. See Chapters 12 and 15.

7-45 Hermetic Motor Electrical Characteristics

The design characteristics of electric motors used in hermetic machines will depend on whether the unit starts under load or whether it starts under a no-load or balanced pressure condition.

However, the basic operation of the motor is the same as for open-type motors. Brushes and/or open points cannot be used in the hermetic motor, because the arcing would gradually disintegrate the refrigerant and the oil in the unit. Therefore, an external switch must be used to connect and disconnect the various windings. All torque must be developed by induction only.

The higher starting torque needed (turning effort) for those units which start under load necessitates the use of larger conductors in the starting circuit. This required starting torque is usually obtained by using one of several electrical devices. Usually, manufacturers try to provide starting power equal to twice the running power. In other words, a one-sixth hp motor is designed to produce one-third hp during starting. In some cases more frequent power surges are put into the motor during the starting time. Various methods are used to shut off the special starting devices after the motor has approached its full speed.

The external wiring of a capacitor start hermetic motor including a starting relay is shown in Fig. 7-50.

7-46 Hermetic Motor Types

Motors used in hermetic compressors are of the induction type. These motors have two field windings (stator) and induce an electric current and therefore magnetism in the rotor.

Capacitor hermetic motors are available in several electrical types:

1. Capacitor-start, induction-run motor.
2. Capacitor-start, capacitor-run motor.
3. Capacitor-run motor.

Hermetic motors may be either 4-pole motor 1700 rpm or 2-pole motor 3400 rpm.

Five types of single-phase induction motors are:

1. Split-phase type (SP).
2. Capacitor-start, induction-run motor (CSIR).
3. Capacitor-start, capacitor-run motor (CSR).
4. Capacitor-run motor (CR).
5. Permanent-split capacitor motor (PSC).

The split-phase motor has a low starting torque. It may be used in small units in which the pressures equalize during the off-cycle such as in capillary tube units. It has both a starting winding and running winding. A thermal, current, or potential relay located outside the compressor, is used to disconnect the starting winding after the motor reaches sufficient speed.

The capacitor-start, induction-run motor has a good starting torque. This extra

torque is obtained by placing a capacitor in series with the starting winding.

The capacitor-start, capacitor-run motor has a good starting torque and a high power factor running characteristic. It has two capacitors. The starting capacitor is in series with the starting windings and the starting relay. The running capacitor is also in series with the starting winding but is in use continuously while the motor is running.

The permanent-split capacitor motor has a fair starting torque. It may be used on some air conditioning units and small commercial units, provided these units use a capillary tube or bypass type expansion valve refrigerant control.

7-47 Hermetic Split-Phase Induction Motor

This motor is the basic type motor for all the hermetic condensing units in use today. It has the advantage of relatively low cost, since no extra devices are needed. The principle of operation is simple. There are two windings, a running winding and a starting winding.

A split-phase motor used in hermetic motor-compressor systems must use some type of outside starting relay since there must be no arcing or sparking inside the dome. There are two types of starting relays which may be used with the hermetic type split-phase motor. One type is known as the current relay since its operation depends on the current draw through the main winding.

There are also thermal type relays. A schematic wiring diagram showing the current-type starting relay is shown in Fig. 7-51. The relay control winding is in series with the main winding. The magnetic effect of the current flowing through the main winding will close the relay switch "0" as soon as the motor starts. The switch will remain open as soon as the motor is running but will close each time the motor starts again. A sche-

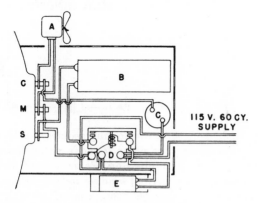

Fig. 7-50. Schematic wiring diagram for capacitor-start hermetic motor-compressor:
A—Fan motor.
B—Starting capacitor.
C—Overload protector.
D—Starting relay.
E—Temperature motor control.
(Servel Inc.)

matic wiring diagram showing the potential type starting relay is shown in Fig. 7-52. The relay control winding is in parallel with the starting winding. The magnetic effect of the current flowing through the relay control winding will open the switch (S) as soon as the motor starts and it will remain open as long as the motor is running. For a four-pole motor the starting windings are made into four coils in series. These starting windings are positioned an actual 45 degrees around the stator from the running winding. This positioning puts the starting winding 90 electrical degrees from the running winding electrical angle.

A smaller wire is used in the starting winding. This smaller wire has more turns than the running winding and the counter emf slows the current and builds up magnetism more slowly than in the running winding. When the unit control thermostat points close, current flows through the larger windings a little faster than the starting winding. The starting winding current follows very quickly, and its magnetism is a little slower building up than in the running winding. This slower build up causes a shift or side movement to one side in the field, thereby producing a twist or torque effect on the rotor.

The magnetism of the running winding therefore builds up a little sooner and induces an opposite magnetism in the rotor. Very shortly after this, 1/1000 of a second or so, the starting winding builds up to its maximum magnetism and this magnetism attracts the induced magnetism in the rotor and causes a twist or turning effect in the rotor. The starting winding is continued in use (energized) until the motor reaches at least one-half of its full speed. From this speed up to the full speed of the rotor the 60 cycle time interval and the four-pole stator will automatically run the rotor at 1800 rpm. This 1800 rpm is the true unloaded speed of a four-pole, 60 cycle motor, because the rotor must travel from one pole to the next in one change

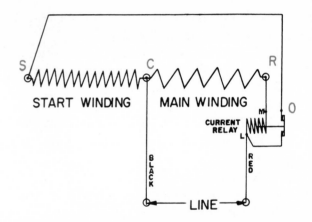

Fig. 7-51. Schematic wiring diagram of current type starting relay as used on split-phase motor. Relay as shown is in starting position. Relay control winding is in series with main winding and magnetic effect of field winding current flowing through current relay will open switch O as soon as motor starts:

C—Common terminal.
R—Running terminal.
S—Starting terminal.
O—Relay control switch.

(Copeland Refrigeration Corp.)

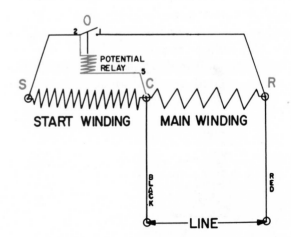

Fig. 7-52. Schematic wiring diagram of potential type starting relay as used on split-phase motor. Relay as shown is in running position. Relay control winding is in parallel with starting winding and magnetic effect of current flow through relay control winding will open switch O as soon as motor starts:

C—Common terminal.
R—Running terminal.
S—Starting terminal.
O—Relay control switch.

of the current. In a 60 cycle circuit the current changes direction each 1/120 sec-

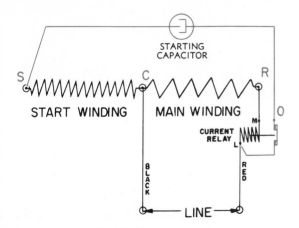

Fig. 7-53. A schematic wiring diagram of capacitor-start induction motor using current type relay. Relay is shown in starting position:

C—Common terminal.
R—Running terminal.
S—Starting terminal.
O—Relay control switch.

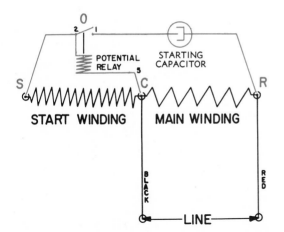

Fig. 7-54. A schematic wiring diagram of capacitor-start, induction-run motor using potential type relay. Relay is shown in running position:

C—Common terminal.
R—Main or running terminal.
S—Starting terminal.
O—Relay control switch.
(Copeland Refrigeration Corp.)

onds. This means the rotor makes one revolution (four poles) in 4/120 seconds or 1/30 of a second. In one minute or 60 seconds, therefore, the motor will turn 60 x 30 or 1800 revolutions at an unloaded speed (synchronous speed).

Actually there is a slight slippage of the rotor in its magnetic field, and these motors will actually run 1750 to 1775 rpm. The speed is slightly different for different motors, but for any particular motor it will be constant as the slippage will be constant. Some motors have two poles and revolve at twice the speed of the 4-pole motors.

These motors are used most often on small units 1/10, 1/6, 1/4 hp that have no starting load (capillary tube) or have an electric, mechanical, or hydraulic pressure unloading device.

Electrical relays are the most common devices used to disconnect the starting winding. These relays are explained in Chapter 8.

7-48. Hermetic Capacitor-Start, Induction-Run Motor

This is a very popular type hermetic motor for refrigerating units. A capacitor is placed in series with the starting winding. A current relay, a potential relay, or a hot wire (thermal) relay may be used to disconnect the starting winding when the motor reaches almost full rated speed.

A schematic wiring diagram showing capacitor-start; induction-run motor is illustrated in Fig. 7-53. It should be noted that a current type starting relay is used.

A schematic wiring diagram for a similar installation but using a potential type relay is shown in Fig. 7-54.

7-49 Hermetic Capacitor-Start, Capacitor-Run Motor

The capacitor-start, capacitor-run motor generally uses two capacitors. One capacitor is in the starting winding circuit. The other capacitor is in the running winding circuit. When the motor is started, the capacitors turn the motor power surges into two-phase power. After the motor reaches two-thirds or three-fourths of its

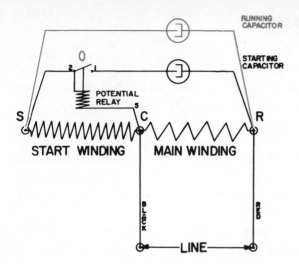

Fig. 7-55. A schematic wiring diagram of capacitor-start, capacitor-run motor using potential relay. Relay shown is in running position:

C—Common terminal.
R—Main or running terminal.
S—Starting terminal.
O—Relay control switch.

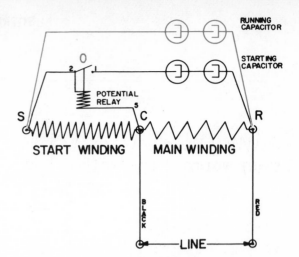

Fig. 7-56. Schematic wiring diagram of hermetic motor using two capacitors in series in starting winding and two in running winding. This starter uses potential relay and it is shown in running position:

C—Common terminal.
R—Running terminal.
S—Starting terminal.
O—Relay control switch.

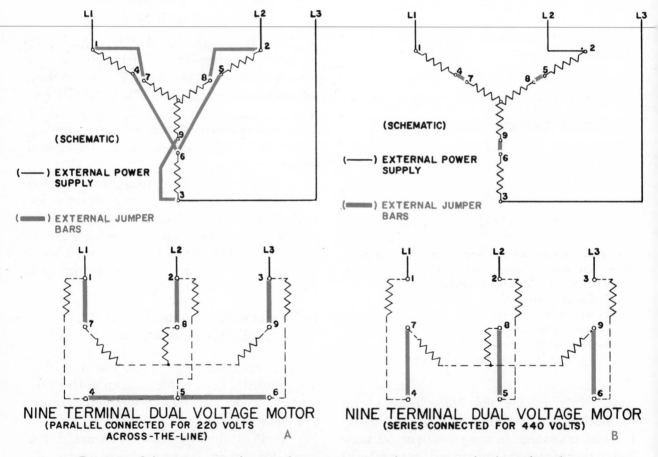

NINE TERMINAL DUAL VOLTAGE MOTOR
(PARALLEL CONNECTED FOR 220 VOLTS ACROSS-THE-LINE)   A

NINE TERMINAL DUAL VOLTAGE MOTOR
(SERIES CONNECTED FOR 440 VOLTS)   B

Fig. 7-57. Schematic wiring diagram showing circuits and connections for three-phase hermetic motor: A—Circuit as connected for 220 volts. B—Circuit as connected for 440 volts. Note that L_1, L_2 and L_3 are the three-phase line connections.

rated speed, the relay opens the circuit to the starting capacitor, but the running capacitor is left in the circuit. This action produces a two-phase motor at all times and results in a very efficient motor. It improves the power factor of the motor. This motor is used in the larger hermetic units in commercial systems, but its cost has practically eliminated it from the domestic field. Fig. 7-55 shows a capacitor-start, capacitor-run hermetic motor wiring diagram. Note that the running capacitor is in series with the starting winding. A motor wiring circuit with two starting capacitors and two running capacitors is shown in Fig. 7-56. These capacitors are connected in series to increase the voltage capacity (two 120V capacitors in series can be used in a 240V circuit). The μf (microfarad) capacity is less than the capacity of the smallest capacitor.

The resultant capacity value of capacitors in series may be expressed by the formula:

$$\frac{1}{\mu f} = \frac{1}{C_1} + \frac{1}{C_2}$$

μf = field capacitance (effective value)

C_1 = Capacity of Capacitor #1 in microfarads

C_2 = Capacity of Capacitor #2 in microfarads

The value of capacitors in parallel may be expressed by the formula:

$$\mu f = C_1 + C_2$$

or by simply adding together the values of all of the capacitors connected in parallel.

7-50 Hermetic Polyphase Motor

The larger hermetic compressors usually use three-phase motors to drive the compressor. These motors are usually of the 220V or 440V type. The dome terminal has nine terminals to enable the serviceman or installation man to wire the motor for either 220V or 440V as shown in Fig. 7-57. Some of these motors use a

550V supply. Three-phase motors are available from one-half hp up. The building in which the unit is to be placed must be wired for three-phase service. Very few residences have three-phase, but most industries and some commercial buildings have three-phase current.

THE HIGHER VOLTAGES ARE VERY DANGEROUS. YOU MUST DISCONNECT THE POWER AND LOCK THE SWITCH OPEN (USE AN ACTUAL LOCK) BEFORE STARTING TO SERVICE THE MACHINES.

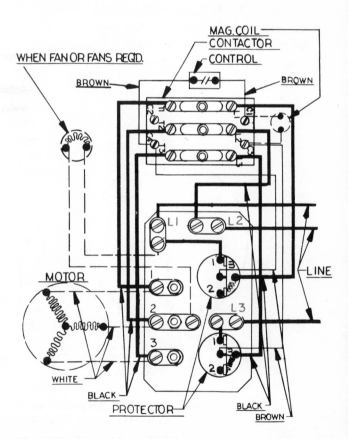

Fig. 7-58. Three-phase hermetic motor circuit wiring diagram. L_1, L_2 and L_3 are the three-phase line connections. Overload protector is shown in L_3 circuit. Special magnetic type starter is required for this installation. Automatic temperature control would be connected to control at top of illustration.
(Copeland Refrigeration Corp.)

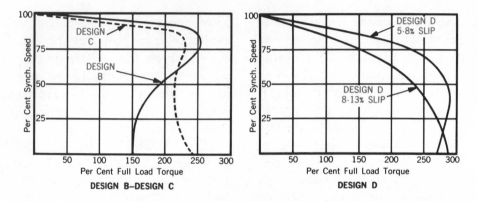

DESIGN B—DESIGN C **DESIGN D**

Fig. 7-59. Speed torque curves compared for two polyphase motor designs. It should be noted that design B and C motors provide starting torque of 150 to 250 percent of full load torque. Design D motors provide starting torque of 260 to 280 percent of full load torque; however, speed of these motors will fluctuate much more than B and C motors as load fluctuates. (Century Electric Corp.)

The three-phase motors use contactors or motor starters and the need for relays or capacitors does not exist. These motors are more efficient than single-phase motors.

may have certain differences, it is important to obtain from the manufacturer the wiring diagram for the unit, when servicing the system.

Operating characteristics of two types

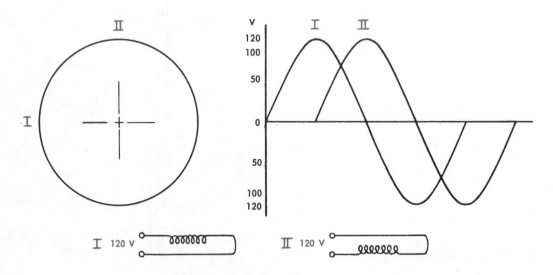

Fig. 7-60. Two sine curves of two-phase power circuit. Note that there are two separate circuits. The two circuits are 90 deg. out of phase.

Fig. 7-58 shows a three-phase motor wiring circuit and its starting and protector circuit. It is always best to have an electrical journeyman perform the electrical work on these units. Since each unit

of polyphase motors are shown in Fig. 7-59.

The sine curves for a two-phase motor are shown in Fig. 7-60, while the sine curves for a three-phase motor are shown in Fig. 7-61.

7-51 Hermetic Motor Terminals

The electrical terminals, which carry the circuit through the dome, must be electrically insulated from the dome or housing, and must also be leakproof.

nals are fused to glass and the glass in turn is fused to a metal disk. This assembly may be welded to the hermetic dome or housing, as shown in Fig. 7-62. The terminal must be leakproof after thousands of heating and cooling, expansion and con-

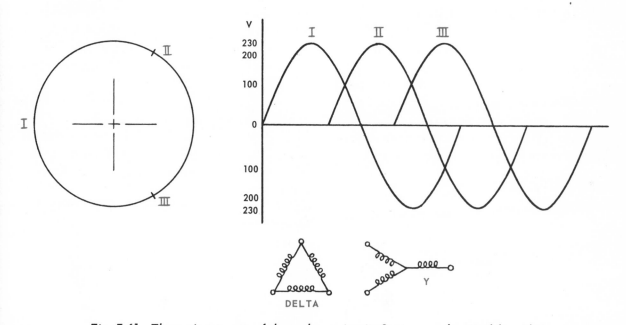

Fig. 7-61. Three sine curves of three-phase circuit. System can be wired for either Delta design or Y design.

Many terminal designs have been used. Metal terminals, that clamp against the housing, using synthetic rubber insulators and gaskets are used. Also, metal termi-

traction cycles and must also have a high insulating value. A fused glass multiple terminal installed is shown in Fig. 7-63.

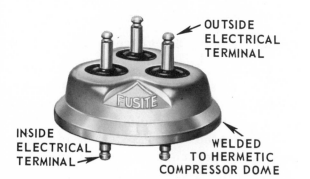

Fig. 7-62. Metal terminals which are fused to glass. and in turn glass is fused to metal disk which may be welded to hermetic compressor dome. This provides safe electrical insulation and leak tight assembly. (Fusite Corp.)

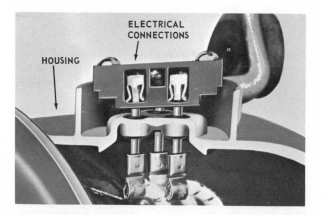

Fig. 7-63. Metal-glass fused hermetic electrical terminal installed. Wires to control relay are connected by means of spring loaded clips. Note metal structure surrounding terminals to protect them from abuse.

The wire terminals are spring clips that tightly clamp on the hermetic terminals.

Replacement terminals are used by many servicemen. These replacement terminals use synthetic rubber gaskets to make a leakproof joint.

7-52 Direct Current Motors

Areas which use DC power must have direct current motors for their refrigerators. These motors are compound wound and mechanically are similar to both the capacitor and repulsion-start induction type motors; however, the electrical circuits are quite different. A circuit diagram is shown in Fig. 7-64.

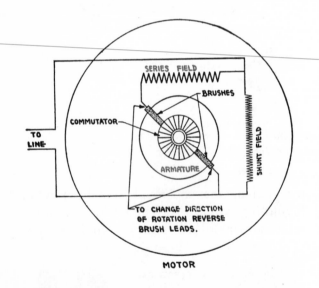

Fig. 7-64. Wiring diagram of compound wound direct current motor. Note that current going through armature must pass through series field. Series winding gives motor high starting torque. (Norge Div., Borg-Warner Corp.)

Compound wound motors have two types of field windings; one is in parallel with the armature winding, and one is in series with the armature winding. Because DC is used, the field poles always have the same magnetic polarity. Also since a DC current is going through the armature coil,

the magnetic polarity of the armatures will remain constant. It is positioned to cause a turning effect or torque in the armature. The series field helps to keep the motor speed constant. The series winding strength builds up to increase the rpm if the motor tends to slow down or weakens to reduce the rpm if the motor tends to speed up. One has only to reverse the brush leads to reverse the direction of rotation of these motors (it reverses the armature magnetic polarity).

The possibilities for wear are a little greater in the direct current motors than in the others because of the armature design. The brushes are in constant contact with the commutator, giving rise to possible troubles, such as dirty commutator, worn brushes, high mica insulation between the bars, shorted armature and squeaky brushes.

7-53 Motor Horsepower and Motor Characteristics

Energy, work, and power are explained in Chapter 1. Motors are rated by horsepower. One horsepower is equal to lifting 33,000 ft. lbs. per minute or 550 ft. lbs. per second. At 100 percent efficiency, 778 watts equals one horsepower. Refrigeration motors of $\frac{1}{100}$ hp to several hundred horsepower are in use. Motors as small as $\frac{1}{20}$ horsepower have been used to drive compressors. In refrigeration the torque of a motor is as important as its horsepower. Torque is the ability to twist or turn (such as turning the crankshaft of a compressor). It is measured in pounds feet or in pounds inches. A person pulling on a one foot wrench with a force of 50 pounds is developing 50 pounds feet of torque. The term "pounds feet" or "pounds inches" is the correct technical term for units of torque, however common usage has allowed the term foot pounds and inch pounds to also

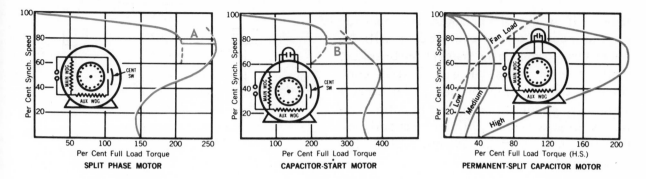

Fig. 7-65. *Torque and speed characteristics of three types of single-phase motors:*

Split-phase motor. Starting winding is disconnected by centrifugal switch at approximately 75 percent of synchronous speed as shown at A. This type of motor provides fair starting torque. It is available in hp ratings up to 1/2 hp and for either 115 or 230V.

Capacitor-start motor. Starting winding is disconnected by a centrifugal switch at approximately 75 percent of synchronous speed as shown at B. Higher starting torque is obtained by adding capacitor in starting circuit. This motor is generally available in hp rating up to 3 hp and for either 115 or 230V.

Permanent-split capacitor motor. This motor has no separate starting winding. Its use is limited to easy-to-start loads such as fans and blowers. These motors may be operated as multi-speed motors using simple and inexpensive controls. Its use is usually in low hp applications and is available for either 115 or 230V current.
(Century Electric Co.)

indicate torque. This is somewhat confusing since units of work are the foot pound. The student must be prepared to accept either of these terms as units of torque. A motor used to start a compressor against a 150 psig head pressure must have good starting torque.

It is important to know the properties of the most popular motors, the single-phase motors. Fig. 7-65 shows the operating curves of the various types of motors based on motor speed and percent of full load torque.

7-54 Fuses and Circuit Breakers

A motor that is started and stopped automatically and is placed or controlled from a distance should use a fuse having a rated capacity of not more than 100 percent to 110 percent of the rated ampere capacity of the motor. This size of fuse is ample, under normal conditions, to allow a motor to start and reach its rated speed fully loaded.

Some motors have to develop maximum rated capacity for short periods, and to start quickly under a heavy load. If the motor is being started and operated under the direct supervision of an attendant, a fuse may be used having a short time period rated capacity of 125 percent. In no case should a fuse larger than 150 percent of the rated full load current of the motor be used. The above applies to plug and cartridge type fuses approved by the National Board of Fire Underwirters. Experience shows that link and wire fuses often do not provide enough protection for refrigeration unit motors.

A plug fuse will not protect an overloaded motor well enough because the fuse must be of enough capacity to withstand the starting load of the motor, which can be from 2 to 6 times more than the running current. If the motor running winding draws this extra load long enough after it has started it may burn out the motor.

Many homes and business establishments now use circuit breakers rather than fuses. A circuit breaker is an automatic switch which will open a circuit if the current draw is too great. Circuit breakers are usually rated the same as fuses. If a circuit breaker is "opened" as the result of an overload it will be necessary to manually "reset" the breaker. Just as with fuses, if a circuit is continually opening the breaker, the circuit should be carefully examined to determine if the breaker has sufficient capacity or if there is a short or other trouble in the circuit.

7-55 Motor Protection

Originally refrigerators had only plug or cartridge fuses to protect them. The fuse had to be large enough to carry the starting current which is often 100 percent over the running current. Fig. 7-66 shows the full load current draw in amperes for various size motors for both AC and DC motors. However, because the

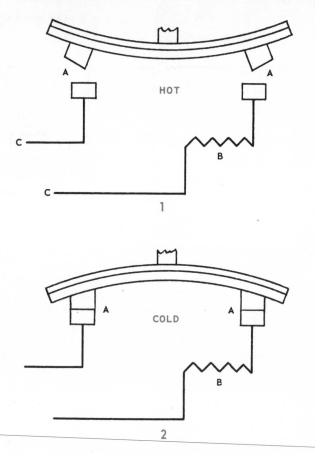

Fig. 7-67. Bimetal type motor overload protector: A—Contact points. B—Heater-coil. C—Motor winding connections. 1—Shows circuit open because of increased temperature or voltage. 2—Shows points closed as in normal operation.

HP	AC Motors Single-Phase Split-Phase or Capacitor		DC Motors Compound Wound	
	115V	230V	120V	240V
1/6	4.4	2.2	- - -	- - -
1/4	5.8	2.9	2.9	1.5
1/3	7.2	3.6	3.6	1.8
1/2	9.8	4.9	5.2	2.6
3/4	13.8	6.9	7.4	3.7
1	16.0	8.0	9.4	4.7
1 1/2	20.0	10.0	13.2	6.6

Fig. 7-66. Table of maximum fuse ratings for motor running protection.

starting current is larger than the running current, the fuse was often too large to protect the motor while it was running. If the running winding of the motor were to draw the full fuse amperage for any length of time, the motor would overheat and be ruined.

To eliminate this danger, time fuses may be installed in the circuit. These devices allow an excessive current flow for a very short period of time (such as in

starting), but they will break the circuit if the current flow is excessive for any length of time. Two designs are used:

One type uses a gear soldered to a shaft, and a lever under a spring load is attached to this gear. If the motor consumes too much current for too long, the heat from a resistance coil will melt the solder and the gear will turn allowing the spring loaded shaft to open the circuit.

Another type uses a heating coil and a bimetal strip. The bimetal will bend if the heating coil becomes warm and will open the circuit.

An overload cut-out device consisting of a heating coil and spring loaded ratchet throw-out arrangement has been used. Some are built into the thermostat and some are separate units. Bimetal overload devices are now the most common safety device and are located at various important places in the unit. If these parts overheat for any reason, the circuit will be opened by the bimetal snap switches.

All these devices, however, will only stop the mechanism if the current load is too high. If the motor should overheat from other troubles, the unit may still run and damage may result. Other sources of excessive heat may be: high exhaust temperatures, poor air circulation, poor refrigerant circulation, and friction.

Present refrigerating systems have safety devices installed which open the electrical circuit if the motor draws too much current, if the motor overheats for any reason and/or if the compressor becomes too hot.

Fig. 7-67 illustrates a bimetal device that opens the circuit if the bimetal disk reaches a temperature that will cause it to snap in the other direction. Fig. 7-68 shows the construction of a motor protector.

Considerable damage may result to the compressor or the motor from overheating. This overheating could occur without the current draw becoming excessive. It is therefore necessary to use overload devices which will open the circuit if any type of overheating occurs. These controls are temperature operated and receive their heat from the motor, the compressor, and

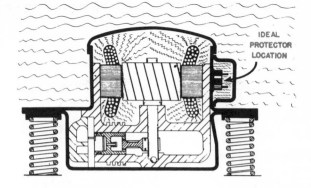

Fig. 7-69. Illustration showing a suitable location for motor-compressor overload or excessive temperature protector. (Texas Instruments Inc.)

the current draw of the motor. Fig. 7-69 shows an overload protector located on the motor-compressor dome or housing. An external overload protector as used on polyphase motors is shown in Fig. 7-70.

Fig. 7-70. Wiring circuit diagram for three-phase hermetic motor which uses two external motor protectors. (Copeland Refrigeration Corp.)

EXTERNAL INHERENT PROTECTION
(2) 3 TERMINAL PROTECTORS & CONTACTOR

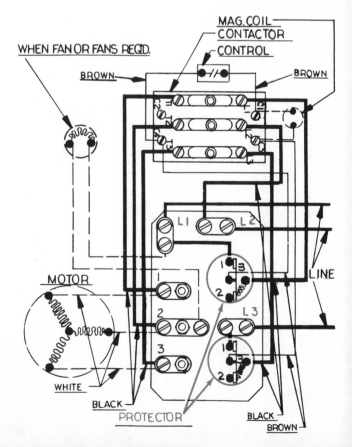

Fig. 7-68. Motor overload protector. Excessive heat will cause bimetal disk to bend and open contact points. (Franklin Appliance Div., Studebaker Corp.)

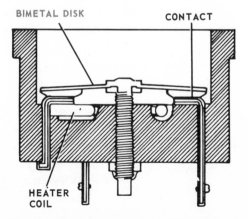

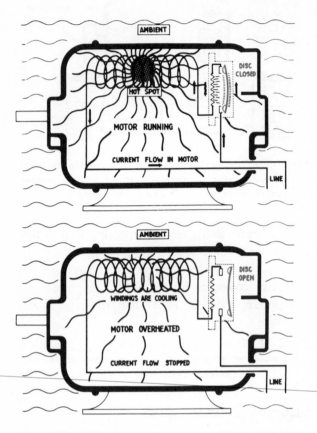

Fig. 7-71. Bimetal overload protector installed inside open type electric motor.

The action of a bimetal snap action current-actuated and heat-actuated overload protector as used on an open type motor is shown in Fig. 7-71.

Some of the temperature sensitive motor protectors are quite compact and may be easily installed inside the motor winding. Such a motor protector is described in Par. 7-56.

7-56 Motor Internal Overload and Overheating Protection

Internal overload motor protectors are mainly used on hermetic motors. They have been developed along with the two-pole motor and the application of large hermetic motors.

Refrigeration systems must be protected against too much current draw and against overheating. In most refrigeration

and air conditioning equipment the motor-compressor unit is designed to start under a condition of balanced pressures. There is danger of overheating the motor if it attempts to start against a high head pressure. The motor may also overheat if there is a lack of refrigerant (the refrigerant gas cools the motor). The motor may overheat if the unit attempts to start too soon after shutting off. Too much current draw may also be caused by a stuck or locked rotor or compressor.

If there is an increased starting load, the internal overload protector will open the motor circuit and protect the motor from such abuse.

The units normally operate at 125 F. When the temperature reaches 200 to 250 F. the protection device will open the circuit and stop the motor. It will then close at about 150-175 F. Do not tap on the controls in an attempt to operate the points. If this is done, the points may vibrate and arc and cause them to burn out quickly.

The internal motor overload protectors are of two types: (1) bimetal disk and a series heater coil, or (2) thermistor.

In the bimetal type, the contact points are on a bimetal strip and are normally in a closed position as shown in Fig. 7-72.

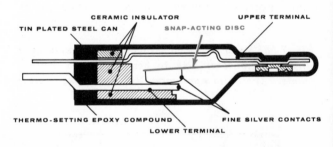

Fig. 7-72. Compact motor protector which is designed to be fitted into motor windings.

When there is too high a temperature rise they will open the circuit. The temperature rise may be due to overheating from excessive current draw due to a high head pressure, or other factors. When the temperature in the disk decreases enough, the strip will return to its normal position and the contact points will close.

In the thermistor type, an electronic material, similar to transistor and diode material, is placed in a capsule and this material is placed in the control circuit. As the material temperature increases its current carrying capacity increases. If the temperature rises too much (to about 200 F.) the increased current flow will operate a relay circuit and the circuit will open.

The overload protector is placed inside the hermetically sealed compressors, directly on or in the windings. The internal overload protector will open if there is either excessive current draw or excessive temperature or both. Loss of refrigerant, a restriction in the system, or low suction pressure -- all could lead to a motor burn out if the overload protector were not installed.

Depending on ambient temperature conditions, it may be an hour to two hours after the protector opens the circuit before it will close. Cooling the dome with forced air, dry ice, or carbon dioxide spray will hasten the cooling process. You should never attempt to bypass the leads of these protectors because even a few moments of operating a unit without this protector may burn out the motor. These protectors cannot be taken out of the circuit and they are therefore the best possible protection for a hermetic compressor. Motors having this protection are usually labeled "Internal Overload Protected."

In the Y type three-phase motors the internal overload is located at the common terminal of the three windings and it will open all three circuits when it points open, as shown in Fig. 7-73. These internal protectors are very reliable. Cases of failure are almost unknown. Fig. 7-74 shows an instrument used to check the three circuits of a three-phase system.

7-57 Motor Temperature

The temperature of the hottest spot in a motor should not rise more than 40 C. (72 F.) over the room temperature. This means an average maximum temperature of approximately 150 F. Because this temperature is difficult to measure except in a laboratory, it is better to check the ambient (surrounding) temperature to be sure it is not excessive. Check the motor for cleanliness and air flow. Then check the current draw of the motor. If this current

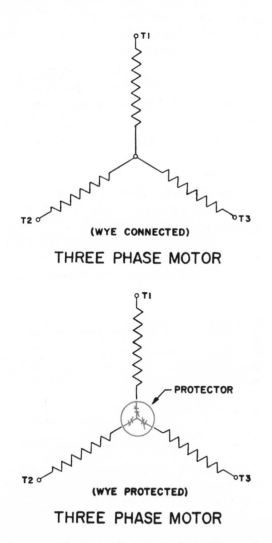

Fig. 7-73. Illustration showing method of connecting motor protector in three-phase Y type motor. In this position protector will open all three circuits. (Copeland Refrigeration Corp.)

draw exceeds the rating on the nameplate or in the motor manual, the motor is overheating.

To judge the temperature of a motor, always use a thermometer. A motor with too high a frame or stator temperature may have motor winding temperatures so high that the insulation on the wires may fail.

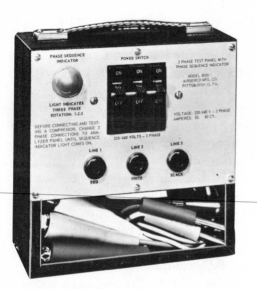

Fig. 7-74. *Instrument which may be used to test three circuits of three-phase system.*
(Airserco Mfg. Co.)

The thermal overload protector for motors usually opens the circuit when the temperature reaches 200 F. and closes the circuit when the temperature drops to about 150 F. Motors depend on rather cool ambient air for cooling. If this air is too warm or if the air flow is restricted, this cooling effect is lost and the motor will overheat.

7-58 Standard Motor Data

The split-phase motor including the repulsion-start induction type is obtainable in 25, 30, 40, and 60 cycles and may use either 120 or 240 volts. The 30 and 60 cycle four-pole motors run at 1750 rpm while the 25 and 50 cycle motors have a speed of 1425 rpm. The 40 cycle runs at a speed of 1150 rpm. The DC motor voltages are usually 32, 115, and 230 volts and the motor runs at 1725 rpm. These motors are supposed to run continuously with a temperature rise not exceeding 40-55 C., which is about 90 F. above room temperature.

Compressor speed on open systems can be controlled by using either two or four-pole motors and by changing pulley sizes. Direct connected compressors must operate at motor speed. If a four-pole motor is used to replace a two-pole motor, a compressor of greater displacement must be used with the slower rpm motor.

The wire size used in the refrigeration mechanism is very important. If the wire is undersize or if it is too long, it will heat up and may eventually cause a fire. Long circuits also add an unnecessary resistance to the flow of electricity causing an excessive voltage drop. If the voltage to the motor is less than 90 percent of the rating of the motor there is danger of the motor being overheated and ruined. A table of wire sizes recommended for 115V circuits is given in Fig. 7-75.

Wire No.	Diameter of Wire in Inches	Ampere Capacity Plastic Insulation
18	.040	5
16	.051	10
14	.064	20
12	.081	25
10	.102	30
8	.128	50
6	.162	70
4	.204	90
2	.258	125

Fig. 7-75. *Table of recommended wire sizes for various ampere capacity circuits. This table is calculated on basis that it is used on 115V circuit.*

The efficiency of small motors is only 50 to 60 percent; therefore, they consume nearly twice as much current as they should, compared to larger motors such as

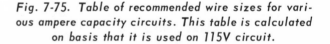

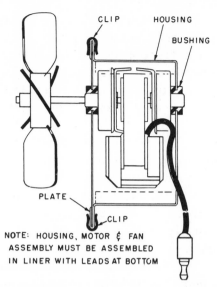

Fig. 7-76. Domestic refrigerator "inside cabinet" mounted air circulating fan. (Kelvinator Div., American Motors Corp.)

CLIP HOUSING
BUSHING
PLATE
CLIP
NOTE: HOUSING, MOTOR & FAN ASSEMBLY MUST BE ASSEMBLED IN LINER WITH LEADS AT BOTTOM

1/2 hp and over. A 1/6 hp motor which should theoretically use only 124 watts or 1 1/4 amperes will be found to need approximately 2 1/2 to 3 amperes to develop the 1/6 hp.

When making electrical connections to a domestic refrigerator, the thermostat, which is installed in the circuit should be connected into the hot wire of the circuit. This hot wire in the alternating current circuit may be easily recognized if a trouble lamp is connected to one of the lines and then grounded to a good ground such as a water pipe, the lamp will light if that particular wire happened to be the hot wire of the two. This wire usually has black insulation. If a trouble lamp is not available, an AC voltmeter will serve the same purpose.

The other wire is called the ground wire of the circuit. It usually has white insulation. It should be run directly to the motor.

7-59 Fan Motors

Many hermetic units use motor-driven fans to (1) force condenser cooling air through the ducts and over the condenser

and condensing units, (2) to circulate air in refrigerated parts of domestic and commercial units as shown in Fig. 7-76. To obtain efficient air movement the fan and condenser are carefully shrouded or housed in sheet metal. The fans are carefully balanced and run almost noiselessly. The fans are usually fastened to the motor shaft with Allen setscrews. Some of these motors have sealed bearings (bushings) and require no oiling while others need oiling (SAE 10 or 20) amounting to one drop per bearing each six months. A few motors are on the market that use only one bearing. The motors are usually fastened on brackets and are mounted in rubber. Fig. 7-77 shows a replacement condenser fan and motor with a universal mounting bracket.

Fig. 7-77. Replacement motor and fan with universal mounting brackets which may be used with variety of condensing unit designs. (Airserco Mfg. Co., Inc.)

The motors are usually of the shaded pole type. The shaded pole produces a moving magnetic field perpendicular to the field pole and starts the rotor turning as shown in Fig. 7-78. Approximately one-half of each pole face has a small copper plate insert (A). This insert slows the buildup of the magnetic field through the

copper plate enough to cause a magnetic motion toward the copper plate. This action gives a delayed time for induced magnetism in the rotor (opposite magnetism). The rotor turns as it is attracted by it. This action continues as the alternating current changes the polarity of the poles and rotor. Although this design has less starting torque than other type motors, it is very successful in small motors 1/6 to 1/100 hp. Fig. 7-79 shows a double shaft fan motor. The end bell of this motor is shown in Fig. 7-80.

Generally, the condenser fan motor leads are connected to the common terminal and the running winding terminal of the compressor motor. This connection puts the fan motor in parallel with the compressor motor and allows it to be controlled by the thermostat. The safety overload cut-out is also put in the circuit ahead of the fan so its functioning will also cut out the fan motor. Some fan motors have their own thermal safety controls.

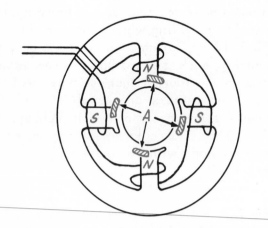

Fig. 7-78. Shaded-pole fan motor. S—South polarity. N—North polarity. A—Shaded pole (copper).

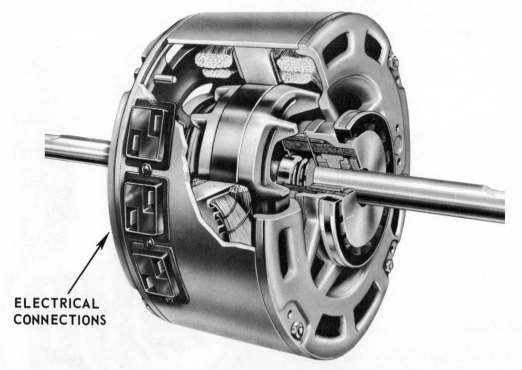

ELECTRICAL CONNECTIONS

Fig. 7-79. High starting torque shaded-pole, double-shaft fan motor. Choice of electrical connections provides choice of fan speeds. (General Electric Co.)

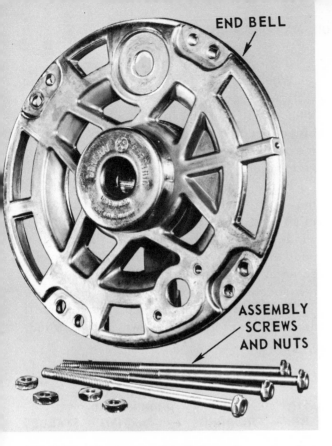

END BELL

ASSEMBLY
SCREWS
AND NUTS

Fig. 7-80. Aluminum end bell for a fan motor. Note assembly screws and nuts.

7-60 Transistorized Motors

A method employing transistor switching instead of the brush or commutator method has been developed for low hp motors. The brushless motor operates electronically through the use of silicon rectifiers, transistors and special circuitry. The advantages of the transistorized motor are its high speed, performance, durability, variable speed, elimination of sparking and brush noise, and its compactness.

It is also possible to vary the speed by the addition of a small potentiometer which will vary the resistance within the circuitry.

7-61 Servicing Electric Motors

The maintenance, trouble shooting, removal, repair and installation of electric motors and their accessories is a major portion of a serviceman's job.

He must know how to use instruments and have a knowledge of electricity to accurately determine the trouble. The following paragraphs describe these service operations:

1. General service.
2. Open motors.
3. Hermetic motors.
4. Fan motors.

It is basic that a solid foundation should be provided for the installation of any motor. When the motor is mounted upon the foundation, it should be bolted down securely; when so fastened the armature shaft should be level for a horizontal motor and should be plumb for a vertical motor.

Refrigeration motors are commonly mounted on a steel base which also holds the compressor and the condenser. A rubber or spring suspension is often used on the motor to reduce the vibration and to take up the starting torque. Some motors are mounted on cradles, and springs are used to provide the proper belt tension. An innovation is to mount the motor in a cradle in such a manner that, as the motor starts, the starting torque loosens the belt, and the belt tension returns to normal when the motor reaches its full speed.

7-62 Watt Readings to Determine Motor Troubles

One of the means to determine the condition of a motor-compressor unit is to observe the wattage consumption of the unit. An instrument which is used to obtain voltage, amperage and wattage values is shown in Fig. 7-81. The proper method of connecting the meter into the wiring circuit to obtain a watt reading is shown in Fig. 7-82.

The meter will give three wattage readings:

1. Over swing reading.
2. Combined starting and running winding reading (of only 1 to 1 1/2 seconds duration).
3. The running winding reading.

Fig. 7-81. Combination volt, ampere and wattmeter. Note that this instrument provides different terminals for use with various voltages and wattage ranges.

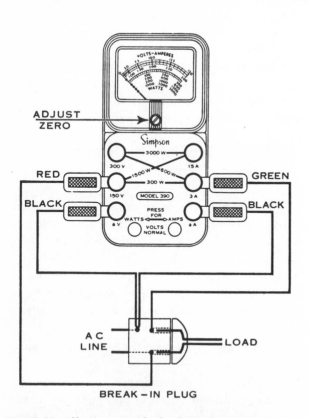

Fig. 7-82. Illustration which shows how to connect instrument, shown in Fig. 7-81, into circuit to measure wattage drawn by the load (compressor).

When the thermostat contacts close, the wattmeter pointer will swing to the right; then it will quickly move back to the combined reading, and then in a few seconds the pointer will fall to the running winding reading only.

If the starting winding circuit is open, the wattmeter pointer will swing to the right and then move back to the running winding value only. This action indicates a bad relay or starting winding. The overload safety cut-out should open the circuit in a few seconds (2 to 3 seconds).

Approximate wattage readings for small hermetic motors are shown in Fig. 7-83.

WATTS AT 115 VOLTS

MOTOR HP	RUNNING 70 F.	110 F.	COMBINED RUNNING AND STARTING	STALLED
1/16	66	100	1000	375
1/9	117	160	1800	740
1/8	108	163	1850	743
1/7	160	218	1850	970
1/5	242	295	1800	1450
1/4	235	320	2300	1250

Fig. 7-83. Table of approximate wattage readings for small hermetic motors. Temperatures indicated are ambient temperature of motor.

7-63 Radio Interference

Some conventional refrigerators cause a slight amount of radio or TV interference. This interference will usually amount to a slight snap or click in the radio or TV at the instant the refrigerator stops or starts, and should not be more noticeable than turning off a light. This interference may be partly eliminated by grounding the frame of the motor to a water pipe or by placing a condenser between the frame of the motor and a ground. In general, the interference is not disagreeable and need not be given any attention.

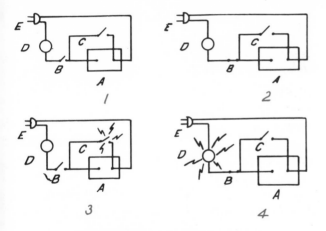

Fig. 7-84. Method of testing a condenser:
   A—Capacitor being tested.
   B—Charging switch.
   C—Shorting switch.
   D—Fuse or circuit breaker.
   E—Attachment plug to 120V circuit.
      1—Switches open.
      2—Charging switch closed.
      3—Good capacitor.
      4—Shorted capacitor.

Excessive radio interference of a continuing nature when the refrigerator motor operates or when it starts, indicates a loose electrical connection or some fault in the mechanism of the motor such as worn brushes, badly pitted commutator, or loose connections. The particular trouble can be easily determined by a careful examination of the motor.

Occasionally a static charge will be built up on the belt of a belt-driven compressor. The discharge of this charge will cause radio interference. If the motor and compressor are grounded together, this noise will be eliminated.

7-64 Servicing Capacitors

Most motors have one capacitor, the starting capacitor, but some have two or more capacitors; either one starting capacitor and one running capacitor or two or more capacitors connected in parallel or series for additional capacitance. The starting capacitor is connected in series with the starting winding and is usually connected into the circuit between the relay and the starting winding terminal of the motor (off-and-on operation).

The running capacitor is also in the starting winding circuit but stays in operation while the unit runs (continuous operation).

There are two types of capacitors:
1. The dry capacitor (for intermittent operation).
2. The electrolytic capacitor (for continuous operation).

The dry capacitor is described in Par. 7-39.

The simplest capacitor test is to substitute a good capacitor for the capacitor being tested. If the motor operates, it is known that the old capacitor is faulty. The replacement capacitor should be the same capacity as the old one. If the only one available is of a different capacity, use one 5-10 percent over capacity rather than one under capacity.

Another way to check a capacitor is to disconnect it from the circuit and connect the proper voltage power to its terminals (be sure a fuse is in the circuit as shown in Fig. 7-84; then, short the terminals of the capacitor. If the capacitor is good, it will spark. If it has an open circuit no charging will occur and therefore no sparking will take place. If it is shorted or grounded, the fuse will blow.

The capacitor should be put in a protective case while testing it because a shorted capacitor may explode when put in a circuit.

In (1), the tester is connected to the terminals of the capacitor (A) with rubber covered spring clips. Both switches (B) and (C) are open; some models have button switches similar to door bell switches that are spring loaded to stay open. In (2) the charging switch (B) is closed momentarily; just touch it. Note that switch (C) stays open. If the capacitor is shorted, the fuse or circuit breaker will blow, (4) (D). If nothing happens, then proceed as in (3). With the switch (B) open, touch the shorting switch. If the capacitor is good, the switch will spark. If it does not spark the first time, try it three or four times before scrapping the capacitor. Fig. 7-85 illustrates a commercial model of a capacitor tester. These testers are recommended. Testing a capacitor by shorting is not recommended.

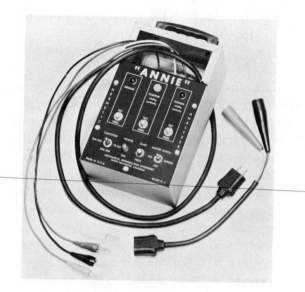

Fig. 7-85. Capacitor tester and analyzer. This unit may be used to detect hermetic motor troubles. It may also be used to reverse the motor.
(Mechanical Refrig. Enterprises)

Important: Never put your fingers across the terminals of a capacitor as it may be charged and give you a shock. Always short it with a wire first before handling it.

Some capacitors have resistors connected across the terminals for slowly discharging the capacitor when it is not in use. This resistor is visible at the terminal end of the capacitor. The resistor slowly bleeds the capacitor of its charge mainly to minimize the arcing of the motor control points, which may happen if the unit cycles frequently.

A capacitor must be accurately sized to the motor and the motor load. It is

general practice to permit a 25 percent overload capacity, i.e., a 125 μf can be used for a 100 μf capacitor, but an undersized capacitor should never be used. If it is at all possible, use an exact replacement capacitor. The make, model and model number are usually placed on each capacitor. If this information is unavailable, or if an emergency capacitor must be used temporarily, there are several ways to determine the proper size unit. One of the quickest methods is to put the temporary capacitor in the circuit, and if it brings the unit up to running speed and the relay operates in 3 seconds, the capacitor is very nearly correct. A better method is to use a specially designed capacitor selector unit. This selector has a variable capacitance and increasing amounts of μf's are put in the circuit (in series) until the correct voltage reading is reached for the unit. The capacitance registered on the selector indicates the capacity of the capacitor to be put in the circuit.

Another method that may be used to check the capacity of a capacitor is as follows: the capacitor should be connected to a double-fused line and the voltage leads of the meter connected across the capacitor. The ammeter reading is obtained by placing the heavy probes of the ammeter around the wire.

The two types of capacitors, electrolytic (oil type) or the dry type may be tested in the same way. However, the oil type is usually used only as the continuous operating type (capacitor-run type of motor) and is usually of much smaller μf capacity.

Some of the capacitors have mechanical connectors (machine screws) while some have solder-type leads. It is necessary to use a small electric soldering copper or soldering gun to connect these latter units.

There are some hermetic testing units or analyzers that may be used to check capacitors, motor windings, relays, overload cutouts, etc. Some are equipped with light

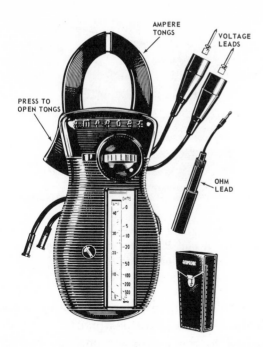

Fig. 7-86. Ammeter-ohmmeter which may be easily connected to an electrical circuit to check voltage, amperage or resistance (ohms) in circuit. (Amprobe Instrument Div., Soss Mfg. Co.)

Fig. 7-87. Instrument, shown in Fig. 7-86, fitted for use as an ohmmeter.

indicators while some use voltmeters, ammeters, ohmmeters, and wattmeters.

A very popular instrument for checking the electrical flow to a refrigerator unit is shown in Fig. 7-86. This unit can be used to measure amperes, volts and ohms. Fig. 7-87 shows the instrument fitted for use as an ohmmeter.

Be sure the capacitors are discharged before testing a circuit with an ohmmeter or the discharge may ruin the meter.

7-65 Servicing Open Type Motors

Troubles found in the open type motor are few, and they can be classified as:
1. Electrical troubles.
2. Mechanical troubles.
The electrical troubles found in electric motors may be:
1. An open circuit, short circuit, or ground may occur in the field windings. In these cases, replacing the motor is recommended.

2. Frequent starting of the motor may result in overheating; the capacitor and the switch, also the insulation may fail. If the motor will not start but simply has the characteristic AC hum until you spin the pulley and then the motor starts satisfactorily, it is a sign that the capacitor or the centrifugal switch points have failed. It is easy to replace the old capacitor with a good capacitor of the same capacity. If the motor still will not start, the trouble is probably in the centrifugal switch.

The mechanical troubles are almost the same in all open type motors:
1. There is a possibility that the centrifugal switch used for connecting and disconnecting the condenser and/or the starting winding may become worn, in which case a replacement of the switch is necessary. Fig. 7-88 shows a centrifugal switch for a capacitor type electric motor

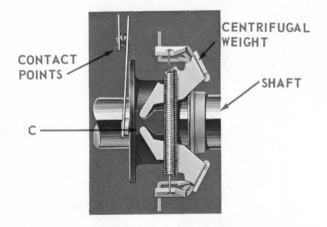

Fig. 7-88. Centrifugal switch mechanism which may be used on an "open type" unit compressor. Counterweights and spool C revolve with motor shaft. At about 75 percent of full operating speed counterweights cause spool C to move to right which allows contact points to open and starting winding is disconnected. (Century Electric Co.)

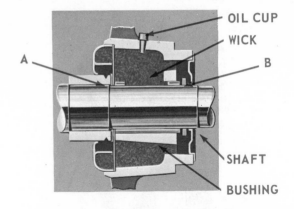

Fig. 7-89. Motor end bearing which uses wick oiler. Oil slingers A and B prevent oil from migrating into motor or out along motor shaft.

2. Other troubles may include bearing wear, end play, excessive vibration, orientation of the motor to the compressor, and the air gap between the rotor and stator. Repair and testing of motors is covered in Chapter 15.

7-66 Open Motor Lubrication

Open motors may be lubricated in various ways based on the type of bearing used and the position of the motor. Open motors using bronze bushings, plain or sleeve, may be lubricated in two different ways: (1) Wick system, (2) Slip ring system.

The wick system uses a well or reservoir in the end bell and a wick (cotton or wool yarn) carries oil from this well to the top of the bushing and shaft. This system allows long intervals between servicing bearings, and prevents excessive oiling of the bearing. This type lubrication system is shown in Fig. 7-89.

Motors with this system of lubrication, when shipped from the factory, have the cotton or wool yarn saturated with oil. However, before starting the motor, the oil wells should be filled by adding to each well the amount of oil designated on the tag attached to the motor, or until oil appears in the lower oil level cup.

If the bearing is to be removed from the shaft, or if the bushing is to be removed from the end bell, the yarn should be lifted from the bearing before removing and/or replacing the bearing to prevent the yarn being forced between the shaft and the bearing. When replacing the yarn, equal amounts should be packed on each side of the bearing, and put over the slot of the bearing so the spring on the oil well cover will push the yarn down on the shaft. Wick lubricated bearings should be oiled with one or two drops every six months.

Some larger refrigeration motors use the ring lubricating method. A brass ring rests on the motor shaft through a slot in the top of the bearing. The ring is large enough to dip into the oil pocket below. As the motor shaft turns, the ring turns slowly and the wet portion lubricates the bearing. Be sure to check the rings when working on these motors. Use a medium viscosity oil for a lubricant (SAE 30).

Some motors use ball bearings, as shown in Fig. 7-90. These bearings are grease lubricated. Most of them are sealed bearings and do not need any lubrication service. Some, however, come with grease cups and can be grease gun lubricated. These motors, when new, are supplied with enough grease in the bearings to lubricate them for a number of months. A small amount of grease should be added every two or three months. Use a high grade "medium" grease on fully enclosed motors. Too much grease may cause the bearings to overheat. The life of the bearings depends to a considerable extent on cleanliness. Use only clean grease and keep all dirt out of the bearing. Clean all the connections before using the grease gun. Most greases and oils oxidize and also collect dirt while in use. When a motor is reconditioned, the old lubricant must be discarded, the lubricated portions thoroughly cleaned, and new lubricant used.

Another method of lubrication presently used is the "oilless" bushing. In this type of arrangement the shaft passes through a sintered (porous bronze bushing which has been impregnated with oil at the factory. The total tolerance between the shaft and bushing is less than .001 in. and may have a tolerance of as little as .0003 in. As the bushing-shaft tolerance increases, due to wear, the motor becomes noisy. The "oilless" bushing is considered permanently lubricated

by the serviceman. This type of bushing is often used on fan motors and on other low horsepower applications.

7-67 Open Motor Bearings

Check the bearings to see if they are worn. If the rotor is hitting the metal of the stator, this is a sure sign that the bearings are worn out and must be replaced. The clearance between the rotor and stator varies from .015 in. to .030 in., depending on the size of the motor. This clearance should be the same for the full distance around the rotor. A bearing should be replaced which shows sign of wear. A heavy rumbling sound at the time of starting usually indicates that the bearing is badly worn, even though the rotor does not quite touch the field poles.

The bearings are usually made of phosphor bronze and are pressed into the end brackets or end bells. Sometimes these bearings are locked in by a pin pressed through the bearing housing and into the bearing. The bearing must always be pressed inward to remove it. Care should be taken not to put an out-of-line force on the end bell when pressing the bearings out, as this will probably crack the end bell. A special tool used to remove or install bushings or sleeve bearings is shown in Fig. 7-91. After the bearing is pressed into the bracket, when installing a new one, the bearing must be reamed. It is best to ream the two in line with adjustable reamers. The surface of the shaft in contact with the bearing must be perfectly smooth. A scored shaft may be repaired in a lathe with the use of a grinder mounted on the tool post.

The bearing on the commutator end of all motors will usually show a normal temperature rise in excess of the bearing on the pulley end because less air circulates around it. However, the temperature rise should not exceed 40 C. (72 F.) above the surrounding (or ambient) temperature.

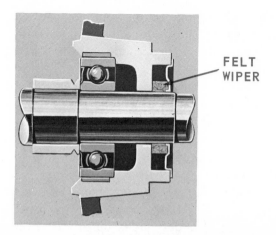

FELT WIPER

Fig. 7-90. Motor shaft mounted on ball bearings. Ball bearings are grease lubricated. Felt wiper keeps out dirt and dust.

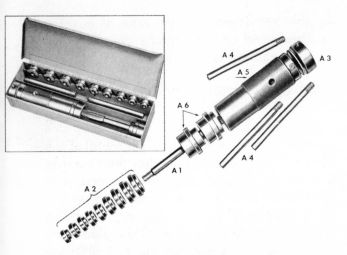

Fig. 7-91. Special motor bearing tool kit. Kit contains necessary tools for removing and replacing motor bearings:

A-1 Main shaft.
A-2 Bushing puller disks of various sizes.
A-3 Take up nut.
A-4 Nut turning handles.
A-5 Main spacer.
A-6 Bushing socket spacers.
(Cleveland Sales Co.)

Any one of the following causes may result in a hot bearing:

1. Oil too heavy.
2. Oil too thin (select a good grade of mineral lubrication oil which is not greatly affected by a change in temperature and does not foam or bubble too freely).
3. Dirt or grit in the oil.
4. Belt too tight.
5. Pulley hub rubbing against the bearing.
6. Motor not properly lined up, causing the armature shaft shoulder to pull or be pushed against one bearing.

7-68 Cleaning Open Motors

While in service, the motor should be cleaned at regular periods. Dust and lint in the motor will prevent proper air circulation through the inside of the motor. Compressed air or a hand bellows should be used frequently to blow dirt out of the motor. Any oil which may overflow from the bearings should be wiped from the motor. A little attention will result in continued good operating results and enable the motor to give the best service for many years.

If the motor is dismantled, all the parts should be carefully cleaned before being worked on or reassembled. Cleaning fluids must be used that are not harmful to the electrical insulation material or to your health. There are many cleaning fluids on the market. Be sure to check the one being used for safety to equipment and personnel. The motor interiors are well designed but abuse in handling may harm them. Fig. 7-92 illustrates typical internal wiring construction.

All cleaning fluids should be used in well ventilated and fireproof situations. Only enough cleaning fluid for the job should be used as too much may be dangerous. Always avoid using CARBON TETRACHLORIDE as the fumes are toxic and dangerous.

7-69 Pulleys

Pulleys that are mounted on motor shafts are available in many sizes and types of construction. Some are made of cast iron and some of steel stampings. They are made with various shaft size openings and diameters.

The pulleys are made with and without fans.

The most popular shaft sizes for fractional horsepower motors are 1/2 in., 5/8 in. and 3/4 in. diameter. Practically all pulley bores have a keyway and a setscrew. The setscrew usually has a 5/16 in. NC thread.

The pulley sizes vary from 2 in. diameter to a 5 1/4 in. diameter in 1/4 in. increments. Larger sizes up to 15 in. diameter are available.

The V-pulleys come in two popular widths. The A width is for belts up to

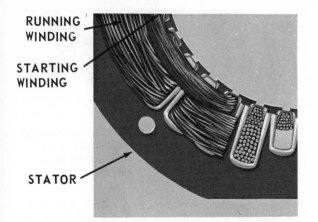

RUNNING
WINDING

STARTING
WINDING

STATOR

Fig. 7-92. Section through stator windings showing method of installing, insulating and retaining windings. Wire insulation is heavy modified polyester. Slots are lined, and "cuffed" ends prevent grounds where coils cross corners of core. Slots are closed with shaped sticks of heavy electrical paper.

17/32 in. width while the B width is for belts that are 1/2 in. to 11/16 in. wide.

Multiple groove pulleys are available for units that use two or more belts to drive the flywheels. Some air conditioning units use step pulleys for driving the air movement fan. By changing the belt from one groove to another, the speed of the fan can be changed.

Special pulleys that are of variable pitch are also available. These pulleys are made with one half of the pulley threaded on the hub of the other half, as shown in Fig. 7-93. A setscrew locks the variable half in place when it is adjusted. By turning the variable half, the V-groove can be widened to let the belt ride closer to hub and thereby reduce speed of driven flywheel or pulley. The speed of the driven unit can be varied by as much as 30 percent using these pulleys. Fig. 7-94 illustrates a double-groove, variable-pitch pulley.

Bushings are available to adapt large

Fig. 7-94. Adjustable double V-pulley. Both grooves are adjustable.

A

B

Fig. 7-93. V-pulley adjustable in width used to change speed of belt-driven appliances. Widening V gives effect of using smaller diameter pulley. Narrowing V gives effect of using larger diameter pulley. A shows the pulley in wide position, B shows pulley in narrow position. (Maurey Mfg. Corp.)

bore pulleys to small shafts; for example, a bushing can be used to reduce a 3/4 in. bore to a 1/2 in. bore.

7-70 Belts

The most popular way to drive the open compressor is through the use of a V-belt. These belts are made of rubber, layers of fabric, and cord. Some belts are a mixture of natural rubber and synthetic rubber. A cross section through a V-belt is shown in Fig. 7-95.

The belts are made in a multitude of lengths varying from as short as 15 in. outside length to as long as 364 in. outside length. The outside length is the complete distance around the outside of the belt. A steel tape, a cloth tape, or a special belt measuring fixture can be used to quickly determine the length of a belt.

Most belts are in one of three standard widths. This width is the widest or outside width of the belt. The widths are A 1/2 in. wide and B 5/8 in. wide. However, many special width belts have been made such as 33/64, 9/16, 37/64, 19/32, 5/8, 41/64, 23/32, 3/4, 7/8, 29/32, and 31/32. Some heavy-duty applications use the C width belt which is 15/16 in. wide.

When the motor is belted to the driven machine, it is necessary to have both shafts parallel to make the belt ride properly on the pulleys.

Whenever possible, the direction of rotation should be such as to cause the pull to be on the bottom side of the belt.

The development of new rubber, new cording design, and materials has permitted the use of smaller cross section belts. When installing these belts be careful to adjust for proper belt tension and alignment. The belts should be snug but not tight. The belt should have about a 1/2 in. of vertical movement when pressed with approximately a 10 lb. force. The compressor flywheel and the motor pulley must be in line with each other in two different ways to give long life to the belt and to the electric motor. First, the center line of the compressor must be parallel with the center line of the electric motor shaft; second, the pulley grooves must be in line with each other. A poorly aligned belt will decrease the life the motor because the motor is not designed to stand an excessive end load, and a noisy, poorly operating motor may result.

Automobile air conditioner belts are especially designed to transmit the power to the compressor. It is very important

Fig. 7-95. Cross section through a V-belt. Note cords running lengthwise through belt at neutral axis. (Gates Rubber Co.)

that the factory instructions be followed when adjusting these belts as explained in Chapter 25.

7-71 Open Motor Testing Stand

Electric motors, when in need of repair, are frequently taken to an electric motor repair shop to be overhauled. However, some of the refrigeration service companies prefer to repair as many of these motors as possible. In case rewinding the motor is necessary, this should be done in a shop equipped for this kind of work. In many cases when motors come in, it is a question whether the motor should be repaired or rewound. It is then necessary to test the motor carefully to determine its operating characteristics. To do this, a torque testing stand should be used. Chapter 15 describes this unit.

This testing stand consists of a stand and a group of pulleys with equal diameters to fit various size motor shafts. The surface of these pulleys is smooth and flat. A torque arm lined with automobile brake lining is arranged to fit the pulleys. The length of the torque arm should be exactly one foot between its point of support on the scales and the center of the motor pulley. A spring loaded adjustment mechanism should be arranged on the friction surfaces of the torque arm to enable various frictions to be produced between the torque arm and the motor pulley. The extremity of the torque arm is placed either on a spring scale or preferably on a platform scale. The torque arm should be balanced to prevent any prior loading of the scale. The torque arm must be level at the time the readings are taken. The torque of the motor can then be very accurately checked for stall condition and full speed load. The torque obtained in this way may then be read directly from the scales in pounds feet. This data, if compared with the manufacturers torque ratings, will indicate the condition of the motor. The switch mechanisms and brush mechanisms of these motors may be checked by using this stand. It is recommended that ammeters, voltmeters, and wattmeters be used to determine the current draw of the motor. The temperature rise of the bearings should be carefully noted when testing the motors. A thermometer placed in the bearing oil reservoir is recommended for this purpose. The temperature rise should not exceed 72 F. above the room temperature.

Electric dynamometers are available for measuring the power output of electric motors and they can also motorize the motor to determine its friction losses.

Electric meters should be installed in a panel in such a way that push switches can put an ammeter, a voltmeter, or a wattmeter in the circuit.

7-72 Servicing Fan Motors

The most common fan motor troubles are:

    A. Loose connections.
    B. Dry bearings.
    C. Worn bearings.
    D. Burned-out motor.
    E. Loose fan.
    F. Out-of-balance fan.
    G. Fan blades touching housing.

Loose or dirty connections will cause too much voltage drop at the motor and the fan motor will lose speed, hum loudly, and overheat. A sensitive voltmeter or an ohmmeter will quickly locate the faulty connection. Do not rely on visual inspection.

Dry bearing will cause the same symptoms as in the previous statement, but this condition will last only a short time before the bearings will either seize (bind) or become badly worn. Worn bearings will permit the rotor to vibrate in the stator causing noise. Also, the magnetic air gap will vary and cause an annoying hum or rumble. When the bearings wear badly enough to permit a rotor to rub on the stator the motor will probably burn out quickly.

Occasionally, the end play D as shown in Fig. 7-96 of the rotor becomes excessive and causes the motor to produce a distinct knock as the rotor shifts back and forth. Also, a reconditioned motor may

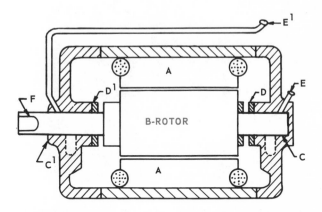

Fig. 7-96. Rotor running in its magnetic center:
    A—Stator.
    B—Rotor.
    C—Bearings.
    D—End play bearings.
    E—Oil cups.
    F—Pulley setscrew contact surface.

have the bearing (bushing) inserts off position to the extent of forcing the rotor out of its magnetic center along its shaft. When the motor is running, it should float between the extremes of its end play. One may check this by touching the end of the rotor shaft with a wooden stick, lightly as the motor is running. It should move back and forth and then settle in between the extremes of the end play. If the rotor cannot assume its magnetic center, it will hum excessively and heat. When running, the heaviest magnetic flow from the stator tries to line up with the heaviest magnetic flow from the rotor B. This aligning must take place with end play clearance at D and D'. The total clearance is usually about .030 or 1/32 in. Fig. 7-97 shows the bushing and end play bearing washer on a fan motor.

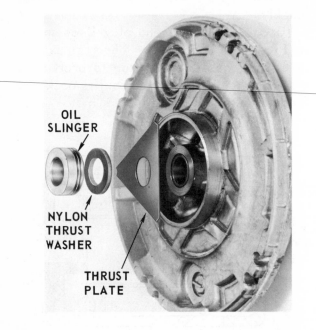

OIL SLINGER

NYLON THRUST WASHER

THRUST PLATE

Fig. 7-97. An illustration of a fan motor bearing and thrust bearing washer. (General Electric Co.)

A rattle in the fan motor may sometimes be caused by the fan becoming loose on the motor shaft. This noise can be easily remedied by tightening the setscrew that fastens the fan hub to the shaft. The smaller fans have either a round shaft or a flat spot milled on the shaft. If the fan is abused, the blades may be forced out of position and one or more blades may vibrate causing undue noise. The easiest

repair is to replace the injured fan. Any attempt to rebalance the blades is difficult unless special static and dynamic balancers are available. If the fan blades touch the fan housing, it may be caused by the motor being out of line or the shroud or housing may be warped. The contact spot is usually easily detected and remedied, by moving the fan on the shaft or moving the shroud or housing. Do not bend the fan blades as this will cause the unit to vibrate.

7-73 Servicing and Repairing Hermetic Motors

Servicing hermetic motors may be divided into two major sections: (1) external servicing, (2) internal servicing. Most of the hermetic motor troubles are external. The trouble may be in the wiring or in the motor control devices. It is important to determine exactly where the electrical troubles are, before deciding the motor is at fault.

Furthermore, it is essential that any external trouble be remedied as soon as possible, because this trouble may eventually cause the motor to fail.

The motor may need rewinding, and because the windings are always in the stator, this stator must be removed. The motor-compressor dome must be unbolted or the weld removed by cutting or grinding. Be careful of the oil. Oil in a burned out motor is usually very acidic and may burn your hands, face, and clothing. The motor stator is usually bolted to the compressor body and dowel pinned to obtain extreme accuracy of alignment. First, disconnect the wires from the terminals and carefully label them, also the three terminals. Then mark (center punch) the parts to assure they will be assembled in the correct manner. Keep the parts in a separate labeled tray. It is good practice to torque the nuts and bolts as they are removed, to learn how much to tighten them on assembly.

Improper tightening may warp the body out of its normal tolerance and cause considerable trouble.

Some stators are pressed in the dome to increase the cooling action on the stator windings. This type of stator must be power pulled and gear pullers or special pullers are used to carefully remove it as shown in Fig. 7-98.

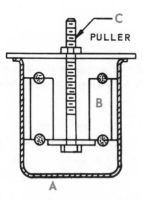

Fig. 7-98. *Puller which may be used for removing a press fit stator from its dome: A–Dome. B–Stator. C–Puller.*

After the stator is removed, it can be rechecked electrically for grounds, opens, and shorts. The trouble may sometimes be repaired quickly without the motor needing to be rewound. If the motor needs rewinding, this operation must be done by an expert motor rewinder. It is necessary to see that the following important things are done:

A. Wire size must be the same.
B. Number of turns must be the same.
C. Insulation must be immune to the refrigerant and oil even in the presence of moisture.
D. Work must be done in a dry, clean, and dust-free place.

Many of the refrigeration supply houses have replacement stators for hermetic units. It is important to remember that the workmanship must be of the highest quality. It is costly to do all the dismantling over again. The first repair job must be right.

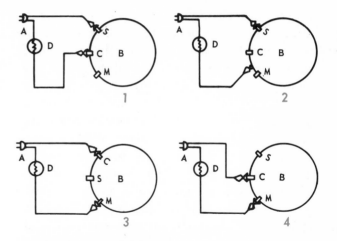

Fig. 7-99. *Method of testing motor electrical circuits:*
A–Power circuit plug 115V AC.
B–Motor being tested.
C–Motor common terminal.
D–25 watt electric light bulb.
S –Starting winding terminal.
M–Running winding terminal.

7-74 External Testing and Servicing Hermetic Motors

The condition of the refrigeration motor can be readily and easily determined with the use of instruments, without the necessity of opening the unit. This may be done by disconnecting the wires that are connected to the motor terminals and then testing the motor independent of all its external electrical connections as shown in Fig. 7-99. A is the plug, B is the hermetic motor, D is the light bulb (25 watt), while the starting winding terminal is S, the common terminal is C, and the running or main winding terminal is M. In part (1) the starting winding is being checked for continuity. If the bulb (D) lights, it means the current is flowing through the starting winding (S to C), and that there is no open spot in the windings.

In part (2) the windings are being checked for a ground; that is to see if any part of any of the internal wiring or the terminals are touching or making electrical contact with the metal parts of the unit.

If the bulb (D) lights when one of the electrical leads is touched to any of the terminals, and the other lead or clip is touched to the clean or bare metal body of the dome, it means that electricity is flowing along the internal wires and through a grounded wire into the metalwork. Be sure the terminals are clean and dry during the test, or they may be temporarily grounded by dirt. The insulator of the windings should show no breakage (ohmmeter) to the casing (dome) at 1000 to 1500 volts. In part (3) the continuity of both the running and starting windings is being checked. An instrument to check motor windings at high voltages is shown in Fig. 7-100. You must be extremely cautious and not touch the parts when the power is on.

Another trouble that sometimes occurs, especially if the unit has been overheated, is the shorting of some motor windings without a ground being formed. Any short-

Ohmmeter Readings

HP	Running Winding	Starting Winding
1/8	4.7	18
1/6	2.7	17
1/5	2.3	14
1/4	1.7	17

Fig. 7-101. Table of approximate ohmmeter readings for fractional horsepower single-phase motor.

ing of the motor windings will increase the current draw, decrease the power and overheat the unit. A shorted unit can sometimes be detected by an interruption in the steady hum of the motor when it is running; that is, a noticeable beat occurs in addition to the steady hum. To check for this short, one can roughly determine its existence by the test light (D). The test light (D) will be brighter than normal if some of the windings are shorted. A better way is to use an ohmmeter and check the resistance of the coils. As models are checked, record the data. Many servicemen use an ohmmeter to check for continuity, shorts, and grounds. An ohmmeter is more accurate than a test light. Repeated tests have shown that the approximate resistance of domestic unit windings are as shown in Fig. 7-101.

7-75 Starting a Stuck Hermetic Motor-Compressor

Occasionally a unit may be found that will not start, even though all the electrical tests indicate that the unit is in good condition. This stuck condition may be caused by the unit standing idle for a considerable time, a particle of dirt, or some electrolytic plating may have taken place. A more

Fig. 7-100. High voltage test instrument for checking motor windings. Use 1,000 volts for units up to 1/3 hp and 1,500 volts for units 1/2 hp and higher. Duration of test should not be for longer than one second. (Airserco Mfg. Co.)

ELECTRIC MOTORS

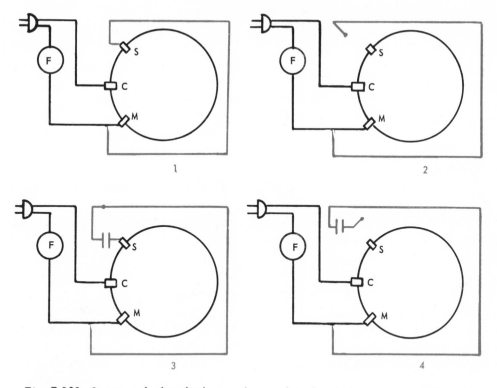

Fig. 7-102. Some methods which may be used to break loose a stuck hermetic compressor:
1 and 2—Without a capacitor in the starting circuit.
3 and 4—With a capacitor in the starting circuit.

than normal amount of liquid refrigerant in the compressor may also bind the unit. Three methods are recommended to break loose a stuck unit:

A. Connect the power line direct to the motor connections eliminating the starting relay as shown in Fig. 7-102.

B. Use above-normal voltage, such as 230V on a 115V circuit, to break it loose as shown in Fig. 7-103, part (1). This method can only be used for a very short period of time.

C. Reverse the unit; that is, make it run backward. This reversal rotation may be done by putting a capacitor in series with the running winding as shown in Fig. 7-103, part (2).

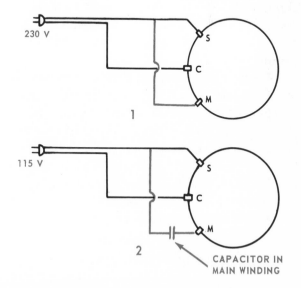

Fig. 7-103. Methods which may be used to start a stuck compressor: 1—Using above normal voltage. 2—Using capacitor in series with running winding. CAUTION – Apply the above methods for only a few seconds.

It is important to be continually on the alert to avoid handling high voltage circuits. You should short circuit capacitors to discharge them before handling.

7-76 Review of Electrical Safety

Electrical hazards can be considered in two parts:

1. Electricity as a source of ignition to start fires (electrical sparks near combustible material or in an atmosphere of combustible gases are an all too frequent source of fires).
2. Electrical shock. When electricity is passed through a part of an animal or human it causes muscle spasms. If it passes across the heart or brain it can be fatal. If enough current (amperes) are present, the electric current can actively overheat the body, cause burns and high temperature which may result in permanent body damage.

It is necessary to disconnect the electrical power source before performing any repair or service on electrical parts. You should lock the switches open to prevent someone from closing them during installation or service operations. The switch should also be tagged to warn other people.

Always short a capacitor before touching its terminals. If it is charged, it may discharge 200 to 500 volts into your body.

If a person has been subjected to electrical shock, he should be made to lie down and kept warm. If unconscious, artificial respiration is necessary. Always call a physician if someone has suffered severe electrical shock.

7-77 Test Your Knowledge - Chapter 7

1. List the types of motors used in domestic refrigeration.
2. How many field windings are used in a 115-230V repulsion-start induction motor?
3. Why must an open motor be cleaned regularly?
4. Why do some capacitors explode when charged?
5. Where is a thermistor used?
6. Why do some capacitors have resistors?
7. What is the running winding wattage of a 1/8 hp hermetic motor?
8. Why is a plug fuse inadequate protection for a motor?
9. What advantage does a capacitor motor have over a repulsion-start induction motor?
10. How often should open motor bearings be oiled?
11. Why do some motors have rubber or spring mountings?
12. What kind of electric motors are usually used in hermetic refrigerators?
13. What are the common voltages used on direct current motors?
14. How can radio interference caused by the refrigerator motor be reduced?
15. How many terminals does a domestic hermetic motor usually have?
16. How many windings does a single-phase hermetic motor stator have?
17. Why are some motors called split-phase motors?
18. What is the most common design problem with hermetic motors?
19. Why are hermetic motor field windings insulated in a special way?
20. What kind of rubber does a replacement terminal have?
21. What is a capacitor?
22. Is the capacitor connected in series with the starting winding?
23. What usually happens in the starting winding circuit when the motor reaches the correct speed?
24. What type motors are used to power the fans used on hermetic systems?
25. How is the fan motor electrically connected to the compressor motor?

26. Why is the hermetic motor sometimes run backwards?
27. How may a shorted capacitor be detected?
28. What is voltage drop?
29. How much may the voltage drop at the motor terminals before it causes trouble?
30. How should the wiring be marked for easy circuit tracing?
31. What is the magnetic center of a motor?
32. What is electrical continuity?
33. Why do some systems use two running capacitors connected in series?
34. How long does current flow in one direction when 60 cycle current is used?

Console for the automated control of the heating, comfort cooling and ventilating of a large office building.

Chapter 8

ELECTRIC
CIRCUIT CONTROLS

A thorough knowledge of the electrical circuits used in refrigeration and air conditioning is very important if you are to correctly install and service these systems. Elementary electricity is explained in some detail in Chapter 7. You are advised to master these fundamentals.

This Chapter explains the more common electrical controls and also explains various electrical circuits used in refrigerating systems. The application of electrical instruments is also explained. The correct use of electrical instruments is necessary if the electrical parts of the system are to be understood and serviced correctly.

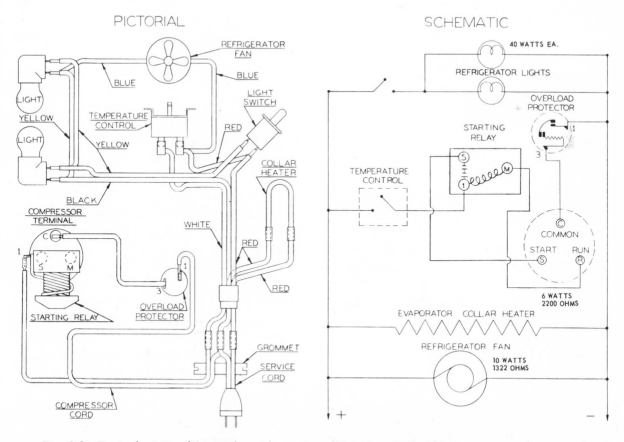

Fig. 8-1. Typical wiring diagram for a domestic refrigerator. Left. Electric circuits in pictorial form. Right. Diagram using conventional electrical symbols.
(Franklin Appliance Div., Studebaker Corp.)

A small diameter tube which is used as a refrigerant control is called a capillary tube refrigerant control. See Fig. 8-4. In this application it is a carefully calibrated refrigerant flow control device and becomes an active part in the refrigerating cycle.

"Capillary tubes" are used for two other common applications:

1. It may be used to connect a power element or sensing bulb to a bellows or diaphragm, as found on thermostatic motor controls or thermostatic expansion valves.
2. A capillary tube may also be used to connect either the low side pressure or high side pressure or both to the bellows of a pressure operated motor control.

8-1 Electrical Controls

There are several types of electrical controls commonly used on refrigerating mechanisms:

1. Motor cycling controls.
    A. Thermostats.
    B. Pressure motor controls.
2. Relays.
    A. Amperage.
    B. Potential.
    C. Hot wire (thermal).
3. Solenoids.
4. Timers.

Air conditioners for heating have a variety of electrical controls depending on type of heating system and type of fuel. Chapter 23 describes and illustrates many of these controls.

8-2 Motor Cycling Controls

The purpose of automatic refrigeration is to provide correct refrigerating temperatures with a minimum of attention. To produce these temperatures under a variety of conditions, it is necessary to use a refrigerating unit with more capacity than is ordinarily needed. Under average conditions, this unit would over-refrigerate under continuous operating conditions.

There are two ways to stop heat removal when a satisfactory temperature has been reached:

1. The most popular way is to stop the motor when the correct temperature is reached.
2. The second method is to stop the flow of refrigerant in the system when the correct temperature is reached.

This latter system is frequently used in multiple commercial systems but seldom in single units.

Motor controls for most hermetic systems are more involved than those used for open systems. The hermetic system frequently uses a starting relay, and as many as three safety devices in the electrical circuit. Many modern hermetic units also incorporate automatic defrosting. Fig. 8-1 shows a complete electrical system for a domestic refrigerator. Note the two types of illustrations, pictorial and schematic. See Fig. 7-5 for a list of electrical symbols.

8-3 Refrigeration Electric Motor Controls

The temperature maintained by a refrigerating unit should be within certain limits. The machine must shut off (cut-out) when the low limit of the desired temperature is reached. As the temperature in the refrigerated space rises, at a predetermined temperature, the machine must start (cut-in) and refrigeration (cooling) is again supplied.

To operate the cut-in and cut-out, two different types of motor controls may be used:

1. Pressure type.
2. Thermostatic type.

This Chapter discusses the thermostatic type extensively as it is the one in general use. The pressure type is used to some extent in commercial refrigeration, and its operation is discussed in more detail in Chapter 13.

The running time varies depending on the ambient temperature, load to be cooled, quality of insulation, and size of refrigerating unit.

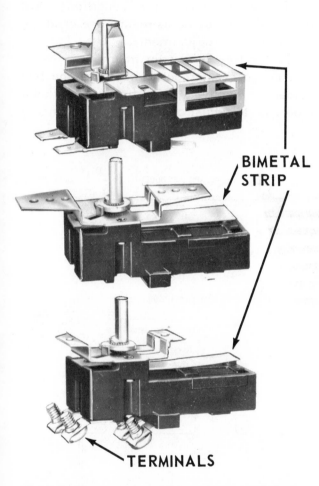

Fig. 8-2. *Three types of bimetal operated thermostats. These units are used for refrigeration control, for electric heat control and air conditioner control.* (*Therm-O-Disc Inc.*)

Motor controls are available for many different applications, including:
1. Domestic refrigerators.
2. Freezers.
3. Water coolers.
4. Air conditioners.
5. Ice makers.
6. Display cases.

In domestic refrigeration, for the northern states the running time will usually be 35 to 40 percent of the time; for the southern states about 50 percent of the time. Domestic refrigerators usually run 5 to 10 minutes, and are idle 10 to 20 minutes.

Most refrigerator manufacturers design their units so the electric motor operates a total of only 8 to 14 hours out of the 24, which is approximately 40 percent of the time.

This fourteen-hour operating time is based on average use of the cabinet. If the cabinet is used more, the running time will be longer. If the usage is less, the running time will be less.

Frost free refrigerators and some automatic defrost refrigerators may run a little longer or more often than the conventional older style machine because the defrosting energy adds to the heat load.

8-4 Motor Control Principles

Devices which change position or shape as the temperature varies or as the pressure varies, are used as motor control devices.

A bimetal strip is commonly used to produce motion as the temperature changes. It may be used where very small differentials are desired, such as in a house heating thermostat. It may also be used as a safety switch for motors. Its principle is to magnify a minute, metal size change into useful motion. This motion can be gradual as is done with a bimetal strip as shown in Fig. 8-2, or it can be a snap action as is done by using a disk.

Pressure changes from either a confined fluid, or from the low pressure side of the system, operating on a bellows or diaphragm, may also be used to control a motor circuit. This latter system is the one most frequently used. Fig. 8-3, shows some devices that power the switch in motor controls. Other designs are shown in Fig. 8-4. As the pressure rises in the low side, or in

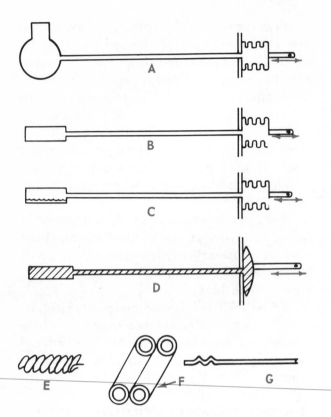

Fig. 8-3. Methods used to obtain motion from temperature and pressure changes. A—Low side pressure bellows. B—Gas charged temperature response bellows. C—Vapor pressure temperature response bellows. D—Liquid charge temperature response diaphragm. E—Capillary tube coil used as a bulb. F—Enlarged cross section of E sensitive element. G—A capillary tube used as a bulb.

the temperature lowers, the system is turned on. The control performs two functions:

1. It maintains certain temperature limits.
2. It controls the cycling time of the unit.

To obtain these two conditions, two different control adjustments are used:

1. A range adjustment.
2. A differential adjustment.

The range adjustment is to make the box colder or warmer. The differential adjustment, is to adjust and regulate the running

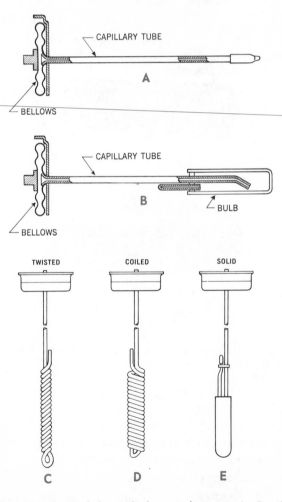

Fig. 8-4. Several thermal element designs. A—Capillary tube sensitive element. B—Bulb sensitive element. C—Twisted sensitive element. D—Coiled sensitive element. E—Solid (bulb) sensitive element. (Ranco Inc.)

the sensitive bulb, due to a temperature rise, the pressure rises in the bellows or diaphragm, and the bellows moves against atmospheric pressure and any spring pressure present. This movement, when connected to a snap-action switch will cause the switch to snap closed, and current will flow to the motor. When the pressure and temperature in the sensitive bulb decrease, the bellows or diaphragm will move in the opposite direction, and the toggle or snap switch will be pulled into the open position as shown in Fig. 8-5.

When used in a heating system the results are reversed. As the temperature rises, the heating system is shut off. When

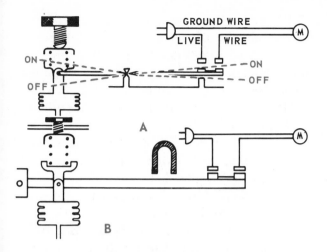

Fig. 8-5. *Methods of connecting bellows to snap action motor control switch. A—Toggle snap action. B—Magnet snap action.*

time of the unit. The control knob operated by the user of the refrigerator to adjust the temperature is a range adjustment. The differential adjustment is generally located so that only the serviceman changes the cycling interval.

8-5 Range Adjustment

Range adjustment provides for the correct minimum and maximum temperature or pressure, in an automatically operated system. Examples: the range adjustment will keep a refrigerator between certain minimum and maximum acceptable temperatures, an air conditioned room between certain temperatures, an air compressor between certain pressures. It is very difficult to keep any device at a certain temperature and/or pressure (at exactly 34.4 F. or 150.2 psig). It is the slight raising or lowering of the temperature or pressure which forces the control contact points together to start the unit, or forces the control contact points apart to stop the unit as the case may be.

A sample range adjustment is shown in Fig. 8-6. The unit cuts in at 25 F. and cuts out at 15 F. evaporating unit temperature. To make the box operate at a warmer tem-

perature, the range adjustment may be adjusted so the cut-out becomes 16 F. and the cut-in 26 F., as shown in Fig. 8-6 (A). Note that the temperatures are higher, but the temperature distance between the two has not been changed. This distance is still 10 F. The new settings will only slightly affect the running time of the unit due to the fact that the condition desired is not as cold, and therefore, the condensing unit will not have to do so much work.

The temperature of the refrigerator may be lowered a degree by adjusting the range adjustment to cut in at 24 F. and cut out at 14 F., as shown in Fig. 8-6 (B).

8-6 Range Adjustment Mechanisms

The range adjustment is easily recognized by the fact that it is an adjustable force pressing directly upon the bellows or diaphragm which operates the switch. This force is always being exerted on the bellows whether the switch is in the cut-out position, or in the cut-in position.

The adjustable force may be either an adjustable weight that always presses

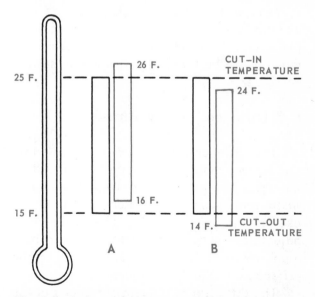

Fig. 8-6. *Range adjustments. The basic range is shown in black. A—Range is raised to 26 F. cut-in and 16 F. cut-out. B—Range is lowered to 24 F. cut-in and 14 F. cut-out.*

against the bellows, or more commonly, it is a spiral spring with an adjustable screw which in some cases changes the pressure or in other cases changes the tension of the spring.

The spring may press, or pull, either directly on the bellows or diaphragm, or it may press or pull on a lever which is attached to the bellows, as shown in Fig. 8-7.

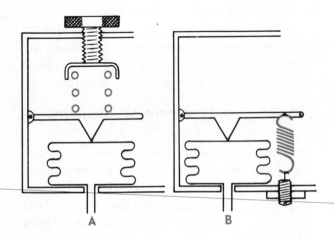

Fig. 8-7. Adjusting range settings of motor control. A—Compression spring range adjustment. B—Tension spring range adjustment.

Most of the range adjusting screws have a calibrated dial, or a pointer connected to the screw that indicates the direction the dial should be turned for a warmer setting or colder setting.

8-7 Differential Adjustment

The differential adjustment is built into the temperature control mechanism. It is not adjusted or changed by the operator when making a temperature selection by use of the control knob. The differential adjustment should be made by a serviceman who understands the working of the differential adjustment mechanism.

The differential adjustment controls the temperature difference between the cut-out and the cut-in settings. If the evaporating coil is set to cut in at 25 F. and cut out at 15 F., the difference or differential is 10 F. Whenever the differential (the distance between the settings) is changed, the range is also changed. If the range only is adjusted the differential will not be affected.

Three types of differential adjustments are shown in Fig. 8-8.

A. Cut-in type: The cut-in point may be moved without changing the cut-out as in A-1 and A-2.

B. Cut-out type: The cut-out point may be moved without changing the cut-in setting as shown in B-1 and B-2.

C. Double type: The cut-in and cut-out settings may be either brought closer together or moved farther apart as shown in C-1 and C-2.

A differential adjustment of the first two types may be recognized by the fact that it affects the operation of the switch mechanism. In the first case, only when the switch is in the cut-out position; in the second case, only when the switch is in the cut-in position. The third type differential adjustment is usually an adjustable arrangement which affects the effort of the toggle to snap off and on. This adjustment affects both the cut-in and the cut-out. They may be adjusted farther apart or closer together.

To obtain a desired cabinet temperature it is usually necessary to adjust both the range and the differential. To keep the same average cabinet temperature, the differential may be adjusted to 14 and 26 F., shown in Fig. 8-9, A-1. With this setting, the compressor will run longer, but will not cycle as often.

If this control is adjusted to cut in at 25 F. and cut out at 13 F., as shown in Fig. 8-9, A-2, the compressor will run longer than normal, and the cabinet temperature will be lower than normal.

If this control is adjusted to cut in at 27 F. and cut out at 15 F., as shown in Fig. 8-9, A-3, the compressor will run less and the cabinet temperature will be higher.

If the control is adjusted to cut in at

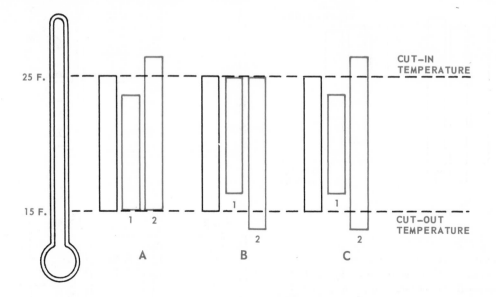

Fig. 8-8. Effect of different types of differential control adjustments. A–Cut-in setting type. B–Cut-out setting type. C–Cut-in and cut-out type. Note in each illustration the normal setting is shown in black.

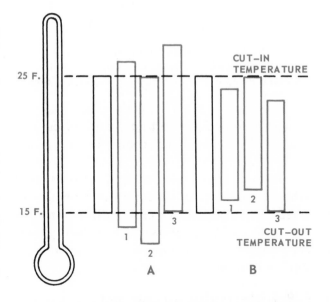

Fig. 8-9. Some differential adjustment characteristics. A–1. Differential increased. A–2. Range lowered. A–3. Range raised. B–1. Differential decreased. B–2. Range raised. B–3. Range lowered.

24 F. and cut out at 16 F., as shown in Fig. 8-9, B-1, the cabinet temperature will be normal, however, both the on and off cycles will be shorter and the cabinet temperature will vary less than normal.

With the control adjusted to cut in at 25 F. and cut out at 17 F., as shown in Fig. 8-9, B-2, the cabinet temperature will be warmer than normal, and the on and off cycles will be shorter than normal. The cabinet temperature will vary less than normal.

A control adjusted, as shown in Fig. 8-9, B-3, which cuts in at 23 F., and cuts out at 15 F. will provide a below normal cabinet temperature, which will vary less than normal. The on and off cycles will be shorter than normal.

If a slightly lower cabinet temperature is desired, with little or no increase in running time, the differential may be adjusted to cut out at 14 F., as shown in Fig. 8-10, A-1. If an increase in running time is desired it may be adjusted, as shown in Fig. 8-10, A-2. An adjustment as shown in Fig. 8-10, B-1, will provide a slightly warmer cabinet temperature and a shorter cycle interval. Also the cabinet temperature will vary less than normal. An adjustment as shown in Fig. 8-10, B-2, will provide a normal cabinet temperature, which varies less than normal, and a shorter than normal cycling interval.

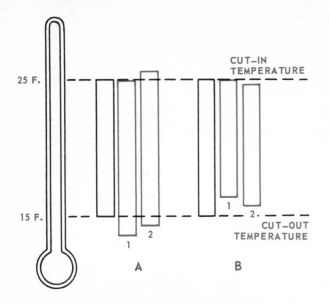

Fig. 8-10. *Some differential adjustments. Lower than normal temperature will be maintained by A–1. Normal temperature will be maintained by A–2 and B–2. Higher than normal temperature will be maintained by B–1. Adjustments for A–1 and A–2 will provide longer than normal running time.*

A typical control adjustment may be described as follows: To increase the cycling time when a control with a cut-in differential is used, first adjust the differential from a 25 F. cut-in to a 27 F. cut-in, as shown in Fig. 8-11, A-1. Then adjust the

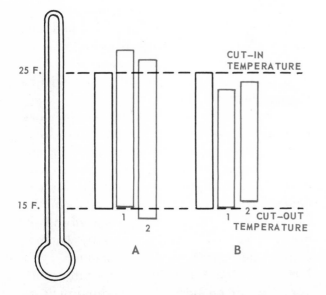

Fig. 8-11. *Effect of a cut-in differential adjustment.*
A–1. Cut-in differential raised.
A–2. Range lowered.
B–1. Cut-in differential lowered.
B–2. Range raised.

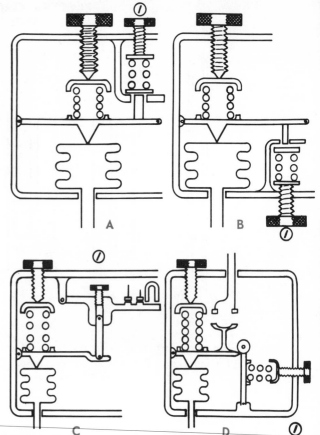

Fig. 8-12. *Various types of differential adjustment mechanisms. A–Cut-in type. B–Cut-out type. C–Cut-in type using a slot and magnet. D–Double type.*

range to move the settings to 26 F. cut-in, and 14 F. cut-out, as shown in Fig. 8-11, A-2.

To decrease the cycling time (interval) when a control with a cut-in differential is used, first adjust the cut-in differential to cut in at 23 F., as shown in Fig. 8-11, B-1, then adjust the range to the settings of 24F. cut-in and 16 F. cut-out.

8-8 Differential Adjustment Mechanisms

Two types of differential adjustments have a spring that affects the movement of the bellows, either just before the contact points cut out or cut in, but not both. This limited action is obtained by using a stop on the spring as shown in Fig. 8-12, parts A, B and C.

The third type of differential adjustment

278

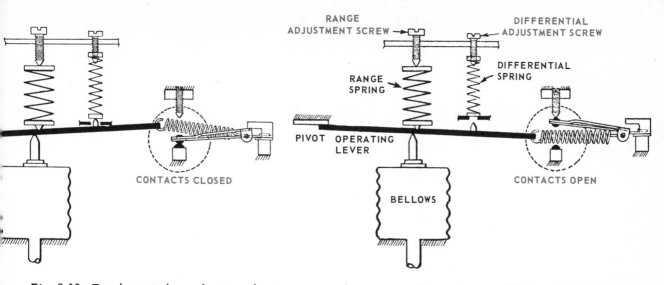

Fig. 8-13. *Toggle switch mechanism showing range adjustment, and a cut-in type differential adjustment.*

affects both the cut-out and cut-in by using a spring to make it easier for the points to open and close, or more difficult for the control to open or close the electrical contact points, as shown in Fig. 8-12, part D.

Fig. 8-13 shows a mechanism with a cut-in differential.

A control with a cut-in calibration screw and lever and a cut-out calibration screw and lever, is shown in Fig. 8-14.

Fig. 8-14. *Cross section of thermostat which shows operating mechanisms and adjustments. Range adjustment is shown at 1. Contact points are shown in red.*

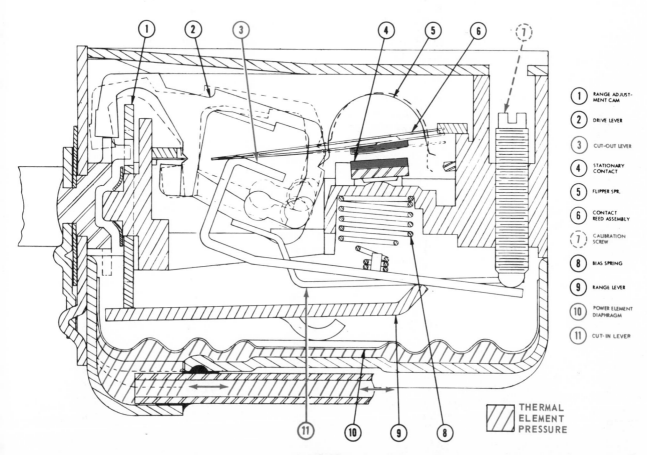

8-9 Adjusting Controls

It is advisable to adjust the controls according to the manufacturer's specifications. Some controls are marked "Cut-in adjusting screw" and "Cut-out adjusting screw." Some are marked "Range."

1. If the control has a cut-in differential and the control is marked step one, "cut-out adjustment" for one adjusting screw and step two, "cut-in adjustment" for another adjusting screw, the cut-in screw is the differential adjustment, and the cut-out is the range.

2. If the control has a cut-out differential, it will be just the opposite; the cut-in will be the range and the cut-out will be the differential.

3. If the differential adjustment controls the distance between the cut-out and the cut-in, the first setting should be adjusted by using the differential adjustment to adjust to the correct distance between the settings, then the range adjustment is turned to obtain the correct settings.

The adjustment used by the owner is usually a limited range adjustment. However, some models are designed to allow the owner to adjust only the cut-out setting. This design insures a safe cut-in temperature at all times.

Many controls of the thermostat type have an altitude adjustment. When a refrigerator is used at higher than normal altitude, the atmospheric pressure decreases enough to reduce the pressure on the control diaphragm or bellows, a sufficient amount to affect the settings. The altitude adjustment, range control, pressure for the bellows or diaphragm is therefore increased to make up for the decreases in atmospheric pressure. Fig. 8-15 shows such a control and its altitude adjustment table. Note that the dial is divided into 60 equal calibrations.

Fig. 8-16 shows two different controls and a table of adjustments used to correct for various altitudes for each control.

Some controls have a small heater unit and the heat from this unit keeps the bellows and diaphragm from being cooled too much by the adjacent cold parts of the re-

Fig. 8-15. Thermostat equipped with altitude adjustment. Table indicates correct setting of altitude adjustment for any particular altitude.
(Gibson Refrigerator Div., Hupp Corp.)

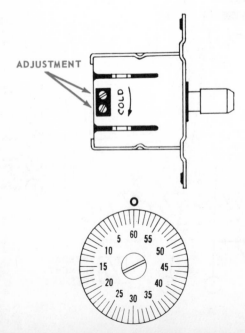

ALTITUDE ADJUSTMENT CHART
(Cutler Hammer Control)

ALTITUDE IN FEET	COUNTERCLOCKWISE TURNS OF SCREWS	
	CUT-IN SCREW	CUT-OUT SCREW
2,000	7/60	4/60
3,000	13/60	7/60
4,000	19/60	10/60
5,000	25/60	13/60
6,000	31/60	16/60
7,000	37/60	19/60
8,000	43/60	22/60
9,000	49/60	25/60
10,000	55/60	28/60

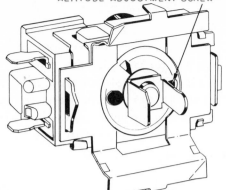

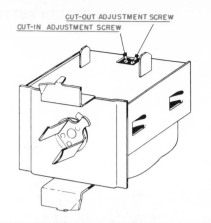

Altitude Above Sea Level - Feet	Constant Cut-In
	Altitude Screw Adjustment (Turns Clockwise)
1000	No Change
2000	1/16
3000	1/8
4000	3/16
5000	1/4
6000	5/16
7000	3/8
8000	3/8
9000	-

ALTITUDE ADJUSTMENT

<u>Both</u> Cut-In And Cut-Out Screws <u>Must</u> Be Adjusted

Altitude Above Sea Level - Feet	Constant Cut-In	
	Turns Counter-Clockwise	
	Cut-In Screw	Cut-Out Screw
2000	1/8 CCW	1/16 CCW
3000	7/32	1/8
4000	5/16	5/32
5000	13/32	7/32
6000	1/2	1/4
7000	19/32	5/16
8000	11/16	3/8
9000	13/16	13/32
10000	15/16	7/16

Altitude Above Sea Level - Feet	Variable Cut-In
	Range Screw Adjustment (Turns Clockwise)
1000	3/32
2000	3/16
3000	7/32
4000	1/4
5000	3/8
6000	7/16
7000	15/32
8000	1/2
9000	9/16

Altitude Above Sea Level - Feet	Variable Cut-In	
	Turns Counter-Clockwise	
	Cut-In Screw	Cut-Out Screw
2000	1/16 CCW	1/16 CCW
3000	1/8	1/8
4000	5/32	5/32
5000	3/16	3/16
6000	1/4	1/4
7000	5/16	5/16
8000	3/8	3/8
9000	13/32	13/32
10000	7/16	7/16

Fig. 8-16. Two domestic type thermostats equipped with altitude adjustments. Left—General Electric. Right—Cutler-Hammer. (Kelvinator Div., American Motors Corp.)

frigerator. A too cold thermostat body will not cut in as soon as it should, and may cause erratic cabinet temperatures.

The complete control is shown in Fig. 8-17.

8-10 Pressure Controls

To cause refrigeration effect, a low pressure must be maintained in the evaporator unit to permit evaporation of the re-

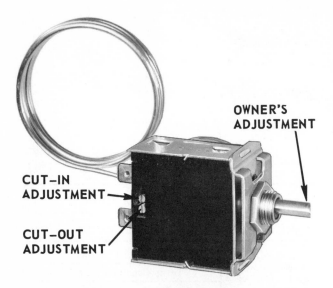

OWNER'S ADJUSTMENT

CUT—IN ADJUSTMENT

CUT—OUT ADJUSTMENT

Fig. 8-17. Domestic cabinet thermostat. Range adjustment used by owner is at the right. Note the cut-in and cut-out adjustment at the left.

frigerant at a low temperature. Therefore, automatic control of the motor may be based on pressure differences in the evaporator. This control is used on commercial systems.

It operates as follows: When the evaporator warms, the low side pressure increases, a bellows expands, a switch is closed, and the motor starts. When the pressure (and temperature) becomes low enough the pressure is reduced, the bellows contracts, the contacts open and the motor is automatically shut off.

The electrical switch may be of either the mercury bulb or of the open-contact point type. A bellows operated low pressure control is shown in Fig. 8-18. A pressure rise in the bellows chamber causes the contact points to close. As soon as the compressor reduces the pressure sufficiently, bellows will contract, opening circuit.

The range adjustment will lower both the cut-in and cut-out an equal distance if the screw is moved out (counterclockwise), and will raise the cut-out and cut-in pressure if turned in (clockwise). The spring is under compression and presses on the bellows at all times. The differential ad-

justment will raise the cut-out pressure when turned farther to the right (clockwise). This is the cut-out type differential adjustment. If the spring tension is increased by turning the screw clockwise, it is harder for the bellows to reach its cut-out setting but the spring has no affect on the cut-in setting.

Some models of the pressure control are also equipped to act as a safety control. A bellows construction with a pressure tap to the high pressure side of the compressor is used. If the compression pressure or head pressure should become too high, the bellows will expand and this movement will open the switch and stop the mo-

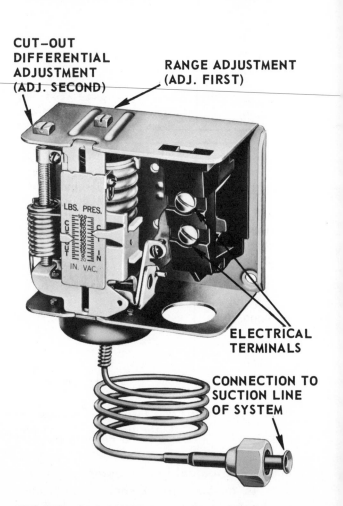

CUT—OUT DIFFERENTIAL ADJUSTMENT (ADJ. SECOND)

RANGE ADJUSTMENT (ADJ. FIRST)

ELECTRICAL TERMINALS

CONNECTION TO SUCTION LINE OF SYSTEM

Fig. 8-18. Pressure type motor control with cover removed to show mechanism and adjustments. Note the electrical terminals. (Penn Controls, Inc.)

tor. This control is a safety device for the motor. It is especially necessary when a water-cooled unit is used. See Chapter 13 for more information on commercial controls.

The low pressure type of control is of such a nature that it is easy to adjust while on the job. It can also be easily adjusted with a vacuum pump and a compound gauge after it has been removed from the unit.

Some larger units also use a safety control device connected to the oil pressure. These operate to shut off the unit if the oil pressure decreases or fails below a predetermined safe pressure. The construction is similar to a low pressure control but usually with a fixed or nonadjustable differential.

The adjustment of these controls is important, because lasting satisfactory operation of the unit depends to a great extent on their proper adjustment.

8-11 Thermostatic Motor Controls

Thermostatic motor controls may be classified into three types according to internal construction and operation. These types are:
1. Self-contained type.
2. Remote power element type.
3. Double remote power element type.

8-12 Remote Power Element Type Control

The remote power element type control operates on the same principles as described in Pars. 8-2, 8-3, 8-4, and 8-5. In addition, it may be equipped with safety devices and a defrosting switch. Its design is also different in that it has a remote power element which is connected to a bellows in the electrical control by means of a capillary tube, but its operation is identical. Fig. 8-19 shows two controls equipped with remote temperature sensing tubes. That is, as the power element warms, its internal

Fig. 8-19. *Two motor controls which have remote temperature sensing capillary tubes. Note voltage and current rating of controls. (Cutler-Hammer, Inc.)*

pressure operates upon a flexible bellows or diaphragm, located in the rear of the temperature control. This bellows presses against an arm under spring tension. When the pressure becomes high enough, it throws two contacts together to complete the electrical circuit and start the motor.

The adjustment of this temperature control consists of turning the knob in the direction specified on the cold control. Increasing the large spring pressure will make the unit warmer, and releasing the spring pressure will make the unit colder. See Fig. 8-20.

To increase or decrease the temperature difference or differential between the cut-in and cut-out points, a small screw is located in the bottom of the case. The more the small screw is turned in, the less the differential. The more the small screw is turned out (counterclockwise) the more the differential.

The differential screw adjusts the distance the arm can move in the open position. By turning the screw in, the cut-in temperature can be raised or vice versa. However, this screw has no effect on the cut-out, as the lever is away from the screw in the points closed position. This differential is not to be touched, however, unless absolutely necessary.

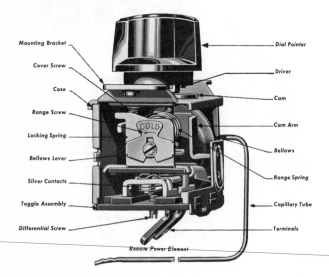

Fig. 8-20. Thermostatic motor control which uses remote power element. This control is used in domestic units and small commercial units.

After the evaporator has become cold enough, the power element will cool; the resultant drop in pressure will cause a contraction of the bellows which in turn allows the spring pressure to make the contacts fly apart. These contacts are built into a lever toggle system controlled by springs. When they are opened and closed, they move rapidly with a snapping action. This reduces arcing at the points. A thermostatic control using two remote power elements is used on many units equipped for automatic defrosting.

Special devices, such as overload cut-out, automatic defrosting, manual switch, and range adjustments, which provide control of evaporator temperatures, are incorporated in many of the thermostatic motor controls.

Another type of temperature control is shown in Fig. 8-21.

8-13 Remote Power Element Design

Remote power elements are available in several designs.

One major difference in type is based on the pressure in the element. Two common designs are as follows:
1. Above atmospheric pressure in the element (used for controlling refrigeration temperatures).
2. Below atmospheric pressure in the element (used for controlling heating units).

The above atmospheric pressure type is used for controls which close the electrical circuit on temperature rise. If the element loses its charge, the unit is unable to start. This element is used where continuous running would be harmful such as refrigerators and comfort cooling units.

The below atmospheric pressure type is used for controls which open the electrical circuit on temperature rise and are used on electric heating units and electric defrost units. If the element loses its charge,

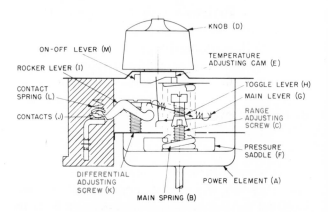

Fig. 8-21. Thermostatic motor control. Note control knob, range adjustment and differential adjustment. (Cutler-Hammer, Inc.)

the points will open (they are designed to close on temperature drop and open on temperature rise). These controls are called "fail safe" controls. They prevent an electric heating coil from overheating.

The power element may also be classified according to the charge in the element as follows:

A. Liquid.

B. Cross charge (approximately one-half liquid and one-half vapor).

C. Vapor charged.

These various elements are shown in Fig. 8-22.

The liquid charged unit (A) responds to the expansion and contraction of the liquid as the temperature changes. There is no vapor in the element at any time.

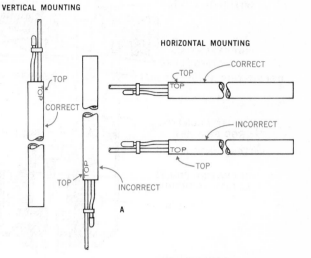

Fig. 8-23. *Some typical thermostat bulb mountings. Note how the bulbs are marked and also note correct and incorrect positions for mounting temperature sensitive bulb. (Ranco Inc.)*

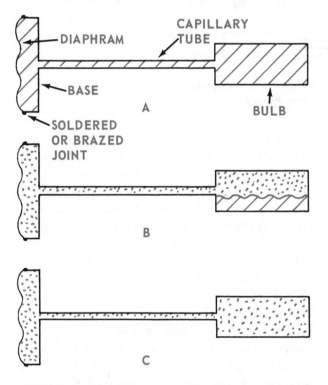

Fig. 8-22. *Three types of sensitive element charges: A–Liquid charged (hydraulic). B–Cross charged (always some liquid and some vapor in the element). C–Vapor charged (all vapor above a certain "safe" temperature.*

The cross charged element (B) always has some liquid and some vapor in the sensitive bulb. The bulb temperature may be either above or below the temperature of the other parts of the control.

The vapor charged element (C) responds to the vapor pressure as the temperature changes. The vapor charged element operates in a temperature range which makes certain that no liquid is present in the element above its operating range. The bulb must always be the coldest spot in the control.

The important thing to remember is that the bulb or the capillary tube end must control the thermostat. Some bulbs are marked to show the position that they should be in when mounted on the evaporator coil or attached to a tube or pipe as shown in Fig. 8-23.

8-14 Defrosting Switch Safety Overload

Some manual defrosting switches include a safety overload device. A long arm is attached to the defrosting switch button which, when pulled out, has a little catch on the arm which holds the contacts apart until the control button is pushed back again.

A small ratchet rack and gear attachment is connected to a safety fuse or time fuse and operates as follows: directly in series with the wires going to the contact points is a heating coil which is wrapped

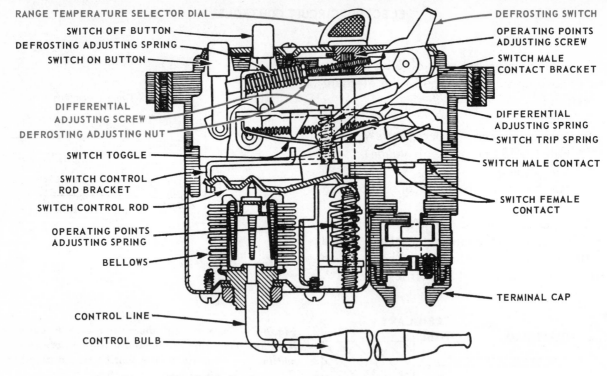

Fig. 8-24. Semiautomatic defrosting motor control.
(Kelvinator Div., American Motors Corp.)

Labels on figure:
RANGE TEMPERATURE SELECTOR DIAL
SWITCH OFF BUTTON
DEFROSTING ADJUSTING SPRING
SWITCH ON BUTTON
DIFFERENTIAL ADJUSTING SCREW
DEFROSTING ADJUSTING NUT
SWITCH TOGGLE
SWITCH CONTROL ROD BRACKET
SWITCH CONTROL ROD
OPERATING POINTS ADJUSTING SPRING
BELLOWS
CONTROL LINE
CONTROL BULB
DEFROSTING SWITCH
OPERATING POINTS ADJUSTING SCREW
SWITCH MALE CONTACT BRACKET
DIFFERENTIAL ADJUSTING SPRING
SWITCH TRIP SPRING
SWITCH MALE CONTACT
SWITCH FEMALE CONTACT
TERMINAL CAP

around a shaft holding the ratchet gear. This coil is so designed that if the motor runs too long or draws too much current, it will get so warm that it heats the solder holding the ratchet gear to the ratchet axle. When the solder gets hot enough it will melt, freeing the ratchet gear.

The ratchet rack has a spring tension, when this is released it pulls the rack up. The rack has a shoulder which catches the contact point lever, breaking the circuit. That is, as soon as the solder melts, this arm will move up, pulling the defrosting button out and shutting off the electric motor. As soon as the circuit is cut, the heating coil, being in series with the rest of the electrical line, ceases to heat, and the solder will resolidify so that when the housewife pushes the button back in, the unit will operate as before.

8-15 Semiautomatic Defrosting Controls

Some domestic refrigerators use semiautomatic defrosting controls. These devices were made to do the following: (1) de-

frost the unit when the housewife presses the button, and then (2) return to regular operation automatically after the unit has defrosted. The housewife has only to start the defrosting; the rest is automatic. Another system is as follows: raise the range a fixed amount by pressing a button. With this action, the cooling coils will run at a warm enough temperature to permit defrosting, but will still give satisfactory refrigeration. Return to regular operation by pulling on the button. A third system, incorporates a clock arrangement that will automatically (by time) start the defrosting and return the control to normal operation automatically. This latter type usually operates once every 24 hours. It is fully automatic.

A sample of an earlier model manual defrost is shown in Fig. 8-24. The range adjustment is the long screw with a moveable nut. This nut is attached to the switch control rod by means of the operating points adjusting spring. The differential adjustment controls the distance the toggle is allowed to snap open; therefore, it adjusts the cut-in point.

The defrosting switch when turned to the left puts a load (spring) on the lever extending from the lever so that the bellows pressure must be higher (meaning a higher temperature) to make the contact points snap closed. When the lever does move the defrost switch knob, it returns this knob to its normal operation setting (to the right).

The present day refrigerators which use manual defrost frequently use a double capillary tube control, Fig. 8-25. This control uses a power element for normal cycling and the other as a cut-in control for the defrost. The defrosting is started by the housewife pushing the control knob in. This movement opens the motor circuit and closes the circuit to either a defrost solenoid (hot gas) or to electric heater elements.

When the coils are defrosted, the defrost capillary tube will create enough bellows pressure to open the defrost circuit and return the control connections to the motor circuit.

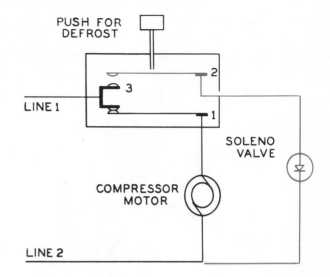

Fig. 8-26. Wiring diagram for a "hot gas" defrosting device which uses a combination control. The control is shown in the refrigerating position. Defrost system is solenoid valve controlled hot gas defrost. (Ranco Inc.)

A wiring diagram of the control connected to a hot gas defrost system is shown in Fig. 8-26. The circuits used for an electric defrost system are shown in Fig. 8-27.

The hot gas method of defrosting uses a solenoid valve to open and close the bypass

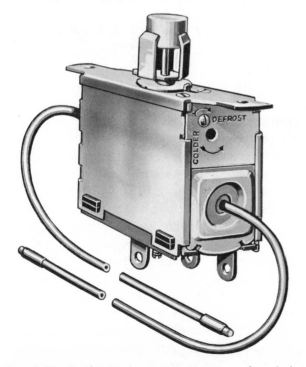

Fig. 8-25. Combination temperature control and defrost control. (Ranco Inc.)

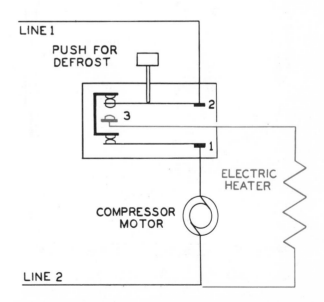

Fig. 8-27. Wiring diagram for electric heater defrost system using combination control. Control is shown in refrigerating position. Heater circuit is shown in red.

from the compressor discharge to the evaporator coil. Fig. 8-28 shows the valve equipped with connector lines. This valve

Fig. 8-28. Solenoid valve which may be used with thermostats for either hot gas defrosting or secondary system control.

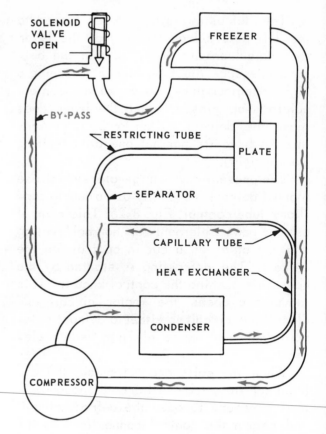

Fig. 8-30. Bypass system using solenoid valve. With valve open as shown, main refrigerating effect will be in freezing compartment. With valve closed both PLATE evaporator and FREEZER evaporator will be refrigerated.

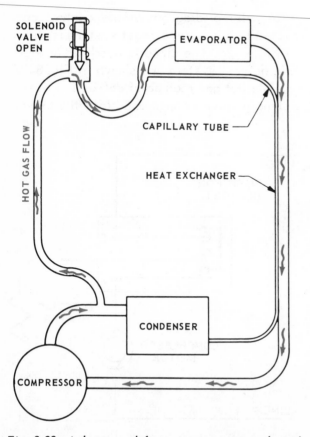

Fig. 8-29. A hot gas defrost system using solenoid valve. The illustration shows valve open and hot gas passing directly from compressor into evaporator.

is similar to the solenoid valves used to control refrigerant flow in secondary systems of two-temperature refrigerators. The valve must be mounted in a vertical position to function correctly. Fig. 8-29 shows the solenoid valve installed in a hot gas defrost system, while Fig. 8-30 shows it installed in a bypass refrigeration system.

Some refrigerators use two separate controls. One control is the regular thermostat while the other control is the defrost control. Fig. 8-31 illustrates such a specialized control. It can be used with either the hot gas or electric defrost systems. The control is designed with a vacuum in the sensitive element. If the bellows loses its charge the pressure will rise and open the circuit (a fail safe control).

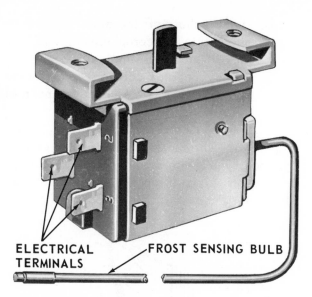

<figure>Fig. 8-31. Defrost control. This control is used in addition to regular temperature control. (Ranco Inc.)</figure>

8-16 Full Automatic Defrost Controls

There are a number of refrigerators that have a standard temperature section in the cabinet and a frozen foods section. These dual-purpose cabinets necessitate a special series of motor controls. First, the controls must give correct temperatures in both sections. Second, the controls must provide complete automatic defrost.

Several different types of controls are shown in Figs. 8-32 and 8-33.

There are four different basic means of determining the defrosting interval:

1. Electric timer which defrosts the unit at certain time intervals.
2. Device which defrosts the unit based on the number of times the refrigerator door is opened.
3. Clock which runs only when the unit is running and which defrosts the unit after a predetermined number of hours of running time.
4. No-frost system which uses forced convection evaporator coils and defrosts these coils during each off-portion of the operating cycle, either by hot gas or, more often, by the use of electric heating elements.

An example of a defrost system which uses a timer to operate the defrost cycle every twelve hours is as follows:

A. It shuts off the compressor and the evaporator fans and starts the electric heaters. The heaters will be on for about 15 minutes.

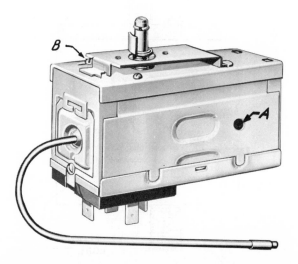

Fig. 8-32. Fully automatic defrost control. A—Electric timer motor. B—Range adjustment.

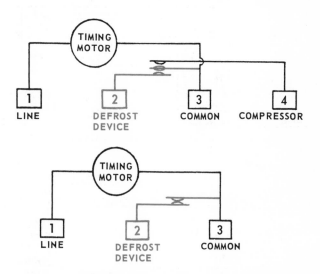

Fig. 8-33. Wiring diagram of an automatic defrost control. Control terminals are labeled. The top illustration is for an electric defrost system; motor circuit is broken during defrost time. Bottom diagram is for hot gas defrost system; compressor continues to run during defrost cycle. (Ranco Inc.)

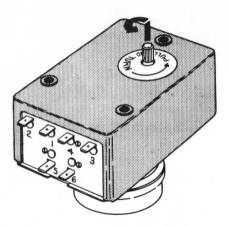

Fig. 8-34. Defrost timer as used to operate defrost cycle in non-frost refrigerator.
(Gibson Refrigerator Sales Corp., Hupp Corp.)

B. It then shuts off the electric heaters and starts the compressor. The fans stay off about 5 minutes.

C. The evaporator coil fans are started and the unit is returned to normal operation.

Fig. 8-34 shows such a timer, while Fig. 8-35 shows the electrical circuit changes. The thermostat which controls the on-and-off circuit for the electric heater elements is shown in Fig. 8-36.

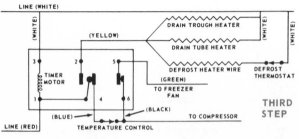

Fig. 8-35. Electric circuits used on three step defrost method.
(Gibson Refrigerator Sales Corp., Hupp Corp.)

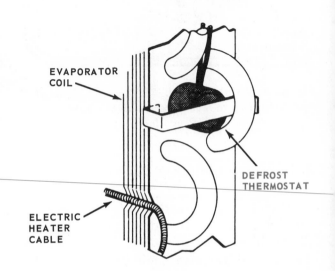

Fig. 8-36. Bimetal defrost thermostat. Control closes at 20 F. and opens at 50 F. during defrost.

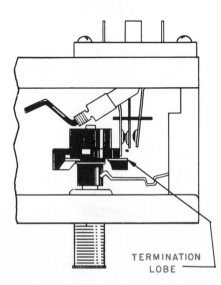

Fig. 8-37. Timer operated cam which returns unit to normal cycling after about 45 minutes.

One control has a timer operated termination cam, as shown in Fig. 8-37. This turns the refrigerating circuit to normal operation after a certain time interval (approximately 45 minutes) even though the thermostat may not call for cooling. This device prevents too long a defrost interval and also serves as a safety device.

8-17 Ice Cube Maker Controls

Many domestic refrigerators now have an automatic ice cube maker as part of the refrigerator. A small fresh water line is connected to the refrigerator. A combination

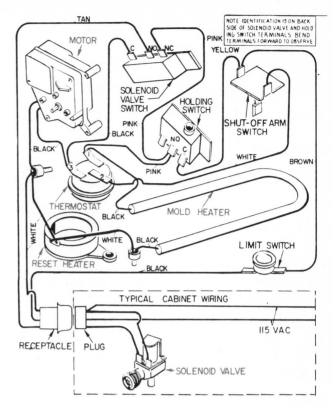

Fig. 8-39. Electrical circuits which control automatic ice cube maker. Note motor, thermostat, reset heater, mold heater and water solenoid valve.

using a solenoid valve, a timer, an evaporator coil, a defroster and a bin level control enables the refrigerator to keep a storage bin full of ice cubes at all times. Fig. 8-38 shows the construction of a typical unit.

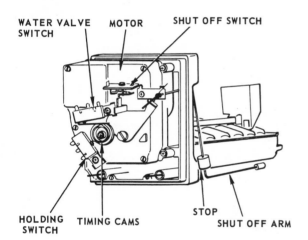
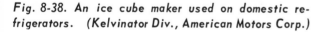

Fig. 8-38. An ice cube maker used on domestic refrigerators. (Kelvinator Div., American Motors Corp.)

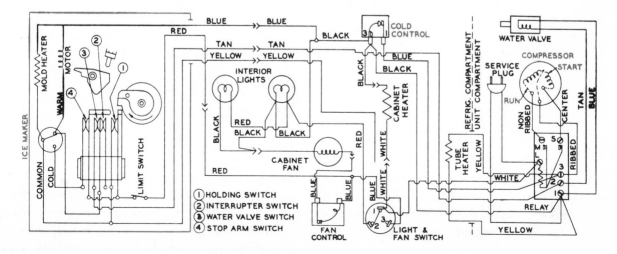

Fig. 8-40. Complete wiring diagram of domestic, compression system refrigerator, including ice cube maker.

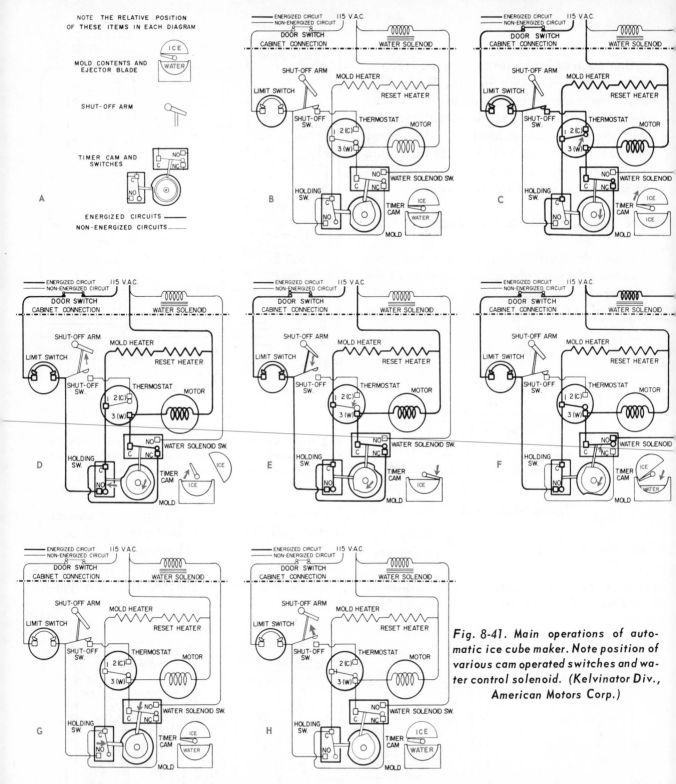

Fig. 8-41. Main operations of automatic ice cube maker. Note position of various cam operated switches and water control solenoid. (Kelvinator Div., American Motors Corp.)

Fig. 8-39 shows a diagrammatic view of the electrical circuits of an automatic ice cube maker. Note the water-in solenoid valve, the mold heater, the shut-off arm switch, etc.

The electrical wiring diagram for the refrigerator is shown in Fig. 8-40. The automatic ice cube maker mechanism is shown on the left. The cam on the motor controls the sequence of water fill, freezing of the water, mold heater, and removal of the crescent shaped cubes from the mold.

The step-by-step operation is shown in a sequence of drawings in Fig. 8-41.

A. Indicates the parts which change position during the cycle.

B. Is the freezing cycle.

C. Shows the water frozen into ice and the timer cam starts to move.

D. Is the holding portion and the stored ice is being dumped into the basket.

E. Shows the ice removal lever against the newly formed ice.

F. Shows the ice being removed as the mold fills with more water. Note the water solenoid switch position.

G. Shows the water switch open and the holding switch open.

H. Shows the unit ready to repeat the cycle.

Connecting the system to a water supply is usually done using a saddle valve as shown in Fig. 8-42. Some of these valves are self piercing, others require that a small hole be drilled in the water pipe.

There are many types of commercial ice cube makers. These units are described in Chapters 13 and 14. These units have normal units except for the evaporator coil and the cycling thermostat. In operation, these units continue to operate until the ice cube storage bin has enough cubes stored. Several types of controls are in use:

1. Lever operated.
2. Sensitive element filled with water.
3. A photoelectric cell sensitive element.

The lever type has a lever extending into the storage compartment. As the quantity of ice cubes increase this lever raises until it opens a switch when the cube level is high enough. It then turns on again when the ice cube level drops to about one-fourth to one-third full.

The sensitive element filled with water has a rubber diaphragm which moves out as the water in the element freezes. This freezing occurs when enough ice has collected in the storage bin. As the diaphragm moves out it opens a switch.

The photoelectric cell element uses a

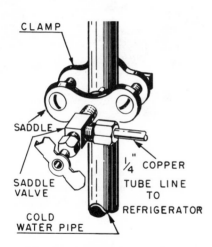

Fig. 8-42. *Saddle type water pipe valve used for connecting house water supply to automatic ice cube maker.*

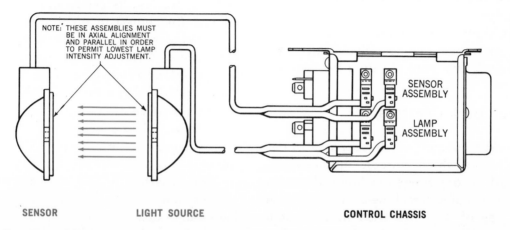

SENSOR   LIGHT SOURCE   CONTROL CHASSIS

Fig. 8-43. *Schematic diagram of photoelectric cell ice cube maker bin control installation.*

light source on one end of the storage cabinet and a photocell (sensor) accurately in line with it at the other end of the cabinet. When enough ice cubes collect in the cabinet the light beam is interrupted, the small current generated in the photoelectric cell and a solid state control transistor (control chassis) shuts off the current flow to the motor-compressor.

Fig. 8-43 shows the basics of this control, while Fig. 8-44 shows the control.

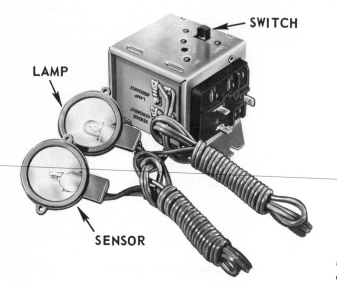

Fig. 8-44. *Photoelectric cell type ice cube maker bin control. When bin is filled, beam of light will be broken and ice cube maker will be stopped.*
(Ranco Inc.)

This control has a thermal delay which causes a two minute delay after the light beam impacts the photoelectric cell before the unit starts. This delay prevents an ice scoop movement or a hand movement across the beam from stopping the ice cube maker.

8-18 Ice Bank Controls

A motor control which operates in response to ice which collects on an evaporator coil is sometimes used on milk coolers and vending machines. The control makes use of the difference in electrical resistance between ice and water. The

thicker the ice the greater the resistance to current flow. It is used on refrigerating machines which use a bank of ice as a refrigeration reserve where the service requirement is not steady but fluctuates greatly. Fig. 8-45 shows an ice sensitive element and the electronic control. The printed circuit can be seen on the side of the control.

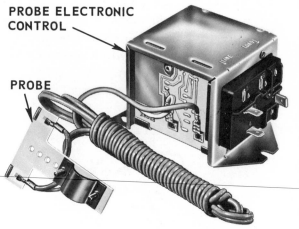

Fig. 8-45. *An electronic ice bank control. Increased electrical resistance of ice compared to water causes control to start and stop the compressor.*

The sensitive element is mounted on the evaporator. When this part of the evaporator freezes, the water on the sensitive element plate (probe) freezes between the two electrodes, as shown in Fig. 8-46. The change (increase) in electrical resistance of the ice rather than the water reduces the current flow to the control (probe assembly) and the circuit to the motor-compressor is opened. When the ice melts on the sensitive element the increased current flow will operate the control, the motor-compressor circuit will close and the unit will start.

The sensitive probe voltage is AC, which is obtained from a transformer built into the control box. The installation of the control is shown in Fig. 8-47.

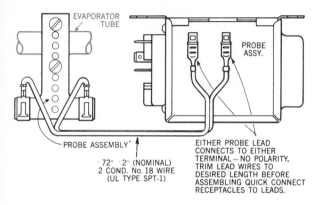

Fig. 8-46. Ice bank control shown mounted on evaporator tube.

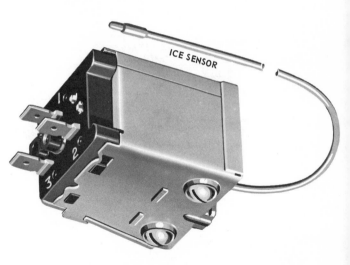

Fig. 8-48. Air conditioner control used to prevent ice formation on evaporator. (Ranco Inc.)

8-19 Air Conditioning Controls

Comfort cooling air conditioners have a variety of controls:
1. Thermostat.
2. Humidistat.
3. Defrost control.

The thermostat usually has its sensitive element located in the return air duct of the air conditioner. When this air cools enough, the thermostat will stop the unit.

The humidistat is described in Par. 8-21.

The defrost control is used to prevent ice formation on the air conditioner evaporator. The control is shown in Fig. 8-48. This control opens the circuit if the evaporator temperature approaches the freezing temperature. This control has a factory

adjustment only and should not require adjusting on the job. The details of the mechanism are shown in Fig. 8-49. The control

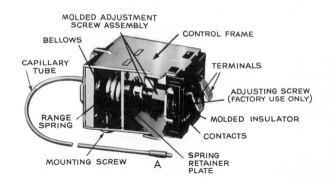

Fig. 8-49. Mechanism of air conditioner defrost control. In operation control bulb A, is mounted on the evaporator.

is a SPST (single pole, single throw) control if used for defrost only. It is a SPDT (single pole, double throw) control when defrost heating units are used on the off cycle. These controls are also used in refrigerators and heat pumps. Fig. 8-50 is a schematic diagram of the control which shows how it is connected into the air conditioning electrical and refrigerating circuits. At (A) it is shown without a defrost heater, at (B) with a defrost heater.

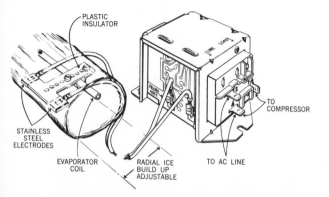

Fig. 8-47. Ice bank control installation and wiring diagram.

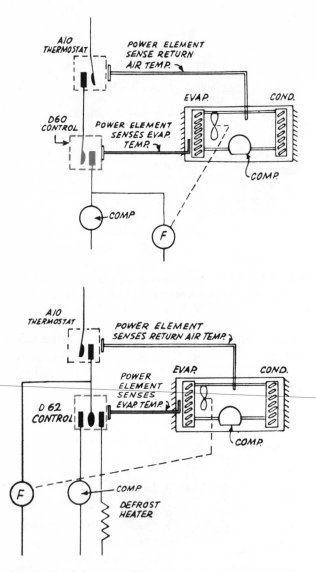

Fig. 8-50. Schematic diagram of air conditioning defrost control. Above. Control without defrost heater. Below. Control with defrost heater.

8-20 Deice Controls

Air-to-air heat pumps which have an outdoor coil sometimes have an icing problem. Ice accumulates on the outdoor coil during the cold season when the heat pump is used as a heating unit. This ice reduces the heat flow into the outdoor coil and it also tends to block the air flow through the coil.

A special control called a deice control is used to prevent this ice accumulation.

The control is a combination timer and thermostat. Fig. 8-51 shows the control with its sensitive element and timer adjustment.

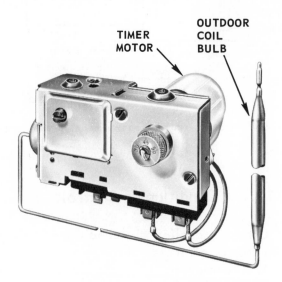

Fig. 8-51. Heat pump deice control. Control reverses heat pump cycle and defrosts outdoor coil each thirty to ninety minutes if outdoor coil is at 26 F. or below. (Ranco, Inc.)

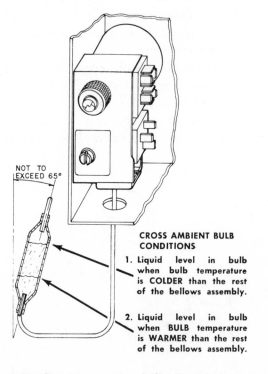

CROSS AMBIENT BULB CONDITIONS

1. Liquid level in bulb when bulb temperature is COLDER than the rest of the bellows assembly.

2. Liquid level in bulb when BULB temperature is WARMER than the rest of the bellows assembly.

Fig. 8-52. Deicer sensitive bulb. Note how temperature sensitive bulb is positioned.

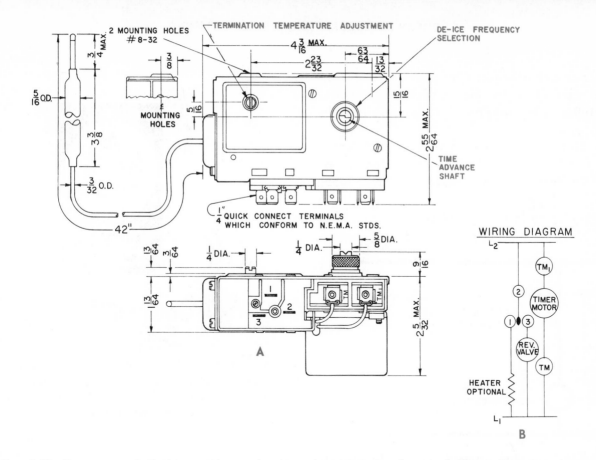

Fig. 8-53. *Deicer control. Mechanism of control and its adjustments are shown at A. Wiring diagram is shown at B.*

The timer is adjustable for a coil defrost cycle of 30, 45 or 90 minutes. The sensitive bulb is cross charged to insure bulb control at all times. The bulb control permits the defrost cycle only if the coil is at 26 F. or below. If above this temperature the defrost cycle is skipped until the next defrost interval. The sensitive bulb is usually mounted at the place where the ice last melts from the coil. Fig. 8-52 shows the sensitive bulb details. The temperature cut-in adjustment, the dimensions, and the wiring diagram are shown in Fig. 8-53. Note the defrost cycle reverses the heat pump and the outdoor coil temporarily acts as a condenser during the defrost cycle.

8-21 Humidity Controls

Humidity controls are used to control humidifiers and are also used to control dehumidifiers.

For humidifiers the humidistat closes the circuit when humidity drops or decreases. Chapter 20 explains the design and operation of a humidifier.

TYPICAL WIRING DIAGRAM
FOR HUMIDIFIER

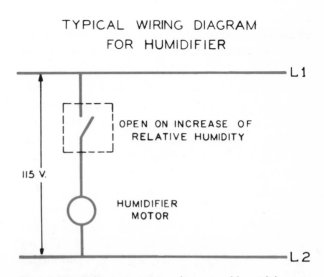

Fig. 8-54. *Schematic wiring diagram of humidifier circuit. Control is adjustable to control relative humidity between 20 and 80 percent.*

For dehumidifiers the humidistat closes the circuit when the humidity increases. Chapter 21 explains the dehumidifier in more detail.

The wiring diagram of a humidifier is shown in Fig. 8-54; the wiring diagram of a dehumidifier is shown in Fig. 8-55.

TYPICAL WIRING DIAGRAM FOR DEHUMIDFIER

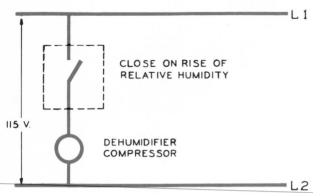

Fig. 8-55. Schematic wiring diagram of dehumidifier circuit. Control is adjustable between 20 and 90 per-cent relative humidity.

8-22 Defrosting Clocks

To ease the burden of the housewife and to permit more efficient operation of the refrigerating unit, several companies have used defrosting clocks as standard equipment on their domestic refrigerators (as explained in Par. 8-16).

Defrosting clocks are available which may be used with any make refrigerator. These may be installed by plugging them into the power outlet and then connecting the refrigerator extension cord into the clock, as shown in Fig. 8-56.

Cabinets with frozen foods compartments will collect excessive amounts of ice and frost on the low temperature evaporator coil. Manufacturers have developed means to defrost these coils quickly without warming the food. Hot gas defrost systems and electrical heating elements are the two basic means used.

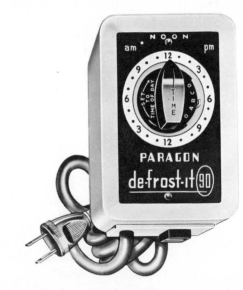

Fig. 8-56. Defrosting clock. This may be plugged into power circuit and used to defrost refrigerator at selected time. Clock has a 24 hour dial. Time of defrost may be selected.

8-23 Non-Frost System

A popular control system to provide a non-frost condition in combination with a regular refrigerator compartment and a freezer compartment, is in common use. Compartments in these refrigerators are cooled by cold air, which is circulated by one or more electric fans, which force air over the evaporator coil which is located in a duct system separate from the refrigerated space.

This circulating cold air cools the refrigerator compartments (removes heat and moisture), the warmer and moisture laden air returns to the evaporator coil, is cooled and the moisture condenses on the coil and becomes frost. As the thermostat stops the unit for each off cycle, the thermostat turns on the electric heaters or hot gas defrost. The evaporator coil fans are turned off during the off cycle. The evaporator coils are defrosted and the defrost water drains to the condensing unit. When the unit starts again the cooling starts again. The fan operates

Refrigerator Section Air Flow Control

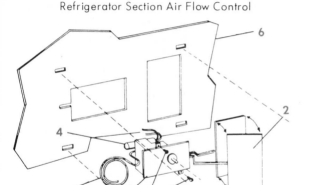

1. Air Flow Control
2. Air Flow Control Damper
3. Air Flow Control Capillary
4. Air Flow Control Heater
5. Mounting Screws for Air Flow Control
6. Cabinet Liner

Fig. 8-57. Air flow damper and control which is used on some non-frost refrigerators. (Franklin Appliance Div., Studebaker Corp.)

only after the evaporator has cooled the air. Many units use damper motors which close the air flow opening into the refrigerated compartments during the defrost cycle. Fig. 8-57 shows such a control and how it is mounted.

Chapter 10 explains the design and construction of the evaporator coil fans and the ducts.

8-24 Special Thermostats

A special thermostat is shown in Fig. 8-58. A mercury-filled thermometer is used. Two electrodes are fused through the glass and contact the mercury column. When the mercury column extends from one electrode to the other a small electric current will flow. This current operates relays or transistors which in turn connect power to operate the refrigerating unit or solenoid valves. This control has the special ability to maintian extremely small differentials. Differentials as small as .009 F. are obtainable (useful in research and laboratory work).

8-25 Installing Thermostats

Thermostats must be correctly installed or the system will not operate accurately or regularly.

The electrical connections must be clean and tight. Use wire terminals. Just wrapping stranded wires around a terminal screw is not a good or permanent connection. One or more wires of the stranded wire may work loose and ground the wire or short the terminals. The connections should be cleaned with clean steel wool.

The sensitive bulb must be very carefully mounted. It should be mounted tightly on the evaporator coil or the tubing. The sensitive bulb, and the place to which it is clamped, should be cleaned with clean steel wool.

When installing the control be careful not to bend the capillary tube back and forth as the copper tube will work harden and may break. Also be sure the capillary

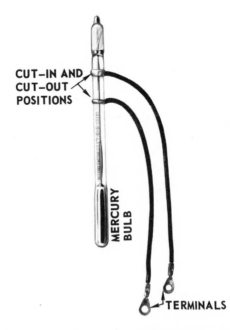

Fig. 8-58. Thermometer type thermostat. Electrical circuit is completed when mercury column rises to connect two electrodes. Only a small current is carried by thermostat. Relays are used to connect power to motor. (H-B Instrument Co.)

tube does not touch any part of the evaporator coil. If any of the capillary tube is coiled, tape the coil to prevent vibration. If any of the tubing rubs against any part it may wear through or work harden at that spot and crack.

8-26 Thermostat Testing and Servicing

Troubles that may be encountered in thermostats include:

1. Corrosion occurring at the contact points causing a poor electrical circuit. This trouble may be remedied by sanding the points with sandpaper, (not emery cloth) and it is advisable to use the finest grade that can be obtained. A fine clean mill file may also be used to clean open contact points.

Thermostats must have good electrical connections. They must also be adjusted to correct temperatures, and the sensitive element must accurately sense the temperature of the evaporator coil or the cabinet temperature.

Electrical connections must be clean and tight. Only metal terminals should be used. Clean the terminals, the terminal jacks or the screw posts with clean steel wool. The contact points must be clean. Corroded or pitted points (best detected by using an ohmmeter) usually should not be repaired. The control should be replaced. In an emergency, the points can be cleaned with a small clean file. A single cut or mill file is best but even a clean nail file may do a temporary job.

2. The overload protection devices may also have dirty contact points, and poor current flow will result.

3. The power element and bellows may lose its charge. This may be detected, since, if the charge is lost, the bellows are very easily compressed. If the bellows were charged, the pressure inside would probably be around 75 pounds per square inch or more, and finger pressure would

not affect it. In the event of leakage, replace this part of the switch.

4. Frequently the control bulb is not attached lightly to the coil, causing a great change of temperature range before the motor will cut in and cut out. The servicing of these particular types of switches is rather difficult; therefore the best policy is simply to replace the complete unit.

The power element must be firmly clamped to the evaporator coil. Good thermal contact must be obtained between the thermal bulb and the coil. Many evaporator coils have metal sockets into which the thermal elements are inserted. The contact surfaces must be clean.

The sensitive element must have good thermal contact with the coil or tube. Be careful not to bend the capillary tube any more than necessary as it might work harden and crack.

To adjust to the correct temperature settings, you may mount a thermometer at the bulb then cycle the unit. Because it is difficult to obtain accurate settings until the unit cycles several times, time may be saved by using a thermal bath or a thermostat adjusting tool.

A method of checking and adjusting a thermostat is similar to the test shown in Fig. 6-42. It consists of a clamp for the thermostat bulb, an accurate thermometer, and a small cavity for refrigerant. With this instrument mounted on the thermostat bulb, and the cavity charged with liquid

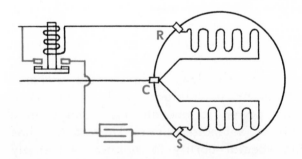

Fig. 8-59. *Magnetic type current relay. Relay is shown in open position. R–Running winding terminal. S–Starting winding terminal. C–Common terminal.*

R-12, a screw is used for adjusting the boiling pressure. The temperature of the R-12, and the bulb temperature can be quickly and accurately lowered or raised to adjust the control.

Pressure controls may be adjusted easily by using the system valves and running the unit to obtain the correct pressures or you may use a pressure-vacuum hand pump.

8-27 Starting Relays

Hermetic units use external circuit breakers or relays. It is impractical to use open electrical contacts inside a sealed system. These relays are usually of the following types:

1. Current (magnetic) type.
2. Potential (magnetic) type.
3. Thermal (hot wire) type.

The purpose of the relay is to permit electricity to flow through the starting winding of the motor until the motor reaches about two-thirds of its rated speed, and then to disconnect or open the starting winding circuit. The starting winding should be energized only for three or four seconds at a time. If current flows through this winding for a longer period of time, the winding may overheat. Many relays have current and/or thermal protection devices to prevent the starting winding from being abused.

To operate correctly, these relays must be sized accurately to the motor. When replacing one, be sure it has the same electrical specifications as the original relay.

8-28 Current (Magnetic) Relay

The magnetic type relay uses the electrical characteristics of the motor to operate it. The running winding consumes more current when the stator is not turning, or is turning slowly, than it does when it reaches full speed. As the rotor picks up speed, the magnetic fields build up and collapse in the motor, producing a bucking or

counter electromotive force (EMF) or voltage on the running winding. Relay switches used to close and open the starting winding operate on the change in current flow, or in the change in voltage of the running winding, as it goes from start to run.

The magnetic relay is an electromagnet similar to a solenoid valve. Either a weight or a spring holds the starting winding contact points open when the system is idle. The weight operated unit is shown in Fig. 8-59. Then, when the motor control contacts close and the high current flows into the running winding, the magnetic current relay coil is heavily magnetized and lifts the weight to overcome the spring pressure and close the contacts. This action closes the starting winding circuit and the motor will quickly accelerate to two-thirds or three-fourths of the rated speed. As it does so; the amperage draw of the running winding of the motor decreases, the magnetic strength of the magnetic current relay decreases, allowing the weight or the spring to open the points. Fig. 8-60 shows a magnetic current relay in the closed position (starting) and also the open position (running). There is one

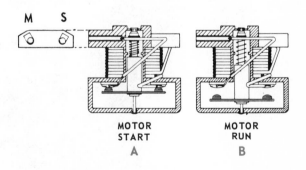

Fig. 8-60. A current (amperage) relay. A—Relay in starting position. B—Relay in running position. (Franklin Appliance Div., Studebaker Corp.)

type of magnetic current control which uses a rotary solenoid. This type can be mounted in any position. The weight type must be mounted level.

Another diagrammatic view of a cur-

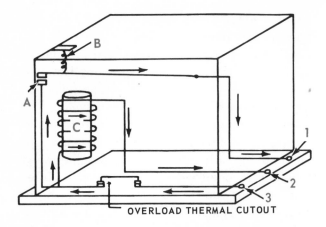

Fig. 8-61. Current type magnetic starting relay in running position. A—Contact points. B—Spring. C—Solenoid. 1—Starting winding terminal. 2—Running winding terminal. 3—Common terminal.

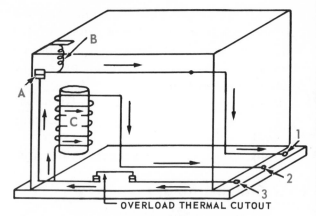

Fig. 8-62. A current type magnetic starting relay in starting position. A—Contact points. B—Spring. C—Solenoid. 1—Starting winding terminal. 2—Running winding terminal. 3—Common terminal.

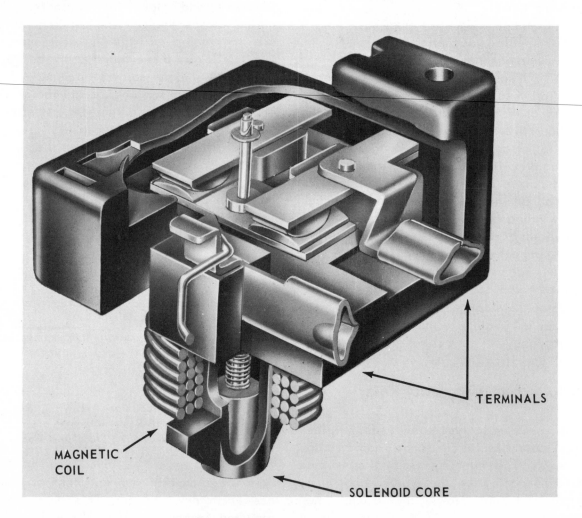

Fig. 8-63. Current type magnetic relay. Plastic housing contains solenoid which has a movable center. Heavy current draw on starting raises the center plunger and closes the starting winding circuit. (Tecumseh Products Co.)

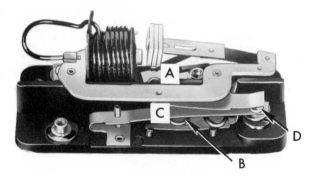

Fig. 8-64. Current type magnetic starting relay. In this starting relay, starting winding points are kept open by means of cantilever spring. At instant of starting, magnetism pulls spring down and closes starting points at (A). If for any reason current draw is too great resistance wire (B) will heat and cause bimetal strip (C) to bend and open circuit at (D). (Copeland Refrigeration Corp.)

rent starting relay in the open position is shown in Fig. 8-61. The same unit in a closed or starting position is shown in Fig. 8-62. One type of magnetic current relay is shown in Fig. 8-63; while another type is shown in Fig. 8-64. A method of installing a current starting relay is shown in Fig. 8-65.

These relays are available in a number of capacities. The relay must be accurately sized to the motor. The difference between the closing amperage and the opening am-

perage settings is small. It is this small difference in current flow which will close the starting circuit, and then open it when the motor reaches approximately three-fourths speed. Fig. 8-66 shows a circuit using a current relay.

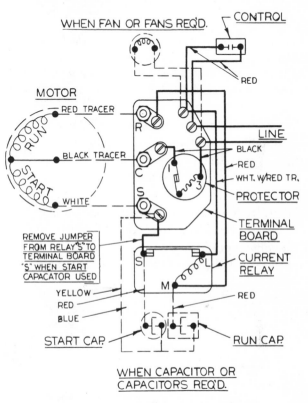

Fig. 8-66. Complete wiring diagram of system using current relay.

8-29 Potential (Magnetic) Relay

The potential relay is growing in popularity especially in the larger units. Fig. 8-67 shows a potential (voltage) magnetic relay. This relay looks somewhat similar to the amperage relay, but its operation is based on the increase in voltage as the unit approaches and reaches its rated speed. See Par. 7-47. This relay remains closed on the off cycle. This feature is its

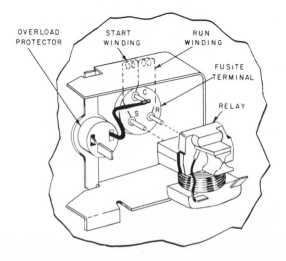

Fig. 8-65. A starting relay mounted on the compressor housing. (Kelvinator Div., American Motors Corp.)

Fig. 8-67. *Potential starting relay. Weight (A) closes points (C) during off cycle. On starting, increasing voltage through coil (B) will pull contact points apart and stop flow of current through starting winding.*

biggest advantage. If the points are closed when the thermostat turns on the power, there will be no arcing of the relay points as quite frequently occurs with the current relay. As the motor speed increases, higher voltage creates more magnetism in the relay coil pulling the contact points apart thereby opening the starting circuit. The relay coil connected across the starting

winding, is made of small wire so very little current passes through it, thus minimizing the heating of the coil and core.

The voltage needed to open the contact points must be high enough to prevent the points from opening before the motor reaches 80 to 90 percent of its full speed. It also must be low enough to positively

Fig. 8-69. *Potential type relay. As armature lever is pulled down by electromagnet, lever at left will open starting circuit points.*

open the points and remove the starting winding from the circuit at the right time, or the motor would overheat. Fig. 8-68 is a circuit diagram of a unit with a potential relay. A potential type relay is shown in Fig. 8-69. The wiring diagram for its installation is shown in Fig. 8-70.

8-30 Thermal (Hot-Wire) Relay

The theory of this control is that electrical energy can be turned into heat energy; it takes time to raise the temperature of a substance, and as a substance increases in temperature, it expands.

The thermal (hot-wire) relay uses a specially calibrated wire (A) Fig. 8-71 of high oxidation resistance.

Two bimetal strips are mounted near this resistance wire. One bimetal strip controls two contact points in the starting

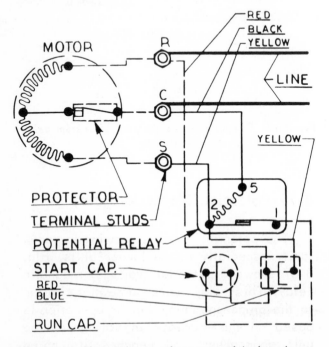

Fig. 8-68. *Wiring diagram for potential (voltage) type magnetic starting relay.*
(Copeland Refrigeration Corp.)

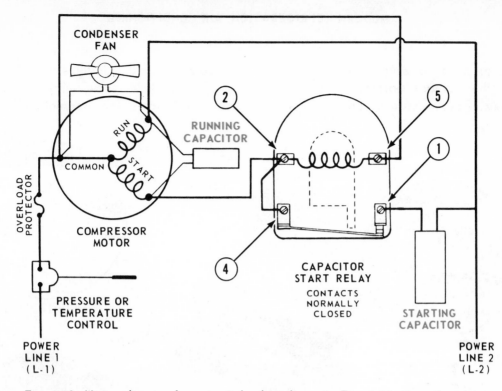

Fig. 8-70. Wiring diagram for potential relay shown in Fig. 8-69. Note that this is a capacitor-start, capacitor-run motor.

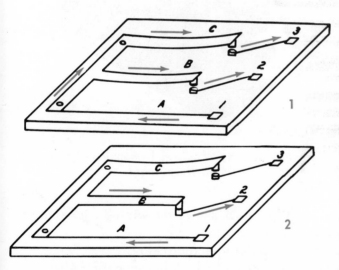

Fig. 8-71. Schematic diagram of thermal starting relay. A—Heating wire. B—Running winding bimetal. C—Starting winding bimetal. 1—Power wire connection. 2—Running winding connection. 3—Starting winding connection. At 1. Both circuits are open, circuits have been drawing too much current. At 2. Starting circuit is open, unit is operating on the running winding only.

winding circuit (C), the other is in the running circuit (B). When the relay is closed, both sets of points are closed. As the

thermostat points close, electricity flows through the hot wire along both bimetal strips into both the starting and running windings. As this current passes through the wire (A), it heats up, and it is sized so it heats just enough to cause the starting winding bimetal strip (C) to bend as the motor reaches its proper speed (two-thirds to three-fourths of full speed) and the starting winding contacts open. The current going through the hot wire now decreases, and the running winding bimetal (B) does not move enough to open. If the compressor is overloaded, or if for any other reason the running winding draws too much current, the resistance wire will heat up enough to make the running winding bimetal strip open, and the unit will be shut off. Because it takes time for the hot wire to heat and cool, and also for the bimetal strips to heat and cool, it is necessary to wait for the temperatures to change before trying to make the hot-wire relay function again during any testing.

Another type of hot-wire relay operates on the same general principle, with an adaptation of a wire under tension to operate the contact points, as shown in Fig. 8-72. The tension of this wire when

Tecumseh and Universal Cooler. Figs. 8-73 and 8-74 show wiring diagrams of refrigerators using thermal relays.

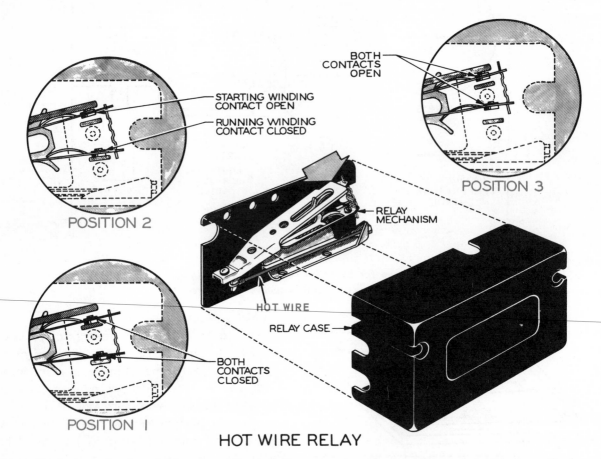

HOT WIRE RELAY

Fig. 8-72. A thermal relay which uses a "hot wire" in tension. Starting — Position 1. Running — Position 2. Overload — Position 3. (Gibson Refrigerator Sales Corp., Hupp Corp.)

cold, keeps both sets of contact points closed.

1. As the current passes through the wire, it heats and expands or stretches at a carefully predetermined setting, the stretch of the wire opens the starting winding contact points.

2. If the motor should use an excessive amount of current, the wire will stretch or expand enough to open the running winding contact points (safety cutout).

3. Some units that use or have used the thermal relay are Crosley, Gibson, Kelvinator, Norge, Philco, Stewart-Warner,

Fig. 8-75 shows the wiring connections to three relays:

A. Delco thermal relay.
B. General Electric magnetic relay.
C. Klixon magnetic relay.

8-31 Servicing Relays

In general, relays should be replaced, not repaired. The serviceman's job is mainly to determine if the relay is defective, and if it is, to replace it with an exact duplicate. These relays are accurately designed. The wire size, the contact point area, and the spring tension or weight plus the air gaps must be accurately set for each unit. A slight difference in weight or spring tension, for example, might result in a hundred motor revolutions difference in the functioning time of the points if they function at all.

The most effective way to determine if the relay is causing the trouble is to check the other parts of the circuit, i.e., the motor, the capacitor, the overload cut-out, and the thermostat. Only if these parts test all right should the relay be replaced. A relay tester is shown in Fig. 8-76. It will test either a current relay or potential relay. It also checks the relay for line voltage. The test may be quickly done. Connect the numbered leads from the numbered jacks on the tester to the same numbered terminals on the relay. First, test using 115V before using the 208-230V switch.

It is necessary to keep the relay cover in place; never discard it, as dust collecting on the contact points will quickly cause the points to burn resulting in excessive voltage drop across the points and poor functioning of the control. The weight-type amperage relay must be mounted in a straight up-and-down position so the plunger will not rub and bind against the sides of the relay body. The relay should open in approximately 4 to 5 electrical cycles (up to three seconds) if it is functioning correctly.

When replacing the relay, it is important to disconnect the power supply, to label each wire as it is disconnected, and to use the correct size screwdriver. The terminals are usually numbered, and a tag or clip on each wire with the corresponding number makes it easy to connect the new relay. Masking tape and a marking pencil are useful for labeling wires. As a dropped screw is sometimes hard to locate, it is recommended that a screw holding type of screwdriver be used.

If an exact potential relay replacement is not available, replace with one of a lower rather than higher voltage rating

(90%). Because capacitors can discharge at 300V or higher, potential relay points may be burned (fuse) by this discharge if the unit short cycles. To eliminate this

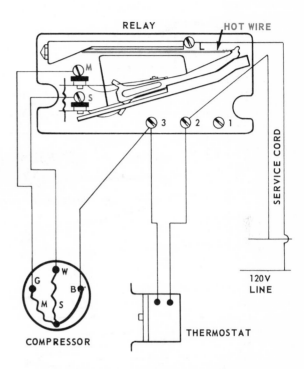

Fig. 8-73. *The circuit diagram for a thermal (hot wire) relay. The current draw will cause the "hot wire" to heat and stretch in length. A slight heating will cause the starting points at (S) to open. Further heating by a too heavy current will cause the points at (M) to open and stop the unit.*
(Kelvinator Div., American Motors Corp.)

trouble, use capacitors equipped with resistors across the capacitor terminals or use a time delay switch to prevent the short cycling.

Frequently a unit will short cycle because the thermostat is exposed to vibration (on a shaky wall, or a stairs, etc.). Be sure to mount the thermostat in a firm position. You should avoid tapping a relay to check it. Tapping the relay may cause the points to touch but this short contact may ruin the points and injure the motor. The relay must function correctly without being tapped, or it should be replaced.

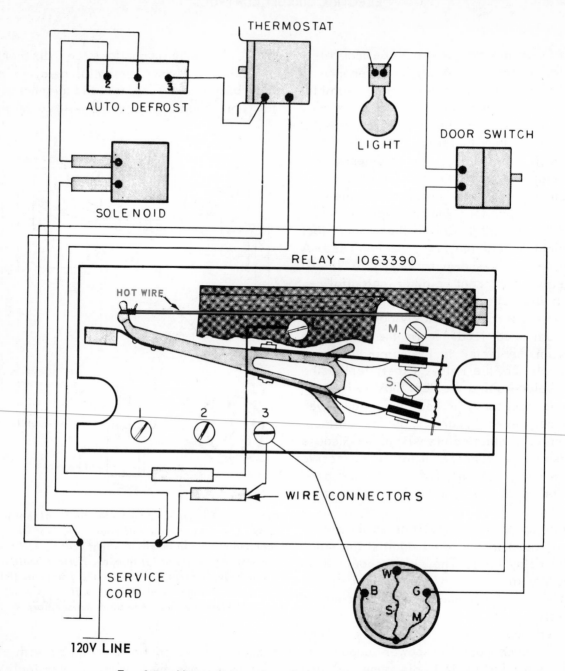

*Fig. 8-74. Wiring diagram for refrigerator using thermal relay.
(Kelvinator Div., American Motors Corp.)*

8-32 Electrical Circuits

Electrical circuits of refrigerators include:

  A. Motor.
  B. Motor control.
  C. Starting relay.
  D. Overload controls.
  E. Cabinet light and switch.

Other frequently used devices are:

  A. Condenser fan motor.
  B. Ultraviolet ray lamp.
  C. Evaporator fan motors.
  D. Defrost resistance circuits.
  E. Butter warmer.
  F. Mullion heater.
  G. Contactors or starters used on commercial units. (See Chapter 13)

Electrical power is obtained through an insulated extension cord usually of No. 18 stranded wire for domestic refrigerators and up to No. 12 for the heavier duty air

Fig. 8-79. A schematic wiring diagram which has a thermostat operated butter warming coil, mullion heater to stop sweating around the freezer door, light circuit,

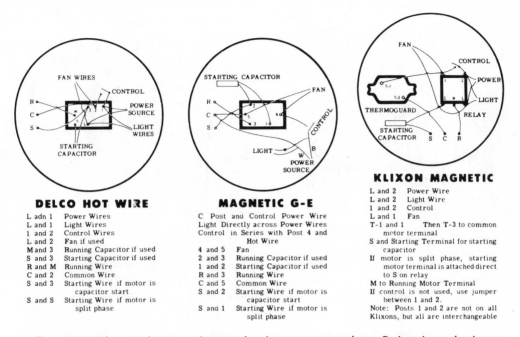

DELCO HOT WIRE

L adn 1	Power Wires
L and 1	Light Wires
1 and 2	Control Wires
L and 2	Fan if used
M and 3	Running Capacitor if used
S and 3	Starting Capacitor if used
R and M	Running Wire
C and 2	Common Wire
S and 3	Starting Wire if motor is capacitor start
S and S	Starting Wire if motor is split phase

MAGNETIC G-E

C Post and Control	Power Wire
Light Directly across Power Wires	
Control in Series with Post 4 and Hot Wire	
4 and 5	Fan
2 and 3	Running Capacitor if used
1 and 2	Starting Capacitor if used
R and 3	Running Wire
C and 5	Common Wire
S and 2	Starting Wire if motor is capacitor start
S and 1	Starting Wire if motor is split phase

KLIXON MAGNETIC

L and 2	Power Wire
L and 2	Light Wire
1 and 2	Control
L and 1	Fan
T-1 and 1	Then T-3 to common motor terminal
S and	Starting Terminal for starting capacitor
If motor is split phase, starting motor terminal is attached direct to S on relay	
M to Running Motor Terminal	
If control is not used, use jumper between 1 and 2.	

Note: Posts 1 and 2 are not on all Klixons, but all are interchangeable

Fig. 8-75. Electrical circuit diagram for three starting relays. Delco thermal relay. General Electric magnetic relay. Klixon magnetic relay.

conditioners. These cords are insulated to withstand at least twice their normal voltage. These power-in cords are either of the two-wire or three-wire (one ground wire of green color) types. Fig. 8-77 shows several types of three-wire connectors. The other end of the extension cord is connected to a junction box mounted on the condensing unit. The junction box often houses the starting relay too. A cord having several wires extends from the junction box to the refrigerator cabinet. These wires are usually colored white, black, red, green, yellow, or blue and are used for the cabinet light, motor control, (thermostat) motor, etc. Fig. 8-78 shows a domestic unit wiring diagram. The wire colors are indicated.

A wiring diagram of a domestic refrigerator equipped with lights and an automatic electric defrost system is shown in

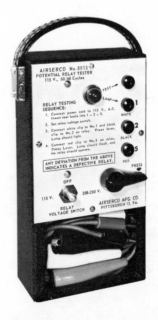

Fig. 8-76. Motor starting relay tester which will test both current and potential type relays. May be used on both 115 and 230 volt circuits.
(Airserco Mfg. Co.)

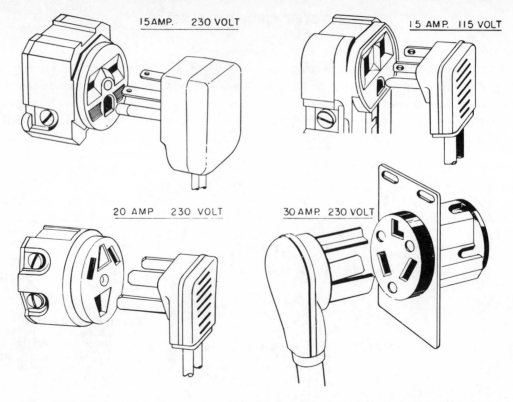

15 AMP. 230 VOLT

15 AMP. 115 VOLT

20 AMP. 230 VOLT

30 AMP. 230 VOLT

Fig. 8-77. Four types of extension plug cord attachment plugs and receptacles. Three types of 230 volt assemblies are shown. Use is dependent on amperage capacity. (Kelvinator Div., American Motors Corp.)

Fig. 8-78. Wiring diagram of external circuits for hermetic refrigerating mechanism. This circuit uses a natural convection evaporator and a static condenser. Note wiring of overload protector. (Franklin Appliance Div., Studebaker Corp.)

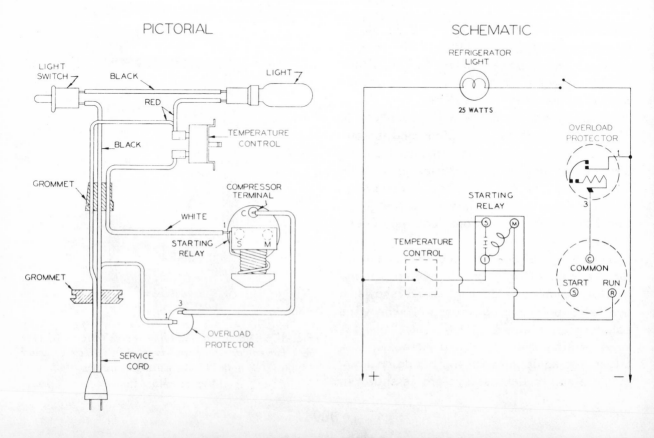

PICTORIAL

SCHEMATIC

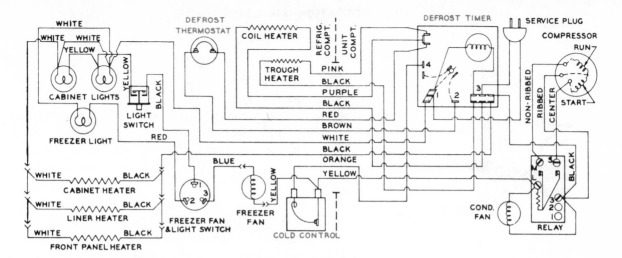

Fig. 8-79. Wiring diagram for "no-frost" type household refrigerator.
(Gibson Refrigerator Div., Hupp Corp.)

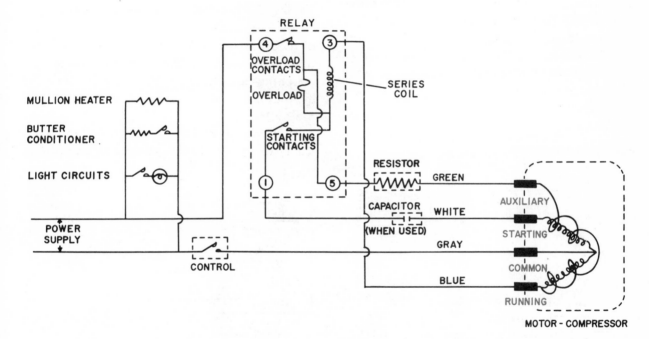

Fig. 8-80. Wiring diagram for four terminal motor-compressor. This unit has three motor windings and operates
at 3400 rpm. A capacitor is used on larger units. (General Electric Co.)

and a four terminal 3600 rpm motor is shown in Fig. 8-80. It is important that these electrical units be tested by using a test light or an ohmmeter. Never test them by shorting, as shorting the resistor or relay for only one or two seconds may permanently damage the motor. Old wire loses some of its conductivity, and old insulation loses its qualities. Where wire replacement is required (insulation cracks when

wire is bent into a loop), wire terminals may be put on with a pair of pliers. See Figs. 8-81 and 8-82.

8-33 Wiring

Fig. 8-83 shows the complete external electrical circuit for a sealed unit freezer refrigerating mechanism. The wire is stranded, usually of No. 18 wire size, and

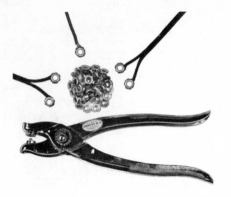

Fig. 8-81. *Wire terminal replacement tool. Note attaching pliers and terminals.*

is plastic or rubber insulated. The other end of the cord is connected to mechanical terminals in the junction box. The junction box is part of the starting relay or is under the same metal or plastic cover. The wires are moulded in plastic. Small brass screws

with 10-32 or 8-32 threads are used to hold the terminals, or friction tight slip terminals may be used.

A screwdriver with an external or internal clamp to hold the screw as it is being started in the threaded hole, or as it is being removed from the hole should be used.

When relay covers or junction box covers are opened, there seems at first to be an endless number of wires connected to the junction terminals. But when it is remembered that the power source, the thermostat, and the interior light each have two leads, while the motor has three leads, the number of wires is understandable. Fig. 8-84 shows the wiring diagram of a combination domestic unit and freezer.

It is important that the full voltage is reaching the motor. This may be checked by placing a voltmeter across the leads of the motor.

All the electrical connections must be tight, or they will cause excessive voltage

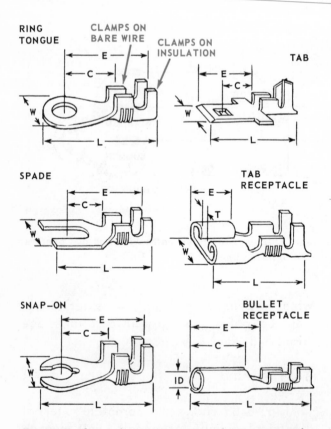

Fig. 8-82. *Several common types of wire terminals. Ring and spade type are used on screw terminals. Tab and bullet types are used on quick disconnects.*

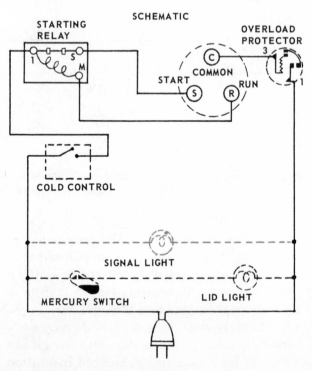

Fig. 8-83. *Wiring diagram for chest type freezer. Note signal light which indicates when power is on.*

PICTORIAL   SCHEMATIC

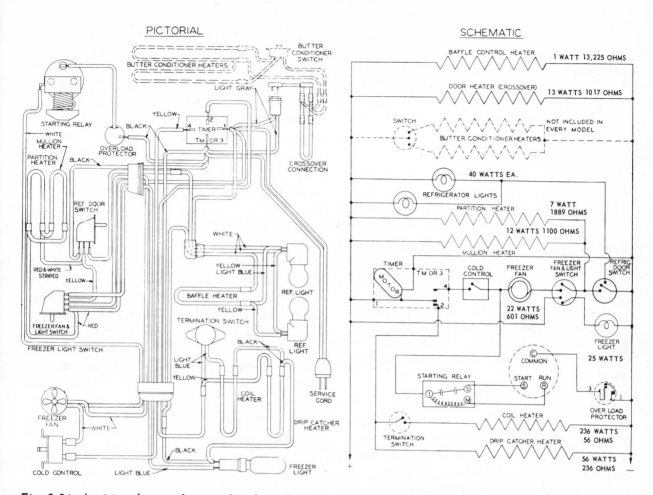

Fig. 8-84. A wiring diagram for a modern household refrigerator. Note the circuits for a mullion heater, butter conditioner, lights and other devices. (Franklin Appliance Div., Studebaker Corp.)

drop (resistance). If there is a loose connection, the terminal may be warm or hot to the touch.

Some wires have soldered and some clamped terminals. These terminals must be in good condition. Just wrapping loose ends of stranded wire around screws to make a connection is an inefficient and unsafe practice. Such connections may work loose and loose wire strands contact other terminals and cause short circuits.

8-34 External Electrical Troubles (Hermetic Units)

It is necessary to understand a little about electricity before one can easily check a hermetic system. Electrical trou-

bles are actually quite simple and can be easily checked. Study Chapter 7. It is important to remember that voltage is pressure, and that amperage is rate of flow of electricity. Both must be available to supply electrical power (watts). Just like water in pipes, the wires must be large enough to carry the current (amount). The joints must be good as in water pipes in order for the full flow of current to take place.

What is not generally understood is that there is always a loss of pressure (volts) in a wire as electricity flows along it. This action is due to a heating action in the wire (resistance) caused by the electron movement as the electrons collide with each other.

Fig. 8-85 (1) shows a water pipe with

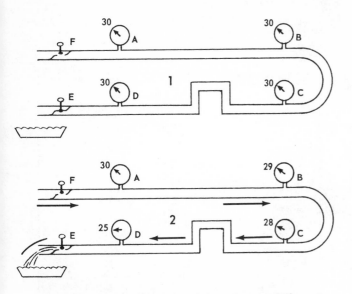

Fig. 8-85. Water flow compared to electrical flow. 1—Valve E closed, valve F open. No water flow, all gauges read the same. 2—Valve E open, valve F open, water flowing. All gauges show a pressure drop. Most of drop is between C and D due to U bend in pipe.

the inlet valve open and the outlet valve closed. The pressure is produced by water pumps. The pressure is the same throughout the system when the water is not flowing. When the outlet valve is opened and water flows, the pressure drops. Notice that it drops a little for each distance. This pressure drop indicates the energy lost pushing the water that distance. Between gauges C and D the pressure drop is greatest, because additional effort is needed to push water around four bends in the pipe.

In Fig. 8-86 a similar setup is shown, but this time for an electrical system. Electricity is furnished for residential use by electrical companies at 115 to 120 volts or at 230 to 240 volts pressure. Most homes and small commercial places use the lower voltage. Electricity comes into the building on one white wire and one black wire with a pressure or potential of 115 to 120 volts. It is wired so the white wire is also connected to the ground. The black wire is the hot wire, and a voltmeter between it and the ground should show 115 to 120 volts.

The 230 to 240 volt circuit usually consists of three wires; two black and one white. The voltage (pressure) between the two black wires is 230 to 240 volts while the voltage between either of the black wires and the white wire is 115 to 120 volts. Sometimes wiring is not done correctly. You must use a voltmeter or test light to indicate which wire is hot and which is the ground wire.

As most electric refrigerators, freezers, and window air conditioners are plugged into wall receptacles, it may not be known which lead or wire is hot. Reversing the plug will sometimes minimize radio noise and, in some extreme cases, even cause the unit to operate better. In Fig. 8-86 a black wire extends from the switch at point G to the right side of the resistance, light bulb or motor at point C. The switch at point (1) is closed, but the one at point (2) is open. The potential or voltage is 120 volts up to the number 2 switch. However, no electricity is flowing (open circuit) and, therefore, there is no

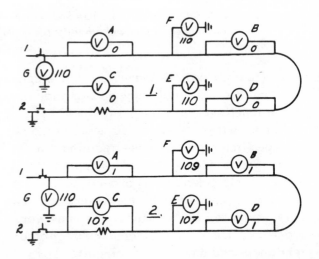

Fig. 8-86. Electricity flow showing how the potential (pressure), resistance, and potential drop operate in a system. 1—Electricity not flowing with switch 1 closed and 2 open. Pressure to ground is 115 volts, but other pressure drops are 0. 2—Electricity is flowing with switches 1 and 2 closed. Voltage drop at A, B, and D is 1 volt each and the resistance at C has a 107 volt drop.

voltage drop along the line. Voltmeters A, B, C, and D show no voltage (there is no pressure difference between their connections to the main line). The voltmeters at E, F, and G show the full 120 volts, because that is the pressure difference between anywhere along the line and the ground.

In Part 2 the switch at (2) is closed and current starts to flow through the circuit (closed circuit). Note that now there is a small voltage drop at A. This voltage drop occurs in any line in which current is flowing. If the line is large enough, the voltage drop is very small (.001 to .0001 of a volt). If the line is too small for the current flow, the voltage drop will be greater. Usually an undersize wire may be detected by the fact that it gets warmer than usual while current is flowing. The voltage difference between the line and the ground is less at F and E because of the voltage drop in the line up to these measuring points. At C the voltage drop is 117 volts, the remaining pressure difference between the hot wire and the ground. If there was more voltage drop at A, B, and D, the voltage at C would be less. This is one serious source of motor trouble. If a motor is designed to operate at 100 to 120 volts and the voltage drop in the circuit is large, the motor voltage may be so low at the motor that the motor will lose speed and start slipping its magnetic fields (slow up too far below its synchronous speed). This causes the magnetic fields to grow large at the wrong time, and the motor will heat up, and it may even burn up.

It is necessary that external electrical circuits to the refrigerator are in good order and of the proper capacity. All the connections must be clean and tight.

In actual practice a voltmeter using several scales and with needle point leads should be used to check voltages and voltage drops. The voltmeter should have three scales; 0-15 volt, 0-150 volt, and 0-300 volt.

8-35 Electrical Instruments

It is necessary when working on electrical circuits or electrical devices to use accurate electrical instruments.

Some of the more common instruments are:

1. Voltmeter.
2. Ammeter.
3. Ohmmeter.
4. Wattmeter.
5. Megohmmeter.

These instruments come in a variety of sizes, scale readings and ranges. They are also available as recording instruments as well as in direct reading types. A recording type voltmeter is shown in Fig. 8-87. A recording instrument may be connected into a circuit and left for a period of several hours or a day, then the serviceman by examining the recorded chart will know exactly what happened in the electrical circuit as the unit cycles.

Fig. 8-87. Recording voltmeter which records voltage on two scales, 70 to 130 volts, or 150 to 270 volts.

To be of any use, the instruments must read accurately. They should be checked (or calibrated) with a master instrument at least once a year. They are delicate instruments and must not be dropped or exposed to rough usage. Chapter 7 describes some of these instruments and their use in connection with motors.

Some important things to remember are:

Always be sure the meter has a scale with a maximum reading above the maximum possible in the circuit. For example, if a 220V meter is put across a 440V circuit, the meter may be damaged.

A voltmeter is connected across a circuit or across an electrical part in a circuit. It should not be put in series in the circuit.

An ammeter is always put in series in the circuit (except the inductive type such as the Amprobe ammeter).

Always set the meter on maximum scale reading when it is first used on a circuit, and only adjust to the lower scales after it is determined that the meter can safely read the lower scale calibration.

Always disconnect the power before using an ohmmeter. Any power surge into an ohmmeter from a power line will ruin it. This is also true of a capacitor discharge into an ohmmeter. Be sure capacitors are discharged before using an ohmmeter to test them.

8-36 Test Lights

One of the best ways to test electrical circuits without causing damage is to use a test light as shown in Fig. 8-88. The test light with the two prongs may be used when the device being tested is connected to electrical power. For example, if the refrigerator is plugged in and will not start, this test light may be used to determine if power is coming to the wall outlet. The lighting of the light will indicate power is available up to the wire probes. If the wall outlet has power, then the open circuit is in the refrigerator wiring. Plug the refrigerator into the wall outlet. Use the test light to see if power is coming to

the end of the extension cord that attaches to the junction box or relay terminals. Continue this testing until the open spot in the circuit is found.

The test light shown in Fig. 8-88, lower drawing, is used to check electrical devices that are not connected to power. This test light should be connected to a power source. If the bulb lights when the probes are touched together, the test light is functioning. To use this light put one probe on one end of a wire and the other probe on whatever that wire is supposed to connect to. If the bulb lights the circuit is continuous (there is continuity).

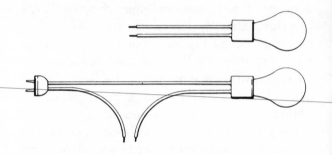

Fig. 8-88. Two types of test lights. Above. Light bulb with two prongs. Below. Test light connected to electric power source and used to check circuits not connected to power source.

Fig. 8-89 shows a special test light used to test a three-phase circuit. It may be used to determine which leads of a three-phase circuit connect leads to the three-phase power lines. If the tester glows, the rotation is 1, 2, 3. Reverse any of the two leads, the tester should not glow. If the tester glows, one of the three-phase circuits is open.

8-37 Review of Safety

Safety is a challenge to all of us. Anything in motion, anything which holds back a pressure, anything which can conduct electricity or heat, anything which is rough or sharp, and anything which can drop due to gravity, is a potential safety hazard.

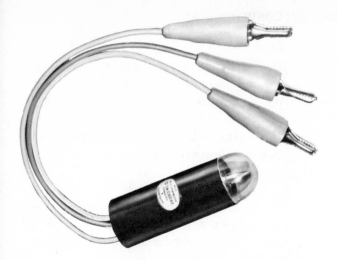

Fig. 8-89. *Test light used to test a three-phase circuit. To use instrument, connect three leads to three-phase terminals. If tester bulb glows, rotation is 1, 2, 3. If it does not glow, reverse pairs of leads until it does glow. If tester glows regardless of connections, one circuit is open.*
(Airserco Co.)

Most accidents are the result of carelessness. The basic problem is that when one is concentrating on a job, or is concentrating on getting a job done, he tends to momentarily neglect safety.

Therefore, one must train himself to do things safely. He must either study the job for its safety problems and their solutions or have a person schooled in safety to watch every move he makes.

Remember before each step of a job is performed: stop and think of the safety aspects.

YOU SHOULD ALWAYS DISCONNECT THE ELECTRICAL POWER AND MAKE SURE NO ONE CAN TURN IT ON WHILE YOU ARE WORKING ON THE ELECTRICAL PARTS OF A REFRIGERATOR OR AIR CONDITIONING SYSTEM. You should replace worn electrical wires or wires with brittle insulation (the insulation cracks when the wire is bent into a loop).

Use only screwdrivers with insulated handles (wood or plastic). Use only wrenches and pliers with insulated handles. This habit is double insurance to avoid shocks.

If you must work in a damp or wet room--stand on a dry and insulated platform.

Always use instruments to check a circuit to see if it is electrically charged before handling wires, terminals or parts.

8-38 Test Your Knowledge - Chapter 8

1. Can a motor control be operated by low side pressure? High side pressure? Both?
2. In what way are pressure and thermostatic types of motor controls essentially similar?
3. What two purposes does a motor control serve?
4. How many types of differential adjustments are there?
5. What are thermostatic motor control bulbs charged with?
6. Why are starting relays used in connection with hermetic motor controls?
7. What does the range adjustment control?
8. What does the differential adjustment control?
9. What provisions are built into motor controls to protect the motor from drawing too much current?
10. Will turning the cut-in differential adjustment affect the cut-out temperature?
11. Will turning the double type differential adjustment affect the cut-out temperature?
12. What is the purpose of a timer on a domestic refrigerator?
13. What is another name for a relay?
14. How many types of relays are in use?
15. What type screwdriver is recommended for small terminal screw handling?
16. How may a thermostat be checked quickly?
17. How does a bimetal disk respond to a temperature change?
18. What is voltage drop?
19. Why does a loose connection in an electrical circuit become warm?

20. Which magnetic relay coil uses the largest size wire?
21. Does a hot-wire relay have to be mounted level? Why?
22. How should open contact points be cleaned?
23. Why do electrical wires have different colored insulations?
24. Is the current draw more when the motor is starting or when it is running?
25. Is the voltage drop more when the motor is starting or when it is running?
26. How does altitude affect a diaphragm or bellows type thermostat?
27. Why are some thermostat bodies heated?
28. Why do some refrigerators have dampers and damper controls?
29. Are potential relay contact points open or closed during the off cycle?
30. What size wires are most commonly used on domestic refrigerators?
31. What type of unit uses a deice control?
32. What type of refrigerating device uses a photoelectric cell sensing device?
33. Can a test light be used to test continuity?
34. Explain the operation of a cross-charged sensitive element.
35. Why are some sensitive elements vapor charged?

Chapter 9

REFRIGERANTS

To transfer heat from the interior of a cabinet or room to the outside, some type of a heat carrier must be used.

In a standard mechanical cooling system, heat is removed by evaporating a liquid refrigerant in the evaporator, and expelling heat at the condenser. This causes the refrigerant to change from a vapor to a liquid.

Fluids which can be changed easily from a liquid to a vapor, and from a vapor to a liquid, are used as the medium because such a change is accompanied by a change in heat content. Some fluids are better suited to this purpose than others. The most popular ones, especially for automatic refrigeration, will be discussed in this Chapter.

If you desire information concerning refrigerants which are not covered in this Chapter, consult Chapter 27, Technical Characteristics, or, The American Society of Heating and Refrigerating and Air Conditioning Engineers Guide and Data Book (ASHRAE).

9-1 Requirements for Refrigerants

There are certain desirable characteristics which a fluid used as a refrigerant should possess:
1. It should be nonpoisonous.
2. It should be nonexplosive.
3. It should be noncorrosive.
4. It must be nonflammable.
5. Leaks should be easy to detect.
6. Leaks should be easy to locate.
7. It should operate under low pressure (low boiling-point).
8. It should be a stable gas.
9. Parts moving in the fluid should be easy to lubricate.
10. It should be nontoxic.
11. It should have a well balanced latent heat of evaporation value per unit of weight.
12. It should have a small relative displacement to obtain a certain refrigeration effect.
13. A minimum difference between the vaporizing pressure and the condensing pressure is desirable.

The first requirements are almost self-explanatory because it is only natural that an automatic mechanism be safe from the possibility of being poisonous, flammable, and explosive.

The refrigerant must be noncorrosive in order that the more common metals may be used for construction and for giving a long life to all the parts.

The refrigerant should be such that its presence and its source may be easily detected in case of leaks. This is mainly a service feature.

It is desirable to keep normal pressures in the refrigerator as close to atmospheric pressure as possible, because excessive differences aid leaking tendencies, overwork the compressor, and decrease the efficiency of the valves.

The standard comparison of refrigerants as used in the refrigeration industry is based on an evaporator temperature of

5 F. and a condensing temperature of 86 F. In this Chapter, this basis of comparison is given for each refrigerant discussed.

9-2 Identifying Refrigerants by Number

The present practice in the refrigeration industry is to identify refrigerants by number.

You should therefore become familiar with refrigerant numbers, as well as the names.

The number is preceeded by the letter R, which means refrigerant. The identifying system of numbering has been standardized by the American Society of Heating, Refrigerating and Air Conditioning Engineers (ASHRAE).

Some refrigerants in common use are:

R-12, R-30, R-22, R-13B1, R-744, R-502, R-13, R-14, R-500.

Group Two – Toxic and somewhat flammable refrigerants:

R-1130, R-611, R-160, R-764, R-40, R-717.

Group Three – Flammable refrigerants:

R-600, R-601, R-290, R-170, R-1150, R-50.

The National Board of Fire Underwriters has also classified refrigerants mainly on their degree of toxicity. There are six divisions in this scale. Class one is the most toxic, while Class six is the least toxic. Fig. 9-1, lists some refrigerants by group and by toxicity.

9-4 Group One Refrigerants

The Group One refrigerants are considered the safest refrigerants on the basis

REFRIGERANT NO.	NAME AND CHEMICAL FORMULA	DATA INFORMATION
R-11	Trichloromonofluoromethane CCl_3F	Par. 9-5
R-12	Dichlorodifluoromethane CCl_2F_2	Par. 9-6
R-22	Monochlorodifluoromethane $CHClF_2$	Par. 9-7
R-500	Azeotropic mixture of 73.8% of (R-12) and 26.2% of (R-152a)	Par. 9-9
R-502	Azeotropic mixture of 48.8% of (R-22) and 51.2% of (R-115)	Par. 9-10
R-503	Azeotropic mixture of 40.1% of (R-23) and 59.9% of (R-13)	Par. 9-11
R-504	Azeotropic mixture of 48.2% of (R-32) and 51.8% of (R-115)	Par. 9-12
R-717	Ammonia NH_3	Par. 9-14

See Chapter 27 for a more complete list of refrigerants.

9-3 Classification of Refrigerants

Refrigerants have been classified by two different national organizations. They are: The National Refrigeration Safety Code, The National Board of Fire Underwriters.

The National Refrigeration Safety Code catalogs all the refrigerants into three groups. Some of these are:

Group One – Safest of the refrigerants:

R-113, R-611, R-11, R-21, R-114,

of not being a fire hazard and not being toxic. Some refrigerants in Group One are:

R-11   Trichloromonofluoromethane CCl_3F

R-12   Dichlorodifluoromethane CCl_2F_2

R-13   R-13B1, R-14

R-21   Dichloromonofluoromethane $CHCl_2F$

R-22   Monochlorodifluoromethane

R-30   Methylene Chloride CH_2Cl_2

R-113   Trichlorotrifluoroethane CCl_2FCClF_2

R-114 Dichlorotetraflouromethane
$C_2Cl_2F_4$
R-152a, R-500, R-502, R-503, R-504
R-744 Carbon Dioxide CO_2

The pressure-temperature curves for five of the common Group One refrigerants are shown in Fig. 9-2.

The refrigerants in this group may be used in the greatest quantities in any in-

NATIONAL REFRIGERATION SAFETY CODE GROUP		CLASS
GROUP 1		
R-744	Carbon Dioxide	5
R-12		6
R-13B1	Kulene-131	6
R-21		6
R-114		6
R-30	Carrene No. 1	4
R-11		6
R-22		5
R-113		4
R-500		6
R-502		6
R-503		6
R-504		6
R-40	Methylene Chloride	4
GROUP 2		
R-717	Ammonia	2
R-1130	Dichloroethylene	4
R-160	Ethyl Chloride	4
R-40	Methyl Chloride	4
R-611	Methyl Formate	3
R-764	Sulphur Dioxide	1
GROUP 3		
R-600	Butane	5
R-170	Ethane	5
R-601	Iso Butane	5
R-290	Propane	5

Fig. 9-1. Grouping and classification of some popular refrigerants. The grouping is according to the National Refrigeration Safety Code. The classification is according to the National Board of Fire Underwriter's Refrigerant Toxicity Classification.

stallation. The code as given in Chapter 27, "American Standard Safety Code for Mechanical Refrigeration," allows systems

to use up to 20 pounds of these refrigerants in hospital kitchens; up to 50 pounds (indirect system) in public assemblies; up to 50 pounds in residential use provided special precautions are taken, and up to 20 pounds in residential air conditioning systems.

9-5 R-11 Trichloromonofluoromethane (CCl_3F)

R-11 is a synthetic chemical product especially made for refrigeration use. It is a stable refrigerant, nonflammable, and nontoxic. This refrigerant is considered a low pressure refrigerant. It has a low side pressure at 5 F. of 24 inch vacuum and a high side pressure of 18.3 psia at 86 F. The latent heat at 5 F. is 84.0 Btu. This refrigerant is extensively used in large centrifugal compressor systems. As much as 35 pounds of this refrigerant may be used for each 1,000 cubic feet of air conditioned space (a room approximately 10 ft. by 12.5 ft. by 8 ft.). Leaks may be detected by using the electronic detector or by using a halide torch. R-11 is often used by many servicemen as a flushing agent for cleaning the internal parts of a refrigerator when overhauling systems, especially after a system has had a motor burn out or has had an excess of moisture in the system.

9-6 R-12 Dichlorodifluoromethane (CCl_2F_2)

R-12 is a colorless, almost odorless liquid with a boiling-point of -21.7 F. at atmospheric pressure. It is nontoxic, noncorrosive, nonirritating, and nonflammable. Chemically it is inert at ordinary temperatures and thermally stable up to 1022 F. A table of properties of R-12 is shown in Fig. 9-3.

R-12 has a relatively low latent heat value which is a decided advantage in the smaller refrigerating machines, because the large quantity of refrigerant circulated

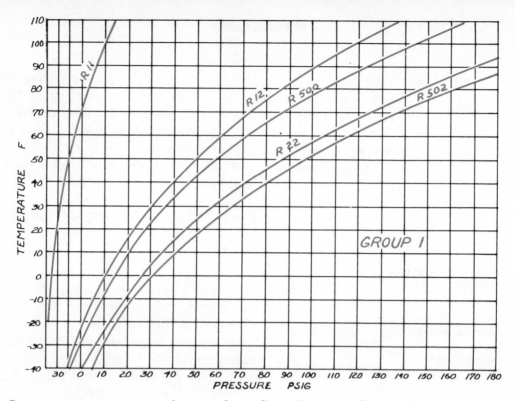

Fig. 9-2. Pressure-temperature curves for some Group One refrigerants. R–11 is known as a low pressure refrigerant and R–502 is a medium pressure refrigerant.

Temp. F.	PRESSURE		VOLUME VAPOR	DENSITY LIQUID	HEAT CONTENT BTU/LB.	
	Psia	Psig	Cu. Ft./Lb.	Lb./Cu. Ft.	Liquid	Vapor
−150	0.154	29.61*	178.65	104.36	−22.70	60.8
−125	0.516	28.67*	57.28	102.29	−17.59	83.5
−100	1.428	27.01*	22.16	100.15	−12.47	66.2
− 75	3.388	23.02*	9.92	97.93	− 7.31	69.0
− 50	7.117	15.43*	4.97	95.62	− 2.10	71.8
− 25	13.556	2.32*	2.73	93.20	3.17	74.56
− 15	17.141	2.45	2.19	92.20	5.30	75.65
− 10	19.189	4.49	1.97	91.70	6.37	76.2
− 5	21.422	6.73	1.78	91.18	7.44	76.73
0	23.849	9.15	1.61	90.66	8.52	77.27
5	26.483	11.79	1.46	90.14	9.60	77.80
10	29.335	14.64	1.32	89.61	10.68	78.335
25	39.310	24.61	1.00	87.98	13.96	79.9
50	61.394	46.70	0.66	85.14	19.50	82.43
75	91.682	76.99	0.44	82.09	25.20	84.82
86	108.04	93.34	0.38	80.67	27.77	85.82
100	131.86	117.16	0.31	78.79	31.10	87.63
125	183.76	169.06	0.22	75.15	37.28	88.97
150	249.31	234.61	0.16	71.04	43.85	90.53
175	330.64	315.94	0.11	66.20	51.03	91.48
200	430.09	415.39	0.08	60.03	59.20	91.28

*Inches of mercury below one atmosphere.

Fig. 9-3. Table of properties of liquid and saturated vapor of refrigerant R–12. Note pressures corresponding to standard evaporating temperature of 5 F. and condensing temperature of 86 F.
(Freon Products Div. E. I. du Pont de Nemours and Co.)

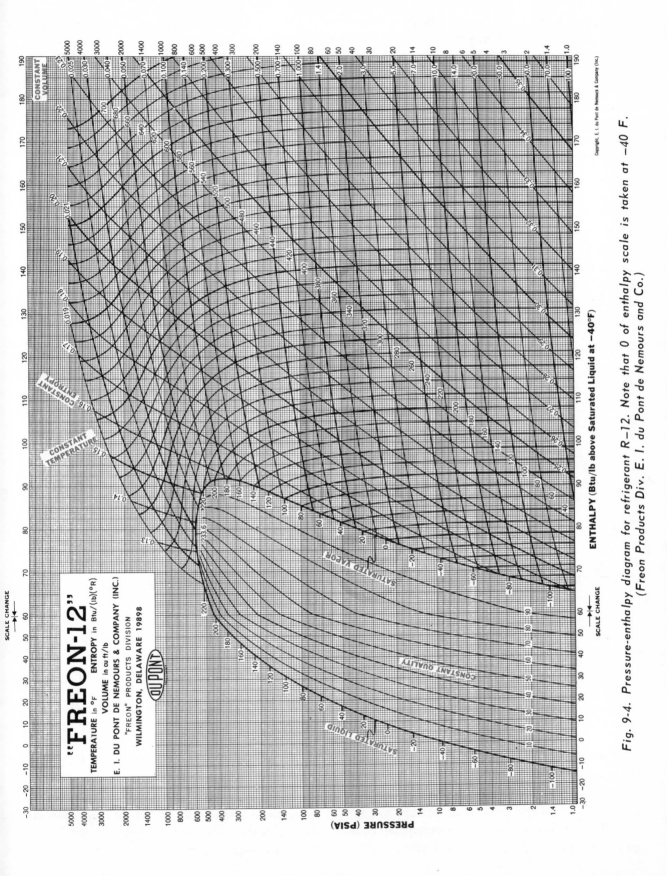

Fig. 9-4. Pressure-enthalpy diagram for refrigerant R–12. Note that 0 of enthalpy scale is taken at –40 F. (Freon Products Div. E. I. du Pont de Nemours and Co.)

will permit the use of less sensitive, more accurate, and more positive operating and regulating mechanisms. It is used in reciprocating, rotary and large centrifugal compressors. It operates at a low but positive head and back pressure, and with a good volumetric efficiency. R-12 has a pressure of 26.5 psia at 5 F. and a pressure of 108.0 psia at 86 F. The latent heat of R-12 at 5 F. is 68.2 Btu/lb. Latent heat is vapor heat minus the liquid heat.

An R-12 leak may be detected by means of a halide lamp, or electronics leak detectors. See Chapter 12 concerning the use of various types of leak detectors. Water is only slightly soluble in R-12. At 0 F. it will only hold 6 parts per million by weight, and the solution formed is slightly

R-12 is more critical as to its water content as compared to R-22 and R-502. R-12 is soluble in oil down to -90 F. The oil will begin to separate at this temperature and because it is lighter than the refrigerant, will collect on the surface of the liquid refrigerant.

The Pressure-Heat diagram (enthalpy) for this refrigerant is shown in Fig. 9-4. See Par. 1-47 for a description of enthalpy.

It is safe to use 30 pounds of this refrigerant per each 1,000 cubic feet of air conditioned space.

This refrigerant is available in a variety of cylinder sizes and may be obtained in hermetically sealed throw-away cans. The cylinder code color is white.

A typical R-12 cycle for a frozen foods unit is shown in Fig. 9-5. The dotted line labeled C' to D' indicates the increased refrigerating effect when the liquid is sub-cooled in the condenser or liquid line. This sub-cooling is done by a low ambient condition, or by using a heat exchanger.

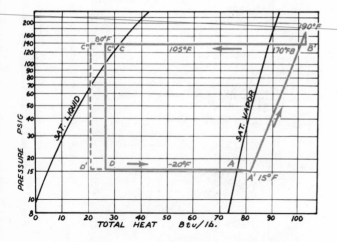

Fig. 9-5. Pressure heat diagram for freezer application using R-12 as refrigerant. Heat is absorbed in evaporator D to A. Vapors are compressed by compressor A' to B'. Heat is given off in the condenser B' to C'. Pressure drops from C' to D as refrigerant passes through refrigerant control without change in heat content.

9-7 R-22 Monochlorodifluoromethane (CHClF$_2$)

R-22 is a synthetic refrigerant specially developed for refrigeration installations that need a low evaporating temperature. One example of this application is in fast freezing units which maintain a temperature of -20 F. to -40 F. It has also been successfully used in air conditioning units and common household units. It is used only with reciprocating compressors. The operating pressures of R-22 are such that it is not necessary to operate at below atmosphere pressures in order to obtain these low temperatures.

corrosive to any of the common metals used in refrigerator construction. The addition of mineral oil to the refrigerant has no effect upon the corrosive action, except possibly to decrease the amount of discoloration caused by the free water.

R-22 has a boiling point of -41 F. at atmospheric pressure. It has a latent heat of 93.21 Btu per pound at 5 F. The normal head pressure at 86 F. is 172.87 psia as shown in the table in Fig. 9-6. This refrigerant is stable and is nontoxic, noncorrosive, nonirritating, and nonflammable. The evaporator pressure of R-22 at 5 F. is 43 psia.

Water is more soluble in R-22 than R-12 by a ratio of 3 to 1 (19.5 ppm by weight). Therefore, water must be kept at

9-8 Azeotropic Mixtures

Azeotropic mixtures are, as the name implies, mixtures of refrigerants, however, these azeotropic mixtures act as a single refrigerant.

Temp. F.	PRESSURE		VOLUME VAPOR	DENSITY LIQUID	HEAT CONTENT BTU/LB.	
	Psia	Psig	Cu. Ft./Lb.	Lb./Cu. Ft.	Liquid	Vapor
−150	0.272	29.37*	141.23	98.34	−25.97	87.52
−125	0.886	28.12*	46.69	96.04	−20.33	90.43
−100	2.398	25.04*	18.43	93.77	−14.56	93.37
− 75	5.610	18.50*	8.36	91.43	− 8.64	96.29
− 50	11.674	6.15*	4.22	89.00	− 2.51	99.14
− 25	22.086	7.39	2.33	86.78	3.83	101.88
− 15	27.865	13.17	1.87	85.43	6.44	102.93
− 10	31.162	16.47	1.68	84.90	7.75	103.46
− 5	34.754	20.06	1.52	84.37	9.08	103.97
0	38.657	23.96	1.37	83.83	10.41	104.47
5	42.888	28.19	1.24	83.28	11.75	104.96
10	47.464	32.77	1.13	82.72	13.10	105.44
25	63.450	48.75	0.86	81.02	17.22	106.83
50	98.727	84.03	0.56	78.03	24.28	108.95
75	146.91	132.22	0.37	74.80	31.61	110.74
86	172.87	158.17	0.32	73.28	34.93	111.40
100	210.60	195.91	0.26	71.24	39.67	112.11
125	292.62	277.92	0.18	67.20	47.37	112.88
150	396.19	381.50	0.12	62.40	56.14	112.73
175	525.39	510.70	0.08	56.14	66.19	110.83
200	686.36	671.66	0.05	44.57	80.86	102.85

*Inches of mercury below one atmosphere.

Fig. 9-6. Table of properties of liquid and saturated vapor of refrigerant R-22. Note pressures corresponding to standard evaporating temperature of 5 F. and condensing temperature of 86 F.
(Freon Products Div. E. I. du Pont de Nemours and Co.)

a minimum in these refrigerants; and, consequently, driers or dessicants should be used to remove most of the moisture. Because of the affinity of R-22 for water, more dessicant is needed to dry it. R-22 has good solubility in oil down to 16 F. The oil will begin to separate at this point. Because it is lighter than the refrigerant, it will collect on the surface of the liquid refrigerant. Leaks may be detected with a halide torch or an electronic leak detector. Some of the properties of R-22 are shown in Fig. 9-7.

Four commonly used azeotropic refrigerants are:

R-500 – composed of 73.8% R-12 and 26.2% R-152a.

R-502 – composed of 48.8% R-22 and 51.2% R-115.

R-503 – composed of 41.1% R-23 and 59.9% R-13.

R-504 – composed of 48.2% R-32 and 51.8% R-115.

These are patented refrigerants and the manufacturing process is rather complicated. The serviceman should never at-

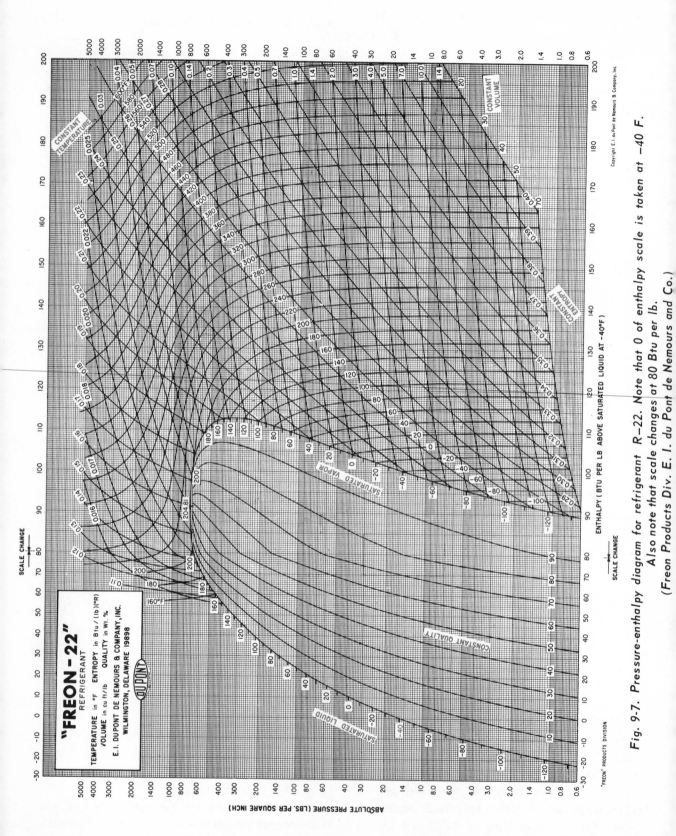

Fig. 9-7. Pressure-enthalpy diagram for refrigerant R-22. Note that 0 of enthalpy scale is taken at -40 F. Also note that scale changes at 80 Btu per lb.
(Freon Products Div. E. I. du Pont de Nemours and Co.)

tempt to make his own mixtures of these refrigerants.

Characteristics of these refrigerants are explained in the following paragraphs.

capacity than R–12 when used for the same applications. The evaporator pressure of R–500 at 5 F. is 31.21 psia. It has a boiling point at atmospheric pressure of –28 F.

Temp. F.	PRESSURE		VOLUME VAPOR	DENSITY LIQUID	HEAT CONTENT BTU/LB.	
	Psia	Psig	Cu. Ft./Lb.	Lb./Cu. Ft.	Liquid	Vapor
–40	10.95	7.62*	4.0	84.28	0.00	87.74
–30	14.10	1.22*	3.15	83.35	2.38	89.04
–20	17.92	3.23	2.52	82.40	4.79	90.31
–10	22.52	7.82	2.03	81.44	7.22	91.57
0	27.98	13.3	1.66	80.46	9.71	92.81
10	34.43	19.7	1.36	79.46	12.23	94.03
20	41.96	27.3	1.13	78.45	14.79	95.22
30	50.70	36.0	0.94	77.41	17.40	96.39
40	60.75	46.1	0.79	76.34	20.05	97.53
50	72.26	57.6	0.67	75.26	22.75	98.64
60	85.33	70.6	0.57	74.14	25.48	99.71
70	100.1	85.4	0.48	72.98	28.28	100.75
80	116.7	102.0	0.42	71.80	31.12	101.75
86	127.6	113.0	0.38	71.06	32.85	102.33
90	135.3	121.0	0.36	70.56	34.01	102.70
100	155.9	141.0	0.31	69.28	36.97	103.60
110	178.8	164.0	0.27	67.95	40.00	104.44
120	204.1	189.0	0.23	66.55	43.10	105.22
130	231.9	217.0	0.20	65.08	46.29	105.91
140	262.4	248.0	0.17	63.51	49.58	106.51

*Inches of mercury vacuum.

Fig. 9-8. A table of the properties of the liquid and saturated vapor of the refrigerant R–500. Note the pressures corresponding to the evaporating temperature of 10 F. and the condensing temperature of 86 F. (Industrial Chemicals Div. Allied Chemical Corp.)

9-9 R–500 Refrigerant (R–152a + R–12) (CCl$_2$F$_2$/CH$_3$CHF$_2$)

Refrigerant R–500 is used only in units with reciprocating compressors and is used in both industrial and commercial applications. It is an azeotropic mixture of 26.2% of R–152a and 73.8% of R–12. It has a fairly constant vapor-pressure temperature curve, which is different from the vaporizing curves for either R–152a or R–12.

R–500 offers approximately 20% greater

and its condensing pressure at 86 F. is 127.6 psia. Its latent heat at 5 F. is 82.45 Btu per lb. as shown in the table in Fig. 9-8.

R–500 can be used whenever a higher capacity than that achieved with R–12 is needed and with little change in condensing temperatures as shown in Fig. 9-9. R–500 is also recommended for use where electrical service varies from 60 cycle to 50 cycle.

The solubility of water in R–500 is highly critical. R–500 has fairly high solubility with oil. Leaks may be readily detected through the use of the halide leak detector,

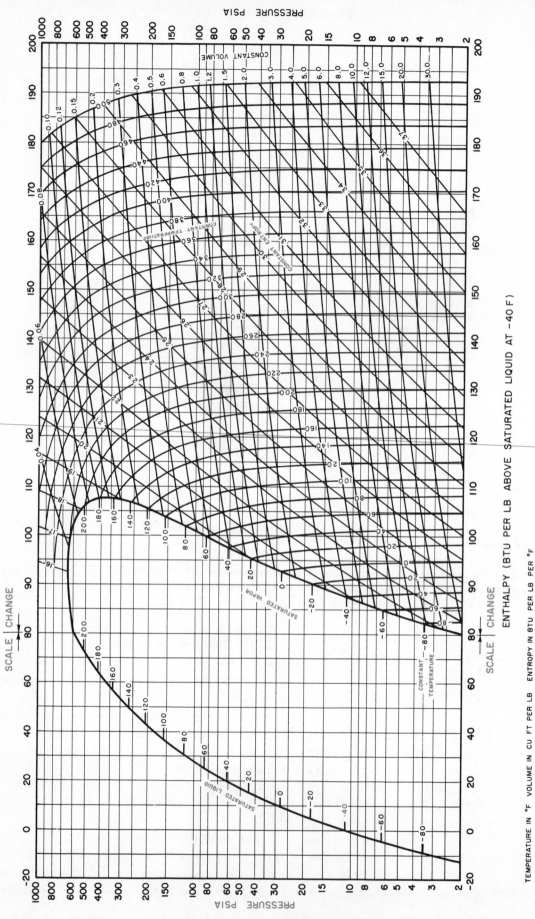

TEMPERATURE IN °F   VOLUME IN CU FT PER LB   ENTROPY IN BTU PER LB PER °F

Fig. 9-9. Pressure-enthalpy diagram for refrigerant R-500. Note that 0 of enthalpy scale is taken at −40 F. Also note that scale changes at 80 Btu per lb.

© BY INDUSTRIAL CHEMICALS DIV. ALLIED CHEMICAL CORP.

electronic leak detector, soap solution or a colored tracing agent. The color code for R-500 cylinders is red.

Servicing refrigerators using this refrigerant does not present any unusual service problem. It should be noted however, that water is quite soluble in this refrigerant and it will be necessary to be sure that moisture is kept out of the system by careful dehydration and the use of driers.

is a nonflammable, noncorrosive, practically nontoxic liquid. It is a good refrigerant for obtaining low temperatures and it is used in applications requiring temperatures from 0 to -60 F. It is often used in frozen food lockers, display cases, and storage for frozen foods and ice cream. It is also often used in frozen food processing plants. It is used only with reciprocating compressors.

Temp. F.	PRESSURE		VOLUME VAPOR	DENSITY LIQUID	HEAT CONTENT BTU/LB.	
	Psia	Psig	Cu. Ft./Lb.	Lb./Cu. Ft.	Liquid	Vapor
-100	3.230	23.34*	10.84	98.49	-15.15	67.37
- 75	7.318	15.02*	5.07	96.05	- 8.90	70.63
- 50	14.74	0.04	2.64	93.47	- 2.57	73.97
- 25	27.02	12.33	1.50	90.74	3.90	77.07
- 20	30.22	15.52	1.35	90.18	5.21	77.69
- 15	33.69	18.99	1.22	89.60	6.54	78.32
- 10	37.46	22.76	1.10	89.02	7.86	78.93
- 5	41.53	26.84	1.00	88.44	9.20	79.54
0	45.94	31.24	0.91	87.84	10.54	80.15
5	50.68	35.99	0.82	87.24	11.89	80.75
10	55.79	41.09	0.75	86.63	13.25	81.33
15	61.27	46.57	0.69	86.02	14.62	81.92
20	67.14	52.45	0.63	85.39	15.99	82.49
25	73.42	58.73	0.57	84.86	17.37	83.05
50	111.6	96.89	0.38	81.44	24.42	85.67
75	162.7	148.0	0.26	77.84	31.74	87.88
86	198.8	175.1	0.22	76.13	35.06	88.68
100	229.1	214.4	0.18	73.80	39.37	89.47
125	313.4	298.7	0.12	69.05	47.33	90.02
150	418.6	403.9	0.08	62.84	55.32	88.79
160	467.3	452.6	0.07	59.49	58.21	87.74

*Inches of mercury below one atmosphere.

Fig. 9-10. Table of properties of liquid and saturated vapor of refrigerant R-502. Note pressure corresponding to standard evaporating temperature of 5 F. and condensing temperature of 86 F. (Freon Products Div. E. I. du Pont de Nemours Co.)

9-10 R-502 Refrigerant (R-22 + R-115) (CHClF_2/CClF_2CF_3)

Refrigerant R-502 is an azeotropic mixture of 48.8% R-22 and 51.2% R-115. Refrigerant R-502 was first used in 1962. It

The boiling point of R-502 is -50.1 F. at atmospheric pressure, and its condensing pressure is 175.1 psi at 86 F. and its evaporating pressure at 5 F. is 50.68 psia. Its latent heat at -20 F. is 72.5 Btu per pound, as shown in the tables of properties in Fig. 9-10.

Refrigerant R-502 combines many of

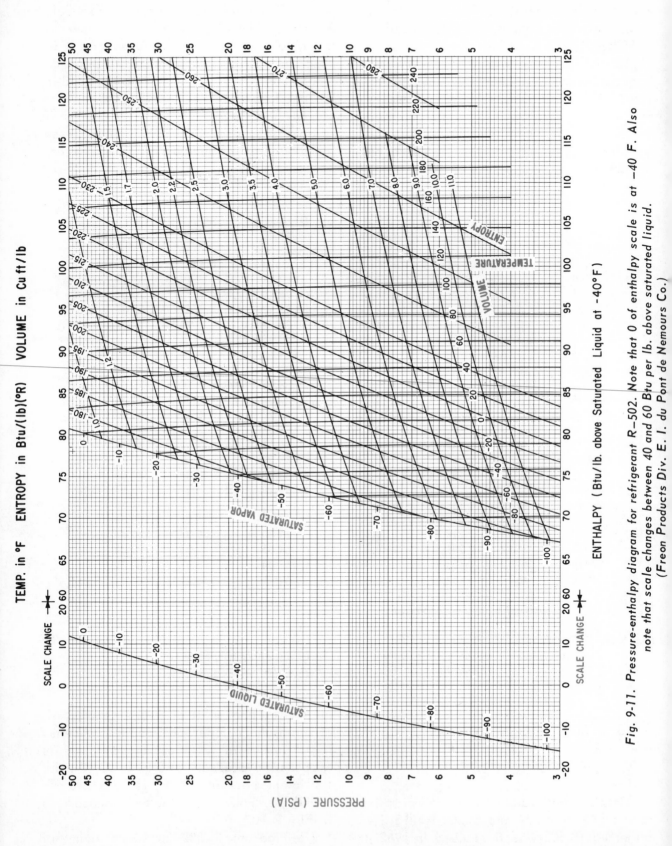

Fig. 9-11. Pressure-enthalpy diagram for refrigerant R-502. Note that 0 of enthalpy scale is at -40 F. Also note that scale changes between 40 and 60 Btu per lb. above saturated liquid.
(Freon Products Div. E. I. du Pont de Nemours Co.)

the desirable features of both R-12 and R-22. It gives a machine the capacity about equal to the use of R-22 and still maintains approximately the condensing temperature of a system using R-12. A pressure-enthalpy diagram of the refrigerant is shown in Fig. 9-11.

By reducing the condensing pressure as compared to R-22, and still obtaining the desired low side temperature, the compressor will operate at a lower condensing pressure and temperature, thereby prolong-

sures, it is possible to eliminate liquid injection to cool the compressor which is often necessary with R-22. R-502 maintains all the qualities found in the other halogenated (flourocarbon) refrigerants. It is nontoxic, nonflammable, nonirritating, stable, and noncorrosive, and leaks may be readily detected by using a halide torch or an electronic leak detector.

The cylinder color is purple and the cylinders are available in the usual capacities.

Temp. F.	PRESSURE		VOLUME VAPOR	DENSITY LIQUID	HEAT CONTENT BTU/LB	
	Psia	Psig	Cu. Ft./Lb.	Lb./Cu. Ft.	Liquid	Vapor
−140	9.94	9.69*	3.88	96.0	−43.58	31.27
−130	13.67	2.09*	2.89	94.7	−41.96	32.36
−120	18.45	3.57	2.19	93.4	−40.25	33.45
−110	24.48	9.78	1.69	92.0	−38.46	34.52
−100	31.97	17.3	1.32	90.6	−36.55	35.57
− 90	41.15	26.5	1.04	89.2	−34.54	36.60
− 80	52.27	37.6	0.83	87.7	−32.42	37.59
− 70	65.59	50.9	0.67	86.1	−30.17	38.54
− 60	81.38	66.7	0.54	84.5	−27.79	39.45
− 50	99.90	85.2	0.44	82.8	−25.29	40.31
− 40	121.5	107.0	0.37	81.1	−22.64	41.10
− 30	146.3	132.0	0.30	79.2	−19.83	41.81
− 20	174.8	160.0	0.25	77.2	−16.87	42.44
− 10	207.1	192.0	0.21	75.2	−13.73	42.96
0	243.7	229.0	0.18	72.9	−10.38	43.35
10	284.7	270.0	0.15	70.5	− 6.82	43.57
20	330.5	316.0	0.12	67.8	− 3.00	43.58
30	381.3	367.0	0.10	64.7	2.03	43.29
40	437.3	423.0	0.08	61.1	5.77	42.54
50	499.0	484.0	0.07	56.6	11.10	40.97
60	566.4	552.0	0.05	49.8	18.59	35.91

*Inches of mercury below one standard atmosphere.

Fig. 9-12. Table of properties of liquid and saturated vapor of refrigerant R-503. Note that temperature of −120 F. with evaporator pressure above atmospheric. To operate in above 0 F. temperature range evaporator pressures in excess of 250 psig will be required. (General Chemical Div. Allied Chemical Corp.)

ing the life of the compressor valves and other components. The lower condensing temperature permits better lubrication because of the increased viscosity of the oil at the lower condensing temperature.

Because of the lower condensing pres-

R-502 will hold 1.5 times more moisture at 0 F. than R-12 (12.0 ppm by wt.). R-502 has fair solubility in oil above 180 F. Below this temperature the oil will tend to separate and collect on the surface of liquid refrigerant. This action may result in

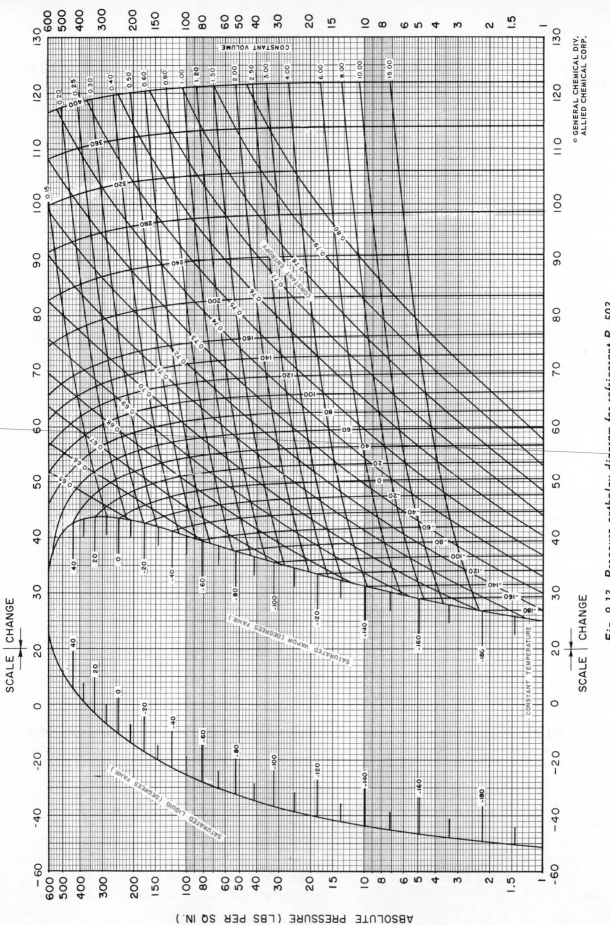

SCALE CHANGE

SCALE CHANGE

Fig. 9-13. Pressure-enthalpy diagram for refrigerant R-503. (General Chemical Div. Allied Chemical Corp.)

© GENERAL CHEMICAL DIV.
ALLIED CHEMICAL CORP.

	PRESSURE		VOLUME VAPOR	DENSITY LIQUID	HEAT CONTENT BTU/LB.	
Temp. F.	Psia	Psig	Cu. Ft./Lb.	Lb./Cu. Ft.	Liquid	Vapor
−100	5.96	17.8*	8.08	90.49	−65.91	43.36
− 90	8.30	13.0*	5.94	89.22	−62.86	44.78
− 80	11.30	6.9*	4.46	87.93	−59.81	46.19
− 70	15.12	0.43	3.40	86.63	−56.82	47.59
− 60	19.89	5.20	2.63	85.31	−53.80	48.97
− 50	25.77	11.1	2.07	83.96	−50.79	50.34
− 40	32.91	18.2	1.64	82.60	−47.76	51.67
− 30	41.50	26.8	1.32	81.22	−44.69	52.98
− 20	51.72	37.0	1.07	79.81	−41.59	54.25
− 10	63.75	49.1	0.88	78.37	−38.44	55.48
0	77.80	63.1	0.73	76.90	−35.25	56.67
10	94.06	79.4	0.61	75.40	−31.99	57.81
20	112.8	98.1	0.51	73.85	−28.65	58.89
30	134.1	119.0	0.43	72.27	−25.23	59.91
40	158.3	144.0	0.36	70.63	−21.72	60.85
50	185.6	171.0	0.31	68.94	−18.11	61.71
60	216.2	202.0	0.26	67.18	−14.37	62.47
70	250.3	236.0	0.22	65.35	−10.49	63.11
80	288.3	274.0	0.19	63.41	− 6.45	63.63
90	330.2	316.0	0.16	61.36	− 2.22	63.99
100	376.4	362.0	0.14	59.15	2.24	64.14

*Inches of mercury below one standard atmosphere.

Fig. 9-14. Table of properties of liquid and saturated vapor of refrigerant R–504. Note that density of liquid decreases very rapidly as temperature increases. (General Chemical Div. Allied Chemical Corp.)

very little oil being carried into the condenser. Oil in the evaporator will separate from the refrigerant and special devices may have to be used to return the oil to the compressor.

9-11 R-503 Refrigerant (R-23 + R-13) (CHF₃/CCIF₃)

This is an azeotropic refrigerant which consists of a mixture of 40.1% R-23 and 59.9% R-13.

This is a nonflammable, noncorrosive, practically nontoxic liquid classified under Group 6 in the Underwriter's Laboratories Classification Scale.

Its boiling temperature at atmospheric pressure is -128.6 F. which is a lower boiling temperature than that for either R-23 or R-13.

Its evaporating pressure at 5 F. is 264 psia. Its critical temperature is 67.1 F. and its critical pressure is 607 psia.

This is a low temperature refrigerant and is particularly adaptable for use in the low stage of Casade systems which require temperatures in the -100 F. to -125 F. range. Properties of R-503 are shown in Fig. 9-12. A pressure-enthalpy diagram for this refrigerant is shown in Fig. 9-13.

The latent heat of vaporization at atmospheric pressure (-127.6 F.) is 74.2 Btu/lb.

Leaks in R-503 systems may be detected with the use of a halide torch or an electronic leak detector. This refrigerant has the ability to hold a greater portion of moisture than some other low temperature refrigerants. It should be remembered however, that all low temperature applications require extreme system dryness since any moisture not in solution with the refrigerant is likely to form ice at the refrigerant control devices.

Oil does not circulate well at low temperatures. Casade and other low tempera-

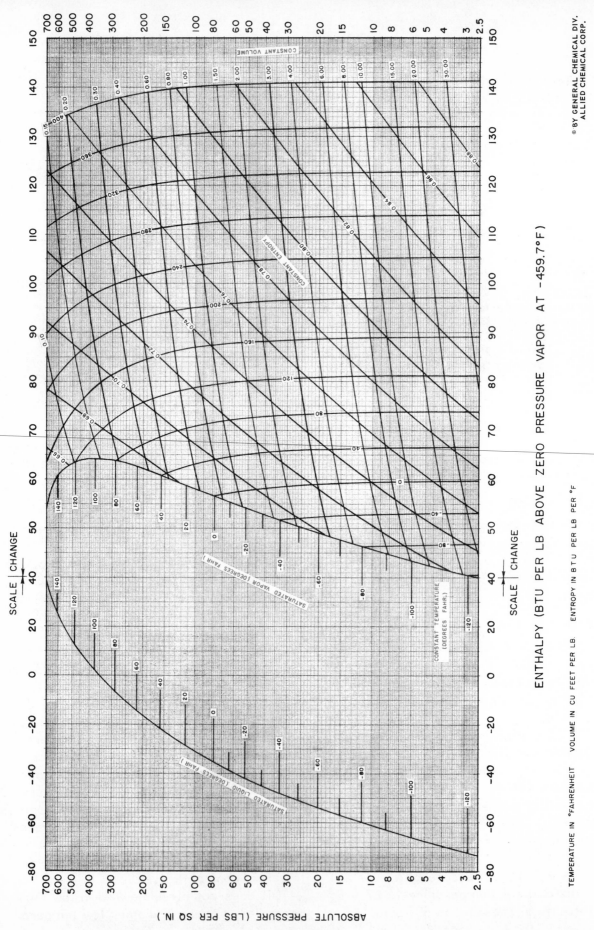

ENTHALPY (BTU PER LB ABOVE ZERO PRESSURE VAPOR AT -459.7°F)

TEMPERATURE IN °FAHRENHEIT   VOLUME IN CU FEET PER LB   ENTROPY IN BTU PER LB PER °F

Fig. 9-15. Pressure-enthalpy diagram for refrigerant R-504.

© BY GENERAL CHEMICAL DIV.
ALLIED CHEMICAL CORP.

ABSOLUTE PRESSURE (LBS PER SQ IN.)

ture equipment is usually fitted with oil separators and other devices for returning the oil to the compressor.

9-12 R-504 Refrigerant (R-32 + R-115) ($CH_2F_2/CClF_2CF_3$)

This is an azeotropic refrigerant which consists of a mixture of 48.2% R-32 and 51.8% R-115. It is a nonflammable, non-corrosive and nontoxic liquid and is classified under Group 6 in the Underwriter's Laboratories classification scale.

The boiling temperature at atmospheric pressure is 71 F.

Its evaporating pressure at 5 F. is 85.93 psia and its critical pressure is 690 psia. Properties of R-504 refrigerant are shown in Fig. 9-14. A pressure-enthalpy diagram for this refrigerant is shown in Fig. 9-15.

As with all low temperature refrigerants, some difficulty may be experienced with the oil circulation. With the addition of 2% to 5% ethane, the oil will be taken into the solution with the refrigerant and will circulate through the system with it.

Leaks in the R-504 system may be easily detected with the use of a halide torch or an electronic leak detector.

This refrigerant is used in industrial processes in which a low temperature range of -40 F. to -80 F. is desired.

9-13 Group Two Refrigerants

The Group Two refrigerants are toxic refrigerants. They are irritating to breathe and may or may not be slightly flammable. Refrigerants in Group Two:

R-717	Ammonia	NH_3
R-113	Dichloroethylene	$C_2H_2Cl_2$
R-160	Ethyl Chloride	C_2H_5Cl
R-40	Methyl Chloride	CH_3Cl
R-611	Methyl Formate	$C_2H_4O_2$
R-764	Sulphur Dioxide	SO_2

Pressure-temperature curves for some common Group 2 refrigerants are shown in Fig. 9-16.

R-717 was one of the first refrigerants

Fig. 9-16. Pressure-temperature curves for some Group 2 refrigerants.

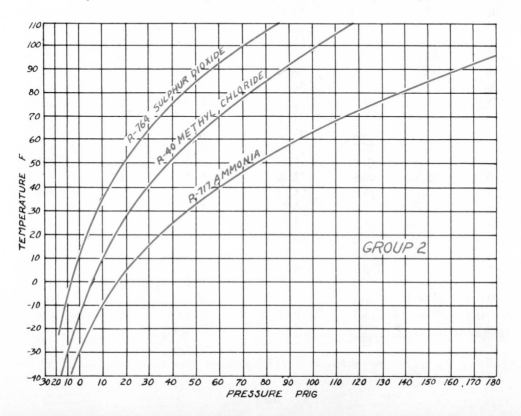

used. However, with the exception of the absorption refrigerators, it is now used only in large industrial installations. The use of R-764 has practically disappeared although at one time it was almost the only refrigerant used in domestic refrigerators. R-40 is no longer used in new machines. However, there are many sulphur dioxide (R-764) and methyl chloride (R-40) charged units still in use.

Additional information concerning Group Two refrigerants can be found in Chapter 27.

9-14 R-717 Ammonia NH₃

R-717 is a refrigerant commonly used in industrial units. It is a chemical compound of nitrogen and hydrogen NH₃) and under ordinary conditions is a colorless gas. Its boiling temperature at atmospheric pressure is -28 F. and its melting point

from the solid is -108 F. The low boiling point makes it possible to secure refrigeration at temperatures considerably below zero without resorting to pressures below atmospheric in the evaporator. Its latent heat is 565 Btu per pound at 5 F. so that large refrigerating effects are possible with the use of relatively small-sized machinery. Condensers for R-717 are almost always of the water-cooled type. Under ordinary operating conditions, the condenser pressure at 86 F. will vary from 150 to 200 psi, as shown in Fig. 9-17.

R-717 is somewhat flammable and with the proper mixture of air will form an explosive mixture. Accidents from this source, however, are rare. R-717 gas is not classed as poisonous, but its affect on the respiratory system is so violent that only very small quantities of it can be breathed safely. About .35 volumes per 100 volumes of air is the strongest concentra-

	PRESSURE		VOLUME VAPOR	DENSITY LIQUID	HEAT CONTENT BTU/LB.	
Temp. F.	Psia	Psig	Cu. Ft./Lb.	Lb./Cu. Ft.	Liquid	Vapor
-100	1.24	27.4*	182.4	45.52	-63.3	572.5
- 75	3.29	23.2*	72.81	44.52	-37.0	583.3
- 50	7.67	14.3*	33.08	43.49	-10.6	593.7
- 35	12.05	5.4*	21.68	42.86	5.3	599.5
- 25	15.98	1.3	16.66	42.44	16.0	603.2
- 20	18.30	3.6	14.68	42.22	21.4	605.0
- 15	20.88	6.2	12.97	42.00	26.7	606.7
- 10	23.74	9.0	11.50	41.78	32.1	608.5
- 5	26.92	12.2	10.23	41.56	37.5	610.1
0	30.42	15.7	9.12	41.34	42.9	611.8
5	34.27	19.6	8.15	41.11	48.3	613.3
10	38.51	23.8	7.30	40.89	53.8	614.9
15	43.14	28.4	6.56	40.66	59.2	616.3
20	48.21	33.5	5.91	40.43	64.7	617.8
25	53.73	39.0	5.33	40.20	70.2	619.1
35	66.26	51.6	4.37	39.72	81.2	621.7
50	89.19	74.5	3.29	39.00	97.9	625.2
75	140.5	125.8	2.13	37.74	126.2	629.9
86	169.2	154.5	1.77	37.16	138.9	631.5
100	211.9	197.2	1.42	36.40	155.2	633.0
125	307.8	293.1	0.97	34.96	185.1	634.0

*Inches of mercury below one atmosphere.

Fig. 9-17. Table of properties of refrigerant R-717 (Ammonia). Note high latent heat of this refrigerant.

tion one can bear for any length of time. Because of its pronounced and distinguishable odor, and also the white smoke-like fumes that it forms in the presence of sulphur candle or sulphur spray vapor, R-717 leaks may be quickly and easily detected.

R-717 attacks copper and bronze in the presence of a little moisture, but does not corrode iron or steel. It presents no special problems in connection with lubrication unless extreme temperatures are encountered. R-717 is lighter than oil and no problems are encountered in dealing with the separation of the two. Excess oil in the evaporating coil may be removed by opening a valve in the bottom of the evaporating coil. The solubility of oil in liquid R-717 is only 20 ppm at 5 F. and only 125 ppm at 86 F. R-717 gas is extremely soluble in water. It is used in large compression machines using reciprocating compressors and in many absorption type systems. Fig. 9-16 shows the vapor pressure curve for this refrigerant.

9-15 Group Three Refrigerants

Refrigerants that have a high tendency to burn or form a combustible mixture with a wide range of concentrations of air are classified as Group Three refrigerants. Under proper design and installation conditions some of these refrigerants perform remarkably well.

Some refrigerants in Group Three are:

R-600	Butane	C_4H_{10}
R-170	Ethane	C_2H_6
R-290	Propane	C_3H_3

Since these refrigerants are no longer commonly used their characteristics are not covered in detail in this chapter. See Chapter 27 for further information.

9-16 Cryogenic Fluids

The range of temperatures from -250 F. to absolute zero (-459.69 F.) is called the Cryogenic range.

These low temperatures may be easily reached by evaporating Cryogenic fluids which have very low boiling temperatures. Common Cryogenic fluids are:

R-702	Hydrogen
R-704	Helium
R-720	Neon
R-728	Nitrogen
R-729	Air
R-732	Oxygen
R-740	Argon

The use of these fluids is becoming quite general. Some information concerning these Cryogenic fluids is given in the following paragraphs.

There are certain cautions which anyone handling these fluids must observe.

Containers for the fluids must be of special material capable of withstanding extremely low temperatures without losing their strength.

Containers are heavily instulated and the temperature of the fluids inside the containers is very low. This is to reduce the loss of the fluids by boiling. Pressures inside the containers are maintained at a relatively low level which corresponds to the vapor pressure relationship for the fluid. No attempt should be made to seal the fluid in a pressure tight container because the extreme pressures which would result if the container became warm would probably burst the container. The insulation, the heat absorbed by vaporizing the fluids, and the preset pressure release keeps both the temperature and the corresponding pressure of the fluid within safe handling limits.

DO NOT ATTEMPT TO USE ANY OF THESE FLUIDS IN ANY CONTAINER OR MECHANISM WHICH WAS NOT DESIGNED FOR ITS USE.

In general, these fluids for low temperature application are expendable. The fluids evaporate (boil) at a very low temperature at atmospheric pressure and use is made of the low temperature created, however, no attempt is usually made to reuse the vaporized fluid, as is done in the usual refrigerator application. See Par. 1-49 and Fig. 1-22, also Chapter 27, for further information on Cryogenic fluids and temperatures.

In Cryogenic work, temperatures are measured from absolute 0 and are usually recorded in degrees Kelvin (K). This is the absolute centigrade scale taking absolute 0 as the 0 for the scale. Pressures are indicated in atmospheres (atm).

To convert degrees Kelvin (K) to Rankin (R) (absolute F), multiply degrees K by 1.8.

To convert pressures listed in atmospheres (atm) into psia multiply atm by 14.69.

9-17 Color Code for Refrigerant Cylinders

All cylinders used for transporting refrigerants are color coded to permit easy identification of the refrigerant in the cylinders. This practice helps to prevent accidental mixing of refrigerants within a system. Popular refrigerants, their R-number, chemical formula, cylinder color coding, and boiling points follow:

amount, and that all cylinders shall not be "liquid full" at 130 F. or less. If a cylinder is completely filled with liquid at room temperature, it may burst due to excessive pressure caused by the expansion of the liquid as it warms up. The I.C.C. further states that cylinders which have contained a corrosive refrigerant must be checked every five years. Cylinders containing noncorrosive refrigerants must be checked every 10 years. All cylinders over 4 1/2 inches in diameter and 12 inches in length must contain some type of pressure release protective device such as a fusible plug, or a spring operated relief valve.

9-18 Refrigerant Storage Cylinders

Refrigerant storage cylinders are available in sizes from 4 pounds to 150 pounds capacity. Some types of refrigerants such as R-114B2 are also available in drums. See Chapter 2 for more information on service cylinders.

Many storage cylinders are presently available with new liquid-vapor valves. The two-way valve permits charging in the usual manner from a standard outlet,

REFRIGERANT NUMBER	REFRIGERANT NAME	CHEMICAL FORMULA	CYLINDER COLOR CODE	BOILING TEMP. AT ATMOSPHERIC PRESSURE
R-764	Sulphur Dioxide	SO_2	Black	14
R-40	Methyl Chloride	CH_3Cl	Orange	-10.4
R-12	Dichlorodifluormoethane	CCl_2F_2	White	-21.62
R-22	Monochlorodifluoromethane	$CHClF_2$	Green	-41.44
R-113	Trichlorotrifluoroethane	CCl_2FCClF_2	Purple	117.63
R-114	Dichlorotetrofluoroethane	$CClF_2CClF_2$	Dark Blue	38.39
R-500	Refrigerant 152A/12	$CCl_2F_2/CH_3C\,HF_2$	Red	-28
R-502	Refrigerants 22/115 (48.8% R-22/51.2% R-115)	$CHClF_2/CClF_2CF_3$	Orchid	-50.1

To further insure the safety of those working with cylinders containing refrigerants, regulations are prescribed by the Interstate Commerce Commission. These regulations provide that a cylinder shall not be filled in excess of the prescribed

either as a vapor or as a liquid, without having to invert the cylinder.

Fig. 9-18 shows a double cylinder valve called a liquid-vapor valve. The ability to transfer either a liquid or vapor is accomplished by the use of two valve stems.

Fig. 9-18. Two-valve unit for refrigerant storage cylinder. Refrigerant may be drawn from cylinder either as a liquid or as a vapor.

One is on top of the valve body and one is on the side of the valve. The side hand wheel operates a valve which is attached to a tube which extends to the bottom of the cylinder. The vapor hand wheel is located at the top of the cylinder and is

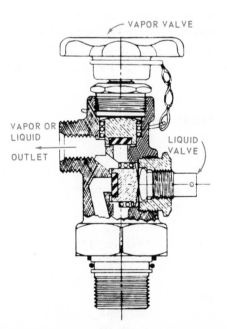

Fig. 9-19. Cross section through refrigerant cylinder valve used to provide either liquid refrigerant or refrigerant vapor.
(Kaiser Aluminum and Chemical Corp.)

marked "vapor." The liquid hand wheel is located on the side of the valve and is marked "liquid." Note the built-in safety device. A standard hood cap is placed over the valve when it is not in use.

Fig. 9-19 shows a cross section of the liquid-vapor valve.

9-19 Head Pressures

The proper head pressure, sometimes called the high side pressure or condensing pressure, is important. If the condensing pressure is too high, the compressor has to work too hard. Too much vapor left in the compressor clearance pocket decreases the volumetric efficiency. The temperature of the exhaust vapor will become excessive and may cause oil deterioration. Above normal head pressures are usually caused by:

1. A noncondensible gas trapped in the condenser; air, for example. The air will not condense. Due to Dalton's Law the head pressure will be the vapor pressure of the refrigerant plus the air pressure.

2. An overcharge of refrigerant in systems using a low side float, an expansion valve, or a thermostatic expansion valve may fill some of the heat radiating space in the condenser with liquid refrigerant and reduce the condenser's heat radiating ability.

3. If either side of the heat transfer surface is dirty, this dirt will act as an insulator and the heat radiating capacity of the condenser will be lowered and the condenser temperature will rise to overcome this handicap.

4. If the air movement or the water movement through the condenser is reduced by blocked air passages, or poor water flow, there will not be enough heat removing media to remove the heat from the condenser.

5. A restriction in the system, for example, a clogged capillary tube or a stuck shut refrigerant control.

In air cooled condensers, the head pressure should correspond to a temperature between 30 F. and 35 F. higher than the ambient temperature or the temperature of the air passing over the condenser.

In a water-cooled condenser, the head pressure should correspond to a temperature 15 F. to 20 F. above the exhaust temperature of the water.

In all cases the condensing temperature will rise until the heat loss from the condenser equals the heat input into the condenser.

9-20 Low Side Pressures

The low side pressure in a refrigerating system depends on the use the refrigerating system is put to, and type of evaporating coil used.

You must first determine the temperature that is desired in the cabinet or fixture, then adjust the motor control until this temperature is maintained. However, there are many cases where both a certain evaporating coil temperature and a cabinet temperature relationship should exist.

Cabinet temperatures are fairly standard and the following is a widely accepted list of cabinet temperatures:

FIXTURE (Cabinet)	TEMP. F.
Back Bar	37–40
Beverage Cooler	37–40
Beverage Pre-Cooler	35–40
Candy Case (Display)	60–65
Candy Case (Storage)	58–65
Dairy Display Case	36–39
Double Display Case	36–39
Delicatessen Case	36–40
Dough Retarding Refrigerator	34–38
Florist Display Refrigerator	40–50
Florist Storage Case	38–45
Frozen Food Cabinet (Closed)	−10 to −5
Frozen Food Cabinet (Open)	−7 to −2
Grocery Refrigerator	35–40

Retail Market Cooler	34–39
Pastry Display Case	45–50
Restaurant Service Refrigerator	36–40
Restaurant Storage Cooling	35–39
Top Display Case (Closed)	35–42
Vegetable Display Refrigerator (Closed)	38–42
(Open)	38–42

The proper refrigerator temperature to be maintained is dependent on the material placed in the fixture. The following list is based on the application of the fixture:

APPLICATION	TEMP. F.
Service	34–38
Meats	30–34
Bananas	60–65
Fresh Meats	28–32
Aging Room	30–34
Chill Room	35–39
Curing Room	32–36
Freezer Room	−15
Poultry	30–34
Vegetables, Fresh	36–42
Ice Cream Hardening	−25
Ice Cream Storage	−20 to −10
Plants and Flowers	38–50
Fur Storage	33–37
Locker Room	−5 to 0

It is necessary to have the correct size evaporating coil to produce the temperature desired. If the coil is over capacity compared to the cooling needs, it will be at above normal temperature. If the coil is undersized, it will be at a below normal temperature.

The refrigerant will be colder than the coil when the unit is running and for the same reason the evaporator coil will always have a lower temperature than the fixture temperature.

Normally the refrigerant will be 10 F. colder than the coil temperature when the unit is running and the refrigerant and the coil will become the same temperature during the off cycle.

The evaporator coil surface temperature is dependent on its size as compared to the heat it must remove from the fixture per unit of time.

The temperature of a typical frosting

type evaporator coil (domestic type) will vary from 0 F. to 25 F. and the refrigerant temperature will be about 10 F. lower than this or in the range of -10 F. to 15 F. while the unit is running.

9-21 Use of Pressure-Temperature Curves

The pressure-temperature curves illustrated in this chapter show pressures produced by refrigerants under various temperatures. The vertical scale is the temperature scale in degrees F. The horizontal scale is pressure in psig. To determine the pressure of the refrigerant at any particular temperature, read horizontally from the temperature reading until the curve of the particular refrigerant is reached, then move directly down and the pressure may be read on the horizontal scale. For example, the vapor-pressure of R-12 refrigerant at a temperature of 100 F. is 116.9 psig. The temperature is always the temperature of the refrigerant. The same curve may be used for determining both the condensing and evaporation temperatures and pressures. The condensing values are the higher values. When using this chart, several things must be kept in mind:

1. The temperature of the refrigerant in the evaporating coil is approximately 8 F. to 12 F. colder than the coil when the compressor is running.
2. The temperature of the refrigerant in the evaporating coil is the same as the coil temperature when the compressor is stopped.
3. The temperature of the refrigerant in an air-cooled condenser is approximately 30 F. to 35 F. warmer than the room temperature.
4. The temperature of the refrigerant in a water-cooled condenser is approximately 20 F. warmer than the water temperature at the drain outlet.
5. The temperature of the refrigerant

in the condenser will be approximately the same as the temperature of the cooling medium after the unit has been shut off for 15 to 30 minutes.

9-22 Use of Pressure-Temperature Tables

The pressure-temperature relationship of the refrigerants under saturated conditions can be shown in the tables as well as pictured in graphs.

The table can also be used to show the volume of one pound of the gas at that temperature, as well as the latent heat, the specific heat of the liquid, and the density of the liquid. These values are of considerable value to an engineer.

To use the tables, select the temperature being investigated in the left hand vertical column and then move across to the other columns horizontally to determine the pressure, as shown in Fig. 9-20.

9-23 Refrigeration Oil

The primary purpose of oil in the refrigerating mechanism is to provide lubrication. Refrigerant oil must have certain properties, because of the necessity of its mixing with the refrigerant in the compressor. The oil circulates through the system with the refrigerant and is in direct contact with motor windings in hermetic units. Refrigerant oil must be able to withstand extreme temperatures, be compatible with refrigerants and not damage the equipment.

Oil in the refrigeration system is chilled to extremely low temperatures yet must be able to withstand high temperatures at the compressor. Consequently, the oil must remain fluid with the refrigerant. The fluidity of an oil-refrigerant mixture is determined upon its solubility in refrigerant and also the refrigerant used, and the temperature, as well as the properties of the oil used.

TEMPERATURE °F.	REFRIGERANT 12	22	500	502	717	TEMPERATURE °F.	REFRIGERANT 12	22	500	502	717	TEMPERATURE °F.	REFRIGERANT 12	22	500	502	717
-60	*19.0*	*12.0*	---	*7.0*	*18.6*	12	15.8	34.7	21.2	43.2	25.6	42	38.8	71.4	48.4	83.4	61.6
-55	*17.3*	*9.2*	---	*3.6*	*16.6*	13	16.4	35.7	21.9	44.3	26.5	43	39.8	73.0	49.6	85.0	63.1
-50	*15.4*	*6.2*	---	*0.0*	*14.3*	14	17.1	36.7	22.6	45.4	27.5	44	40.7	74.5	50.7	86.6	64.7
-45	*13.3*	*2.7*	---	2.1	*11.7*	15	17.7	37.7	23.4	46.6	28.4	45	41.7	76.0	51.8	88.3	66.3
-40	*11.0*	0.5	7.9	4.3	*8.7*	16	18.4	38.7	24.2	47.7	29.4	46	42.6	77.6	53.0	90.0	67.9
-35	*8.4*	2.6	4.8	6.7	*5.4*	17	19.0	39.8	24.9	48.9	30.4	47	43.6	79.2	54.2	91.7	69.5
-30	*5.5*	4.9	*1.4*	9.4	*1.6*	18	19.7	40.8	25.7	50.1	31.4	48	44.6	80.8	55.4	93.4	71.1
-25	*2.3*	7.4	1.1	12.3	1.3	19	20.4	41.9	26.5	51.2	32.5	49	45.7	82.4	56.6	95.2	72.8
-20	0.6	10.1	3.1	15.5	3.6	20	21.0	43.0	27.3	52.4	33.5	50	46.7	84.0	57.8	96.9	74.5
-18	1.3	11.3	4.0	16.9	4.6	21	21.7	44.1	28.2	53.7	34.6	55	52.0	92.6	64.1	106.0	83.4
-16	2.0	12.5	4.9	18.3	5.6	22	22.4	45.3	29.0	54.9	35.7	60	57.7	101.6	71.0	115.6	92.9
-14	2.8	13.8	5.8	19.7	6.7	23	23.2	46.4	29.8	56.2	36.8	65	63.8	111.2	78.1	125.8	103.1
-12	3.6	15.1	6.8	21.2	7.9	24	23.9	47.6	30.7	57.4	37.9	70	70.2	121.4	85.8	136.6	114.1
-10	4.5	16.5	7.8	22.8	9.0	25	24.6	48.8	31.6	58.7	39.0	75	77.0	132.2	93.9	148.0	125.8
- 8	5.4	17.9	8.9	24.4	10.3	26	25.4	49.9	32.4	60.0	40.2	80	84.2	143.6	102.5	159.9	138.3
- 6	6.3	19.3	9.8	26.0	11.6	27	26.1	51.2	33.5	61.4	41.4	W.C. 85	91.8	155.7	111.5	172.5	151.7
- 4	7.2	20.8	11.0	27.7	12.9	28	26.9	52.4	34.3	62.7	42.6	90	99.8	168.4	121.2	185.8	165.9
- 2	8.2	22.4	12.1	29.4	14.3	29	27.7	53.6	35.2	64.1	43.8	95	108.2	181.8	131.3	199.8	181.1
0	9.2	24.0	13.3	31.2	15.7	30	28.4	54.9	36.1	65.4	45.0	100	117.2	195.9	141.9	214.4	197.2
1	9.7	24.8	13.9	32.2	16.5	31	29.2	56.2	37.0	66.8	46.3	A.C. 105	126.6	210.8	153.1	229.8	214.2
2	10.2	25.6	14.5	33.1	17.2	32	30.1	57.5	38.0	68.2	47.6	110	136.4	226.4	164.9	245.8	232.3
3	10.7	26.4	15.1	34.1	18.0	33	30.9	58.8	39.0	69.7	48.9	115	146.8	242.7	177.4	262.7	251.5
4	11.2	27.3	15.7	35.0	18.8	34	31.7	60.1	40.0	71.1	50.2	120	157.6	259.9	190.3	280.3	271.7
Ev 5	11.8	28.2	16.4	36.0	19.6	35	32.6	61.5	41.0	72.6	51.6	125	169.1	277.9	204.0	298.7	293.1
6	12.3	29.1	17.0	37.0	20.4	36	33.4	62.8	42.0	74.1	52.9	130	181.0	296.8	218.2	318.0	---
7	12.9	30.0	17.7	38.0	21.2	37	34.3	64.2	43.1	75.6	54.3	135	193.5	316.6	233.2	338.1	---
8	13.5	30.9	18.4	39.0	22.1	38	35.2	65.6	44.1	77.1	55.7	140	206.6	337.2	248.8	359.1	---
9	14.0	31.8	19.0	40.0	22.9	39	36.1	67.1	45.2	78.6	57.2	145	220.3	358.9	265.2	381.1	---
10	14.6	32.8	19.8	41.1	23.8	40	37.0	68.5	46.2	80.2	58.6	150	234.6	381.5	282.3	403.9	---
11	15.2	33.7	20.5	42.2	24.7	41	37.9	70.0	47.2	81.8	60.1	155	249.5	405.1	300.2	427.8	---

Fig. 9-20. A temperature-pressure chart which may be used to determine the operating pressures for various temperatures and for various refrigerants. Ev—Average low side pressures. W.C.—Average water-cooled system head pressures. A.C.—Average air-cooled system head pressures. (Sparlan Valve Co.)

The properties of a good refrigerant oil are:

1. Low wax content. Separation of wax from the oil in a refrigerant oil mixture may plug refrigerant control orifices.

2. Good thermal stability. Ability to eliminate hard carbon deposits at hot spots of the compressor such as valves or discharge ports.

3. Good chemical stability. Little or no chemical reaction with the refrigerant or materials normally found in a system.

4. Low pour point. Ability of the oil to not congeal at the lowest temperatures in the system.

5. Low viscosity. Ability of the oil to maintain good composition at high temperatures and good fluidity at low temperatures consequently providing a good lubricating film at all times.

In order to improve the performance of the oil many manufacturers produce oils with additives which are designed to inhibit the formation of sludge or foaming. Oil which contains moisture or air will form sludge or varnish and may cause damage to the unit.

When oil is removed from a system, it should be clear. Discoloration of the oil means that it is impure. If this has happened, new dryers and filters should be placed on the system to keep the new oil clean. Another indicator of impure oil is odor. If the oil from a system has an odor it is a good indication that it is contaminated. For additional information on oil, see Chapters 2, 12, and 15.

Oil recommended by manufacturers of the equipment should be used. Fig. 9-21 indicates viscosity of oil which may be used for most applications, if the manufacturer's recommendation cannot be found.

9-24 Selection of a Refrigerant

To provide an economical refrigerator mechanism the designer must choose a refrigerant that will rate high in the following respects: The refrigerant, when passing from a liquid to a vapor, must absorb a considerable amount of heat per pound as it changes its state. The specific volume of the vapor and volume per unit of weight, must be kept small so a compressor of minimum size may be used. It must be remembered too that cost and availability have a bearing on the refrigerant used.

9-25 Refrigerants Used in Hermetic Systems

The first hermetic units produced used R-764 (sulfur dioxide) refrigerant. The properties of this refrigerant are explained in Par. 9-13. Then the refrigerant used in hermetics was R-40. The Grunow refrigerator used R-30. In 1934 the Frigidaire Corp. introduced their hermetic unit which used R-114. Frigidaire has been the exclusive user of this refrigerant in most of their small hermetic units. The Crosley Corporation first used R-12 in their units. The most popular hermetic refrigerant

SERVICE CONDITION	REFRIGERANT	VISCOSITY
Compressor Temperature		
Normal	All	150
		150/additives
High	Halogen	150/additives
	Ammonia	300
		300/additives
Evaporator Temperature		
Above 0 F.	Halogen	150
		150/additives
	Ammonia	300
0 F. to -40 F.	Halogen	150
		150/additives
	Ammonia	150
		150/additives
Below -40 F.	Halogen	150
		150/additives
	Ammonia	150
		150/additives

Fig. 9-21. Table of refrigerant oils. Oils should be selected according to compressor temperature, evaporator temperature and kind of refrigerant used.

has been, and still is, R-12, except for low temperature units (frozen foods units) where R-22 is quite popular. The properties of R-12 are described in Par. 9-6. Refrigerants used in hermetic refrigeration units must be of top quality. They must contain an absolute minimum of foreign matter and moisture. It is imperative to transfer refrigerants in chemically clean cylinders and lines. Always charge a unit, except large commercial units, with the refrigerant in the vapor form. Never charge liquid refrigerant into a domestic or small commercial unit. Always keep the charging cylinder at room temperature or warm it with hot water. Avoid using stoves or flames to heat cylinders as the cylinders may explode.

9-26 Refrigerant Identification

The basic method of refrigerant identification is through the use of a pressure temperature chart. Identification of refrigerants by smell or color is very difficult, with the exception of R-764 and R-717.

One mechanism which may be used to help identify refrigerants is the Airserco Refrig-I-Dent, as shown in Fig. 9-22. This instrument allows the serviceman to test and identify an unknown refrigerant in an operating system or from a refrigerant cylinder. The instrument provides a thermometer and pressure gauge attached to a special manifold, and a pressure temperature chart. The refrigerant sample is obtained from the system and entrapped in the manifold instrument. The indicated pressure-temperature for the refrigerant is then checked against the pressure-temperature chart and the type of refrigerant is determined.

9-27 Changing Refrigerants

Usually it is not advisable to change refrigerants in a unit that was designed for a particular refrigerant. Engineering features that were incorporated in the unit to provide efficiency may be lost.

If for some reason the refrigerant must be changed, it is generally advisable to use an expansion valve designed for the new refrigerant. If the unit uses a capillary tube, and the density or pressure differences are changed, the tube should be replaced.

Be sure to clean the mechanism thoroughly and replace the oil. Installing a drier-filter is good practice when a system is being converted from one refrigerant to another.

9-28 Replacing R-40 (Methyl Chloride) with R-12

Because of the flammability of R-40, refrigerant R-12 is often used as a replacement. If the unit is of the small domestic type the only conversion necessary will be the replacement or adjustment of the refrigerant control. If the unit is a larger open type, the compressor speed may have to be reduced to compensate for the reduced volume of gas needed and the higher operating pressure. This decrease in motor pulley size may require using a shorter belt. The pulley diameter may be reduced approximately 20 percent, that is, a 2 1/2 in. diameter pulley may be replaced by a 2 in. diameter pulley.

9-29 Replacing R-22 with R-502

It is possible to change a system from R-22 to R-502 when lower temperatures and pressures are desired, or if greater cooling capacity is required without replacing the unit. The conversion of R-22 to R-502 to obtain greater capacity should be done only with those units which operate at temperatures of 0 F. or lower. If the reason for the change is to obtain lower operating temperatures with an open system, the compressor speed should be re-

Fig. 9-22. An instrument which may be used to identify the refrigerant in use in a system.

duced if the same capacity is desired. Compressor speed reduction may be obtained by decreasing the size of the motor pulley. The motor horsepower should remain the same. In the case of a hermetic unit, 10 percent to 30 percent more capacity may be obtained from the same unit by converting from R-22 to R-502. In all conversions, a refrigerant control which is designed to operate with R-502 should be used. To obtain even greater performance from the conversion of R-22 to R-502, a suction-line heat exchanger should be used. In all cases where changing refrigerant is being considered, it is recommended that the manufacturer of the equipment be consulted first.

9-30 Replacing R-12 with R-22

Replacement of R-12 with R-22. This substitution is sometimes done in limited cases where there is a need to have more cooling effect, and where the condensing unit cannot be replaced. The serviceman should be very careful; he should first inquire of the equipment manufacturer to determine if the unit can withstand the high operating pressures of R-22. As in most conversions, the refrigerant controls should be changed. Because of the higher low-side pressures and greater latent heat, it may be necessary to decrease the suction line diameter to make sure the oil will return down the suction line.

9-31 Amount of Refrigerant Required in a System

The amount of refrigerant that should be in a system varies with the type of system. The low side float, automatic expansion valve, and thermostatic expansion valve systems are not sensitive to the amount of refrigerant in the system. The method of checking is to charge gas refrigerant into the low side of the system until the evaporator has its normal amount, the liquid line is at room temperature, and there is no hissing sound at the refrigerant control valve. If one or two extra pounds are put in the unit, this extra refrigerant will become a reserve and will be stored in the liquid receiver. The smaller the unit, the less the amount of refrigerant needed as a reserve. A sure way to determine if the system has sufficient refrigerant is to put a sight glass in the liquid line. The appearance of gas bubbles in this sight glass is a sign that the system is short of refrigerant, and it should be charged until the gas bubbles disappear.

Most systems which use a high side float or a capillary tube are very critical as to their refrigerant charge. If the system is overcharged, the evaporator will be overcharged or flooded. The use of accumulator spaces at the outlet of these evaporators relieves the problem somewhat, but you must be careful of the amount charged into these systems. A common method of charging these units is to slowly charge these systems with refrigerant in the vapor state until the suction line starts to sweat and/or frost back and then purge a little at a time until the "frost back" disappears. Another method is through the use of a charging cylinder which will allow the serviceman to charge the system to the manufacturer's recommended amount.

Remember that you should, if possible, always charge a system into the low side, and that the refrigerant should be put into the system in vapor form. Forcing liquid refrigerant into a system may damage the pump and may even injure the serviceman.

You should always remember that if a system is short of refrigerant, there is a leak in the system. This leak should be located and corrected before the system is charged.

9-32 Review of Safety

When a leak in a system is suspected, make certain that the room is thoroughly ventilated before starting to work on the unit. Always check for recommended operating pressures for each refrigerant. Check refrigerant R-number before charging. Make certain that the service cylinder is not overcharged when charging it from a storage cylinder. Make certain there are no lighted flames near the unit which is using a fluorocarbon refrigerant that is suspected of have a leak. Always check I.C.C. cylinder stamp for assurance of a safe cylinder. WEAR GOGGLES AT ALL TIMES ESPECIALLY WHEN CHARGING OR DISCHARGING TO PROTECT YOUR EYES IN CASE OF A SUDDEN LEAK.

Always charge refrigerant vapor into a system. Liquid refrigerant entering a compressor may injure the compressor and may cause the unit to burst.

Liquid refrigerant on the skin may freeze the skin surface and cause a "frost bite." If this should happen, quickly wash away the refrigerant with water. Treat the damaged surface for the "frost bite."

If one accidentally gets refrigerant in

his eyes and a doctor is not immediately available, in the emergency, wash with mineral oil, (for refrigerants except ammonia), as the oil will absorb the refrigerant. Then wash the eyes with a boric acid solution. If the refrigerant is ammonia wash immediately with water.

Water may also be used for washing refrigerant from the eyes.

9-33 Test Your Knowledge - Chapter 9

1. Why is R-717, Ammonia, not popular in the compression type, domestic machines?
2. How may one test for R-502 leaks?
3. What is a common head pressure for air-cooled R-12 refrigerators?
4. What is the method used to locate R-22 leaks?
5. What are the low side pressures at 5 F. for R-22 and R-12?
6. What does "halide" mean?
7. What does toxic mean?
8. What oil properties are required with R-12?
9. What other name is R-12 known by?
10. What is the pressure of R-12 at 105 F.?
11. What is the temperature of R-12 under a pressure of 20 pounds per square inch gauge?
12. What is the pressure of R-22 at 0 F.?
13. Is it advisable to substitute refrigerants in a system?
14. How may one determine the refrigerant temperature in an air-cooled condenser?
15. Name the refrigerants that may be tested for leaks with the halide torch.
16. What will be the high side pressure (gauge) in an air-cooled condenser using R-502 while the condensing unit is running, if the room temperature is 75 F.?
17. What is the normal head pressure for an air-cooled R-22 system?
18. Is the refrigerant temperature in the evaporator coil the same temperature as the coil when the unit is running?
19. What affect does air in the system have on the head pressure?
20. Name two refrigerants that may not be tested with the halide torch.
21. Name two ways an R-22 or R-12 system may be checked for leaks.
22. How does one determine the correct head pressure of a water-cooled condenser?
23. What is latent heat?
24. What is the meaning of Group 1, Group 2, and Group 3 refrigerants?
25. Is carbon dioxide used as a refrigerant?

Chapter 10

DOMESTIC HERMETIC SYSTEMS AND MECHANISMS

The domestic hermetic refrigerator system (sealed unit) consists of a single housing in which the motor and compressor are sealed with leakproof joints.

Hermetic units for domestic refrigerators and freezers may be grouped according to the following general classifications:

1. All of the joints are silver brazed and/or welded and there are no service valves.
2. Some of the joints are mechanical (assembled with bolts or screws) and there are no service valves.
3. All the joints are silver brazed and/or welded and there are service valves.
4. Some of the joints are mechanical and there are service valves.
5. Combinations of the above four general types.

10-1 Development

The refrigeration industry has long recognized the engineering and production problems involved in designing, producing and servicing the open compressor with its crankshaft seal and the various mechanical joints in order to make them leakproof over a long period of time. A natural evolution was the elimination of the need for the compressor crankshaft seal by installing the motor inside a housing with the compressor. This improvement has been dependent on the development of motor insulation materials, refrigerants, motor designs, and motor controls.

The General Electric Monitor Top was the first hermetic unit that reached the market in large quantities. This was introduced in 1926. It was a R-747 (sulphur

CONDENSER AIR BOTH IN AND OUT

Fig. 10-1. Late model refrigerator with compact mechanism which provides considerable usable space. (Kelvinator Div., American Motors)

dioxide) charged unit with the compressor and motor under a dome surrounded by the condenser. It was mounted on top of the refrigerator cabinet. The system used a high side float refrigerant control and had an amperage relay starter as explained in Chapter 8.

Several hermetics appeared on the market during the period of 1926 to 1934 such as the Majestic, the Grunow and others. In 1934 the Frigidaire Corp. introduced the Meter Miser in their domestic units. The following six years found many of the manufacturers developing the hermetic system. Today, all domestic units are either full hermetic or semihermetic. The present condensing units are being made more compact, permitting the cabinets to be refrigerated their full height as shown in Fig. 10-1.

Modern refrigerators are available in a wide range of styles. They can be equipped at one extreme with two complete independent refrigeration units; one for the frozen foods compartment and the other for normal food storage. At the opposite extreme they may have one evaporator to cool both the freezer compartment and the food storage.

10-2 Typical Hermetic Cycles

Most condensing units are located in the bottom of the cabinet. They are hermetically sealed and use a split-phase motor connected to either a reciprocal or rotary compressor. The condenser is either a natural convection type, called a static condenser, or forced convection type (blower coils). The refrigerant control is usually a capillary tube. The evaporator is commonly made of aluminum or stainless steel and provides considerable volume and shelf space for frozen food storage, ice cube making, and cooling the refrigerator cabinet.

The refrigerant lines are usually silver brazed in place and the complete unit is designed to be removed in one piece, usually from the back of the cabinet. The electrical system on some units consists of a

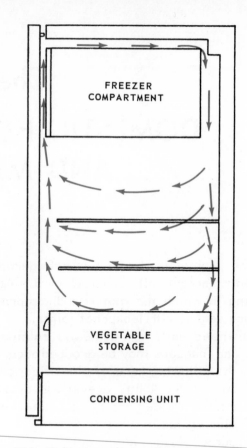

Fig. 10-2. Cold air spill-over from frozen foods compartment refrigerates normal storage cabinet.

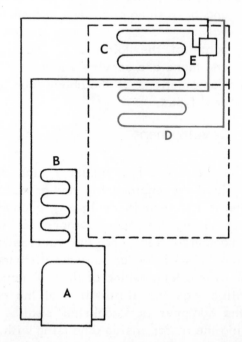

Fig. 10-3. Refrigerant spill-over from frozen food coil refrigerates normal storage cabinet. A—Compressor. B—Condenser. C—Low temperature evaporator coil. D—High humidity evaporator coil. E—Accumulator.

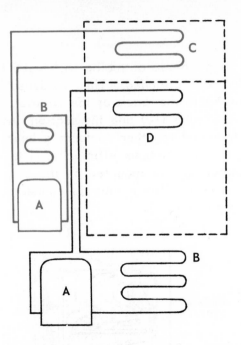

Fig. 10-4. *This two-temperature box is refrigerated by two complete and independent refrigerating mechanisms. A—Motor-compressor. B—Condenser. C—Low temperature evaporator coil. D—High humidity evaporator coil.*

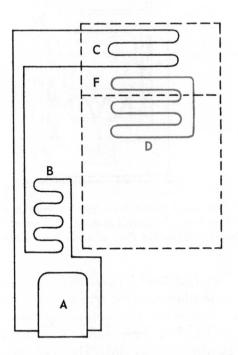

Fig. 10-5. *In this refrigerator a single condensing unit is used; however, a secondary refrigerant in a closed system picks up heat in the refrigerator cabinet and gives it up to the frozen foods compartment coil. A—Motor-compressor. B—Condenser. C—Low temperature evaporator coil. D—High humidity evaporator coil. F—Secondary condenser.*

starting relay, several protective devices, a temperature motor control, automatic defrosting mechanism, door switch and various heater coils.

Various methods have been developed to provide two different temperatures required in refrigerators:

1. Frozen foods temperatures. The frozen foods compartment temperature must be maintained at 5 F. or below.
2. The refrigerated compartment temperature which must not fall below 32 F. (usually maintained between 35 and 45 F.). If below 32 F. many foods would freeze.

Some methods of obtaining controlled temperatures in each compartment are:

1. Air spill-over using one evaporator as shown in Fig. 10-2.
2. Refrigerant spill-over using two evaporators as shown in Fig. 10-3.
3. Two complete and independent refrigerating mechanisms as shown in Fig. 10-4.
4. Secondary refrigerant system in which a secondary refrigerant in a closed system picks up heat in the refrigerator cabinet and transfers it to the freezing compartment coil as shown in Fig. 10-5.
5. Two-temperature valve operating on the refrigerator (highest temperature) coil as shown in Fig. 10-6.
6. Forced convection type evaporator using a fan to circulate the cooled air in both the freezer compartment and the food compartment as shown in Fig. 10-7.
7. Forced convection type evaporator using independent fans to circulate the cooled air for each compartment, Fig. 10-8.

A diagram of the cycle used in a cabinet which uses a frozen foods evaporator and the fresh foods portion cooled by spilled air is shown in Fig. 10-9. Note the use of a heat exchanger number 3 to increase efficiency. The condenser (8) is the

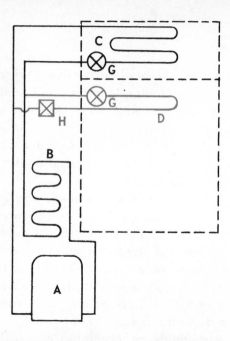

Fig. 10-6. *In this refrigerator a two-temperature valve on the refrigerator coil (highest temperature) provides the two temperatures required. A—Motor-compressor. B—Condenser. C—Low temperature evaporator coil. D—High humidity evaporator coil. G—Refrigerant controls. H—Two-temperature valve.*

Fig. 10-7. *Forced convection type of evaporator using a single fan to circulate cooled air.*

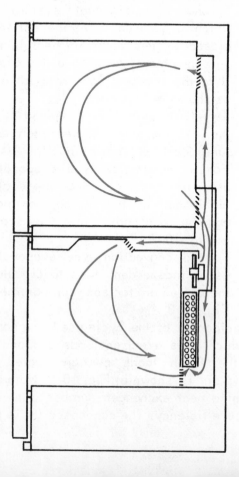

static type made of tubing with wire heat dissipators attached. The condenser is mounted on the back of the cabinet. The capillary tube (10) and the suction line (4) are fastened together to form a heat exchanger to increase efficiency. The accumulator (2) is mounted on the evaporator. The capillary tube is connected to the evaporator (1).

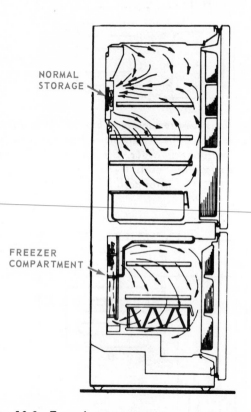

NORMAL STORAGE

FREEZER COMPARTMENT

Fig. 10-8. *Forced convection type evaporator using independent fans. 1—Normal storage. 2—Freezer compartment. (Franklin Div. of Studebaker Corp.)*

A refrigerator cycle with the fresh foods cold plate and the frozen foods evaporator connected in series is shown in Fig. 10-10. The main refrigerant control is a capillary tube (6). The refrigerant is fed to the fresh foods coil first (2). The pressure in this coil is kept higher than the pressure in the frozen foods coil (1) by the resistance of the restrictor. The accumulator is shown at (3), the suction line at (5), the condenser at (8), and the

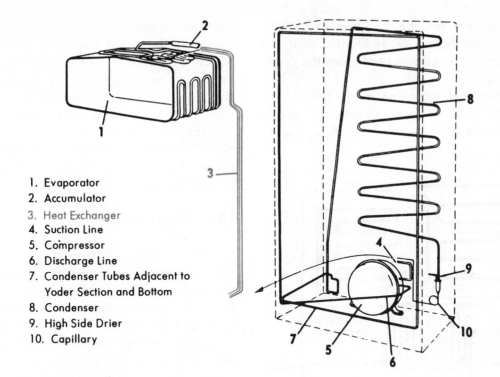

1. Evaporator
2. Accumulator
3. Heat Exchanger
4. Suction Line
5. Compressor
6. Discharge Line
7. Condenser Tubes Adjacent to
   Yoder Section and Bottom
8. Condenser
9. High Side Drier
10. Capillary

Fig. 10-9. Typical domestic refrigerating unit. Note use of heat exchanger (3) to increase performance.

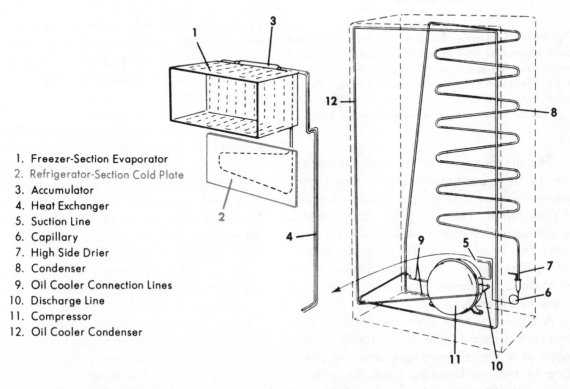

1. Freezer-Section Evaporator
2. Refrigerator-Section Cold Plate
3. Accumulator
4. Heat Exchanger
5. Suction Line
6. Capillary
7. High Side Drier
8. Condenser
9. Oil Cooler Connection Lines
10. Discharge Line
11. Compressor
12. Oil Cooler Condenser

Fig. 10-10. Chest type freezer section with a cold plate connected in series (2).

discharge line for the compressor at (10). A special condenser (9) is located near the compressor to remove heat from the compressor oil.

Another refrigerating cycle for a cabinet with a fresh foods evaporator and a frozen foods coil is shown in Fig. 10-11.

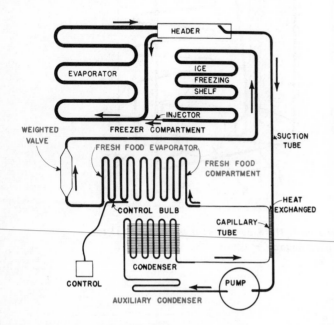

Fig. 10-11. Schematic diagram of cycle with fresh foods evaporator coil in series; and a weight valve maintaining the pressure difference. Note the auxiliary condenser for evaporating defrost water. The injector keeps the liquid refrigerant circulating in the freezer evaporator. (General Electric Co.)

The discharge vapor from the compressor is first passed through a small condenser located in a flat position in the base of the cabinet. The heat from this condenser evaporates the drain water which comes from the frost on the fresh foods evaporator. The vapor is completely condensed in a static condenser mounted on the back of the refrigerator.

A capillary tube then delivers reduced pressure liquid to the fresh foods evaporator at a higher pressure than the pressure in the ice freezing shelf. An injector carries the remaining liquid refrigerant

plus the vapor into the frozen foods cooling coil. Note that both ends of the frozen foods evaporator are connected to the header or accumulator. The injector forces the liquid around the frozen foods evaporator until it is all evaporated. If liquid refrigerant reaches the header it drains back into the evaporator. The refrigerant vapor then returns to the compressor by way of the suction line.

10-3 No-Frost Cycles

The no-frost or nonfrost refrigeration systems were developed for domestic refrigeration during the late 1950's and early 60's. The units consist of finned evaporators and forced air (fan and motor) such as shown in Fig. 10-12. Because the frost will collect at the coldest spot or area, the air is forced or induced to flow over the finned coil where it is cooled and some of the moisture in this air is condensed and frozen to the coil. The dry cold air is then distributed to the food compartment, cools the food, and picks up any moisture or frost which may be on the food or beverages in the compartment. The dry, moisture-free, and frost-free food packages and beverage containers are attractive and easy to handle.

To keep the evaporator fins from clogging with frost and to maintain a high efficiency of heat transfer, the evaporators are usually defrosted during each off-cycle of the machine. This defrosting is commonly done with heat generated by electric heating coils (resistance coils). These heating wires are mounted adjacent to, or are built into, the evaporators.

It is further necessary to provide drainage for the drain water. A collecting baffle is mounted under the coil and a drain tube carries the water to the condensing unit. Because this baffle, and also the drain tube, may collect frost or ice; these devices are sometimes heated with an electric resistance wire. The heat from the compressor and condenser plus electric heaters evaporate the drained water during the on-cycle of the machine. See Fig. 10-13.

10-4 Refrigerant Controls

Hermetic systems generally use the capillary tube refrigerant control. This control which has proven to be successful

10-5 Hermetic Compressor Designs

The development of hermetic compressors and their manufacture has required some of the most accurate craftsmanship industry has produced. Parts are being fitted to micoraccuracies under production conditions.

1. Evaporator
2. Defrost Heater
3. Compressor
4. Termination Thermostat
5. Fan Assembly

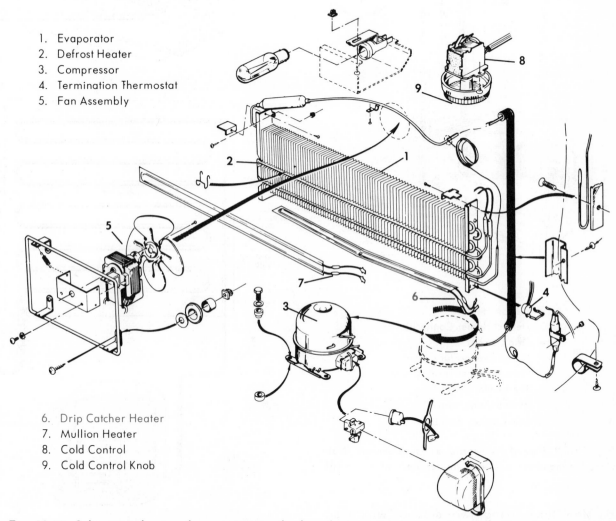

6. Drip Catcher Heater
7. Mullion Heater
8. Cold Control
9. Cold Control Knob

Fig. 10-12. Schematic showing the components of a forced convection type cooling unit. Note 6, a drip trough heater to aid in evaporating defrost water.   (Franklin Div. of Studebaker Corp.)

requires a carefully measured refrigerant charge. Fig. 10-14 shows a capillary tube installation.

The design, construction, and operation of capillary refrigerant control is explained in Chapters 6 and 27.

There are two types of compressors in popular use, namely:

A. Reciprocating compressor.

B. Rotary compressor.

Both give quiet and efficient service. These compressors have been covered in detail in Chapter 5. The motors in most domestic hermetic units operate on 120 volt, 60 cycle, single-phase alternating current. They are of the split-phase in-

hot refrigerant vapor is discharged from the compressor and:

1. Passed through oil condenser (2).

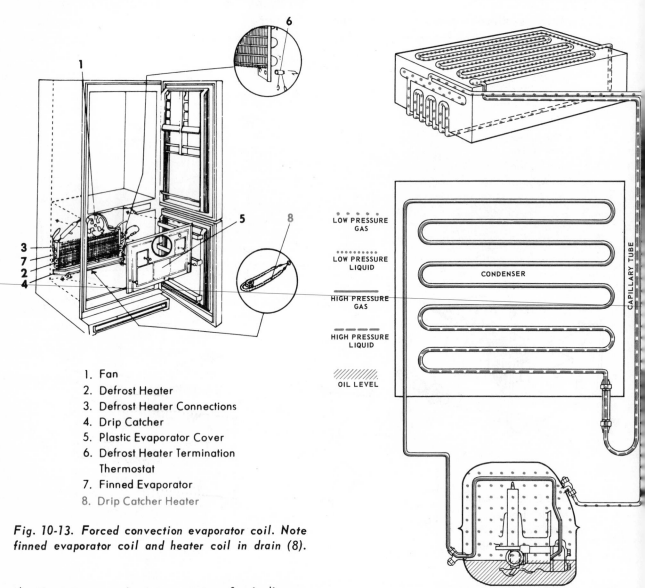

1. Fan
2. Defrost Heater
3. Defrost Heater Connections
4. Drip Catcher
5. Plastic Evaporator Cover
6. Defrost Heater Termination Thermostat
7. Finned Evaporator
8. Drip Catcher Heater

Fig. 10-13. Forced convection evaporator coil. Note finned evaporator coil and heater coil in drain (8).

Fig. 10-14. Refrigerant cycle showing various states of refrigerant throughout system. Note change from high pressure liquid to low pressure liquid after passing through capillary tube.
(Gibson Refrig. Sales Corp., Hupp Corp.)

duction type using two sets of windings; starting and running. The heat produced by the motor and by compression is dispelled by spraying the hot oil over the inner housing of the unit. The housing then transfers the heat to the surrounding air. In the larger fractional horsepower units as seen in Fig. 10-15, the coil (3) is submerged in the oil and partially cooled refrigerant is used for heat removal. The

2. Reenters the compressor passing through the oil cooler coil which is submerged in the compressor oil (3).

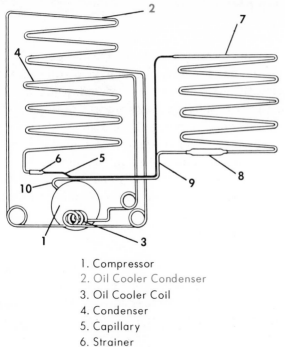

1. Compressor
2. Oil Cooler Condenser
3. Oil Cooler Coil
4. Condenser
5. Capillary
6. Strainer
7. Evaporator
8. Accumulator
9. Heat Exchanger
10. Suction Line

Fig. 10-15. Domestic cycle diagram in which condenser is in two parts. Heat from oil cooler condenser is used to evaporate defrost condensate.

Fig. 10-16. Three types of domestic condenser designs: A—Wire on tube. B—Finned tube. C—Tube on plate or shell.

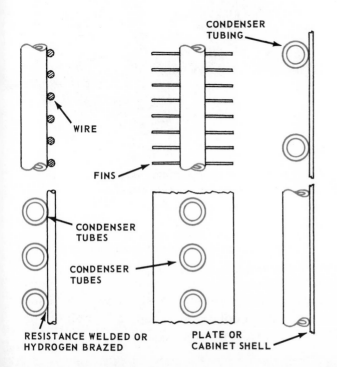

10-6 Condenser Design

Three types of condensers used in hermetic units are:
A. Finned.
B. Wire.
C. Plate.

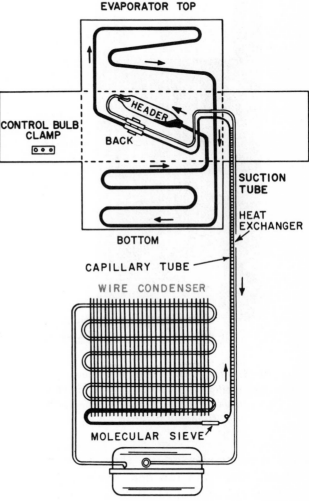

Fig. 10-17. Natural convection wire condenser. Wires are usually resistance welded to condenser tubes.

Fig. 10-16 shows the three types of condensers. Fig. 10-17 shows a wire condenser unit while Fig. 10-18 shows a plate type condenser. These two latter types are usually static or natural convection condensers. Condensers that do not use a fan to provide forced air are sometimes called static condensers.

The condenser is usually made of copper or steel tubing with either copper, tin dipped or aluminum fins. In the fan cooled

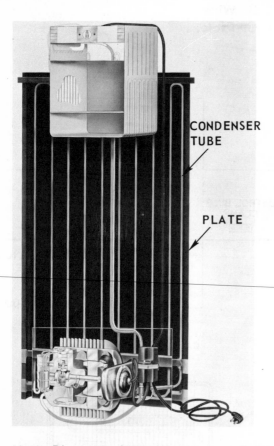

Fig. 10-18. Plate type hermetic system condenser. Note that tubing is attached to large sheet of metal for maximum air contact and "chimney effect." (General Electric Co.)

fin type condenser, a shroud is usually placed over the fan and condenser to increase the control of air flow over the condenser, Fig. 10-19. Some companies install air-in and air-out ducts to improve the condenser cooling and also to decrease noise. These ducts are usually made of some acoustic (noise absorbing) substance, such as felt or cardboard.

It is important that these ducts remain intact and that the air flow does not become restricted. These ducts should be cleaned at least twice a year.

The plate condenser is the easiest of the three to manufacture and clean externally. However, it is more bulky in order to provide sufficient cooling area and takes up more space than the other two types. Another design of the plate condenser is accomplished by soldering, brazing, or welding the condenser coil to the inside surface of the outer cabinet shell.

10-7 Evaporator Coils

Many evaporator coil designs are being used. The shape of the evaporator coil depends to a considerable extent on the use of the coil, space allotted to the coil and type of refrigerant control.

Evaporator coils are made of copper, aluminum or stainless steel. Some evaporators are stamped or formed into sections which include the refrigerant tubes, the collector headers, and the shelves all in one piece. The complete unit takes the form of a freezer chest.

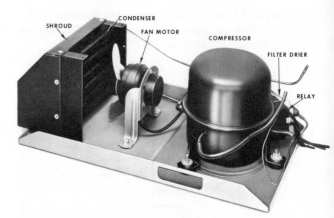

Fig. 10-19. Fan cooled condensing unit with shroud over condenser to help direct air flow. (Kelvinator Div., American Motors)

Refrigeration cabinet evaporators may be divided into six general groups:

1. Freezer chest located in refrigerator cabinet with spill-over air used to cool remainder of cabinet as shown in Fig. 10-20.

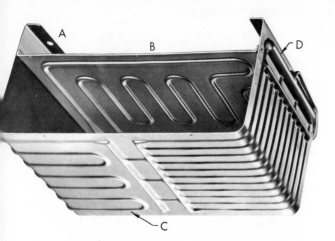

Fig. 10-20. *One-piece type evaporator coil in which tubes, headers, and shelves are formed in single piece. A—Mounting bracket. B—Shelf. C—Refrigerant passage. D—Accumulator.*
(Houdaille-Hershey Corp.)

2. Independent freezer chest located in freezer compartment and a cold plate located in food section, Fig. 10-21.

3. Finned evaporator located in freezer section using fan for forced air circulation and an aluminum cold plate located in normal food section, Fig. 10-22.

4. Finned evaporator located in freezer section with use of fan and duct work to provide cooling to freezer compartment and food compartment, Figs. 10-23 and 10-24.

5. Two independent refrigeration units, one for freezer section and one for food compartment.

6. Secondary evaporator condenser for freezer compartment and conventional evaporator system for food compartment.

Any of these methods for cooling the freezer compartment may also be used to cool the normal refrigerated foods compartment.

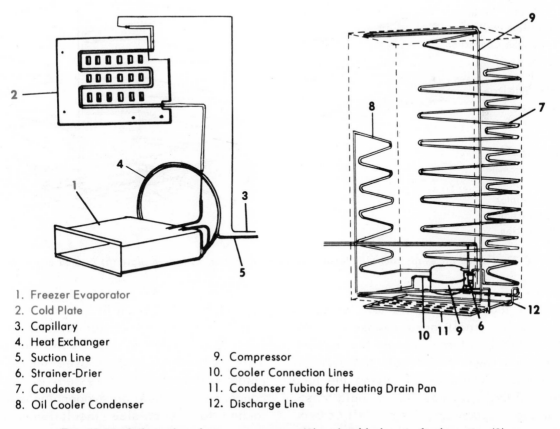

1. Freezer Evaporator
2. Cold Plate
3. Capillary
4. Heat Exchanger
5. Suction Line
6. Strainer-Drier
7. Condenser
8. Oil Cooler Condenser
9. Compressor
10. Cooler Connection Lines
11. Condenser Tubing for Heating Drain Pan
12. Discharge Line

Fig. 10-21. *Independent freezer evaporator (1) and cold plate in food section (2).*
(Franklin Div. of Studebaker Corp.)

The ideal domestic refrigerator should quickly freeze ice cubes, freeze foods, provide storage for frozen foods, and provide a nondrying (high humidity) refrigerated space for storage of open and perishable foods.

To accomplish this triple function, several types of evaporator coil designs are used. (A) One evaporator coil held to a low temperature may be used to make ice cubes compartments in the cabinet, one compartment for ice cubes and frozen foods, and the other compartment for fresh produce. This design is more expensive since it means using two evaporator coils, equipped with either a two-temperature valve, secondary cooling system, overflow coil with restriction between the two coils, or two condensing units. (C) One of the simplest and most effective solutions is to use a

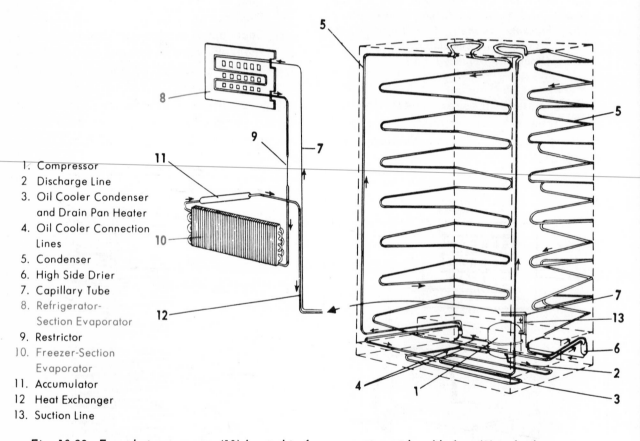

1. Compressor
2. Discharge Line
3. Oil Cooler Condenser and Drain Pan Heater
4. Oil Cooler Connection Lines
5. Condenser
6. High Side Drier
7. Capillary Tube
8. Refrigerator-Section Evaporator
9. Restrictor
10. Freezer-Section Evaporator
11. Accumulator
12. Heat Exchanger
13. Suction Line

Fig. 10-22. Forced air evaporator (10) located in freezer section with cold plate (8) in food compartment.

and keep frozen foods. Its low temperature and its small area exposed to the large cabinet volume, keeps the cabinet temperature nearly correct; however, it has the disadvantages of drying the food quite rapidly. This results in rapid frosting of the evaporator coils as well as producing low humidity in the cabinet. (B) Some manufacturers have provided two secondary refrigerant in a separate evaporator coil and condenser system sealed from the regular system as in Fig. 10-25. This secondary system uses the evaporator coil of the first system to cool its condenser. It has an evaporator coil attached to the outside (insulation side) of the inner lining of the cabinet or a finned coil, located in the rear of the inside of the cabinet. One manufacturer called the arrangement a "Cold Wall." (D) Others use a large surface coil for the high humidity, 35 F. to 45 F. portion of the cabinet. (E) A two-temperature system that uses a solenoid valve to produce the two temperatures is shown in Fig. 10-26. When the thermostat in the food compartment

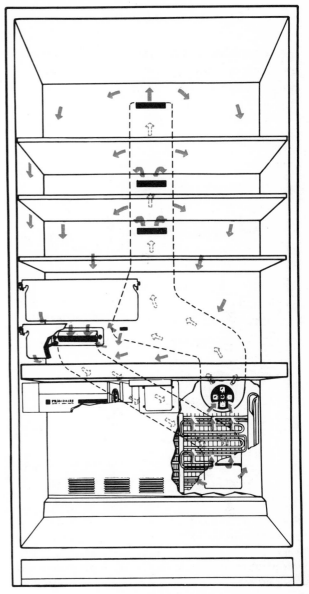

Fig. 10-24. Finned evaporator. Note ducts which carry cooled air to narrow parts of refrigerated cabinet. (Frigidaire Div., General Motors Corp.)

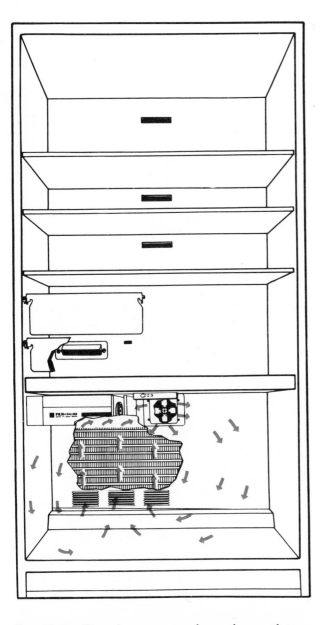

Fig. 10-23. Finned evaporator located near freezer compartment. Note flow of air across evaporator coil and in cabinet part of freezer compartment.

calls for more cooling, the solenoid valve closes and the refrigerant passes the plate coil before it reaches the freezer coil. When the food compartment is cool enough, the solenoid valve is energized and opens as shown in Fig. 10-27. The refrigerant then bypasses the plate coil, due to ease of flow. The thermostat operated by the freezer coil cycles the motor-compressor unit.

10-8 Forced Convection Coils

A popular design uses forced convection evaporator coils. Finned coils using fans and motors cool the air, which is then force-circulated around the food. These

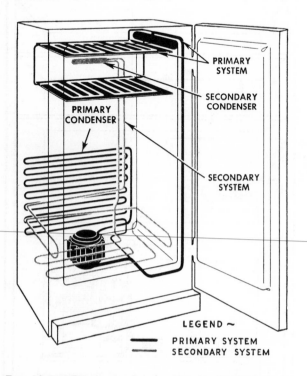

Fig. 10-25. Diagram of secondary refrigeration circuit. Evaporator coil in freezing compartment (primary circuit) contacts condenser coil of secondary refrigeration circuit by temperature difference only. Both primary and secondary systems are charged with same kind of refrigerant.

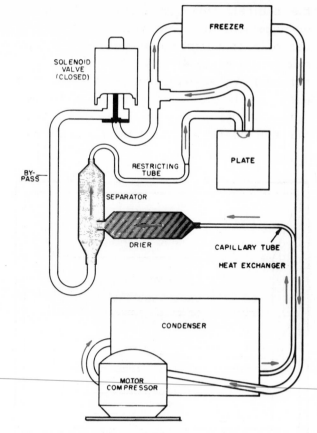

Fig. 10-26. Refrigeration cycle that uses solenoid bypass to control plate temperature. Valve is closed and plate is being cooled.
(Philco Corp.)

coils are mounted in a duct system which enables the evaporator coil to be mounted outside the cooling compartment. This design uses the fan operation to control the temperature of the food compartment. In this arrangement the refrigerator and freezer sections are separated and insulated from one another by a divider. Air is drawn into the return ducts through openings in both compartments, then passed across the evaporator where it is chilled, and the moisture is removed and deposited

as frost on the coils. This action eliminates all frost from the interior of the cabinet and the foods compartment. See Fig. 10-28.

Cold dry air is discharged through the fan openings into the freezer section, the remainder of the air is directed into the refrigerator air duct opening in the back of the lined wall. An air flow control, or baffle, to allow the proper amount of cold air into the food compartment, is used in the cold air duct when a single evaporating coil and fan is used. In some units a separate evaporator and fan are used in the freezer and refrigerator sections. Fig. 10-29 shows a freezer section for a forced convection bottom type freezer compartment.

In the air circulation system of a single fan unit as shown in Fig. 10-30, a two-speed fan is sometimes used to deliver air to both the freezer and refrigerator compartments. The operation of the fan is continuous except during the defrost cycle, or when the freezer door is opened.

The operation of the two-speed fan is dependent upon the fan thermostat located in the refrigerant compartment. As the temperature in this compartment increases, the need for more cooling occurs and the fan automatically runs at a higher speed. When the proper temperature is reached the fan switches back to the low speed. An air flow control is used in conjunction with the single evaporator coil fan to direct the air flow to the proper compartment as needed.

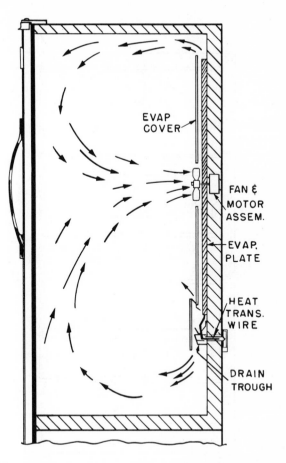

Fig. 10-28. *Forced convection evaporator coil. Note use of cover over evaporator to improve air distribution. (Kelvinator Div., American Motors Corp.)*

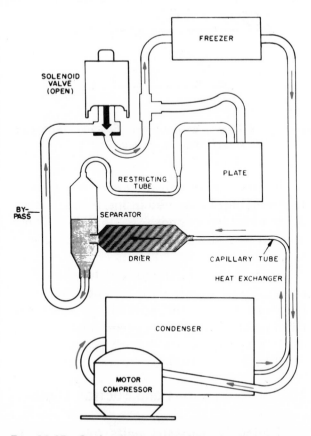

Fig. 10-27. *Cycle that uses solenoid valve to control plate temperature. Valve is open and refrigerant is bypassing the plate coil which therefore is not being refrigerated.*

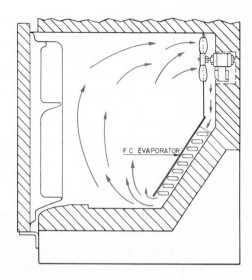

Fig. 10-29. *Bottom type freezer section. Note forced connection fan and path of air flow through evaporator coil.*

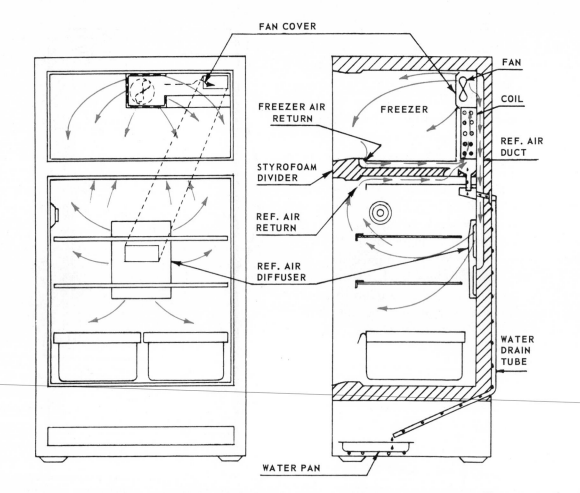

Fig. 10-30. Single fan circulates air through both refrigerator and freezer compartment. Fan runs with condensing unit "on" cycle but will be "off" when freezer door is opened.

The operation of a unit containing a fan in both the refrigerator and freezer compartments is similar to the single fan unit. Fig. 10-29 shows a forced convection cooled freezer compartment. In this type of system the fans are single speed and operate independently of each other. The unit cycling thermostat located in the freezer compartment controls the cycling of the unit and the operation of the fans. The refrigerator compartment fan is also controlled by the operation of an independent air flow thermostat. Both fans are connected in series with their respective door switches and the automatic defrosting unit, so the fan will not operate when the door is open or during the defrosting cycle.

In this type of unit a freezer thermostat (air sensing) is located in the freezer compartment. Its purpose is to control the operation of the compressor and condenser fan.

Some form of automatic defrost cycling is also used on this unit. Its operation may be dependent on the number of times the refrigerator door is opened and closed, or it may be a clock type defroster as described in Par. 10-14.

10-9 Liquid Lines and Suction Lines

Tubing in domestic units may be made of copper, steel, or aluminum. Tubing joints in domestic units are either soft soldered or silver brazed. The tubing is attached permanently to the evaporator unit and condensing unit and the mechanism must be removed from the cabinet to separate the joints. Usually the liquid line and suction line are permanently fastened together to provide efficient heat exchange.

Copper or steel tubing is usually brazed to the condenser and motor-compressor as these parts are also of copper or steel. Where evaporators are made of aluminum, attachments cannot be silver brazed to them. The manufacturer, in some cases, flash welds (a resistance welding operation) a short length of copper tubing to the aluminum tubing of the coil. This copper tubing must be left connected to the aluminum evaporator coil during service operations so it may be easily connected into the system after the service operation has been completed.

The tubing should be kept from rattling (vibrating) or rubbing against cabinet or mechanism parts. Grommets are usually used where tubing passes through walls to minimize the chance of vibration or rubbing damage.

You should always avoid putting a strain (pulling) or sharply bending the tubing as this may rupture the tubing. For more information on tubing, refer to Chapter 2.

10-10 Air Flow Control

In refrigerators using a forced air evaporator coil with a single fan, some type of air flow control must be used in the duct connecting the freezer compartment and the normal food compartment to prevent equalizing of temperatures. Some units have a manual adjustable damper to restrict the air flow, some have automatic dampers operated by a thermostatic control. By adjusting the thermostatic control for the damper, varying temperatures can be obtained in the normal food compartment. However, it is recommended that the flow control setting be adjusted simultaneously with the thermostatic control.

The control damper extends into the duct and its movement is controlled by the setting of the thermostatic control. The temperature of the normal food compartment is determined by the amount of air allowed to enter this section. Many units use a small heating element next to the bellows of the air control. This heating element helps to offset the passing cool air which might cause the bellows to act ahead of time. Without this heating element the damper may close too soon. An air flow control installation is shown in Fig. 10-31.

10-11 Electrical Circuits

The electrical circuits on all domestic hermetic mechanisms are similar.

A typical circuit is shown in Fig. 10-32. Power to the refrigerator is obtained

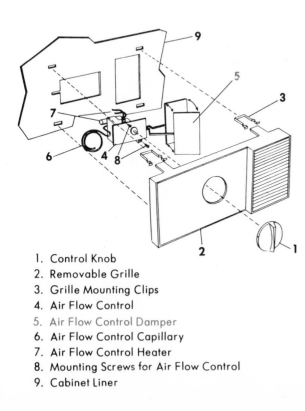

1. Control Knob
2. Removable Grille
3. Grille Mounting Clips
4. Air Flow Control
5. Air Flow Control Damper
6. Air Flow Control Capillary
7. Air Flow Control Heater
8. Mounting Screws for Air Flow Control
9. Cabinet Liner

Fig. 10-31. An "exploded" diagram of an air flow control damper. Note movement limits of damper.

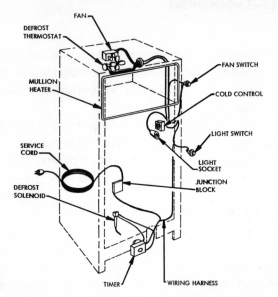

Fig. 10-32. Arrangement of electrical wiring in a typical refrigerator cabinet. (Norge Div., Borg-Warner Corp.)

Fig. 10-33. Wiring diagram of conventional hermetic refrigerator which has an electrical heating coil for defrost. (Hotpoint Co.)

through a supply cord usually of No. 14 stranded wire. This cord is connected to a junction box mounted on the condensing unit. The junction box often houses the motor starting relay. A wiring diagram in a domestic refrigerator is shown in Fig. 10-33.

A three-wire cord extends from the junction box to the refrigerator cabinet. The three wires (usually white, black, and red or green) are used for the cabinet light and the motor control, thermostat, etc. It is general practice that the black wire is the "hot" wire and goes from the plug up to the motor control. The white wire returns from the motor control, down through the junction box, into the relay and then into the motor. The third wire is red or green and carries the current from the light switch and back to the white wire of the extension cord, as shown in Fig. 10-34.

Fig. 10-34. Wiring diagram for hermetic refrigerator which incorporates heating coil to keep frozen foods door joint from sweating. Note motor-compressor wiring diagram in lower left hand corner.

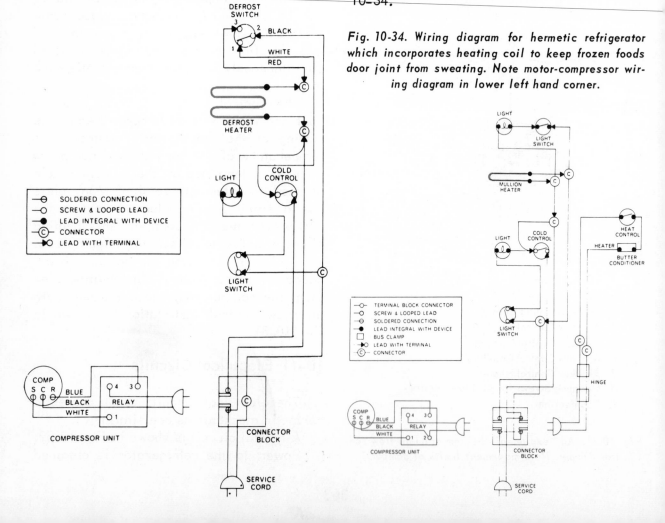

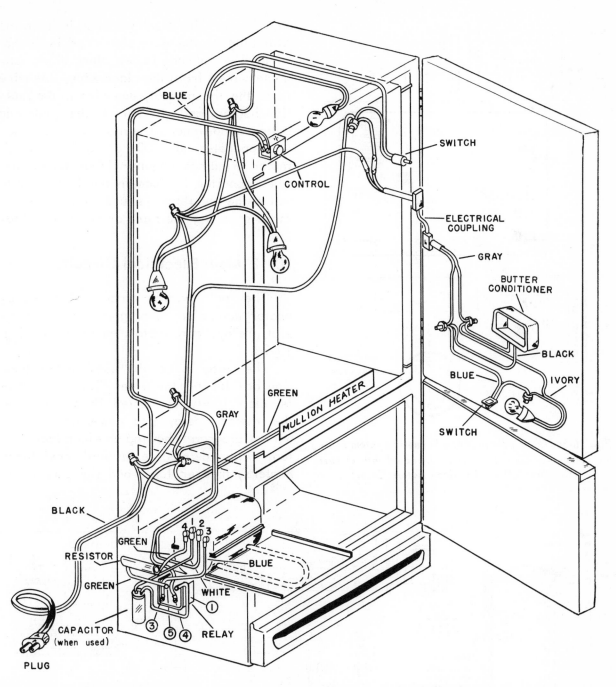

Fig. 10-35. Pictorial drawing of the wiring in a refrigerator. Note mechanical connections used. The number and color code is similar to those commonly used. The compressor motor has four terminals as it is a 3400 rpm motor and uses an auxiliary winding.

Most of the electrical connectors are of the mechanical type. Even the terminals on the end of the wires are mechanically attached to the wires. Stranded wires should never be wrapped around terminal posts. Always use approved wire terminals.

The wiring of a refrigerator that uses a four terminal motor-compressor unit, butter conditioner, mullion heater, cabinet lights and thermostat operated from the fresh foods compartment is shown in Fig. 10-35. A definite color code is followed in

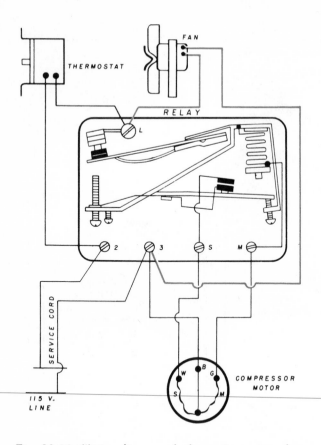

Fig. 10-36. Wiring diagram of a hermetic system showing condenser fan electrically connected into circuit. (Kelvinator Div., American Motors Corp.)

the wiring. The black wire fed in from the wall plug or the extension cord is the hot wire. The current is fed along three separate wires from the black wire. One wire is to the thermostat, one wire to the mullion heater, and one wire to the lights and butter conditioner. The motor-compressor unit operates at 3400 rpm and has three motor windings requiring four terminals. The capacitor is used in the larger units while the resistor is used on all those models having the third or auxiliary winding.

10-12 Main Electrical Circuits

The main wiring circuit of a refrigerator comprises a plug-in cord, thermostat, relay, and motor as shown in Fig. 10-36.

The relay is usually used as the junction box for all the wires. The thermostat is electrically connected in series with the motor, relay and power-in plug. A wiring diagram showing an electrical system with defrost electrical resistance heaters, freezer fans, and lights is shown

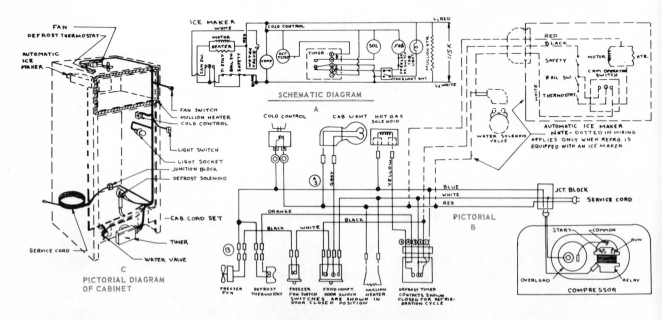

Fig. 10-37. Wiring diagram showing some of the more important parts of a modern refrigerator. (Norge Div., Borg-Warner)

in Fig. 10-37. The light switch and light are located in parallel with the motor. These connections mean that the cabinet light can operate even though the system is not running. The light switch is a spring-loaded switch mounted in the cabinet door jamb, and a switch spring closes the circuit as the door opens.

compressor motor. All of the electricity used by the compressor motor and the fan motor passes through the thermostat switch.

Some refrigerators have small heating elements in the butter compartments. These heating elements keep the butter a few degrees above the normal 35-45 F.

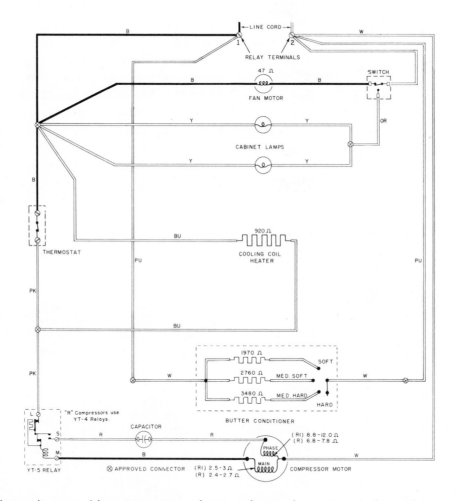

Fig. 10-38. *Wiring diagram of hermetic system showing electrical connections for such items as motor relay, cabinet light, and butter conditioner and thermostat. It also shows connections between starting relay and motor.*

10-13 Electrical Circuit Accessories

Many refrigerators also have other electrical accessories. Some have motor driven fans to help cool the condensers. The fan motor is connected in series with the thermostat and is parallel with the

compartment temperature. The resistance is connected in the system in parallel with the other units. It has its own thermostat. See Fig. 10-38.

Occasionally the breaker strips around the freezer compartment door will sweat or frost. Formerly double rows of gaskets were used to minimize this condition, but at present small electrical resistance wires are mounted in back of the breaker strips to eliminate this condition. Fig. 10-39 illustrates a wiring diagram of a domestic unit. In addition to a mullion and

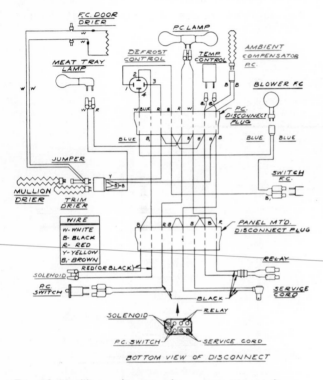

Fig. 10-39. *Wiring diagram of two-compartment domestic refrigerator. Note defrost control unit, solenoid, and ambient compensator.*
(Kelvinator Div., American Motors Corp.)

trim heater, it has an ambient compensator adjacent to the provision compartment and temperature control to prevent condensation from forming on the control and keep it operating correctly.

Some refrigerators have a small heating element mounted inside the cabinet liner near the evaporator of the nonfreezer section of the box. This heating element operates during the time the unit is not running and prevents condensation from forming on the cabinet liner. See Fig. 10-40.

Ultraviolet ray lights are used in some refrigerators as an air purifying agent.

These lights operate from a transformer. The electrical circuit is in parallel with the other main units of the system.

10-14 Defrosting Systems

The method of defrosting domestic refrigerators has improved considerably in the past few years. Some years ago defrosting was accomplished by shutting off the system until the frost melted and then turning the units on again manually or automatically. Trays which caught the defrost water were emptied manually.

Since the development of frozen food compartments in domestic refrigerators a better way had to be developed for defrosting. The new systems defrost the coils quickly to prevent raising the temperature of the frozen foods, and the defrost water is removed from the cabinet automatically.

There are five principal ways in which

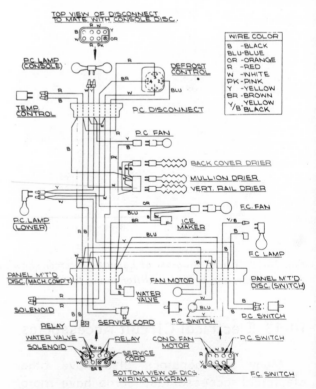

Fig. 10-40. *Wiring diagram for two-compartment refrigerator having a back cover drier heating element to insure against condensation forming on cabinet.*

the automatic defrost interval is determined. The mechanisms for each are different. These methods are:

1. Daily by clock timing.
2. Accumulated running time of the condensing unit.
3. Accumulated door open time.
4. Counted number of door openings.
5. Defrosting during each off cycle.

The daily clock timing system uses an electric clock mechanism wired into the electric circuit to defrost the refrigerator daily at a time at which the clock is set. This time is usually set sometime after midnight. It may be set to suit the wishes of the owner. The length of the automatic defrost is approximately 12 minutes and during this time the blower fan is in operation. During the defrost interval the automatic defrost system will operate the heater coils or hot gas defrost. In some instances a Thermo-disc control located on the evaporator, is set to turn on the system when a temperature of approximately 55 F. is reached or the specified length of time of defrost period is achieved.

Accumulated running time of the condensing unit defrosting is timed by means of an electric clock mechanism connected in parallel with the compressor motor. The clock will run all of the time that the compressor is operating. The clock mechanism is set to operate the automatic defrost after a certain number of hours of operation of the condensing unit (usually about eight to twelve hours). This interval of defrosting is adjustable to accomodate various conditions of use of the refrigerator.

Accumulated door open time also times the defrost interval through an electric clock mechanism which operates the automatic defrost after a total number of minutes that the refrigerator door has stood open. The principle of this timing is based on the fact that each time the refrigerator door is opened, the cold air in the cabinet spills out. Part of the moisture in this air has been deposited on the evaporator coil

and as the door is opened, fresh moisture laden air enters and will be deposited on the evaporator coil. Frequent and prolonged opening of the cabinet door will hasten frost accumulation on the evaporator coil. This defrost timing device, therefore, provides automatic defrosting on the basis of cabinet use.

The counted number of door openings defrost interval is based on the same principle as the accumulated door open time. Instead of using a clock mechanism, a ratchet mechanism on the door operates the automatic defrost system. After a certain number of door openings (usually about 60) the automatic device will be brought into operation.

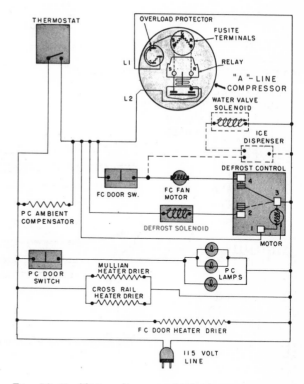

Fig. 10-41. Wiring diagram which shows circuits and controls for hot gas type automatic defrost system.

A popular system used in the no-frost refrigerator is to defrost the evaporator coil during each off part of the cycle. These automatic defrost systems control the length of the defrost time by a thermostat

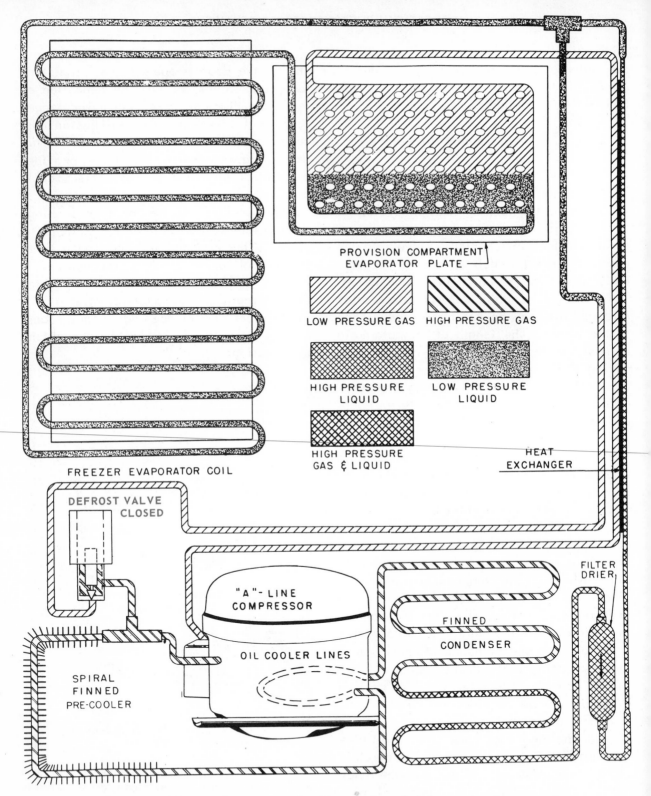

Fig. 10-42. *Diagram showing normal cooling cycle with defrost valve deenergized.*

Labels in figure:
PROVISION COMPARTMENT
EVAPORATOR PLATE

LOW PRESSURE GAS   HIGH PRESSURE GAS

HIGH PRESSURE
LIQUID

LOW PRESSURE
LIQUID

HIGH PRESSURE
GAS & LIQUID

HEAT
EXCHANGER

FREEZER EVAPORATOR COIL

DEFROST VALVE
CLOSED

"A"-LINE
COMPRESSOR

OIL COOLER LINES

FINNED

CONDENSER

FILTER
DRIER

SPIRAL
FINNED
PRE-COOLER

attached to the evaporator coil. Automatic defrosting is accomplished by stopping refrigeration and rapidly heating the evaporator coil.

The two sources of heat used to quickly defrost the coils are:
1. Hot condenser gas (vapor).
2. Electrical heating coils.

Primarily, all of the automatic defrost systems depend on electrical controls for their operation. Fig. 10-41 shows a domestic refrigerating wiring diagram with the conventional automatic defrost controls connected into the circuits.

10-15 Hot Gas Defrost Systems

To defrost the evaporator coil with hot gas, the hot gas coming from the compressor is temporarily circulated into the evaporator where it melts the frost from within. The vapor then returns to the compressor.

The mechanism consists of a solenoid valve located in a bypass line running from the outlet of the compressor to the evaporator as in Fig. 10-42. This illustration shows an automatic defrost system on the refrigerating cycle. The liquid refrigerant flows through the freezer evaporator coil on its way to the provision compartments refrigerated plate. Heat is first absorbed from the freezer compartment and any extra liquid refrigerant passes upward to cool the food storage area.

The lubricating oil has the ability to absorb refrigerant in increasing amounts as oil temperatures are reduced and releases refrigerant as oil temperatures are increased. On the "off" cycle, the compressor and the oil will absorb some of the refrigerant in the unit, leaving an insufficient amount of refrigerant to refrigerate both coils completely. At the beginning of the "on" cycle, all of the available refrigerant will be evaporated in the lower freezer coils and little or no refrigerant will reach the upper coils. During this period, frost on the upper plate may melt. After the compressor has operated for a few minutes and has warmed up, the oil will release the absorbed refrigerant and this additional refrigerant will pass to the upper refrigerant plates.

The thermostat contact bulb is attached to the upper refrigerated plate so the com-

pressor will continue to operate until the upper plate has been completely refrigerated. The freezer compartment will continue to be refrigerated during the entire "on" cycle while the food storage space will receive cooling during only a part of the cycle. In this manner the refrigerated food space is maintained at a satisfactory temperature automatically.

The automatic defrost cycle places the mechanism on the defrost cycle once every 8 hours. Its operation is shown in Fig. 10-43. On the defrost cycle, a solenoid

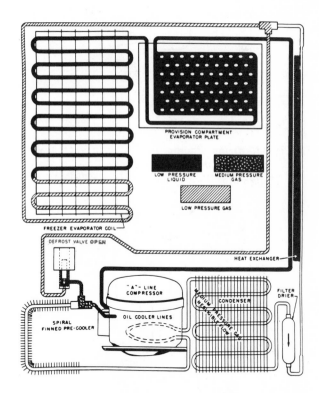

Fig. 10-43. Diagram showing defrosting cycle with defrost valve energized.

valve opens and directs the flow of warm refrigerant vapor from the compressor directly to the lower freezer coils. This hot vapor helps melt the frost which has accumulated on the evaporator coils. The warm vapor is then drawn back down the suction line to the compressor. An electric heater which is mounted on the bottom of the

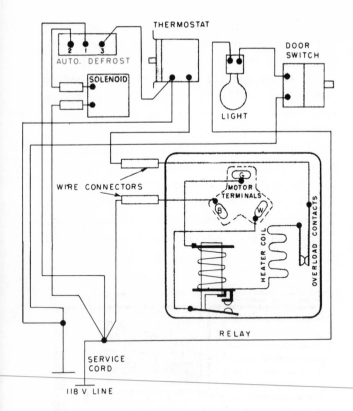

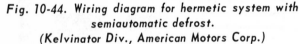

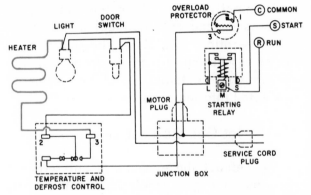

Fig. 10-46. Electrical defrost system which is started by means of a push button and which automatically returns to its normal cycle. Note overload protection for motor-compressor and current type relay. (Franklin Mfg. Co.)

freezer compartment is also turned on during the defrost cycle to prevent any freeze-up of the drain at the bottom of the compartment, and to remove any frost

Fig. 10-44. Wiring diagram for hermetic system with semiautomatic defrost. (Kelvinator Div., American Motors Corp.)

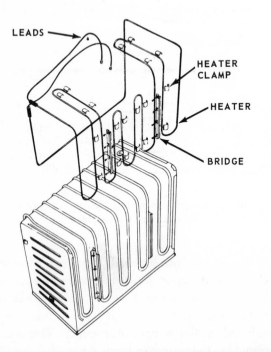

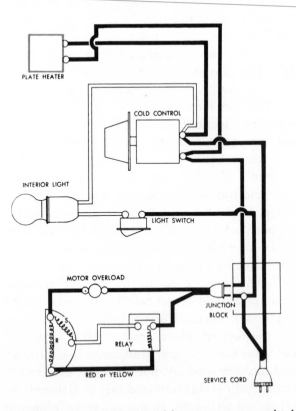

Fig. 10-45. Electrical heating unit applied to an evaporator coil and used to provide automatic defrost facilities.

Fig. 10-47. Wiring diagram of hermetic system which uses electrical resistance defrost unit that is turned on manually and which automatically returns to normal operation. (Norge Div., Borg-Warner Corp.)

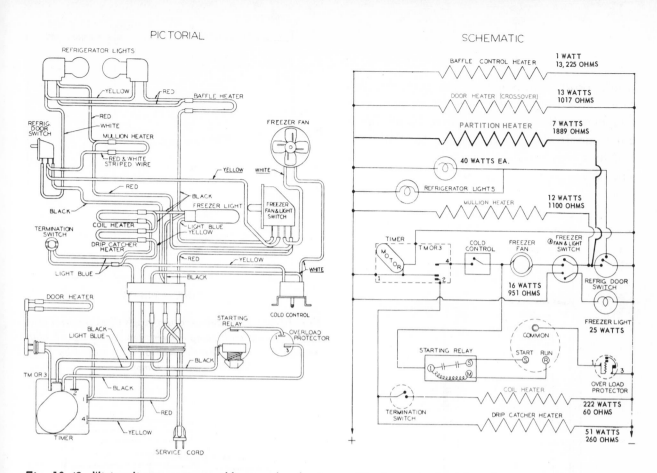

Fig. 10-48. Wiring diagram using coil heater, door heater, mullion heater and partition heater to prevent sweating.

that may have formed on the interior of the walls of the freezer. The defrost cycle continues until the temperature of the defrost control bulb rises to approximately 40 F., or for one hour -- whichever occurs first.

The defrost control will return the system to normal operation after the defrost interval.

Some semiautomatic systems require opening the solenoid valve with a manual electric switch. When the defrost is complete, a slight rise in temperature activates a sensitive bulb which returns the system to normal operation. Fig. 10-44 shows the wiring diagram for this type of automatic defrost.

10-16 Electric Heater Defrost System

To defrost the unit with electrical heating elements requires installing heating coils or electrical resistance wires be-

neath those parts of the coils needing defrosting, as shown in Fig. 10-45. The resistance wires are placed to melt the frost from the coils in a minimum of time. These coils are rated at 400 watts and up. The system is automatically shut off during the defrost cycle and a thermostat returns the unit to normal operation after the coil is defrosted. The electrical heating elements are well insulated, and the circuit is usually equipped with a fuse. Some of these circuits have a safety thermostat which will open the circuit in case the temperature rise is too high. Fig. 10-46 shows the wiring circuit of an electrical defrost system which is started by pressing a push button. After defrost, it is automatically returned to normal operation. Fig. 10-47 is another semiautomatic electrical defrosting system. The wiring diagram of a full automatic system is shown in Fig. 10-48. The water collected may be disposed of in several ways. Some systems run the defrost water down to a pan near the compressor-motor where the heat from the compressor evaporates it, as shown in Fig. 10-49. Some units drain the water into a special tray and this tray must be periodically emptied. The drain pipe usually has a liquid trap.

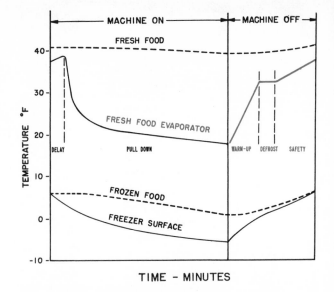

Fig. 10-50. Time-temperature graph of evaporator coil temperatures and compartment temperatures of two-door refrigerator. The thermostat is operated by fresh food evaporator temperature.

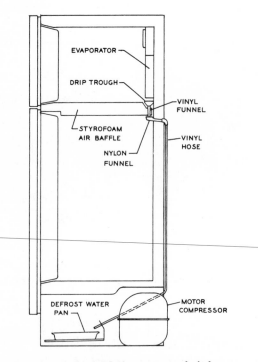

Fig. 10-49. A method of disposing of defrost water through use of heat generated by motor-compressor and temperature difference between cool water and condenser.

One refrigerator uses a thermostat actuated by the fresh foods evaporator. The freezer section evaporator is in series with the fresh foods coil. A graph of the temperature time relationship for an automatic defrost refrigerator is shown in Fig. 10-50.

When the unit first starts at a fresh foods coil temperature of 37.5 F., the fresh foods coil will warm up a little but the freezer coil immediately starts to become colder (starts at 8 F.). As the unit runs the fresh foods coil temperature lowers quickly and the freezer coil slowly. At the end of the running cycle, the fresh foods evaporating temperature opens the thermostat

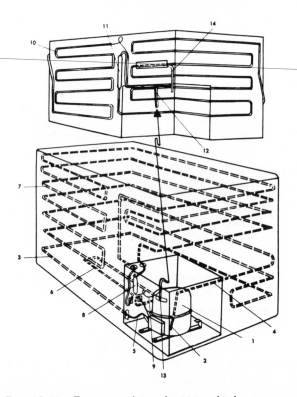

Fig. 10-51. Freezer cabinet liner in which evaporator coils are attached directly to outside of inner liner surface. The condenser coils are attached to inside of outer shell. 1—Compressor. 2—Discharge line. 3—Oil cooler condenser. 4—Oil cooler inlet line. 5—Oil cooler outlet line. 6—Bottom coil. 7—Condenser. 8—Drier strainer. 9—Capillary tube. 10—Evaporator. 11—Accumulator. 12—Heat exchanger. 13—Suction line. 14—Control well. (Franklin Div., Studebaker Corp.)

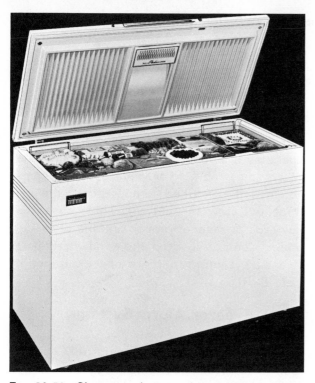

Fig. 10-52. *Chest type domestic freezer. In this freezer evaporator coils are attached to outside of inner liner.*

were obtained with the refrigerator operating in a 100 F. room. It should be noted that the temperature of both the fresh food and frozen food varied very little during the entire cycle time.

10-17 Evaporating Coil Design for Frozen Food Refrigerators

There are three common designs of evaporating coils used in frozen food freezers. They are shell liner, plate or shelf and forced convection coil.

The shell liner is shown in Figs. 10-51 and 10-52. In this diagram the evaporator coils are located adjacent to the inner liner of the freezer cabinet and between the inner and outer shell of the cabinet. The plate or shelf type as shown in Fig. 10-53 and the forced convection coil as shown in Fig. 10-54 are used in many upright freezer in-

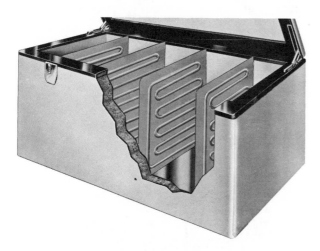

Fig. 10-53. *Freezer cabinet using refrigerant plates. (Kold-Hold Mfg. Co.)*

at approximately 17.5 F. and the freezer coil has cooled to -5 F. During the off cycle the fresh foods coil must warm up past 32 F. (defrost temperature) and up to 37 F. before the unit starts running again. The dotted line at the top represents the fresh food temperature during the cycle. The bottom dotted line indicates the frozen food temperature during the cycle. The curves

Fig. 10-54. *Forced convection coil used in upright freezer; note use of drain heater to evaporate condensation formed on defrost cycle. (Kelvinator Div., American Motors Corp.)*

stallations. Most of the chest type freezers use the tank or liner type coil. Some of the chest types and upright types use a plate coil. A recent innovation in upright freezers has been the nonfrost forced convection freezer. The operating principle of this unit is basically the same as that of the forced convection evaporating coil used in domestic units as explained in Par. 10-8.

10-18 Freezer Refrigerants

Refrigerants for freezers should be capable of giving the desired low temperatures, -10 F. to -20 F., at approximately atmospheric low side pressure. The high side pressure should not be excessive. The gas volume pumped must be small in order to keep the size of the compressor at a minimum.

Three refrigerants often used, which meet freezer requirements, are R-12 and R-22 and R-502. See Paragraphs 9-6, 9-7, and 9-10, for characteristics of these refrigerants.

10-19 Freezer Refrigerant Controls

The small modern frozen foods cabinets generally use a capillary tube as a refrigerant control. For a description of this control see Par. 6-28. Some units employ a thermostatic expansion valve as the refrigerant control. See Par. 6-9 for a discussion of this valve. Older cabinets may be found with a low side float valve, but these are no longer produced. Some experimenting has been done using high side floats.

10-20 Freezer Motor Controls

Home and farm type freezers usually employ a thermostatic motor control designed for a lower temperature setting but otherwise identical to the domestic refrigerator type. The controls are explained in Par. 8-11.

Some larger farm type freezers and locker plants use a thermostat and liquid line solenoid valve and a pressure motor control to control the box temperature (see Par. 13-35). The thermostat in the cabinet operates a solenoid valve in the liquid line. When the cabinet or refrigerated space reaches the desired temperature, the refrigerant flow is shut off. This causes the low side pressure to drop and the pressure motor control to stop the condensing unit. Pressure motor controls are explained in Par. 8-10.

10-21 Freezer Alarm Systems

Since frozen foods cabinets may contain food worth a considerable amount of money, and a rise in temperature could cause con-

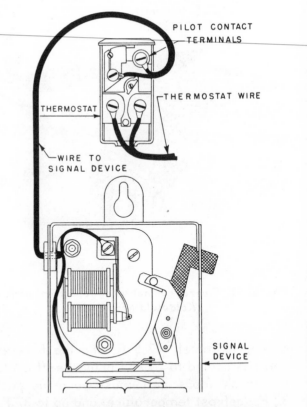

Fig. 10-55. Typical freezer alarm system. Battery operated unit is independent of electrical power failure. It must be connected to thermostat or to special unit thermostat. Batteries are good for 50 hours, or 12 months idle time. It has both a sound and a visible indicator.

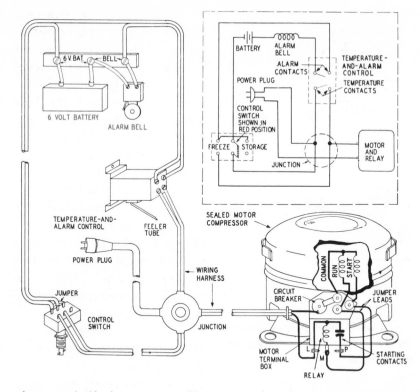

Fig. 10-56. Wiring diagram of 6V alarm system. Thermostat also includes alarm switch. Alarm bell will ring if for any reason there is an excessive temperature rise. (Philco Corp.)

siderable spoilage, some device is needed to warn the consumer in case the unit fails. There are several types of alarm systems on the market, but basically they are similar. They consist of a control bulb suspended inside the cabinet which is connected to a mechanism which operates a light, a bell, a buzzer or other signaling device.

A source of electrical power completes the system. The source of power may be batteries as shown in Fig. 10-55, or a transformer may be connected to any other electrical circuit in the house except the one to which the freezer is connected.

In operation, if the freezer temperature rises above a safe limit, it causes the control to close and complete the electrical circuit. This causes the light to operate or the bell or buzzer to ring. The alarm should start to operate when the compartment temperature reaches 15 F. The alarm control bulb should be located near the food that would become warm first. If the alarm circuit type requiring 120V is used, it should be connected to a different circuit than the one operating the unit. If a battery type alarm is used, the batteries should be checked at frequent intervals.

A wiring diagram of a 6V alarm system connected into the regular wiring system is shown in Fig. 10-56. The combination thermostat and alarm control will cycle the control, but if the unit will not start, or if the temperature continues to rise, the alarm circuit is closed. The control switch is used to eliminate the cycling control during freezing operations (control is moved to the left). When normal cycling is desired this control switch is moved to the right. If the control switch is left open, it will indicate red.

Some units have what is known as a power interruption signal light. In these units, a signal light is located on the outside of the cabinet. The signal light will

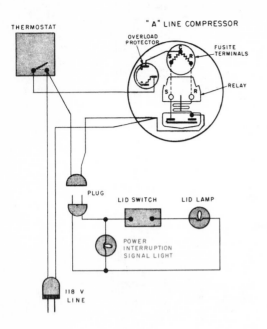

Fig. 10-57. Wiring system which incorporates circuit signal light to indicate when there is an interruption of the circuit.

glow as long as voltage is supplied through the circuit. An interruption of the circuit because of a blown fuse or disconnected plug, will open the circuit, the light will go out and indicate to the owner that there is something wrong. See Fig. 10-57.

It is important to remember that a well-filled frozen food cabinet will maintain a safe temperature for 48 to 72 hours after the unit is stopped, and also that dry ice may be used to maintain below 0 F. temperatures until service can be restored.

10-22 Defrosting Frozen Food Systems

Frost will slowly form on the cold walls of some freezers. This frost must be removed when it interfers with the use of the cabinet or the closing of the lid. A chest type freezer normally needs to be defrosted only once or twice a year. Use only a wooden paddle or a fiber brush to remove the frost. Be careful not to scratch or otherwise damage the inside surface of the cabinet. When a more complete defrosting

job is required or desired, select a time when the food supply in the cabinet is low. Wrap all the food in newspapers or pack it in dry ice, and then proceed to defrost the cabinet by shutting off the power. It is a good idea to wash the inside with baking soda and water. The inside of the cabinet must be thoroughly dry before starting the unit. Replace the food after the cabinet temperature is below 32 F.

On some freezers an automatic defrosting system is used. The arrangement varies according to manufacturer but follows one of the two basic methods, hot gas defrost or resistance heater defrost.

The hot gas defrost has a control with a timer, single-pole, double-throw switch, and a temperature-sensitive power element. The contacts connected in series allow the freezer fan motor to operate at the same time as the condensing unit. During the defrost period, the fan and condens-

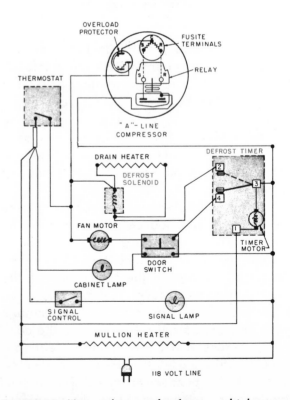

Fig. 10-58. Wiring diagram for freezer which uses a hot gas defrost system. Note defrost solenoid wired to defrost timer.

ing unit circuit No. 4, Fig. 10-58, is open and No. 2 is closed. By completing the circuit through No. 2, the solenoid and drain heater are energized defrosting the evaporator and evaporizing the condensate.

10-23 Freezer Condensing Units

Home and farm freezers employ various types of condensing units. The small home freezer usually has a hermetically sealed

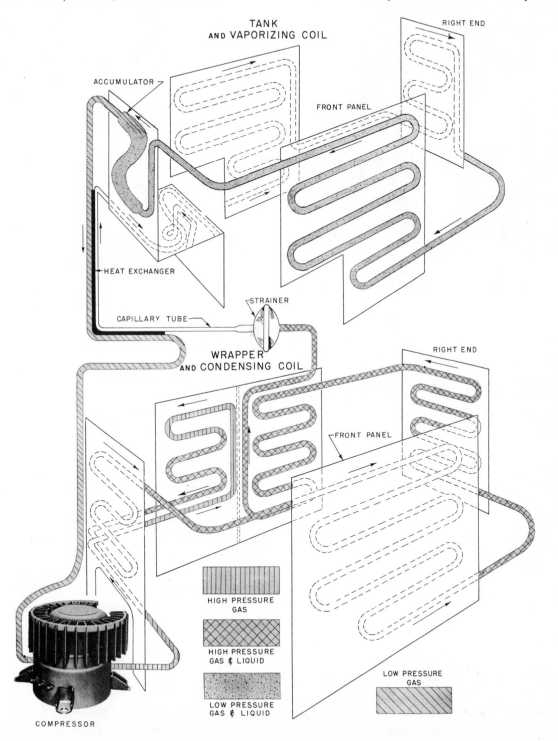

Fig. 10-59. Freezer cabinet refrigerating unit (condenser arrangement).

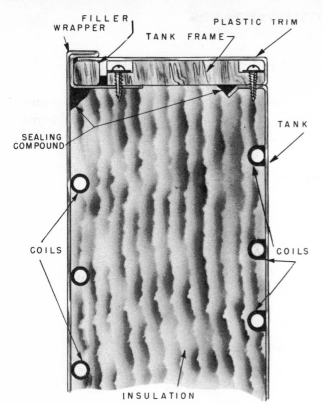

Fig. 10-60. *Wall construction of Kelvinator freezer showing condenser coils (left side) against outer wall of cabinet.*

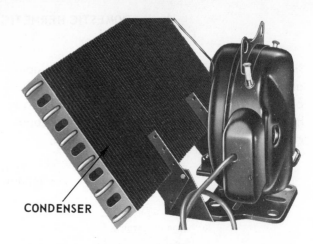

Fig. 10-61. *Sealed unit with natural convection condenser. (Tecumseh Products Co.)*

condensing unit. For complete information on this type of unit, refer to Chapters 4, 12, and 15. Kelvinator has a rather unusual condensing unit arrangement as shown in Figs. 10-59 and 10-60. The condenser for this unit mounted on the inside of the outside shell, is of the plate type. The condensing unit of a frozen food unit must be about 50 percent larger for the same volume cabinet as the typical domestic refrigerator. This increase in size is mainly due to the low suction pressure causing the suction vapor to occupy more volume and the greater difference between the suction pressure and the condenser pressure. Fig. 10-61 illustrates a small freezer condensing unit using a natural convection (static) condenser.

10-24 Freezer Motor-Compressors

Freezer condensing units are manufactured which use a reciprocating or a rotary compressor. Modern models have sealed compressors. Some older models used open-type compressors. Motor-compressors are explained in Paragraphs 4-5 through 4-12.

Motor-compressors used on freezers are similar in design to those used on refrigerators. However, as stated in Par. 10-23, the displacement is larger due to the lower volumetric efficiency of the compressor, since it operates at a lower suction pressure than a refrigerator.

10-25 Freezer Motors

The types of motors used on freezers can be divided into two principal groups. The sealed-type condensing unit uses an induction motor with a starting winding operated by a relay. For more information on induction motors consult Chapter 7. A small fan motor sometimes is used to increase the air flow over the condenser, and it is also of the induction type.

The second type of motor widely used on conventional condensing units is the capacitor type. For more information on this motor, also consult Chapter 7. Fig. 10-62 illustrates a wiring diagram for a hermetic type frozen food cabinet. Note how the warning light is energized by a thermostat built into the same device that controls the cycling of the unit.

A complete wiring diagram for a chest type frozen foods unit is shown in Fig.

10-63. Many of the cabinets use electrical heating elements to prevent sweating and freezing at the door gasket joints. Fig. 10-64 illustrates a wiring diagram showing a mullion coil (heater), a signal light, motor circuit, etc.

10-26 Freezer Condensers

Condensers used on freezers are the same as used on domestic refrigerators. This includes the finned condenser, both forced and natural convection; and the plate condenser. On one model mentioned earlier, Par. 10-6, the condenser is mounted just inside the outside shell while others are placed with the condensing unit. On larger units water-cooled condensers are used, see Chapter 13.

10-27 Freezer Receivers

On some freezing units, particularly older models, the conventional liquid receiver is used. The small home freezers today employing a capillary tube control do not have a separate part for a receiver,

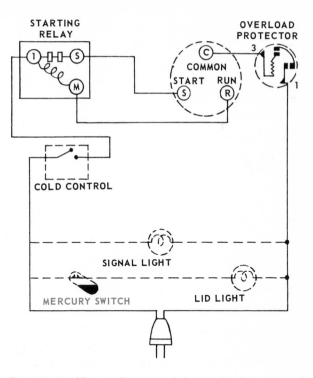

Fig. 10-63. Wiring diagram of frozen foods unit and cabinet. Mercury switch completes lid light circuit when lid is lifted. Signal light is energized while unit is running. (Franklin Mfg. Co.)

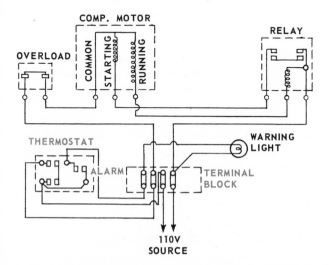

Fig. 10-62. Wiring diagram of frozen foods refrigerating unit. Note relay, terminal block, and warning device with special thermostat.
(Carrier Corp.)

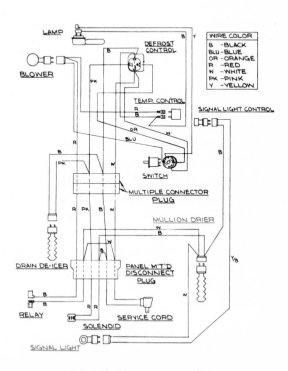

Fig. 10-64. Wiring diagram of domestic freezer. Note mullion drier and signal light.
(Kelvinator Div., American Motors Corp.)

but the lower section of the condenser serves a similar purpose.

It should be noted that in freezers using the capillary tube refrigerant control the greater portion of the liquid refrigerant will remain in the evaporator coils during both the running and off part of the cycle.

10-28 Freezer Belts

Many older models and some recent model condensing units use belts. For more complete information on belts, alignment and care, refer to Chapter 7.

10-29 Freezer Liquid Lines

The liquid lines are now practically all connected by silver brazing. On capillary units, the liquid line is the capillary tube. These liquid lines are generally soldered to the suction line for a distance of two to four feet for heat exchange purposes. They must be carefully mounted to prevent vibration rattles.

10-30 Freezer Suction Lines

Because of the low temperatures, and because some refrigerants tend to frost back, it is sometimes necessary to use heat exchangers to warm the return gas and it may also be necessary to insulate the return line with sponge rubber to prevent sweating and dripping. Mount the suction line carefully to prevent vibration rattles. The suction line fittings are usually silver brazed. The openings into the cabinet where the lines must go to reach the evaporator must be made airtight with some mastic tape, or ice will accumulate. See Fig. 10-65.

10-31 Starting Freezer Units

The first step is to see that the freezer has been located properly for good air circulation and that sufficient space for open-

ing of doors or lids has been provided. The next step is to check the freezer electrical circuit. This circuit should be a separate circuit starting at the main entrance panel, with no other appliances or switches connected to it. This precaution is required by the electrical code in many sections and should be followed in all cases, as any interruption of electric current might become costly to the owner. To actually start the unit, plug it in to the outlet plug and turn the thermostat control knob to the "on" position. There are no valves to be opened on the smaller home freezers using sealed units. On other freezers, check starting instructions supplied by the manufacturer be-

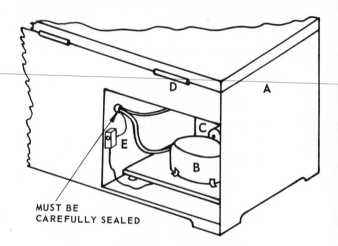

MUST BE
CAREFULLY SEALED

Fig. 10-65. Sealing cabinet openings. A—Cabinet. B—Compressor. C—Condenser. D—Balanced door hinges. E—Motor control.

fore turning on the unit. Be sure to remove the shipping bolts that are used to hold the condensing unit during shipment. Carefully file the warranty and operating instructions for future reference.

10-32 Cycling of Freezers

Cycling time on home and farm freezers cannot very well be stated in definite limits of time. This will vary depending on the amount of storage space being used, on the outside temperature of the box, on the condition of the compressor, etc. Putting food in the cabinet to be frozen will also affect the cycling time. In general, it can be said that the condensing unit will run about one-third of the time. In other words it may run 5 minutes and be off 10 minutes, or it may run 1 hour and be off 2 hours. The important point here is that any unusual change in cycling time should be investigated immediately, as it may indicate that trouble is developing in the system.

10-33 Shutting Down Frozen Food Units

When shutting down a frozen food unit, special precautions should be taken to prevent rusting and to eliminate odor. After the electrical plug has been removed or the current shut off by a switch, allow several hours for the unit to completely defrost. When the defrosting is complete, remove excess water and wash the inside of the cabinet with a solution of baking soda and water. Thoroughly dry the inside of the box. A portable heater set inside the cabinet will speed up this step. Leave the doors or lids ajar slightly to allow circulation of air during the shut down period.

10-34 Freezer Unit Troubles

Home freezers are subject to troubles that may occur in domestic refrigerators (Chapters 11 and 12) and in addition, due to the lower temperature involved, there are some different troubles. These include (a) ice formation, (b) moisture in the system, and (c) wax separation in the system. These will be covered in more detail in the following paragraphs.

10-35 Freezer Ice Accumulation

Ice formation is a condition which will interfere with (a) the operation of the lid or doors, and (b) the running time and tem-

perature of the unit if sufficient accumulation of ice occurs inside the box. Ice forming between the outside and inside liners of the cabinet in the insulation may cause considerable trouble.

The condition mentioned in the preceeding paragraph is usually caused by a leaky gasket seal or the gasket electric heater may not be working. It may be that the seal has lost its life or is broken. In either case, the rubber gasket should be replaced. The trouble may be that the hinges or lock needs adjusting. A flat slip of paper inserted between the door and the cabinet should be held tightly when the lid is closed. If this paper may be pulled out easily, the gasket is not tight enough. The hardware must be adjusted and the gasket replaced.

An excessive accumulation of ice in the food storage space acts as insulation and may result in poor cooling down time for foods placed in the cabinet.

Ice accumulation in the insulation is a more serious trouble as it indicates an air leak in the exterior cabinet seal allowing warm, moist air to enter this space. The warm air being cooled on contact with the inner liner gives up some of its moisture in the form of ice in the insulation or on the liner. If this condition is not corrected, enough ice will eventually build up to buckle the sides of the cabinet.

The only way to remedy this trouble is to remove the insulation, dry out the space between the liners, repack with dry insulation, and completely seal the outside liner against the entrance of air.

Ice accumulation is one of the main troubles occurring with improperly or carelessly constructed units; it also reduces the insulating ability of the cabinet, and the unit will run more.

An accumulation of ice in the insulation of a freezer will generally be indicated by a cold spot on the outside surface of the freezer or by condensation on the outside surface. Also, if the insulation is badly iced up, the condensing unit may run continuously. Iced up insulation will melt and drain if the freezer is shut down and allowed to warm up for a few days.

10-36 Wax in the System

All oils, including those used in refrigeration systems, contain a small amount of wax. This presence of wax has presented a real problem to refrigeration engineers ever since the earliest low-temperature cabinets were built. A small amount of oil circulates with the refrigerant, and due to the sudden expansion occurring at the refrigerant control and the low temperature and pressure at which this expansion occurs, a small amount of wax is separated from the oil and collects in the refrigerant control. It accumulates over a period of time until the refrigerant control becomes restricted or clogged completely. The only remedy after this clogging has occurred, is to remove the valve or capillary tube and clean it or to replace the valve. When servicing frozen foods equipment, be sure to use a thoroughly dewaxed oil.

For ordinary household and commercial refrigeration and in air conditioning service most refrigerant oils are satisfactory. However, for service in food freezers, a completely dewaxed oil is necessary.

Moisture in the system will form in the refrigerant control at the point of expansion. This moisture may be effectively removed by putting a drier in the liquid line. Warm the refrigerant control enough to melt the ice and the dryer will absorb this moisture as it circulates in the system.

10-37 Inefficient condensing Unit

The efficiency of the condensing unit depends on several factors. Each must be considered to determine which is causing the unit to be inefficient. The compressor is the most important factor, and any one of several things may cause it to be inefficient. The most frequent reason is leaking compressor valves. Worn pistons, piston rings, (if used), and/or a worn cylinder bore may all cause inefficient pumping. The motor and its parts (capacitor, relay, etc.) must be checked to determine if it is at fault.

The next most important factor is the condenser and air flow over the condenser. The condenser surface must be clean for highest efficiency. Enough clearance must be allowed around the cabinet for free movement of the air into and through the condenser.

Various parts of the condensing unit must be checked carefully and put in good condition to get top efficiency from the unit.

10-38 Servicing Frozen Food Unit

For servicing the open type condensing units, refer to Chapter 15. For servicing hermetic units, refer to Chapter 12. The procedures vary greatly due to the differences in cabinet design and construction. However, some of the more common service pointers are as follows: during the overhaul or exchange of the refrigerating unit, it is essential that the frozen foods be kept refrigerated. These foods will stay at a safe temperature in the cabinet for 48 to 72 hours after the unit is shut off. The serviceman can make a temporary frozen foods box from any available container and use dry ice to keep the food frozen. Rumpled newspapers provide a good temporary insulation.

When dismantling a cabinet, the tar (hydrolene) seals may be easily and neatly removed with a hot knife. Use this tar generously when resealing. The tar should be carefully melted in a double boiler with water in the outside boiler. The melting of the tar is an extremely dangerous operation as a fire or an explosion may occur, so it is necessary to be very cautious.

If the unit has a bad thermostat, it is safe to connect the unit directly so it runs continuously until a new thermostat can be obtained and installed. In this latter case, the owner can be instructed to shut the unit off for an hour every other hour or two hours, or allow it to run continuously as this will do no harm and will assure ample refrigeration.

When it is suspected that there is moisture or wax clogging the refrigerant control, a good service procedure is to keep the ice or wax locked in the control until the control is removed. This precaution will enable the serviceman to remove the wax or moisture from the system. The simplest way to keep the wax or ice in the control is to pack the valve in dry ice until it can be removed from the system. The valve may then be warmed and the moisture or wax removed.

Always check the unit for the correct operating pressures and the correct amount of refrigerant (Chapter 12).

10-39 Review of Safety

Pressures in any part of a refrigerating system should be adjusted to atmospheric pressure, open to the atmosphere and continuously purged with CO_2 or nitrogen if they are being brazed, welded or soldered.

Heat tar (hydrolene) only with hot water. Use goggles to protect your eyes. Open flames or a high temperature may cause a violent fire.

Avoid putting your hands near revolving fans, motor pulleys, or motor belts.

Always disconnect the electric power (open the switch or pull the plug) before working on the electrical parts of the system to avoid the possibility of unpleasant and perhaps fatal shocks.

Frost and ice should be removed by heating (hot water or electric heat). The use of a knife or a metal scraper may produce holes in the unit.

Solder or use solid metal terminals on the wire ends to attach the electrical wires. Avoid using wire ends to attach the wire to the terminals.

10-40 Test Your Knowledge – Chapter 10

1. What is a hermetic refrigeration mechanism?
2. What is another name for a natural convection condenser?
3. How may copper tubing be joined to aluminum tubing?
4. What are some of the devices in the electrical circuit of a hermetic domestic refrigerator?
5. How is the temperature controlled in a butter compartment?
6. Why are systems being defrosted faster at the present time?
7. What is used to control the flow of hot gas through the evaporator for defrosting?
8. What is meant by a semiautomatic defrosting system?
9. Where are most of the refrigerant lines located in the latest model domestic refrigerators?
10. How is the defrost water removed after the defrost cycle?
11. What are the two refrigerant control systems commonly found on frozen food cabinets?
12. How often should a freezer be defrosted?
13. A 6 cu. ft. home freezer would probably have what kind of condensing unit?
14. Why are the suction line and the liquid line sometimes soldered together?
15. What is the best temperature range for any home freezer?
16. Most frozen foods cabinets use what kind of motor control?
17. Why is it important to have open space around a freezer, especially near the condenser?

18. Which condition of ice accumulation mentioned in this chapter is the most serious?

19. How does wax get in a refrigeration system?

20. Give two (2) ways moisture may enter a system.

21. What may be used to remove moisture from a refrigeration unit?

22. What service jobs can be performed on a hermetic unit?

23. How does a no-frost refrigerator prevent sweating and frosting?

24. What is a drain heater?

Chapter 11

DOMESTIC REFRIGERATOR AND FREEZER CABINETS

The refrigerator cabinet has undergone considerable change during the forty years of its evolution as a kitchen necessity. The original cabinets were replicas of the wooden icebox. Wood cabinets of multiple door construction and natural wood finishes were common practice. Solid brass, nickel plated hardware was standard. The cabinet lining was galvanized iron or sheet zinc. Wood or wire mesh shelves were used.

Fig. 11-2. A domestic single-door refrigerator. Note compactness of unit by placing condensing unit at rear of unit and using modern insulation.

Fig. 11-1. Modern two-door refrigerator-freezer. Note use of door panels for additional storage. (Kelvinator Div., American Motors Corp.)

Originally the electric refrigerator consisted of a cooling (evaporator) coil installed in the ex-ice compartment of an icebox. The condensing unit was ordinarily installed in the basement.

Refrigerators today provide maximum storage space for minimum exterior dimensions. See Fig. 11-1. Modern refrigerators have air conditioned interiors and efficient, lightweight, refrigeration units. They provide temperatures in the freezing compartment as low as -20 F. They have fingertip door control, automatic ice cube makers, plenty of shelf space and functional beauty. These features are all results of modern research.

Most manufacturers have taken advantage of the greater compactness of the hermetic unit to decrease the condensing unit space, and to enlarge the refrigerated space. See Fig. 11-2.

The hardware has been considerably improved for ease of operation and for durability. The practice of concealing the hinges and the latch is common. The cabinets are lighter as manufacturers improve on structural design, provide more efficient insulation, and use lighter mechanisms.

Several concerns have produced refrigerators with overall heights of 30 in. so they may be used as tables, as shown in Fig. 11-3. Some refrigerators are being

FORCED CONVECTION EVAPORATOR OUTLET

Fig. 11-4. A side-by-side refrigerator-freezer using forced convection evaporator coils for nonfrost. (Gibson Refrig. Sales Corp.; Hupp Corp.)

use of forced convection evaporators in both domestic refrigerators and domestic freezers as shown in Fig. 11-4. Most cabinets now use a white or color matching lacquer exterior and a porcelain interior.

Frozen foods refrigeration has grown rapidly in the last few years. This field of quick or fast frozen foods has caused the development of new types of domestic and commercial equipment. It has presented new problems in design, use, and servicing of frozen food equipment. Domestic frozen food cabinets can be classified into two categories:
1. Chest type freezer, Fig. 11-5.
2. Upright freezer, Fig. 11-6.
The use and servicing of domestic equipment necessary to quick freeze foods and store these foods will be studied in this chapter, and in Chapter 12.

Fig. 11-3. Table height refrigerator, used in apartments, recreation rooms, etc. (Glascock Bros. Mfg. Co.)

incorporated in stove-refrigerator sink combinations. Automatic defrosting and nonfrosting models are popular, as is the

11-1 Preserving Foods by Refrigeration and Freezing

Foods (vegetables and fruits) last longer when kept at temperatures just above the freezing temperature. The lower temperatures slow the oxidation of the food, reduce the multiplication of the bacteria in the living cells and fibers, and reduce the aspiration (removal of fluid) trend in the food. At first snow and natural ice was used in caves, then it was discovered that ice inside insulating materials kept longer, and soon cabinets or small buildings built with thick walls were used. The cutting and storing of ice became a big business in the 1800's. The industrial revolution, the use of steam engines and electric motors in the 1800's soon caused the development of mechanical refrigerating machines.

Today, modern cabinets for refrigerated and frozen foods is an industrial, commercial and domestic necessity.

Man's effort to preserve foods so that no change in flavor, aroma, or texture takes place, dates back many years, but it has been only in the last few years that this dream could actually be accomplished and controlled. Perishable foods were first frozen commercially in the United States about 1875. By 1890, mechanical refrigeration was adapted to freezing foods but only in large applications of cold storage.

Foods frozen by the processes used at that time, are now known as slow frozen foods.

A retail line of packaged frozen foods first appeared on the market in Springfield, Mass., in 1930. Its growth has been accelerating ever since. The home freezer and the domestic storage cabinet of the present design dates to just prior to World War II, about 1939.

11-2 Advantages of Refrigerated and Frozen Foods

The advantages of frozen foods are many and varied. Probably the most important advantage is that freezing provides the opportunity to preserve a food supply for long periods without seriously affecting the taste, aroma, or texture of the food. Frozen foods allow the consumer

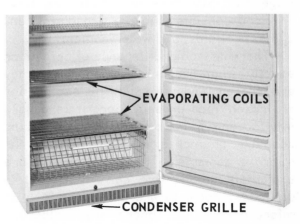

Fig. 11-6. Upright domestic freezer. Note shelf type evaporating coils and thinness of walls due to use of polystyrene insulation.

to purchase in larger quantities and in season, thereby saving money. It allows the farmer to freeze his surplus foods and to hold them until needed. Frozen foods offer the housewife a method of preparing foods in quantity and ahead of demand.

Research has indicated that microorganisms (bacteria, yeasts, and molds) suspended in water, frozen, and stored at

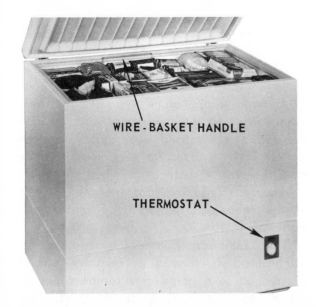

Fig. 11-5. Chest type freezer. Wire baskets are used to help in the storage and removal of food. (Amana Refrig. Inc., Sub. of Raytheon Co.)

freezing temperatures (15 F. or below) are soon killed. Enzymes which cause food spoilage, are controlled by low temperatures. Research indicates that to preserve some foods for long periods (one year or more) the temperatures must be held well below 0 F. (-20 F. or lower for best results).

Meat, poultry, and fish have important colloidal (miniature cell) changes that must be minimized, and low temperatures are an aid in minimizing this action.

Commercial frozen food must be of good quality, must be carefully prepared for freezing. It must be kept at low temperatures all the time until it is being made ready for consumption.

11-3 Principles of Preserving Food

It is important to understand why refrigerating and freezing preserves food.

Food consists of micro-organisms, enzymes, colloids, and water content.

There is some difference of opinion on exactly what happens to foods when they are frozen, and the scientific explanation of frozen food preservation. It is generally accepted, however, that the freezing destroys or makes dormant most of the micro-organisms. These organisms are extremely small, live cells that exist in all foods. Bacteria are a common form of micro-organisms. Others are molds and yeast.

Enzymes are miniature particles of matter that exist in food substances. They are not destroyed by fast freezing, but their increase is minimized by the low temperatures. They seem to serve as catalytic agents (stimulants) of organic change. They are destroyed by pasteurization.

Colloids are peculiar to meats. They are miniature cells in meats, fish, and poultry. If they are abused in any way, such as cell disruption, the food quickly becomes rancid. They seem to be cell

containers or capsules. If the container is ruptured the food rapidly deteriorates.

Fast freezing produces exceedingly small ice crystals; slow freezing provides time for larger crystal growth. The larger the ice crystals the more the food cell walls are ruptured.

Air in a freezer is relatively dry and unless foods are packed in a moisture-vapor proof container, there will be a steady loss of moisture from the food. After periods of only two or three months light gray spots or areas may appear on the surface of meats. These spots known as "freezer burn," are caused by loss of moisture (drying or dessication). Freezer burn may affect all foods, but the indications of it will vary. Freezer burns may not injure the food value or taste of food. Proper packaging will eliminate the danger of this condition, particularly if in packaging, the air is expelled, and a vapor-proof container is used, and thoroughly sealed.

11-4 Storage Time for Refrigerated and Frozen Foods

Most foods kept at 35 to 45 F. and at humidities around 50% keep fairly well for three days to one week.

The maximum storage time for frozen foods is influenced by many factors such as storage temperature, type of container, condition of food when frozen, and the kind of food. Fruits and vegetables may be stored from season to season with little loss in flavor or color.

The fast freezing temperature depends on the freezing method used and varies from -50 F. to -20 F.

The indirect immersion method in which food is placed in containers and submerged in a brine at a temperature of -45 F. to -50 F. is quite effective. The method used to freeze poultry is to pump refrigerant through a tube inserted in the poultry which freezes rapidly at a -30 F.

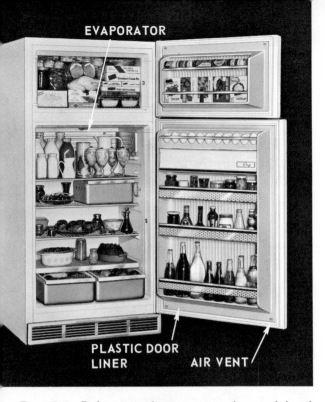

EVAPORATOR

PLASTIC DOOR LINER

AIR VENT

Fig. 11-7. Refrigerator-freezer; a two-door model with freezer at top. Note evaporator in upper part of lower compartment. (Kelvinator Div., American Motors Corp.)

to -50 F. temperature. High velocity low temperature air blasts (up to 2000 ft./min.) are used successfully for fast freezing.

Freezing in a refrigerated room at temperatures only slightly below freezing with only moderate air circulation cannot properly be termed fast freezing, but is known as "sharp" freezing.

Zero to -10 F. is accepted as the best storage temperatures for most frozen foods. These temperatures are practical for the owner of a freezer who must store various foods in one cabinet. These temperatures are also used in most locker plants. Large warehouses are usually equipped to store foods at temperatures best adapted to prolong the safe storage period for each food. The lower the temperature the higher the cost of operation.

11-5 Preparation of Food for Refrigerating and Freezing

All food placed in a refrigerator should be clean. Food in glass or metal containers should be sealed. Fruits and vege-

tables should be kept in a high humidity atmosphere, preferably in a covered pan. They should not be slow frozen. The best temperatures for storage are listed in Chapter 16. Fresh meat should be kept as close to freezing as possible and in high humidity atmosphere.

It is important to freeze only high quality fruits and vegetables, and to pick varieties that freeze satisfactorily. Freezing will preserve good quality, but it will not make good quality foods out of bad quality foods.

When freezing fruits, speed is important as fruit loses flavor and color rapidly. Apples require blanching. Fruits may be packed in syrup, dry sugar, or without sugar. Sugar solutions give protection to frozen fruits and are used extensively.

Frozen fruits discolor rapidly (by oxidation) when thawed for which reason only meal size quantities should be frozen in each package.

Vegetables should be thoroughly cleaned and prepared as if they are to be served at once. They should be blanched in boiling hot water for a period (length of time depends on vegetable) to preserve natural flavor, texture, color, food value and to stop the action of enzymes (Par. 11-3). After blanching, cool in cold running or ice water and pack in small containers made of vapor-proof materials. Several kinds of containers are available. Freeze the food as soon as possible, at low temperatures of -10 F. to -20 F.

The three major items to guard against are drying (freezer burn), rancidity (oxidation of the fat tissue), and discoloring (oxidation of other muscle tissues).

Freezing of meat is simple, requiring only that it be cut into pieces suitable for meal preparation, packaged and frozen. Freeze the meat as quickly as possible to retain the best flavor and quality. Wild game and poultry may be frozen like beef.

Many other foods may be frozen, and the preparation is simple in most cases.

Simply prepare the food as you would for immediate consumption, package in an appropriate container and freeze. The list includes cooked dishes, sauces and dressing, soups, melons, dried fruit, packaged foods, cereals, pies and pastries, bread

11-6 Cabinets

Two popular ways to classify cabinets of domestic refrigerators are by style and size. One way is by the door design such as single door, double door, multiple door,

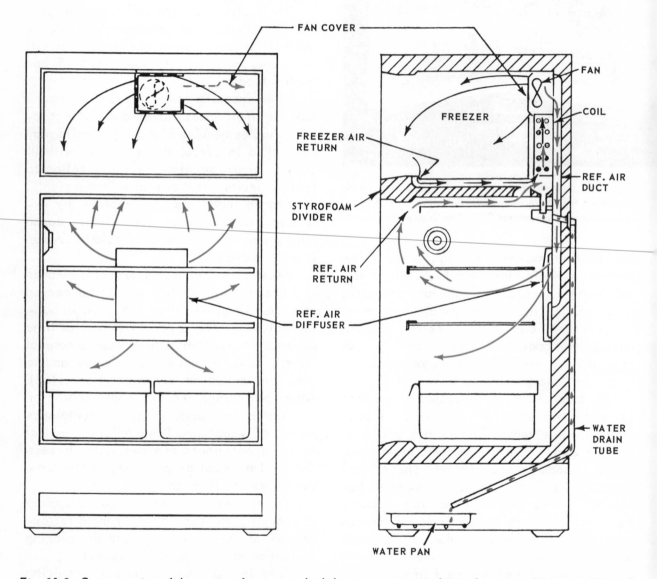

Fig. 11-8. Cross section of domestic refrigerator which has an evaporator located at rear of freezer and uses duct with motor-fan to circulate cooled air to both compartments.

and rolls, lunches, desserts and salads, and leftovers. Bread may be stored by freezing it and it will stay fresh indefinitely in the freezer.

etc. The second way to classify cabinets is by capacity in cubic feet. This varies from about 4 cu. ft. up to 15 cu. ft. or more. In the large cabinets, the number of

FREEZER
COMPARTMENT

Fig. 11-9. Two-door refrigerator showing outer shell and inner shell, shelving and basket for holding frozen foods. (Gibson Refrig. Sales Corp.; Hupp Corp.)

doors usually increases with the capacity of the unit.

The capacity in cubic feet may be designated in two ways: Gross cubic feet, or net cubic feet. The gross cubic content is measured by multiplying the three interior dimensions together. The net cubic feet (usable space) is this volume less the space occupied by the evaporator or ice maker. The net cubic feet volume is the one generally used when comparing cabinet sizes.

11-7 Domestic Cabinet Designs

Cabinets having shelf type evaporators have two features:
- A. Maximum ice cube and frozen food space.
- B. Maximum refrigerated space compared to external dimensions of the cabinet.

The growing popularity of frozen foods has caused refrigerator manufacturers to redesign the interiors of their cabinets to enlarge the evaporators and to make more space available for frozen food storage. To accommodate high container storage and to use the interior volume efficiently, most of the evaporators are now mounted in the middle top of the interior, as in Fig. 11-7.

Many manufacturers use a forced convection evaporator which permits them to use a high percentage of the total area for a freezer compartment. This is accomplished by either using a single evaporator with a duct to direct air to the provision compartment and frozen food section, or the use of independent coils and fans as shown in Fig. 11-8.

11-8 Domestic Cabinet Construction

The inner shell of the refrigerator is usually made of one piece of sheet steel. It is formed in a large press. Most outer shells are made of two or more pieces of of steel spot welded or seam welded into one rigid shell. The outer shell has a frame welded to its interior. The shell is usually painted with a durable enamel or is porcelain finished. The inner shell is also fabricated from sheet steel. It is usually finished with porcelain, or a synthetic organic finish. The inner shell has provisions for mounting evaporators, fans and shelf brackets. See Fig. 11-9.

The inner design of a cabinet of this type is shown in Fig. 11-10. Note the direction of air flow through the duct work to the provision compartment and back again to the freezer. Space between the inner and outer shell is capped with a plastic strip. This plastic strip is sometimes called a breaker trim, breaker collar, or "cold ban" trim. Fig. 11-11, shows the breaker trim installed and the method of removal and replacement. Fig. 11-12, shows one manufacturer's method of at-

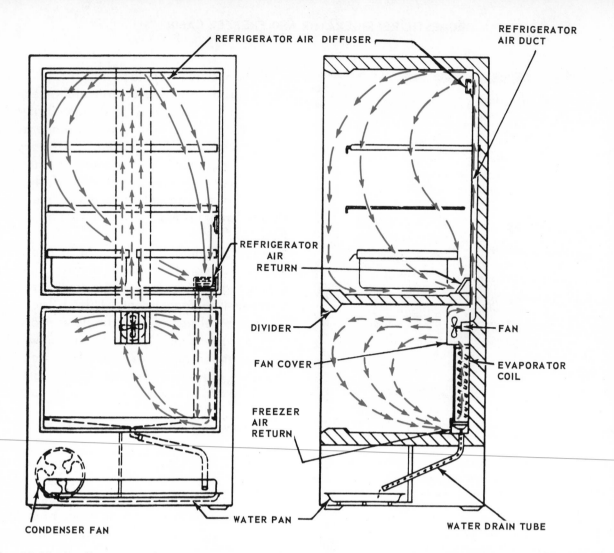

REFRIGERATOR AIR DIFFUSER

REFRIGERATOR AIR DUCT

REFRIGERATOR AIR RETURN

DIVIDER

FAN COVER

FREEZER AIR RETURN

CONDENSER FAN

WATER PAN

FAN

EVAPORATOR COIL

WATER DRAIN TUBE

Fig. 11-10. Air flow in two-door refrigerator with freezer compartment at bottom. Note location of evaporator.

taching the cold ban trim with the use of trim clips. The term "cold ban" is used to denote a plastic material which will not readily conduct heat from the warm outer wrapper to the cold liner.

The attachment of mullion strip between the freezer compartment and the provision compartment is accomplished by clipping the mullion over the cold ban trim, and fastening it to the cabinet at the center hinge bracket as shown in Fig. 11-13.

11-9 Shelving

Present day refrigerator shelving is usually made from stamped steel or aluminum. The shelves are mounted on small noncorroding wheels (usually hard plastic).

Roll-out shelves must be designed to move easily even though loaded. They must also be designed so they will not tip as they are moved out of the refrigerator. See Fig. 11-14.

Most refrigerators have trays or bins for storage of meats (near the evaporator) and for fruits and vegetables. These trays or bins usually have glass plate covers.

Most cabinets have recessed doors which have provision to hold beverages, eggs, cheese, etc., as shown in Fig. 11-15.

Shelving in a chest type freezer usually consists of wire baskets at the bottom of the compartment. Fig. 11-16, shows a typical example of the chest type storage arrangement. Shelving in some upright models consists of refrigerated shelves made into individual compartments com-

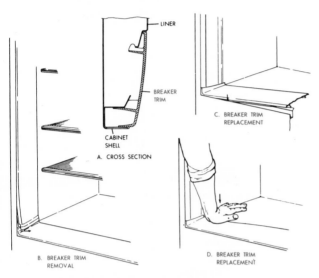

Fig. 11-11. Note breaker trim, and proper method of removal and reinstallation. Care must be taken that palm of hand is used to press down on strip to prevent excessive pressure in one area, which might cause strip to break.

plete with individual doors. In locker plants, tiers of drawers form the lockers. In most cases the shelving used in freezers is part of the evaporator.

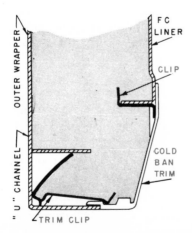

Fig. 11-12. Method of attaching cold bar trim to freezer compartment liner, and outer shell through use of trim clips. (Kelvinator Div., American Motors Corp.)

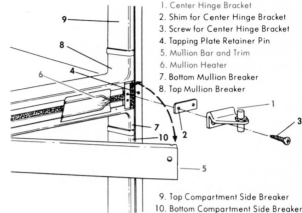

1. Center Hinge Bracket
2. Shim for Center Hinge Bracket
3. Screw for Center Hinge Bracket
4. Tapping Plate Retainer Pin
5. Mullion Bar and Trim
6. Mullion Heater
7. Bottom Mullion Breaker
8. Top Mullion Breaker

9. Top Compartment Side Breaker
10. Bottom Compartment Side Breaker

Fig. 11-13. Method of fastening mullion strip between freezer compartment and food provision compartment. Note center hinge bracket which is also used to hold mullion in place.
(Franklin Appliance Div., Studebaker Corp.)

11-10 Freezer Cabinet Construction

The modern chest type freezer cabinet is constructed of steel with welded, sealed external steel seams to prevent the entrance of air and moisture. The outer wrapper is formed from one piece of

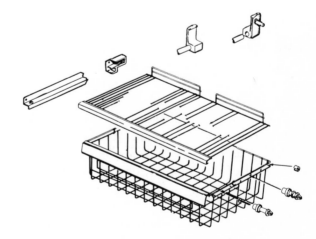

Fig. 11-14. Refrigerator roll-out shelf assembly.

sheet steel with a vertical seam located in the back. The bottom is cut and formed and then welded to the sides and ends. Reinforcement plates are frequently fastened to the inside of the outer wall to increase rigidity. Several companies use a stamped steel or angle iron frame. The outside is usually finished with baked enamel.

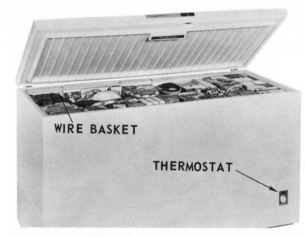

WIRE BASKET

THERMOSTAT

Fig. 11-16. Domestic chest type deep freeze using wire baskets for orderly storage of food.

joint to prevent moisture from freezing the door shut. The condensing unit is generally mounted in the bottom or end of the cabinet, making it a self-contained unit.

IN-THE-DOOR STORAGE

Fig. 11-15. Modern domestic cabinet. Note recessed door which provides additional storage space.

The inside liner is made of a plated steel, copper, or aluminum to prevent corrosion. It is usually welded into a moisture tight tank. The tubing for the refrigerant is then attached to the outside of the inner liner, as shown in Fig. 11-17. In the cabinets, separate liners are assembled, and space between them and the outer wall of the cabinet, usually 4 to 5 in., is packed with an insulating material, as shown in Fig. 11-18.

The top edge is covered with a plastic or metal strip. The joints are sealed against air and moisture. The lid is usually constructed of steel, is made airtight by using gaskets made of soft synthetic material. Some units use an electrically heated resistance wire at the door or lid

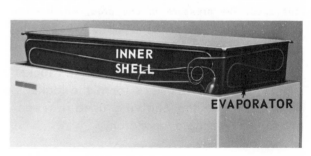

INNER SHELL

EVAPORATOR

Fig. 11-17. Chest type freezer with inner shell partly removed. Note evaporator coil fastened to liner.

The upright freezer cabinet construction is dependent on the type of evaporator used, forced convection, plate or tubing. See Fig. 11-19. Cabinet construction is similar to that of a normal domestic refrigerator.

The upright type combination freezer and household refrigerator is now in common use. Some manufacturers construct the cabinet in several enclosed sections. These sections form the drawers, or have fixed shelves with a door in front of each section. These freezers are made for use in the kitchen along with a regular refrigerator. The shelves are usually made of

cost of operation may be a little high because of cold air spilling out when the outside door is opened.

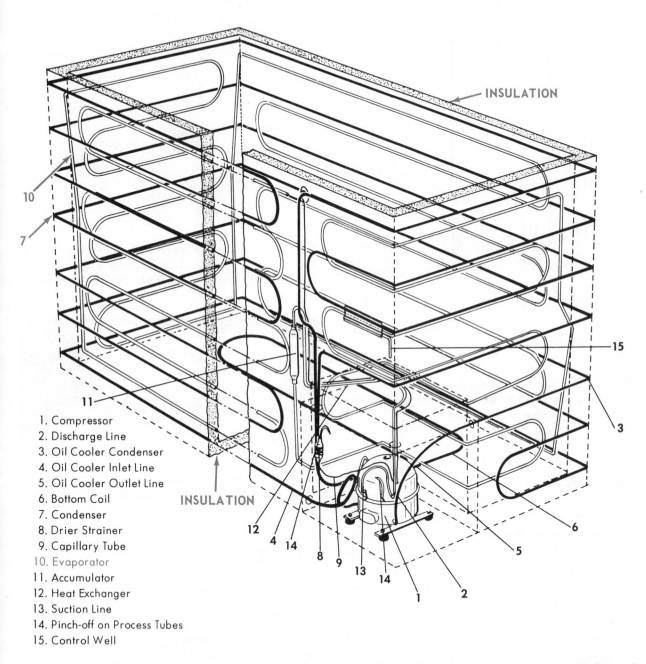

1. Compressor
2. Discharge Line
3. Oil Cooler Condenser
4. Oil Cooler Inlet Line
5. Oil Cooler Outlet Line
6. Bottom Coil
7. Condenser
8. Drier Strainer
9. Capillary Tube
10. Evaporator
11. Accumulator
12. Heat Exchanger
13. Suction Line
14. Pinch-off on Process Tubes
15. Control Well

Fig. 17-18. Chest type evaporator (10) in freezer compartment. Note: Special oil cooler condenser (3) located at bottom of condenser, oil cooler inlet line (4), and oil cooler outlet line (5).

flat evaporator coils, or have forced convection blower cooling, as shown in Fig. 11-20. They are easily accessible but the

The lift top cabinet is known commonly as the chest type. An advantage of this type is minimum loss of cold air when

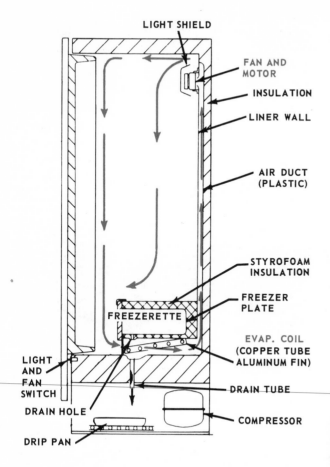

LIGHT SHIELD

FAN AND MOTOR

INSULATION

LINER WALL

AIR DUCT (PLASTIC)

STYROFOAM INSULATION

FREEZER PLATE

FREEZERETTE

EVAP. COIL (COPPER TUBE ALUMINUM FIN)

LIGHT AND FAN SWITCH

DRAIN HOLE

DRIP PAN

DRAIN TUBE

COMPRESSOR

Fig. 11-19. "Non-frost" forced convection evaporator coil. Note placement of evaporator coil and air flow developed by the use of fan.

AIR FLOW DUCT

Fig. 11-20. Frost-free freezer. Note air ducts at top and bottom of freezer. As evaporator coil is outside freezer compartment, no frost will form within cabinet.

INDICATOR LIGHT

Fig. 11-21. Chest type freezer. Note indicator light which warns owner if freezer temperature is too high.

opened. Fig. 11-21 shows a typical chest type freezer. It is not quite as convenient to put food into or to remove food from, but otherwise it is a desirable type of cabinet. Many freezers are of this construction. In normal defrost, chest type freezers, it is necessary to remove the condensate from the cabinet formed during the defrosting. Fig. 11-22 shows one method of removing the condensate through the use of a drain located in the center of the bottom of the cabinet.

Frozen food system capacities vary from a small kitchen size storage unit to large storage warehouse where tons of frozen foods are stored. Many domestic refrigerators have frozen foods space in combination with the regular refrigerator

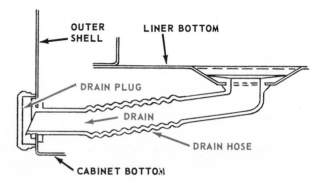

OUTER SHELL

LINER BOTTOM

DRAIN PLUG

DRAIN

DRAIN HOSE

CABINET BOTTOM

Fig. 11-22. Drain arrangement located in bottom of chest type freezer to aid in removing water from freezer when defrosting.

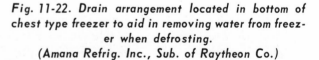
(Amana Refrig. Inc., Sub. of Raytheon Co.)

storage space. See Fig. 11-23. These are known as dual-temperature boxes.

11-11 Insulation

Heat is kept from leaking through the refrigerator cabinet walls by lining the walls with heat insulating substances such

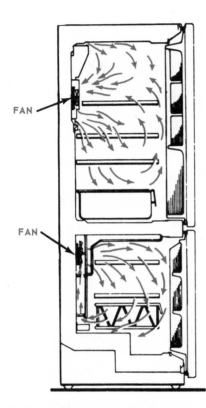

Fig. 11-23. A dual-temperature refrigerator. Note air circulation through both normal temperature and frozen foods compartment. Each refrigeration compartment has a motor fan.
(Franklin Appliance Div., Studebaker Corp.)

as cork, corrugated paper, glass wool, fiberglass, wood fiber, aluminum foil, urethane foam, or other insulating material. See Figs. 11-24 and 11-25.

11-12 Urethane Insulation

A popular type of insulation used in many refrigerator applications is rigid urethane foam. This should not be confused with Styrofoam. Rigid urethane foam has

high mechanical strength, low moisture pickup, and a low K factor (see Chapter 16). It can be formed in place to provide a well insulated unit.

One of the most successful methods of producing urethane foam is by the expansion of plastic granules through the use of R-11 or R-12 to produce a foam substance which is injected into a mold or cavity and forms a rigid piece of insulation. Another method is to have the urethane blown be-

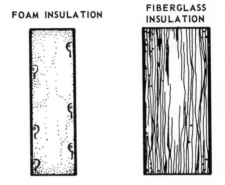

Fig. 11-24. Relative thickness of foamed in-place insulation is compared to fiber glass insulation.

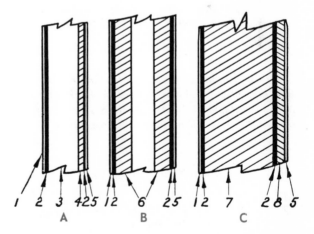

Fig. 11-25. Three different refrigerator wall constructions. A—Older type. B—Modern icebox. C—The usual electric refrigerator box insulation. 1—Inner lining usually steel with porcelain finish. 2—Cardboard backing or a coating of odorless asphaltum. 3—Dead air space. 4—Hair felt or equal. 5—Exterior of steel — usually lacquered. 6—Cork or hair felt. 7—Slab insulation which is wrapped in waterproof paper. 8—Veneer or paper backing.

tween the inner and outer walls of the refrigerator after the cabinet has been assembled, so the foamed insulation completely surrounds the wiring and refrigerant lines which pass through the walls, as shown in Fig. 11-26. The foamed in-

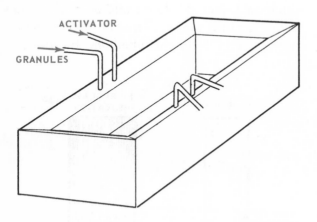

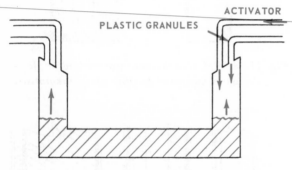

Fig. 11-26. Method of installing foamed-in-place urethane insulation. Cabinet is laid on back with door opening up. Inner and outer shells are held in place by fixture during insulating operation.

sulation is blown into the cavity and adheres to the inner walls of the refrigerator. This gives the unit stability and strength. Some manufacturers produce rigid urethane foam in a solid piece, as shown in Fig. 11-27. This process produces positive insulation because there are no joints or cavities. By using foam, the thickness of the insulation can be reduced allowing extra refrigerated space without increasing the external size of the cabinet. After filling the cavity between the inner and

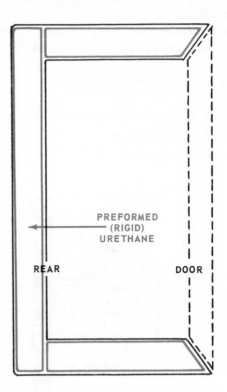

Fig. 11-27. Rigid urethane installed in refrigerator cabinet. Insulation is sometimes put into sealed plastic bag prior to installation.

outer walls, the breaker collar, Fig. 11-28, is connected to the shell.

The problem of moisture getting into the insulation is usually eliminated by hermetically sealing the outer portions of the cabinets and doors against the entry of moisture laden air. There are several

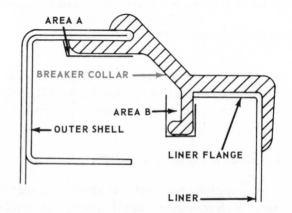

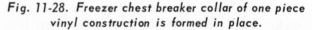

Fig. 11-28. Freezer chest breaker collar of one piece vinyl construction is formed in place.

methods of accomplishing this sealing. Briefly it is a process of welding the cabinets into sealed containers after the insulation has been put in. The welding is done in a place where humidity has been reduced to a minimum. The interior must be dried as thoroughly as possible before it is sealed, to eliminate moisture. If the cabinet is not thoroughly sealed, ice will eventually form in the insulation causing severe sweating, and may damage the cabinet.

It is especially important that the outer shell be sealed as an outer shell leak produces an accumulation of moisture in the insulation. An inner shell leak will remove moisture from the insulation. See Fig. 11-29. In servicing freezers, it is sometimes necessary to remove and install all refrigerant, motor control, electrical and thermometer lines which pass through the cabinet insulation. It is important that all openings be thoroughly sealed with a plastic sealer immediately after the repairs

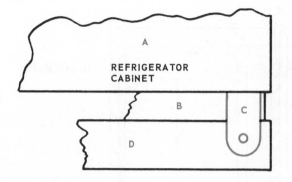

Fig. 11-30. Hinge design which allows door to open within total space of refrigerator. A—Refrigerator. B—Gasket. C—Hinge. D—Door.

have been completed, otherwise such openings will allow moisture to collect in the insulation.

11-13 Refrigerator Doors

Refrigerator and freezer doors are now built to cover almost the entire front of the refrigerator. Fig. 11-30 shows a typical door hinge design.

The inner liner of the door is usually recessed to provide space for small shelves. Small vent holes are provided in the door to release entrapped moisture; some have low wattage heater coils to help keep the inner liner from sweating. Some refrigerators have built-in butter cavities. As most of these use a small heating element, an electric cord must be run from the cabinet to the door on the hinge side. Many cabinets use plastic as the inner liner of the door.

Secondary doors are doors used on individual inner compartments of an upright type frozen foods cabinet, as shown in Fig. 11-31. Such doors prevent the spilling out of cold air from the compartments

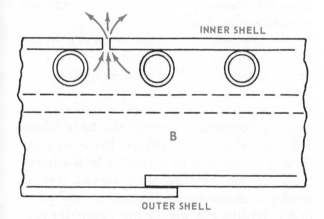

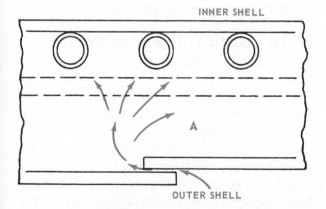

Fig. 11-29. Results of a leak in outer shell and in inner shell of a freezer cabinet. A—Shows a leak in the outer shell. B—Shows a leak in the inner shell.

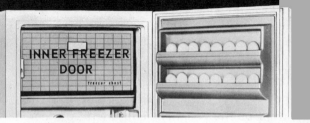

Fig. 11-31. Domestic refrigeration cabinet with secondary door for freezer compartment.

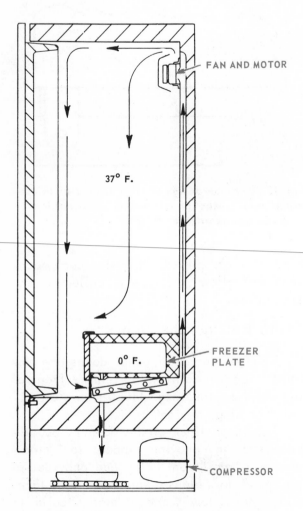

Fig. 11-32. A domestic refrigerator with compressor unit mounted at bottom rear of cabinet. Note freeze plate and fan and motor.

Fig. 11-33. Two-door domestic refrigerator. Note storage space in door. This refrigerator has an automatic defrost. (Kelvinator Div., American Motors Corp.)

and minimize frost collection. The doors are made of metal, glass, or plastic and are usually spring operated.

11-14 Condensing Unit Location

Manufacturers have placed the condensing unit in the domestic refrigerator and domestic freezer self-contained cabinets in various locations.

At present most manufacturers mount the unit in the bottom rear of the cabinet, or in the back wall of the refrigerator, as shown in Fig. 11-32.

A popular design uses a forced convection condensing unit in the base of the cabinet. The motor driven fan draws air through a portion of the grills at the lower front of the refrigerator, forces the air over the condenser and motor-compressor, and exhausts the air to the room through another portion of the same grill.

11-15 Location of Refrigerator Evaporators

Many domestic refrigerator evaporators are in the form of a shelf across the top of the cabinet.

Cabinets with frozen food compartments have several arrangements for cooling the regular section of the cabinet. The cabinet construction varies according to the type evaporator used. Some models use a wrap-around freezer coil, which is commonly made of aluminum. This coil is bolted to the roof on the inner side. It has a metal or plastic tray shelf mounted underneath. Controllable air ducts along the sides and back of the shelf allow cold air to settle into the regular portion of the cabinet to cool it. Another type cabinet construction insulates the frozen foods space from the regular space and a separate evaporator is used to cool the regular space. The separate coil is a secondary coil or is in the regular cycle as an overflow coil using a suction pressure valve. Or, it may have a separate condensing unit.

Figs. 11-33 and 11-34 illustrate types of popular cabinet design.

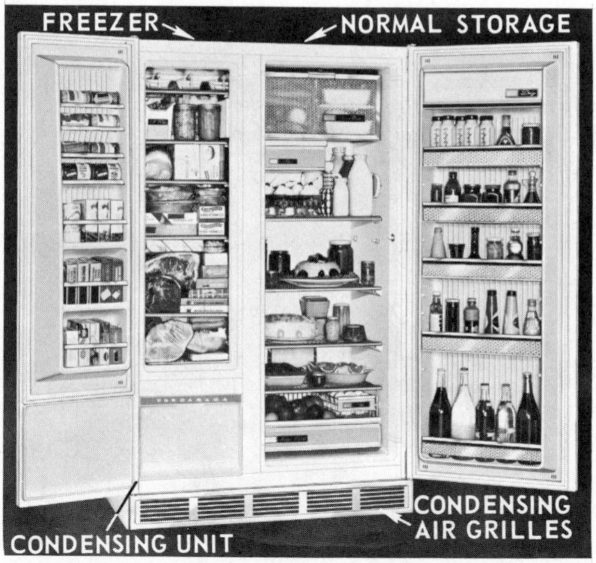

Another type across-the-top evaporator model is shown in Fig. 11-35. This is an 11.6 cu. ft. cabinet (2.2 in the freezer

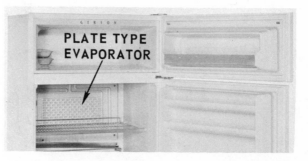

Fig. 11-36. A two-door cabinet design. Normal food storage compartment is cooled by a plate type evaporator coil.

Fig. 11-34. Double-door domestic refrigerator having full length doors on both freezer and normal storage compartment.

FREEZER

Fig. 11-35. One-door cabinet design with across-the-top freezer. (Hotpoint, Div., General Electric Co.)

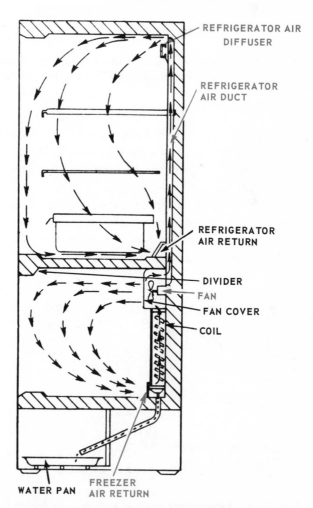

Fig. 11-37. Frost-free refrigerator system. Note air ducts and circulating fan.

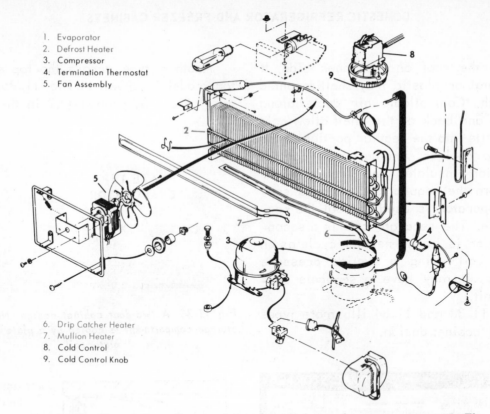

1. Evaporator
2. Defrost Heater
3. Compressor
4. Termination Thermostat
5. Fan Assembly

6. Drip Catcher Heater
7. Mullion Heater
8. Cold Control
9. Cold Control Knob

Fig. 11-38. Forced air cooling system used in non-frost refrigeration system. 1—The evaporator coil. 2—The defrost heater. 6—Drip trough heater. 7—Mullion heater.

and 9.4 in the fresh food space). A two-door cabinet is shown in Fig. 11-36. It has a plate type evaporator for the lower compartment.

A frost-free refrigerator is shown in Fig. 11-37. In this type refrigerator there are no coils or surfaces within the refrigerated spaces. Refrigeration is accom-

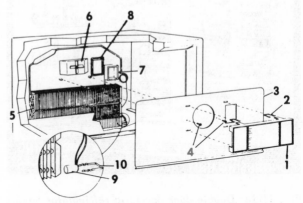

1. Removable Grille
2. Grille Mounting Clips
3. Finned Evaporator Cover
4. Finned Evaporator Cover Mounting Screws
5. Finned Evaporator
6. Fan Assembly
7. Air Duct Seal
8. Sealing Mastic
9. Defrost Heater Termination Thermostat
10. Termination Thermostat Mounting Clip

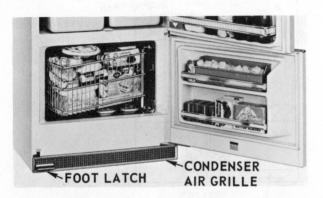

FOOT LATCH   CONDENSER AIR GRILLE

Fig. 11-39. Refrigerator cabinet with freezer located in bottom. Note foot pedal which is used to open freezer door.

Fig. 11-40. Finned evaporator with motor fan. Evaporator is located in rear of freezer compartment.

plished by circulating air from the refrigerated space over the evaporator, cooling it and returning the cold air back inside the storage space. The evaporator may frost some on the "on cycle" but will defrost on the "off cycle." An exploded view of a forced cooling system is shown in Fig. 11-38.

A two-door cabinet with the freezer in the bottom compartment is shown in Fig. 11-39. This cabinet has a foot latch to operate the lower door. The freezer compartment has a swing-out design food basket.

In some absorption type machines, the refrigerator mechanisms are located on the side of the cabinet. In some of the domestic refrigerator designs, the evaporator is placed either in the upper left hand corner of the cabinet, or in the center of the cabinet. In any event, the evaporator is usually placed at the top in order to provide for the best refrigeration of the air, interior of cabinet, and its content. See Fig. 11-40.

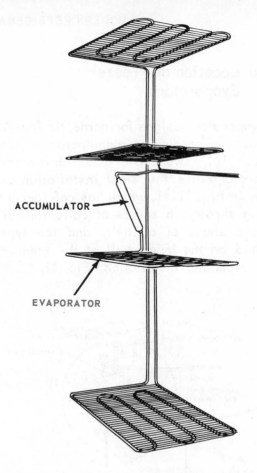

Fig. 11-41. Upright freezer-refrigeration system using wire type, shelf evaporators.

Fig. 11-42. Chest type cooling oil evaporator (1) in freezer compartment, (2) cold plate in food compartment. (Franklin Div., Studebaker Corp.)

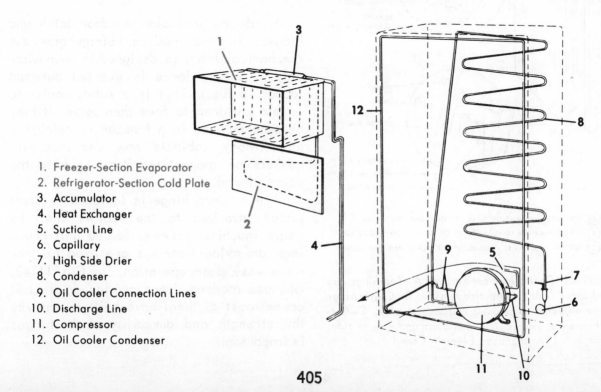

1. Freezer-Section Evaporator
2. Refrigerator-Section Cold Plate
3. Accumulator
4. Heat Exchanger
5. Suction Line
6. Capillary
7. High Side Drier
8. Condenser
9. Oil Cooler Connection Lines
10. Discharge Line
11. Compressor
12. Oil Cooler Condenser

11-16 Location of Freezer Evaporators

Evaporator designs for domestic freezers vary according to manufacturer (see Chapter 10). Two basic types of freezer evaporators are the shelf installation as shown in Fig. 11-41, which has refrigerant flowing through a series of coils formed into the shape of a shelf; and the type mounted on the inner wall of the freezer as in a cabinet installation, Fig. 11-42. A

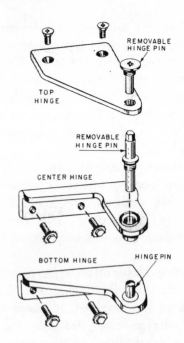

Fig. 11-44. Parts of a three hinge arrangement for a two-door cabinet. (Norge Div., Borg-Warner Corp.)

popular arrangement for upright freezers is the use of the forced convection type evaporator, "nonfrost," Fig. 11-20.

11-17 Cabinet Hardware (Door Latches)

Hardware includes the door latch and hinges. On the modern refrigerator the mechanical latch is designed to open when only a slight force is exerted outward (about 15 lbs.). This is a safety device to enable children to free themselves if they become trapped in a freezer or refrigerator. Many cabinets now use magnetic gaskets or magnetized bars to keep the doors closed.

The modern hinge is fastened to steel plates attached to the cabinet shell by using machine screws. Sealed ball bearings or nylon bearings are used to promote easy door operation. See Fig. 11-43. Because modern doors are larger and because most of them have built-in shelves the strength and durability of the hinges is important.

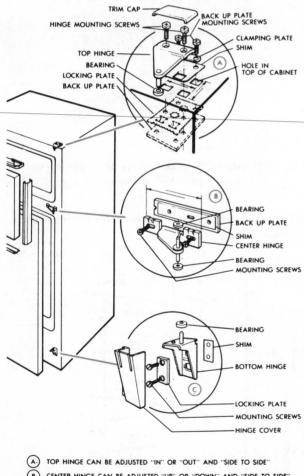

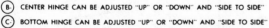

A) TOP HINGE CAN BE ADJUSTED "IN" OR "OUT" AND "SIDE TO SIDE"
B) CENTER HINGE CAN BE ADJUSTED "UP" OR "DOWN" AND "SIDE TO SIDE"
C) BOTTOM HINGE CAN BE ADJUSTED "UP" OR "DOWN" AND "SIDE TO SIDE"

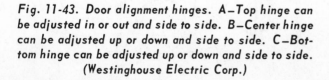

Fig. 11-43. Door alignment hinges. A—Top hinge can be adjusted in or out and side to side. B—Center hinge can be adjusted up or down and side to side. C—Bottom hinge can be adjusted up or down and side to side. (Westinghouse Electric Corp.)

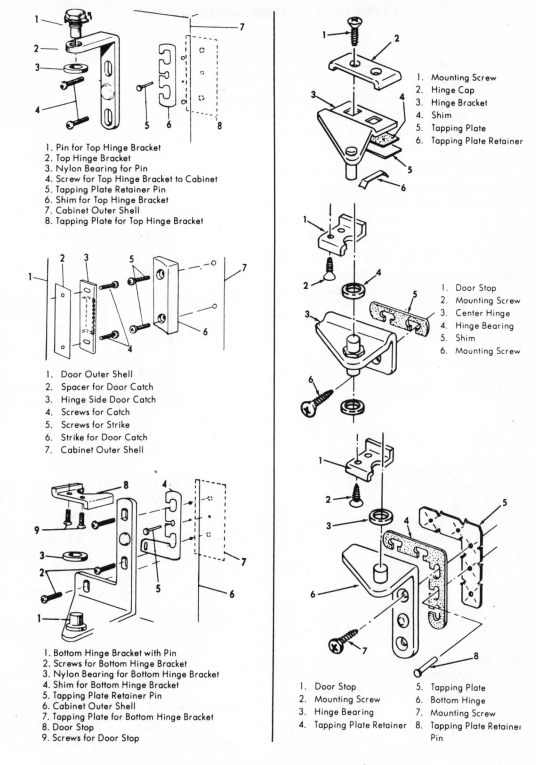

1. Pin for Top Hinge Bracket
2. Top Hinge Bracket
3. Nylon Bearing for Pin
4. Screw for Top Hinge Bracket to Cabinet
5. Tapping Plate Retainer Pin
6. Shim for Top Hinge Bracket
7. Cabinet Outer Shell
8. Tapping Plate for Top Hinge Bracket

1. Mounting Screw
2. Hinge Cap
3. Hinge Bracket
4. Shim
5. Tapping Plate
6. Tapping Plate Retainer

1. Door Outer Shell
2. Spacer for Door Catch
3. Hinge Side Door Catch
4. Screws for Catch
5. Screws for Strike
6. Strike for Door Catch
7. Cabinet Outer Shell

1. Door Stop
2. Mounting Screw
3. Center Hinge
4. Hinge Bearing
5. Shim
6. Mounting Screw

1. Bottom Hinge Bracket with Pin
2. Screws for Bottom Hinge Bracket
3. Nylon Bearing for Bottom Hinge Bracket
4. Shim for Bottom Hinge Bracket
5. Tapping Plate Retainer Pin
6. Cabinet Outer Shell
7. Tapping Plate for Bottom Hinge Bracket
8. Door Stop
9. Screws for Door Stop

1. Door Stop
2. Mounting Screw
3. Hinge Bearing
4. Tapping Plate Retainer
5. Tapping Plate
6. Bottom Hinge
7. Mounting Screw
8. Tapping Plate Retainer Pin

Fig. 11-45. Hinge assemblies used on two-door cabinets.
(Franklin Appliance Div., Studebaker Corp.)

11-18 Cabinet Hinges

Present day hinges are usually made of chrome-plated steel or extruded aluminum, corrosion proofed to prevent rusting. See Fig. 11-44.

The part fastened to the cabinet is called the hinge; the part fastened to the door, the hinge butt. The joining piece is the pin. The hinge is usually adjustable on the cabinet. Shims may be used under both the hinge and the hinge butt to adjust the distance between the door and the frame.

Fig. 11-45 shows a type of hinge which permits opening of the door in a space no wider than the refrigerator.

Nylon bushings are placed in the outer door panel to support the hinge pin, and nylon washers on the hinge pins act as the weight bearing surfaces at pivot points. The hinges may have elongated mounting holes for adjustment of the door as shown in Fig. 11-46.

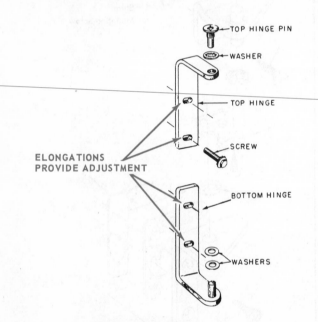

Fig. 11-46. Hinge assembly for one-door cabinet. Note adjustable slots.
(Kelvinator Div., American Motors Corp.)

Most chest type freezers use hinges similar to the one shown in Fig. 11-47. The hinges are usually concealed by using plastic or metal snap-on covers.

11-19 Cabinet Latches

Latches on some freezers are constructed with a spring operated latch bolt that maintains a constant tension on a

roller equipped bar, and the spring pressure against a tapered cabinet fitting holds the door tightly closed.

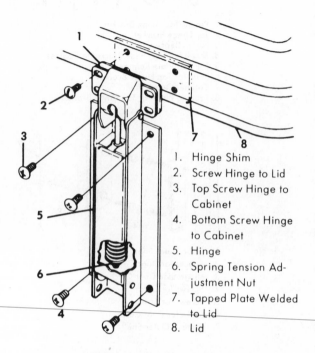

1. Hinge Shim
2. Screw Hinge to Lid
3. Top Screw Hinge to Cabinet
4. Bottom Screw Hinge to Cabinet
5. Hinge
6. Spring Tension Adjustment Nut
7. Tapped Plate Welded to Lid
8. Lid

Fig. 11-47. Lid hinge for chest type freezer.
(Franklin Appliance Div., Studebaker Corp.)

The latch consists of a handle and latch. The part that is fastened to the cabinet is called the strike. See Fig. 11-48. The strike is usually adjustable in two directions.

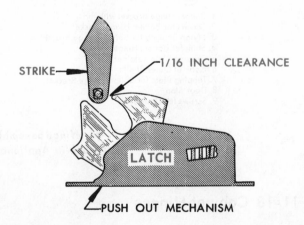

Fig. 11-48. Latch and strike assembly. Note clearance adjustment.

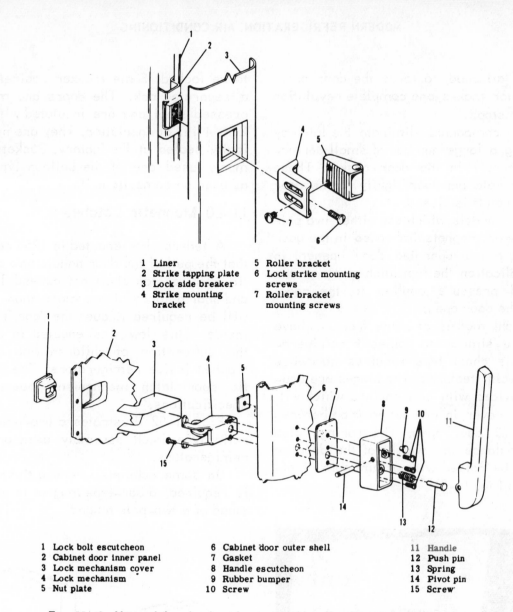

1 Liner
2 Strike tapping plate
3 Lock side breaker
4 Strike mounting bracket
5 Roller bracket
6 Lock strike mounting screws
7 Roller bracket mounting screws

1 Lock bolt escutcheon	6 Cabinet door outer shell	11 Handle
2 Cabinet door inner panel	7 Gasket	12 Push pin
3 Lock mechanism cover	8 Handle escutcheon	13 Spring
4 Lock mechanism	9 Rubber bumper	14 Pivot pin
5 Nut plate	10 Screw	15 Screw

Fig. 11-49. View of door latch with a vertical handle. Note names of parts.

The handle may be removed by removing the latch cover on the door liner or by removing the complete liner.

Fig. 11-49 illustrates a door latch with a vertical handle. A horizontal handle door latch is also in common use.

A foot-operated door opener is shown in Fig. 11-50. This mechanism eliminates stooping and enables one to open the door even though both hands are full.

An electrically operated door closer is used on some models. A push-button switch is located on the front of the door. When the button is pushed, a small motor is energized causing a shaft, to which an

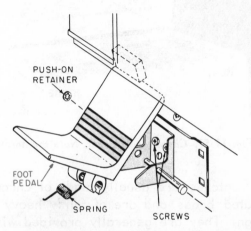

Fig. 11-50. Foot pedal door opener mechanism. (General Electric Co.)

arm is attached, to force the door open. The motor makes one complete revolution and then stops.

Some companies eliminate the latch by inserting a large number of small permanent magnets in the door gasket. These magnets hold the door tightly to the door frame when it is closed.

Some models which use either two pole magnets or magnets imbedded in the gasket use a foot-operated door opener. In this application the foot latch pivots on the pin and pressure applied to the pedal forces the door open.

Upright models of home freezers have hardware similar to domestic refrigerators. The chest type requires hardware with special features. The hinges are usually provided with coil springs which will hold the cover in any set position between 5 and 90 deg. open. The springs also counterbalance the weight of the door so it may be raised with a minimum of effort. See Fig. 11-51.

to be locked. Some freezer cabinets have a separate lock. The doors are made of pressed steel and are insulated with from 2 to 4 in. of insulation. They are hermetically sealed at the factory. Gaskets commonly used are of the balloon type such as used on domestic units.

11-20 Magnetic Latches

A federal law enacted in 1958 requires that the pull of the door handle on a domestic refrigerator shall not exceed 13 lbs., and that a force of not more than 15 lbs. will be required to open the door from the inside. This law was enacted to prevent the suffocation of children who become trapped inside refrigerators. The magnetic door latch mechanism meets these specifications.

Fig. 11-52 illustrates a two-pole magnetic type latch assembly used on many refrigerators.

On some cabinets where a tighter seal is required, a bar-type magnet is used instead of a two-pole magnet.

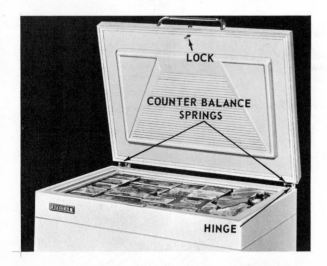

Fig. 11-51. Chest type freezer. Note the hardware.

Latches are usually made of chrome-plated brass and are of fairly heavy design. They are generally provided with a hole through the handle and striker or some other means to enable the cabinet

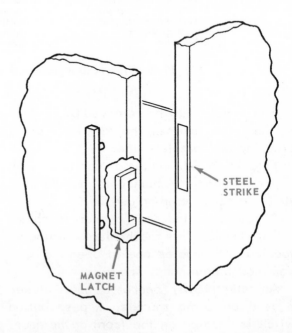

Fig. 11-52. Two-pole magnetic latch installed on refrigerator door.

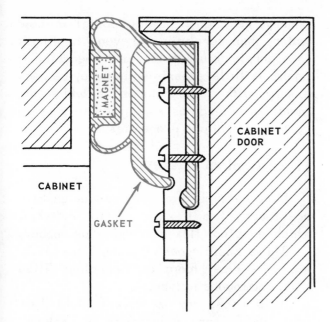

Fig. 11-53. Magnetic door gasket. Note magnet in-bedded in door gasket material.

The magnets should be adjusted so the door will make tight contact without the necessity of slamming it.

A door closer, which contains a magnet within the gasket, and which closes doors silently and automatically, is shown in Fig. 11-53. Another type of magnetic gasket is shown in Fig. 11-54. A magnetic gasket consists of a thin vinyl outer covering and a continuous permanent magnet inside a vinyl envelope. The gasket provides spring action for good closing, and requires a closing force of only about one-seventh of that required for some old

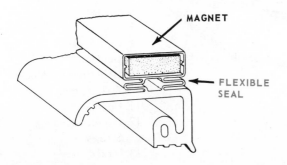

Fig. 11-54. Magnetic gasket with flexible element.

style gaskets. A .003 in. plastic feeler gauge or a strip of paper may be used to check the distance between the gasket and door as shown in Fig. 11-55. If the gauge or a strip of paper requires a definite pull to remove it when the door is closed, the gasket is sealing satisfactorily.

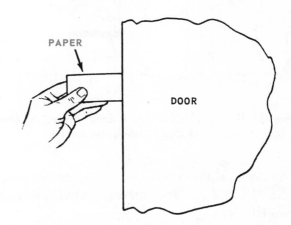

Fig. 11-55. Testing door for air tightness. Pull on narrow strip of paper will indicate if the gasket is tight enough.

11-21 Cabinet Hardware Repairs

Hardware may often be repaired when replacement parts are not obtainable.

An emergency repair for hinges that are worn and cause the door to sag is to dismantle the hinge, and after cleaning and filing the worn surfaces flat, insert washers to replace the wear. See Fig. 11-56.

The hinge pin holes may also wear elliptically (oval shaped). This wear can be repaired by drilling the holes larger and inserting larger pins, or inserting steel or brass sleeves.

Broken die cast parts can be repaired by gas welding if special die cast filler rods are used. A sand or asbestos paste mold should be made to hold and align the parts during the welding operation. A successful weld can only be made if the plating is removed around the welded portion. The parts can be replated after finishing.

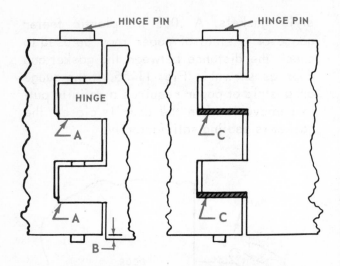

Fig. 11-56. Repairing a worn cabinet hinge. A—Worn surfaces. B—Sag. C—Inserted washers.

Avoid breathing the fumes when welding die castings. Use strong local exhaust ventilation.

Replacement springs can be made by heating spring wire to a low cherry red, cooling slowly (in sand or asbestos) shaping the spring, heating the spring to a dull

cherry red, quenching (dipping) in cold water, then carefully and evenly heating it to a purple (blue) color, and quenching it again. A little experimenting may be necessary with temperatures to which the metal is heated, as spring wires vary in carbon content and properties.

11-22 Cabinet Gaskets

Many refrigerator and freezer gaskets are made of a flexible plastic material which does not flex as readily as rubber.

Three basic types of gaskets are: Hollow tube type, foam or fiberglass filled type, and magnetic type.

It is necessary to have a tight door seal. Before any adjustment or replacement of gaskets is attempted, the serviceman should make certain that the cabinet is level, using a spirit level. A cabinet which is not level may cause the door hinge to bind, or improper door adjustment.

When checking the door seal a feeler gauge .003 in. in thickness may be used.

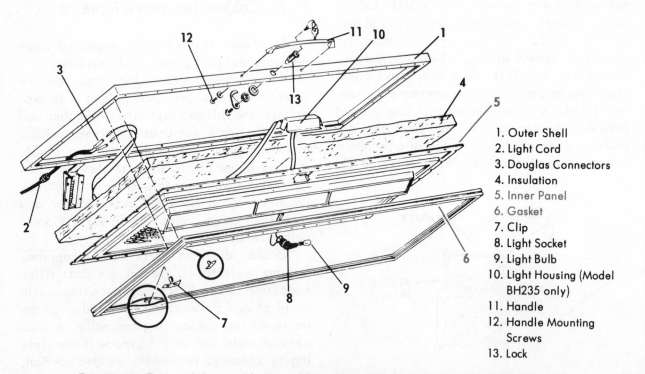

1. Outer Shell
2. Light Cord
3. Douglas Connectors
4. Insulation
5. Inner Panel
6. Gasket
7. Clip
8. Light Socket
9. Light Bulb
10. Light Housing (Model BH235 only)
11. Handle
12. Handle Mounting Screws
13. Lock

Fig. 11-57. Freezer lid assembly components. Note (5), the inner panel and (6) the gasket.

A second way to make a check is to insert a 100-watt lamp inside the cabinet. Use a thin electric wire. Place the lamp near the front of the cabinet. Darken the room; then a gasket leak can be detected by seeing light coming from inside the cabinet.

Another method of checking to see if a gasket is securely sealing the door joint, is to have the cabinet at refrigerating temperature and open the door twice in rapid succession, at 25 to 30 second intervals. The second door opening should require a stronger pull on the door handle than the first. The reason for this is that the first time the door is opened cold air is spilled out of the cabinet and is replaced by warm air. When the door is closed during the 30 second period, the warm air cools, contracts, and a partial vacuum is created.

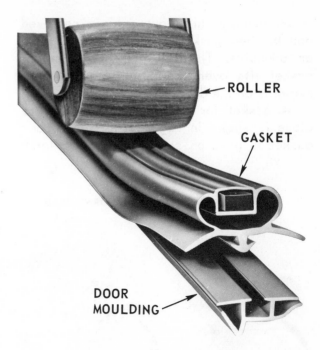

Fig. 11-59. *A method of mounting a gasket on door moulding. (Jarrow Products, Inc.)*

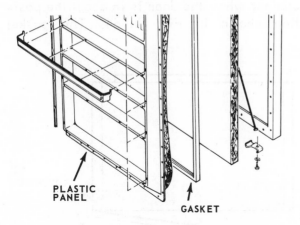

Fig. 11-58. *Door assembly. Note inner plastic panel.*

To replace gaskets, it is usually necessary to remove a plastic or metal inner panel under the gasket. See Fig. 11-57. Care must be taken that the plastic inner panel does not drop. Fig. 11-58 shows an exploded view of a door and inner panel. By using a special plastic holding strip on the door, the sealing gasket can be easily removed and installed. See Fig. 11-59.

Suitable replacement gaskets are usually available. Replacement gaskets may

clamp in place similar to the original, or they may be fastened by using an adhesive, as shown in Fig. 11-60. The gasket sealing surface is the part that wears

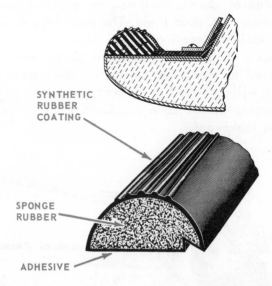

Fig. 11-60. *Replacement gasket that is fastened with adhesive. Bead only of old gasket is removed. Adhesive is applied and replacement is installed with lip placed over old gasket.*

first, usually this part only is removed and the new gasket head is installed using an adhesive. The lip of the replacement gasket fits over the original gasket that remains on the door.

A gasket for doors that are easy to close is shown in Fig. 11-61. This rubber gasket is used on safety-type spring latch

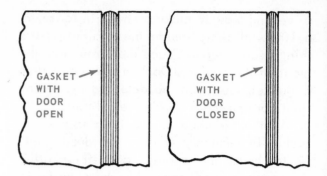

GASKET WITH DOOR OPEN

GASKET WITH DOOR CLOSED

Fig. 11-63. Correct amount typical gasket should be compressed to provide leakproof joint between door and cabinet.

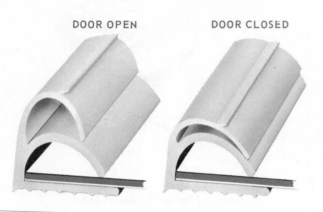

DOOR OPEN   DOOR CLOSED

Fig. 11-61. Door gasket developed for magnetically latched doors and safety latch doors. It seals tightly with force of only 4 lbs.
(Jarrow Products Inc.)

doors, and on magnetic refrigerator and freezer doors. Note how the gasket clamps under the door liner. The open tube design enables a sealing action with slight pressure. Fig. 11-62 shows a gasket notcher used to notch the corners of the gasket so it will not have a tendency to bunch up or buckle at the corners. Gasket joints must be leakproof.

The door must be carefully adjusted to permit easy operation and still provide a tight joint. Fig. 11-63 shows a gasket adjustment which provides a good joint. To obtain this fit, the hinges should be adjusted first. The shims should be arranged until the hinge edge gasket contacts the cabinet when the door is in about the position shown in Fig. 11-64. The gasket

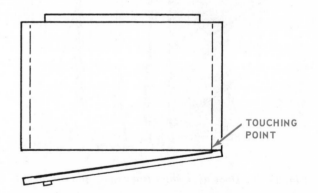

TOUCHING POINT

Fig. 11-64. Position door should be in when gasket touches cabinet evenly for full length on hinge edge.

should touch the cabinet evenly the full length of the door. If the side of the door with the handle does not contact the cabinet evenly, it usually means that the door is warped. See Fig. 11-65. This misalignment can usually be remedied by loosening the door liner screws, straightening the door, and tightening the screws.

Fig. 11-62. Gasket notcher. Note adjustable single cutting blade. (Watsco Inc.)

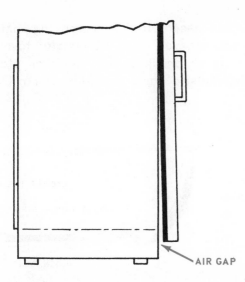

Fig. 11-65. When latch side of door does not contact cabinet evenly, door can be adjusted by means of door liner screws.

11-23 Cabinet Assembly Devices

Modern metal refrigerator and freezer cabinets make use of a wide variety of assembly devices. Where strength is needed the parts need not ordinarily be removed, spot or seam welding is used extensively. For example, plates to which the hinge and hinge butt are attached and the frame of the cabinet that supports the motor-compressor are usually welded.

Hinge parts and the latch parts are generally held in place by countersunk machine screws. In some cases lock washers are used.

Small parts may be held in place with sheet metal screws. When tightening sheet metal screws care must be taken as slight excess in tightening torque may strip the threads in the sheet metal.

Fasteners known as quick fasteners are used extensively. These devices come in great variety. They are usually made of spring steel and use hard sharp edges to hold them in place. Various fastening devices are also used for assembling of plastic panels to door liners. In Fig. 11-66, part B, the shelf support is made of a plas-

tic (polystyrene). It is fastened by inserting the cloverleaf in the panel hole and driving in the pin to expand the cloverleaf.

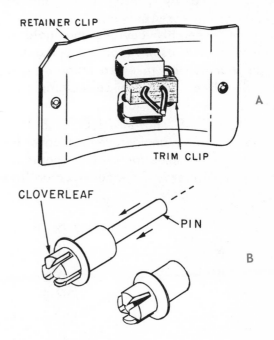

Fig. 11-66. Fastening devices. A—Trim and retainer clips used on mouldings and liners. B—Door shelf supports made of polystyrene.
(Kelvinator Div., American Motors Corp.)

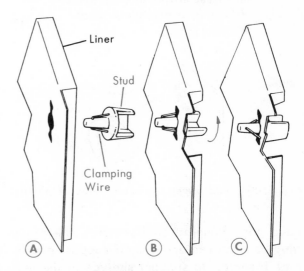

Fig. 11-67. Shelf studs used to support shelves. Note clamping wire which locks in place by twisting the stud. A—Note the shape of the hole in the liner. B—Stud being inserted and twisted 1/4 turn. C—Position of installed stud.
(Franklin Appliance Div., Studebaker Corp.)

Rivets may be used to fasten small door hinges, such as used on dairy bars and bottle keepers. The rivets can usually be removed by prying under the rivet heads with a screwdriver.

The assembly devices that hold shelf brackets are usually of a spring-loaded type that can be inserted from the inside of the liner and are self-clamping and locking. See Fig. 11-67.

Fig. 11-68 shows a type of hole plug used by some manufacturers to cover holes which are not used for shelf supports at the time of delivery. If the serviceman finds a

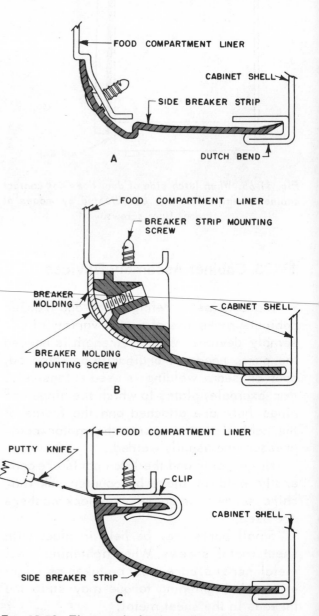

Fig. 11-68. Hole plug used to cover holes which are not needed at time of manufacture. (Norge Div., Borg-Warner Corp.)

Fig. 11-69. Shelf support grommet made of plastic.

need for changing shelf heights the plugs may be removed and a shelf support grommet inserted to support shelves at the new desired heights. See Fig. 11-69.

Assembly devices used to fasten the breaker strip to the food compartment liner and to the cabinet shell are shown in Fig. 11-70.

When assembling or removing parts of the cabinet you must be careful to avoid buckling or breaking the metal or plastic parts. Plastic parts should be warm (75 to

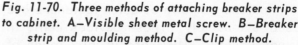

Fig. 11-70. Three methods of attaching breaker strips to cabinet. A—Visible sheet metal screw. B—Breaker strip and moulding method. C—Clip method.

100 deg.) before being removed or installed. Some plastics, when cold, break or crack easily. Flexible broad-faced tools should be used to pry or force plastic

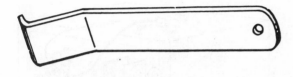

Fig. 11-71. Tool for removing plastic strips from cabinets and door.
(Gibson Refrig. Sales Corp., Hupp Corp.)

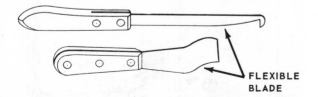

FLEXIBLE BLADE

Fig. 11-72. Tools for removing plastic strips from cabinets and doors.

parts. Fig. 11-71 shows a tool design; Fig. 11-72 shows two tools used on cabinet assemblies.

11-24 Finishes

Most modern cabinets have a porcelain interior (inside of the liner) and are finished with lacquer or baked enamel on the outside of the cabinet and door. Porcelain is a relatively expensive finish and only the more deluxe cabinets are usually finished with it on the exterior. Some baked enamels today are virtually as durable as porcelain. Because they are chip and crack resistant, they are being used on many refrigerators.

11-25 Refinishing Metal Surfaces

Metal to be refinished must be carefully prepared before being painted. All dirt, rust, grease, alkalies, and dust must be removed from the metal. Temperature and humidity in the paint room must be controlled according to the paint manufacturer's recommendations. The air must be as free from dust as possible. The spray room must be carefully designed for safety. Explosion proof lamps and explosion

proof switches should be used. The air in the spray room should be carefully filtered.

Enamels to be baked are sprayed on the metal and the units are then baked in special drying ovens or bins. The drying devices are usually electric heat lamps (infrared).

11-26 Cleaning Finishes

When cleaning lacquer surfaces, care must be taken to make sure the cleaning materials do not harm the finish. Gritty cleaning materials should not be used. To clean lacquer finished cabinets, solutions and materials are now on the market which have the property of cleaning and polishing the surface simultaneously. All cleaning and polishing materials should be applied according to the manufacturer's directions.

11-27 Repairing Finishes

Enamel finished cabinets may be repaired by using high grade enamel made especially for the purpose. Examine the damaged area carefully. All wax and rust must be removed, down to the bare metal. Sand edges of the damaged area with fine waterproof paper (6/0) so the old finish slopes toward the center. This is called "featheredging" and is done so the primer and finish coat blend smoothly with the old finish. See Fig. 11-73. Soapy water may be used as a sanding lubricant. The metal surface must be dry before applying primer.

Apply metal primer to exposed bare metal with a brush or spray gun (follow manufacturer's instructions). The primer provides a hard surface for good adhesion of the finish coat. Allow the primer to dry thoroughly. When the primer is dry, sand lightly using 6/0 waterproof paper and soapy water as a sanding lubricant.

Spray or brush on the enamel, blending new coat to the old finish as smooth as possible. Allow enamel to dry thoroughly, then sand (wet) with 6/0 paper until the edges are invisible. For a gloss finish rub entire surface including patched area with rottenstone and paraffin oil or rubbing oil. When desired gloss has been reached, wipe off rottenstone and oil by using moistened

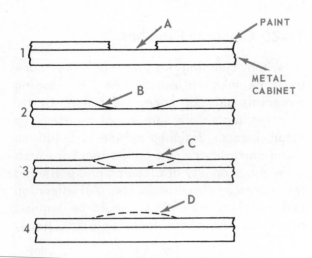

Fig. 11-73. Steps in finishing a chipped surface: A—Paint chipped from cabinet. B—Surface sanded in preparation for repairing. C—New finish applied. D—Excess finish must be sanded down to level as shown.

cloth or chamois. Paint spraying must be done in a fireproof, well ventilated booth. The air must be free of dust and the spray gun air must be free of moisture and oil.

11-28 Porcelain

The porcelain process is a method of covering metal with a white opaque glass coating. At the corners, the porcelain may be black (the primary coat) as black porcelain is less likely than white porcelain to chip or crack. The finishing process consists of thoroughly cleaning the metal, and then fusing black opaque glass to this metal at a high temperature. This is a factory operation, beyond the scope of the repair shop. The black finish is porcelain with an iron content that expands, the same as that of the metal and white porcelain. White porcelain is bonded to the black porcelain at a high temperature and a smooth-

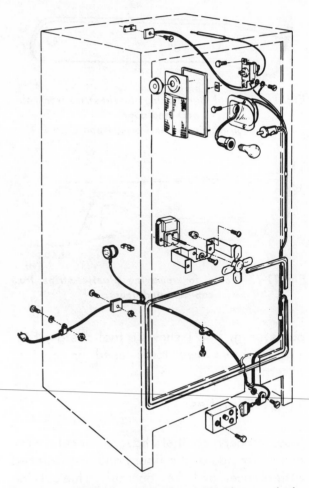

Fig. 11-74. Refrigerator wiring system showing the location of the wiring and electrical parts inside cabinet.

glassy finish is obtained. Porcelain has the disadvantage of being brittle and easy to chip.

11-29 Patching Porcelain

When filling in cracks or chipped places of a porcelain finish, a special porcelain patching material should be used. Because of the inherent nature of porcelain, its color shade will vary somewhat. A patching kit may be obtained with several colors.

In doing this work it is necessary to clean the surface to be patched, warm the area to be patched, then apply the patching material with a small, fine brush or air brush. After the material has dried, it should be smoothed down with waterproof

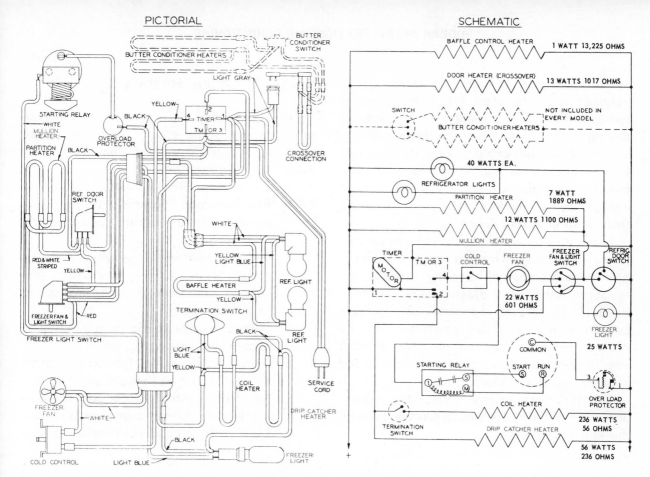

Fig. 11-75. Wiring diagram for refrigerator. Note variety of special heaters. Also the butter conditioner heater. (Franklin Appliance Div., Studebaker Corp.)

abrasive paper and polished with a soft cloth, or with rottenstone (available from paint stores) and rubbing oil.

11-30 Accessories

Many devices have been created to make refrigerators more useful. Some of the accessories available are:
1. Cabinet lights.
2. Butter conditioner.
3. Electrically operated door closers.
4. Crispers.
5. Wire baskets.
6. Beverage holders including built-in units.
7. Egg nests.
8. Storage bins.
9. Automatic ice cube makers.
10. Fresh meat storage.
11. Deodorizers.
12. Thermometers.

The cabinet light is usually a 25-watt bulb mounted in the rear of the cabinet. It is 120V controlled by a spring activated switch that closes the circuit when the cabinet door is open. This switch is usually located near the bottom rear of the door on the pilaster. It usually controls the evaporator fan motor too, by shutting off the fan when the door is open. The wiring is in the same harness as the thermostat wires and the wires connect into the main circuit at the junction box (usually the relay).

The butter conditioner is a small cavity built into the cabinet liner or the door liner. It usually has a small heating element that maintains the butter at an easy spreading temperature (about 50 F. to 60 F.). Wiring to this conditioner connects into the main circuit at the relay and it is in parallel with the thermostat. It operates only when the unit is running. See Figs. 11-74 and 11-75.

Crispers, or covered containers in the refrigerator are used for storing vegetables, fruits, and meats. They prevent drying of the food from the dehumidifying action of the evaporator. Some designs use glass shelves as the cover for the containers and the containers slide out on racks. Some models use built-in doors (metal) to seal this space.

For convenience of storing, some refrigerators have wire baskets to hold certain foods for ease of handling.

Some units have plastic beverage containers, built into the door. An outside beverage tap may be provided so the cooled beverage can be obtained without opening the door. Specially built shelves and baskets hold standard shaped articles such as bottles, eggs, oranges, etc. The orderly arrangement provides for maximum use of the storage space.

11-31 Electrical Heaters

Most domestic refrigerators and freezer units use some electrical heaters. See Fig. 11-76. Some of the more common heater applications are:

1. Butter conditioner heater.
2. Freezer door heater: to prevent condensation from forming and freezing on freezer door.
3. Mullion heater to prevent condensation from forming on mullion (the cabinet structure between two doors of a cabinet).
4. Defrost heater to aid in defrosting of evaporator on defrost cycle.
5. Drip catch heater (to heat drained defrost water and evaporate it).
6. Air flow control heater (to prevent frost from forming around air flow control in forced convection units).

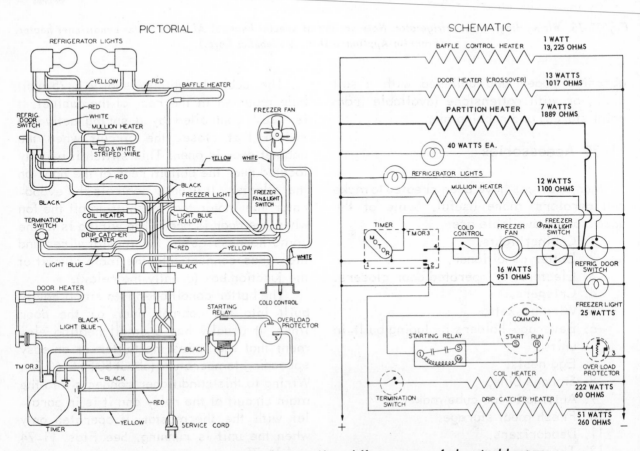

Fig. 11-76. Refrigerator wiring diagram. Note different types of electrical heaters.

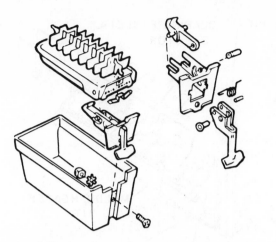

Fig. 11-77. Ice bucket with lever for releasing ice into bucket. (Frigidaire Div., General Motors Corp.)

7. Drain tube heater (to prevent defrost water from freezing and clogging drain tube).
8. Thermostat heater (to warm body of thermostat to insure that sensitive element only operates thermostat).

These are low wattage heaters, and their operation is best checked by using an ohmmeter. Refer to the wiring diagram of the unit, or the manufacturer's service manual to obtain the correct value for each heater.

11-32 Ice Cube Trays

Practically all refrigerators provide facilities for making ice cubes. The ice is usually made by filling shallow trays with tap water. The trays have grids (about 1 1/2 in. square) that shape the ice into easily handled cubes.

Aluminum trays are prevalent throughout the industry, however, rubber, stainless steel and plastic trays are also used.

Some companies have installed ice bucket holders in the freezer compartments as shown in Fig. 11-77. The ice trays are inverted and levers engage the top of the grid mechanism to release the ice cubes.

Also available are automatic ice cube makers that are self-filling. They freeze cubes, free the cubes and dump them into a basket. The operation continues until the basket is full, (refer to Par. 8-17 for additional information).

Ice formed in ice cube trays is usually translucent (not clear). The foggy appearance is due to the release of air from the water as it freezes. Clearer ice may be produced by first boiling the water, and allowing it to cool to room temperature before putting it in the freezing trays. Automatic ice cube machines as described in Par. 11-33 and Chapter 14, usually produce clear ice.

11-33 Automatic Ice Cube Makers

The automatic ice cube maker is designed to produce and store an adequate quantity of ice cubes for normal household use. A series of compartments are automatically filled with water, then subjected to a low temperature to form the ice cubes. The cubes are automatically removed and stored.

Two basic systems are in use: Ice mold system and plastic conveyer belt system.

The basic operation of the ice mold system, Fig. 11-78 is: water enters the ice mold through the rear of the mold. Each individual ice cube compartment has a small opening which allows the water to enter. Flow of water to the mold is controlled by the use of a small cam, which allows water to enter the mold for a predetermined period of time.

A sensing bulb is located in the front of the ice mold. The thermostat switches to a cold or operating temperature of approximately 16 F. The warm position (or off) is approximately 31 F. When the cold temperature is reached and water in the mold is frozen, and the ejection cycle begins. A thermostatically controlled switch causes the motor and the heater coil to be energized. A series of ejection blades or fingers eject the ice cubes. The ejection blades connected to the motor rotate until

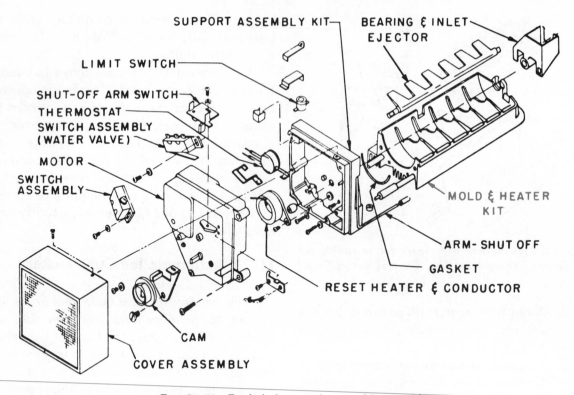

SUPPORT ASSEMBLY KIT

LIMIT SWITCH

SHUT-OFF ARM SWITCH

THERMOSTAT

SWITCH ASSEMBLY
(WATER VALVE)

MOTOR

SWITCH
ASSEMBLY

BEARING & INLET
EJECTOR

MOLD & HEATER
KIT

ARM- SHUT OFF

GASKET

RESET HEATER & CONDUCTOR

CAM

COVER ASSEMBLY

*Fig. 11-78. Exploded view of ice mold assembly.
(Kelvinator Div., American Motors)*

the ice is ejected from the mold. A series of cams attached to the motor shaft operate the ice ejection cycle. After the ice cubes are ejected, one of the cams closes the water solenoid valve circuit, allowing it to again fill the mold. The operation is then repeated. An arm inserted in the ice cube bucket, when lifted by the ice cubes as the bucket fills, shuts off the unit. A refrigerator with this type ice cube maker requires a water supply (usually a 3/8 in. copper tube equipped with a hand shutoff valve).

The quantity of ice manufactured and the length of time to produce the ice is dependent on load conditions, ambient temperature, number of door openings, etc.

A manufacturer who uses a forced convection evaporator has a plastic conveyor belt, as shown in Fig. 11-79. In this arrangement, a continuous plastic mold revolves around two shafts, one of which is connected to a motor. Each link has three molds which have grooves to allow the

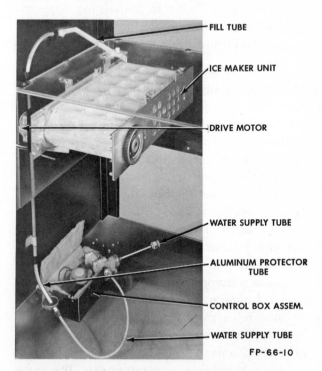

FILL TUBE

ICE MAKER UNIT

DRIVE MOTOR

WATER SUPPLY TUBE

ALUMINUM PROTECTOR TUBE

CONTROL BOX ASSEM.

WATER SUPPLY TUBE

FP-66-10

*Fig. 11-79. Automatic ice cube maker used in domestic refrigerator showing component parts.
(Frigidaire Div., General Motors Corp.)*

water to flow between them. After filling, the conveyor belt moves forward at approximately the rate required to freeze three cubes every 24 minutes. As the conveyor moves forward, it reaches a point in the track near the front, which causes the plastic belt to twist and the ice cubes to drop into a reservoir. Ice cubes will continue to be produced even on the off cycle of the refrigerator unit. The freezer blower fan located in back of the ice cube maker, operates when the ice maker is in operation. During the defrost cycle no ice freezing takes place.

11-34 Installing a Refrigerator or Freezer

The sale of a refrigerator to the customer should not end the dealer's reponsibility. It is important that the installation should be carefully and accurately, made in order to keep the customer convinced that he has made a wise purchase. The shipping and moving of a refrigerator must be done carefully to avoid damage. Fig. 11-80 shows a hand truck with a hold-on strap. The side rails may be used as skids to aid in moving the appliance in and out of the truck.

A consideration of importance is proper ventilation for the unit. The refrigerator should be carefully leveled, using a spirit level, because of the ice cube trays, and to provide ease of door opening and closing. Usually the two front legs of the refrigerator are adjustable (screw type) to aid the leveling of the cabinet. See Figs. 11-81 and 11-82.

11-35 Uncrating a Refrigerator or Freezer

The critical areas which may be easily abused when uncrating or removing a cabinet are:

1. Bottom: Refrigeration unit may be damaged.

Fig. 11-80. Appliance hand truck. (Stevens Appliance Truck Co.)

2. Back: Refrigeration condenser coils may be damaged. (Not all cabinets have condensers in the back.)
3. Door: The doors may be forced out-of-line or buckled.

Avoid putting the blades of a fork lift truck under a cabinet as the blades may injure the refrigerating unit.

The carton usually has printed instructions on it relative to safe handling. These instructions should be carefully followed.

11-36 Location of Refrigerator or Freezer

The location of the refrigerator or freezer is usually determined by the convenience of the cabinet to the other devices in the kitchen. Factors to be considered in obtaining an ideal location include:

1. The refrigerator or freezer should not be exposed to direct rays of the sun because this will add to the cost of operation.
2. The refrigerator or freezer should be close to an electrical outlet as overloaded or lengthy extension cords may reduce the line voltage to a dangerous level.
3. It should be located to provide good air circulation through the condenser.
4. Avoid placing a refrigerator or freezer over or close to a hot air register or a radiator.
5. If the refrigerator has an automatic ice cube maker, a water supply must be available.

11-37 Electrical Connections

Most refrigerators and freezers are electrically connected to the house electrical system by a flexible extension cord fitted with a three-prong plug. The third prong is for a ground. The power supply is complete when the plug is inserted in the outlet. It is important that the extension cord be put in such a place that it will not be kinked sharply or pinched.

In all electrical refrigeration hookups it is of the utmost importance that the refrigerator motor have the same characteristics as the power line. The frequencies must be the same; that is, 60 cycle, 25 cycle, etc. The voltage must be the same, i.e. 32, 120 or 240 volts. The phase must be the same, single-phase, three-phase, etc. Single-phase motors are used almost exclusively for domestic refrigerators.

Sufficient current must be available for motor consumption and the voltage must be up to the voltage required by the motor. To check on these values an AC ammeter and

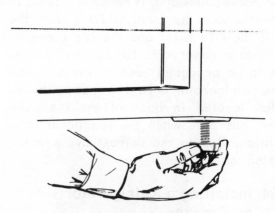

Fig. 11-81. Adjustable leg leveler.

voltmeter may be used. The voltage at the outlet should be checked with the unit both running and off. A voltage drop of over 15 volts will necessitate correcting the elec-

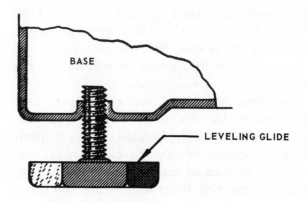

Fig. 11-82. Detail of leveling glide.

trical service supply. In most cases it is advisable to install a separate circuit for the refrigerator, rather than use the supply already available in the kitchen.

11-38 Instructions to Owner

Before leaving the refrigerator or freezer in the hands of the housewife it is important to instruct her concerning the method of defrosting (as directed by the manufacturer), and the correct use of the temperature control.

Leave your name, address, and telephone number in a convenient place (attach decal if available) so service calls, if required, can be made with minimum of trouble.

When a refrigerator is moved, the condensing unit, if mounted on springs or rubber supports, should be clamped or bolted to the cabinet. After a refrigerator has been moved, it should always be leveled carefully, using a spirit level.

11-39 Care of Refrigerator or Freezer

In the operation of any domestic refrigerator or freezer, the owner should be instructed not to allow the door to remain open. Due to the great difference in temperature between the inside of the cabinet and the room temperature, convection currents will be set up as soon as the door is opened. This will bring a great deal of heat into the cabinet quickly. When removing articles from, or placing articles in the cabinet, do it as quickly as possible.

The cabinet must be kept clean outside as well as inside. The hinges and latch should be lubricated periodically. The condenser and motor-compressor should be wiped clean at least every six months. The door gasket should be checked for tightness periodically.

11-40 Defrosting Refrigerator or Freezer

Many present day refrigerators or freezers have automatic defrost devices or nonfrost type systems. Some defrost devices are clock operated to turn on each day at a certain time (1 or 2 A.M.). Others are activated by mechanical devices such as a ratchet controlled by opening the door. These controls either turn on electrical heating elements to melt the frost (the unit is shut off) or open a solenoid valve to send hot gas through the evaporator until the frost is melted (the unit continues to operate). The water formed then drains into a pan in the condensing unit compartment and evaporates, aided by the heat from the condensing unit. See Fig. 11-62. See Chapters 8 and 10 for more complete information concerning automatic defrosting systems. Another reason an evaporator should be defrosted and the water drained is that this collection of frost on the evaporator is usually odor-laden and the odor may permeate the food. Instructions supplied by the manufacturer should be followed carefully.

11-41 Review of Safety

Refrigerators and freezers must be carefully handled in order not to injure those handling them or to damage the cabinets or mechanisms.

Never use a pointed or sharp metal tool to remove ice from the evaporator. You may puncture the refrigerating unit.

Remember, if an old style refrigerator is taken out of service, the door latch must be removed immediately; better still, remove the door. Too frequently, children are suffocated by allowing an out-of-service refrigerator to stand where they may use it to play in.

Some refrigerants, such as R-764 (sulphur dioxide) and R-717 (ammonia) are irritating to eyes, nose, and respiratory system. Always purge these refrigerants into a proper purging line and never into the work room.

Some refrigerants, such as Group Three refrigerants, if mixed with air may form explosive mixtures. Use great caution when working with these refrigerants, to be sure no vapors are present in any space where there is danger of the mixture being ignited by a spark or an open flame.

11-42 Test Your Knowledge - Chapter 11

1. Why are refrigerator cabinets insulated?
2. What is the average thickness of the insulation if polyurethane is used?
3. Why should the insulation be moisture proof?
4. What is meant by net contents of the cabinet?
5. What are some possible locations of the condensing unit?
6. Why must an evaporator be defrosted?
7. Name three substances used for insulation.
8. How are cabinet door joints made airtight?
9. List two evaporator locations in the cabinet.
10. Why should some evaporators be located near the top of the cabinet?
11. What may clog an air-cooled condenser, externally?
12. Why should the voltage of the electrical line to the refrigerator be checked?
13. What happens to defrost water in modern refrigerators?
14. What is the best way to check a door gasket for leaks?
15. How are most latches and strikes adjusted?
16. Why is it required that refrigerators be openable from the inside?
17. List three advantages of frozen foods.
18. What type of insulation is used in modern freezers?
19. What is meant by hermetic insulation?
20. What is meant by featheredging when repairing an enamel or lacquer finish?

Chapter 12

DOMESTIC HERMETIC SYSTEMS, SERVICING

Hermetic units are made in various styles. The service procedure depends on the design. Late designs generally have condensing units in the base and run the refrigerant lines back of the cabinet door-jamb breaker strip. The evaporators are removed from the front of the refrigerator.

A competent serviceman must be well acquainted with the fundamentals of refrigeration and must be adept in the proper use of tools, before he is qualified to work on a refrigerating mechanism. A good knowledge of fundamental refrigeration is needed to enable the serviceman to dismantle and assemble the mechanism and to locate troubles. A knowledge of the handling of tools is necessary in order to lap valves properly, to fit tubing, and to assemble the parts in the proper manner.

The ability to locate trouble and determine its cause is a requirement of a competent refrigerator serviceman. Practically any careful mechanic can overhaul a refrigeration mechanism once it is taken apart, but it requires a specially trained mechanic to safely and correctly dismantle and assemble a refrigeration system. It also requires special training to diagnose troubles and make repairs on the mechanism.

12-1 Tools and Supplies

The serviceman should be equipped with an adequate tool kit. It is good economics to purchase high quality tools. Tools required include: valve wrenches, gauges, storage cylinders for the refrigerant, wrenches, and a torch. See Chapters 2 and 15 for more detailed description of tools needed.

A typical serviceman's equipment connected to service a hermetic unit is shown in Fig. 12-1. This shows the motor-com-

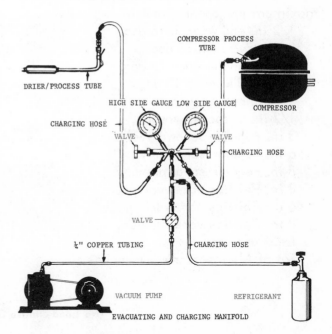

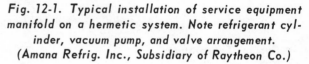

Fig. 12-1. Typical installation of service equipment manifold on a hermetic system. Note refrigerant cylinder, vacuum pump, and valve arrangement.
(Amana Refrig. Inc., Subsidiary of Raytheon Co.)

pressor connected to a gauge manifold, refrigerant cylinder, vacuum pump, drier-process tube, etc.

A serviceman's complete tool kit will comprise one each of the following:

Refrigeration ratchet wrench with 3/16, 7/32, and 1/4 in. square openings.

1/4 in. square to 1/4 in. square ratchet wrench adapter.

1/4 in. square to 3/16 in. square ratchet wrench adapter.

1/4 in. square to 7/32 in. square ratchet wrench adapter.

3/16 in. internal packing nut adapter.

1/4 in. internal packing nut adapter.

Set of bending springs for 1/4, 3/8, and 1/2 in. OD tubing.

Tube cutter.

Flaring outfit to use on 3/16, 1/4, 5/16, 3/8, 7/16, 1/2 in. OD tubing.

Gauge manifold.

Compound gauge 30 in. Hg--0--150 psig.

High pressure gauge 0--300 psig.

8 in. adjustable open end wrench with maximum jaw opening of 1 in.

1/2 in. end wrench 15 deg.

3/4 in. wrench 15 deg.

7/8 in. end wrench 15 deg.

1 in. end wrench 15 deg.

1/2 in. box wrench.

1/2 in. T socket wrench.

3 in. regular screwdriver.

6 in. regular screwdriver.

8 in. regular screwdriver.

3 in. Phillips screwdriver.

6 in. Phillips screwdriver.

8 in. Phillips screwdriver.

Leak detector.

Set of Allen setscrew wrenches.

Set of sockets with from 7/16 in. to 1 in. openings (12 point preferred).

Gasket scraper (a ground file).

T-handle wrench for sockets.

Swivel handle wrench for sockets.

Torque handle wrench for sockets.

Speed handle wrench for sockets.

Pinch-off tool (for extreme emergencies only).

Thermometer -20 to 120 F.

The serviceman should also have the following supplies:

1 5 lb. cylinder of R-12.

1 5 lb. cylinder of R-22.

An assortment of one to five pound and special weight disposable cylinders of R-12 and R-22.

1 Set of fittings; i.e. nuts, elbows, unions, half unions, "tee," caps, plugs, etc.

1 Set of sweat fittings.

1 Purging line (1/4 in. x 15 ft.) equipped with a hand shutoff needle valve and a check valve.

1 Set of tubing mounting service valves.

1 Brush, round with fiber bristles.

1 lb. of 60-40 solder.

1 can of soft solder flux.

1 ounce of silver brazing rod.

1 can of silver brazing flux.

1 pad steel wool.

1 pad medium grade sandpaper.

1 roll of plastic tape.

(No Load and No Door Openings)

	70°F. Ambient Temperature	90°F. Ambient Temperature	100% Run Time
Cabinet Temperature	38°	40°	47°
% Operating Time	38	62	100
Cycles Per Hour	3	2	None
Kwhr/24 hrs.	3.8	6.0	9.9
Control Position	4	4	4
Evaporator Air Temperature	1.5°	-1°	0°
Suction Pressure (Psi) (Min-Max)	2"-13	0.13	-2
Watts (Complete System)	390 ± 20	395 ± 20	395 ± 20

Fig. 12-2. Performance data of 18 cu. ft. combination refrigerator-freezer which has 1/3 hp two-pole motor-compressor. Note Kwhr changes with ambient temperature change.

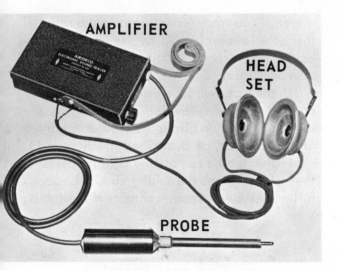

Fig. 12-3. Electronic sound tracer. Note headset, amplifier, and probe. To use instrument, touch suspected part with probe. Sound from headset will indicate if probe is at source of sound.
(Airserco Mfg. Co.)

1 can of refrigerant oil (spout type).
1 can of refrigerant oil, 300 viscosity.
1 can of refrigerant oil, 150 viscosity.
Cleaning cloths.

Assorted service stock such as driers, tubing, copper pipe, refrigerant controls, motor controls, relays, capacitors, and the like.

Small hand vacuum cleaner.

12-2 Servicing Hermetic Units

To successfully service refrigerating units, you must know how they are supposed to perform when in good condition. Fig. 12-2 shows the performance data of a typical domestic unit. This information is for a 1/3 hp two-pole motor unit used in a combination refrigerator-freezer of 18 cu. ft. capacity.

The servicing procedure on a hermetic refrigerator mechanism depends to a considerable extent how the unit was assembled. If the unit was brazed or welded together, extra equipment is required to perform a major repair (an internal repair). If the unit is bolted together, servicing

anything within the unit is still considered a major overhaul but less special equipment is needed for tearing down and assembling the unit.

It is considered good practice to remove the complete hermetic unit from the cabinet and recondition it in the shop if any internal difficulties arise.

Servicing of hermetic refrigerators may be divided into three major divisions:
1. External servicing.
2. Internal servicing.
3. Overhaul of hermetic system.

12-3 External Servicing of Hermetic Units

External servicing means all service operations which do not involve breaking into the refrigerant system. Most external repairs can be done on the customer's premises.

Some of the more common external service operations are:
1. Cabinet hardware.
2. Cleaning.
3. Noise (rattles).
4. Electrical.
   Thermostat.
   Interior light and circuit.
   Power circuit.
   Fan motor.
   Relay.
   Capacitor.
   Motor terminals.
   Defroster.
   Defroster control.
   Heater coil.

12-4 Cleaning Mechanism

The hermetic refrigerating system is basically a heat transfer mechanism. Provisions must be made for air to circulate around and through the unit and condenser. Further, the condenser and dome must be kept as clean as possible, because dirt and lint will act as a heat insulator. Periodic cleaning (approximately every three months) is necessary for economical operation and long life.

The best way to clean the hermetic mechanism is with a small vacuum cleaner or a special vacuum cleaner nozzle with a brush attachment. The vacuum cleaner eliminates raising a lint cloud to circulate in the room or to settle on the floor. It is also quicker and more thorough than hand brushes or cleaning cloths. If a brush or cleaning cloth is used, place a paper or cloth on the floor under the unit. If the unit uses a fan on the condensers, be sure to turn off the power (pull the plug) before proceeding with the cleaning. In some cases it may be necessary to partially remove the unit (especially remove the baffles and un-bolt the condenser guard) to perform a good cleaning job.

Some servicemen use high pressure nitrogen or carbon dioxide to blow lint, etc. from between the fins of coils and other difficult to reach sections.

12-5 Noise Elimination

Most external noise in the refrigerator comes from rattles. Loose baffles or ducts, tubing touching something while vibrating, uneven floor which may cause a list (leaning to one side) of the condensing unit, and fan and motor vibration, are all sources of noise. The source of the noise in a system may usually be located with the use of a stethoscopic type listening device or electronic sound tracer, as shown in Fig. 12-3. This instrument has a built-in sound amplifier.

A loose evaporator coil unit door and loose articles on shelves that are not even-ly placed on supports may also cause annoying rattles. A rattling noise originating in the unit may indicate that the unit is laboring harder than it should. To determine if there is an extra load on the running parts, the electrical load may be best measured by an ohmmeter or a watt-

meter. You may sometimes determine if the unit is overloaded by its starting behavior (3 seconds to operate relay is the average time).

If the cabinet is on an uneven floor the cabinet may be leveled by adjusting the screw type floor glides located at the front of the cabinet, as described in Chapter 11.

If the tubing is rattling against parts of the refrigerator, the tubing should be carefully bent away from contact. If the tubing

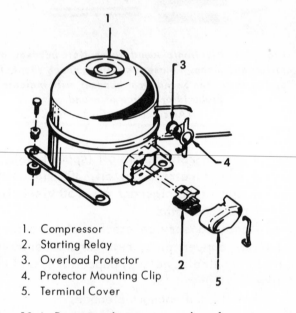

1. Compressor
2. Starting Relay
3. Overload Protector
4. Protector Mounting Clip
5. Terminal Cover

Fig. 12-4. Diagram showing procedure for using replacement starting relay on hermetic unit when checking motor troubles.
(Franklin Appliance Div., Studebaker Corp.)

is taut and has a vibration or hum, this noise can be reduced by clamping rubber blocks on the tubing to stop the harmonic vibration.

Loose baffles and ducts can be easily secured by using self-tapping sheet metal screws.

12-6 Diagnosing Electrical Troubles

Some hermetic units are needlessly replaced because the serviceman concluded that the internal mechanism was faulty when the trouble really existed in the external electrical devices.

For example, if the mechanism will not start, or if the unit hums but will not start, or if the unit short cycles, the trouble could be in the external electrical circuit. The fault may be in the:

1. Power-in connections.
2. Thermostat.
3. Wire terminals.
4. Relay.
5. Capacitor (if the unit has one).

Each of these devices should be checked carefully before the unit itself is determined faulty. These parts can best be checked by removing them from the wiring system and then:

1. Checking them independently or
2. Temporarily substituting a test part of known proper quality to see if the unit will run with the new part. See Fig. 12-4, which shows a motor-compressor with a relay and an overload protector mounted on it. Fig. 12-5, shows a typical electrical circuit for a domestic refrigerator.

Such troubles as open circuits and grounded electrical wires can be easily checked with a test light. A test light can be used to test four-pole motors but two-pole motors should only be tested with a proper size relay as these motors overheat if the starting circuit is connected for more than 2 to 3 seconds.

It is strongly recommended here that Chapters 7 and 8 be carefully reviewed before attempting to trouble shoot in electrical units.

12-7 Field Service Operations

Field service operations consist of jobs which require that the serviceman connect gauges, refrigerant cylinders, oil containers, vacuum pumps, etc., into the refrigerating unit lines or equipment.

A service and gauge manifold is usually used to aid in the performing of these operations.

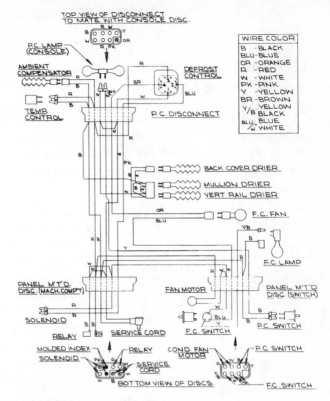

Fig. 12-5. Wiring diagram of domestic system equipped with defrost control, fan and electric heaters. Color code of wiring assists serviceman in tracing circuits. (Kelvinator Div., American Motors Corp.)

Some of the more common field service operations are:

1. Diagnosing of troubles in the unit.
2. Discharging.
3. Charging.
4. Purging.
5. Evacuating.
6. Adding oil.

The unit must be equipped with service valves, service valve attachments, or tubing service valves to perform the operations listed above.

Some basic principles you should keep in mind during all operations which include the inside of the hermetic unit are:

1. The refrigerant must be removed from the system before it is opened.
2. The pressure inside the system should be atmospheric before the system is opened.
3. Clean the joints and the valve fittings before opening or before installing connections.

12-8 Hermetic System Trouble Shooting Chart

Hermetic system trouble shooting should be approached in a logical manner. Always listen to the report of the owners, then begin by checking the most obvious trouble. Gradually check the more remote possibilities. Never replace parts without due reason in an attempt to shorten the length of time required to repair the unit.

The chart which follows lists some common troubles, their causes, and remedies. These data do not apply to all units and should be considered as a general guide only.

TROUBLE SHOOTING CHART
(Franklin Div. Studebaker Corp.)

Trouble	Probable Cause	Remedy
Unit will not run	Blown fuse	Replace fuse
	Low voltage	Check outlet with volt-meter, should check 115 volts ± 10%.
		If circuit over-loaded, either reduce load or have electrician install separate circuit.
		If unable to remedy in any other manner, install an auto-transformer.
	Inoperative Cold Control	Jumper across terminals of control. If unit runs and connections are all tight, replace control.
	Inoperative Relay	Check relay replace if necessary.
	Inoperative Overload	Check overload replace if necessary.
	Inoperative Compressor	Check compressor, replace if necessary.
	Defective service cord	Check with test light at unit if no circuit and current is indicated at outlet, replace or repair.
	Broken lead to compressors, timer or cold control	Repair or replace broken leads.
	Inoperative timer	Check with test light and replace if necessary.
Refrigerator section too warm	Repeated door openings	Instruct user
	Overloading of shelves, blocking normal air circulation in cabinet	Instruct user
	Warm or hot foods placed in cabinet	Instruct user to allow foods to cool to room temperature before placing in cabinet.
	Poor door seal	Level cabinet, adjust door seal.
	Interior light stays on	Check light switch; if faulty, replace.
	Refrigerator section air flow control.	Turn control knob to colder position. Check airflow heater.
		Check if damper is opening by removing grille and with door in open position, damper should open. If control inoperative replace the control.
	Cold control knob set at too warm a position not allowing unit to operate enough	Turn knob to colder position.
	Freezer section grill not properly positioned.	Reposition grill
	Freezer fan not running properly	Replace fan, fan switch, or defective wiring

TROUBLE SHOOTING CHART

Trouble	Probable Cause	Remedy
Refrigerator section too warm (Cont.)	Air duct seal not properly sealed or positioned	Check and reseal or reposition.
Refrigerator section too cold	Refrigerator section air flow control knob turned to coldest position	Turn control knob to warmer position.
	Obstruction causing damper of air flow control to remain open	Remove obstruction
	Defective airflow control	Replace control
	Defective airflow heater	Replace heater
Freezer section and refrigerator section too warm	Inoperative fan motor	Check and replace fan motor if necessary.
	Cold control set too warm or defective	Check thoroughly and replace if necessary.
	Finned evaporator blocked with ice	Check defrost heater termination thermostat or timer. Either one of these could cause this condition.
	Shortage of refrigerant	Check for leak, repair, evacuate and recharge system.
	Not sufficient air circulation around cabinet.	Relocate cabinet or provide clearances to allow sufficient circulation.
	Poor door seal	Level cabinet, adjust door seal.
	Excessive door openings	Instruct customer
Freezer section too cold	Cold control knob improperly set	Turn knob to warmer position
	Cold control capillary not properly clamped to evaporator	Tighten clamp or reposition.
	Defective cold control	Check control. Replace if necessary.
Unit runs continuously	Not sufficient air circulation around cabinet or air circulation is obstructed.	Relocate cabinet or provide proper clearances around cabinet - remove obstruction.
	Poor door seal	Check and make necessary adjustments.
	Freezing large quantities of ice cubes, or heavy loading after shopping	Explain to customer that heavy loading will cause long running time until temperatures are maintained.
	Refrigerant charge	Under charge or over charge - check and evacuate and recharge with proper charge.
	Room temperature too warm.	Ventilate room as much as possible.
	Cold control	Check control if it allows unit to operate continuously and temperatures are maintained - replace control.
	Defective light switch	Check if light goes out. Replace switch if necessary.
	Excessive door opens	Instruct customer

TROUBLE SHOOTING CHART (Cont.)

Trouble	Probable Cause	Remedy
Noisy Operation	Loose flooring or floor not firm	Tighten flooring or brace floor.
	Tubing contacting cabinet or other tubing	Reposition tubing.
	Cabinet not level	Level cabinet.
	Drip tray vibrating	Reposition tray - place on fiberglass pad if necessary.
	Fan hitting liner or mechanically grounding	Reposition fan.
	Compressor mechanically grounded	Replace compressor mounts.
Unit cycles on overload	Inoperative relay	Replace relay.
	Weak overload protector.	Replace overload.
	Low voltage	Check outlet with volt meter. Under load voltage should be 115 volts ± 10%. Check for several appliances on same circuit or extremely long or under-sized extension cord being used.
	Defective compressor	Check with test cord and also for ground before replacing.
Frost or ice on finned evaporator	Inoperative timer	Check with test light and replace if necessary.
	Defective defrost heater	Replace heater.
	Defective termination thermostat	Replace thermostat.
Ice in drip catcher	Defective drip catcher heater.	Replace heater.

12-9 Diagnosing Mechanism Troubles

Before starting to troubleshoot a system, you should check the data plates and wiring diagrams usually found on the system and cabinet. Fig. 12-6 shows a chart of refrigerant and compressor data for an 18 cu. ft. combination refrigerator-freezer.

DATA

Refrigerant	R-12
Charge (in ounces)	10-1/2
Compressor Type	Dome
Compressor HP	1/3
Compressor Speed RPM	3450

Fig. 12-6. Refrigerant and compressor data for 18 cu. ft. combination refrigerator-freezer.

A lack of refrigerant is usually indicated by the evaporator being only partially frosted, but the part which is frosted may be heavily coated.

Fig. 12-7 shows typical pressure curves for a capillary tube system, normal cycle, when it is overcharged, and undercharged.

A leaky check valve will be indicated by the suction line warming rapidly as soon as the compressor stops, starting at the compressor, as oil and hot vapor flow back into it. A restriction on the high side (capillary tube, filter, dehydrator or screen) will be indicated by continuous running, no refrigeration and the liquid refrigerant will be found stored on the high side. This liquid can be detected by carefully using a small torch flame on the condenser as that part which contains liquid will stay relatively cool while the metal with no liquid back of it will warm rapidly.

A partial restriction will be shown by frost starting at that point. This frosting may quite frequently occur at the filter-screen, and dryer.

A compressor housing that is warmer than usual may indicate a unit running at a below normal voltage, a quantity of air in the system or a lack of oil. The voltage can be easily checked with the use of a voltmeter. Air in the system can be checked by purging. A lack of oil will be indicated by a noisy unit. A lack of oil usually means that the oil has become lodged in the evaporator. An inefficient compressor will be indicated by excessive running time.

In older units that have the condensing unit mounted above the evaporator, this condition can sometimes be remedied by putting hot water in the ice cube trays. This extra heat boils the refrigerant violently and it may carry the oil back to the condensing unit. Drastic cases may require removing the unit and setting it upside down for a few minutes to start the oil flowing. An oil-logged evaporator may be indicated by a lazy evaporator, that is, the evaporator does not frost evenly.

Internal electrical troubles (motor and connections) are very rare (about 3 cases out of 1000). Most internal problems come from a lack of oil in the motor-compressor causing excessive wear and eventually cause a burn out. In cases where liquid refrigerant reaches the compressor, it may remove the oil as it evaporates in the crankcase, and carry the oil with it into the condenser.

Some problems may be caused by installing the wrong type of motor-compressor. These units are designed for three applications:

1. High temperature (air conditioners).
2. Medium temperatures (refrigerators).
3. Low temperatures (freezers).

The application must be correct or the unit will fail, or not refrigerate correctly.

12-10 Hermetic Unit Service Valves and Adaptors

Most hermetic refrigerators do not have service valves. Some have fittings to which valves may be attached for service operations. The valves are removed when the service work has been completed. Others have no service valves, neither do they have a provision for fitting them with valves. Where no provision for service valves is provided, it is necessary to fit and attach valves to the mechanism. Valve attachments of various types are available from refrigeration supply wholesalers.

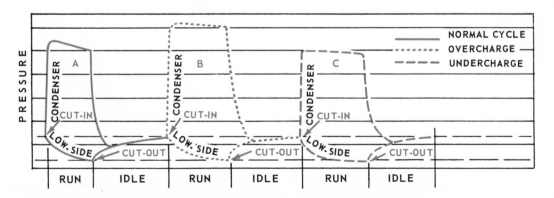

Fig. 12-7. Pressure cycle diagrams for three conditions in capillary tube system: A—Normal charge. B—Overcharged. C—Undercharged. (Allen Mfg. Co., Inc.)

12-11 Systems with Valve Adaptors

A means to connect gauges and charging cylinders to a hermetic system is shown in Fig. 12-8. The device has a removable service valve as shown in Fig.

12-9. Fig. 12-10 illustrates a service valve attachment with an Allen setscrew drive; Fig. 12-11 shows a service valve which has two openings, and the connection for at-

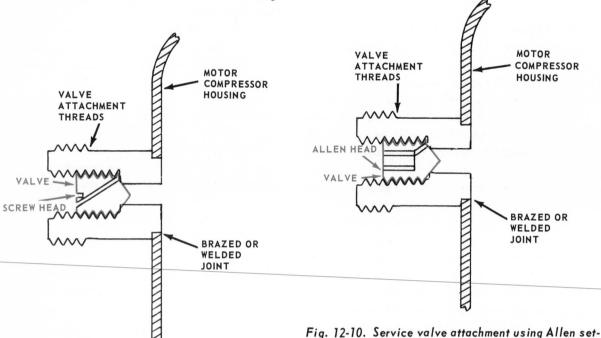

Fig. 12-8. Service valve assembly for hermetic units. Valve attachment must be fastened to valve before valve can be opened or refrigerant will escape.

Fig. 12-10. Service valve attachment using Allen setscrew valve turning device.

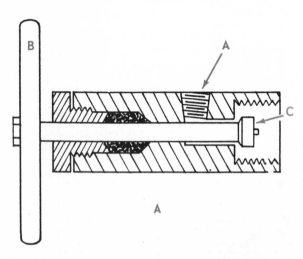

Fig. 12-9. Service valve attachment which may be installed on semi-hermetic or hermetic units. A—Opening for gauge connection and for servicing. B—Handwheel. C—Valve screwhead engagement.

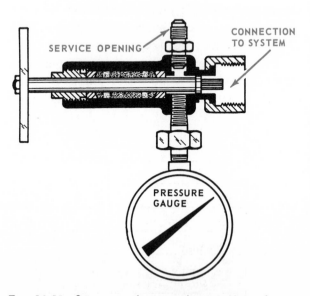

Fig. 12-11. Service valve attachment. Note the two openings. One may be used for pressure gauge, and the other for performing service operations such as discharging, charging, and replacing or adding oil. (Norge Div., Borg-Warner Corp.)

taching it to the refrigeration system. It should be noted that for these refrigerators the adaptor provides a means of operating the valve in the mechanism, also it provides an opening for a service gauge or a refrigerant cylinder, or both. Synthetic gaskets or copper gaskets are used to seal the valve joints. Fig. 12-12, shows an assortment of valve adaptors.

The following procedure should be followed when using valve adaptors:

1. Remove the dust cap from the adaptor mounted on the motor-compressor.
2. Choose the correct valve stem drive.
3. Push the service valve stem forward in the body of the valve.
4. Engage the valve stem in the valve adaptor needle.
5. Thread the body unit into the valve adaptor.
6. Good gaskets must be used.
7. Before opening the valve adaptor needle, tighten the packing unit around the valve stem.

The valve and valve adaptor must be clean. You should blow out the passages using nitrogen gas or carbon dioxide gas. Always test the assembly for leaks using a 15 to 20 psig refrigerant pressure.

12-12 Systems with Process Tubes

The process tube, which the manufacturer uses to evacuate, test, and charge the new unit, which is left on the system at the factory is often used by soldering an extension to it, or by mounting a process tube adaptor on it as a means of servicing a system. The process tube adaptor kit, as shown in Fig. 12-13, makes it possible to extend the process tube without soldering an extension to it or without flaring the tubing.

Through the use of various sized adaptors, the tool may be used on 3/16, 1/4, 5/16, or 3/8 in. copper tubing.

The use of the kit assures the service-

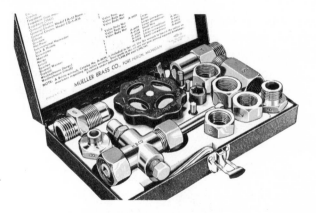

Fig. 12-12. Valve kit and adaptors for use on various makes of semi-hermetic or hermetic refrigeration units. (Mueller Brass Co.)

man of a positive seal and provides a means for attaching charging lines. It permits the serviceman to charge the unit simply by cutting the process tube with a tube cutter and attaching the adaptor to it. The refrigerant in the system must be released before mounting the adaptor or brazing an extension on the process tube. Clean the outside of the tube before cutting. Use clean sandpaper to remove the paint and dirt. If possible, make certain there is

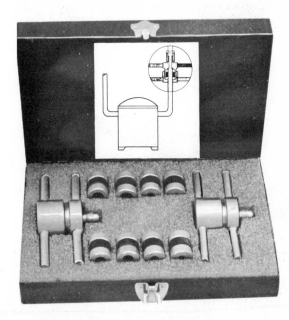

Fig. 12-13. Process tube adaptor and kit. Note in the insert the method of attaching the adaptor to the process tube. (Robinair Mfg. Corp.)

a little internal pressure in the system to blow out any metal chips which may be formed while cutting.

Fig. 12-14 shows a replacement motor-compressor installed, and low side and high side process tubes. Many units have only one process tube.

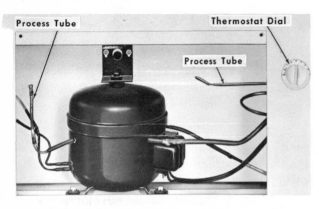

Fig. 12-14. A motor-compressor replacement showing two process tubes.
(Kelvinator Div., American Motors Corp.)

After evacuating the system to dry it and charging the system, close off the process tube through the use of a positive pinch-off tool. Remove the adaptor and braze the end of the process tube.

The pinch-off tool is used wherever it is necessary to seal off soft copper tubing up to 3/8 in. OD. One type of pinch-off tool is shown in Fig. 12-15. The tool has a screw type action shaft with a ball bearing on the end which presses against the tube. The pinch-off tool is placed over the copper tubing in the same manner as a tubing cutter. The tubing should be slowly compressed by tightening the pinch-off tool handle in a clockwise direction.

As pressure is exerted on the tube, the ball bearing presses into the tubing and compresses it against the die on the bottom of the tool, producing a permanently pinched line, as shown in Fig. 12-16. Care

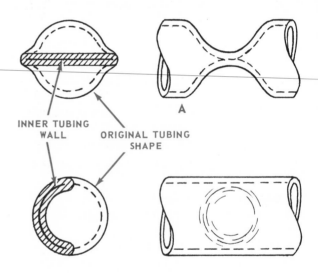

Fig. 12-16. Action of sphere type tubing pinch-off tool. A—"Pinch-off" which may be made with plier-type tool. B—"Pinch-off" made by tool shown in Fig. 12-15.

should be taken that the pinch-off tool is not rotated too far or that excessive pressure is applied. It is best to leave the pinch-off tool in place until the adaptor is removed and the tubing end is sealed by brazing. The pinch-off tool may also be used when an emergency arises which requires isolating parts of the refrigeration system.

Fig. 12-15. Pinch-off tool which is usable on tubing up to 3/8 in. OD. This makes a good seal and also keeps tubing strong at pinch-off spot.

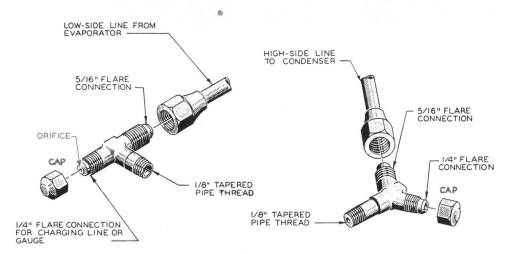

Fig. 12-17. *T and Y fittings being used to attach gauges to hermetic systems. Small orifices prevent any appreciable refrigerant loss. (Gibson Refrig. Sales Corp., Hupp Corp.)*

12-13 Systems with Bleeder Fittings

Another way to attach gauges to a hermetic system is shown in Fig. 12-17. T and Y fittings are connected to the compressor body with pipe threads. A flare connection is used to attach the refrigerant lines. The third opening is capped with a 1/4 in. flare cap. The opening in the fitting at this third connection is small. If the machine is adjusted to produce near atmospheric pressure, the cap may be removed and the gauge or manifold service line attached without losing much refrigerant. The unit should be idle for several minutes before installing the. lines or removing them. Furthermore, the connecting lines should be purged before tightening the connections.

12-14 Systems with Valves Mounted on Tubing

A popular way to gain access to a hermetic system is to mount service valves on the suction tubing, or the discharge tubing (tubing to condenser) or both. Many tubing mounted valves have been developed.

There are two general types:
1. Bolted-on valves.
2. Brazed-on valves.

Fig. 12-18 shows a bolted-on valve. The valve is available in several sizes for vari-

ous size tubing. The tubing should be straight and round. You must clean the tubing (do not scratch). Check to make sure no dents exist in the tubing. Check also to see if the operating valve will have space to be operated, and that the connecting

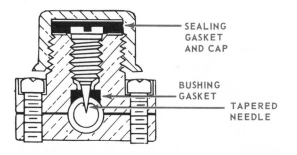

Fig. 12-18. *Bolted-type tubing mounted service valve.*

tubing can be easily mounted on the operating valve. Put a little clean refrigerant oil on the tubing. Be sure the sealing synthetic washer is in place, and the needle point piercing valve stem is all the way out. Mount the valve on the tubing. Tighten the unit clamping screws evenly. Fig. 12-19 shows a cross section of a typical valve. The clamp-on part is usually left on the system. The operating valve is similar in design and construction to those shown in Figs. 12-9 and 12-11. Fig. 12-20 shows two types of these operating valves.

439

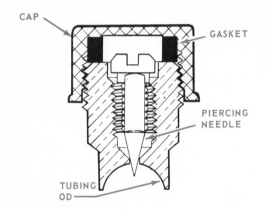

Fig. 12-19. Sectional view of tubing mounted piercing valve. Note use of synthetic material sealing gaskets. Preformed silver brazing ring is usually used to fasten this part to suction or discharge line of unit.

The brazed-on type (saddle design) is possible because both the suction tubing and the condenser tubing have no liquid in them and can be safely heated to a brazing temperature providing there are no flam-

stem and the gasket from the saddle. Put clean fresh brazing flux on the saddle (outer edges) or use a phosphorous-copper brazing filler rod. Mount the saddle on the

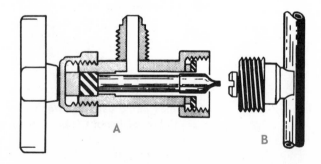

Fig. 12-21. A piercing valve brazed on the line which may be used on hermetic refrigerator systems. Part A can be removed after servicing to prevent tampering with the system. Part B remains on the system. (Kelvinator Div., American Motors Corp.)

Fig. 12-20. Two types of service valves used with tubing mounted valve adaptors. Left. Valve with one 1/4 in. male flare service opening. Right. Valve with two 1/4 in. male flare service openings. (Watsco, Inc.)

mables nearby and no soft-soldered joints close to the brazing. Be sure the tubing is straight and round at the brazing point. Clean both the saddle and tubing mating surface with clean sandpaper or clean steel wool. Remove the piercing valve

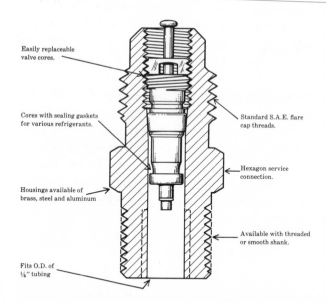

Fig. 12-22. Schrader valve which may be used to enable serviceman to mount service lines on hermetic system. When service line is mounted on the fitting, the valve stem is forced in and the system is open for checking pressures, charging, evacuating, etc. This valve operates similar to an automobile tire valve. The service valve or tubing connected to this fitting must have a depressor to push the stem in. (Scovill-Schrader Division)

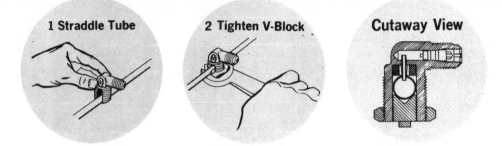

Fig. 12-23. Schrader access valve unit being mounted on tubing. Left. Placed on clean tubing. Center. Clamping nut being tightened. Right. Cross section of finished installation.

tubing. Check to see if there is room (clearance) for mounting the service valve on the tubing mounting valve. Heat both the tubing and the saddle until the filler rod material flows around the saddle. The saddle must not move or shift during the brazing or while the brazed joint is cooling. Some servicemen hold the saddle in place with a small C-clamp during the brazing operation. DO NOT OVERHEAT THE TUBING AS IT MAY BE WEAKENED TO THE POINT OF FAILURE AND MAY BURST. USE GOGGLES DURING THE BRAZING OPERATION. Inspect the brazed joint carefully. Use a mirror to check the hard-to-see edges.

After the brazed joint has cooled, install the piercing needle and gasket. Then the unit is ready for the installation of the service valve, as shown in Fig. 12-21.

12-15 Systems Using Schrader Valves

Many systems use a Schrader valve to gain access to a hermetic system. The Schrader core is similar to the one used in automobile tire cores, Fig. 12-22.

The flexible service tubing or the service valve mounted on this fitting has a pin which depresses the core valve stem as the service device is mounted on the system. Fig. 12-23 shows a clamp-on valve adaptor.

Some servicemen use a Schrader valve service valve. This device has a valve stem which can be used to remove the

valve core after it is mounted on the valve adaptor. The main reason the core is loosened is to allow a more thorough vacuum to be drawn on the hermetic system. Vacuum lines and fittings should be as large as possible. Fig. 12-24, shows the advantage of removing the valve core while evacuating.

12-16 Use of Service Valve Adaptors

After valves have been mounted on a hermetic system, they can be used to check the internal pressures (both low pressure side and high pressure side), or the sys-

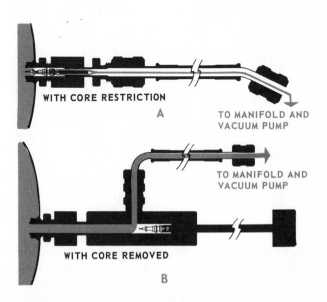

Fig. 12-24. Diagram showing larger evacuating passages obtained when valve core is removed from its fitting. (Robinair Mfg. Co.)

tem can be discharged of its refrigerant, refrigerant can be added, the system can have oil added, the system can be evacuated, etc.

By using these valves, new driers can be installed, replaced, or new motor-compressors can be installed, leaks can be repaired, new refrigerant controls can be installed.

Usually a flexible charging line is connected to the service valve adaptor and a hand valve is mounted on the other end of

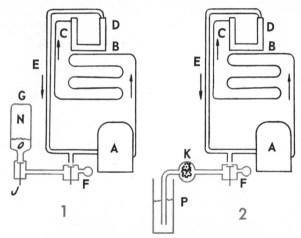

Fig. 12-26. Adding oil to hermetic unit. 1—Bomb method. 2—Pump method. A—Compressor. B—Condenser. C—Capillary tube. D—Cooling coil. E—Suction line. F—Valve attachment. G—Refrigerant cylinders. J—Cylinder valves. K—Pump. N—High pressure refrigerant gas. O—Oil. P—Oil container.

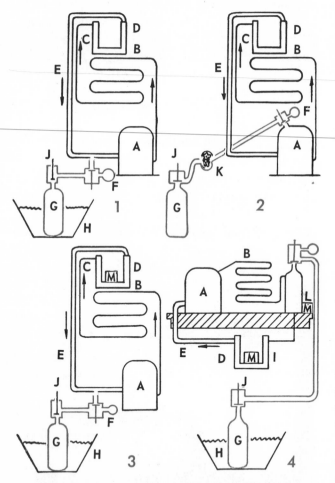

Fig. 12-25. Charging hermetic unit. 1—Boiling refrigerant in. 2—Pumping refrigerant in. 3—Using dry ice in cooling coil. 4—Using dry ice on HSF unit. A—Compressor. B—Condenser. C—Capillary tube. D—Evaporator coil. E—Suction line. F—Valve attachment. G—Refrigerant cylinder. H—Hot water. J—Cylinder service valve. K—Pump. L—High side float. M—Dry ice.

this tubing. This helps the serviceman do the service operations. Fig. 12-25 shows four operations using this type of service connection for charging a hermetic system.

At 1, have the valve loose at (F) and use the cylinder gas in (G) to blow out the lines. In some models (F) may be located on the evaporator (D) or on the compressor dome (A). This process works if the service valve attachment is on the low side.

At 2, a gear pump is shown, but a vane pump or piston pump may also be used. It is important that the refrigerant be carefully weighed as it goes into the unit. This practice calls for the cylinder and the water pail (H) to be mounted or suspended from a weighing scale.

At 3, dry ice or water ice (M), is put around the evaporator coil (D) to help create a low pressure in the system. This is a slow process which requires boiling of the refrigerant in the refrigerant cylinder (G) and condensing it in the evaporator coil (D).

At 4, is illustrated the charging of a hermetic system that has a top-mounted condensing unit and a high side float (L).

Ice is put around the high side float and around the evaporator coil. Remember that loss of refrigerant means a leak in the system. Locate and correct the leak before charging the system.

To add oil, using the one service line technique, installing it as shown in Fig. 12-26. In (1), the correct amount of oil (0) is put in a service cylinder (G) and a small amount of refrigerant, the same as that in

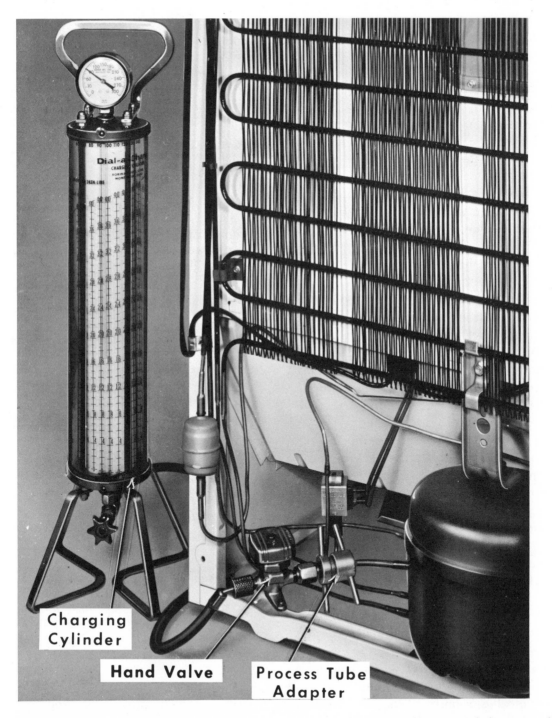

Charging
Cylinder

Hand Valve

Process Tube
Adapter

Fig. 12-27. System being charged using hand valve and process tube adapter. Note use of charging cylinder, usually called a charging tube.   (Kelvinator Div., American Motors Corp.)

the system, is also put in the cylinder to create a pressure (N). The cylinder is inverted and connected by clean lines to the system, (J) and (F). Be sure the cylinder pressure is higher than the system pressure. Then open valves (J) and (F) and the oil will be forced into the system. In (2), a vane or gear pump (K) is used to syphon oil out of a clean and dry graduated container (P) and force it into the service valve attachment (F). A hand pump may be used to perform the same function.

The use of a hand valve and a process tube fitting to charge a system is shown in Fig. 12-27. Note that a charging cylinder is used in this operation.

Another system which is more popular is the use of a service gauge manifold as described in Par. 12-17.

12-17 Gauge and Service Manifold

Gauges and hand valves can be used in connection with the service valves mounted on hermetic systems. However, to purge a system, to check pressures, to evacuate and to charge the system would require disconnecting the devices and connecting new devices for each operation.

A gauge manifold equipped with two gauges, two hand valves and flexible refrigerant tubing enables the serviceman to perform these operations with a minimum of disconnecting of lines. Fig. 12-28, shows a gauge manifold complete with a high pressure gauge, low pressure (or compound gauge), and three flexible hoses equipped with 1/4 in. flare fittings which use fittings with synthetic rubber gaskets which can be made pressure tight with your fingers. Fig. 12-29 shows the design and construction of flexible service and refrigerant tubing.

The serviceman must learn how to use the gauge and service manifold. The hand valves on the manifold can be used for most of operations. It is important to learn about the inside design of the gauge

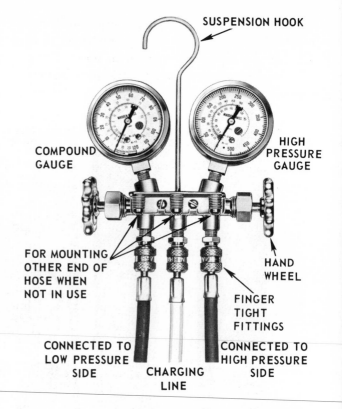

Fig. 12-28. Servicing manifold with hoses and gauges. Note three male flare plugs for sealing other end of hose when unit is not in use. Also, note hook used to hang manifold.
(Madden Brass Products Co., Div. of Robinair Mfg. Co.)

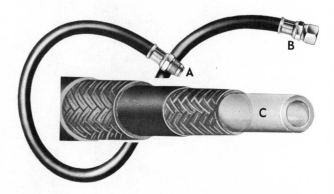

Fig. 12-29. Flexible charging line. A—External flare connection. B—Internal flare connection. C—Cutaway which shows wall construction of tubing.
(Resistoflex Corp.)

and service manifold, so you can use it safely and efficiently. Fig. 12-30, is a diagrammatic view of the manifold, while

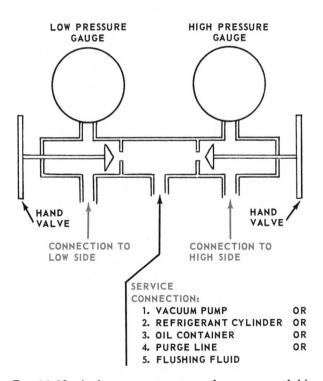

LOW PRESSURE GAUGE

HIGH PRESSURE GAUGE

HAND VALVE

HAND VALVE

CONNECTION TO LOW SIDE

CONNECTION TO HIGH SIDE

SERVICE CONNECTION:
1. VACUUM PUMP   OR
2. REFRIGERANT CYLINDER OR
3. OIL CONTAINER   OR
4. PURGE LINE   OR
5. FLUSHING FLUID

Fig. 12-30. A diagrammatic view of gauge manifold showing hand valves, gauges and refrigerant openings.

Fig. 12-31 shows a test manifold connected to a hermetic system, and to a refrigerant cylinder.

The use of the manifold is described in detail in the remainder of this Chapter and in Chapter 15.

12-18 Adding Oil to the System

The correct amount of oil in a system is very important. A lack of oil will shorten the life of the mechanism, increase friction and cause noise. An overcharge of oil will cause the compressor to pump excessive amounts of oil reducing its refrigerant pumping capacity and also subject the compressor valves to severe strain. It frequently requires some study to determine the amount of oil charge.

Since oil must stay in the system for years, it is vitally important to use the best lubricant obtainable. All reputable oil

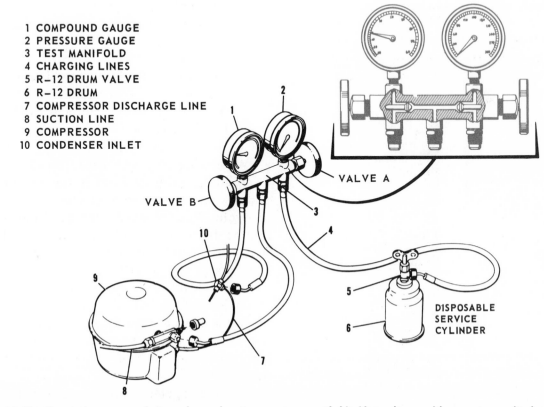

1 COMPOUND GAUGE
2 PRESSURE GAUGE
3 TEST MANIFOLD
4 CHARGING LINES
5 R-12 DRUM VALVE
6 R-12 DRUM
7 COMPRESSOR DISCHARGE LINE
8 SUCTION LINE
9 COMPRESSOR
10 CONDENSER INLET

VALVE A

VALVE B

DISPOSABLE SERVICE CYLINDER

Fig. 12-31. Hermetic system being charged using gauge manifold. Note disposable service cylinder and the use of high side manifold opening for charging.

companies produce refrigerant oils that are quite satisfactory. Remember to clean all charging lines. Refrigerant oils are available in several viscosities (ease of flow at different temperatures). Be sure to follow the manufacturer's viscosity recommendations. See Chapters 2 and 9.

The unit should be charged in much the same procedure followed when adding refrigerant to the system. Information on the exact charge required should be obtained from the manufacturer, or from the identification plate on the unit. Another suggestion is to measure the oil removed from the unit at the time the unit is dismantled. Usually, a rotary compressor requires between 20 and 30 ounces of oil. The exact charge should be placed in a clean charging cylinder and then transferred into the system.

Fig. 12-32 illustrates a practical charging board for accurately measuring the amount of refrigerant or oil charged into a system. This method provides greater accuracy than is possible if charging directly from a storage cylinder into the system. Remember to use clean lines, purged of all air, for transfer purposes.

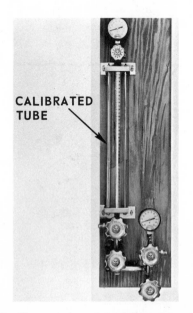

CALIBRATED TUBE

Fig. 12-32. Charging board used for accurately charging hermetic systems. (Airserco Mfg. Co.)

Only rarely is it necessary to add oil to a hermetic system. Occasionally, if there is a leak which results in a considerable loss, it will be necessary to add oil. Leaking refrigerant always carries some oil with it, and this lost oil must be replaced. The conventional method of adding oil to a system may be used if the hermetic unit is completely equipped with service valves. That is, oil can be siphoned in, or poured in.

12-19 Charging a Hermetic System

It may be found that the hermetic unit needs refrigerant by such indications as a partially frosted evaporator, low head pressure, a leak, running too much, etc. You must remember that a pressure difference is needed to move the refrigerant from the refrigerant cylinder into the system. Methods used to add refrigerant are as follows:

1. Evacuate the system.
2. Another compressor or pump may be used to create the pressure difference.
3. The unit is cooled (water ice, or dry ice, or refrigerating unit.
4. The refrigerant cylinder may be heated with hot water, never an open flame or over 120 F.

When charging a partially charged unit, a small quantity of refrigerant should be added and the unit should then be allowed to cycle. Proper charge is best indicated by the frost on the evaporator. When the frost line starts to come down the suction line, purge out a little of the refrigerant.

The service connection lines must be clean and free of air (moisture). This cleaning can be done by purging refrigerant through the lines before the charging refrigerant is allowed to pass through the lines.

Once a system has been evacuated it can be charged by replacing the evacuating pump with a refrigerant cylinder, or by

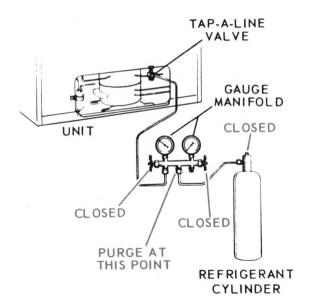

Fig. 12-33. Diagram showing where to purge charging line. Note that the valve adaptor, tap-a-line, is mounted on process tube.
(Franklin Appliance Div., Studebaker Corp.)

using valves to close off the pump and connect the cylinder. Crack the cylinder valve and purge the lines by leaving the charging line loose at the center part of the gauge manifold for a moment, as shown in Fig.

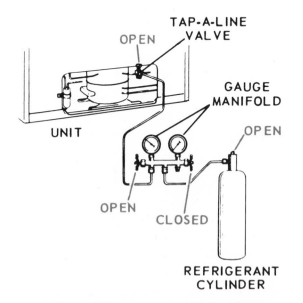

Fig. 12-34. Unit after adjustment of refrigerant cylinder valve. Note position of open tap-a-line valve and refrigerant cylinder.

12-33. Start the unit and open the line service valve, gauge manifold valve, and refrigerant cylinder valve. Watch the low pressure side gauge so that not more than 5 psig is created. This pressure control is accomplished by adjusting the refrigerant cylinder valve. Allow the refrigerant charge to enter the system for approximately 3-5 minutes connected, as shown in Fig. 12-34. Close the gauge manifold valve. Allow the unit to operate and check the frost line on the evaporator. If the frost line is inadequate, continue charging at

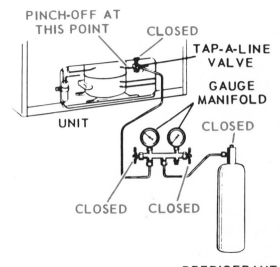

Fig. 12-35. Unit after tap-a-line valve is closed along with refrigerant cylinder and gauge manifold. Note pinch-off point.

short intervals. Make certain the frost line does not go beyond the accumulator dome suction line.

When the proper amount of frost has been observed, close the refrigerant cylinder valve, adaptor valve, and gauge manifold valve. Pinch the process tube between the compressor and the adaptor valve with a pinch-off tool, as shown in Fig. 12-35. Remove the adaptor valve and silver braze the end of the tubing. Check for leaks using a leak detector. Close the adaptor if it was

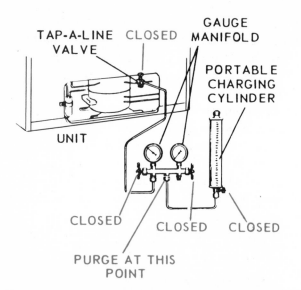

Fig. 12-36. Purging charging line at center port of gauge manifold, when portable charging tube is used.

installed on the suction line. Leave it mounted on the suction line for future service operations.

12-20 Charging a System Using a Portable Charging Cylinder

If a portable charging cylinder, as mentioned in Par. 12-16, is used, the following steps are recommended, after evacuation.

Attach a line from the charging cylinder to the center of the gauge manifold and purge the line at the center part of the gauge manifold, Fig. 12-36. Open the valve adaptor (tap-a-line) and gauge manifold, crack the charging cylinder valve and allow the refrigerant to enter the system, as shown in Fig. 12-37. When the correct amount of refrigerant has entered the system, as can be checked by reading the scale on the charging cylinder, close the cylinder valve. Close the valve adaptor and the gauge manifold valves, as shown in Fig. 12-38. Then use the pinch-off tool and close off the process tube between the compressor and the valve adaptor. Braze the end of the process tube. Remove the valve adaptor and check the system for leaks.

12-21 Evacuating Hermetic System

Prior to completely charging a hermetic system, it is best to evacuate old refrigerant, which is in the system, and also to remove any air or moisture which may be contained in it. Moisture will freeze at the refrigerant control and cause oil sludge. Oxygen in the air will oxidize the oil while the nitrogen will create excessive head pressure. For further details on evacuation, see Par. 12-22.

Basic steps which must be followed in evacuating a hermetic system, without service valves, are: attach a valve adaptor to the process tube, to a process tube extension, or attach a valve adaptor to the suction line. If this is not possible, attach a valve adaptor to some part of the low side of the system.

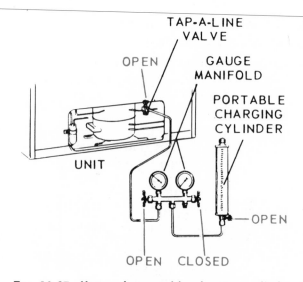

Fig. 12-37. Using the portable charging cylinder to charge refrigerant into the system.

Next, attach flexible lines to the manifold gauge and to the vacuum pump, Fig. 12-39. Start the vacuum pump and open the gauge manifold valve to evacuate the lines for approximately two minutes, Fig. 12-40. When the vacuum gauge registers 29 in. of vacuum, close the gauge manifold valve and wait to see if the vacuum holds for approx-

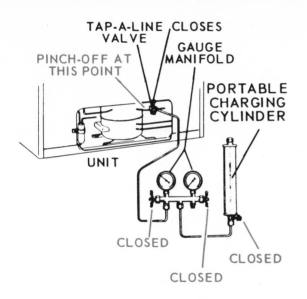

Fig. 12-38. Steps to be followed when removing tap-a-line valve.

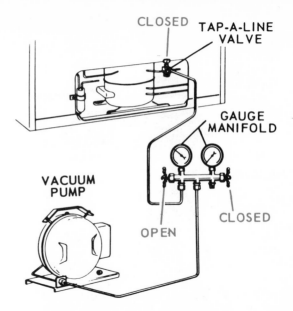

Fig. 12-40. Second step in evacuating a system is to operate vacuum pump and open manifold valve and valve adaptor valve as indicated.

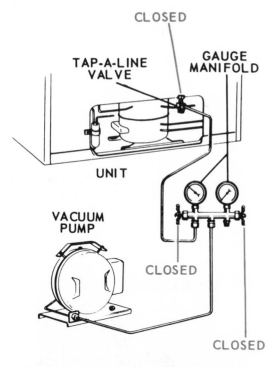

Fig. 12-39. Procedure to use when evacuating system which does not have service valves. Install valve adaptor (tap-a-line), flexible refrigerant line, gauge manifold, and vacuum pump. Make certain valve adaptor and manifold gauge valves are closed as shown. (Franklin Appliance Div., Studebaker Corp.)

imately two minutes. If so, this will indicate there are no leaks in the system.

Start the vacuum pump, open the valve adaptor valve, gauge manifold valve and

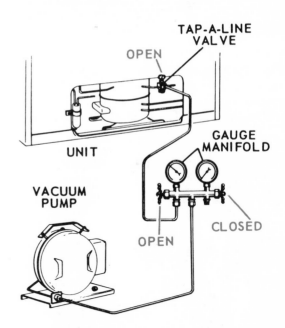

Fig. 12-41. Final check for positive evacuation is with vacuum pump operating and gauge openings in positions as indicated. Check to see if vacuum gauge holds for three (3) minutes.

allow the vacuum pump to operate for approximately 20 minutes, as shown in Fig. 12-41. Then close the gauge manifold valve, stop the vacuum pump and check to see that the vacuum holds for approximately three minutes. If the vacuum holds, you are ready to begin charging the unit.

VACUUM
GAUGE

VACUUM
HOSE

Fig. 12-42. Portable high vacuum pump mounted on stand for service transporting. Note flexible metal evacuating line. This is a large capacity line and will not collapse. Two hand valves are used to control evacuating operation.

12-22 Using High Vacuum Pumps

As a general rule, standard reciprocating type air compressors do not create high enough vacuum, and ordinary refrigeration compressors are not designed to produce the necessary vacuum for evacuating refrigeration systems being serviced.

Small portable high vacuum pumps are available which draw down to 1 micron of mercury column. A micron is 1/1000 of a millimeter, 2.54 centimeters equal 1 inch, 10 millimeters equal one centimeter, and therefore 25,400 microns equal 1 inch. One micron is close to a perfect vacuum. A high vacuum pump is one which will produce a vacuum lower than 29 in. Portable vacuum pumps are shown in Figs. 12-42 and 12-43. Vacuums lower than 29 in. are necessary for complete dehydration or complete moisture removal from the system. The oil sight port permits checking the oil level, also the oil color. This special oil should be replaced frequently.

To determine accurate vacuum, an electronic high vacuum gauge, is used because a regular compound gauge cannot read accurately to micron levels. See Fig. 12-44. A vacuum from 29 1/4 to 29.9

VACUUM
GAUGE

VACUUM LINE
CONNECTION

OIL SIGHT
PORT

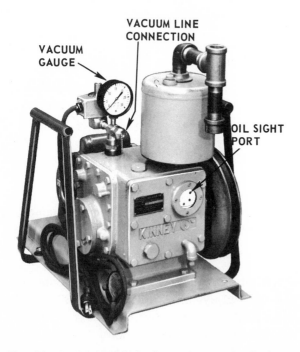

Fig. 12-43. A portable high vacuum pump which may be used to remove air or refrigerant from a system. Note the oil sight glass; also the vacuum gauge.

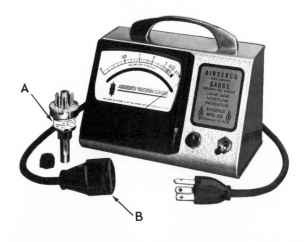

Fig. 12-44. Leak and moisture indicator. A—Gauge tube with 1/8 in. pipe threads. B—Gauge tube electrical connector. In operation, indicator is connected into system to be checked by using pipe threaded portion.

in., which is equal to 20,000 microns to 1,000 microns, is necessary to allow the moisture within the system to dehydrate at room temperature.

The inside design of a vacuum gauge tube is shown in Fig. 12-45. The sensing element is a thermopile. It is important to use the tube in an upright position to keep foreign matter out. The vacuum dial scale is shown in Fig. 12-46.

If a leak exists in a system, the vacuum produced will not be a high vacuum and the dial needle will rise rapidly and steadily when the valves are closed. If there is moisture in the system, the vacuum produced will also be below the desired vacuum. When the valve is closed the dial needle will rise and level off at a pressure corresponding to the water vapor pressure at that temperature. Fig. 12-47 shows the two conditions of a pressure-time graph. These are made with the valve to the vacuum pump closed.

To insure dehydration of a wet system the following procedure is recommended for domestic units. Connect a 250-watt lamp, in place of a fuse, in series with a test cord. Attach the cord to the compressor terminals; then to a 120V outlet.

This procedure allows only about 30V

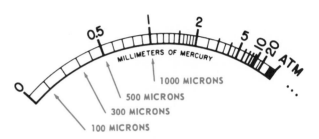

Fig. 12-46. Dial scale of high vacuum gauge. Notice that pressure between 0 and 1,000 microns has been greatly expanded for easy reading. (Airserco Mfg. Co.)

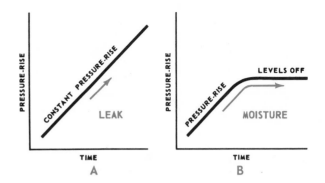

Fig. 12-47. Graphs which show effect of a leak and of moisture on high vacuum gauge reading. A—Shows effect of a leak. B—Shows effect of moisture in system.

to pass to the compressor because the lamp becomes a resistor. This warms the compressor windings to help vaporize the moisture which may be trapped in the system. The compressor should not run during this operation. A chart showing the various pressures obtainable with different type pumps is given in Fig. 12-48. Note the evaporating temperature of water at the various pressures.

Many servicemen use the triple evacuation procedure:

1. Evacuate to 1500 microns pressure.
2. Charge with correct refrigerant until atmospheric pressure is reached and evacuates to 500 microns.
3. Charge with correct refrigerant until atmospheric pressure (0 psig) is reached and evacuate to 500 microns.

During manufacture, systems are evacuated to 50 to 100 microns before oil is

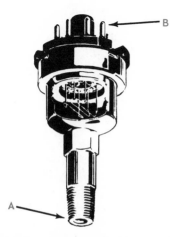

Fig. 12-45. The internal construction of a high vacuum gauge tube. A—Pipe connection to vacuum pump manifold. B—Electrical connections to vacuum gauge.

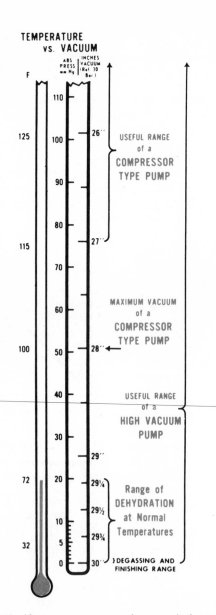

**TEMPERATURE
vs. VACUUM**

USEFUL RANGE
of a
COMPRESSOR
TYPE PUMP

MAXIMUM VACUUM
of a
COMPRESSOR
TYPE PUMP

USEFUL RANGE
of a
HIGH VACUUM
PUMP

Range of
DEHYDRATION
at Normal
Temperatures

DEGASSING AND
FINISHING RANGE

Fig. 12-48. Note pressure scales used during high vacuum evacuation of system. The temperature scale shows evaporating temperature of water at these pressures. For example, water will evaporate (boil) at 72 F. at 20 mm of Hg pressure (20,000 microns). (Airserco Mfg. Co.)

added. In the field, when oil is in the unit, evacuating to 50 microns may cause some of the oil to vaporize.

Because the motor-compressor depends on gas flow to cool the motor windings and compressor, avoid using it for evacuation pumping. The motor and compressor may heat up and be damaged.

12-23 Driers and Filters

It is very important to keep the inside of a refrigeration mechanism as chemically clean as possible. When gauges are put on a system and service operations are performed, it is difficult to prevent foreign matter from entering the system.

A positive method of keeping the system clean and dry inside is to install driers and filters in the refrigerant circuit. A combination filter drier is shown in Fig. 12-49. A solid moisture absorbent will usually do a satisfactory job. Silica gel is an excellent moisture absorber. The silica gel must be of high quality as it must not decompose into dust and start circulating with the refrigerant. One company produces a bead silica gel that gives good results. Many other absorbent chemicals are also used.

You can easily determine if a drier is absorbing water. It will become warm as it absorbs moisture.

It is important not to use a liquid drying agent in a unit equipped with a solid desiccant. The liquid dryer chemical will release the moisture already trapped in the drier. For the same reason, a solid des-

Fig. 12-49. Filter-drier used on domestic systems. Note arrow designating direction of flow of refrigerant through filter-drier.

iccant should not be put in a system that is already using a liquid drier. To avoid this danger, all systems should be labeled if a liquid drying agent has been added.

Activated alumina may be used with good results as a desiccant. Calcium chloride is an excellent drier but it cannot be left in the system as it will decompose and start circulating. It is an excellent temporary drier if it is removed in a short time (24 hours, maximum). The moisture absorbent properties of these desiccants are shown in Fig. 12-50.

Desiccant	Mesh	Absorption From Liquid, Percent of Weight of Desiccant
Silica Gel	8-20	16
Calcium Sulphate	4-6	6.6
Activated Alumina	8-10	12
Calcium Chloride *	12	100

* Temporary Installation Only

Fig. 12-50. Table of moisture absorbing ability of some of desiccants in driers, used on refrigeration and air conditioning systems. This table is for refrigerants R–12 and R–22.

Anhydrous calcium sulphate has also been successfully used as a desiccant. It can be left in the system permanently.

The Refrigeration Electrical Manufacturer's Association has recommended that dehydrators be rated as to cubic inches of desiccant. Fig. 12-51 shows the cubic content corresponding to the horsepower for which each size drier is recommended. All driers are sealed by the manufacturer. Do not remove the sealing caps until just before installation.

Driers absorb water faster at lower temperatures. If at all possible, the drier should be installed inside the refrigerator just ahead of the refrigerant control.

Strainers are of several types. The screen type which is popular is usually made of bronze, brass, or monel wire and should be 100 to 120 mesh. That is, there should be 100 openings along a one inch rule length, or, 10,000 holes per square inch. The popular screens are 100 x 90, 100 x 100, 120 x 108, and 120 x 120. The wire is usually .004 to .005 in. diameter. In this size wire the openings are about .005 in. square. Felts may be used. These felts which are about 1/8 in. thick are made of special felt material. Wool batt is used as a filter in some driers. One company has a specially processed coarse cotton yarn wound in a diamond pattern over a metal frame. One of the latest filters makes use of powdered metal pressure castings.

Many driers are filter-drier combinations. If the unit originally had a strainer placed in the line between the condenser and refrigerant control, it should be removed prior to installing a new filter-drier.

12-24 A Special Field Servicing Technique

One company has a special technique for servicing hermetics in the field. Their method enables a trained serviceman to replace the motor-compressor unit, or any other part of the mechanism without removing the refrigerator from the prem-

DRYER SIZES – DOMESTIC

Cu. In.	Capacity, HP
2	1/8
3	1/6 to 1/4
6	1/4 to 1/2
9	1/2 to 3/4

DRYER SIZES – COMMERCIAL

Cu. In.	Capacity, HP
12	3/4 to 1
18	1 to 1 1/2
30	1 1/2 to 3
50	5 to 7 1/2

Fig. 12-51. Recommended drier capacities in cubic inches based on the horsepower of the condensing unit.

ises. For example, if the motor-compressor needs replacing, a special unit is obtained that can be easily substituted for the malfunctioning motor-compressor. A replacement unit is shown in Fig. 12-52. A

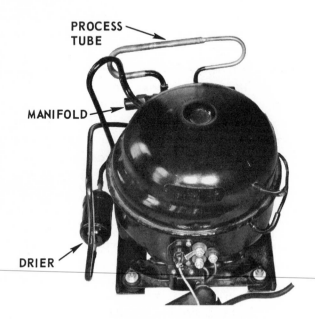

Fig. 12-52. *A replacement motor-compressor equipped with a manifold system.*

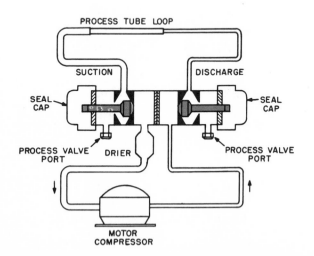

Fig. 12-53. *Schematic diagram of a replacement motor-compressor equipped with service valve manifold.*

diagrammatic view of its assembly is shown in Fig. 12-53. The unit comes equipped with a valve which is similar to

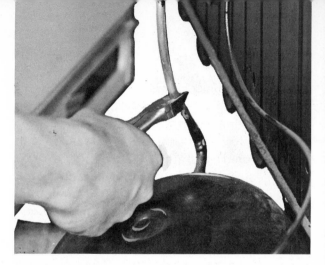

Fig. 12-54. *Pinching suction line prior to wrapping it in cloth and breaking it.*
(Philco Corp., Sub. of Ford Motor Co.)

the gauge manifold valve system used for servicing. Note that the discharge and suction opening lines are soldered together. The valves are two-way valves. Turned all the way in, the valve closes the opening to process valve port (gauge openings).

The faulty unit is removed by cutting the condenser and suction lines in such a place along the tubing that the lines can be resoldered to replacement tubing. The lines are first pinched, as shown in Fig. 12-54, then wrapped in cloth and finally bent sharply at the pinch to sever them. Sawing is not recommended as chips may cause

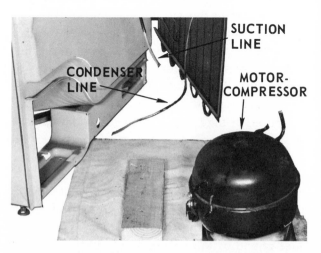

Fig. 12-55. *Old motor-compressor has been removed and its refrigerant lines sealed by pinching. This protects internal structure of unit for shipment.*

internal damage. The cut lines with the old unit now separated from the system are shown in Fig. 12-55, with the lines sealed by pinching them firmly. After the new motor-compressor has been installed and

connections necessary to perform these operations. The R-12 cylinder must contain clean refrigerant. The drier must have fresh, clean desiccant and the connections must be tight. The manifold valves remain turned all the way in. To check for leaks valve V_2 is kept closed. A pressure of 50 psig is built up in the lines and evaporator coil.

To purge the unit, valve V_2 is opened, then the R-12 cylinder valve is opened. You should purge several times to insure complete cleanliness and dryness.

To remove the service lines, close both V_2 and V_1 and turn the manifold valves all the way out. All the lines can then be removed and the gauge opening ports can be capped.

To charge the system, connect as shown in Fig. 12-57. Note that the cylinder is connected to the suction side. With the mani-

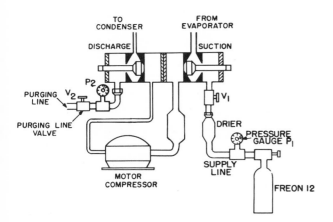

Fig. 12-56. Connections needed to test for leaks and to purge system.

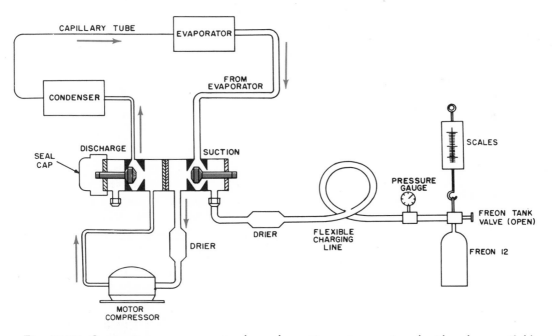

Fig. 12-57. Connections necessary to charge hermetic system equipped with valve manifold.
(Philco Corp., Sub. of Ford Motor Co.)

the joints carefully soldered, the system must be carefully checked for leaks. It must be cleaned of air and moisture, and must be charged. Fig. 12-56 illustrates the

fold valve in its position, the compressor is removing refrigerant from both the evaporator coil and the refrigerant cylinder.

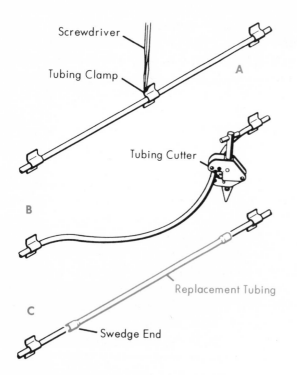

Fig. 12-58. Replacing tubing using swedge ends. A—Removing damaged tubing. B—Cutting old tubing with a tubing cutter. C—Installing swedged and replacement tubing. Joints are silver brazed. (Franklin Appliance Div., Studebaker Corp.)

Occasionally it is necessary to replace tubing which has failed due to abuse, buckling or cracking. Fig. 12-58 shows a typical procedure.

12-25 Overhauling Hermetic Systems

Many manufacturers provide exchange service on complete refrigeration machines exclusive of the external controls, fans, and cabinet. In many cases it is advisable to use this type service, if the unit cannot be repaired in the field. In case a manufacturer has gone out of business or if it is impossible to obtain a replacement mechanism, overhaul procedures described in the following paragraphs may be useful.

Domestic units vary in size from 1/20 hp to 1/3 hp, with the most popular sizes being around 1/6 to 1/4 hp. The construction varies. Some are sealed and welded units with no external valves or moving parts; some are welded but have external fans; some are welded and are equipped with service valves or valve attachments. Some are bolted together and are completely serviceable without special tools. All types can be repaired, but some require more repair equipment and more complicated repair procedures than others.

The general service procedure is to discard the refrigerant and the oil from the machine, and dismantle the machine. Make the necessary repairs (motor, compressor, refrigerant control, drier, etc.) clean the parts with a nontoxic, nonflammable solvent, various spirits, and/or liquids. Clean the parts again, and assemble.

One cleaning solvent is R-11, a refrigerant with a high boiling point, 74.8 F., which is both nontoxic and nonflammable. It is an excellent cleaning solvent for flushing systems which have been contaminated due to hermetic motor burn out. It leaves no noncondensable residue and has no reaction with the electrical insulation. R-11 can be cleaned and reused.

Several degreasing solvents are available which are comparatively safe. Some of their features are low toxicity, noncorrosive, and a high flash point. Suppliers can supply solvents safe to use for this type of cleaning.

Assemble the unit, install temporary valves, test the unit (test for leaks), evacuate, dry the unit, charge it with oil and refrigerant, test the unit (recording thermometers, wattmeters, etc.), test for leaks, disconnect the temporary valves and finally, give the unit a test run in a 100 F. room.

12-26 Removing the System

If in checking a unit you determine there is a mechanical or electrical trouble inside, which cannot readily be repaired in the field, the unit should be removed from the cabinet and sent to a specially equipped shop for repair.

A replacement unit may be used while the original is being repaired. If this cannot be done, it is advisable to supply the customer with a complete refrigerator loaner, to use while the unit is being repaired.

It is important to protect the refrigerating unit while it is being moved. Cradles or crates should be used to hold mechanisms. Wooden frames and C clamps provide means of holding the parts from being injured while in transit.

The complete cabinet, if moved in a truck should be shrouded in a special padded blanket.

The procedure for removing the unit from the cabinet varies because: (1) some of the evaporators are removed from the rear of the cabinet; (2) some of the evaporators are removed from the front of the cabinet (by way of the cabinet door).

The refrigerant lines are sometimes run just under the door frame breaker strips. These breaker strips must be removed in order to remove the lines.

These strips are usually made of a plastic material. Several other designs of cabinet frame breaker strips are shown in Chapter 11. There are several methods used to fasten the breaker strips to the cabinet shell and the liner.

The breaker strips must be removed very carefully or they will break. The material should be at room temperature to guard against brittleness.

The cabinets which have the evaporator unit removed from the rear of the cabinet are not difficult to dismantle.

Cabinets which require removing the unit from the front of the cabinet call for skill and patience on the part of the serviceman. The hardest part is removing and installing the breaker strips. The mechanism is then removed. You must be careful not to kink or buckle the refrigerant lines.

Some cabinets are of the double-door design and the strips between the two com-

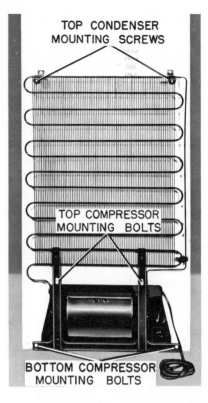

Fig. 12-59. Mounting bolts and screws that must be removed when replacing refrigerating mechanism. (General Electric Co.)

partments must be removed before the unit can be taken out.

The compressor and condenser are sometimes fastened to the rear of the cabinets by four to six mounting screws and bolts, as shown in Fig. 12-59. Be careful not to abuse the mechanism while removing these devices.

12-27 Dismantling the Unit

The procedure to follow in dismantling a hermetic unit depends on the construction of the unit. The general information which follows is applicable to all types of units.

CLEAN THE OUTSIDE OF THE UNIT THOROUGHLY. Mineral spirits, obtainable from most oil companies, is used extensively as a general cleaner. Carbon tetrachloride is sometimes used but it is dangerous. It must be used with caution.

If used, avoid breathing even the smallest amount of the carbon tetrachloride and do not allow it to touch your skin or clothing.

A special booth with a grate bottom, having drainage facilities, equipped with a pump and spray nozzle and ventilated, is desirable, especially for a shop doing volume work. Local fire and industrial hygiene regulations must be followed closely.

REMOVE THE REFRIGERANT. If the unit is equipped with service valves, or service valve attachment plugs, the refrigerant should be purged into the open atmosphere through lines equipped with special oil traps. Do not purge flammable gas into a sewer because of the danger of explosions.

If the system is not equipped with valves, the unit must be cut open. Several methods may be used. One method is to cool the unit (use dry or water ice), put the unit in an exhaust ventilated booth and cut the lines. Be sure to wear goggles. Another way is to use one of the valve adaptors.

REMOVING OIL. It is desirable to remove the oil if the compressor dome is to be mounted in a lathe and cut open, or turned as the old weld is removed using a power grinder. If the sealed unit is of the bolted construction type, the oil may be left in the unit until it is dismantled. The old oil should be drained off and carefully measured to assure replacement of the exact quantity. If the oil is clean and dry, it may be stored for future use in a clean and dry container. If the old oil is acidic (contains hydrochloric and hydroflouric acid) it should not be used again. Handle the acidic oil with extreme care. Be sure to wear rubber gloves and goggles.

DISCONNECTING LINES. The lines (liquid and suction) are usually silver brazed to the evaporator and condensing unit. It is not usually necessary to disconnect the suction line from the evaporator. Occasionally, when the liquid line is a capillary tube, it is advisable to disconnect it

at both ends. The openings should be immediately sealed if the lines and parts are to be used over again. This sealing can be done either by pinching the lines or using expanding corks (synthetic rubber or natural corks). The openings into the condensing unit should also be plugged to keep the unit as clean as possible. Masking tape may also be used to temporarily seal the openings. The welded motor-compressor units may be opened easily by grinding away the welded seam, or removing the weld bead by mounting the unit in a lathe and cutting the weld bead away with a cutting tool.

A device used to remove the motor-compressor weld by grinding is shown in Fig. 12-60. The motor-compressor is

Fig. 12-60. A motor-compressor opener. This special dome welding grinding machine will open a motor-compressor in about 20 min. A—Points to welded bead and grinding wheel. B—Machine controls.
(Airserco Mfg. Co.)

clamped to a turntable and the grinding wheel removes the weld as the compressor slowly turns. The wheel automatically adjusts itself to the contour or shape of the weld seam. The machine will remove both side welds and top welds. The opener mechanism is housed in a steel cabinet equipped with shatterproof windows to enable the operator to watch the grinding operation. Both motors of the unit require single-phase, 120 volt power and use about 11 amps. The machine automatically grinds the weld. One motor is used to operate the turntable while a second motor drives the grinding wheel. The machine may be equipped with either 1/8, 1/4, or 3/4 in. thickness grinding wheels.

Remove a minimum of material as sufficient base metal must be left for the assembly to be arc welded together again.

After the compressor dome weld is removed, the dome can usually be lifted off the base. The motor and compressor will be exposed. Some models have the dome pressed on the base in addition to the weld. In such cases the dome must be pulled off the base. To remove a press fit dome, clamps are generally used to hold the dome and a special arbor press, or screw jacks are used to force the two apart, as shown in Fig. 12-61. These

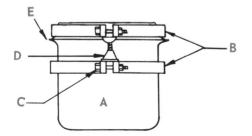

Fig. 12-61. One method of pulling a compressor dome apart. A—Dome. B—Steel straps. C—Clamp bolts. D—Screw jack. E—Welded joint.

clamps are made of heavy steel bars bent to fit the dome and are clamped on tightly by means of bolts. Most domes have mounting lugs that can be used with the clamps. It may occasionally be necessary to weld lugs onto the dome to secure a purchase point to pull them apart. Hydraulic pressure is sometimes used to remove a dome. Clean the inside of the dome thoroughly before proceeding further.

12-28 Motor Repairing

The most common trouble with hermetic mechanisms is a burned (overheated) motor. When the windings overheat, the insulation is destroyed and the stator coils short and ground. If the motor starting winding or running winding is faulty, the stator must be dismantled and rewired (rewound) or replaced. The rewinding should be done by a specialist. The wire used must be the same size and have the same insulation as the original wiring. Replacement or exchange stators are obtainable for most hermetic motors.

A burned-out motor usually indicates the system contains considerable foreign matter. Two methods of cleaning a burned-out system are: Flushing the system with R-11. Installing a high capacity combination drier-filter in the suction line temporarily until all foreign matter and moisture have been trapped. The system must be dismantled and thorougly cleaned.

Hydrochloric and hydroflouric acid are formed by the breakdown of the refrigerant and oil in the system. The acid will cause insulation on motor windings to deteriorate. The motor will run at a higher temperature than normal and the unit will burn out. There are many acid test kits available to determine the amount of contamination. See Chapter 15 for further information along this line.

Acid cleaning kits are useful in flushing out the system and to determine when it is advisable to recharge the unit.

12-29 Repairing Compressors

If parts of a compressor are badly scored and worn, the unit will usually have to be replaced. There are several hermetic replacement units on the market. These can be easily installed in place of the worn out condensing unit (Bendix - Westinghouse - Copeland - Tecumseh - and others).

If the trouble is in the compressor

valves, the check valve, or if there is dirt in the system, all these can be repaired. You must remember that the precision craftsmanship in these mechanisms often holds to tolerances of plus or minus .0001 in.

12-30 Repairing Reciprocating Compressor

The most common compressor troubles are with valves and valve seats. The valve reed may be replaced and the valve seat reground on a surface grinder or in a drill press and then accurately lapped. Replacement valve reeds are available for most hermetic compressors.

It is necessary to test the valves before assembling the unit. The testing can be done by using fixtures and synthetic gaskets or using a synthetic rubber vacuum cup, as shown in Fig. 12-62. Noisy valves

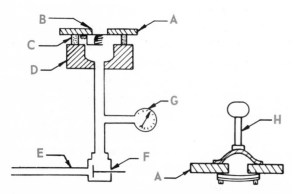

Fig. 12-62. Testing valves. A—Valve plates. B—Refrigerant oil. C—Synthetic rubber gasket. D—Fixture. E—Clean, dry compressed air. F—Air valve. G—Pressure gauge. H—Vacuum cup.

may be caused by excessive valve lift (or excessive pressure differences). The valve movement is usually measured in thousandths of an inch. Valve lift must be accurately adjusted. Check the amount of lift before dismantling the valve (dial indicator). Too little valve lift will result in inefficient compressor operation and overheating.

A check valve can be checked much the same way. It is important to keep these units as quiet as possible so the bearing and bushing clearances must be as small as possible (main bearings, connecting rod bearing, piston pin bushing and piston clearances).

Having accurate micrometers and thickness gauges available for checking is important.

The main bodies or parts of the compressor are usually made of cast iron, the valves of spring steel, and the piston pins of high carbon steel (some repair shops use drill rod as replacement piston pins). If the replaced part is a moving part, it should be the same weight as the old part, to keep dynamic vibrations to a minimum.

End play must be kept to a minimum to eliminate end play slap. Action of the pump should be checked to make sure the pump is operating satisfactorily.

12-31 Repairing Compressor Valves

Practically all compressor valves used on domestic refrigerators are of the diaphragm or disk type. These are usually called flapper valves. The valves are made of thin spring steel, and are held in place by their own spring tension and a machine screw, or by an auxiliary coil or flat spring. After a long period of use, the compressor valves and valve seats, which are usually made of cast iron, may be worn. It is a good policy to replace the valve reed when overhauling a compressor, because the cost is small. It is also good practice to lap the valve seats. In lapping be sure that a fine lapping compound is used and that special care is taken to clean all lapped surfaces carefully after the lapping job has been completed. Compound remaining on the surfaces may ruin the compressor. If raised, valve seats are used, a plate glass surface may be used as the lapping tool, or special lapping blocks may be used. Some companies use fine polishing paper clamped to a flat plate as the lapping surface. If the valve seat is in bad condition, the valve plate should be mounted in a lathe, either in a chuck or on a face plate, and the whole plate trued up. Some repairmen use a surface grinder to true up valve seats.

In compressors using the spring steel type valve it is necessary that the proper surface of the valve come in contact with the valve seat. The proper surface may be detected by the slightly turned over edge of the opposite surface of the valve. This is caused when the valves are stamped out. The stamping process turns the edge of the valve on one side (burrs it). If this side is placed against the valve seat, it might not seal properly. Additional information on valve repairing will be found in Chapter 15. Replacement valve plates are available and their use is recommended.

12-32 Compressor Intake Valve Testing

A poor intake valve will be indicated by poor vacuum, but the compressor holds the vacuum when it stops. This may also be due to the use of too thick a gasket or worn pistons and rings. Keep in mind also that lack of oil will result in poor pumping ability.

12-33 Repairing Hermetic Rotary Compressors

Most of the instructions in Par. 12-30 are applicable also to rotary compressors. The rotating vane type of rotary compressor has two additional repair requirements:

1. Positioning of the roller housing to accurately locate the contact spot between the concentric roller and the eccentric housing is important. In Fig. 12-63 the contact point X must be carefully adjusted. In this

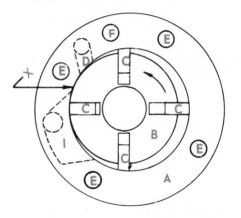

Fig. 12-63. Diagram of parts and adjustments on hermetic rotary compressor. A—Housing. B—Rotor. C—Blades. D—Exhaust port. E—Bolts. F—Dowel pin. I—Intake port. X—Contact point.

drawing four cap screws hold the housing (A) and an end plate up against the main housing. Point F is a dowel pin. The assembly is assembled and the housing is tapped lightly until the rotor B binds when the shaft is turned by hand or by using the electric motor. Then the housing is relieved a very small amount by tapping opposite to X until the binding is released. Dial micrometers may be used to measure the distance the housing moves.

2. Vanes C must be accurately fitted to the roller (B) and housing (A). These vanes (C) must match accurately in length to the roller (B) and housing length (A). The vanes must also fit the slots in the roller accurately. They must not be too long or they will bind as they pass point (X). If they are too short they will permit blow-by as they pass point (X). The length of the vanes must match the length of the roller and the length of the housing to prevent vapor leakage past the ends of the blades.

The single or stationary vane type compressor has much the same fit problem as the rotating vane type. The parts

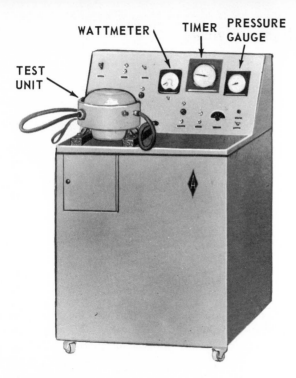

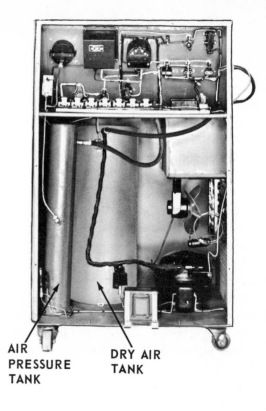

Fig. 12-64. Motor-compressor analyzer stand which checks motor wattage, pressures, and time to pump certain volume of dry air up to certain pressure (volumetric efficiency).

Fig. 12-65. Photo which shows inside construction of unit shown in Fig. 12-64.

must be accurately fitted together. The main bearing or bearings must be in excellent condition. The length of roller, housing and vane must be matched accurately. There must be no evidence of scoring.

The vane is usually spring loaded to keep it riding on the roller. If this spring is too weak, vapor will bypass the vane and cause a loud clicking noise. If it is too strong it will cause an unnecessary load on the roller and cause rapid wear. Dowel pins are used to align housing with shaft.

Both compressors need sufficient oil at all times to keep the parts in a constant oil bath. It is necessary to clean all oil passages and to clean or replace the oil metering screws.

12-34 Compressor Testing After Overhaul

After the compressor has been overhauled, it should be charged with the correct amount of the proper viscosity oil and then tested. Use the type and quantity of oil recommended by the manufacturer.

To charge a compressor, connect a charging line to the service valve. Connect this tubing to a manifold and to both a vacuum pump and an oil container. Run the vacuum pump to pump a vacuum on the system with the tubing immersed in fresh refrigerant oil. The oil will quickly fill the crankcase. Oil starting to spray through the discharge service valve, is an indication that the compressor has enough oil.

Next equip the compressor with a high pressure gauge and a compound gauge; 126 psi for R-12 and 213 for R-22. If the compressor tests all right, it should be baked for a period of 8 hours or more at a temperature of 150 F. to 200 F. with at least a 20 in. vacuum on the system.

It can also be evacuated for several hours at 50 to 500 microns of pressure or lower.

This evacuating will remove practically all of the air and moisture from the system.

Test benches are available which may be used to test newly repaired hermetic motor-compressors. Fig. 12-64 shows a test bench electrically connected, with flexible motor and discharge lines connected to the motor-compressor. Inside construction of the unit is shown in Fig. 12-65.

12-35 Servicing Check Valves

All rotary compressors are equipped with check valves in the suction line or in the suction passages. This check valve prevents the oil in the compressor from backing into the suction line and into the evaporator during the off cycle. As mentioned previously, the indication of a leaky check valve is the rapid warming of the suction line as soon as the compressor stops, due to the warm oil backing into the suction line. Another indication is the defrosting of the evaporator starting at the suction line connection of the evaporator.

Whenever possible, replace the defective check valve. Always test the check valve for leaks by using the air pressure or vacuum test in a manner similar to the way a compressor valve is tested.

See Chapter 6 for more information on check valves.

12-36 Servicing Capillary Tubes

Broken or clogged capillary tubes are troubles commonly encountered. Metal chips, flux, oil residue (wax) etc. are common clogging materials. Capillary tube

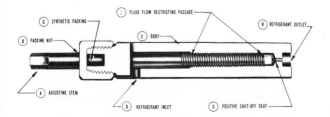

Fig. 12-66. Adjustable capillary valve. (Standard Refrig. Co.)

troubles may be corrected by installing a new correct size capillary tube, or an adjustable capillary tube, as shown in Fig. 12-66 or 12-67.

To check a capillary tube for restrictions, compare its pressure drop with the pressure drop of a new tube of like specifications, using the same refrigerant and the same inlet and outlet pressures.

In some cases the capillary tube may be cleaned and the obstruction removed

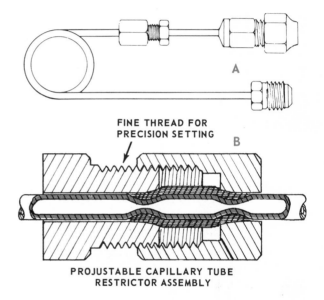

Fig. 12-67. Internal design of adjustment used on capillary tube. A—Shows complete assembly. B—Shows how adjustment operates.

without replacing the tube. To clean a capillary tube it is not necessary to remove the entire tube, merely disconnect the tube at its outlet end. There will be little loss of refrigerant because the system has already been pumped down. A capillary tube cleaner, as shown in Fig. 12-68, is connected to the outlet of the tube and pressure is used to force the restricting material out of the tube. The tube cleaner operates by creating a fluid pressure, usually oil, up to 20,000 psig by turning the handle of the cleaner.

If the serviceman finds the restriction is difficult to remove, it may be necessary to replace the capillary tube with a new one.

After the capillary tube has been cleaned the fluid flow should be continued to flush out the tube thoroughly. The ma-

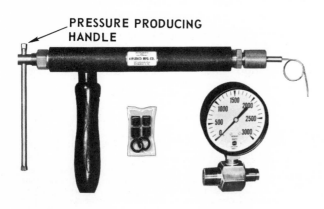

Fig. 12-68. Capillary tube cleaner used to clean obstructions from capillary tubes.

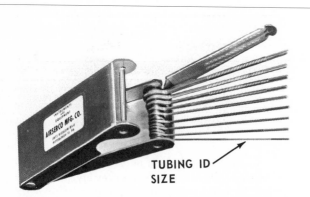

Fig. 12-69. Capillary tube sizing kit. (Airserco Mfg. Co.)

terial removed is trapped in a drier-filter. Fig. 12-69 shows a capillary tube sizing kit which may be used to determine the correct ID of the capillary tube to insure proper size replacement.

12-37 Repairing Condensers and Receivers

When trouble is encountered with either a condenser or a receiver, it is usually better to replace the unit than to re-

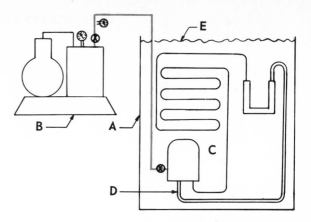

Fig. 12-70. Testing rebuilt hermetic system for leaks. A—Water tank. B—Air compressor or inert gas source. C—Submerged unit. D—Refrigerating lines. E—Water level.

pair it. This is also true in regard to the evaporator.

If a leak is to be repaired, welding, brazing or soldering may be used. Careful work is required. Joints should be silver brazed to insure a lasting leakproof joint.

12-38 Checking for Leaks

After any installation, or the replacement of any part of the refrigerator circuit, it is necessary that a very careful test be made of all joints to make sure there are no leaks. The methods of testing for leaks vary with the different refrigerants used. However, they are common in this respect: a positive pressure (greater than atmospheric) of from 5 to 30 lbs. is necessary throughout the circuit to test for leaks.

There are several ways to do the testing. Carbon dioxide or nitrogen may be used. It may be charged into the unit through the attachment or auxiliary valves. Build up a 20 to 30 psig pressure and test for leaks by immersing the unit in a water tank as shown in Fig. 12-70, or you may use soap suds or a special foaming solution. Then increase the pressure to 75 or 100 psig and check again. Finally, raise the pressure to 200-250 psig and check carefully for leaks once more.

There is an element of danger in this operation in that the high pressures may

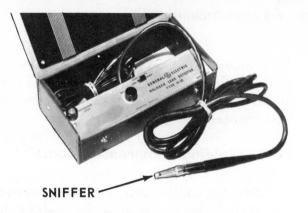

SNIFFER

Fig. 12-71. Electronic leak detector. (General Electric Co.)

cause serious injury to the tester if the unit should fail suddenly. It is therefore important to stand in a safe place while building up the pressure, and also to use a high side wall on the tank to deflect any sudden erruption.

Following the test it is necessary to thoroughly evacuate the system since all vapor used in the test must be removed from the system.

Many companies prefer to use a refrigerant to test for leaks. A process similar to the one just described is used, but a sensitive leak detector is used instead of soap suds or water. An electronic leak detector is shown in Fig. 12-71. Note that the unit is checked for leaks before it is evacuated as any leaks would allow moisture to enter the system during evacuation or pump-down.

If a leak is detected and repaired it is of vital importance to check the complete unit for leaks again.

CAUTION: NEVER USE OXYGEN TO DEVELOP PRESSURE WHEN CHECKING FOR LEAKS. IF HIGH PRESSURES ARE NEEDED, USE NITROGEN.

12-39 Repairing Leaks

Refrigerator systems are made of copper, steel, and/or aluminum materials. Leaks may occur in any part of the system and the repair of the leak depends on the material that has failed or combination of materials at the leaky point.

To determine the metal used, scrape the metal. Steel is gray-white, is hard and is magnetic (use a small magnet to test). Copper is reddish in color when scraped and is nonmagnetic. Aluminum is white and soft and is nonmagnetic. Steel may be silver brazed; copper may be silver brazed; aluminum may be aluminum soldered or brazed. Aluminum to steel or copper may be resistance welded. Aluminum evaporators can be repaired using epoxy cement. Instructions supplied by the manufacturer should be followed.

12-40 Leak Testing Devices

An alcohol (halide) torch with a long air intake tube may be used to good advantage to test for R-12 and R-22 leaks. With this torch (alcohol) ignited, pass the intake tube near the different joints. If vapor is leaking out it will go up the intake tube to the flame and give forth a brilliant green hue, a sure indication of a refrigerant vapor leak. A halide torch should be filled with alcohol and pumped up with air out-of-doors or in a room in which there is no possible chance of vaporized refrigerant being present. If some refrigerant is pumped into the torch in charging it, it would give a continuous indication of the presence of a leak and would therefore be of no use in detecting leaks in the refrigeration mechanism. The alcohol used must be clean as the liquid passages are very small. To light the torch, the flame chamber should be preheated and the air intake tube opening stopped with one finger until the flame is burning well.

Halide leak torch detection units are also available which use natural gas, acetylene, or propane as the fuel. Fig. 12-72 shows a halide leak detector which uses propane.

Another way to locate leaks is with a viscous fluid which is applied to the piping or equipment as a thick creamy foam,

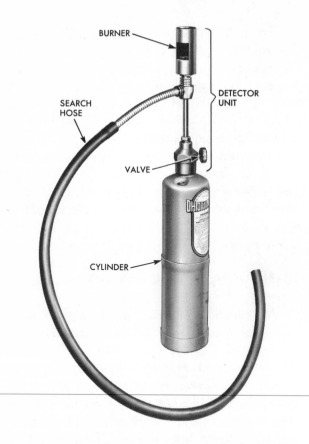

Fig. 12-72. Halide torch used to test for leaks. Note the small propane cylinder, the torch indicating element, air intake hose used to search for leaks.

Fig. 12-73. Foam placed on a connection that is suspected of leaking. Note the bubbles which indicate a leak. (Highland Chemicals, Inc.)

Fig. 12-73. When a leak is present, large bubbles form. The serviceman places foam on areas that are suspected of leaking. The foam will stay around the joint, yet is fluid enough to spread.

The most sensitive leak detector of all is the electronic type shown in Fig. 12-71.

This measures the electronic resistance of vapor samples and if the refrigerant is in the air sample being tested the current flow changes.

12-41 Welding Compressor Dome

After the compressor has been checked and tested, the dome may be welded in place. The best way to seal the dome is by arc welding. This requires such a short time, heat does not travel to the interior of the dome (compressor and winding).

A good safety practice is to bleed the dome with carbon dioxide or nitrogen while the welding is being done to prevent an explosive mixture of oil fumes and air from collecting. See Fig. 12-74. Use reverse polarity coated electrodes during arc welding to minimize heat that is released into the dome metal. Before welding it is important to clean the metal surfaces for at least one-half inch on each side of the weld area to prevent dirt inclusions. These may form blow holes which would cause future leaks. The welding should be done by an experienced operator. The welding station must be well

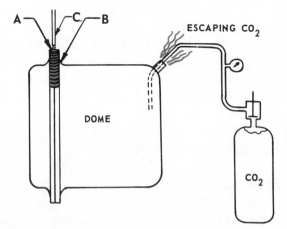

Fig. 12-74. Welding hermetic dome. A—Arc welded seam. B—Dome flange. C—Arc welding electrode. Always clean all surfaces before welding. Note CO_2 being used as flushing gas to prevent collection of explosive mixtures.

ventilated. The arc must be shielded from the eyes of passersby. Tack weld the dome in at least three places (equally spaced) before proceeding with the welding. Do all the welding with the weld in the downhand position; i.e., turn the dome as the welding progresses. After the welding is completed, the motor should again be tested for running characteristics. It is important to cool the metal as quickly as possible after the weld is completed. Use a damp cloth, or a stream of cool air.

Brazing, gas welding, and silver brazing with a gas flame are slower and may in some cases overheat the wiring and ruin the insulation.

12-42 Assembling System

Insuring cleanliness of internal parts of the mechanism is one of the most important steps in the assembly process. The inside of the compressor and the motor windings are usually the hardest parts to clean. One of the best procedures is to use an air gun and a mineral spirits spray. Immersing the parts in a mineral spirits bath is also effective. CARBON TETRACHLORIDE IS AN EXCELLENT CLEANER BUT ITS FUMES ARE DANGEROUS AND IT IS INJURIOUS TO THE SKIN. After being cleaned with carbon tetrachloride the iron and steel parts must be oil dipped immediately to prevent rusting.

It is essential to run the compressor after it has been assembled, before welding the dome. It can be run for a few moments and its pumping ability and its noise level checked without danger of scoring the parts due to lack of oil. A vacuum gauge equipped with a synthetic rubber tip can be held against the inlet opening of the unit while checking its pumping ability. A similarly equipped high pressure gauge may also be used on certain models. Running the motor provides a check of the electrical work for opens, shorts, grounds and suitable power.

12-43 Connecting Tubing

After the motor-compressor dome has been assembled and welded, the suction tubing and the condenser tubing must be fastened to the dome.

These joints are best attached by silver brazing. Silver brazing methods are described in Chapter 2. It is important to remember that the joint must be clean, the parts must be securely mounted to prevent movement during brazing, and both parts to be joined must be brought up to the correct temperature at the same time (the compressor end of the joint usually requires more application of heat).

12-44 Evacuating and Drying Unit

The evacuating and drying of the unit is a very important part of the assembly work. The system should be as close to 100% clear of air, moisture and other foreign matter as possible. Steps to follow are:

1. Evacuate unit to a 1 to 50 micron pressure level.
2. Charge with CO_2 to 50 to 100 pounds per sq. in.
3. Evacuate unit again.
4. Charge with refrigerant gas (no liquid).
5. Evacuate unit (warm unit again).

It must be remembered that the most careful evacuating and purging will not satisfactorily clean a unit that was carelessly put together with dirt in the system. To determine the extent of damage within a unit which has had a burn out, an acid test kit can be used after all contaminants have been removed. See Chapter 15 for additional information.

A vacuum pump should be used to remove as much air as possible from the unit, as explained in Par. 12-22. No pump will remove all of the air. A pump that produces a 28 in. vacuum will remove only about 93% of the air. With a 28 in. vacuum moisture particles must be heated to 100 F. or above, before they will evaporate and can be pumped out as water vapor.

To remove the moisture you must heat the unit to a temperature that will not only vaporize the moisture, but will drive the moisture out of all the crevices. For the same reason, the unit should be run for part or all of this operation. This is to in-

To eliminate still more of the air, charge some refrigerant into the system. Next, evacuate the system again. This will take out more of the air. Only about .8% of the original air will then remain in the system. The remaining air may best be removed by purging the condenser after the system has been in operation for a short time.

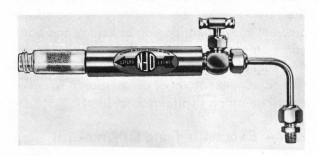

Fig. 12-75. Indicator used to show presence of moisture in system. Lower left fitting connects to service gauge opening. If system refrigerant contains moisture and if some is purged through green desiccant in plastic cylinder, chemical will turn purple.

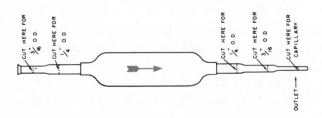

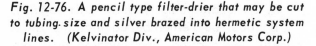

Fig. 12-76. A pencil type filter-drier that may be cut to tubing size and silver brazed into hermetic system lines.   (Kelvinator Div., American Motors Corp.)

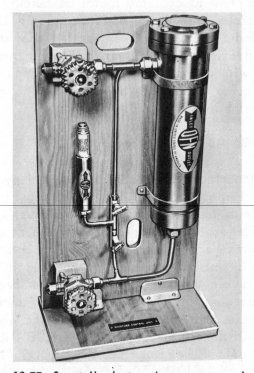

Fig. 12-77. Specially designed apparatus used to dehydrate any refrigerating system. Incorporates moisture indicator which accurately indicates moisture content in system.
(McIntire Co., Sub. of Superior Valve and Fittings Co.)

sure that all pockets in the compressor and in the bearings are agitated to release pocketed air, plus warming the motor windings which are an additional source of trapped moisture. It is considered good practice to evacuate for 8 hours at 250 F. or for 24 hours at 150 F. A drying oven, temperature controlled, is of utmost importance. Carbon dioxide has an affinity or attraction for moisture and circulating it in the system helps to solve the moisture problem.

In addition to the electronic vacuum gauge on high vacuum pumps described in Par. 12-22, there is a device on the market which indicates moisture in the system by use of a silica gel cartridge and a litmus solution. Refrigerant or air is passed through the device and if there is moisture present, the silica gel will be discolored. See Fig. 12-75.

A small pencil type strainer designed for hermetic systems is shown in Fig. 12-76. This unit may be silver brazed into

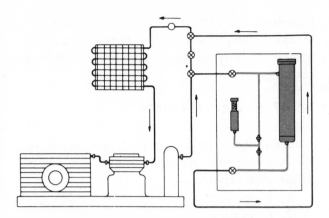

Fig. 12-78. Complete dehydrating apparatus connected into liquid line of refrigerating system by bypass arrangement.

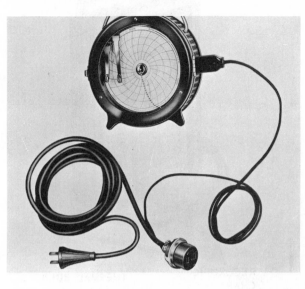

Fig. 12-79. Recording thermometer which records temperatures and indicates cycling intervals on 72 hour basis. (Bristol Co.)

the refrigerant circuit without injury to the strainer.

Fig. 12-77 shows a dehydrating and indicating system which may be used in drying a refrigerating system.

Fig. 12-78 illustrates diagrammatically how a dehydrating and indicating system should be connected to the refrigerating circuit.

By means of such a system, the refrigerant can be circulated through the oversize drier by positioning the valves as shown. After the system has been operated for several hours, the test unit can be fed some of the refrigerant. If there is still moisture in the refrigerant, the green colored crystals in the test tube will change to purple color. This operation is continued until the test tube crystals do not change color when refrigerant is admitted.

The dehydrator and the test tube can be removed without disturbing the system, by simply closing the two dehydrator line valves and opening the middle valve.

12-45 Testing the Unit

After unit has been assembled, tested, evacuated, and charged with oil and refrigerant, it should be run with a thermostatic control for at least 24 hours to ascertain its behavior. A recording thermometer is of great help during this test period to enable the repairman to know what is happening during the entire test period. Many servicemen neglect this very important part of repair work. Fig. 12-79 shows a 72 hour temperature recorder. The recorder is put in the refrigerator and it is connected to a wall plug and the refrigerator cord is then connected to the special socket on the cord. The chart is a three (3) day chart which shows the cabinet temperature at all times. The other needle records the running times of the unit. If possible, the cabinet should be placed in a 100 F. room for the test.

If a cabinet is not used, the evaporator may be covered with a canvas bag to provide a load situation similar to what the unit will encounter in actual service. The testing room should be a quiet room in order to aid in checking for noise. A portable temperature recorder is shown in Fig. 12-80.

The testing should also include close observation of the temperature of the dome, the lines, and the even frosting of the evaporator.

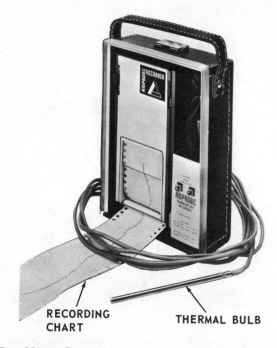

RECORDING CHART

THERMAL BULB

Fig. 12-80. Portable temperature recorder for up to 30 hours recording, is placed inside cabinet. (Amprobe Instrument, Div. Soss Mfg. Co.)

An ammeter and voltmeter or a wattmeter should be used to check the electrical section of the unit. Many servicemen use a combination hermetic compressor analyzer and electrical tester. There are numerous types available. Fig. 12-81 illustrates a heavy-duty analyzer which provides the serviceman with a hermetic motor analyzer, dual range volt-ammeter, capacitor analyzer, 3-phase tester, motor resistance tester, potential relay tester, and insulator tester. For additional information on the use of electrical instrumentation see Chapter 8.

12-46 Miscellaneous Service Notes

Pinching lines is a practice to be used in cases of emergency only. Some servicemen follow this practice needlessly and it leads to future trouble. One must remember that when refrigerant is added to a system, some of the oil in the system will be dissolved in the refrigerant. If the unit becomes noisy soon after the refrigerant has been added, some refrigerant oil should be added. Electric motors, when installed, should have clean and tight electrical connections. The motor must be very carefully aligned with the fan and fan housing.

12-47 Review of Safety

When servicing refrigeration systems, the serviceman must be alert to several dangerous conditions:
1. Electrical.
2. Pressure.
3. Heat.
4. Freezing.
5. Dropping heavy objects.
6. Lifting heavy objects.
7. Fire.
8. Acid.
9. Pointed or sharp tools and objects.
10. Exposed power-driven parts (drills, shafts, fans, etc.).

Always open the electrical circuit or make sure all electrical devices are safe before starting on a job.

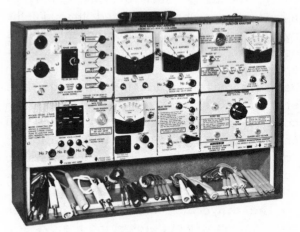

Fig. 12-81. Combination hermetic compressor analyzer and electrical tester. (Airserco Mfg. Co.)

Wear goggles when working on a charged system. When using a flame be sure there are no flammables nearby. Be sure the pressure in the system is close to atmospheric pressure before opening a system. Do not permit oil from a hermetic unit to contact your skin; the oil may be acidic.

Each time an operation is planned, train yourself to think, "Is there a possible safety hazard in the operation?" Then take precautions needed to minimize the hazard.

There is often a temptation to use carbon tetrachloride for cleaning. Remember its effects are accumulative in the human body and its continued use may be fatal.

12-48 Test Your Knowledge - Chapter 12

1. Do all hermetic systems have service valves?
2. Which refrigerants are in most common use in hermetic units being built today?
3. Why are some of the condenser air passages controlled by ducts?
4. How many evaporators are used in domestic refrigerator cabinets?
5. What happens to the suction line when a rotary compressor check valve leaks?
6. What causes tubing to create noise?
7. How may a motor-compressor dome be opened?
8. What is a good way to clean the outside of the mechanism?
9. How should hermetic mechanism be prepared for moving?
10. What is the most popular method of sealing tubing joints in hermetic servicing?
11. What trouble is indicated by a hot liquid line?
12. What is the size of the service valve stem wrench?
13. Give several reasons why a gauge installation must be tested for leaks.
14. Why must a leak testing torch be charged and pumped up out in the open air and not in the same room in which a refrigerator is located?
15. What trouble results if a 250 lbs. per square inch head pressure exists in an air-cooled R-12 system?
16. A frosted suction line with an excessive low side pressure is the indication of what trouble?
17. To what part of the system is the compound gauge usually connected?
18. To what part of the system is the high pressure gauge usually connected?
19. Why must the pressures be balanced before a system is opened?
20. What should the average low side pressure be for R-12, operating at 15 F. evaporator temperature?
21. What should the average high side pressure be for R-12 operating in a room temperature of 85 F.?
22. What indicates the presence of air in a condenser?
23. Name two methods of adding oil to a system.
24. What is a micron?
25. How many microns are in a millimeter?
26. How does a process tube adaptor fasten to a process tube?
27. At what temperature does water evaporate at a 29 in. vacuum?
28. What should be used to trap the clogging material when a capillary tube is unplugged?
29. How does a motor-compressor analyzer test for volumetric efficiency?
30. Why is the oil in a burned out motor-compressor dangerous for a serviceman to handle?

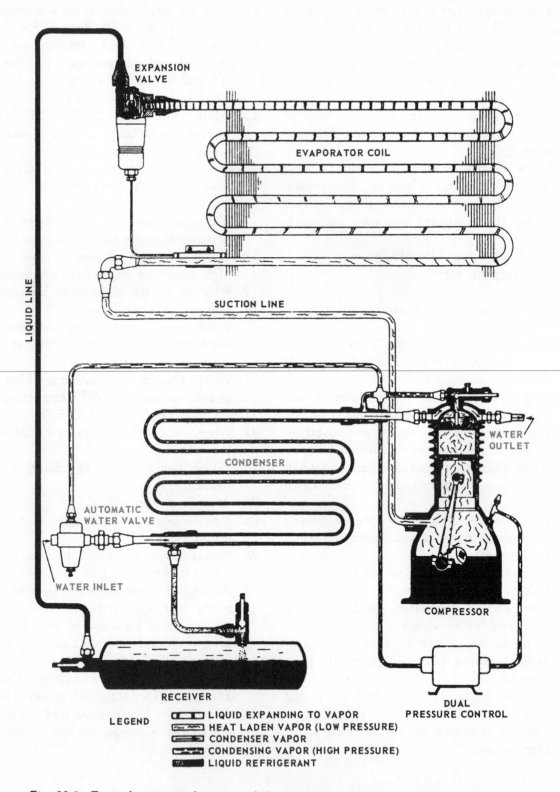

Fig. 13-1. Typical commercial water-cooled unit showing tube-within-a-tube condenser and water-cooled compressor head.

Chapter 13

COMMERCIAL SYSTEMS

The machines which refrigerate the multitude of commercial refrigeration applications vary considerably in size and in appearance. Machines as small as 1/8 hp are used for beverage coolers, vending machines, dehumidifiers, etc. Machines of 7 1/2 to 15 hp and more are used for frozen food walk-in cabinets, industrial cooling, etc. See Fig. 13-1.

In this chapter we will discuss the design, construction and operation of commercial units.

13-1 Construction of Refrigerating Mechanisms

Fundamentals of operation applicable to domestic refrigeration mechanisms are also applicable to commercial refrigeration mechanisms.

Commercial units using the absorption cycle are similar in construction and operation to those studied in Chapter 17. Absorption units are used for water-cooling, air conditioning, and other commercial applications.

Commercial units using mechanical cycle mechanisms vary from the domestic mechanisms mainly in the multiplicity of evaporating units connected to one condensing unit, and the special designs required for the larger units.

13-2 Mechanical Cycle

Most of the large commercial refrigerating apparatus is of the semihermetic design (completely serviceable). Many single unit applications, such as bottle coolers, beverage dispensers, and ice cream cabinets use a full hermetic unit with parts of the system being similar to the designs shown in Chapter 10, except that the design of the cabinet varies according to the application.

In the commercial refrigerating system, the unit is designed to vaporize a refrigerant under a controlled pressure in an evaporator. The vapors formed are then compressed and passed to the condensing unit, which removes heat from the vapor and converts it back into a liquid, as shown in Fig. 13-2. In some cases the cycles are complicated by the addition of unloading or defrost devices. Fig. 13-3 shows a hot-gas defrost system.

13-3 Complete Mechanical Mechanism

The single unit commercial refrigerating mechanism apparatus consists of:
A. High pressure side:
  1. Compressor.
  2. Condenser (usually air cooled).
  3. Liquid receiver (when a thermostatic expansion valve or automatic expansion valve is used).
  4. High pressure safety motor control.
  5. Liquid line.
The refrigerant control is at the division point between the low side and the high side of the system, (thermostatic expansion valves, automatic expansion valves or capillary tubes).
B. Low pressure side:
  1. Evaporator.
  2. Low pressure or temperature motor control.
  3. Suction line.

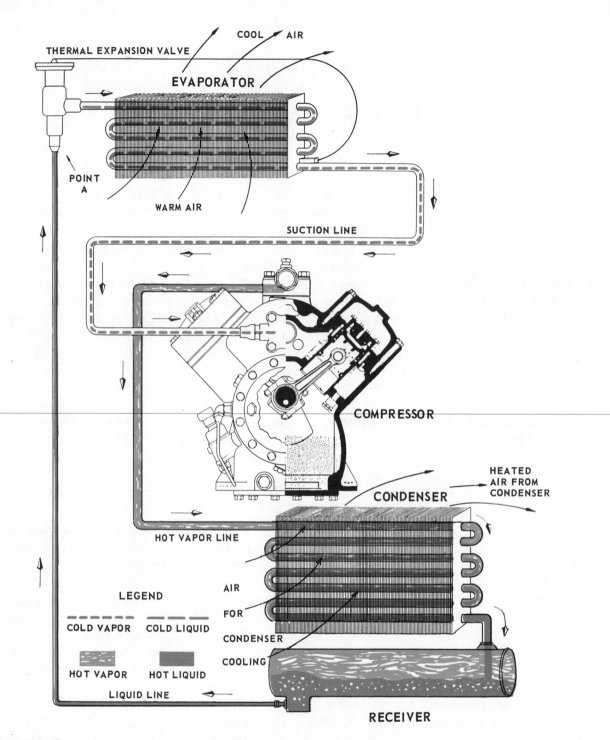

THERMAL EXPANSION VALVE

COOL AIR

EVAPORATOR

POINT A

WARM AIR

SUCTION LINE

COMPRESSOR

HEATED AIR FROM CONDENSER

CONDENSER

HOT VAPOR LINE

LEGEND

COLD VAPOR   COLD LIQUID

HOT VAPOR   HOT LIQUID

AIR

FOR

CONDENSER

COOLING

LIQUID LINE

RECEIVER

Fig. 13-2. Typical commercial system cycle using air-cooled condenser, thermostatic expansion valve and V-type compressor.   (Carrier Air Conditioning Co.)

The multiple mechanism consists of:
A. High pressure side:
  1. Compressor.
  2. Condenser.
    a. Water or air-cooled.

3. Liquid receiver (with thermostatic expansion valve).
4. High pressure motor control.
5. Liquid lines (with a distributing manifold).

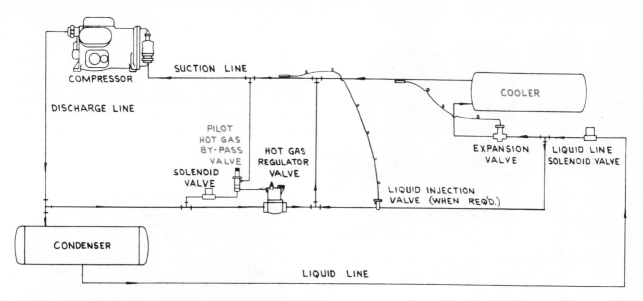

Fig. 13-3. Commercial refrigerating cycle showing water cooler and hot gas bypass system.

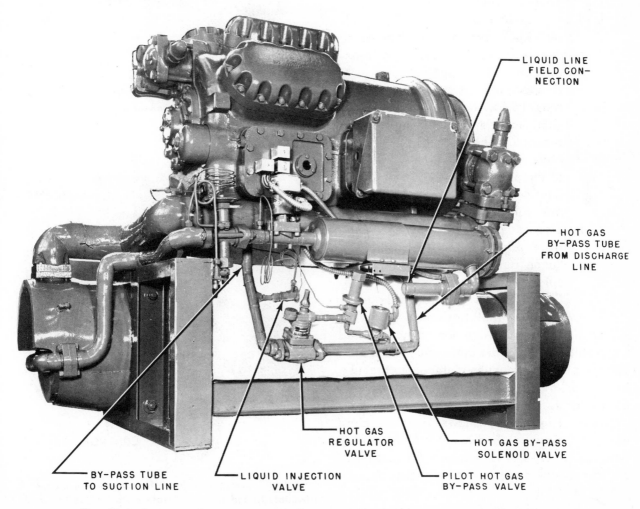

Fig. 13-4. Large condensing unit complete with hot gas bypass and compressor unloader.
(Airtemp Div., Chrysler Corp.)

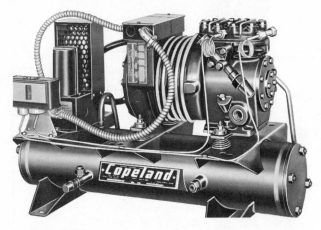

Fig. 13-5. Commercial hermetic condensing unit. (Copeland Refrig. Corp.)

6. Water valve (used with a water-cooled unit).

B. Low pressure side:

1. Refrigerant controls (two or more which are of the thermostatic expansion valve type).

2. Evaporators (two or more which may be of the natural convection, forced convection, or submerged type).

3. Motor control (which is usually of the pressure type).

4. Suction lines with suction line manifold.

5. Two-temperature valves (for multiple temperature installations).

6. Surge tanks (for absorbing pressure fluctuations).

7. Check valves (for multiple temperature installations).

Condensing units are normally mounted on a steel base. In the open unit, the motor operates the compressor through the use of one or more belts. In the hermetic unit the motor is connected directly to the compressor. Fig. 13-4, shows a 25 hp condensing unit which has two 2 1/8 in. solder type liquid lines. It is designed for low temperature work and has a 40,600 Btu/hr. capacity at -52 F.

A fabricated steel frame is used to hold the shell and tube condenser on the hermet-

ic unit shown in Fig. 13-5. Note the water coil around the electric motor, the oil level sight glass in the lower right of the compressor, and the spring mounted hermetic unit. Fig. 13-6, shows a multiple cylinder belt-driven commercial condensing unit.

Fig. 13-6. Water-cooled commercial condensing unit, which has four cylinder, V-type compressor, shell-and-tube water-cooled condenser and flange type suction line connections.

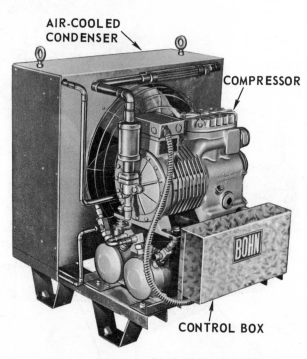

Fig. 13-7. Commercial hermetic condensing unit with air-cooled condenser. Separate motor is used to drive condenser fan. (Bohn Aluminum & Brass Co.)

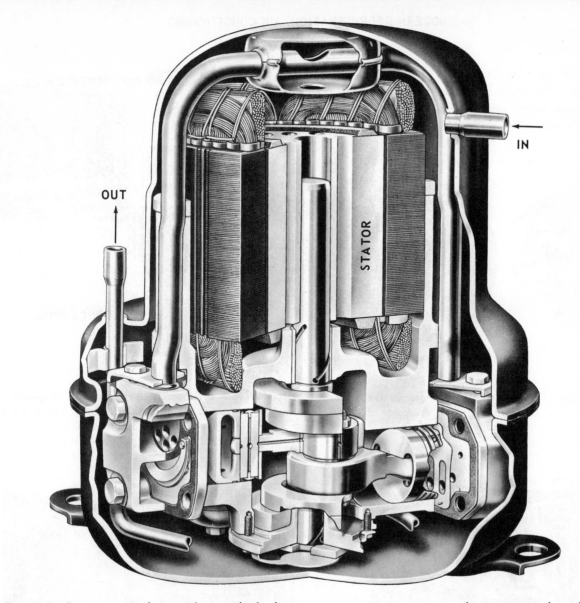

Fig. 13-8. Cross-sectional view of two cylinder hermetic motor-compressor as used on commercial condensing units. (Tecumseh Products Co.)

13-4 Commercial Hermetic Units

A number of companies now produce hermetic units in excess of 20 hp. Some of the units are of the bolted assembly type, often referred to as field serviceable. See Fig. 13-4. Some units are sealed in a welded casing. These are equipped with service valves and may be connected to any desired type of evaporator coil and used for a variety of applications.

An advantage in the use of hermetics in the commercial field is the elimination of the crankshaft seal and belts.

Because any trouble in the compressor mechanism involves both the compressor and the motor, it is essential that the serviceman be cautious when working on these units so that moisture and dirt will not enter the system.

A motor-compressor equipped with a fan condenser, a shroud, and service valves is shown in Fig. 13-7. The internal combination of a hermetic motor-compressor is shown in Fig. 13-8. The motors are single phase in the smaller units but three-phase motors are generally used in units over 1/2 hp, Fig. 13-9.

The condensing units are installed in many different ways. Some are mounted on the roof, some on the same floor level with the evaporator but in different rooms or

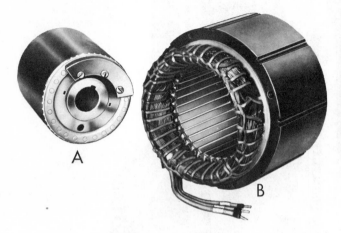

Fig. 13-9. Three-phase electric motor as used in larger hermetic refrigeration units. A—Rotor. B—Stator. (Emerson Electric Co.)

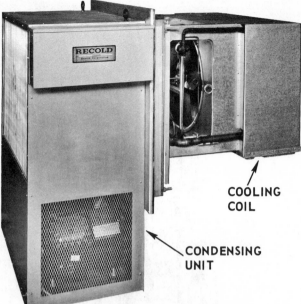

Fig. 13-11. A self-contained commercial refrigerating unit. These units are available in 3 to 10 hp and are equipped with defrosting devices. (Recold Corp., Borg-Warner Corp.)

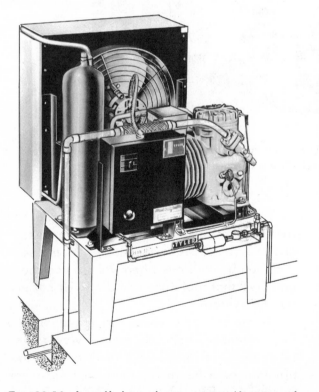

Fig. 13-10. Installed condensing unit. Note trough in concrete slab. Similar piping installations are often found in supermarkets. (Tyler Refrig. Div., Clark Equipment Co.)

Fig. 13-12. Evaporator of self-contained thru-the-wall commercial unit. Drain pan has defroster tubes. The suction line is shown at left center with TEV thermal bulb mounted on it.

outside the building as shown in Fig. 13-10. Note the suction service valve on the compressor dome, the liquid receiver service valve on the receiver, and the forced convection condenser. One method of installing a factory assembled condensing unit and evaporator coil combination is shown in Fig. 13-11. These straddle or plug in units eliminate the need to install piping, to charge the units, when they are installed. The installation, therefore, consists of preparing the opening, mounting the unit, running the electrical lines and opening the shutoff valves. The evaporator coil side is installed as shown in Fig. 13-12.

13-5 Outdoor Air-Cooled Condensing Units

To conserve space within commercial buildings, and in homes, (for air conditioning) there is an increasing use of outdoor air-cooled condensing units, Fig. 13-13. Air-cooled units save the cost of plumbing for water circuits, and are desirable where chemicals in the water make water cooling impractical. These units may be mounted on the roof, on the outside wall, or at ground level immediately adjacent to the building.

Air-cooled condensing units must be designed, built, installed and maintained, keeping in mind four major considerations:

1. There must be a head pressure control, especially if the unit is exposed to outdoor weather which may go below the operating cabinet temperature. Fig. 13-14 shows how a check valve and a limiter valve are used to maintain a good head pressure in the condenser device where low outdoor temperature conditions may be present.
2. A method of preventing short cycling must be designed into the system.
3. A means must be provided to prevent dilution of the compressor oil by liquid refrigerant.
4. The completed condensing unit must be constructed and installed so it is virtually weatherproof.

These units require approximately 1000

cfm of condenser air circulation per horsepower of the unit. They are less costly to operate than indoor air-cooled units.

Some units are enclosed with motorized air dampers operated by a thermostat, others use pressure operated dampers.

AIR IN

AIR OUT

Fig. 13-13. Air-cooled condensing unit for outdoor installation. Unit is shown with casing in place. (Bohn Aluminum and Brass Co.)

One of the main problems with outdoor units is maintaining the thermostatic expansion valve capacity during cold weather. The capacity depends on the pressure difference across the valve. If the condensing pressure reduces from 136 psig (90 F. for R-12) to 47 psig (30 F. for R-12) the valve capacity will drop drastically and refrig-

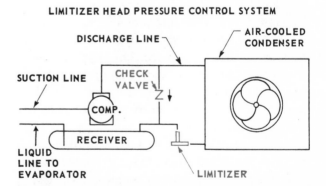

LIMITIZER HEAD PRESSURE CONTROL SYSTEM

DISCHARGE LINE

AIR-COOLED CONDENSER

SUCTION LINE

CHECK VALVE

COMP.

RECEIVER

LIQUID LINE TO EVAPORATOR

LIMITIZER

Fig. 13-14. Outdoor condensing unit cycle. The check valve and limiter valve insure good condensing temperatures during cold weather.

erated fixture temperatures may rise to dangerous levels. Also, a small pressure difference may cause short cycling of the condensing unit.

The condensing temperature may be kept at a good operating level by designing the unit to fill the condenser tubes with enough liquid to leave just enough condensing surface to maintain the pressure. The pressure on the limitizer valve on the outlet of the condenser will not open and allow liquid to leave the condenser, until the condensing pressure reaches the proper level. The limitizer valve is located at the outlet of the condenser and opens on a pressure rise. The installation specifications must be carefully checked. The receiver must be large enough to provide flooding most of the condenser in the winter and still safely hold the refrigerant during the warm season. Standard size receivers do not have this capacity. The condensing pressure may also be controlled by limiting the air flow to the condenser. Damper controls, on the air-in and air-out louvers (usually adjustable) of the housing are used in some cases. Other systems shut off the condenser fan when the condenser pressure falls to a minimum level.

To keep the receiver warmer than the cabinet temperature, electric heating elements in or around the receiver are sometimes used to prevent the receiver and the compressor crankcase from becoming a condenser (too cold). Some systems use a bypass from the compressor to the condenser outlet line to the line from the condenser to the receiver. This bypass feeds a certain amount of hot refrigerant vapor to the receiver to keep it warm. The bypass has a check valve mounted in it to insure one-way flow.

The compressor is kept warm enough to prevent dilution of the oil by the liquid refrigerant during cold weather, by using electric heating elements in or around the motor-compressor, which are thermostatically operated to energize the heating ele-

ment at approximately 50 F. This heater usually has a 100 to 200 watt capacity.

Another method used is to install a solenoid valve in the liquid line operated by the cabinet thermostat. When cut-out is reached, the solenoid closes, the unit continues to run, and the evaporator coil is pumped down before the unit stops.

However, the design capacity to overcome low ambient temperatures is not enough if the outdoor unit is exposed to above normal winds. These winds can prevent damper operation, fan operation, and even cause more cooling effect than the electric heating element can overcome. The unit must be installed in such a position to avoid the harmful effects of these high velocity cold winds.

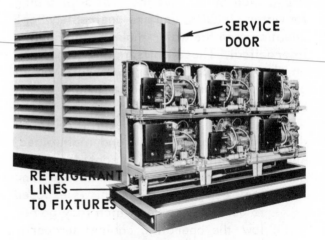

Fig. 13-15. Photo which shows six commercial air-cooled condensing units mounted on rack. The weather protecting shroud has been removed and is in the background. (Tyler Refrig. Div., Clark Equip. Co.)

The unit should be made of nonferrous construction or should be exceptionally well weatherproofed. The electrical installation should be protected from the weather as much as possible. Fig. 13-15 shows six separate air-cooled condensing units mounted on a rack. The weather protection shroud is removed and is shown in the background.

AIR-COOLED RADIATING FINS

AIR-COOLED CONDENSER

OIL PUMP

LIQUID RECEIVER

OIL LEVEL SIGHT GLASS

Fig. 13-16. Four cylinder V-type commercial compres-sor. Note cooling fins on cylinder head and cylinder. (Lehigh Mfg. Co.)

Fig. 13-17. Bolted type motor-compressor. Note oil pump used for forced lubricating system. (Copeland Refrig. Corp.)

13-6 The Compressor

Commercial compressors are of two general types:

1. Open.
2. Hermetic.

The typical open commercial compressor is of vertical reciprocating construction, made of cast iron-steel nickel-alloy cylinders which use cast iron pistons, is driven by means of a drop forged connecting rod and a hardened steel, full-floating piston pin.

The connecting rod is attached to an eccentric type or crank throw type of crankshaft which is drop-forged and casehardened. The bearings are typically bronze alloy. Main bearings are usually made of a similar material, but some companies use the same material for the crankcase and for the main bearings.

In the open units, the crankshaft seal may be of either type wherein the bellows is stationary and presses against a crankshaft shoulder, or it may be of the type where the bellows is sealed to the crankshaft and revolves with it. The oiling of the compressor is done either by the splash system, or by force-feed lubrication to some moving parts.

Compressors usually have a double cylinder head. The intermediate head or valve plate has intake and exhaust valves. The cylinder heads are made of the same ma-

terial as the cylinder body, although some companies make the intermediate head of steel. The intake valves and the exhaust valves are made of thin spring steel, similar to those used in the domestic models. The design, however, changes with the size of the unit. Large compressors use multiple disks and port openings instead of the single openings employed in domestic units.

The pistons are usually fitted with two or more piston rings. Clearances permitted for all moving parts are one thousandth of an inch (.001) or less. This is a little more than allowed for domestic type mechanisms. The cylinder heads of these compressors must be cooled. Radiating fins are constructed in the cylinder head and cylinder body of the smaller sizes, Fig. 13-16. Refrigerant-cooled or water-cooled heads are used in larger models. Speed of these compressors is kept to a minimum, since the belief is that a compressor operated at slow speed (300 to 500 rpm) will be more efficient and last longer. The means for driving these compressors is usually multiple V-type belts.

There are several types of commercial hermetic compressors available. Fig. 13-17 shows a bolted hermetic two cylinder compressor with a force-feed lubrication system.

Some large units have either hydraulic or electric unloading devices to control the number of cylinders which are pumping.

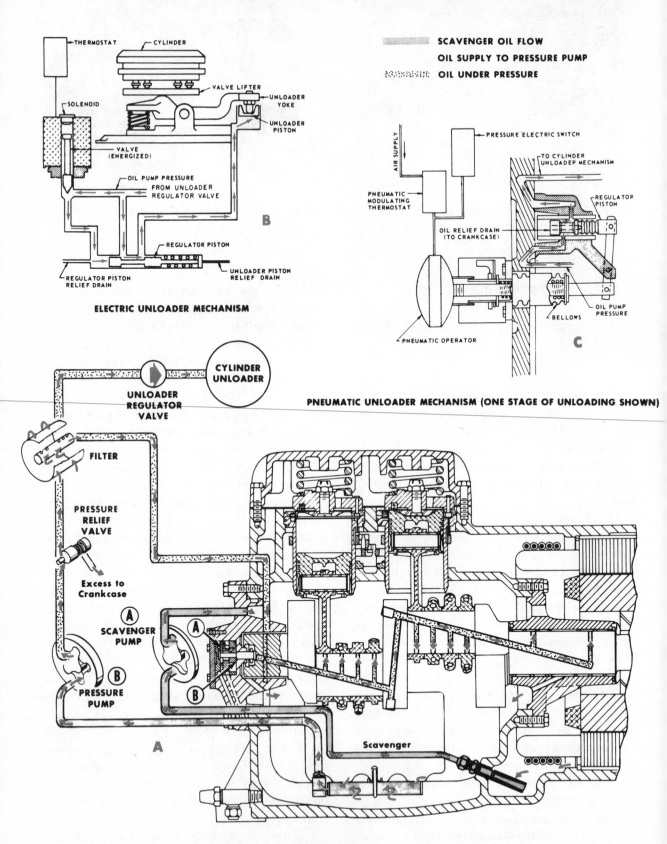

SCAVENGER OIL FLOW

OIL SUPPLY TO PRESSURE PUMP

OIL UNDER PRESSURE

THERMOSTAT

CYLINDER

VALVE LIFTER

UNLOADER YOKE

SOLENOID

UNLOADER PISTON

VALVE (ENERGIZED)

OIL PUMP PRESSURE FROM UNLOADER REGULATOR VALVE

B

REGULATOR PISTON

UNLOADER PISTON RELIEF DRAIN

REGULATOR PISTON RELIEF DRAIN

ELECTRIC UNLOADER MECHANISM

AIR SUPPLY

PRESSURE ELECTRIC SWITCH

PNEUMATIC MODULATING THERMOSTAT

TO CYLINDER UNLOADER MECHANISM

REGULATOR PISTON

OIL RELIEF DRAIN (TO CRANKCASE)

OIL PUMP PRESSURE

BELLOWS

C

PNEUMATIC OPERATOR

CYLINDER UNLOADER

UNLOADER REGULATOR VALVE

PNEUMATIC UNLOADER MECHANISM (ONE STAGE OF UNLOADING SHOWN)

FILTER

PRESSURE RELIEF VALVE

Excess to Crankcase

Ⓐ SCAVENGER PUMP

Ⓑ PRESSURE PUMP

Ⓐ

Ⓑ

A

Scavenger

Fig. 13-18. Oil circuit of compressor with oil take-off to operate compressor unloader. A—Circuit. B—Electric control. C—Pneumatic control. (Airtemp Div., Chrysler Corp.)

The higher the load, the more cylinders used to pump the vapor. Fig. 13-18 shows the oil circuit and how it is controlled to operate the compressor unloader.

Another type of hermetic compressor unit is the welded motor-compressor design (nonfield serviceable). These units vary in size from 1/16 hp up to approximately 20 hp. The internal design varies

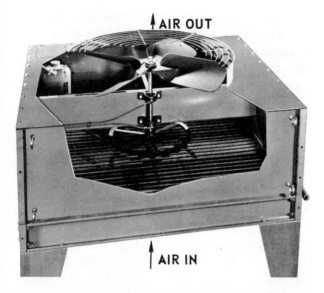

Fig. 13-19. *Air-cooled condenser. Condenser may be flat or horizontal. Belt driven axial flow fan is shown (note motor in upper left corner). Air enters underneath and leaves from top. The condenser has a shroud to protect fan and condenser, and to improve air flow.*

with size and manufacturer. Some are spring mounted internally, while some use external mounting springs. The smaller units usually have one cylinder while the larger units (1/2 hp and up) have two or more cylinders. For small units, motors may be either two or four-pole design (single-phase). Three-phase motors are generally used in the larger units.

13-7 Air-Cooled Condenser

Air-cooled condensers are quite common in the smaller commercial units, and where cooling water is not available or is

too corrosive. The smaller units use static condensers (thermal air flow). The larger condensers are cooled by a large fan located on the motor or built into the compressor flywheel on conventional units. Larger hermetic units use separate motors to drive the fan.

See Chapter 9 for determining condensing temperatures and pressures when an air-cooled condenser is used.

The efficiency of the fan, air-cooled condenser may be increased by the use of a metal shroud around it and the use of a cooling fan as shown in Fig. 13-19. Air can be drawn through the condensers induced, or driven through. These condensers have fins and frequently use a double or triple layer of tubes. Another type of commercial air-cooled condenser is shown in Fig. 13-20.

Fig. 13-20. *Commercial system air-cooled condenser. Air enters on fan side.*
(Bohn Aluminum and Brass Co.)

In order to cool the compressor head and valves, a dual air-cooled condenser is sometimes used. This condenser is so arranged that the refrigerant, when leaving the compressor, passes through one condenser, and is then led back through the motor-compressor. From there it goes into the second condenser where it is finally cooled and condensed into liquid.

13-8 Outdoor Air-Cooled Condensers

Outdoor air-cooled condensers are for use in systems which have the motor-compressor and occasionally the receiver is located inside the building. The condenser only is located outdoors. The compressor discharge line carries the hot, high pressure vapor to the outdoor air-cooled condenser and the condensed liquid is piped back into the building. There are several variations of this type of installation. Par. 13-5 describes several of these installations.

13-9 Water-Cooled Condenser

Most large commercial refrigerating units use the water-cooled type condenser. This condenser is built in two styles:
1. Shell and tube.
2. Tube-within-a-tube type.

One style is constructed so the refrigerant goes directly from the compressor into the interior of a tank or shell.

The other type uses two pipes or tubes, one within the other. The refrigerant passes one way through the outer pipe, while the condenser water passes the other way, through the inner tube.

13-10 Shell-Type Condenser

The shell-type condenser, or shell and tube as it is commonly called, is a cylinder made of steel with copper tubes inserted in the shell. Water circulates through the tubing and condenses the hot vapors into a liquid. The bottom portion of the shell serves as the liquid receiver, as shown in Fig. 13-21. The advantages of this style of construction are compactness of design, the elimination of fans and the need for

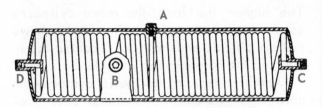

Fig. 13-21. Water-cooled condenser which also serves as liquid receiver. A—Refrigerant out. B—Refrigerant in. C—Water in. D—Water out.

separate condenser and receiver. Also, it enables a flexible type of assembly. Two designs are used. One design has the water tubing coil inside the receiver. The other type uses a number of straight tubes inside the receiver with a water manifold on both ends. When these manifold ends are removed the water tubes can be easily cleaned of deposits which may reduce heat transfer.

13-11 Tube-Within-A-Tube Condenser

The double tube type of water-cooled condenser is popular because it can easily be made to fit the size of the unit to be cooled. Water passing through the inside tube cools the refrigerant in the outside tube, Fig. 13-22. The outside tubing is also

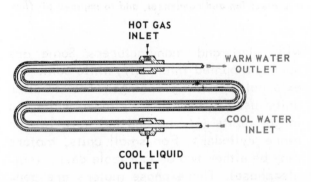

Fig. 13-22. Tube-within-a-tube condenser. Note that water flows in inner tube.

cooled by air in the room providing an efficient operation. The condenser may be constructed in the cylindrical, spiral style, rectangular style, or in a rectangular style

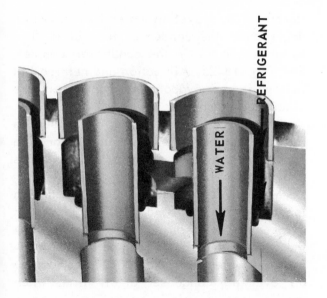

Fig. 13-23. Detail of construction of tube-within-a-tube condenser. Note how both refrigerant tubes and water tubes are silver brazed into header.

of soft copper tubing. See Fig. 13-23. Or, it may be made of copper pipe with end plate manifold as shown in Fig. 13-24.

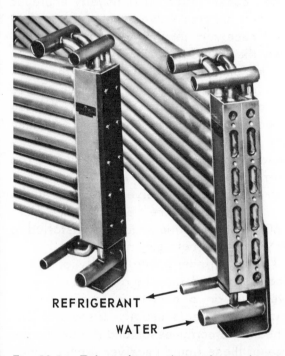

Fig. 13-24. Tube-within-a-tube condenser designed to permit cleaning water tubes (inner tube). The clean-out plate is removed in right-hand view. (Halstead and Mitchell Co.)

Water enters the condenser at the point where the refrigerant leaves the condenser and leaves the condenser at the point where the hot vapor from the compressor enters the condenser. This is called contraflow or counterflow construction. The warmest water is adjacent to the warmest refrigerant, and the coolest refrigerant to the coolest water. The cylindrical spiral design is made with soft tubing. In this design the water tube is difficult to clean.

The rectangular type uses straight, hard copper pipe with manifolds on the ends. When the manifolds are removed, the water pipes can be cleaned easily.

Water-cooled compressors are sometimes used with water-cooled condensers. The water flow, with few exceptions, is through the condenser first, then through the cylinder head, and finally into the drain. Water flow through these condensers is regulated by means of an automatic water valve. See Par. 13-52.

13-12 Cooling Towers

In some localities water contains chemicals causing it to be unsuitable for use as a coolant. In other localities water may be very scarce, expensive, or its use may be limited by law.

To permit using a water-cooled mechanism, and save on water consumption, water-cooling towers are used. These cooling towers serve the same purpose as spray towers used in large industrial refrigeration systems.

One system connects the water lines of the condenser to a water coil in an enclosure. A pump forces the water through the coil in the tower. The coil is pierced with holes and the water is sprayed into the enclosure. Air rushing through the sprayed water, evaporates some of it and the evaporation cools the remaining water to the outdoor temperature or even lower. The cooled water collects in the bottom of the enclosure and passes through a screen to

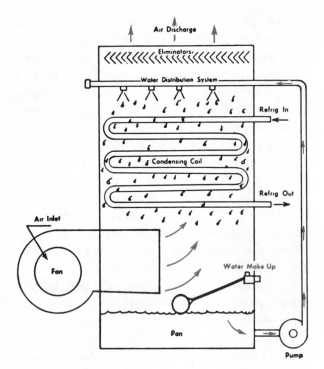

Fig. 13-25. Evaporative condenser. Note air and water flow. Water make-up is controlled by float valve. (Baltimore Aircoil Co., Inc.)

remove leaves or other foreign material and is then recirculated through the condenser. A float controlled valve in the lower water pan provides for makeup or refill water as needed. This float operates similarly to a refrigerant low side float mechanism. Chemicals may be put in the water to retard rust formation, fungus growth, and the like.

The cooling towers are made of corrosion resistant materials such as steel zinc dipped after assembly, copper, stainless steel, or of wood treated to resist rot. The cooling tower has overflow pipes, that carry any excess water to the drain system of the building.

See Chapters 16 and 24 for details of sizes and capacities.

13-13 Evaporative Condensers

The evaporative condenser system carries the refrigerant into a condenser located in an enclosure similar to a cooling tower. In this system water is sprayed or drips over the condenser to cool it. The water cycle is in the condenser cabinet. See Fig. 13-25. Air action and refrigerant action in an evaporative condenser are discussed in Chapter 19.

Usually the evaporative condenser is mounted outdoors; however, an evaporative condenser may be used indoors if air ducts are provided to the outside.

Some systems pump water to a trough located above the condenser and the water drips over coils as air is forced through the coils. A thermostat can be used to control the water flow. A fan operates to blow air over the condenser at all times when the condensing unit is operating. Water is turned on by thermostat only when the condenser temperature exceeds a certain level (100 F. or more).

13-14 Liquid Receiver

The liquid receiver is a steel tank of welded construction. It is usually equipped with two service valves; one is a typical liquid receiver service valve mounted between the liquid receiver and the condenser. The other is located between the compressor discharge and the receiver. These two valves enable the serviceman to disconnect the liquid receiver and condenser from the system separately. Receivers should be equipped with safety devices. The minimum safety device is a thermal release plug. Some receivers have both the thermal and pressure releases. See Par. 13-60. A special line should be installed to carry released refrigerant outdoors.

These cylinders are usually of cylindrical form and may be mounted either in a vertical or a horizontal position. The horizontal style is usually suspended underneath the compressor and motor frame. Some of these liquid receivers are provided with a device whereby the level of the liquid refrigerant may be easily determined.

In the construction involving a water coil inside the liquid receiver, the shell is similar to the one just described, but is usually larger for the same size compressor unit.

13-15 Commercial Evaporator Coils

Because of the great variety of demands in commercial refrigeration, special evaporator unit designs are required for many installations. These evaporator units vary from coils of tubing immersed in a sweet water bath, to forced circulation evaporator units which have the air driven over the coils by means of a motor driven fan.

Evaporating coils may be divided into two main divisions:

1. Coils that are used for cooling air which in turn cools the contents of the cabinet.
2. Coils that are submerged in a liquid such as brine or a beverage.

Coils for cooling air are of two principal types:

1. Natural convection evaporator coils.
2. Forced convection evaporator coils.

In the natural air convection coil, air circulation depends on gravitational or thermal circulation. Three different classes of natural convection, air cooling coils are:

1. Frosting type.
2. Defrosting type.
3. Nonfrosting type.

The condition under which a coil operates determines its classification. The governing conditions are the desired temperature range of the cabinet and the temperature difference between the coil and the cabinet.

13-16 Frosting Type Evaporator

The frosting type coil was the first one produced by refrigerating companies for use in cabinets of all kinds. The coils were of the low side float control type and consisted of a small amount of fin area held at a low temperature. The coils did not become warm enough (over 32 F.) to allow the frost accumulation to melt. They operated at 5 F. refrigerant temperature cutout and 25 F. refrigerant cut-in. The units were constructed of coils of seamless copper tubing brought out of the low side float chamber and run back into the same chamber. These coils were soldered to large copper fins. The coils had to be manually defrosted because gradual accumulation of ice on the fins of the coil decreased the heat removing capacity of the coils. Frost which formed on the coils came from moisture in the air. This left the air dry, and the dry air in turn rapidly dried out food in the cabinet.

13-17 Defrosting Evaporator

To eliminate difficulties encountered in defrosting the frosting type coils, manufacturers produced a coil which may be classified as the defrosting type. This coil

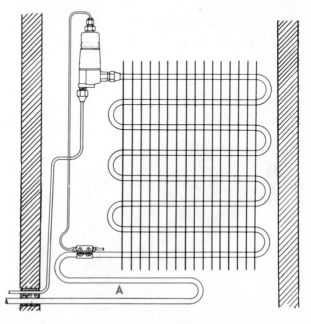

Fig. 13-26. Use of "drier" coil (A), to prevent sweating or frosting of suction line outside fixture. This type of coil is usually of defrosting type. (Detroit Controls Corp.)

is used with the thermostatic expansion valve refrigerant control as shown in Fig. 13-26. The area of the coil is increased so it will behave as follows: during the running of the compressor this coil stays at a temperature of 20 F. to 22 F. This causes frost accumulation on the coil, but after the compressor stops, the coil warms up and the frost melts from the coil before the compressor starts again. This arrangement works in some installations, but in others, it presents problems. It appears that during the off part of the cycle the top of the coil may defrost and its moisture runs down the fins, but before the moisture has time to escape it often freezes around the lower parts of the fins. This ice accumulation on the bottom fins may eventually block the air circulation around the coils and interfere with proper refrigeration.

13-18 Nonfrosting Evaporator

Because of troubles experienced with frosting coils, some companies are producing nonfrosting coils. These coils use only the thermostatic expansion valve type of refrigerant control. The area of the coils is large and to cool the box down to 36 F.

to 38 F. the coils need never become colder than 21 F. to 32 F. It is for this reason the coils are called nonfrosting. However, the refrigerant inside the coil is usually 20 F. or 22 F. to produce the required temperature. See Chapter 15 for information on temperature differances between refrigerants and coils. Occasionally the coils accumulate a light coat of frost just before the compressor shuts off. This frost disappears after the compressor stops. The big advantage of this type coil is the coil is not below freezing and does not have a tendency to rapidly draw moisture out of the air. It is possible to maintain a 75 to 85 percent relative humidity in the cabinet, which is the humidity required to keep produce fresh and from shrinking in weight. Nonfrosting coils are slightly more bulky than the frosting types. See Fig. 13-27.

Evaporators are sometimes classified according to their construction. The two most common constructions are the tube-and-fin type, and the plate type as shown in Fig. 13-28. This coil is made of two

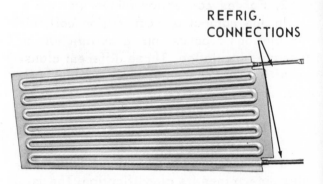

REFRIG. CONNECTIONS

Fig. 13-28. A plate-type evaporator coil. Refrigerant tubes are formed by two plates fused together. (Kold Hold Div., Tranter Mfg., Inc.)

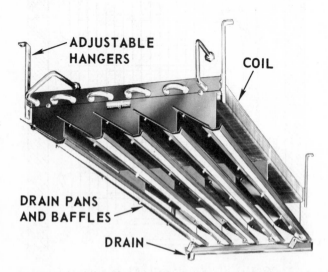

ADJUSTABLE HANGERS

COIL

DRAIN PANS AND BAFFLES

DRAIN

Fig. 13-27. Nonfrosting evaporator. Note baffles used to collect and remove condensate. (Dunham-Bush, Inc.)

plates with one plate formed into grooves or recesses. When the two plates are fused together a plate-type evaporating coil is formed. As explained in Chapter 15 the part of the evaporator coil contacting the air needs more surface than the part in

Fig. 13-29. *Plate-type evaporator coil in which good heat transfer and refrigeration effect are obtained by using eutectic solution liquid. A—Front plate. B—Tubing in eutectic solution. C—Refrigerant outlet. D—Refrigerant inlet. E—Eutectic connection. F—Front plate. (Dole Refrigerating Co.)*

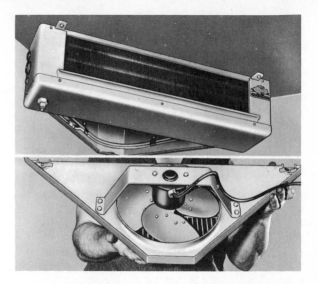

Fig. 13-31. *Forced circulation evaporator coil partially installed and with fan unit removed. (Refrigeration Engineering, Inc.)*

contact with the refrigerant. The fins and the plates are means to furnish greater air contact surface. Another type plate coil is shown in Fig. 13-29. This uses refrigerant tubing mounted between two plates. A vacuum is created between the plates to create a tight contact between the tubing and the plates.

Some of these coils have an eutectic solution between the plates. (A mixture that has a predetermined freezing temperature.) This solution freezes at a certain predetermined temperature and produces a longer operating cycle.

13-19 Forced Circulation Evaporator

Forced circulation evaporators consist of a compact arrangement of refrigerant cooled tubes and fins over which air is blown by means of a fan driven by an elec-

Fig. 13-30. *Blower-type evaporator coil designed for mounting in corner of refrigerator. Note small amount of space required. The air enters at the bottom, is cooled, and exits at front. Unit requires liquid line, suction line, electrical line, and drain pipe.*

tric motor. Both the coil and the fan are usually enclosed in a metal housing. The coils take up only a small amount of space, and do not need any extra baffling. See Fig. 13-30. These coils are designed for ease of servicing, Fig. 13-31. They do have a tendency to cause rapid dehydration of foods unless special care is taken. If the coil is large and operates at a small temperature difference (10 F. to 12 F.) and the air is circulated slowly, the tendency to dehydrate foods is minimized.

In installations where dehydration is permissible, small coils may be used and operated at a greater temperature difference (20 F. to 30 F.), and the air may flow rapidly through the coil. Thermostatic expansion valve refrigerant controls are usually used with forced convection coils.

The motor which drives the fan may be from 1/50 hp and up and may run continuously, or may be controlled by the coils or the box temperature. The refrigerant temperature is usually held quite low, but the coil does not frost because of the rapid air circulation. However, considerable sweating does occur and facilities for drainage must be incorporated in the installation.

The forced circulation evaporator coil will cool a refrigerator cabinet quickly, making it well suited for installations in

Fig. 13-32. An angular air flow evaporator coil. Air enters fan grille and leaves coil at back.

Fig. 13-33. Compact blower evaporator coil for use in low head-room fixtures. Equipped with electric defrost when used for low temperature fixtures.

Fig. 13-34. Vertical, flat-type blower evaporator coil, designed to be mounted behind either window or door frames of fixture. (Peerless of America, Inc.)

storage cabinets used for bottle beverages, foods in sealed containers, and for air conditioning work. See Figs. 13-32, 13-33, and 13-34. An evaporator coil for large fixtures and which has two fans for air return is shown in Figs. 13-35 and 13-36.

A high capacity blower evaporator coil used for low temperature fixtures is shown in Fig. 13-37.

A condensate pump as shown in Fig. 13-38 may be used to provide a positive method of removing the condensate. The pump is mounted on the drain and is self-priming. It uses only about 10 watts and operates continuously.

13-20 Liquid Cooling Evaporators

Liquids require refrigeration for purposes such as making consumption more enjoyable, preserving liquid, improving a manufacturing process, and minimizing the evaporation of liquid.

Examples are water, soft drinks, alcoholic beverages, and brines. Three types of liquid cooling evaporators are:

1. Bottled liquids.
2. Liquids under atmospheric pressure.
3. Liquids under pressure.

Fig. 13-35. Two blower evaporator coil. Motor drives two propeller-type fans and cooled air exits at two ends of coil.

13-21 Immersed Evaporator (Brine)

In the immersed type of liquid cooling, the coil may be surrounded by a brine, beverage, or water. A small plain, tube-type evaporator, submerged in a liquid provides good heat transfer. The efficiency of the coils is increased because of the fact that liquids transfer heat to metals faster than air can transfer heat to metals; a ratio of 50 or 100 to 1 is common. That is, a submerged coil can remove 50 to 100 Btu per hour, per degree temperature difference, per square foot of coil surface, whereas air-cooling coils can only remove 1 Btu under the same conditions. These coils may use either a low side float or a thermostatic expansion valve refrigerant control, when used in multiple installations. Smaller self-contained installations usually use a capillary tube refrigerant control.

The cooled liquid may be circulated and used for various purposes.

13-22 Immersed Evaporator (Sweet Water)

Another type of submerged evaporator coil uses a coil submerged in ordinary tap water which is termed a sweet water bath. An example of this type is the water-cooling device used in soda fountains. The evaporator is submerged in the sweet water. Another coil in which the water is to be cooled and consumed by the customer may also be submerged in the same water.

It is the feature of this design to allow the sweet water to freeze a bit around the coil during what is called the nonload period. The light ice accumulation around the evaporator coil acts as a storage reserve of refrigeration. These systems usually use the thermostatic expansion valve refrigerant control as shown in Fig. 13-39. In the event a thermostatic expansion valve refrigerant control is used the thermostatic bulb should be clamped to the outlet of

Fig. 13-36. Low velocity blower evaporator coil. Air enters at two fan grilles and exits on both sides.

Fig. 13-37. Low temperature blower evaporator coil. This unit has two axial flow fans and is equipped with electric defrost.
(McQuay, Inc.)

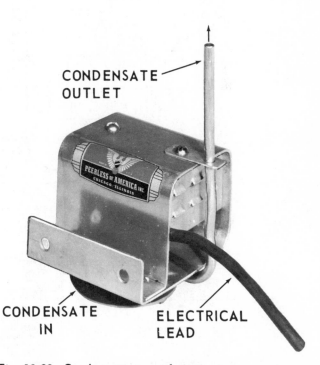

CONDENSATE OUTLET

CONDENSATE IN

ELECTRICAL LEAD

Fig. 13-38. Condensate pump for use on evaporator coil drains. Used when condensate is to be raised above drain pan level.

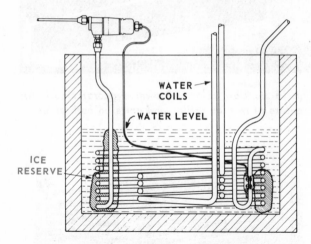

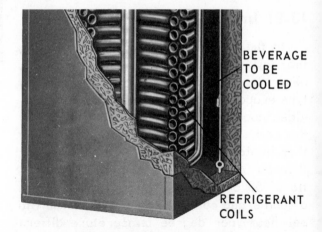

Fig. 13-39. Sweet water bath. Ice accumulation is controlled by location of thermostatic expansion valve thermal bulb. (Detroit Controls Corp.)

Fig. 13-40. Pressure-type beverage cooler. The refrigerant coils are submerged in the beverage to be cooled. (Filtrine Mfg. Co.)

Fig. 13-41. A beverage cooling evaporator, for two different beverages, using low side float refrigerant control. (Temprite Products Corp.)

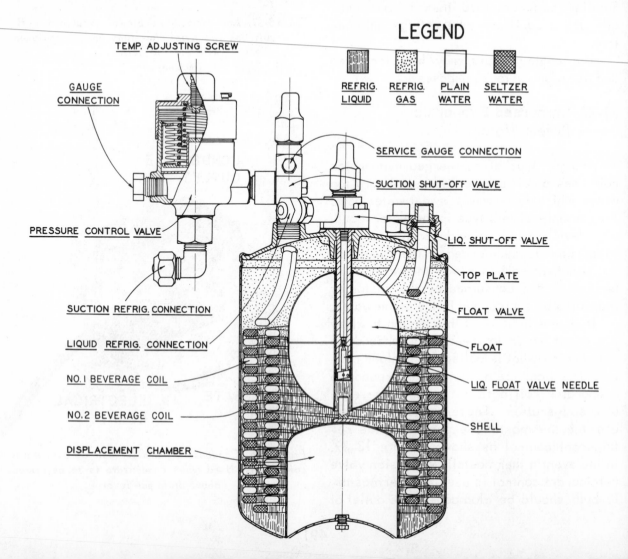

the coil. The coil should reach to the bottom of the bath if the temperature of the bath is to be less than 39.1 F. Water between 39.1 F. and 32 F. tends to expand and rise. Therefore, the coldest water, between these temperatures, will be at the top.

13-23 Pressure Type (Beverage) Evaporator

A type of evaporator coil which may be classed as the submerged type is the pressure type beverage cooler. In this coil the liquid refrigerant is carried in a tube submerged in the beverage to be cooled. This beverage is under pressure. Its construction is similar to that of the liquid receiver type of water-cooled condenser. This construction is quite common for instantaneous water coolers, and is shown in Fig. 13-40. A precaution to be observed in this type, is that the temperature of the beverage should never be such that it will freeze to any extent.

Another type of submerged evaporator coil design is illustrated in the beverage cooler shown in Fig. 13-41. This unit consists of a coil of tubing carrying the beverage to be consumed, submerged in a quantity of liquid refrigerant. The quantity of liquid refrigerant is controlled by a low side type float which also serves as the refrigerant control.

A beverage evaporator coil that takes advantage of the high heat conductivity of aluminum is the all-metal beverage evaporator coil.

Two separate copper tubes are coiled in a helix design, they are placed in a permanent mold and liquid aluminum is poured into the mold. After solidification, the two tubes are completely encased in a hollow cylinder of aluminum, as shown in Fig. 13-42. The heat transfer is excellent. If refrigerant is evaporated in one coil, heat will flow from the liquid flowing in the other coil.

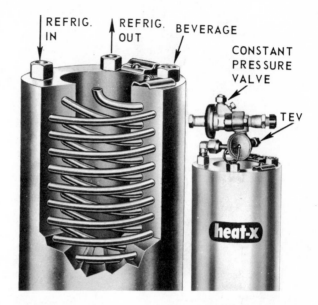

Fig. 13-42. Dry-type beverage cooling evaporator coil. Aluminum casting surrounds both refrigerant and beverage coils, and permits rapid heat transfer. Refrigerant control used is a thermostatic expansion valve. (Dunham-Bush, Inc.)

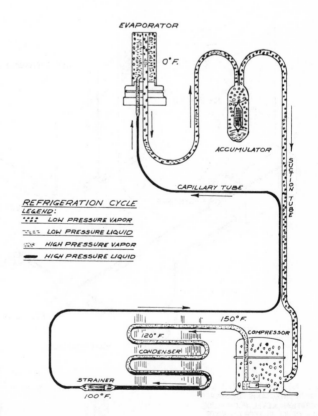

Fig. 13-43. Refrigeration cycle for self-contained ice maker (flake ice). Evaporator coil refrigerant temperature is 0 F. (Rosstemp, Inc.)

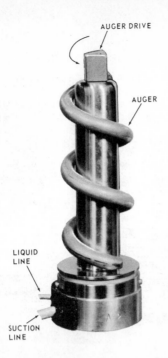

AUGER DRIVE

AUGER

LIQUID LINE

SUCTION LINE

Fig. 13-44. Evaporator and auger of flake ice making unit. Note auger drive and refrigerant line connections.

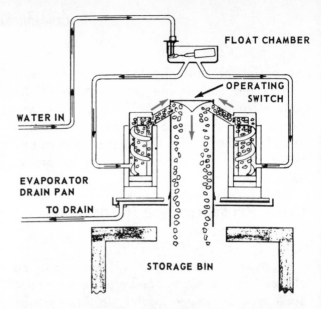

FLOAT CHAMBER

OPERATING SWITCH

WATER IN

EVAPORATOR DRAIN PAN

TO DRAIN

STORAGE BIN

Fig. 13-45. Automatic flake ice system showing water and ice cycle. Water flow is float controlled. When enough ice flakes have been made, operation switch shuts off refrigerating unit and auger motors. (Rosstemp, Inc.)

Fig. 13-46. Flake ice refrigerating system. Layout diagram provides for efficient operation and access for maintenance and service. Water circuit is in red. (Howe Corp.)

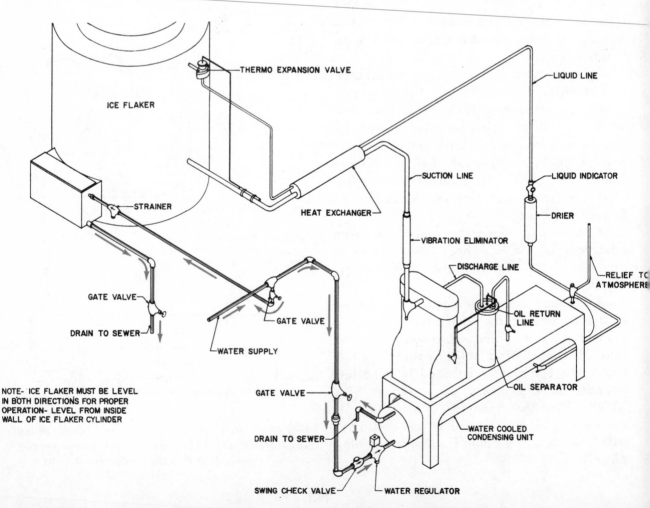

ICE FLAKER

THERMO EXPANSION VALVE

LIQUID LINE

SUCTION LINE

LIQUID INDICATOR

HEAT EXCHANGER

DRIER

STRAINER

VIBRATION ELIMINATOR

RELIEF TO ATMOSPHERE

DISCHARGE LINE

GATE VALVE

DRAIN TO SEWER

GATE VALVE

OIL RETURN LINE

WATER SUPPLY

OIL SEPARATOR

NOTE- ICE FLAKER MUST BE LEVEL IN BOTH DIRECTIONS FOR PROPER OPERATION- LEVEL FROM INSIDE WALL OF ICE FLAKER CYLINDER

GATE VALVE

WATER COOLED CONDENSING UNIT

DRAIN TO SEWER

SWING CHECK VALVE

WATER REGULATOR

Surrounding the tubing with the casting produces a strong coil that can survive freezing of water in the tubes.

Stainless steel tubing may also be used as one of the tubes when beverages that require storing in that metal are to be refrigerated.

Some of the coolers have three or more separate tubes encased by the aluminum when more than one liquid is to be cooled.

13-24 Ice Cube Maker Evaporators

There are many different ice maker mechanisms. The simplest, and the one used in domestic refrigeration mechanisms, freezes water in ice cube trays.

Since a large portion of artificial ice is used for beverage cooling, ice in shapes other than cubes and in smaller sizes is frequently desirable. One type machine pro-

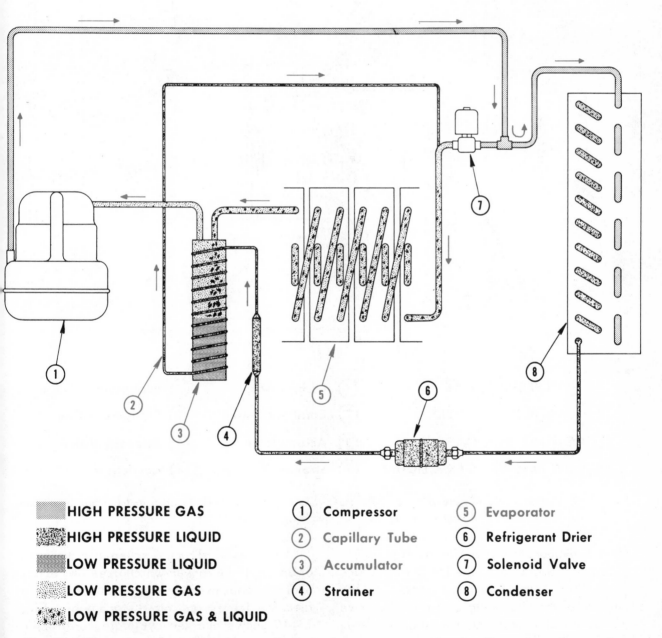

HIGH PRESSURE GAS	① Compressor	⑤ Evaporator
HIGH PRESSURE LIQUID	② Capillary Tube	⑥ Refrigerant Drier
LOW PRESSURE LIQUID	③ Accumulator	⑦ Solenoid Valve
LOW PRESSURE GAS	④ Strainer	⑧ Condenser
LOW PRESSURE GAS & LIQUID		

Fig. 13-47. Ice cube maker refrigeration cycle during freezing process. Note capillary tube and accumulator.

duces ice in the form of flakes. The cycle diagram for a flake ice maker is shown in Fig. 13-43. This consists of a cylindrical

heavy steel auger driven by an electric motor cuts and scrapes the ice from the surface of the evaporator.

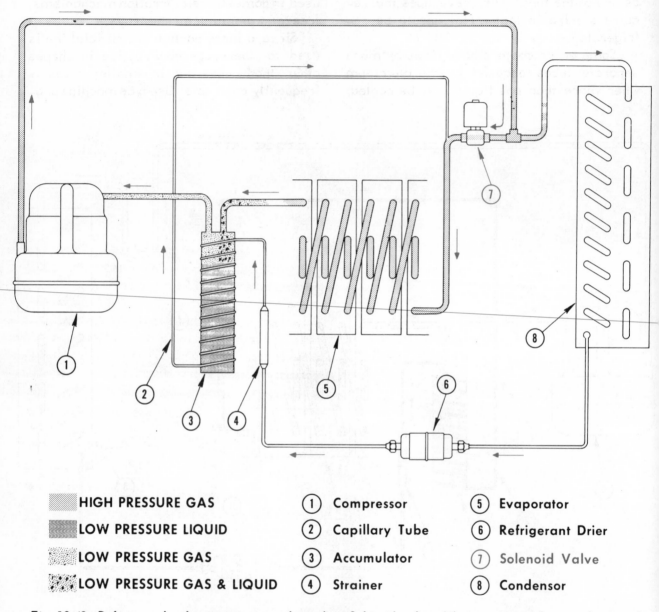

▨ HIGH PRESSURE GAS	① Compressor	⑤ Evaporator
▨ LOW PRESSURE LIQUID	② Capillary Tube	⑥ Refrigerant Drier
▨ LOW PRESSURE GAS	③ Accumulator	⑦ Solenoid Valve
▨ LOW PRESSURE GAS & LIQUID	④ Strainer	⑧ Condensor

Fig. 13-48. Defrost cycle of automatic ice cube maker. Solenoid valve, (7), is open and hot gas heats and frees ice cubes which then fall into storage bin.

shaped evaporator over which water is allowed to flow. Due to the low temperature (0 F.) the water is rapidly frozen to the surface of the evaporator. Fig. 13-44 shows the evaporator coil and the method of removing the ice from the evaporator. A

Fig. 13-45 shows a schematic diagram of an ice flake maker which uses two evaporators and two harvesting augers which feed the ice flakes into a storage bin. Fig. 13-46 shows another cycle diagram for an ice flake maker. All of these ice flake mak-

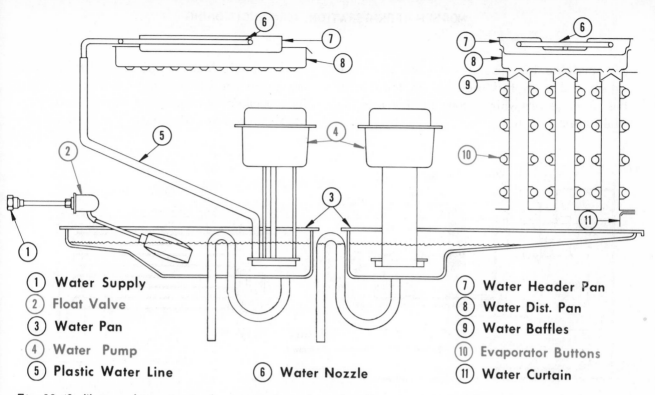

Water and ice circuit labels

1. Water Supply
2. Float Valve
3. Water Pan
4. Water Pump
5. Plastic Water Line
6. Water Nozzle
7. Water Header Pan
8. Water Dist. Pan
9. Water Baffles
10. Evaporator Buttons
11. Water Curtain

Fig. 13-49. Water and ice circuit of automatic ice cube maker. Note water control float (2), recirculation pumps (4), and ice cube forming tubes (10). (American Automatic Ice Machine Co.).

Fig. 13-50. Automatic ice cube maker freezing cycle. Note two capillary tubes, two accumulators, water-cooled condenser, and motor-compressor.

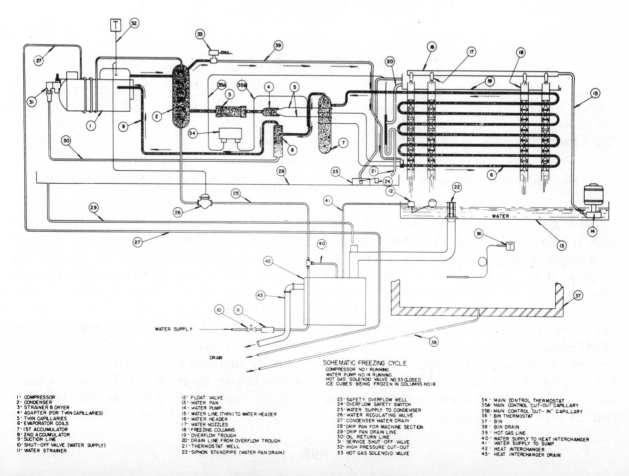

SCHEMATIC FREEZING CYCLE
COMPRESSOR NO I RUNNING
WATER PUMP NO 14 RUNNING
HOT GAS SOLENOID VALVE NO.33 CLOSED
ICE CUBES BEING FROZEN IN COLUMNS NO 18

1- COMPRESSOR
2- CONDENSER
3- STRAINER & DRYER
4- ADAPTER (FOR TWIN CAPILLARIES)
5- TWIN CAPILLARIES
6- EVAPORATOR COILS
7- 1ST ACCUMULATOR
8- 2ND A CCUMULATOR
9- SUCTION LINE
10- SHUT-OFF VALVE (WATER SUPPLY)
11- WATER STRAINER

12- FLOAT VALVE
13- WATER PAN
14- WATER PUMP
15- WATER LINE (TWIN) TO WATER HEADER
16- WATER HEADER
17- WATER NOZZLES
18- FREEZING COLUMNS
19- OVERFLOW TROUGH
20- DRAIN LINE FROM OVERFLOW TROUGH
21- THERMOSTAT WELL
22- SIPHON STANDPIPE (WATER PAN DRAIN)

23- SAFETY OVERFLOW WELL
24- OVERFLOW SAFETY SWITCH
25- WATER SUPPLY TO CONDENSER
26- WATER REGULATING VALVE
27- CONDENSER WATER DRAIN
28- DRIP PAN FOR MACHINE SECTION
29- DRIP PAN DRAIN LINE
30- OIL RETURN LINE
31- SERVICE SHUT-OFF VALVE
32- HIGH PRESSURE CUT-OUT
33 HOT GAS SOLENOID VALVE

34- MAIN CONTROL THERMOSTAT
35A- MAIN CONTROL CUT-OUT CAPILLARY
35B- MAIN CONTROL CUT-IN CAPILLARY
36- BIN THERMOSTAT
37- BIN
38- BIN DRAIN
39- HOT GAS LINE
40- WATER SUPPLY TO HEAT INTERCHANGER
41- WATER SUPPLY TO SUMP
42- HEAT INTERCHANGER
43- HEAT INTERCHANGER DRAIN

ers provide for float level control of the water and a shutoff mechanism located in the storage bin which stops the ice making when the bin is full.

The basic freezing portion of the freezing cycle for an automatic hollow core ice cube maker is shown in Fig. 13-50. Fig. 13-51 shows the defrosting portion of this

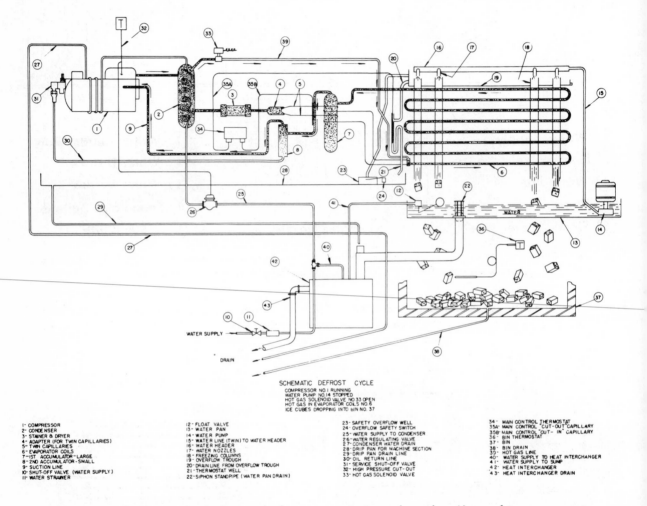

SCHEMATIC DEFROST CYCLE
COMPRESSOR NO. I RUNNING
WATER PUMP NO.14 STOPPED
HOT GAS SOLENOID VALVE NO 33 OPEN
HOT GAS IN EVAPORATOR COILS NO. 6
ICE CUBES DROPPING INTO BIN NO. 37

1- COMPRESSOR	12- FLOAT VALVE	23- SAFETY OVERFLOW WELL
2- CONDENSER	13- WATER PAN	24- OVERFLOW SAFETY SWITCH
3- STAINER & DRYER	14- WATER PUMP	25- WATER SUPPLY TO CONDENSER
4- ADAPTER (FOR TWIN CAPILLARIES)	15- WATER LINE (TWIN) TO WATER HEADER	26- WATER REGULATING VALVE
5- TWIN CAPILLARIES	16- WATER HEADER	27- CONDENSER WATER DRAIN
6- EVAPORATOR COILS	17- WATER NOZZLES	28- DRIP PAN FOR MACHINE SECTION
7- 1ST ACCUMULATOR - LARGE	18- FREEZING COLUMNS	29- DRIP PAN DRAIN LINE
8- 2ND ACCUMULATOR - SMALL	19- OVERFLOW TROUGH	30- OIL RETURN LINE
9- SUCTION LINE	20- DRAIN LINE FROM OVERFLOW TROUGH	31- SERVICE SHUT-OFF VALVE
10- SHUT-OFF VALVE (WATER SUPPLY)	21- THERMOSTAT WELL	32- HIGH PRESSURE CUT-OUT
11- WATER STRAINER	22- SIPHON STANDPIPE (WATER PAN DRAIN)	33- HOT GAS SOLENOID VALVE

34- MAIN CONTROL THERMOSTAT
35A- MAIN CONTROL "CUT-OUT" CAPILLARY
35B- MAIN CONTROL "CUT- IN" CAPILLARY
36- BIN THERMOSTAT
37- BIN
38- BIN DRAIN
39- HOT GAS LINE
40- WATER SUPPLY TO HEAT INTERCHANGER
41- WATER SUPPLY TO SUMP
42- HEAT INTERCHANGER
43- HEAT INTERCHANGER DRAIN

Fig. 13-51. Defrosting cycle (hot gas) of an automatic ice cube maker. Note refrigerant system.

The square or cylindrical shape cube with a hole in the center is formed by running water through a tube within a tube. Ice is formed on the inside of the inner tube. The refrigerant flows between the inner and outer tube. The cube is released from the tube during the defrost cycle. Fig. 13-47 shows such a cycle during the freezing part of the cycle and Fig. 13-48 the defrost cycle (hot gas). Fig. 13-49 shows the water circuit with the recirculating pump and ice cube forming tubes.

same cycle. A schematic of the ice cube water circuit for this machine is shown in Fig. 13-52. Note the use of the ice cube deflector screen which moves ice cubes into the bin and allows surplus water to drain into the water reservoir.

An automatic unit which makes solid ice cubes is shown in Fig. 13-53. Water flows over an inclined plate which is the evaporator coil. A layer of ice is formed about 5/8 in. thick. During the defrost cycle (hot gas) this layer of ice is freed from the

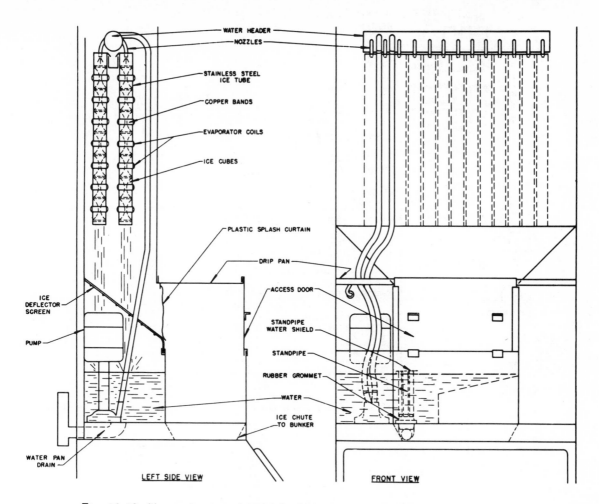

Fig. 13-52. Water circuit and ice cube formation of an automatic ice cube maker.
(Carrier Air Conditioning Co.)

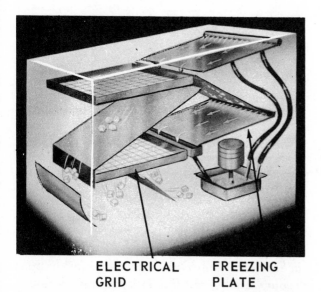

ELECTRICAL GRID   **FREEZING PLATE**

Fig. 13-53. Automatic ice cube maker which makes slab of ice and cuts the slab into cubes.

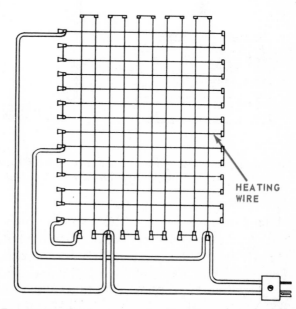

HEATING WIRE

Fig. 13-54. Grid arrangement for changing ice slabs into ice cubes.

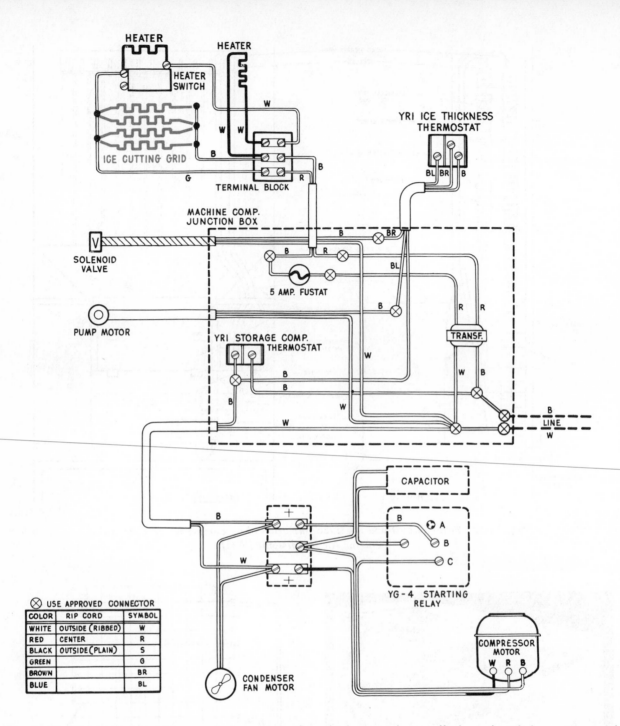

Fig. 13-55. Wiring diagram of automatic ice cube maker which uses electrically heated grid. Ice cutting grid has four parallel circuits. (Frigidaire Div. – Copyright – General Motors Corp.)

plate and by gravity slides over the electric grid. When the grid wires are heated, the wires cut the plate of ice into cubes. The design of the electrically heated grid is shown in Fig. 13-54. A wiring diagram for the unit is shown in Fig. 13-55. The grid circuit has a transformer to reduce the grid voltage to an efficient level.

13-25 Evaporator Defrosting

Many evaporators operate at temperatures below freezing. The demand for open display cases and frozen food has necessitated low temperature installations. The coils operate at refrigerant temperatures of 0 F., –10 F., and even –20 F. Blower coils are used in many cases. The low temperatures and small fin spacings make frequent defrosting necessary. If the coils are not defrosted frequently, the frost accumulation will soon make the evaporator inoperative. Other type coils also need defrosting even though not so frequently. It is desirable to defrost these coils with very little fixture temperature rise.

The coils are usually defrosted automatically. Some are defrosted during each off part of the cycle. On some, a time clock control either turns on the defrosting mechanism once each day or turns on the defrost system after a given number of hours of compressor operation.

The types of defrosting methods are:
1. Hot refrigerant vapor system.
2. Nonfreezing solution system.
3. Water system.
4. Electric heater system.
5. Reverse cycle defrost system.
6. Warm air system.

These defrosting devices may either heat the coil internally (from the inside) or externally (from the outside) to melt the frost.

It is important that the user be reminded to clean the coil, the drain pans, and the drain lines frequently to prevent detrimental odors.

13-26 Hot Refrigerant Vapor (Gas) Defrost System

In a "hot gas" system hot refrigerant vapor is pumped from the compressor directly through the evaporator tubing. This type system consists of a refrigerant line running from the compressor exhaust line up to the evaporator coil and connecting this line into the system between the thermostatic expansion valve or the capillary tube and the evaporator coil. The operation of the line is controlled by a solenoid shutoff valve.

At the predetermined time (usually 12 midnight or 1 A.M.), the time clock closes a circuit which starts the compressor, opens the solenoid valve and stops the fan motors. The hot compressed vapor rushes through the evaporator coil (warming it) and then back to the compressor along the suction line, as shown in Fig. 13-56.

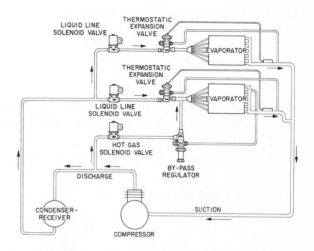

Fig. 13-56. Typical schematic of "hot gas" bypass from compressor discharge to evaporator inlet. (Alco Valve Co.)

This type system will usually defrost the coil in 5 to 10 min. of operation. To keep defrost water from freezing in the

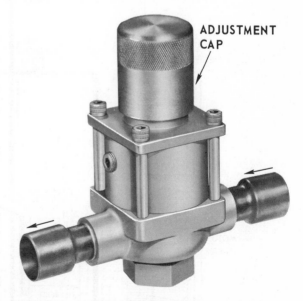

Fig. 13-57. "Hot gas" bypass valve. Valve has 2 to 11 ton capacity.

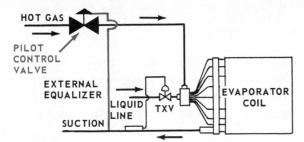

HOT GAS BYPASS TO ENTRANCE OF EVAPORATOR

*Fig. 13-58. Schematic diagram of hot gas bypass regulator. Note the external equalizer line which operates valve dependent on suction line pressure.
(Refrig. Specialities Co.)*

drain pan and tube, part of the defrost line or an electric heater is installed under the drain pan and the drain pipe.

It is desirable to evaporate the refrigerant that condenses in the evaporator coil during the defrost cycle. Heat is applied to the returning refrigerant (electric in some cases) to do the vaporizing. A special blower-evaporator is installed in connection with the suction line and air forced over this reevaporator insures that only vapor can get back to the compressor. The blower works only while the unit is on defrost.

A suction line pressure reducing valve, (a regulator valve) is installed in the suction line to keep the low side pressure of the vapor going to the compressor at a safe pressure level as shown in Fig. 13-57. The pilot controlled valve is installed in a system as shown in Fig. 13-58.

It is important that slugs of liquid refrigerant be prevented from entering the compressor. Reevaporation should be as thorough as possible.

13-27 Nonfreezing Solution System

A system that has been used for years is a "hot gas" defrost system that uses a container in which a brine is stored. The

Fig. 13-59. Nonfreeze solution defrosting system. During defrost glycol solution is pumped through inner tubing of evaporator and along the drain piping.   (Dunham-Bush Corp.)

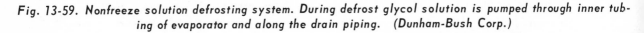

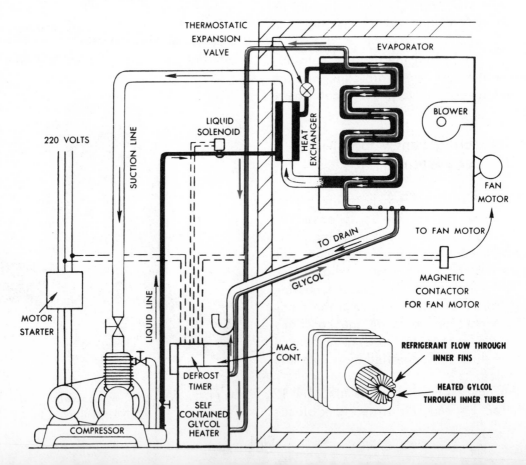

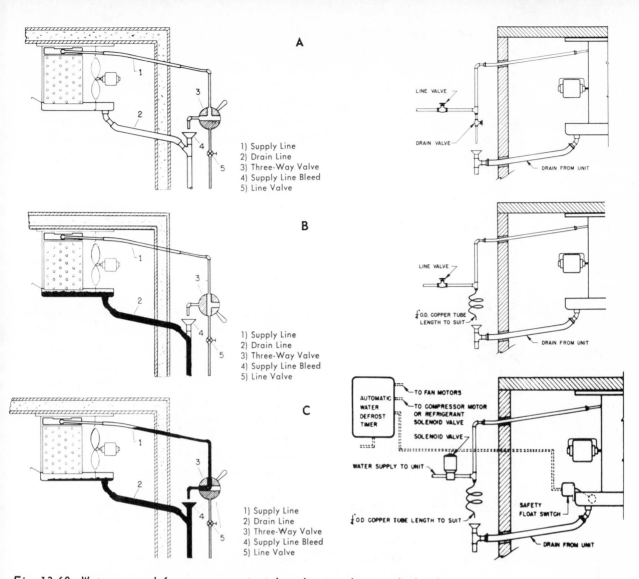

1) Supply Line
2) Drain Line
3) Three-Way Valve
4) Supply Line Bleed
5) Line Valve

1) Supply Line
2) Drain Line
3) Three-Way Valve
4) Supply Line Bleed
5) Line Valve

1) Supply Line
2) Drain Line
3) Three-Way Valve
4) Supply Line Bleed
5) Line Valve

LINE VALVE

DRAIN VALVE

DRAIN FROM UNIT

LINE VALVE

½" O.D. COPPER TUBE LENGTH TO SUIT

DRAIN FROM UNIT

AUTOMATIC WATER DEFROST TIMER

TO FAN MOTORS
TO COMPRESSOR MOTOR OR REFRIGERANT SOLENOID VALVE
SOLENOID VALVE

WATER SUPPLY TO UNIT

½" OD COPPER TUBE LENGTH TO SUIT

SAFETY FLOAT SWITCH

DRAIN FROM UNIT

Fig. 13-60. Water spray defrost system principles showing three methods of operation. A—Manual defrost and manual drain. B—manual defrost and automatic drain. C—Automatic defrost. (Refrig. Eng., Inc.)

refrigerant vapor from the compressor is pumped through this heat storage unit before it goes to the condenser. The brine in the condenser may be electrically heated. The brine is heated during the normal freezing part of the refrigerating cycle.

To defrost the system when the refrigerating system shuts off, the defrost timer closes a solenoid valve in a line running from the condenser line to the evaporator coil. The cooling fan is usually shut off. The brine solution is pumped through its own piping along the drain line, the drain pan, and the evaporator coil. The brine then returns to its container. Fig. 13-59 shows such a defrost cycle.

13-28 Water Defrost System

The water defrost system either manually or automatically runs tap water over the evaporator coil during the off part of the cycle. The water is warm enough to melt the ice and the water is drained away by means of the evaporator coil drain pan. It is important to drain the water from the water lines before the unit is turned on or this water will freeze. The water is either sprayed over the evaporator coil or is fed to a pan located over the coil and holes in the pan feed the water evenly over the coil.

The system uses an electric timer for automatic operation. Fig. 13-60 shows the principle of water defrost, and the two types of manual water defrost as well as an automatic defrost system.

Some special systems have been designed to defrost by spraying a brine over the evaporator coil. A lithium chloride brine may be recirculated by means of a pump. Eliminator plates are needed to prevent brine spray from passing into the refrigerated space.

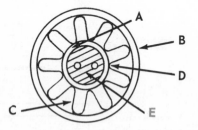

Fig. 13-61. Electric defrost system with electric heating elements installed within evaporator tubing. A—Fin. B—Outer tube. C—Inner fin. D—Inner tube. E—Heating element.

13-29 Electric Heater Defrost System

A popular way to defrost low-temperature coils is with electric heat. Electrically heated coils are installed in the evaporator coil, around the coil, or within the refrigerant passages to furnish heat to defrost the evaporator coil.

One type uses resistance wire heating elements mounted underneath the evaporator coil, under the drain pan, and along the drain pipe. A timer stops the refrigerating unit, and the blowers and the electric heaters are turned on. Heat from the heaters quickly melts the frost from the coil and the water formed drains away. When the coils are warm enough to insure that all the frost is gone, a thermostat returns the system to normal operation.

Another electric defrost system uses an immersion type electric heater to heat a separate charge of refrigerant. This warm refrigerant then circulates around the evaporator coil in its own passageways

to warm the coil and defrost the system, while the refrigerating unit is turned off.

Still another application of the electric heater defrost system is to use a double tube evaporator coil. The evaporator coil refrigerant passes through the passageway between the tubes during normal refrigeration. When defrosting is needed, the system is stopped and electric heating elements inserted in the center tube, as shown in Fig. 13-61, heat the evaporator tubes and cause defrosting from the inside.

13-30 Reverse Cycle Defrost System

Another system used to defrost coils is to reverse the flow of refrigerant in the system. This causes the evaporator coil to become the condenser and the condenser to become the evaporator coil. When the evaporator coil functions as a condenser it melts the accumulated frost.

This reversing is accomplished by installing a four-way valve. Chapter 26 describes the reverse cycle (heat pump) in detail.

To operate on defrost, the four-way valve is turned, either manually or automatically and "hot gas" from the compressor travels up the suction line, heats the evaporator coil by gas condensing in it, and bypasses the refrigerant control by means of a check valve. It passes through the receiver and is then bypassed by means of a check valve through another refrigerant control. The refrigerant boils in the condenser and is returned to the compressor in a vapor state.

The liquid receiver is designed to permit the reverse flow of vapor to travel over the reverse liquid in the receiver and not return it to the condenser.

13-31 Warm Air Defrosting

Where sufficient warm air is available, it can be used to defrost low temperature coils. If the cabinet air is warm enough, it can be used for defrost purposes. The cycles must be frequent enough and often enough to defrost the coil completely.

Some installations bring in outside air to perform the defrosting by using a controlled duct system with blowers and fan.

13-32 Heat Exchangers

To increase the efficiency of operation of larger commercial units and air conditioning comfort-cooling installations, a heat exchanger is often mounted in the liquid and suction line.

A heat exchanger, as shown in Fig. 13-62, provides for a heat transfer from the warmer liquid in the liquid line to the cool vapor coming from the evaporator.

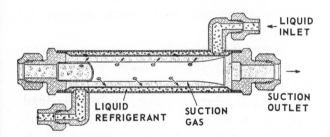

Fig. 13-62. Cross section of heat exchanger used on commercial systems. Note flared connections. (Mueller Brass Co.)

If the liquid is cooled 10 to 20 F. at the prevailing head pressure, the liquid can absorb more latent heat as it changes to a vapor.

The reduction of flash vapor sometimes called "flash gas" is important. Vaporized refrigerant which comes from the instantaneous change of some of the liquid to a vapor as the refrigerant passes through the refrigerant control, reduces the valve capacity, increases the low side pressure drop, and reduces the amount of heat each pound of refrigerant can absorb as it evaporates. The "flash gas" is developed by some of the liquid vaporizing to cool the remainder of the liquid to the evaporating temperature.

The heat exchanger also helps prevent sweat backs or frost backs on the suction line. If there is low temperature liquid refrigerant in the returning suction vapor, it will evaporate in the heat exchanger as it absorbs heat from the liquid line.

13-33 Refrigerant Controls

For single installations involving one evaporator unit and one condensing unit, five types of refrigerant controls which can be used are: thermostatic expansion valves, automatic expansion valves, high side floats, low side floats and capillary tubes. These are explained in Chapter 6. In multiple installations which cover a greater magnitude of uses, two types of refrigerant controls which are usable are the low side float and the thermostatic expansion valve. Thermostatic expansion valves are used extensively, but there are also some low side float systems in use.

The thermostatic expansion valve is explained in Chapter 6. You should study its design, operation, installation, care and repair before proceeding with this chapter.

13-34 Motor Controls

Two basic types of motor controls used in commercial refrigeration which are identical to those used in domestic refrigeration, are the thermostatic motor control and the pressure motor control. Large systems use magnetic starters operated by motor controls.

In multiple commercial work, pressure motor controls are used extensively because (1) the low side pressure is an indication of the temperature in the coil, and (2) one control works well regardless of the number of coils connected to it. The controls provide both range and differential adjustments as shown in Fig. 13-63. Explanation of various range and differential adjustments will be found in Chapter 8.

The control consists of a switch built

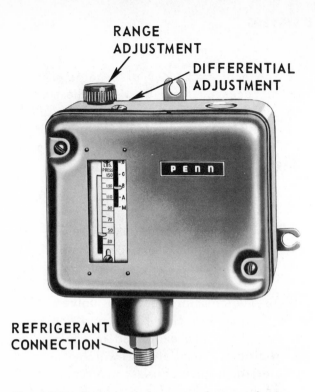

RANGE
ADJUSTMENT

DIFFERENTIAL
ADJUSTMENT

PENN

REFRIGERANT
CONNECTION

Fig. 13-63. Pressure motor control as used on commercial installations. Note range and differential adjustments.

into a toggle arrangement which is acted upon by a bellows whose pressure may be either temperature (thermostatic motor control) or pressure operated (pressure motor control). As the pressure in the bellows builds up, the toggle is snapped and the switch contact points close, starting the motor. Fig. 13-64 shows the internal construction of such a control.

The current draw of larger motors is enough to make a motor starter necessary for AC motors of single-phase over 1 hp. Three-phase AC motors require a starter. Electrical work should be done by a licensed electrician and the work should comply with the local electrical codes.

As the compressor runs, it reduces the temperature, or the pressure on the bellows, until the toggle is snapped the other way, opening the switch and stopping the motor.

These controls have a range adjustment, (usually an adjustable spring pressing against the bellows). When the spring pressure against the bellows is increased, cut-in and cut-out points are raised equally. The range adjustment controls the desired cabinet temperatures.

The distance between the cut-in and cut-out points registered either in degrees F. or in pounds per square inch is called the differential. It is an adjustment which controls the amount of pressure needed or the distance the toggle snaps. The differential controls the cycling interval. Three types of differential adjustments are:

1. Adjusting cut-out.
2. Adjusting cut-in.
3. Adjusting both (putting them farther apart or closer together).

13-35 Pressure Motor Control

A pressure motor control is usually located on the condensing unit, and is operated by low side pressure. Some companies recommend connecting the control into the low side suction line about 10 to 15 ft. from

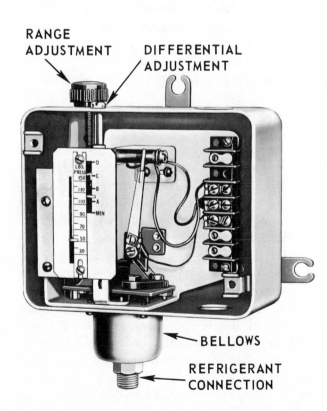

RANGE
ADJUSTMENT

DIFFERENTIAL
ADJUSTMENT

BELLOWS

REFRIGERANT
CONNECTION

Fig. 13-64. Pressure motor control. Cover is removed to show electrical connections and pressure scales. (Penn Controls, Inc.)

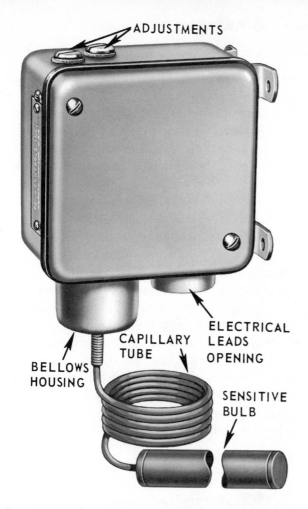

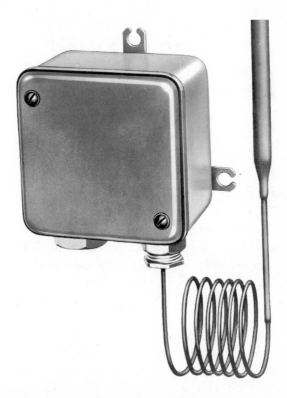

Fig. 13-65. Thermostatic commercial motor control. Sensitive bulb is located in fixture while control proper is usually located outside fixture.

13-36 Thermostatic Motor Control

The thermostatic motor control is similar to the pressure motor control on construction and arrangement except for the power bulb and capillary tube as shown in Fig. 13-65. This type control is generally used in large single installations. However, satisfactory set-ups have been made in multiple installations which assume that, when the one controlled cabinet is at the desired temperature that the others are also. These controls have also been used together with a solenoid valve to control one fixture in a multiple installation.

Thermostatic motor controls are popular in brine cooling installations with the power element being submerged in the brine. Ice cream cabinets are a typical example. When used in single cabinet installations the power element is usually mounted in the cabinet four feet up from the floor between the cold and warm air flues and at the compressor. The range settings vary with the application. The cut-out pressure should correspond to a temperature approximately 10 F. below the desired coil temperature, while the cut-in pressure should correspond approximately to the highest allowable coil temperature.

The differential setting will vary depending on the temperature accuracy desired. A wide pressure difference will allow some variation in cabinet temperature and will lengthen the cycle interval of operation of the condensing unit. A differential set to close limits will maintain a more uniform cabinet temperature but will shorten the cycling interval of the condensing unit. A pressure difference between the cut-in and cut-out point commonly used is approximately 20 psi for R-12.

Fig. 13-66. Thermostatic motor control. Note mounting brackets and electrical wiring opening.

least two inches from the wall. Fig. 13-66 shows the exterior of a thermostatic control, while Fig. 13-67 shows the control with the cover removed.

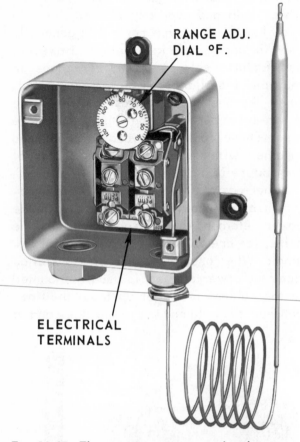

RANGE ADJ. DIAL °F.

ELECTRICAL TERMINALS

Fig. 13-67. Thermostatic motor control with cover removed. Note temperature range dial and electrical terminals.

13-37 Safety Motor Controls

An important difference between commercial and domestic controls is the fact that commercial controls incorporate safety devices known as (1) a high pressure safety cut-out, (2) an oil pressure safety cut-out.

The high pressure safety device consists of a bellows built into the control and connected to the high pressure side of the system, as shown in Fig. 13-68. It is frequently connected to the cylinder head to permit easy disconnecting of the control

from the system. The bellows is attached to a plunger in such a way that if the head pressure becomes too high due to air in the system, the condenser water being shut off, or other causes, the bellows will expand, push the plunger against the switch, and shut off the motor.

This control is called a safety device because its action prevents the building up of dangerous pressures within the system; more important is the fact that it prevents ruining the motor through overloading and overheating. These controls are usually set to cut out at about 125 psi pressure, except in R-12 systems, in which case the control is set at about 150 to 160 psi.

The oil pressure safety cut-out is a safety device that will shut off the electrical power if the oil pressure fails or dips below normal. It is a differential control, using two bellows. One bellows responds to

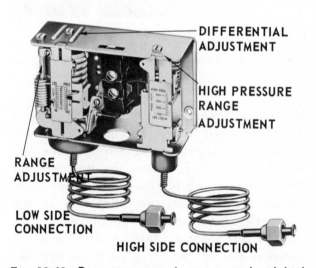

DIFFERENTIAL ADJUSTMENT

HIGH PRESSURE RANGE ADJUSTMENT

RANGE ADJUSTMENT

LOW SIDE CONNECTION

HIGH SIDE CONNECTION

Fig. 13-68. Pressure operated motor control with high pressure safety cut-out. Note the three types of adjustments.

the low side pressure and the other responds to the oil pressure as shown in Fig. 13-69. The wiring diagram for an oil pressure safety control is shown in Fig. 13-70. The control will open the circuit if the pressure difference between the two

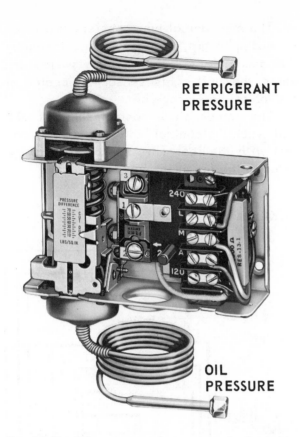

REFRIGERANT
PRESSURE

OIL
PRESSURE

Fig. 13-69. Oil pressure safety cut-out for large commercial systems. Operates on difference between refrigerant and oil pressures.

bellows drops below the required oil pressure needed. This type control is used in large commercial systems. When the pressure difference is too low the mechanism

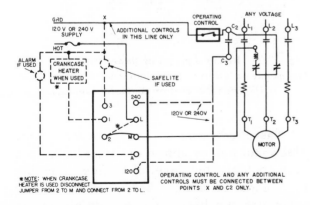

Fig. 13-70. Wiring diagram for oil pressure safety cut-out. Motor is three-phase unit. Note possible use of alarms, safety lights, and crankcase heater. (Penn Controls, Inc.)

sends the current through a bimetal strip. If this strip heats up before the pressure returns to normal, the power will be disconnected.

13-38 Motor Starters

The control contacts (open or sealed) are limited to the amount of current they can carry safely. The National Electric Code and the local electric codes usually specify the limitations of these controls.

However, these same commercial controls can be used for larger motors (larger loads) by using a device called a magnetic starter.

The magnetic starter is an electromagnetic device. The magnetism is controlled by the electricity that flows through the motor control. The magnetism attracts a piece of steel (or armature). When this armature moves, it closes large contact points that safely carry the large currents needed for the large motors. Fig. 13-71 shows a schematic wiring diagram of a magnetic starter. These starters are

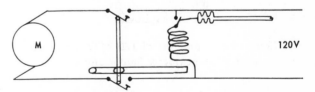

Fig. 13-71. Schematic diagram of automatic control on magnetic starter. Circuit allows high current flow to motor without overloading control contact points.

mounted in an approved metal box with a safety access door. Some of the units incorporate a manual shutoff switch, fuses and an overload thermal safety breaker. The safety switch is a heating element located in the motor line. Fig. 13-72 shows a wiring diagram of a 120-240V single-phase system using a magnetic starter. If the motor demands too much current (shorts, grounds, or overloads) this heater will cause a thermal bimetal strip to bend, opening the electromagnet circuit, which in turn will open the main switch.

2 TERMINAL INTERNAL PROTECTOR & FUSITE

POTENTIAL RELAY & CONTACTOR

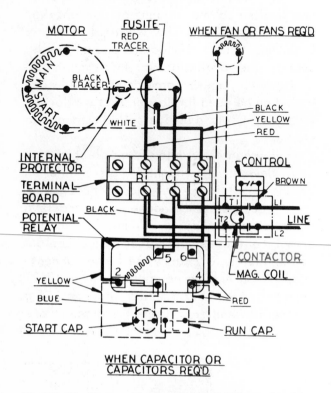

Fig. 13-72. Wiring diagram of 120-240V single-phase unit. Note contactor (motor starter).

A wiring diagram for a three-phase electrical system is shown in Figs. 13-73 and 13-74.

13-39 Ice Maker Controls

Automatic ice cube makers or ice flake makers continue to produce ice until the storage bin is full. A control located in the bin then shuts off the machine until some of the ice is removed or melted. Devices used include:

1. Mechanical levers.
2. Temperature controls.
3. Electronic controls (photo cell).

The mechanical type consists of a lever or a diaphragm, which, when contacted by the accumulated ice, opens a switch and stops the unit. This sensor is located at the top of the storage bin.

The temperature control shuts off the unit when the control bulb is in direct contact with the ice. This sensor is also located at the top of the bin.

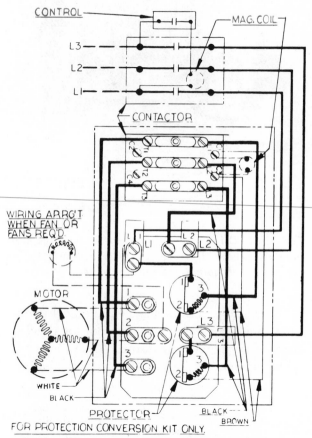

Fig. 13-73. Wiring diagram of three-phase system using magnetic starter. Note that control is in series with magnetic coil of contactor (starter).

The electronic device may be of the electrical nature shown in Fig. 13-75. This unit controls the level of the ice in the bin by means of a light beam. When the ice interrups the beam, the minute electronic circuit stops flowing and a relay shuts off the machine. Fig. 13-76 shows this principle of operation.

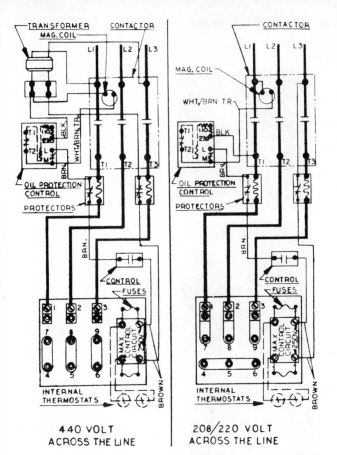

440 VOLT
ACROSS THE LINE

208/220 VOLT
ACROSS THE LINE

Fig. 13-74. Wiring diagrams of 440V circuit and 208-220V circuit as used with three-phase power. (Copeland Refrigeration Corp.)

13-40 Vending Machine Controls

Most vending machines which use refrigeration are automatic in operation. Some of the units automatically heat, if necessary, and move the items being dis-pensed (bottles, bulk fluids, packages of ice cream, and the like). Thermostats, relays, micro-switches, positioning motors, and solenoids of many types are used.

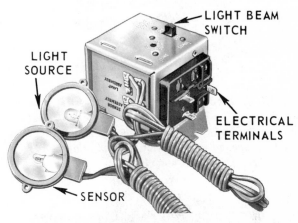

Fig. 13-75. Photoelectronic bin level control used in automatic ice cube makers.

A constant frost condition on the evaporator coils may be maintained by using an electronic icebank sensor control, Fig. 13-77. When the electrodes are mounted on a cooling coil, an electronic current flows between the electrodes when there is water present. When the water turns to ice or frost, the current flow will cease and by means of relays, the refrigerating unit will be shut off.

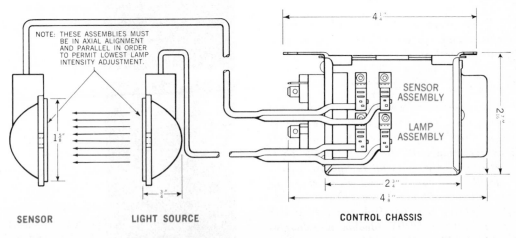

Fig. 13-76. Diagram of light beam type ice cube level control in automatic ice cube maker. Light source and sensor must be carefully aligned and mounted.

ELECTRODES

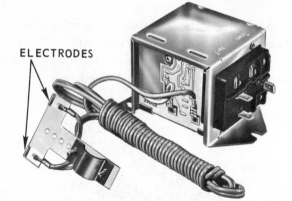

Fig. 13-77. Electronic ice control. Control circuit, AC, flows only when there is water on electrodes. As soon as ice forms, AC flow stops and motor circuit is opened by means of thermal relay.
(Ranco Inc.)

Fig. 13-78. Time switch used for controlling defrost cycles in commercial systems. Note wiring diagram and instructions on inside cover.
(Tork Time Controls, Inc.)

Fig. 13-79. Wiring diagram for several types of defrost control arrangements. A—SPDT (single-pole-double-throw) circuit which activates defrost heaters as it shuts off refrigerating unit. B—DPST (double-pole-single-throw) which only shuts off refrigerating unit. C—DPDT (double-pole-double-throw) which shuts off compressor and fan, and turns on two defrost circuits. D—Circuit for delayed fan shutoff during defrost and one defrost circuit. E—DPDT (double-pole-double-throw) circuit for delayed fan shutoff and two defrost circuits.

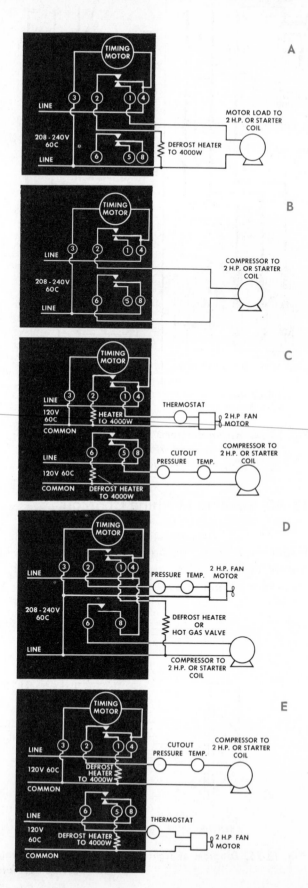

13-41 Defrost Timers

Automatic defrosters require an automatic device for starting the defrost cycle. In installations, which use a defrost timer, an electric self-starting clock mechanism is used to operate a cam which actuates the switches, as shown in Fig. 13-78. These timers are usually of the 24 hour or the 7 day design.

Some of the time clocks are connected directly to the electric power and will defrost the system at the intervals necessary to maintain an efficiently operating coil. Some coils need to be defrosted during each on-cycle, some every few hours, while some coils need to be defrosted only once each day. The cams can be adjusted to control the length of the defrost cycle.

Some timers are connected to the electric power in parallel with the motor. The clock mechanism registers the running time of the condensing unit. These mechanisms also are adjustable for starting the defrost cycle based on hours of running time.

The timer wiring differs according to the type of defrost system. In one "hot gas" system, the timer energizes the solenoid valve, stops the fan motors, energizes auxiliary electric heater element, runs the compressor, etc. It also may be used to prevent the normal cycle from starting until the low side pressure is reduced to normal levels. Some basic electrical circuits using timer controls are shown in Fig. 13-79.

Another type of automatic timer for defrosting is shown in Fig. 13-80. A timer starts the defrost cycle and the temperature bulb returns the unit to normal operation only after the evaporator coil reaches a temperature above 32 F.

A timer that can be used with either "hot gas" or electrical heat is shown in Fig. 13-81. It uses the timer motor to start the defrost action and a pressure control connected to the low pressure side of the

Fig. 13-80. Timer and thermal bulb combination used to control defrost cycle. Thermal bulb is mounted on evaporator.

Fig. 13-81. Defrost timer with pressure attachment which operates from low pressure side. Timer starts defrost action while pressure device returns system to normal operation.
(Paragon Electric Co., Inc.)

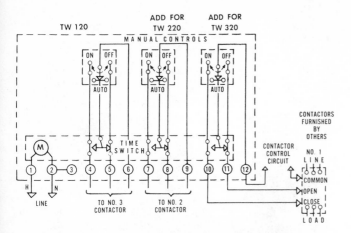
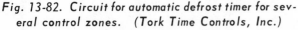

Fig. 13-82. Circuit for automatic defrost timer for several control zones. (Tork Time Controls, Inc.)

system to return the system to normal operation.

Some commercial installations use several timers on one multiple fixture system. Fig. 13-82 shows the wiring diagram of a multiple defrost system with separate refrigerating systems for each fixture. An electrical panel consisting of four timers and six motor starters (contactors) is shown in Fig. 13-83.

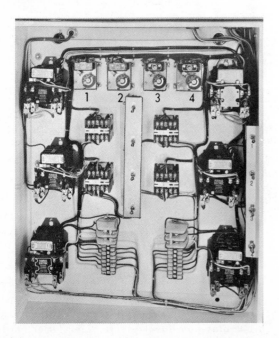

Fig. 13-83. Electric control panel with four timers. Each timer controls production of 10 tons of ice on each cycle. (Turbo Refrigerating Co.)

Timers with transistorized circuitry are used with a relay. The transistor eliminates contact points.

13-42 Two-Temperature Valves

In many multiple installations it is necessary to maintain different temperatures in various coils connected in the same system. Thermostatic expansion valves may be used if the temperature differences are

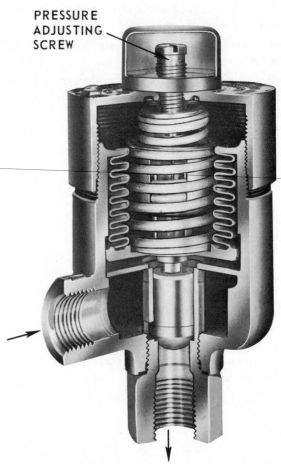

Fig. 13-84. A metering type two-temperature valve. Note adjusting screw. (Temprite Products Corp.)

not too great (not over 5 F.) but in some instances, such as with a storage cabinet and an ice cream cabinet combination, the temperature differences are too great to be taken care of in this manner. To provide for this, a two-temperature valve is put into the suction line. This prevents pressure of the warmest coil from going below a predetermined setting.

The controlled coil or coils should not constitute more than 40 percent of the total load of a system. If the controlled coil is too large, erratic cycling will result. (See surge tanks, Par. 13-49.) If the controlled load amounts to more than 40 percent, separate condensing units should be used.

13-43 Types of Two-Temperature Valves

Two-temperature valves are sometimes called constant pressure valves or pressure reducer valves. The valves are sometimes used to insure a constant low side pressure. Their construction consists of a bellows, a needle, and seat arranged in such a way that the bellows is actuated by

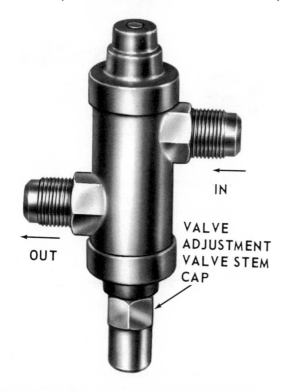

IN

VALVE
ADJUSTMENT
VALVE STEM
CAP

OUT

Fig. 13-85. Metering type two-temperature valve with flare fitting connections. This is a pressure operated throttling valve. (A C and R Components, Inc.)

the pressure in the warmest coil. As the compressor pumps the low side down to this predetermined pressure, the bellows shuts off the valve, preventing the pressure in the warmest coils from going below the pressure desired. As the pressure in the coil builds up, due to vaporizing of the refrigerant in the coil, the bellows again opens the valve allowing vapor to travel to the compressor.

Since the pressure maintained on the surface of a quantity of liquid refrigerant determines the temperature at which the refrigerant will evaporate, this suction line valve will control the temperature of the coil to which the suction line is attached, even though the suction pressure of the compressor is considerably below the coil pressure.

Two general types of two-temperature valves are:
1. Pressure operated.
    a. Metering.
    b. Snap-action.
2. Temperature operated.
    a. Vapor pressure.
    b. Thermostat and solenoid.

13-44 Metering Type Two-Temperature Valve

The metering type, two-temperature valve acts more as a throttling device than as a shut-off valve, Fig. 13-84. Another type with the adjustment on the bottom of the control is shown in Fig. 13-85. It opens and closes when the pressure varies only a fraction of a pound, having no differential. This control is popular in an ice cream cabinet and soda fountain installation. The needle may be better termed a plunger because the valve openings must be made large enough to offer efficient vapor flow. Many of these metering controls have a small adjustment range, being especially designed to maintain beverage temperature pressures. The parts are heavily cadmium plated because the valve is often

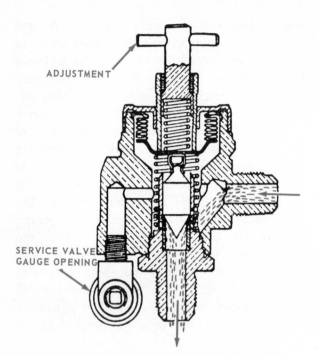

Fig. 13-86. A two-temperature valve. Note adjusting screw and service valve used for checking controlled pressure. (Fedders Corp.)

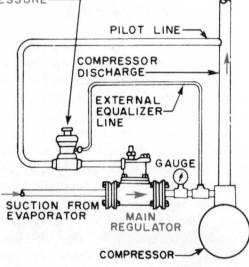

Fig. 13-87. A suction pressure throttling valve controlled by automatic expansion valve which bypasses high pressure gas to open and close main regulator. (Alco Valve Co.)

located in damp places. It must not corrode.

Some of these valves are equipped with a gauge opening to permit the serviceman to adjust and check the warmer coil pressure as shown in Fig. 13-86.

Large systems must rely on forces other than spring force to control the pressure for efficient operation. Fig. 13-87 shows a vapor pressure controlled metering two-temperature valve. Another two-temperature valve is shown in Fig. 13-88. It has a Teflon seat and has connections for silver brazing to the suction line piping.

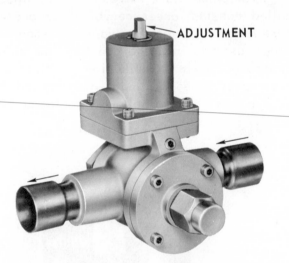

Fig. 13-88. Large capacity evaporator coil pressure regulator. Note fittings for brazed connections to suction line pipe.
(Refrigerating Specialities Co.)

13-45 Snap-Action Type Two-Temperature Valve

The snap-action type valve is such that, when the valve closes, there is a decided rise in pressure in the warm coil before the valve opens again. An important function of the snap-action pressure-operated valve is that it establishes a definite cut-in pressure and temperature. Fig. 13-89, shows a cutaway of a two-temperature snap-action valve. This type valve is used where it is desired to defrost the coil on each cycle.

The snap-action type two-temperature valve is normally used with multiple evaporator systems, such as a walk-in cooler and a display case which do not operate at a wide temperature difference. The two-temperature valves should be located on the suction line to the display case.

13-46 Thermostatic Type Two-Temperature Valve

Another type of two-temperature valve has a temperature control and is built much like a thermostatic expansion valve. Its operation is similar in that it operates from the temperature of the coil. It has a capillary tube and a power bulb similar to the thermostatic expansion valve, along with a bellows arrangement to utilize the different pressures created in the power bulb.

When the coil which this particular two-temperature valve controls becomes cool

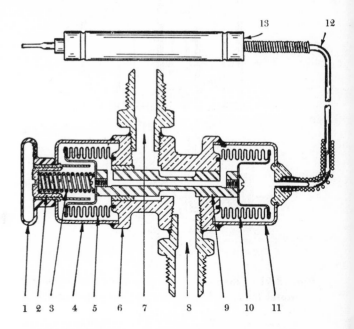

Fig. 13-90. *Thermostatic type, two-temperature valve. 1—Bellows case cap. 2—Adjusting screw. 3—Adjusting spring. 4—Bellows case. 5—Adjusting bellows. 6—Body. 7—Outlet or inlet. 8—Inlet or outlet. 9—Control rod. 10—Control bellows. 11—Bellows case. 12—Control line. 13—Control bulb.* (Kelvinator Div., American Motors Corp.)

enough, the power bulb in cooling also lowers the pressure in the bellows, thus operating the valve plunger and shutting off the valve, as shown in Fig. 13-90. This prevents the pressure from becoming lower in the coil to which the valve is attached, thereby controlling the minimum temperatures of the coil.

As the coil warms up, the power bulb also warms up and the increase in pressure is transmitted to the bellows. The valve is then opened permitting the compressor to draw vaporized refrigerant from that coil again. This type of valve is always located in the suction line to the warmest coil.

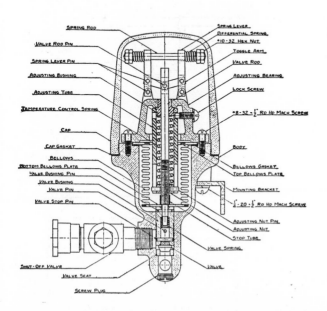

Fig. 13-89. *Snap-action, two-temperature valve. Note service valve. Differential adjustment is double type. It moves to open and close, either farther apart or closer together.* (Fedders Corp.)

13-47 Solenoid Two-Temperature Valve

A fourth way to obtain various fixture temperature in a multiple installation is to use a thermostat connected in series with

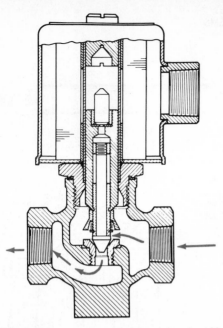

Fig. 13-91. Cross section of solenoid valve. Note that water tends to force valve against valve seat. (Detroit Controls Corp.)

Fig. 13-92. Some systems have the solenoid valve in the suction line to prevent removing the refrigerant from the evaporating coil. The thermostat is operated by the fixture temperature. When the fixture reaches the correct temperature, the thermostat opens. The electric solenoid loses its magnetism and the valve closes. No more refrigerant is fed to the coil and the cabinet will gradually warm up until the thermostat points close, the solenoid valve opens, and refrigeration starts again.

This system of refrigeration control is based on fixture temperature. The condensing unit is controlled by a pressure type motor control, and the motor will not stop until all the fixtures are cooled to their correct temperature.

In another application of a solenoid valve it is used to stop flooding the low pressure side during the off cycle. This solenoid is also located in the liquid line. It is electrically connected in parallel with the pressure motor control, as shown in Fig. 13-93.

a solenoid valve. Fig. 13-91, shows a cross section of a solenoid two-temperature valve.

The solenoid shutoff valve is usually located in the liquid line and is electrically connected to a thermostat, as shown in

Fig. 13-92. Installation of solenoid valve. Valves and thermostats are using line voltages.

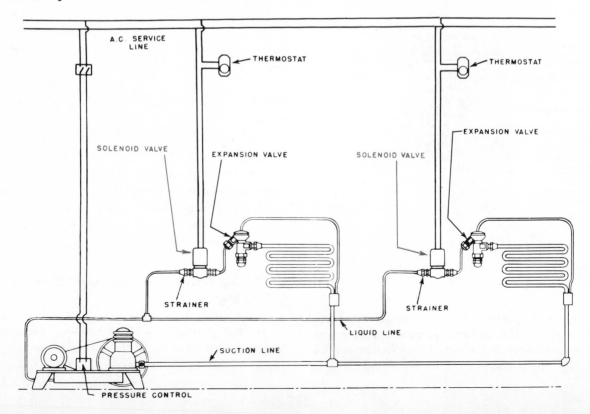

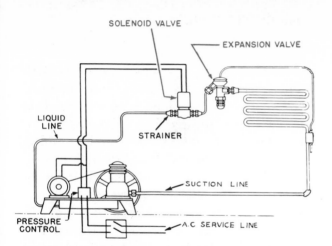

Fig. 13-93. Solenoid valve located in liquid line and controlled by pressure motor control. (Detroit Controls Corp.)

13-48 Check Valves

In many multiple installations one condensing unit is connected to several evaporator coils all of which are at different temperatures. Two-temperature valves are used to procure the desired temperatures. Check valves, as shown in Fig. 13-94, are sometimes put in the suction line of the coldest coils to eliminate erratic refrigeration.

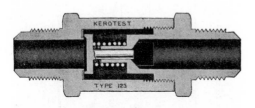

Fig. 13-94. Suction line check valve used in multiple temperature installations. (Kerotest Mfg. Co.)

After the condensing unit has stopped, one of the two-temperature valves may open before the condensing unit turns on, tending to flood the low side with warm refrigerant vapor. This vapor will also travel along the suction line of or to the coldest coil. If it enters this coil it will start condensing, releasing its latent heat. This will make the cold coil defrost or at least warm up somewhat. The check valve when installed in the suction line of the coldest

coil will only allow vapor to be drawn from this coil and it will prevent warm vapor from going into the coil to warm it.

This check valve must have a tight seat and the valve must open easily. If the valve is too small or if it opens with difficulty, it will act as a throttling device and cause too much pressure drop, tending to cause poor refrigeration in the coldest coil.

Fig. 13-95 shows a large capacity check valve.

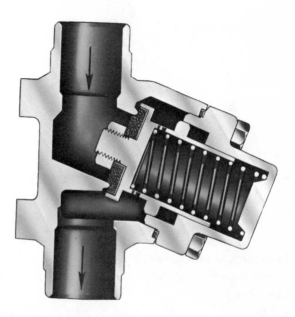

Fig. 13-95. Large capacity check valve. Note double cylinder design to provide smoother operation. (Superior Valve and Fittings Co.)

13-49 Surge Tanks

Multiple temperature installations may have a tendency to short cycle a pressure controlled condensing unit due to the pressure fluctuations resulting from the opening and closing of the two-temperature valves.

For example, if the two-temperature valve is closed and the condensing unit cools the lowest temperature coil enough to open the pressure motor control, the condensing unit will stop. If just after the stopping, a two temperature valve of one of the warmer coils opens, the low side pressure will rise rapidly and turn on the condensing unit, causing a short cycle. To eliminate this trouble a surge tank or a large cylinder may be installed in the main suction line just ahead of the compressor, as shown in Fig. 13-96. This surge tank is made

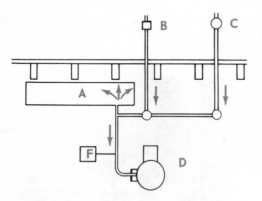

Fig. 13-96. A surge tank installation. A—Surge tank. B—Check valve. C—Two-temperature valve. D—Compressor. F—Motor control.

large enough so if the unit is stopped, and a two-temperature valve opens, the low side pressure will not build up quickly and start the unit too frequently. The capacity of the surge tank is great enough to absorb a large volume of vapor and thereby slow down the pressure changes which affect the motor control. The line connected from the bottom of the tank leads to the compressor and will facilitate the oil return to the compressor.

13-50 Oil Separators

It is very important that the compressor be kept lubricated. Since the compressor pumps a certain amount of oil as it pumps the refrigerant vapor and there is a possible chance that too much oil may leave the compressor, it is important to return the pumped oil back to the compressor as quickly as possible to protect the compressor friction surfaces.

Refrigeration systems are more efficient when the oil is kept in the compressor. The capacity of each part of the system is increased by 5 to 15 percent. It is important to keep the oil from circulating in low temperature installations. Oil separators are used to remove the oil from the hot compressed vapor as the vapor leaves the compressor. The oil separates from the refrigerant vapor because the velocity of the vapor slows down as it arrives in the separator. See Fig. 13-97. Also the separator is insulated to prevent it from acting as a refrigerant condenser. The oil separator collects oil pumped over from the compressor. When a certain oil level is reached in the oil separator, a float opens

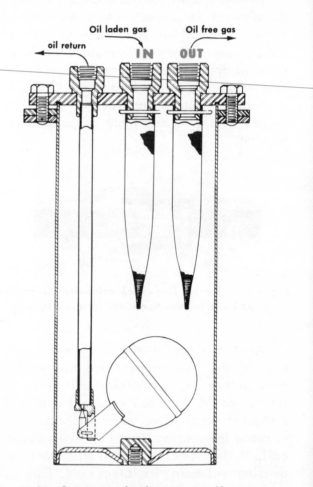

Fig. 13-97. Cut-away of oil separator. Note screens in the inlet and outlet.
(Temprite Products Corp.)

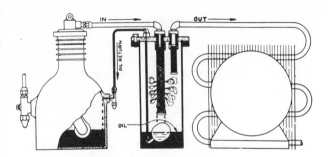

Fig. 13-98. An oil separator installation. Oil is removed from high temperature, high pressure, gaseous refrigerant.

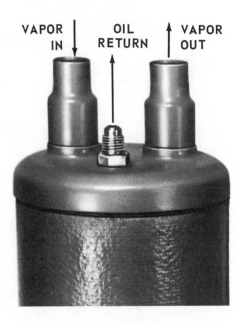

Fig. 13-99. An oil separator designed for brazed line connections.

Fig. 13-100. Internal construction of oil separator. This unit has internal pipe thread oil return fitting. (A C and R Components Inc.)

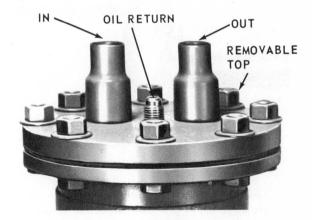

Fig. 13-101. Oil separator with bolted assembly top. This type is cleanable and serviceable.

a needle valve allowing the oil to return to the crankcase of the compressor. Oil separators are placed between the compressor and the condenser, as shown in Fig. 13-98. Fig. 13-99 illustrates a typical oil separator, and Fig. 13-100, the internal construction of an oil separator.

Many oil separators are serviceable (bolted construction). Fig. 13-101 shows a typical bolted design. Large units of up to 150 tons capacity can use the oil separator shown in Fig. 13-102. It has a shell 16 in. in diameter. Note the oil return located at the bottom of this oil separator.

13-51 Compressor Low Side Pressure Control Valves

Starting a compressor places a heavy load on the motor. Inertia of the moving parts, and the fact that the crankcase pressure may be at a maximum just as the

GAS ↑   ↓ GAS AND OIL

OIL → RETURN

Fig. 13-102. Large capacity oil separator. Refrigerant line connections are 3 1/8 in. OD.

reverse metering two-temperature valve because it never permits the crankcase pressure to exceed a certain predetermined value. If the suction line pressure tends to exceed this value, the valve shuts the suction line off from the compressor. The body of the valve is usually made of brass, the diaphragm or bellows of phosphor bronze, and the needle and seat of wear-resisting steel alloy. See Fig. 13-103. The installation of the valve is shown in Fig. 13-104.

INSTALLATION

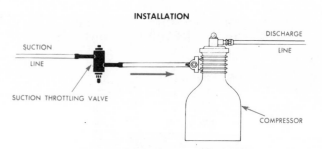

SUCTION LINE

SUCTION THROTTLING VALVE

DISCHARGE LINE

COMPRESSOR

Fig. 13-104. Location of low pressure side throttling valve. (A C and R Components Inc.)

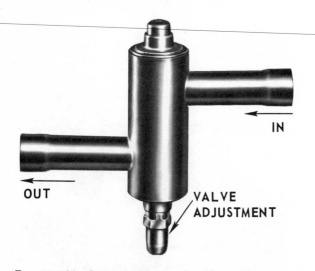

IN

OUT

VALVE ADJUSTMENT

Fig. 13-103. Suction pressure throttling valve. Arrows indicate direction of gas flow. Adjusting screw is located under seal cap (A).

Crankcase pressure regulating valves are needed where the compressor runs too long before the low side drops to a pressure which does not overload the compressor.

Another type of pressure regulating valve is shown in Fig. 13-105. This valve is nonadjustable and is preset to open at 11 psig for standard applications. The valve

compressor starts, necessitates using motors of excessive capacity. Even then the motors are usually taxed to the limit at the moment of starting.

A low side pressure control is used on some installations, which keeps the low side pressures in the crankcase at a reasonable level, even though the low side pressure may be high. It may be termed a

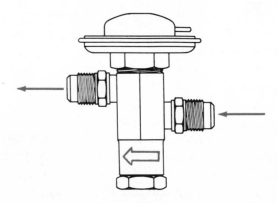

Fig. 13-105. Nonadjustable compressor low side pressure regulating valve. (Sporlan Valve Co.)

is actuated by a pressure difference between the low side and the refrigerant charge in the cap.

A refrigerating system which uses a suction regulator valve is shown in Fig. 13-106. This system uses three-phase power, has a dehydrator, strainer, and solenoid valve in the liquid line.

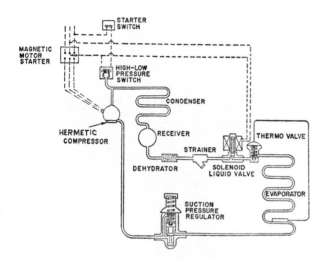

Fig. 13-106. *Refrigerating system showing relative location of some of the more common refrigerant controls. (Alco Valve Co.)*

13-52 Water Valves

Where water is available, many commercial units from 1/2 hp up, use a water-cooled condenser. Due to better heat transfer and the lower condenser temperatures and pressures possible in a water-cooled condenser, the amount of power required to drive the condensing unit will be less than for a corresponding size air-cooled installation. The saving in electrical power compensates to some extent for the cost of the water used.

The purpose of the water valve is to turn the water on and off as needed, and also to vary the amount of water as required. Three types of water valves used are:

1. Electric type.
2. Pressure type.
3. Thermostatic type.

13-53 Electric Water Valve

Electrically operated water valves are of two principal types: a solenoid valve, and a motor-operated valve. The principle of operation of the solenoid valve is: a magnetic coil is connected in parallel with the electric motor. When the electricity is turned on, this magnet creates a magnetic field; a plunger located in the core of the magnet moves in attempting to minimize the magnetic resistance. The plunger movement opens the water valve, and the water flows through the condensing coils. The valve is located between the water supply and the condensing unit and it is usually mounted on the condensing unit base. The moment the motor starts, this valve opens. When the motor circuit is opened the solenoid is deenergized the the plunger closes, stopping the flow of water.

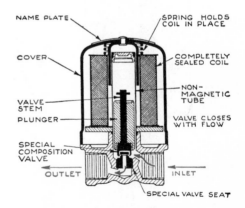

Fig. 13-107. *Solenoid operated water valve. (A-P Controls Corp.)*

Electric water valves, as shown in Fig. 13-107, because of their inherent construction, consume a small amount of current (6 to 10 watts) while in operation. Fig. 13-108 illustrates two typical electric water valve hookups. One uses a low voltage solenoid valve, and the other a 120 volt solenoid valve. Most valves require 120 volts.

A larger capacity solenoid water valve is shown in Fig. 13-109. The body of the

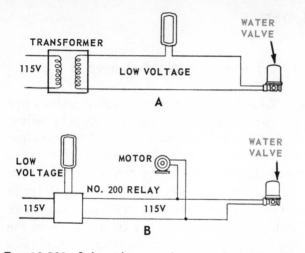

bronze and the valve face is of a special rubber composition. The water flow is constant in this type of control. The valve stem is loosely connected to the plunger to permit a shock action to open the valve. Gravity and water pressure close the valve when the power is shut off. Large volume water flow may also be controlled by motor-operated valves, shown in Fig. 13-110.

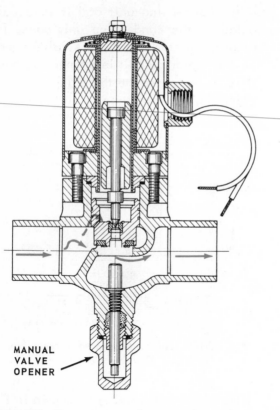

Fig. 13-109. Bypass type electric water valve used on large installations. It should be noted that solenoid only controls water to large piston which in turn operates main water valve.

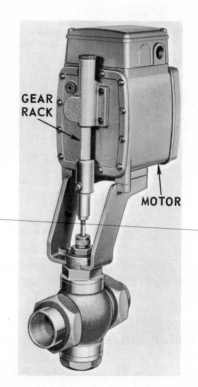

Fig. 13-110. Motorized water valve. Motor raises or lowers valve stem. Note gear rack on stem.

An advantage in the use of the electrically controlled water valve is the fact that these valves may be removed or replaced without disturbing the refrigeration system.

Electrically controlled water valves of the solenoid type are so constructed that the pressure of the water tends to keep the valves closed.

The internal construction of the motor actuated water valve is shown in Fig. 13-111. Pipe joints are of the pipe union design to enable easy removal of the valve. The screen may be serviced by removing

valve is brass and is made with either threaded or soldered connections. The plunger is made of noncorrosive steel. The valve seats are usually made of brass or

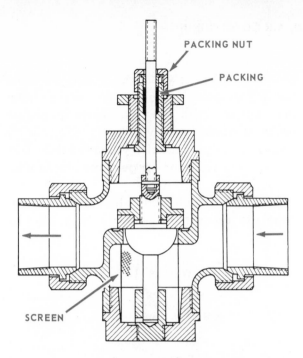

Fig. 13-111. Cross section of water valve body of motor actuated valve. Note direction of flow, screen, valve stem packing and packing nut.

the cap on the botton of the valve. These valves have capacities varying from 1/2 in. pipe size to 4 in. pipe size.

13-54 Pressure Water Valve

The pressure-operated water valve is used in the commercial refrigeration field. It consists of a bellows attached to the high pressure side of the system, preferably to the cylinder head. This bellows operates a water valve, as shown in Fig. 13-112.

Operation: as the pressure rises in the condenser, the bellows in the water valve expands and by various mechanisms, depending on the specific water valve, the valve is opened permitting water to flow into the condenser to cool the compressed vapor. It opens the water circuit only when the water is needed, that is, as the pressure rises. It will keep increasing the water flow just as long as there is a tendency for an increase of pressure in the high side. These valves are adjusted by the tension of a heavy spring which presses against the bellows. The valves are set to open at certain definite head pressures,

the pressure depending on the temperature of the water and the kind of refrigerant used. See Chapter 15. It should be noted that some pressure controlled water valve designs necessitate a regular service operation to remove the valve from the system. Some water valves are made self cleaning

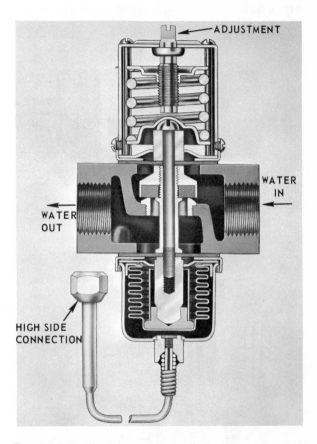

Fig. 13-112. A pressure controlled water valve connected on high side at compressor head. Rate of water flow is adjustable by adjusting spring tension (top) on valve. Water flows through valve from right to left. (Penn Controls Inc.)

to remove dirt particles. The water valve portion of the control may be removed without disturbing the refrigeration system, as shown in Fig. 13-113.

A regulated flow of water is obtained with this valve. As the condensing pressures and temperatures increase, the valve opens farther. When the pressures and temperatures drop, the water flow is shut down.

The valves proper are made of a hard rubber composition, Bakelite or fiber; the seat is usually made of copper or brass. The valves are equipped with either a packing gland or a bellows at the point where the water valve actuating stem goes into the water valve body. The packing construction must be adjusted occasionally to keep it from leaking.

beled and the valves are usually threaded for 3/8 in. standard pipe. Most of the valves are constructed so the water pressure tends to keep the valve closed. Fig. 13-114 shows a large capacity valve used on 1 in. lines. This valve has a gear mechanism for adjusting the pressures.

A valve which controls the flow in two separate circuits is shown in Fig. 13-115.

Fig. 13-113. A self-cleaning type of water valve and seat. (Controls Co. of America)

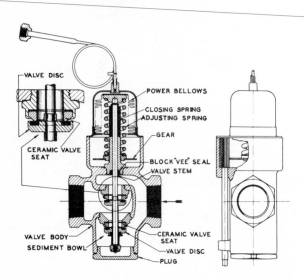

Fig. 13-114. Large capacity pressure operated water valve. Double valve and seat arrangement tends to balance force from water pressure (one valve is opened by water pressure and one valve is closed by water pressure).

The bellows, being a sealed mechanism, will leak only if it corrodes through. These valves usually do not depend on the pipe for support, but are provided with a mounting arrangement or flange. The water-in and the water-out connections are clearly la-

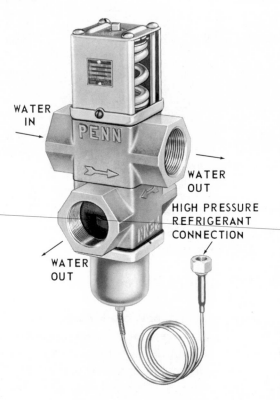

Fig. 13-115. Double water valve, pressure operated. Note water flow direction arrows on two valve bodies. (Penn Controls Inc.)

Both the electric and pressure type should be equipped with filters; that is, they should have screens in the water supply line to remove any solids from the water, Fig. 13-116.

13-55 Thermostatic Water Valve

The thermostatic water valve is controlled by the temperature of the exhaust water. The valve proper is identical to the pressure water valve with the addition of a thermostatic element connected to the bellows operating the valve, as shown in Fig. 13-117. The element is charged with a volatile liquid. The power bulb is clamped to the compressor vapor discharge line.

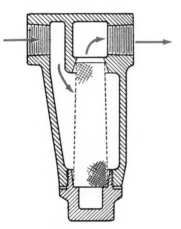

Fig. 13-116. Water line strainer. Opening in upper left-hand corner is water into strain connection. (Kerotest Mfg. Co.)

POWER BULB

ADJUSTMENT

Fig. 13-117. A thermostatic water valve. Valve will start to open with bulb temperature of 120 F., and will be wide open at 125 F. Flow rate is adjustable (bottom screw) from 0 to 50 gallons per hour. (Detroit Controls Corp.)

The pressure created by the volatile liquid in the bulb opens the valve when the discharge line becomes warm and closes the valve as the line cools.

13-56 Manual Valves

Manual servicing valves used on commercial refrigerating machines enable a serviceman to determine the operating pressures, to charge or discharge a system, and to remove any part of the system without disturbing the other parts. These hand valves and service valves must be of a sturdy construction and must be designed to withstand frequent opening and closing without leaking externally or internally. They should be built of the best materials to withstand corrosion and handling.

13-57 Condensing Unit Service Valves

The condensing units are equipped with servicing valves similar to those on domestic systems, however, some of the valves are larger. That is, the valve stems may be 3/8 in. across flats, and larger because the suction and liquid lines are as large as 3 1/8 in. OD. Some of the larger systems may be equipped with additional service valves such as separate valves for installation purposes and/or servicing and a valve between the condenser and the liquid receiver. The gauge connections may be 1/4 in. pipe instead of 1/8 in. pipe.

13-58 Manual Installation Valves

In addition to the usual service valves, multiple installations are usually equipped with what are termed hand shutoff valves, as shown in Fig. 13-118. These valves are required by law to be located so that they may be manipulated easily and be readily accessible. They may be classified as riser valves or manifold valves. In multiple installations it is convenient to run the suction line from the compressor to a man-

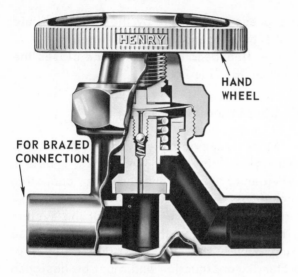

Fig. 13-118. Manual shutoff valve used on multiple installations. Valve uses diaphragm in place of packing. Note that piping openings are in line. (Henry Valve Co.)

ifold and then to have the individual suction lines for each cooling unit go from this manifold to the coils. Between each of these suction lines and the manifold, and mounted into the manifold, is a hand-operated shutoff valve. This valve permits any one of the suction lines to be closed without interfering with the operation of the others. A similar manifold device is also provided for the liquid line. Installation procedure usually provides for mounting these valve groupings in a steel box or cabinet or on a special valve board.

13-59 Riser Valves

Another type of valve, which is used as a shutoff valve and which is also termed a riser valve, is a hand-operated valve

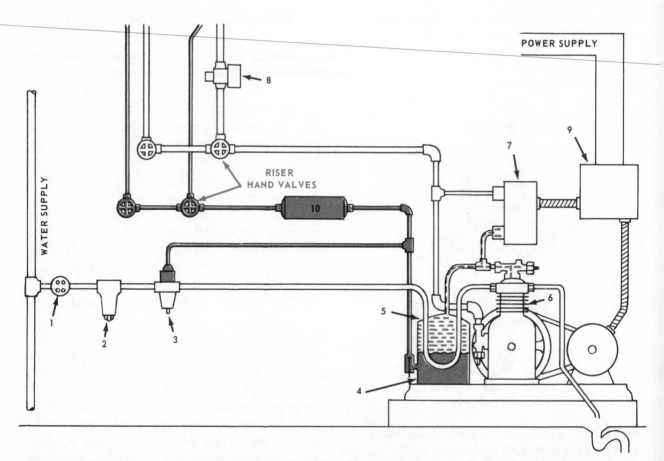

Fig. 13-119. Typical multiple installation showing location of important parts. 1—Water shutoff valve. 2—Strainer. 3—Water valve. 4—Liquid receiver. 5—Condenser. 6—Compressor. 7—Motor control. 8—Two-temperature valve. 9—Magnetic starter. 10—Drier.

with three openings to which refrigerant lines may be connected. Two of these openings are in line with each other on opposite sides of the valve, while the third one is a little closer to the valve wheel and is at

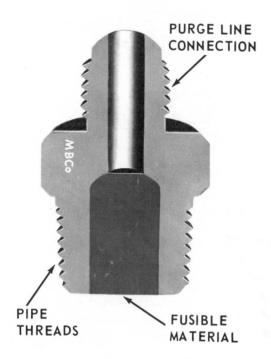

PURGE LINE CONNECTION

MBCo

PIPE THREADS

FUSIBLE MATERIAL

Fig. 13-120. Fusible plug for liquid receivers. Note flared fitting at outlet to permit purge line to outdoors. (Mueller Brass Co.)

right angles to the other two openings. By screwing the hand valve in, the opening at right angles to the other two is closed. This construction permits mounting the valve in either a liquid or suction line, enabling one to connect a second coil to it which may be disconnected at any time from the remainder of the system by screwing the valve all the way in. Fig. 13-119 shows a multiple installation using two liquid line riser valves and two suction line riser valves.

All service valves are of drop forged construction to minimize seepage through the valve. The valve stem may be of either brass or steel. Packing around the valve

stem may be asbestos, lead, and graphite, or the valve may be of the packless type, meaning the type which uses a bellows diaphragm as a sealing device rather than packing. Some valves have self-seating features. This means the valve is easily seated again by tapping the valve stem into the seat. The valve seat is made of a soft lead alloy or Monel metal.

13-60 Relief Valves

A refrigerating system, regardless of size, is a sealed system. It is a pressure container. The pressures vary but, during shut downs, fire, or extreme temperature conditions or faulty electrical control devices may create pressures which could burst some part of the system.

To prevent extreme, dangerous pressures, relief valves are mounted on the units, usually on the liquid receiver. The National Refrigeration Code and most local codes make it a requirement to install this pressure relief device when the unit is of a certain tonnage or more, or if the amount of refrigerant exceeds specified minimums (See Chapter 27).

The relief devices come in three principal types:
1. Fusible plug.
2. Rupture-disk type.
3. Spring-loaded valve.

The fusible plug type is shown in Fig. 13-120. It has a pipe thread for connecting to the liquid receiver. A flared connection is used to fasten the purge line which would carry the released refrigerant outdoors. The low temperature alloy in the plug will melt if the receiver temperature rises above a certain temperature. When the alloy melts, the refrigerant will be released.

The rupture-disk type of relief valve is shown in Fig. 13-121. This is similar in appearance to the fusible plug but it has a thin metal disk inside which will burst before the pressure in the system reaches dangerous levels. It too is threaded into the liquid receiver and the metal is a flared connection for a purge line to carry the released refrigerant outdoors.

The spring-loaded safety valve has the advantage of resealing itself or closing

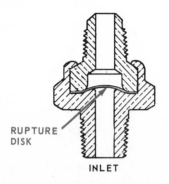

Fig. 13-121. A safety head (ruptured disk type) for R-12. Disk is made of silver. Safety head is obtainable with various rupture pressures from 175 psig to 1000 psig. The safety head is usually designed to rupture at 50 percent above the usual operating pressure. (Reprinted from ASHRAE Guide and Data Book, by permission.)

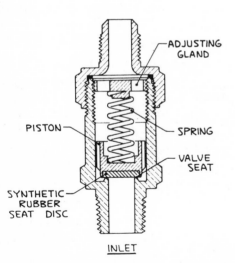

Fig. 13-122. A spring loaded pressure relief valve. Uses synthetic rubber seat. Available in variety of pressure ranges.

when the pressure drops to a safe limit. Fig. 13-122 shows such a valve. Note the spring-loaded valve. The relief pressure is adjustable but once it is set the valve is sealed to prevent tampering as shown

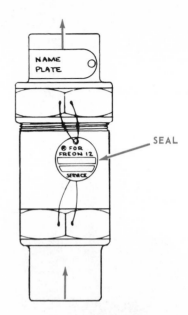

Fig. 13-123. Adjustable pressure relief valve. Note use of wire seal to prevent tampering. (Henry Valve Co.)

in Fig. 13-123. It is important that relief settings not be adjusted in the field. If the seal is broken the valve should be replaced with a correctly adjusted and sealed valve.

13-61 Refrigerant Lines

Hard drawn copper pipe is used to carry the refrigerants around the cycle. This pipe is furnished in iron pipe sizes and the fittings are not interchangeable with tubing sizes. See Chapter 2 for copper tubing sizes. Streamline brazed connections are used to connect the fittings to the pipe.

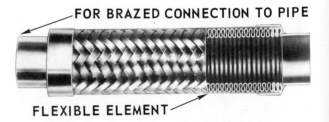

Fig. 13-124. Vibration absorber. Vibration absorber installed in liquid line and suction line prevents condenser circuit vibration from traveling into these lines. (Flexonics Div. of Calumet and Hecla, Inc.)

The National Refrigeration Code and local codes all require the use of hard copper pipe. Soft copper tubing is permissible at the condensing unit end of the lines and also in the fixtures but even these short lengths should be eliminated wherever possible.

To prevent any condensing unit vibrations traveling into the lines, vibration absorbers may be installed in the suction and the liquid lines near the condensing unit. Fig. 13-124 shows the construction of a vibration absorber. Fig. 13-125 shows two designs of vibration absorbers.

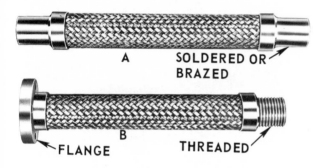

Fig. 13-125. Two designs of vibration absorbers. A—soldered or brazed connection type. B—Flanged and threaded connection type.
(Packless Metal Hose Co.)

Because the appearance of an installation is important, the piping should be put in as neatly as possible. For best sound absorption, it is best to put in two absorbers in each line, one vertically and one horizontally.

13-62 Mufflers

Most domestic refrigerating systems have small mufflers built into the refrigerant circuits to break up the pressure pulses. The mufflers are usually located in the compressor suction and discharge lines within the hermetic unit dome. Compressor action pressure pulses tend to follow the refrigerant lines. The mufflers break up these pulses.

Most refrigerating systems use mufflers; especially systems used for comfort cooling in air conditioning. Fig. 13-126 shows one of the mufflers. The muffler is installed vertically, to provide efficient oil

Fig. 13-126. Refrigerant gas muffler designed for installation in vertical line.

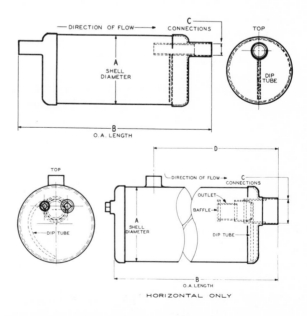

Fig. 13-127. Commercial system muffler. These mufflers reduce noises from gas pulsations. Used in air conditioning installations. Designed for horizontal line installation. (A C and R Components, Inc.)

movement. A muffler that can be mounted horizontally is shown in Fig. 13-127. It has an aspirator device (dip tube) which uses the velocity of the suction line gas to create a lower pressure in the dip tube. This reaches the bottom of the muffler, removes oil from the muffler and puts it into the outlet refrigerant line.

Fig. 13-128. A sight glass designed for soldered or brazed connections. Cap is shown at left of sight opening. (Imperial-Eastman Corp.)

13-63 Sight Glasses

It is usual practice to install a sight glass in liquid lines of commercial installations. The sight glass shown in Fig. 13-128 has an internal device which reads "Full" when there is sufficient refrigerant. It shows nothing when there is no liquid in the line. This sight glass has long extensions which permit soldering or brazing the joints without injury to the sight glass.

Some sight glasses of the see-through type are shown in Fig. 13-129.

A sight glass may be used on a large liquid line by installing a smaller parallel flow pipe, as shown in Fig. 13-130. If bubbles are in the liquid, some of the bubbles will travel through the sight glass tube and indicate a refrigerant shortage.

Fig. 13-129. See-through type sight glass. When both caps are removed you can easily see any bubbles present by looking through liquid refrigerant. (Mueller Brass Co.)

13-64 Dehydrators (Driers)

The efficient operation of a commercial system depends to a considerable extent on the internal cleanliness of the unit. Only clean, dry refrigerant and clean, dry oil should circulate in the system. All foreign particles and water must be removed from the system or must be trapped in some part of the system where they can do no harm. Screens, filters and water absorbents are used. These devices may be in separate units or may be built into one unit.

A common method of removing moisture is with a liquid line drier as shown in Fig. 13-131. If the drying material has sufficient capacity in both the high and low moisture ranges and is fully activated, it can keep

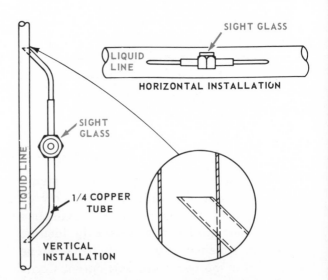

Fig. 13-130. Two methods of installing sight glass in large liquid line. Joints are usually silver brazed. (Airtemp Div., Chrysler Corp.)

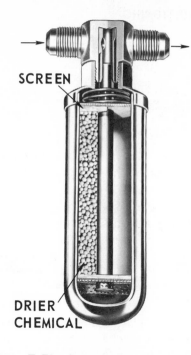

SCREEN

DRIER
CHEMICAL

Fig. 13-131. T-Flo drier. Refrigerant enters at left, passes down through middle tube and upward through dessicant before leaving at right.

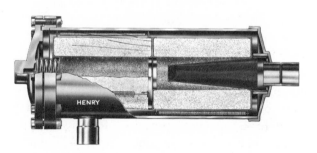

Fig. 13-132. Filter-drier for large commercial system. Chemical cartridges are replaceable.

Fig. 13-133. Replacement cartridge for large commercial filter-drier. (Henry Valve Co.)

the refrigerant both clean and dry. The conventional straight through drier consists of a tube, (brass, copper, or steel) filled with a chemical (desiccant) which will remove moisture by absorption (no chemical change such as activated alumina, or silica gel) or by absorption (some chemical change such as calcium sulphate). Both ends of the tube usually contain filter elements, and the end caps are fitted with either flare or soldered connections. One design of liquid line drier allows the fitting to stay in the line and only the drier cartridge needs to be changed. Fig. 13-132 shows a drier which uses a replacement type cartridge. Fig. 13-133 shows the replacement cartridge.

The most common desiccants (chemicals in drier shells) are Type H and Type F activated alumina, silica gel, and calcium sulfate. Calcium chloride, once widely used, is no longer used in quantity.

Driers are usually installed in the liquid line.

Refrigerant should be dried below 15 parts per million if "R-12" is used and below 25 ppm if "R-22" is used. The beginning of corrosion in "R-12" is 15 ppm. Experience shows that corrosion oil breakdown, and motor burnouts are almost entirely eliminated if the refrigerant has less than 25 parts per million of moisture in the system.

When cleaning a refrigeration system, there are four basic functions to be carried out: water removal, acid removal, filtering out of circulating solids, and some means of indicating when the drying job is complete. Driers will do the first three. A moisture indicator is required to do the fourth. Driers should be left in the systems permanently since oil loses its moisture slowly, also insulation in hermetic compressors and small crevices may release moisture over a long period of time. A drier is like a sponge, however, and can become saturated and leave the refrigerant still wet if the drier is too small. A moisture indicator is the only sure means of recognizing this situation, especially if it is an air conditioning application with no possibility of freeze-up.

Various moisture indicators are available. One liquid line moisture indicator turns pink when the system is dangerously wet and turns blue when it is safely dry. The indicator is under a glass window in the top of the T connector as shown in Fig. 13-134.

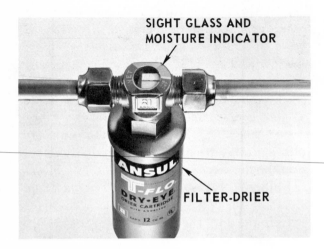

Fig. 13-134. Drier equipped with sight glass and two moisture indicators. Sight glass will reveal shortage of refrigerant and show moisture indication for either R–12 or R–22 refrigerant.
(Ansul Co.)

Other indicators turn purple or orange if dangerous amounts of moisture are present and green if the refrigerant is dry. See Fig. 13-135.

See Chapter 12 for instructions on drier sizes.

Remember that R-22 driers must be three to five times as large as for an equal quantity of R-12. The greater the ability of a refrigerant to hold water, the larger the drier required.

Filters are often mounted in the suction line to prevent foreign particles of over 5 microns in size from entering the compressor. Fig. 13-136 shows a filter designed for suction line use.

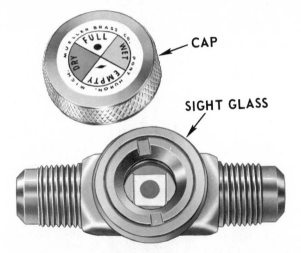

Fig. 13-135. Sight glass and moisture indicator combination. These units are available with either brazed connection fittings or flared connection fittings. (Mueller Brass Co.)

Only two things should be allowed inside a refrigeration system; clean dry refrigerant and good dry oil. A system which is clean, dry, and acid-free will run almost indefinitely without corrosion, freeze-ups, oil breakdown or hermetic motor burnouts. In such a system there is nothing to filter and plugging is impossible. A clean, dry acid-free system remains factory bright and trouble free in operation. A normal system is a completely clean one. A dirty system is a faulty system and must be regarded as a mechanical failure, just as much as a faulty valve plate or connecting rod.

The best assurance that a system is dry is to use and depend on a moisture indicator.

13-65 Engine Driven Systems – Controls

Natural gas, gasoline and propane engines may be used to drive refrigerating machines. The advantages are a variable compressor speed to produce flexible capacity and a comparatively low operating cost. Such units are available in 4 to 75 ton capacities. Engine-compressor units of 1 to 5 tons capacity are available for use on mobile units, and for air conditioning.

13-66 Review of Safety

Commercial systems vary considerably in size. The small self-contained units must be handled with all the care and safety as described in the reviews of safety in earlier chapters.

As the units become larger, the safety precautions become increasingly important both because of the investment in the machines is greater and the damages are more costly. The larger machines are also more dangerous, the energy output of the larger moving parts and the larger refrigerant containers all are potentially dangerous.

Closing the compressor discharge valve on a 10 ton capacity unit while it is operating would almost instantly ruin the compressor or rupture a gasket. Carelessly opening a receiver valve may cause the loss of hundreds of pounds of refrigerant and possible injury to the serviceman. Trapping liquid refrigerant in any part of the system with no gas space may cause a hydraulic pressure sufficient to burst the container.

One must be positive that the pressures inside are atmospheric and that there is no liquid present before opening any part of the system. Goggles should ALWAYS be worn when working on any unit.

Local and national refrigeration and electrical code should be followed when servicing all systems.

It is not safe to work on any part of the system unless you know both the pressure and temperature inside that part and the fundamentals of working on that system as described in Chapters 12 and 15.

Pressure and temperature relief devices are installed on the units for equipment protection, users protection, and serviceman's protection. They should be kept in good condition and accurate. Always keep them in operation.

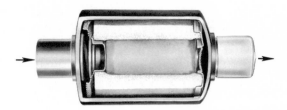

Fig. 13-136. Suction line filter. Filter recovers particles as small as 5 microns. Made in sizes up to 1 5/8 OD pipe sizes.

NEVER USE CYLINDER OXYGEN TO TEST ANY DEVICE FOR LEAKS. EITHER USE REFRIGERANT, CARBON DIOXIDE OR NITROGEN.

13-67 Test Your Knowledge – Chapter 13

1. What are the advantages of a nonfrosting cooling coil?
2. Why must high pressure motor cutouts be used with water-cooled condensing units?
3. What part of the compressor usually contains the intake valves?
4. Why is it advisable to connect the high pressure motor cut-out into the cylinder head of the compressor?
5. Name the three types of water valves.
6. Name the various two-temperature valves.
7. What are the advantages of water-cooled condensers? Air-cooled condensers?
8. What are the advantages of forced circulation cooling coils?
9. Why is the pressure type motor control usually used in multiple installations?
10. In multiple installations which use two-temperature valves, where should the check valves be placed?
11. What percent of a refrigeration load may be placed on a coil controlled by a two-temperature valve?

12. Why does an evaporative condenser save about 85 percent of the water consumption?

13. Are liquid receivers equipped with safety devices? Why?

14. What is inside the inner tube of a tube-within-a-tube condenser?

15. How is cast aluminum used in a liquid cooling coil?

16. What is the contraflow principle in water-cooled condensers?

17. Why is a pressure limiter valve used on an outdoor air-cooled condenser?

18. What principle is used to produce clear ice in an automatic ice cube maker?

19. How is water used to defrost a system?

20. Why must the drain pan and the drain pipe be heated during defrosting cycles?

21. What is the purpose of the check valve in the reverse cycle defrost system?

22. Why is a motor starter necessary?

23. Why is an oil separator insulated?

24. Why do some "hot gas" defrost systems reheat the refrigerant before it returns to the compressor?

25. Which type water valve will not vary the water flow as the refrigeration load changes?

26. Why is a float valve used with an evaporative condenser?

27. Does a flash cooler for a walk-in meat cabinet need an automatic defrost system? Why?

28. What is the purpose of a surge tank?

29. What is a sweet water bath?

30. Where are vibration dampers installed and why are they needed?

31. How is an auger used to produce flake ice?

32. What shuts off an ice cube maker when the storage bin becomes full of ice cubes?

33. How is an electric grid used to produce ice cubes?

34. What does the evaporator coil temporarily become during the defrosting action of a reverse cycle system?

35. In what mechanisms is ice accumulation used to interrupt an electronic circuit?

Fig. 14-1. Condensing unit room or machine room for supermarket. The condensing units are racked on special-ly built stands. Note oil separators and variety of units used.

Chapter 14

COMMERCIAL SYSTEMS, APPLICATIONS

One of the broadest fields of refrigeration is that of commercial refrigeration. This field includes all automatic refrigerating mechanisms other than the domestic or household type; also the comfort cooling field. The field that sometimes is confused with commercial refrigeration is the industrial field. The industrial field uses refrigerating machines which need an attendant, usually a licensed refrigeration engineer, on the job constantly. Industrial plants are manually operated refrigeration machines. They are commonly used for ice making, large storage houses, packing houses, industrial plants, ice cream manufacturing, and frozen food processing plants. Only the commercial field which uses automatic systems will be covered in this chapter.

14-1 History of Commercial Refrigeration

The first refrigerators used for commercial purposes were small semiautomatic ammonia machines. These machines were used for large meat markets and purposes of a similar nature. They appeared between 1913 and 1915 and filled a very definite need. The mechanism was not totally satisfactory, however, because the installation usually required that a competent refrigeration mechanic or engineer be on the premises, or the owner in some localities was required to have an operator's license. Also the cost of the mechanism was considered to be quite high. When the small domestic machines were first experimented with between 1916 and 1920, the possibility of using them for various commercial purposes was very quickly realized. Soon thereafter, the first automatic refrigerators were produced for ice cream cabinets (1920-21). These quickly took the place of the old ice and salt mixtures previously used for ice cream storage. The Nizer Corp. of Detroit was one of the first successful manufacturers of this type of machine. This company merged later with Kelvinator. The Frigidaire Corp. similarly produced products for this field, followed not long after by the Servel and Copeland companies. The second most important use for commercial refrigeration was for water-cooling machines and small automatic machines for grocery and walk-in refrigerator cabinets.

In 1923 mechanical refrigeration made its first real impression on this market, which has grown rapidly since that time. Also, the various types of commercial refrigerating equipment have increased and now include such installations as ice cream making machines, milk and beverage coolers. Fig. 14-1 illustrates a condensing unit room as used in a supermarket. Note the racks and extensive electrical installation. Some commercial installations of the multiple-stacked type have condensing units located outside the building or in a separate room. Fig. 14-2 shows a multiple installation consisting of two condensing units and a separate fan to provide forced-air circulation.

14-2 Scope of Commercial Refrigeration

The commercial refrigeration field covers a multitude of applications.

It is used for long storage, short storage, and display. Typical uses:

Fresh foods: meats, vegetables, fruits, candy, poultry.

It is used for freezing, storing: meats, vegetables, fruits, poultry, ice cream.

It is used for cooling water for: drink-

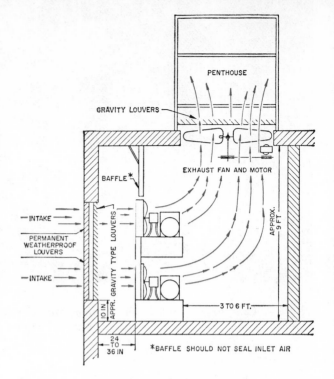

Fig. 14-2. A multiple stacked type condensing unit. Note two independent condensing units and separate exhaust fan. (ASHRAE)

ing, ice making, air conditioning, machine tools, heat treatment.

It is used for storage, display, or distributing: milk, bacteriological specimens, beverages.

Cabinets are usually made of steel inner-and-outer shells, and may be reinforced with steel or wood frame and insulation installed between the shells. Cabinets used for display are built with windows or are open at the top for display and easy access.

Another way to classify commercial refrigeration is by commercial businesses that use the equipment. Typical examples:

Grocery Stores: reach-in cabinets, display cases, ice cream cabinets, frozen food cases.

Meat Markets: walk-in coolers, reach-in cabinets, display cases.

Supermarkets: walk-in coolers, meat cutting rooms, reach-in cabinets, closed display cases, frozen food cases, frozen food display cases.

Restaurants: walk-in coolers, reach-in cabinets, frozen food cases, water cool-

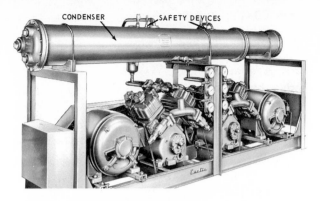

Fig. 14-3. Large dual compressor, dual motor commercial condensing unit. Note shell type condenser, compressor oil sight glasses, gauges.
(United States Air Cond. Corp.)

ers, beverage coolers; ice cream cabinets, ice makers, salad pans.

Drug Stores: ice cream cabinets, bacteriological cabinets, soda fountains, water coolers, ice makers.

Farms: freezers, frozen food cabinets, milk coolers.

Locker Plants: aging rooms, fast freezers, frozen food storage, chill rooms, frozen food display cases.

Trucks: fresh produce, frozen foods.
Ice Cream Parlors.
Frozen Custard Stands.
Metalworking Plants: heat treating, machine coolants.
Bakeries: dough retarding.
Fur Storage.

Three main differences between domestic and commercial refrigeration machines are:

1. Multiple installations, that is, the same condensing unit may be connected to two or more evaporator coils.
2. Water-cooled units.
3. Commercial machines on the average are larger than domestic ma-

Fig. 14-4. Typical non-code commercial installation.

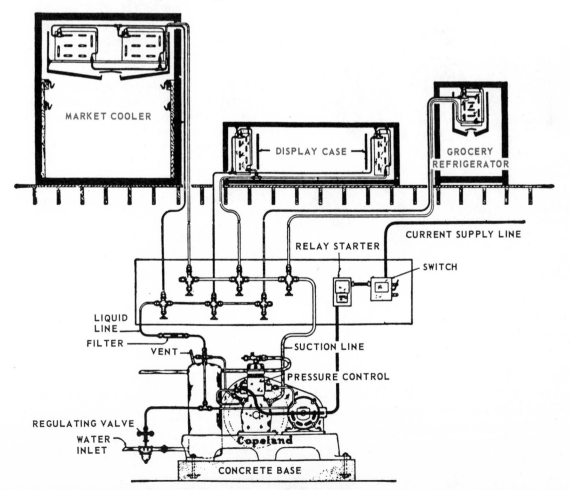

chines, and are available up to as much as 150 tons of refrigeration capacity, Fig. 14-3.

Two types of refrigerant controls are best suited for use in multiple installations; the low side float and the thermostatic expansion valve. Manifolds with hand shutoff valves are recommended for these installations.

The mechanism is similar to the domestic mechanism and includes:

    a. Compressors.
    b. Condensers.
    c. Liquid receivers.
    d. Evaporating units.
    e. Refrigerant controls.
    f. Servicing valves.
    g. Motor controls.
    h. Multiple valves.
    i. Motors and contactors.
    j. Water valves.

and a grocery box. As shown, the system has three evaporator coils and one condensing unit.

A modern self-contained condensing unit evaporator coil combination is shown in Fig. 14-5 and Fig. 14-6. This unit is designed to be mounted in the wall of the refrigerated space.

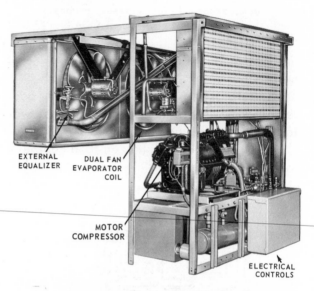

Fig. 14-6. Straddle type refrigerating unit with sheet metal casing removed. Note the external equalizer on the thermostatic expansion valve. This straddle type refrigerator unit is available for applications ranging from −40 F. to +35 F. and is available with Thermobank defrost.

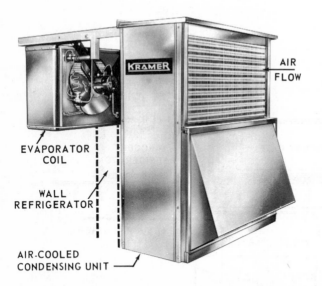

Fig. 14-5. Straddle type refrigerating unit, with blower evaporator coil, thermostatic expansion valve, and air-cooled condenser. (Kramer Trenton Co.)

Fig. 14-4 shows an older model noncode commercial installation. This installation involves a water-cooled compressor and condenser, driven by a 1-hp motor and it cools a walk-in box, a display counter,

14-3 Commercial Cabinet Construction

Since commercial refrigeration covers a considerable number of applications, a study of the various cabinets and applications is necessary. Many different sizes, shapes, and styles of cabinets are available.

All are designed to produce and maintain the correct temperatures needed for items to be refrigerated. All are insulated. The lower the temperature, the more insulation needed. Reach-in windows, display windows, walk-in doors, and the like are used in many applications.

Fig. 14-7. *Four-door reach-in cabinet with a self-contained condensing unit mounted at top.*
(Koch Refrigerators, Inc.)

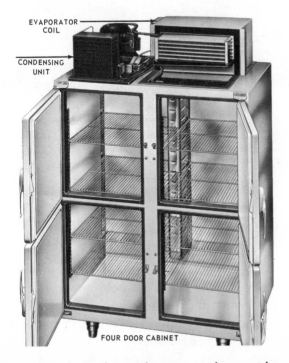

Fig. 14-8. *A reach-in refrigerator cabinet with top-mounted condensing unit and evaporator coil. Cover is removed to show mechanism.*

14-4 Grocery Cabinets (Reach-in Cabinets)

Grocery cabinets have been used for many years to keep perishable products at satisfactory temperatures. Fig. 14-7 shows a typical reach-in cabinet. Internal construction of this cabinet is shown in Fig. 14-8. A blower evaporator coil is mounted on the top and the cooled air is distributed by means of a vertical duct. Fig. 14-9 shows a cross section through the same refrigerator.

Fig. 14-9. *Cross section of reach-in refrigerator showing top-mounted blower type evaporator coil. Note wall construction and air flow.*

Space which contains the evaporator unit is usually called the bunker. This terminology comes from the original use of ice in these cabinets. Blower type evaporator coils are now used almost exclu-

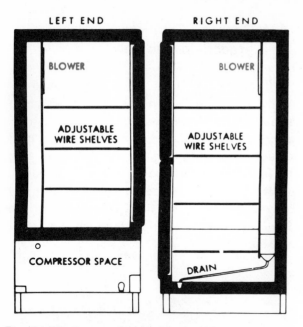

Fig. 14-10. Cross section of a reach-in cabinet. Note location of blower.

pansion valve. The coils are suspended from the top. Insulation most commonly used is foamed-in-place plastic.

Sizes vary considerably, with ranges from 21 to 94 cu. ft. interior net volume being quite common. The temperatures desired are about the same as in domestic boxes with a minimum of 35 F., and a maximum of 45 F. A relative humidity of approximately 80 percent is necessary for uses such as salads, deserts, fresh foods, etc.

A reach-in cabinet for small grocery stores and markets is shown in Fig. 14-11. The evaporator coil is the blower type and is mounted in a vertical position perpendicular to the half doors. This cabinet uses a remote condensing unit. The full height door permits storing beef quarters, etc.

sively for grocery cabinets. Fig. 14-10 shows a unit with the condensing unit located in the base and a blower coil installed inside the cabinet.

The coil is usually located in the upper center of the cabinet; the old flooded coils used a few deep fins, while the newer coils are deep finned and use a thermostatic ex-

Fig. 14-12. Walk-in refrigerator. A low temperature, 0 deg. F., compartment is on left and normal temperature 35 F., compartment is on the right. This cabinet uses hermetically sealed refrigeration system. (Bally Case and Cooler, Inc.)

14-5 Walk-in Coolers

Meat markets usually have a refrigerated cabinet or walk-in cabinet in which to store meat and other perishable products. These cabinets have large doors and windows and are sometimes classified as butcher boxes. The size of these cabinets varies to quite an extent, but two heights are usually considered standard; 9 ft. 10 in.

Fig. 14-11. Reach-in cabinet designed to store and refrigerate a variety of foods. (McCall Refrigerator Corp.)

and 7 ft. 6 in. exterior dimensions, Fig. 14-12. These boxes are of the "knock-down type" which means they may be taken apart for ease in moving, Fig. 14-13.

Some typical walk-in cooler sizes are:

L.	W.	H.
7'	5'	9'10"
8'	6'	9'10"
8'	8'	9'10"
9'	7'	9'10"
12'	10'	9'10"
6'	5'	7'6"
6'	6'	7'6"
7'	6'	7'6"

Many cabinets are made with metal linings and metal exteriors. Porcelain is the usual interior finish and baked enamel is

Fig. 14-14. Prefabricated walk-in refrigerator door. Note foot treadle door opener, part 9.

Door latches for these cabinets must be accessible from the inside for safety, Fig. 14-15. The doors may also be provided with heating wires along the edge to eliminate sweating and freezing.

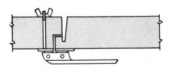

Fig. 14-15. Safety release. Latches are attached by nylon, non-heat conducting bolts. Wing nut inside walk-in refrigerator may be removed to provide emergency door opening. Heater wires located on edges of door eliminate condensation and freezing.
(Bally Case and Cooler, Inc.)

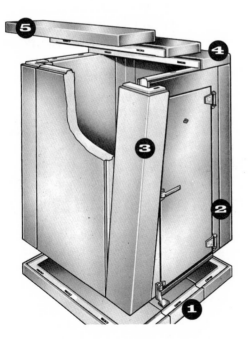

Fig. 14-13. Prefabricated walk-in refrigerator. Note five prefabricated sections and how they lock together.

used on the exterior. Aluminum and stainless steel are also used extensively. Cabinet doors are usually of the same construction as the box and are gasketed to make the box airtight. These gaskets are usually made of built-up rubber. See Fig. 14-14. Note the foot treadle door opener.

In addition to the entrance doors, these coolers may be equipped with small reach-in doors, usually with double or triple glass. That is, instead of having insulation, these doors have two or three panes of glass arranged in such a way that they are airtight, with an air space between the layers of glass. Plate glass is usually used; special chemicals, such as calcium chloride, are used to keep the spaces between the panes free from moisture. The more recent walk-in coolers use rigid urethane foamed-in-place insulation. The urethane is foamed between the inner and outer walls. This produces a very strong wall and eliminates the need for metal framing. Fig. 14-16 illustrates a typical refrigerator wall construction.

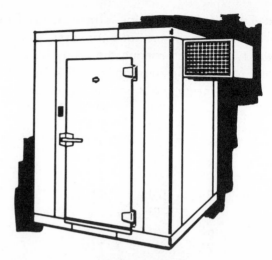

Fig. 14-17. A wall-mounted refrigerating unit, which becomes a completely self-contained refrigerating system.

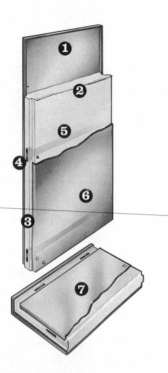

Fig. 14-16. Walk-in refrigerator wall section. 1—Outside metal. 2—Insulation. 3—Tongue and groove joint. 4—Panel locks. 5—Steel straps. 6—Inside metal. 7—Floor section.

There are some walk-in coolers that have a wall mounted evaporating unit which has a vertical baffle located between it and the main portion of the cabinet interior. Forced convection evaporator units are popular, Fig. 14-17.

The temperature maintained in this type of cabinet depends on the use. For meat storage, or fresh produce storage, a temperature of between 35 F. and 40 F. and a relative humidity of about 80 percent is essential. Air movement is necessary. Ul-

traviolet lamps are also used to help keep bacteria and mold growth to a minimum. In those coolers which are maintained at above 32 F. some type of drain must be provided. Fig. 14-18 shows a common method of installing the drain in a prefabricated walk-in cooler which is placed on top of a permanent floor. Because over exposure to ultraviolet rays is dangerous, persons working near these lamps must be protected from the rays, or the lamps turned off when someone is in the cabinet.

For milk storage, beverage cooling, and other service in which the dehydration of

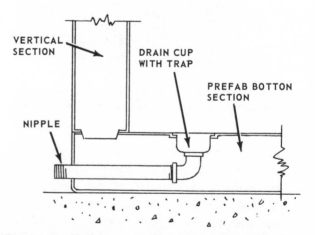

Fig. 14-18. Walk-in cooler drain connection. Note that drain connection is part of prefab bottom section.

foods is not important, colder temperature may be used as desired and less attention may be paid to relative humidity. Blower evaporator coils are commonly used on these installations.

14-6 Florist Cabinets

Florists' cabinets vary in size and construction and differ from grocery cabinets and walk-in coolers in three principal ways: First, the temperature within the cabinet may be kept higher than those in

Fig. 14-21. Activated carbon air filter installed in florist cabinet. Also note evaporator coils, hangers and drains.

the other types of boxes. Temperatures between 55 F. and 58 F. are quite common. Second, the thickness of insulation for these cabinets, as a result of the lesser temperature difference, is usually but 1 to 2 in. thick. Third, the cabinets are usually made with an extensive amount of window surface, permitting the display of cut flowers within the cabinet, Fig. 14-19. Humidity is an important factor in a florist's cabinet, and should be kept as high as possible in order to retard evaporation from the surface of the leaves and flowers. The evaporator coils have large cooling surfaces to keep the coil temperature as high as possible, and natural convection coils are used in most cases. Also, the motor controls are such that there is but little variation in the cabinet temperature. Many florist cases use odor-removing devices to prevent contamination of the flowers. An activated carbon filter, as shown in Fig. 14-20, may be used to reduce mold growth, neutralize ethlene and extract odors given off by flowers. Fig. 14-21 shows a filter installed in a florist's cabinet.

Fig. 14-19. Florist's display refrigerator cabinet. (McCray Corp.)

14-7 Display Cases

To display produce to the best advantage, stores frequently use refrigerated counters. These counters are equipped with glass fronts, enabling the purchaser to see the array of articles handled by the merchant; at the same time the food is safely refrigerated. This refrigeration is neces-

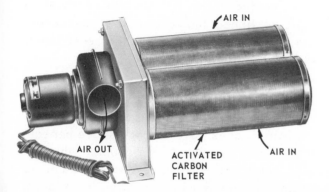

Fig. 14-20. Activated carbon filter used for cleaning air in refrigerator cabinet. (Connor Engineering Corp.)

sary to prevent the spoiling of the food during the 8 to 10 hour period that it is stored in the display case. The temperature in a display case is determined by the usage. Fig. 14-22 shows the recommended temperature for some common applications.

Type Fixture	Temperature—F	
	Min[a]	Max[a]
Meat, unwrapped		
display area	35	38
storage compartment	34	37
Meat, wrapped		
display area	28	36
storage compartment	28	35
Produce, display area	35	45
Produce, storage compartment	35	45
Dairy	35	42
Frozen Food	—[b]	0
Ice Cream	—[b]	-12

[a] These temperatures are air temperatures, with thermometer in the refrigerated air stream and not in contact with the product.
[b] Minimum temperatures for frozen food and ice cream are not critical; maximum temperature is the important factor for proper preservation of product quality.

Fig. 14-22. Recommended temperatures in display cases. (ASHRAE)

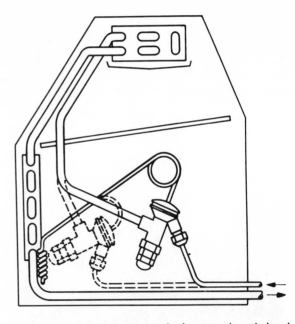

Fig. 14-23. Cross section of glass-enclosed display case. Note use of two evaporator coils connected in series; also use of thermostatic expansion valve. (Detroit Controls Corp.)

Electric lights for lighting display cases are usually installed outside the glass case so heat generated by the lights will not increase the refrigerating load.

Display cases vary as to design, length, and height. Three types are:
1. Glass enclosed display case only.
2. Glass enclosed display case and enclosed storage cabinet.
3. Open display cases for:
   1. Fresh produce.
   2. Frozen foods.
   3. Fresh meats.

Display cases are sometimes classified as to the location of the evaporator coil:
1. Overhead coil.
2. End coil.
3. Base coil.

14-8 Single-Duty Case

A popular display counter is the type using an overhead evaporator coil. The counter frequently makes use of the space below the display portion as a refrigerator storage cabinet as shown in Fig. 14-23. This counter has the main evaporating coils mounted in the upper portion of the display space under the shelf which forms the top of the counter. This provides good refrigerating temperatures all the way through the display space.

In addition, some of the counters have shelf coils. They are called auxiliary evaporating coils. The evaporating coils, which are located under the shelves, consist of coils of tinned tubing containing evaporating refrigerant so placed, that each shelf is individually cooled.

14-9 Double-Duty Case

Some cases have storage space beneath the display portion of the counter which is also refrigerated. The evaporating coil is usually connected in series with the coils above. Temperatures may be kept at 40 F. to 45 F. in both compartments, because they usually serve as temporary containers for food or produce which is transferred to a walk-in storage cabinet overnight. Coils used in these installations must necessarily be narrow and they are made with fins as small as 1 1/4 in. in width. Some of the shelf coils are the plain tubing type. Many of these display cases are now using blower coils for cooling. These coils take little space and provide even refrigeration temperatures throughout the display case.

14-10 End Coil Display Case

Another type of display counter used to some extent is the end coil type. Instead of using evaporator coils running the full length of the counter, the coils are located at each end. If the counter is seven feet long or less, it may have but one coil at the end. It usually has coils at both ends if the counter is longer. These counters vary from 35 to 45 in. in height and the glass extends to the floor. The space within usually contains from two to four shelves which may be viewed either from the front or the top of the case. Sometimes the glass is inclined in front, but more often is vertical. Temperatures maintained in these counters are usually between 40 F. and 50 F. Blower coils are generally used.

14-11 Open Display Case

To make foods more accessible to customers in self-service stores and supermarkets, open display cases are in common use. Fig. 14-24 shows an open frozen foods display case.

These cases may be designed with or without storage space in the base of the unit. Storage space is open at the top. The walls, or the upper part of the wall, may be enclosed in double or triple glass panes. See Fig. 14-25.

The higher temperature cases such as used for fresh meats, dairy products, and the like, do not present any special evaporator coil problems. Blower coils are

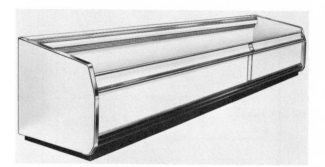

Fig. 14-24. An open display case for frozen foods. Forced circulation cold air serves as a curtain of air to keep food on display at freezer temperatures. (Tyler Refrig. Div., Clark Equip. Corp.)

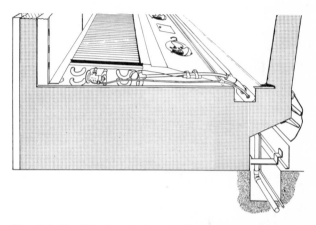

Fig. 14-25. Display case installation. Note trough in floor for refrigeration piping and electrical conduit.

Fig. 14-26. An open meat display case.

used and ducts flow the cold air through grilles at the rear of the case at the same level as the refrigerated foods. The warm air returns down the front of the case. Fig. 14-26 shows an open meat display case. A

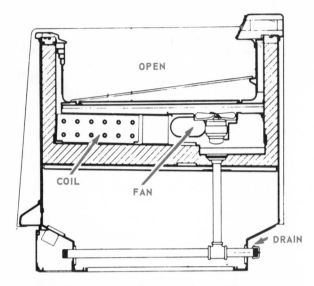

Fig. 14-27. Cross section of open meat display case.
Note evaporator coil location, fan and drain.
(Tyler Refrig. Div., Clark Equip. Corp.)

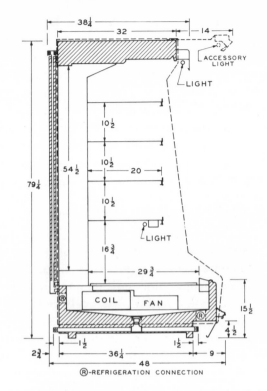

Fig. 14-29. Display case for dairy products and deli-
catessen items. (The Warren Co., Inc.)

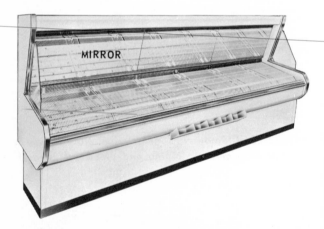

Fig. 14-28. Open display case for produce with canopy mirror.

Fig. 14-30. Dairy case.

shallow open chest type display case is shown in Fig. 14-27.

Many supermarkets have open display cases for produce. These units are kept at approximately 40 F. and at a high humidity. See Fig. 14-28.

A cross section of an air curtain open display case is shown in Fig. 14-29. This unit has sliding doors in the canopy to enable restocking the case from the rear. A complete installation of this unit is shown in Fig. 14-30. Designs of open display units are shown in Figs. 14-31 and 14-32 while Fig. 14-33 shows a display case with the fan and evaporating coil located in a different position.

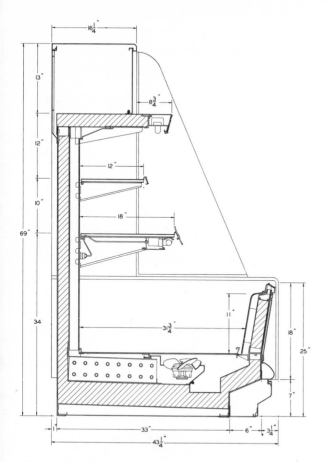

Fig. 14-31. *Cross section of open shelf dairy display case.*

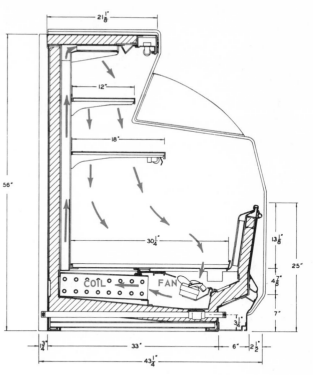

Fig. 14-32. *Cross section of open display case using blower evaporator coil.*

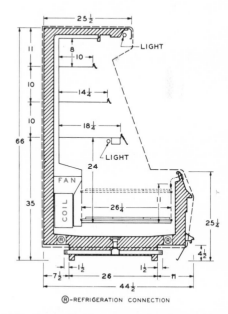

Ⓡ—REFRIGERATION CONNECTION

Fig. 14-33. *Open display case showing coil and fan mounted in lower rear of case.*
(The Warren Co., Inc.)

14-12 Open Frozen Food Display Case

Storing and displaying of frozen foods in both open and closed cabinets has become very popular. These cabinets represent a new problem as temperatures near 0 F. must be maintained. The coils therefore must operate at -10 F. to -15 F. Heater wires are installed along the parts of display cases that may collect condensation from the air. An open frozen foods display case is shown in Fig. 14-34. Some cases are equipped with alarm systems which warn if the case becomes too warm.

Frozen food storage cabinets and closed display cases are constructed in both the chest style and upright cabinet type. Be-

cause of the low temperatures in these cabinets, the openings are gasketed or sealed, and the insulation is thick and care-

Fig. 14-34. Open frozen foods display case. Device being pointed to is an alarm circuit which will signal if produce becomes too warm.
(Tyler Refrig. Div., Clark Equip. Corp.)

fully hermetically sealed. The chest type is popular because the top openings prevent the spillage of cold air when the cabinet is being used. Fig. 14-35 shows a cross section of an open chest type frozen foods display cabinet.

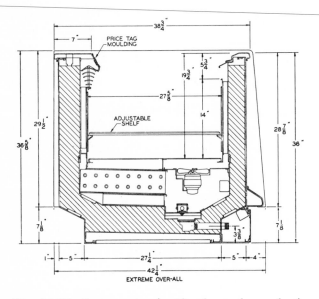

Fig. 14-35. Construction details of open frozen foods display case.

Low temperature units for displaying frozen foods present a difficult coil defrosting problem. The coils must be defrosted at least once a day. The defrosting must be done as quickly as possible to prevent the case from warming up too much. The defrosting must be done automatically.

A time clock is frequently used; this operates a hot gas defrosting system, or an electric heater defroster device. See Chapter 13 for details on these systems.

14-13 Frozen Food Storage Cabinet

The frozen food storage cabinet may be either a chest type or an upright type with 4 to 6 in. of insulation. The doors or access openings are also heavily insulated and are usually provided with a double gasket. Door frames and other parts which may sweat are usually heated by electrical resistance strip heaters.

These cases are used for storage purposes only and the food is moved from these cases to the display cases as needed. These cabinets operate at 0 F. or lower.

14-14 Fast Freezing Case

Cases used for freezing foods rapidly to a frozen condition are similar to storage cases except the temperatures are maintained at about -20 F. and the food is placed as close to the freezing plates as possible. Some cases use refrigerated shelves to provide more heat transfer surface.

14-15 Ice Cream Cabinets

Ice cream cabinets, since their inception, have been made of a steel framework with a sheet metal exterior. The older units were insulated with cork. The insulation was usually four inches thick, except on the top, which was commonly two inches thick. Older units had either a brine tank or dry coils surrounding the ice cream sleeves or holders.

Modern cabinets use polyurethane insulation of 1 in. to 3 in. thickness. The size of bulk ice cream cabinets is determined by the number of ice cream tank sleeves which the cabinet contains. The size of the sleeve or tank holder is standard, therefore, the construction of the various makes of bulk ice cream cabinets is similar. The size of these cabinets is based on the number of sleeves required to contain bulk ice cream cans. They range from one to twelve sleeves. Bulk ice cream cabinets should be kept at approximately 0 F. If the temperature is too cold, it is difficult to scoop out the ice cream; too low a temperature tends to crystallize it.

Dry type evaporator coils are used with a capillary tube, thermostatic expansion valve or automatic expansion valve refrigerant control. Some of the coils consist of tinned tubing wrapped around and soldered directly to the sleeves. Other coils consist of sheet metal with refrigerant passages formed in the metal. The sleeve covers (tops which must be raised to get to the ice cream) are also standardized by manufacturers. Having the openings to these sleeves at the top prevents spilling of cold air from the cabinet, when opened, and provides easy access.

Some ice cream cabinets are self-contained, meaning that the refrigerating machine or condensing unit is built into one end of the cabinet. Some units are of the remote type with the condensing unit located away from the cabinet.

In addition to the chest type ice cream cabinet, upright types and open display types are available. Bulk ice cream, prepackaged, should be kept at approximately -10 F. in order to retain its firmness.

14-16 Soda Fountain

Soda fountains provide compact units for storing and dispensing ice cream, water, beverages, syrups, and ice. They are usually attractive and are designed to facilitate dispensing. The fountain usually has an ice cream cabinet built into it. Another portion of the fountain contains water-cooling mechanism which must be designed to maintain correct water temperature. The evaporator coil outlet tubing from the ice cream cabinet and the drink-

ing water cooler is passed around the syrups, maintaining them at a relatively cool temperature. Beverages are kept at the same temperature as the water. Soda fountains are often difficult to service due to lack of space in which to work.

Syrups should be maintained at about 45 F., water anywhere from 32 F. to 50 F., and ice cream, as mentioned, between 0 F. and 10 F. A two-temperature valve is almost a necessity in this type of installation, as seen in Fig. 14-36. This shows a typical soda fountain cabinet refrigeration installation.

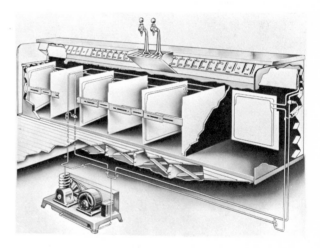

Fig. 14-36. Typical soda fountain cabinet refrigeration installation. (Dole Refrigerating Co.)

A cycle diagram of a complete soda fountain refrigerated by one condensing unit is shown in Fig. 14-37. The soda fountain consists of an ice cream compartment, syrup rail, bottle compartment, and beverage cooler. Thermostatic expansion valves are used; the ice cream coil has a check valve, the syrup coil and bottle compartment coil are controlled by a two-temperature valve, while the beverage cooler has a solenoid liquid line shutoff valve. Note the sight glass, heat exchanger, and dryer mounted in refrigerant lines near condensing unit.

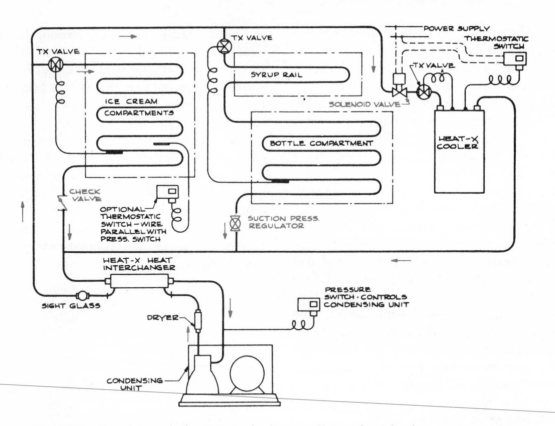

Fig. 14-37. Complete soda fountain cycle diagram. Note solenoid valve, suction pressure regulator, and how these valves are used to control temperatures in various parts of installation. (Dunham-Bush Inc.)

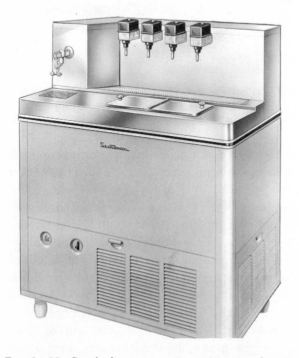

Fig. 14-38. Drink dispenser using pressurized units with mix taking place at outlet valve.

A "bobtail" soda fountain is the same as the one shown in Fig. 14-37, except there are no ice cream cooling coils.

Many drive-ins, soda fountain stores and the like use drink dispensers. Fig. 14-38 shows such a unit designed also to make ice cubes. Fig. 14-39 shows the dispensing circuits for water, syrups, and ice making. A cabinet with beverage valves is shown in Fig. 14-40, while Fig. 14-41 shows the interior design of the unit.

14-17 Soft Ice Cream Makers

A special application of refrigerating systems is the frozen custard or soft ice cream making machines. These units use a large refrigerating machine to fast freeze the mix. The same, or another, motor is used to drive the stirring mechanism (dasher). A 1/2 hp refrigerating unit can fast

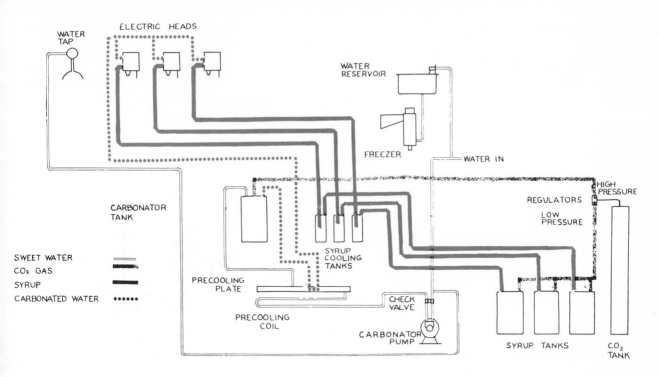

SWEET WATER

CO₂ GAS

SYRUP

CARBONATED WATER

Fig. 14-39. Fluid circuits of drink dispenser. Carbonated water and the syrups are mixed in electric heads. This unit also makes and stores ice flakes. (Scotsman-Queen Products Div., King-Seeley Thermos Co.)

freeze one gallon (32 two-ounce servings) of custard in about six minutes. A combination unit is shown in Fig. 14-42. It has two mixers separated by syrup jars, beverage mixers and dispensers, drain basin, and refrigerated storage unit below the bar top.

Fig. 14-43 shows an exploded view of an ice cream (soft) or custard mixer cabinet. The refrigerating mechanism for these units is shown in Fig. 14-44.

Some units are continuous in operation. Thermostatic expansion valves are usually used as the refrigerant control. The machine is usually adjusted to deliver the custard or sherberts at 20 F. A total of 3 hp can operate the refrigerating unit and drive the dasher. A 12.5 gallons per hour capacity unit usually uses a 2 hp dasher motor and a 3 hp refrigerating unit. The larger units are water cooled.

A mix storage or supply cabinet is usually used with three units to store the mix until it is used.

Fig. 14-40. Drink dispenser, ice maker combination.

14-18 Water Cooler

Water cooler cabinets usually consist of a sheet metal housing built around a steel framework. Inside this sheet metal housing there is usually a condensing unit, located near the floor, and above this is the water-cooling mechanism. The latter is the only part insulated (foamed plastic) from the room. The insulation is usually

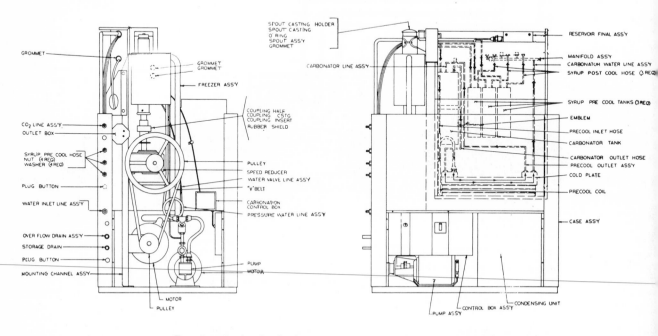

Fig. 14-41. A drink dispenser unit construction details.

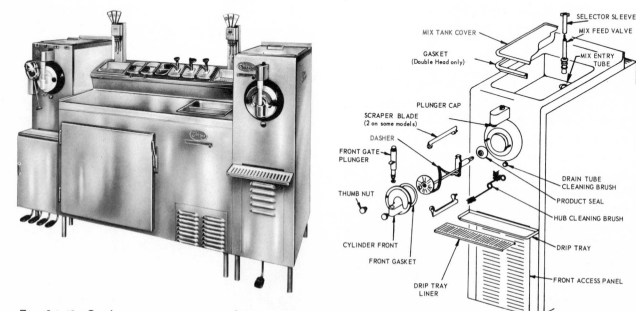

Fig. 14-42. Combination ice cream or frozen custard machine and drink dispenser. (Sweden Freezer Mfg. Co.)

Fig. 14-43. Ice cream (soft) or custard mixer cabinet in exploded view. Note mix tank and dasher.

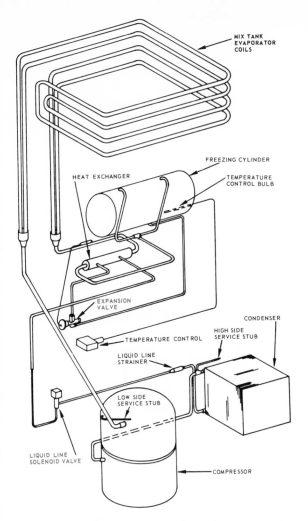

Fig. 14-44. Refrigerating unit for soft server or shake maker. Note solenoid valve and thermostatic expansion valve. (Sweden Freezer Mfg. Co.)

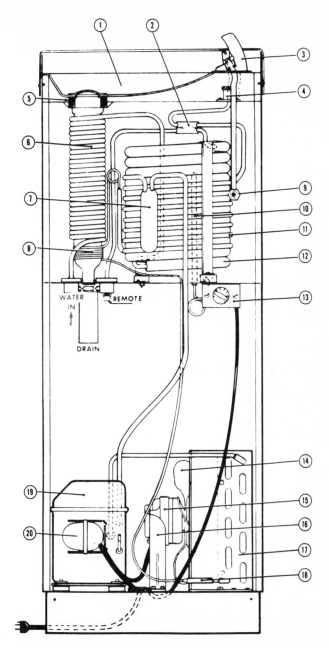

Fig. 14-45. Self-contained water cooler. 1–Top. 2–Cold water distributor. 3–Bubbler guard. 4–Glass filler connection. 5–Drain gasket. 6–Precooler assembly. 7–Accumulator. 8–Capillary tube. 9–Water valve. 10–Thermostat bulb well. 11–Refrigerant coil. 12–Water-cooling coil. 13–Thermostat. 14–Fan blade. 15–Fan motor. 16–Fan bracket. 17–Condenser. 18–Liquid refrigerant strainer. 19–Compressor. 20–Relay, overload protector.
(Temprite Products Corp.)

specially formed and between one and one-half inches and two inches thick. These cabinets are made in such a way that one or more sides may be easily removed to gain access to the interior. The basin of the water cooler is generally made of porcelain-coated cast iron, porcelain-coated steel, or stainless steel. Heat exchangers are frequently used on water coolers. These make use of the low temperature of the waste water and the suction line to precool the fresh water line to the evaporator coil as shown in Fig. 14-45. Self-contained water coolers are of two types:

1. Bottle type..
2. Tap water type.

The bottle type cooler uses a five-gallon bottle of water inverted on the top of the cabinet. Overflow and drain water are stored in a container built into the cabinet. These coolers use air-cooled condensing units exclusively. They are used where water and drains are not available or where the plumbing installation may be expensive.

Water coolers using a plumbing supply and drain connection, must be installed according to the National Plumbing Code and local codes. The plumbing should be concealed, a hand shutoff valve should be installed in the fresh water line, drain pipe at least 1 1/2 in. in diameter provided, and the bubbler opening must be above the

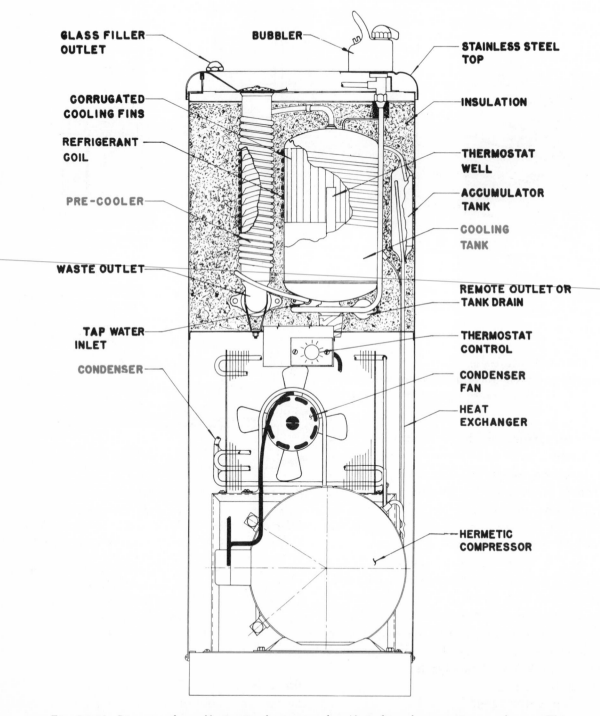

Fig. 14-46. Diagram of a self-contained water cooler. Note forced convection condenser. This unit uses a capillary tube refrigerant control. (Ebco Mfg. Co.)

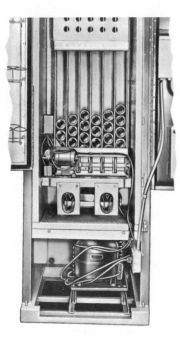

Fig. 14-47. Bottle beverage refrigerated dispenser. Cabinet doors are open and interior structure is shown.

tle dispensers (coin operated). These units contain a refrigeration system. The system is hermetic and usually has a blower type evaporator coil to cool the bottles. The automatic bottle handling devices are powered by a separate motor.

Bottled beverage units are available in several designs. Some dispense only one beverage while some dispense several different kinds. Fig. 14-47 illustrates a bottle unit with the doors open and the condensing unit front cover removed. The coin unit is in the right door while extra bottles are stored in the left door. The condensing

drain in such a way as to eliminate the chance for accidental syphoning of the drain water back into the fresh water system. The tap water models use a variety of evaporator coil designs. Fig. 14-46 shows the evaporator coil wrapped around the water-cooling tank.

Temperatures of the cooling water are variable depending on the persons who are drinking the water. REFER TO PAR. 16-28 FOR RECOMMENDED TEMPERATURES. Clean materials must be used for all water passages.

In large business establishments, in office buildings, or in factories, multiple water coolers, instead of individual ones, are popular. These coolers have one large condensing unit supplying many bubblers and these may be of many different types of construction.

14-19 Beverage Cooler

A popular application of refrigeration is the cooling of bottled beverages. Most people are familiar with the automatic bot-

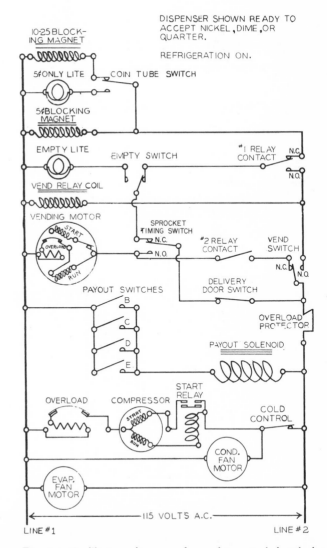

Fig. 14-48. Wiring diagram for refrigerated bottled beverage coin-operated dispenser.

unit is located in the bottom of the cabinet while the blower evaporator coil is mounted behind the two-bottle chute openings.

The automatic operation of this unit with its vending motor, magnets, signal lights, relays, etc., necessitates an elaborate wiring system. Fig. 14-48 shows eight parallel circuits being used in one dispenser. The evaporator coil fan operates continuously.

Fig. 14-51. Automatic ice cube maker. It has a slide back door on ice cube storage bin. The 1/3 hp air-cooled condensing unit is behind removable louvered panels.
(Scotsman-Queen Prod. Div., King-Seeley Thermos Co.)

Fig. 14-49. Dry bottled beverage cabinet. This is a three-door model. Note how doors slide to rear. It uses remote condensing unit.
(National Cooler Corp.)

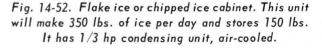

Fig. 14-52. Flake ice or chipped ice cabinet. This unit will make 350 lbs. of ice per day and stores 150 lbs. It has 1/3 hp condensing unit, air-cooled.

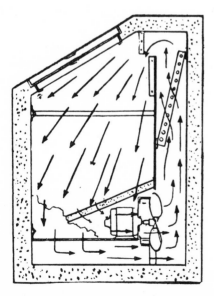

Fig. 14-50. Cross section of dry bottled beverage cooler, with forced convection evaporator coil.
(National Cooler Corp.)

Many commercial establishments use special bulk cabinets for cooling bottled beverages, as shown in Fig. 14-49. A cross section of a typical bulk bottled beverage cooler is shown in Fig. 14-50. Since humidity control is not needed, high velocity air flow is often used to reduce coil size.

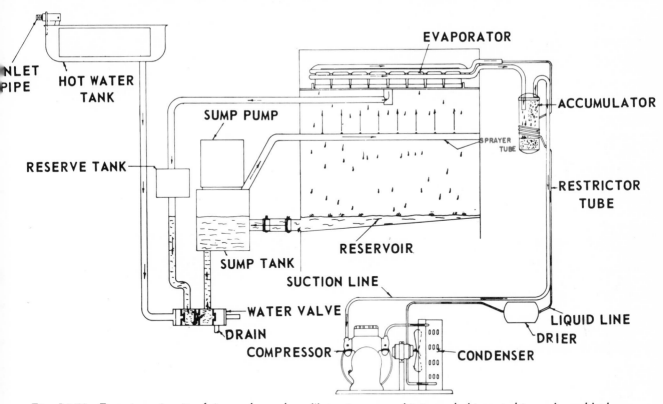

Fig. 14-53. Freezing circuit of ice cube maker. Water is sprayed into cooled inverted ice cube mold where it freezes.

14-20 Automatic Ice Maker

Many commercial establishments have need for large quantities of ice. Ice makers for many years used ice cube trays and shelf cooling coils placed either in separate reach-in cabinets or in back-bar storage units. They were either self-contained mechanisms or connected into multiple installations.

The cubes manufactured in these ice cube trays were cloudy due to entrapped air in the ice.

Automatic ice makers for commercial use are now used extensively. These units automatically control water feed, freeze water into ice, empty the ice into storage facilities, and stop when the storage space is full. The ice cube or the ice chips formed are clear and sanitary.

There are a number of different type units on the market. Floats and solenoids are used to control the water flow. Switch-es are used to operate the storing action when the ice is made. Removal of the ice from the freezing surfaces is accomplished by using electrical heating elements, hot water, hot gas defrosting, or mechanical ice removal.

These cabinets are insulated with such materials as urethane foam or fiber glass. The freezing surface and the bin storage basin are made of stainless steel. Some are self-contained while some use remote condensing units. Both supply and drain plumbing are needed. The units vary in capacity from a few pounds a day up to many tons per day. The capacities of these units decrease as the water temperature and/or the ambient air temperature increase.

An automatic ice cube maker is shown in Fig. 14-51; an automatic ice chip or ice flake maker is shown in Fig. 14-52. These units produce approximately 100 pounds of ice per day. The cycle of operation for the

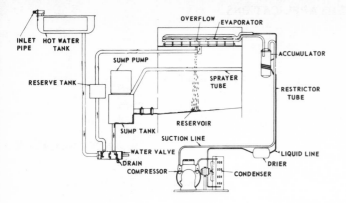

Fig. 14-54. Hot water defrosting cycle of automatic
ice cube maker.

ice cube maker is shown in Figs. 14-53
and 14-54. The ice flaker or ice chip principle of operation of a water-cooled model
is shown in Fig. 14-55.

A refrigeration mechanism is shown in
Fig. 14-56. Water flows through vertical
stainless steel tubes. When a hollow square
length of ice is formed, the refrigeration
stops, hot gas defrosting starts, and as the
long square rods of ice slide down the
tubes they are cut into cubes. When all the
tubes are empty, the refrigeration cycle
starts over again. An ice flake unit cabinet
with the ice making equipment located in
the upper part and the storage bin below
is shown in Fig. 14-57.

Electrical circuits of automatic ice
makers differ to the extent that bin level

controls are necessary or ice cube size
controls are needed. The water pump also
needs controls and wiring. Fig. 14-58 illustrates a typical electrical wiring diagram for an automatic ice maker.

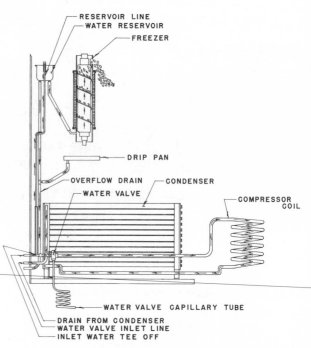

Fig. 14-55. Water circuit of ice flake or ice chip making unit. Inclined screw scrapes ice from inside of
cylinder.
(Scotsman-Queen Prod. Div., King-Seeley Prod. Co.)

① T-1 OVERFLOW THERMOSTAT
② T-2 SUCTION LINE THERMOSTAT
③ COMBINATION BIN SAFETY THERMOSTAT & H.P. CUT-OUT
④ CONDENSER WATER REGULATING VALVE
⑤ HOT GAS SOLENOID VALVE
⑥ RESTRICTOR TUBE
⑦ MAKE-UP WATER VALVE
⑧ WATER RECIRCULATING PUMP

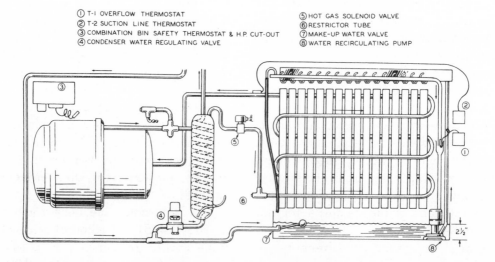

Fig. 14-56. Automatic ice cube making cycle. This system uses a hot gas defrost.
(York Corp., Sub. of Borg-Warner Corp.)

Fig. 14-57. Ice flake making system cabinet. Note sliding door access to ice flake bin. (General Electric Co.)

14-21 Milk Cooler

An important application of refrigeration is the farm milk cooler. State laws require that milk be cooled to 50 F. within one hour after it has been taken from the cow and kept at a 40 F. or lower storage temperature at all times. The refrigeration keeps bacteria increase at a minimum.

The rate that bacteria multiply or increase in milk is dramatically illustrated by noting the rate that bacteria grow at different temperatures. During a 24 hour period, the bacteria will increase to 2,400 at 32 F., and to 2,500 at 39 F., to 3,100 at 46 F., to 11,600 at 50 F., to 180,000 at 60 F., and to 1,400,000,000 at 86 F. One can easily see from this data why the milk should be cooled. Milk coolers are of two types:

1. Can type.
2. Bulk type.

Milk may be kept in 10 gallon cans, standardized as to shape and size. Farmers use milk coolers adapted to these cans. Many of the coolers are of the immersion type and the cans are inserted in refrigerated water, as shown in Fig. 14-59. This water is circulated by a small motor-driven water pump. Some units spray water

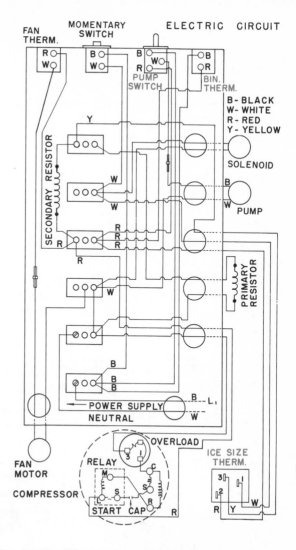

Fig. 14-58. Electrical circuits of automatic ice maker. Note the pump switch, bin thermostat and ice-size thermostat. (American Automatic Ice Machine Co.)

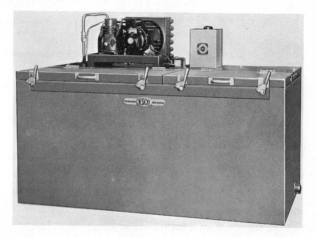

Fig. 14-59. Immersion type dairy milk cooler. Note condensing unit on left and water pump motor housing and control. (Esco Cabinet Co.)

over the cans to achieve quicker heat removal. Other units rock the cans to stir the milk in the cans and the cooling water outside, to produce quicker cooling.

Because milk laden cans are heavy (nearly 100 pounds) some milk coolers have side doors and cold water is sprayed or flowed over the milk cans. These cabinets must have watertight doors and a means to pump the water over the cans and store it while the cabinet is opened to remove the milk cans.

Fig. 14-60 shows a bulk milk cooler. The tank is stainless steel. The agitator and shaft are also made of stainless steel.

Fig. 14-61. Reach-in cabinet designed for use in bakery. Condensing unit and blower coil are located on top of cabinet. (Koch Refrigerators, Inc.)

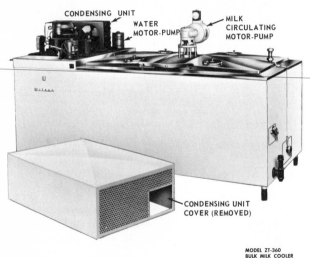

Fig. 14-60. Bulk type milk cooler. Note refrigeration condensing unit and pumps.
(Wilson Refrig., Inc.)

14-22 Bakeries

Many raw products used by bakeries must be kept at refrigerated temperatures to maintain or improve the quality. Frozen ingredients must be stored. Even the water and flour used for bread making must be cooled during certain periods of the year. Creams and custards are kept for longer periods at a cool temperature. Fig. 14-61 shows a reach-in cabinet designed for baking use.

If bread is fast frozen to -1 F. it will remain fresh for almost a month. Air conditioning is also extensively used in bakeries as controlled humidity is important in many baking processes.

14-23 Fur Storage

It has been found that if furs are stored at a low temperature, moths, in the egg, larvae or moth stage, will be destroyed. Common practice is to first cool the furs to approximately 15 to 20 F. then allow the furs to warm up to above 50 F. for 24 to 48 hours. After this cycle, which is found to be the most effective, the furs are stored at 35 to 40 F.

The cabinet for fur storage is usually constructed like a cold storage room, with concrete walls, thoroughly moisture sealed with asphalt, corkboard insulation or its equivalent, and a double door. The inside door is a regular refrigerator door and the outside door is a vault door.

Blower evaporator coils are used to force air circulation around and into the furs. The humidity must be kept at approximately 55 percent to prevent drying the skins. The vaults should be of fireproof construction.

14-24 Industrial Applications

Refrigeration is used extensively in a number of manufacturing processes. There are a great variety of applications. The smaller units are automatic in operation. Two common applications are (1) cooling water which in turn cools electrodes on resistance welders and (2) the cooling of quenching liquids for cooling of metals for heat treating.

14-25 Industrial Freezing of Foods

Industrial freezing of food is carried on in two principal types of establishments:
1. Processing Plants.
2. Locker Plants.
Processors of frozen foods have freezing centers in many large food producing areas. An example of this type of processing is the processing of fish which are packed and frozen along the coast and then shipped to all parts of the country.

A locker plant is a smaller unit used to prepare, freeze and store a great variety of products. Types of refrigerating equipment in processing and locker plants vary considerably, but the plan of freezing the food is similar. Fig. 14-62 shows the flow of produce through a typical plant. The food is weighed and checked for purity and suitability for freezing. Then it moves to the processing room. In the processing room meats are cut, fowl are cleaned and dressed, vegetables blanched and the various items are packaged. Next, the packed foods are sent to the freezing section

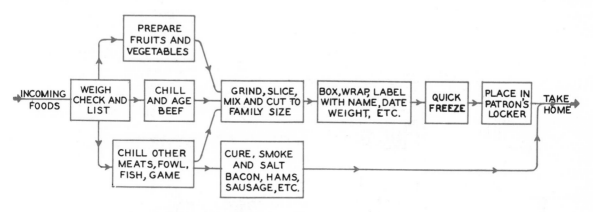

Fig. 14-62. Food flow through freezing plant.

where they are completely frozen and made ready for storage. Fig. 14-63 shows a typical locker plant floor plan. An ultraviolet ray lamp is sometimes placed in the aging room to kill bacteria. It is important to remember that low quality food cannot be made high quality by fast freezing.

Processing plants attempt to freeze food as fast as possible. They also attempt to contact as much of the food as possible with as low a temperature as possible. A fast freezing system, using a rack to hold the produce which is then lowered into an ultralow temperature chamber for fast freezing, is shown in Fig. 14-64. Some foods are immersed in sub-zero liquids, some are pressed between low temperature plates, some are exposed to blasts of low temperature air and some are sprayed with a low temperature liquid.

14-26 Industrial Storage of Frozen Foods

The storage requirements of most frozen foods are about the same, with a temperature of 0 F. to -20 F. desirable, and a variation of 2 to 3 F. allowed normally.

An excessive temperature differential produces "breathing" and volume changes that are detrimental. Humidity in storage rooms should be as high as possible. Cooling of the storage area may be accomplished by blower coils, direct contact plates or brine coils.

terials have been used. Most trucks have all metal bodies with various thicknesses of insulation depending on the application. Fig. 14-65 shows a typical truck body cross section using blanket-type insulation. Foamed-in-place insulation is used in most truck bodies. Fig. 14-66 shows

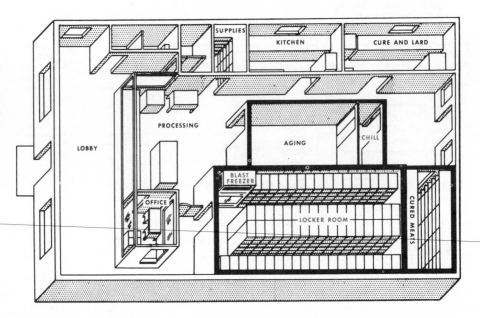

Fig. 14-63. *Typical locker plant. Special blast freezer is used to fast freeze food before it is stored in locker room.*

In smaller plants the customer enters the refrigerated area and pulls out a drawer containing the food. In some locker plants special construction makes it possible to deliver frozen foods from the storage area to the customer without entering the cold area.

14-27 Truck Refrigeration

Truck refrigeration requires specially designed truck bodies and refrigerating units.

The bodies should be light, well insulated, and built to withstand hard usage. The construction, of course, must be sturdy so that continual vibration and rough handling will not destroy the insulating value of the walls. Various insulating ma-

Fig. 14-64. *Freezer rack which is lowered into fast freezing chamber.*

the insulation being installed. The most interesting thing about truck refrigeration is the great variety of applications. Because of the many uses of truck refrigeration, the desired temperatures naturally vary, therefore each problem must be studied before a temperature may be rec-

Fig. 14-66. Truck body being insulated with plastic foam insulation. Gun mixes plastic with foaming activator. Form around lower part of outside of truck body helps shape insulator. (Armstrong Cork Co.)

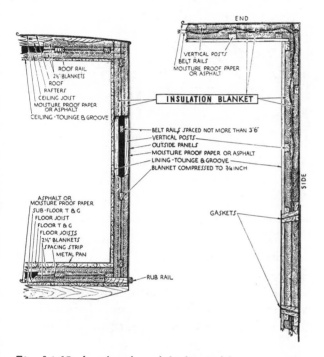

Fig. 14-65. Insulated truck body used for transporting refrigerated material.

ommended. A truck using dry ice for refrigeration must be insulated for -109 F.; ice cream trucks for 0 F. to 5 F.; while other commodities often use 35 F. to 40 F. temperatures. The systems used to produce refrigeration may be divided into four main types:

1. Ice.
2. Dry ice.
3. Mechanical.
4. Chemical (expendable refrigerant).

The ice method is still used, but because of weight and loading requirements, this method is decreasing in popularity.

The use of dry ice as opposed to water ice, is increasing because of weight reduction, elimination of drainage problems, and

servicing problems. However, some difficulty is encountered in controlling temperatures.

Mechanical refrigeration is similar, in most cases, to the typical refrigerating unit, the major variation being in the nature of the compressor drive. These drives are:

1. Engine-driven electric generator and motor.
2. Driven off transmission shaft.
3. Separate gasoline engine.

The electric generator and motor type uses standard voltages, cycles, and phases which permits plugging into a wall outlet in the garage if it is desired to keep the truck cold while it is not on the road.

A transmission power take-off is shown in Fig. 14-67. This operates by the use of

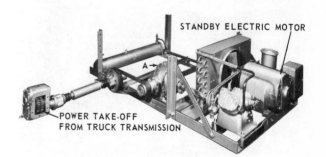

Fig. 14-67. Truck refrigeration condensing unit. Has a transmission power take-off for use on road and standard electric motor for overnight parking cooling and for cool down. Hydraulic clutch (A) operated by a solenoid valve engages and disengages compressor from power sources automatically. (Kold Hold Div., Tranter Mfg. Inc.)

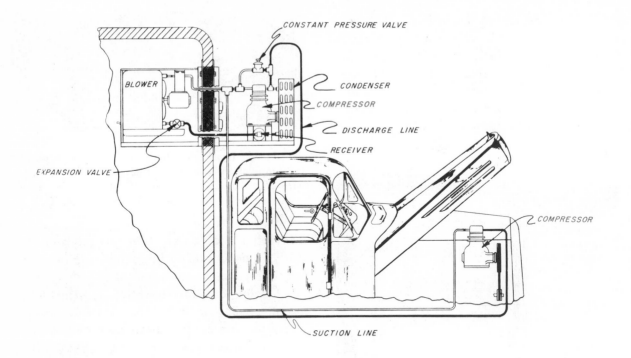

Fig. 14-68. *Truck refrigerating system with engine driven compressor and stand-by motor driven compressor.*

a power take-off from the transmission when the vehicle is running. It uses a standard motor when the truck is parked and the engine is turned off (overnight parking).

Gasoline engine-driven units are automatically controlled to start and stop as the system requires.

Some trucks use a dual refrigeration system. Fig. 14-68 shows a refrigerated truck with a refrigerating unit mounted on the truck body over the cab. This unit is the standby unit and is used only when the

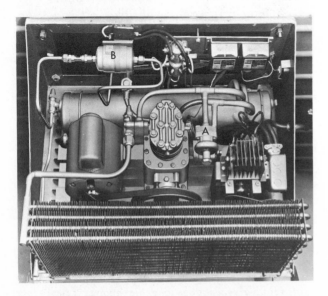

Fig. 14-69. *The stand-by truck refrigerating unit. Note sight glass, pressure regulator (A) and dehydrator (B).*

Fig. 14-70. *Truck engine driven refrigeration compressor. Note idler pulley (A).*

truck is parked for any length of time while on the road. The engine-driven compressor provides the refrigeration needs. Fig. 14-69 shows the inside of the standby motor-driven compressor compartment. In addition to this condensing unit, there is a compressor mounted on the truck engine and driven by the engine as shown in Fig. 14-70.

A typical finished installation of the unit as it is mounted over the truck cab is shown in Fig. 14-71. In addition to blower

Fig. 14-71. Completed installation of condensing unit on upper front of refrigerated truck body. (Kold Hold Div., Tranter Mfg. Co.)

evaporator coils, plate coils are used. Fig. 14-72 shows an installation using two coils.

Liquid nitrogen, which is sometimes called chemical refrigeration, provides excellent low temperature refrigeration. The refrigerant is expendable and therefore a condensing unit is not needed. Liquid nitrogen at atmospheric pressure boils at -320 F. or at 140 R. Temperatures from absolute 0 up to -250 F. are considered to be in the cryogenics range. See Chapter 18.

14-28 Railway Car Refrigeration

Refrigerated railway cars have long been used as a means of transporting perishable goods. Mechanical refrigeration is often used. The car construction is similar to that of truck body construction.

Two general types of refrigeration systems are used on trains: (1) freight refrigeration and (2) air conditioning in passenger cars.

Freight refrigeration may be by:
1. Water ice.
2. Dry ice.
3. Mechanical.
4. Chemical refrigeration (expendable refrigerant).

The present trend is toward mechanical refrigeration. Passenger car air conditioning is by mechanical refrigeration.

The compressors, in mechanical installations, are usually driven from the car axle while the cars are in motion and by an electric motor while the cars are in the yard.

Some train refrigeration systems have been developed using the absorption system. Others have employed the steam jet system of refrigeration.

Fig. 14-72. Two plate coils installed in refrigerated truck body. Note hanger devices and refrigerant lines.

14-29 Marine Refrigeration

Marine refrigeration uses basically the same equipment as land-type refrigeration. However, the refrigerants used are restricted to those which are nontoxic and nonflammable. All cabinets are carefully sealed to exclude the possibility of moisture entering the insulation. Refrigerant lines must be installed to permit some vibration and movement without danger of line or joint failure.

If saltwater-cooled units are used, the water piping, valving, and condenser must be designed to minimize the corrosive effects of salt water.

14-30 Snow Making

Many ski slopes supplement the natural snow on their runs by adding snow made by a "snow maker." The method of making snow consists of a water spray into which compressed air is added in such a manner that the water is broken up into fine mist which freezes very rapidly. The low temperature required for snow making is not created by refrigeration mechanism but comes from the surrounding atmosphere. The atmosphere temperature must be 30 F. or lower in order to manufacture snow although the maximum temperature which may be used depends on the relative humidity. If the relative humidity is low, snow may be made at temperatures as high as 35 degrees. This is because, with low humidity, some of the water evaporates, and in doing so absorbs heat which reduces the temperature of the water droplets below the freezing temperature, and ice crystals (snow) are formed.

In general the ground must be frozen before snow making to prepare a ski slope is practical. Usually manufactured snow is only used to supplement natural snow.

14-31 Review of Safety

The safest way to protect yourself and the public is to check the unit before working on it to be sure the mechanism and cabinet are installed according to local and national fire, electrical, plumbing, building and safety codes.

Floor load limits should be checked before heavy commercial equipment is installed. Wiring and plumbing must be of adequate size, of correct materials, and securely mounted. Remember, you are do-

ing the owner a favor if you locate and call his attention to code violations which might result in serious damage to both the physical structure and his personnel or clients.

Board of Health regulations apply to all equipment which is used in conjunction with foods and beverages and must be carefully followed.

Moving of large commercial cabinets calls for extreme caution. Use handling equipment appropriate for the job at hand and work carefully at all times.

14-32 Test Your Knowledge - Chapter 14

1. What cabinet temperatures are recommended for the following commercial installations: water-cooling, walk-in coolers, florist's cabinet, and ice cream cabinet?
2. Why is it necessary that the doors and windows in commercial cabinets be airtight?
3. What is the purpose of dead air spaces formed between the two and three pane windows in these cabinets?
4. How is moisture kept out from between the glass in multiple pane windows?
5. Why are lights of display counters sometimes located outside the counter?
6. If you were to mount a thermometer in a walk-in cabinet, where would you find the average temperature?
7. Why are most commercial refrigeration installations of the multiple type?
8. To what temperature would you permit water to be cooled, (a) if the bubbler was located in the heat treating room of a tool and die factory? (b) in an office building?
9. What is a wall mounted refrigerating unit?
10. Why must the humidity be kept high in produce storage cabinets?
11. How is cold air kept from spilling from open display cases?

12. What is a double-duty display case?
13. Where are evaporator coils located in open display cases?
14. How are frozen foods open display case coils defrosted?
15. What are the two basic types of ice makers?
16. What is hot gas defrosting?
17. Why does forced convection air flow transfer heat faster?
18. Why must milk be cooled shortly after it has been taken from the cow?
19. Are evaporator coils sometimes mounted outside the refrigerator cabinet?
20. What is the purpose of an activated carbon air filter?
21. How are certain parts of a frozen foods case kept from sweating?
22. How is clear ice manufactured instead of cloudy ice?
23. What is a dasher?
24. Why is a high-velocity blower evaporator coil permissible when cooling bottled beverages?
25. What causes an ice maker to stop making ice when the ice bin is full?
26. How can electric resistance heat be used in making ice cubes?
27. Why do some trucks have two refrigeration compressors?
28. Is a refrigerating system generally used in a snow making machine?
29. Why is floor loading important in commercial applications?
30. An auger is used to make what kind of ice?

Chapter 15

COMMERCIAL SYSTEMS, INSTALLING AND SERVICING

The installation and servicing of commercial units is a very important part of the refrigeration industry. Companies that own equipment may suffer severe losses of equipment investment, perishables may spoil and goodwill may be lost, if equipment fails.

Servicing information in this chapter deals mainly with multiple systems; what goes wrong, and how to provide repairs. Much of the servicing is similar to that described for domestic refrigerators and the information given in Chapter 12 may be used to a considerable extent. Tools and instruments listed in Chapters 2 and 12 are also usable for commercial servicing.

15-1 Types of Commercial Installations

Commercial refrigeration installations vary considerably. The following classification of installations is commonly used:
1. Self-contained Units.
   a. Hermetic.
   b. Conventional.
2. Remote Condensing Unit Installations.
   a. Single cabinet.
   b. Multiple cabinet.

Size of the installation may vary from 1/20 hp self-contained units, to 15 hp units for large cabinets. The size of the larger units is such that the assembly work of the complete system must be performed on the premises.

Small units of the package-type construction do not require this treatment; however, instructions for installing and maintaining them are similar to those given in Chapter 12, for domestic machines.

For example, a self-contained water cooler for an office necessitates only three connections. The electricity is obtained by means of a plugged-in connection. A plumber will be required to connect the water and the drain to the system.

Multiple installations must be installed to handle the refrigeration load efficiently and must be set up to minimize chances of accidents. All installations should be made with permanency and neatness as two main objectives. Many cities have laws and codes designating how and where certain refrigeration apparatus may be installed. See

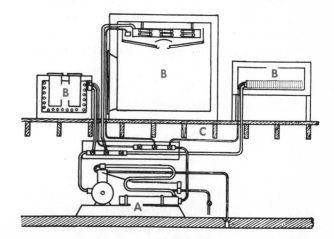

Fig. 15-1. Typical non-code remote type installation. A—Condensing unit. B—Cabinets. C—Floor line.

571

Chapter 27 for the National Refrigeration Code. Also, most refrigerating manufacturing companies have rules for installing their equipment. Prior to the adoption of codes by cities and manufacturers which systemized installation procedures, many installations were made on a careless basis. Fig. 15-1 shows a non-code installation.

Many cities and rural communities are not restricted by code, and installations are usually put in at a minimum cost. One must, therefore, consider two types of installations:

1. Non-code installation.
2. Code installation.

A good practice to follow, if there is no local code, is to install all units according to the National Code as described in Chapter 27.

15-2 Non-Code Remote Installations

A definite procedure should be closely adhered to when assembling a remote system, to safeguard against faults in assembly and to eliminate careless procedures. Refrigeration service departments claim that careless procedures produce more than 90 percent of their servicing difficulties. Assuming that the problem has been solved from the heat load angle, (Chapter 16) and that the units are well proportioned and of such a size that they will efficiently handle the load, the proper installation must be made in a way to take full advantage of these factors. The tubing, safety valves, and protective devices should be incorporated in the installation to produce operating efficiency, permanency, and safety. All refrigeration installation and service work should be done with correct tools, and with good quality tools. Fig. 15-2 shows some of the refrigeration tools commonly used. Chapter 2 describes in more detail tools and supplies needed for good installation and service work.

15-3 Installing Condensing Units

The first problem to be solved is the location of the condensing unit in respect to the cabinet or cabinets. This location should be as close to the various cabinets as possible, i.e., a central location.

Installation should be done in the following order:

1. Put cabinets in place.
2. Locate place for condensing unit and install it.
3. Install evaporating coils.
4. Install valves and controls.
5. Install tubing.
6. Check for leaks.
7. Dehydrate installation.
8. Start unit.
9. Check operation of unit and obtain 24 hour temperature and pressure records of unit in operation.

Cabinets are bulky and are sometimes difficult to move. A dolly, as shown in Fig. 15-3, will come in handy for cabinet moving jobs. Fig. 15-4 shows an appliance truck of the type often used for moving cabinets.

It is recommended that the condensing unit be put in the basement or in an adjacent room to the one in which the cabinet is located. Avoid putting the condensing unit where it will be exposed to low or freezing temperatures. Locating condensing units in the same room with the counters and cabinets is not recommended because of the heat and noise produced. Fig. 15-5 shows another non-code installation.

After the locations of the various units are determined, a sketch or drawing of the entire installation should be made to eliminate mistakes in the estimate of supplies, parts, etc. You should be familiar with the symbols used in these drawings.

The location of the condensing unit may also be determined by source of electrical supply, water supply, and water drainage. Plumbing and electrical connections should

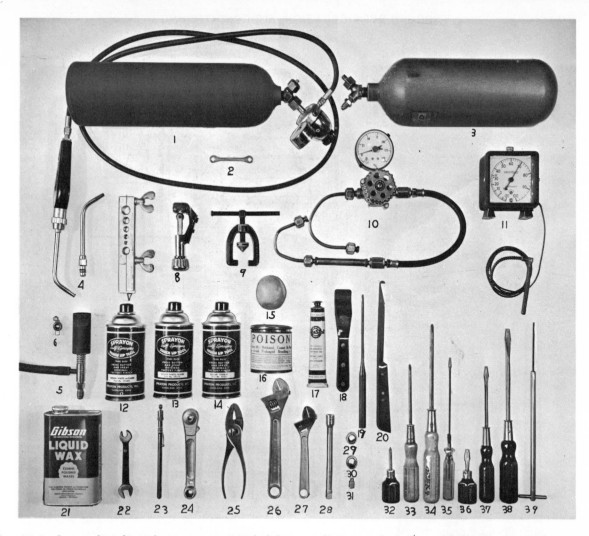

Fig. 15-2. Some of tools and instruments needed for installation and service of refrigerating mechanisms. 1, 2, 4, 5, and 6 are soldering and leak testing units; 7, 8, and 9 are used for tube flaring and cutting; 10 is a compound gauge and connectors; 11 thermometer; 12, 13, and 14 spray cans of touch-up paint; 18 scraper; 19 pin punch; 20 knife; 21 polish; 22 end wrench; 23 thermometer; 24 valve stem ratchet wrench; 26, 27, 28, 29, 30, and 31 are wrenches; 32 through 39 are various types of screwdrivers; 39 Allen setscrew wrench.
(Gibson Refrigerator Sales Corp.; Hupp Corp.)

Fig. 15-3. Dolly for moving refrigerator cabinets. One or more of these under the cabinet enables a service-man to easily move and place heaviest and bulkiest cabinets. Dolly shown will carry 4 tons.
(Airsecro Mfg. Co.)

be done by licensed contractors in those fields. The refrigeration contractor can subcontract these segments of the installation.

Fig. 15-4. Appliance truck with retractable swivel casters. (Stevens Appliance Truck Co.)

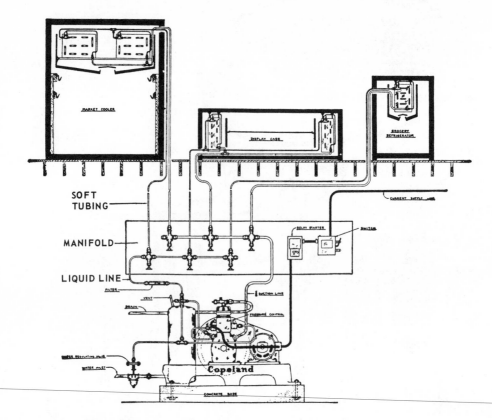

SOFT TUBING

MANIFOLD

LIQUID LINE

Fig. 15-5. Typical non-code commercial installation.

LEVEL ADJUSTMENT

NEOPRENE PAD

Fig. 15-6. Adjustable machine base leg showing neoprene pad to absorb vibration and noise. (Fabcel Div., Fabreeka Products Co.)

Figs. 15-6 and 15-7 show vibration absorbing mountings. Commercial condensing units are usually provided with a base which permits mounting the condensing unit on the floor. However, if the floor is moist or dustier than normal, a sturdy

stand should be constructed of wood, steel, or concrete to enable mounting the unit 20 to 40 in. above the floor. A flimsy base will magnify vibrations or sounds and should not be used.

NEOPRENE PAD IN PLACE

Fig. 15-7. Noise insulated mount used to level condensing units. Square neoprene pad shown at top is cut to fit shape of unit leg (shown below).

The condensing unit should be placed in an accessible place. Do not put it under stairways or in closets. If it is an air-cooled unit, it must have free air flow around it to cool the condenser.

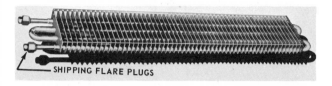

Fig. 15-8. Shelf evaporator coil. Aluminum fins and copper tubing are mechanically bonded together. Fins are offset. (Peerless of America, Inc.)

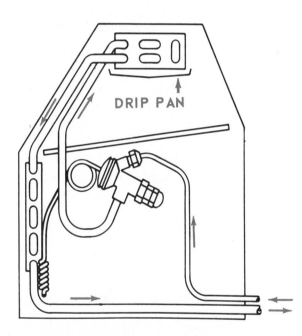

Fig. 15-9. Double-duty display case using two evaporator coils. Note drip pan under coils. (Detroit Controls Corp.)

Where there is possibility of damage from falling objects, protect the condenser by putting a heavy wire cage around it and over it. A valve and accessory board may be installed on the wall just above the condensing unit to support valves, dryer, two-temperature valves, electrical boxes, and necessary instruction cards for service work.

15-4 Installing Evaporator Coils

Evaporator coils should be carefully mounted and firmly fastened in place. The coils should be as level as possible. The type of mounting depends on the type of coil. Fig. 15-8 shows a display case coil, which may be installed as shown in Fig. 15-9. Notice the drip pan under the top coil.

Blower coils are usually equipped with mounting flanges, as shown in Fig. 15-10. Evaporator coils are usually fastened to the ceiling of the cabinet on installations such as a florist cabinet, walk-in cooler, and the like. The coil can be correctly mounted by using a plumb line to locate the holder positions. A cardboard template is a useful means for locating the mounting device.

The hanger may be attached to the ceiling of the cabinet. Bolt directly through the cabinet ceiling with galvanized or tin plated carriage bolts, or the hanger may be fastened to a sheet by means of cap screws (both of these being plated to prevent rusting), and the plate in turn fastened to the ceiling of the cabinet by brass wood screws. Another method is to fasten the bracket directly to the ceiling by means

Fig. 15-10. Small blower coil showing hanger bracket: A—Drain connector. B—Drain pan. Coil must be mounted level for efficient operation and good drainage.

of wood screws. Regardless of the devices used to mount the coil, they should be re-checked after being put in, to make sure they are level.

All natural convection evaporator coils should be properly baffled. Fig. 15-11 shows one type baffle and the means to fasten it to the evaporator coil.

Fig. 15-11. Evaporator coil baffle and drain pan. It is compact, permits good circulation and condensates drainage. A—Hangers. B—Individual baffle drains. C—Collector drain.
(Peerless of America, Inc.)

Display counter coils are usually sup-ported by stands. These stands or brack-ets should be provided with an adjustment to help level the coils in all directions.

15-5 Installing Tubing

The tubing in non-code installations is usually run along the walls and ceiling and is supported only at intervals frequent enough to keep tubing straight and firmly in place. Special clamps are available as tubing fasteners, but a galvanized conduit clamp of the 1/2 in. size is sufficient for most situations, as shown in Fig. 15-12. The tubing should be insulated from these clamps or protected from them by means of a short wrapping of friction tape to pre-vent chafing and galvanic action.

Where the tubing is run through the floor or wall, it should be adequately pro-tected by means of short runs of conduit, or flexible metal tubing (Greenfield). The

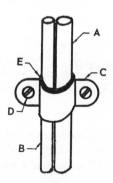

Fig. 15-12. A method of fastening the tubing to the wall. A—Suction line. B—Liquid line. C—Clamp. D—Wood screw. E—Friction tape.

ends should be sealed with a sealing com-pound, otherwise chafing of the tubing and corresponding troubles are likely to re-sult. See Fig. 15-13. In all cases the tubing should be run horizontally and vertically with neat looking bends of as perfect ra-dius as possible.

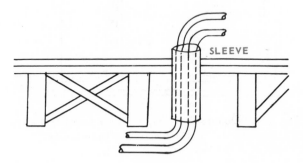

Fig. 15-13. Sleeve to protect tubing as it goes through wall or floor.

The liquid line presents no difficulties as to its slant and position, but you must install the suction lines so the tubing will drain toward the compressor. Any low spots in the suction lines will act as ac-cumulators of return oil, and may eventu-ally form a liquid slug in the tubing. When this oil slug is carried to the compressor it will cause disturbance in the crankcase and may result in temporary oil pumping. If the tubing must slant upward on returning from the evaporator coils to the condensing unit, the construction should be made to permit a steady downward slant of the tubing to a certain point at which a U-bend is located. The U-bend will act as an oil trap, functioning as the low spots mentioned above, insuring a positive return of oil to the compressor.

The tubing should never be run near sources of heat, such as hot water lines, steam lines, furnaces, etc. Such sources of heat will reduce the efficiency of operation.

As previously stated, copper tubing comes in coils usually of 50-foot lengths, and the tubing is dehydrated and sealed at the ends by the manufacturer. In the average commercial installation, 1/4 in. tubing is used for the liquid line and 1/2 in. tubing for the suction line. Only in large installations and sizable air conditioning systems is larger, liquid-line piping required. Large commercial installations use a larger suction line tubing or pipe.

During the installation the tubing should be kept clean. Tubing should never be put aside with the ends open. If possible, all tubing should be installed before being unsealed. Tubing should be sealed if it is not to be used for a period of five minutes or more. A practical method of installing tubing is to uncoil about 10 feet of it at a time by unrolling the coil along the floor, then run the tubing up through floor openings from underneath, gradually working it into place.

You should not have any difficulty installing 1/4 in. tubing. The 1/2 in. tubing must be carefully handled to prevent buckling when it is bent. Tube benders which are available for bending the tubing should be used. See Fig. 15-14.

In a non-code installation where individual suction lines and liquid lines run in-

Fig. 15-14. Tubing bender used to bend tubing to specific angle. Note degrees marked on bender to help serviceman produce proper bend.
(Imperial Eastman Corp.)

to main lines, T-connections may be used and the valves for shutting off the individual coils may be located near the coil itself. Valves, driers, or other heavy objects should not be supported by tubing. These items should be mounted on the wall or some other support. These connections may be of the SAE flare type or of streamline soldered fitting construction (sweat fittings).

When tubing is installed, it should be sealed immediately after flare or streamline connections are made, to keep it clean. The tubing should be attached permanently to the supports along which it runs.

Always try to run the tubing in such a manner that the support will protect the tubing from accidents. Many servicemen use a sponge rubber protective covering over the tubing which serves both as a protector and as an insulator, Fig. 15-15.

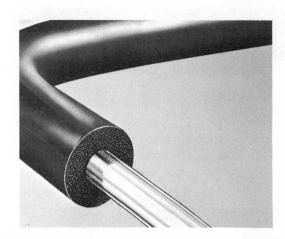

Fig. 15-15. Rubber insulation mounted on a suction line. Insulation is usually installed before tubing or pipe connections are made. (Rubatex Corp.)

Fig. 15-16. Rubber insulating tape being wrapped around a filter-drier to prevent sweating or frosting.

This covering must be placed on the tubing prior to assembly. At tubing connections or where valves have been installed, it is common practice to cover them with insulating tape, as shown in Fig. 15-16. Be careful to place the tubing so it will not be damaged by handling of articles in the room. Do not put loops or unsupported bends in the tubing except at the condensing unit.

A drier and a sight glass should be installed in the liquid line at the condensing unit. Also, a vibration damper, as shown in Fig. 15-17, should be included. One horizontal loop of soft copper tube may be made in the suction and liquid lines if a suitable vibration damper is not available.

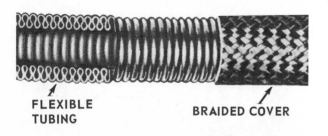

FLEXIBLE TUBING   BRAIDED COVER

Fig. 15-17. Flexible tubing used for vibration dampening. One of these is usually mounted in suction line near condensing unit.

15-6 Electrical Connections

The refrigeration unit must have sufficient electrical power of the correct type to operate the motor, controls, and sole-

noids. Chapters 7 and 8 explain electrical fundamentals and electrical power variables. Before installing a condensing unit, be sure the electrical characteristics of the compressor motor match the electrical power source. Smaller units, 1/8 to 1/4 hp, usually use 120V single-phase AC. Medium size units, 1/4 to 1 hp, may use 230V single-phase or three-phase AC. Larger units may use 208V single-phase AC.

The fans (both evaporator coil and condenser) must be checked to be sure the nameplate data matches the power available. This is also true for solenoid valves and controls.

Wire size is important. The wire should be large enough to carry the load with at least 50 percent extra carrying capacity.

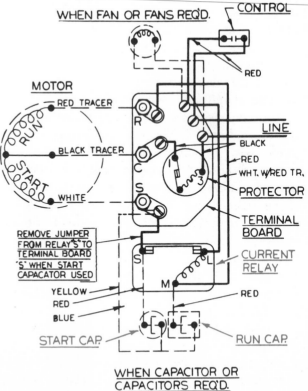

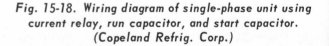

Fig. 15-18. Wiring diagram of single-phase unit using current relay, run capacitor, and start capacitor. (Copeland Refrig. Corp.)

578

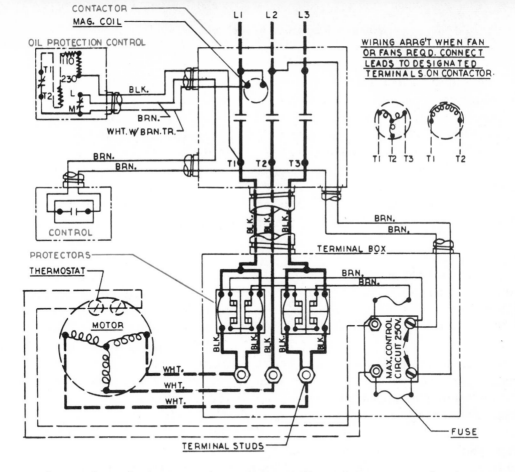

Fig. 15-19. Wiring diagram for 3-phase motor refrigeration unit. Note contactor, control, oil protection control, and motor circuit protectors.

Condensing units are provided with wiring diagrams either fastened to them or in the shipping crate. Fig. 15-18 shows a typical wiring diagram for a single-phase circuit; Fig. 15-19 shows a three-phase refrigerator motor wiring diagram. Correct connections are of extreme importance. Do not turn on the electrical power until you are positive the circuits are correct and all connectors are clean and tight.

Overloaded electrical circuits are dangerous. They may cause unit burn-outs, or electrical wiring fires.

A complete condensing unit installation is shown in Fig. 15-20. The use of an ohmmeter to check all circuits is a recommended procedure.

15-7 Installing Gauges

Before attempting any troubleshooting or service work on any unit, pressure

Fig. 15-20. A typical condensing unit installation. Note vibration damper, drier, sight glass, and electrical installation. (Johnston Refrig. Service)

gauges should be installed and the evaporator temperature should be checked.

A careful procedure must be followed when mounting gauges on a refrigerating system to insure a clean and dry system and long life for the gauges. These gauges are either screwed directly into the service valves, by means of a 1/8 in. pipe or a 1/4 in. pipe connection, or by short runs of 1/4 in. tubing with which the appropriate fittings are used.

A gauge manifold may also be used. Its installation is described in Par. 12-16.

15-8 Installing Gauge Manifold

A service device which has been of considerable aid to servicemen is a service gauge and testing manifold. It enables the serviceman to charge and discharge a system, check pressures, add oil, add liquid driers, bypass the compressor, unload the gauge lines of high pressure liquid and vapor and perform many other operations without replacing gauges and operating almost inaccessible service connections.

A typical manifold, as shown in Fig. 15-23, provides two gauge openings, three or four line connections and two shutoff valves that separate gauge openings from the center line connection. This manifold enables the serviceman to connect gauges to the system, and allows him to do practically all service and adjustment operations without removing the gauges.

The manifold usually has 1/4 in. square drive valve stems; some are equipped with handwheels. The three line attachment fittings are usually 1/4 in. MF.

The manifold is connected to the SSV (D) and the DSV (C) by means of 1/4 in. dia. copper tubing or flexible lines. Because most service valves have 1/8 in. FP gauge openings, two 1/8 in. MP x 1/4 in. MF half unions are installed in the service valves. Be sure the service valve stems are turned all the way out and that the valve is cleaned externally before removing the pipe line plugs and installing the half unions.

After the half unions are installed in the gauge openings, lines from the manifold are attached to these fittings. The line attached to the SSV (D) should be left one to two turns loose while the line to the DSV should be tightened. Then open both the manifold valves (A and B) 1/4 to 1/2 turns and cap the middle opening (E). Now turn the DSV (C) stem in 1/8 to 1/4 turn momentarily. A surge of high pressure refrigerant will then rush through the lines and the manifold and purge to the atmosphere at the loose connection at the SSV (D). The connection at the SSV (D) may now be tightened. This purging is necessary to remove air and moisture from the manifold and lines.

Carefully test for leaks while the manifold and its lines are under high pressure. CORRECT ANY LEAK IMMEDIATELY.

After the testing manifold has been installed as indicated the various service and testing operations may be performed as follows:

1. Observe operating pressures by:
   Closing valve A.
   Closing valve B.
   Cracking open back seat of valve C.
   Cracking open back seat of valve D.
2. Charge refrigerant through compressor by:
   Connecting refrigerant drum to E.
   Opening valve A.
   Closing valve B.
   Cracking open back seat of valve C.
   Closing front seat of valve D.
3. Purge receiver by:
   Closing valve A.
   Opening valve B.
   Back seating then crack open valve C.
4. Charge liquid into high side by:
   Connecting refrigerant drum to E.
   Closing valve A.
   Opening valve B.
   Mid-positioning valve C.

5. Build up pressure in low side for control setting or to test for leaks by:

Sealing E with seal cap.

Opening valve A.

Opening valve B.

Back seating then crack open valve C.

Mid-positioning valve D.

6. Charge oil through the compressor by:

Connecting oil supply to E.

Opening valve A.

Closing valve B.

Turning valve C all the way out.

Turning valve D all the way in.

After completing the service operations, the manifold is removed from the system in a manner that prevents a loss of refrigerant, or admittance of air. Turn the DSV (C) all the way out, then open both the manifold valves 1/4 to 1/2 turn. This arrangement will remove all the high pressure refrigerant from the line and the high pressure gauge. Now turn the SSV (D) stem all the way out and turn the manifold valve stem all the way in. Remove the lines from the service valve, remove the half unions from the service valves and install the service valve gauge opening plugs and tighten them. Immediately plug the lines and all other openings on the manifold to keep out dirt, moisture and air.

15-9 Removing Gauges

Loosen the packing nut one turn and turn the valve stem all the way out. Remove the gauge (using a wrench), fill the gauge opening with refrigerant oil, and then install the plug. After the plug is tightened firmly into its seat, turn the valve stem back in about 1/16 of a turn; then tighten the packing nut. The purpose of putting oil into the gauge opening is to serve as a lubricant to the valve stem and packing. The purpose of turning the valve stem back in 1/16 of a turn is to prevent the valve from

"freezing" against its seat. Such a condition occasionally leads to broken valve stems. Never tighten a cold gauge plug into a hot service valve. This may result in freezing of the plug to its seat. When using a service valve wrench on these valves, apply the turning force gradually. Adjustable end or fixed end wrenches are not recommended for service valve stems. Only the special socket wrenches, sometimes called keys, are to be used.

If the gauge plug is "frozen" in the service valve it can be loosened by first heating the outside of the service valve body with flame from a torch. This heating will cause the body to expand and will weaken the body thread grip on the plug. The wrench can then be used to loosen the valve stem.

15-10 Removing Air

After the tubing is installed the following should be done to prepare the unit for operation.

Air may be forced out of the lines using refrigerant or some clean, noncondensible gas such as carbon dioxide, nitrogen, CO_2, N_2, or Argon. NEVER USE OXYGEN. The air may also be removed by using the condensing unit compressor or a separate vacuum pump. The liquid lines must be free of air before the unit can be operated. The liquid lines should be cleaned before they are connected to the refrigerant control (usually a thermostatic expansion valve) and the condensing unit.

A method used by many installation men is to connect a bypass line from the liquid line to the suction line near the compressor, as shown in Fig. 15-21. This line is controlled by a one-way hand valve and may be used to pump a vacuum on the liquid line. This system is generally used when the evaporator coils have liquid hand service valves and suction line hand service valves at the evaporator coil. In detail, the compressor pumps a vacuum on the suction lines first; then with all the liquid line valves closed, the bypass valve is opened allowing the vacuum to be pumped on the liquid lines also. Do not put a drier

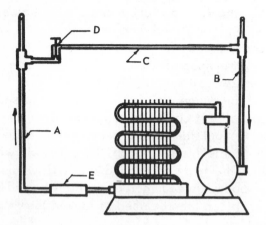

Fig. 15-21. Bypass line for emptying and evacuating liquid lines. A—Liquid line. B—Suction line. C—Bypass line. D—Shutoff valve. E—Drier.

in the system until most of the air has been removed. During the pump down (evacuation) and the purging, use a short length of tubing in place of the drier.

15-11 Purging the Liquid Line

After the system is assembled, the air should be removed from the liquid line, evaporator coil and suction line; in that order. It is best to do the purging with the system shut off. The reason for this order or sequence is because the condensing unit is usually charged with refrigerant and some of the refrigerant can be used to help remove air by pumping.

Dirt may be in the lines and in the evaporator coil, so it is advisable to disconnect the liquid line from the evaporator coil, cap the opening to the evaporator coil, and "crack" the liquid receiver service valve. The high pressure refrigerant will purge away dirt and most of the air from the liquid line. After this is done reconnect the liquid line to the evaporator coil.

15-12 Purging Evaporator Coil

After you have successfully purged the liquid line, disconnect the suction line from the evaporator coil. Plug the suction line to keep it as clean as possible. Crack the liquid receiver service valve, purge the evaporator coil, and then connect the suction line to the evaporator coil.

15-13 Purging Suction Line

Disconnect suction line from the suction service valve. Cap the suction service valve suction line opening. Crack the liquid receiver service valve and purge the suction line. Connect the suction line to the suction service valve.

These three steps will clean most of the solid particles, liquid and gas contaminants out of the tubing and evaporator coil. Some servicemen only perform the last step. However, the three-step method will do a better job.

15-14 Evacuating System

To remove air from the system the usual procedure is to pump the air out of the lines and the evaporator coil by using the compressor, or a vacuum pump.

To use the compressor proceed as follows: put a compound gauge on the compressor suction service valve and remove the refrigerant from the crankcase of the compressor by drawing a 20 in. vacuum or more, as shown in Fig. 15-22. Gauge manifolds are almost universally used. Fig. 15-23 shows a gauge manifold installation and how it may be used to purge, charge, bypass, obtain gauge readings, and the like. Be careful to avoid oil pumping. Then, install a purging line into the gauge opening of the discharge service valve. This purging line must be equipped with a hand shutoff valve. Run this line out-of-doors. Avoid purging refrigerant vapor into the room where the condensing unit

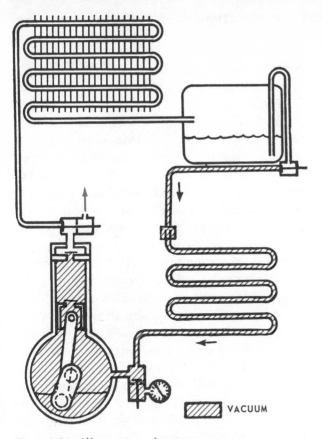

Fig. 15-22. *Illustration showing compressor evacuating liquid line, evaporator coil, suction line, and compressor crankcase to open air.*

is located as refrigerant vapors may be harmful to people in the room. Turn the discharge service valve all the way in, shutting off the condenser openings. Now turn the suction service valve almost all the way out and pump a vacuum on the suction lines. The air being removed will be discharged out the purging line. Fig. 15-24 shows a gauge manifold and a vacuum pump connected to a small hermetic commercial system. After creating as high a vacuum as possible with the compressor, which means that 70 to 75 percent of the air in the suction line has been removed, the refrigerant valve farthest from the compressor on the low side, may be cracked slightly. This will permit a very small quantity of the refrigerant to come down the suction line. When this has been pumped from the system, the amount of air left in the suction line will be negligible (about 5 percent). A second refrigerant flush, followed by evacuating will reduce the air left in the suction line to about 1 percent.

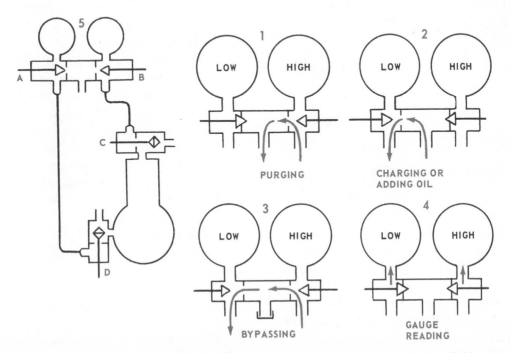

Fig. 15-23. *Schematic of gauge manifold installation on open type compressor. A—Manifold suction valve. B—Manifold discharge valve. C—Discharge service valve. D—Suction service valve. 1—Purging. 2—Charging or adding oil. 3—Bypassing. 4—Gauge reading. 5—In the manifold illustrated all valves are in middle position and all passages are open.*

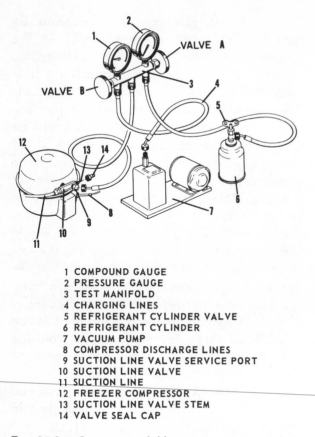

1 COMPOUND GAUGE
2 PRESSURE GAUGE
3 TEST MANIFOLD
4 CHARGING LINES
5 REFRIGERANT CYLINDER VALVE
6 REFRIGERANT CYLINDER
7 VACUUM PUMP
8 COMPRESSOR DISCHARGE LINES
9 SUCTION LINE VALVE SERVICE PORT
10 SUCTION LINE VALVE
11 SUCTION LINE
12 FREEZER COMPRESSOR
13 SUCTION LINE VALVE STEM
14 VALVE SEAL CAP

Fig. 15-24. Gauge manifold, vacuum pump, and refrigerant cylinder connected to small commercial hermetic motor-compressor.

After a system has been purged of air, balance the pressure in the liquid line with refrigerant (gauge to read 0 psig) open liquid line, quickly install the drier, and then seal the connections.

15-15 Testing for Leaks

After these two lines have been cleaned of air, the unit is ready to operate, but it should first be very carefully checked for leaks. To locate leaks, build up a pressure in all parts of the system. Two methods may be used:

1. Using an inert gas.
2. Using refrigerant under pressure.

In case a low pressure refrigerant is used, or if the local code specifies a pressure test above the refrigerant's vapor pressure, some other gas may be used for testing. Carbon dioxide, nitrogen or argon are satisfactory. CAUTION: NEVER USE OXYGEN, AIR OR ANY FLAMMABLE GAS FOR THIS PURPOSE AS AN EXPLOSION MAY TAKE PLACE. This testing should include the liquid line, suction line and all other parts installed by the installation man, except the condensing unit proper of this particular installation. Install a high pressure gauge only (a compound gauge may be ruined by the high pressure). After building up a medium (30 to 100 psig) pressure, close the cylinder valve. If the pressure gauge shows no drop in pressure after an hour or more, you should raise the test pressure to 200 to 300 psig and test again. Do not exceed the pressures as prescribed by the National Code, see Chapter 27, as the excessive pressure may rupture some part of the system. If the pressure shows no decrease during one hour to 24 hours period, the system is safe to operate.

Purge test gas from the system, evacuate by the two or three step method and the unit should be ready to operate.

Testing for leaks using system refrigerant is the most common non-code practice. It is convenient, there is no need for an inert gas cylinder, purging and evacuating is not needed after testing for leaks and the leak testers are a standard part of each installation and serviceman's tool kit. To do this proceed as follows:

Install a pressure gauge in the system. The liquid line valve should be opened just enough to build up a 15 to 30 psig pressure throughout the system.

Test for leaks using one or more of the following:

1. Soapsuds.
2. Halide torch.
3. Electronic leak detector.
4. Liquid tracer.

These tests are described in Chapter 12. A halide torch unit is shown in Fig. 15-25. This apparatus is an oxygen-acetylene unit which can be used for welding, brazing, soldering or leak testing. Only the acetylene cylinder is used when leak testing.

If no leaks are detected at low pressure, increase system pressure to the full pressure of the refrigerant (vapor only) and test for leaks again.

If a leak is found, purge the system to atmospheric pressure, open the system at the leak point, inspect all parts, replace any defective parts, clean and assemble. If a soldered or brazed joint is leaking, take the joint completely apart, clean, and assemble. Then repeat the leak detecting procedure.

If no leaks are found, this part of the unit is ready to operate.

Fig. 15-26 shows an electronic leak detector in use.

15-16 Checking Unit Before Starting

If the motor control has not already been adjusted for installation, this should be done before the system is set in operation. The settings of the motor controls will vary with the demands of the cabinets and with various kinds of refrigerant used.

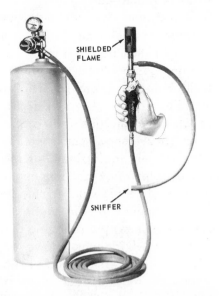

Fig. 15-25. Acetylene cylinder, regulator, hose, and halide leak detector used for checking leaks of most refrigerants. Flame will turn blue-green if there is a leak. (Linde Div., Union Carbide Corp.)

Fig. 15-26. Electronic leak detector being used to check self-contained water cooler. (General Electric Co.)

Be sure the water is turned on, if it is a water-cooled condensing unit, and that the fuses in the electric circuit are the proper size. It is good practice to install recording thermometers, voltmeters, and ammeters on a unit for the first 24 to 48 hours of its operation. The records will reveal malfunctions.

15-17 Checking Refrigerant Charge

One of the most detrimental conditions which may occur in a refrigeration system is to operate the refrigeration unit without sufficient refrigerant. It will result in abuse to valves in the unit, usually results in continuous motor operation, overloading of motor-compressor and poor refrigeration. A lack of refrigerant will be indicated by an increase in the liquid line and drier temperature. A heated drier will release some of its moisture and cause a wet system. Several methods may be used to determine whether or not a refrigerator has an adequate supply of refrigerant.

In a low side float system the lack of refrigerant usually shows up at the most remote coil, or the coil which is the greatest vertical distance from the liquid receiver. If the refrigerant is low, this coil will not have enough liquid refrigerant to close the float valve. As a result, the coil will make a continuous hissing sound while the refrigerant vapor flows through it. This condition will be accompanied by a warm liquid line which may be several degrees warmer than room temperature. This may be easily checked by touching the two lines where they are attached to the coil.

A dry or expansion valve system is more difficult to check for quantity of refrigerant. The first indication of insufficient refrigerant may be obtained from the appearance of the expansion valve body. Under normal conditions the body of the valve frosts over evenly, as far back as the liquid line nut. In case the system has insufficient refrigerant, the expansion valve body adjacent to the liquid line will not frost. This frost method cannot be used for above freezing coil operation conditions.

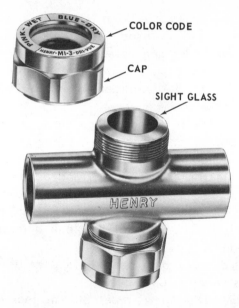

Fig. 15-28. Double part or "see-through" sight glass for larger liquid line. Unit also indicates dryness of refrigerant. Device has brazed connections. Note dryness code on the seal cap (pink for wet, blue for dry).

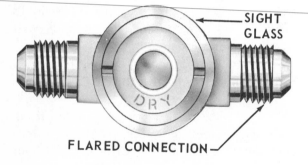

Fig. 15-27. Sight glass which also indicates if the refrigerant in the system is wet or dry. If the refrigerant is dry, the word "dry" will appear, but if the refrigerant has too much moisture in it the word "wet" will appear. Bubbles indicate lack of refrigerant. Note flare connectors.   (Henry Valve Co.)

A common method of checking for quantity of refrigerant is to check the quantity actually in the liquid receiver and condenser. One way to do this is to determine the high side head pressure.

If the unit is water-cooled, the head pressure should correspond to refrigerant temperatures approximately 10 F. higher than the temperature of the water leaving the condenser. The temperature of the wa-

ter in this case should be checked at the point where it leaves the condenser and not at the end of a long drain pipe. If the head pressure, as indicated on the gauge, is below normal as much as 10 psig, lack of refrigerant is indicated.

A very popular way to check for sufficient refrigerant charge is to mount a sight glass in the liquid line and note if there are any gas bubbles going up the liquid line. Bubbles indicate insufficient refrigerant. Fig. 15-27 shows a sight glass which is also a moisture indicator. Figs. 15-28 and 15-29 show see-through sight glasses for larger liquid lines. At low head pressure, bubbles may appear regardless of the amount of refrigerant in the system. If no bubbles appear in the sight gauge at the above pressures, the machine probably has sufficient refrigerant. However, if a restriction is in the line ahead of the sight gauge, bubbles may appear even though there is sufficient refrigerant in the system. If possible, the sight glass should be mounted between the receiver and the dehydrator.

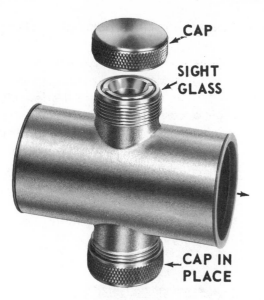

Fig. 15-29. "See-through" or double part sight glass. Both caps are removed, and a light source is used (flashlight) to see if there are bubbles in liquid refrigerant flow. (Mueller Brass Co.)

Some machines are equipped with refrigerant liquid level indicators such as petcocks mounted in the side of the liquid receiver at definite heights. If the petcock is opened and liquid refrigerant comes out, the level of the refrigerant is at least up to this height. Two petcocks are usually provided. When opened, vapor should come from the top petcock and liquid refrigerant should come from the lower one.

In the liquid receiver type of water-cooled unit, in which the water coils are located within the receiver, the amount of refrigerant within the system may be checked by determining the temperature difference of the receiver shell. The division point between the part of the receiver filled with hot vapor and the part filled with cold liquid refrigerant will be indicated by a temperature difference which may be easily checked by feeling the receiver with your hand.

Another method to determine the quantity of liquid refrigerant in the liquid receiver consists of turning off the cooling water to the condenser, and allowing the

compressor to operate. If the liquid line warms up quickly it is an indication of insufficient refrigerant. Also it may be noted in this connection that the head pressure rises quickly after the water is shut off. If the compressor is stopped and the head pressure drops rapidly, it is another indication of a small amount of liquid refrigerant in the liquid receiver.

Still another method of checking for the quantity of liquid refrigerant consists of shutting the machine down and purging the liquid receiver. Boiling of the refrigerant in the liquid receiver when the pressure is reduced, will cause that part of the receiver which is filled with liquid to get cold, sweat and perhaps frost over. This method should only be used as a last resort because it wastes refrigerant.

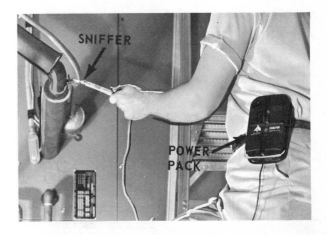

Fig. 15-30. Portable electronic leak detector being used to locate leaks in system. (Bacharach Indus. Inst. Co., Sub. of American Bosch Arma Corp.)

Lack of refrigerant is likely due to a leak in the equipment. A careful check should be made of all joints and parts that could possibly leak before the unit is recharged and put into service. The electronic type leak detector is desirable for detecting these small leaks. Fig. 15-30 shows a portable electronic leak detector in use. Fig. 15-31 shows a transistorized portable electronic leak detector.

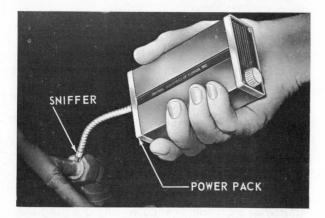

Fig. 15-31. Battery operated transistorized portable electronic leak detector in use. (Thermal Industries of Florida, Inc.)

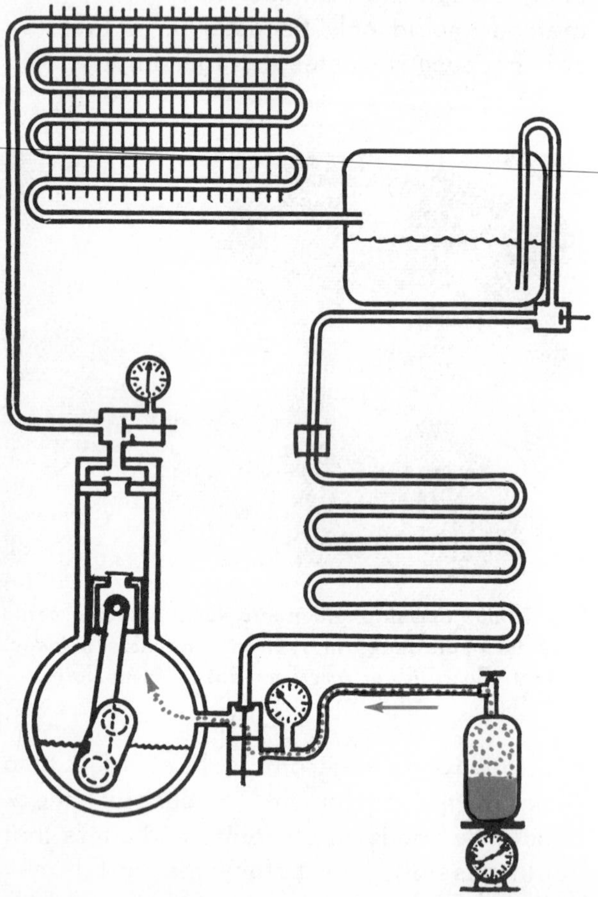

15-18 Charging Commercial System

Charging commercial systems is similar to charging domestic machines and is usually done by charging into the low side. To charge a commercial system the storage cylinder should be attached to the gauge manifold, or the charging can be done as shown in Fig. 15-32. Purging and charging apparatus combinations are popular with servicemen. Fig. 15-33 shows a complete unit with charging table, vacuum pump, vacuum gauge, etc.

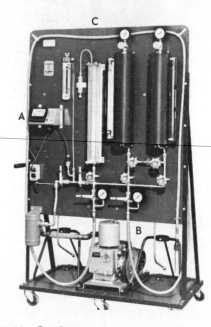

Fig. 15-33. Combination vacuum pump unit. A—Electronic vacuum gauge. B—Vacuum pump. C—Charging tube. (Airserco Mfg. Co.)

The charging lines must be clean, and purged to rid them of air, and connections tested for leaks prior to the actual charging operation. Remember to wear goggles when transferring refrigerants.

The principle of operation is to allow the service cylinder to become a temporary evaporator coil in the system. As the compressor runs, it will remove refrigerant vapor from the cylinder as well as continuing to remove vapor from the evaporator coils.

Fig. 15-32. Method of charging system. Refrigerant cylinder is connected to service valve. After purging, SSV is turned all the way in, unit is started and cylinder valve is opened just enough to keep low side pressure within safe limits. Note weighing scale for indicating amount of refrigerant being put into system.

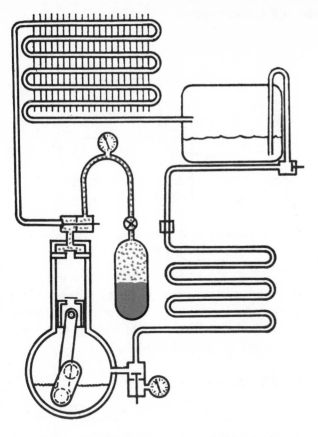

Fig. 15-34. Charging small system through high pressure side. Compressor is used to build up slightly higher than condensing pressure in cylinder and then cylinder is inverted and DSV turned out a turn or two. Small pressure difference will force cylinder refrigerant liquid into condenser receiver.

Charging may be speeded up by using the suction service valve to reduce the flow from the regular evaporating coils and speed the evaporation in the service cylinder. Hot water may be applied to the service cylinder to help speed the evaporation. The low side pressure should be kept at normal levels as too high a pressure may overwork the compressor. Pressures which are too low may cause oil pumping.

This system insures clean refrigerant due to the distilling action during evaporation of the refrigerant. A serviceman must be present at all times during the charging. A service cylinder must not be left connected into a system.

IT IS VERY IMPORTANT THAT LIQUID REFRIGERANT NOT BE ALLOWED TO REACH THE COMPRESSOR. The liquid is not compressible and the compressor valves, and even the bearings and rods, may be ruined if the compressor should pump liquid.

Although it is not usually recommended, some servicemen do put liquid refrigerant into the high pressure side of the system. This is a dangerous practice because dynamic hydraulic pressures are possible which may rupture the lines, and cause considerable damage. However, this system can be used to put the initial charge into a system if done very carefully. If one inverts a cylinder and it has a higher pressure than the system, liquid refrigerant will be forced into the system.

If the unit is water-cooled, the pressure, in the liquid receiver with the water flowing, will be sufficiently below that of the pressure in the cylinder, to permit opening of the two valves after the charging line has been purged. The pressure difference will force refrigerant from the cylinder into the system. If the unit is air-cooled the pressure in the refrigerant drum must be increased. This may be done by using the compressor to pump vaporized refrigerant into the cylinder and increase its pressure. In detail this method is as follows:

1. Connect the refrigerant cylinder to the gauge manifold or to the discharge service valve, as shown in Fig. 15-34.
2. Run the compressor with the discharge service valve turned all the way in, until a pressure of 125 to 135 lbs. is built up in the cylinder.
3. Stop the compressor.
4. Invert the refrigerant cylinder (be careful not to injure the line).
5. Turn the discharge service valve part way out.

High pressure on the surface of the refrigerant in the cylinder will force liquid into the system. While the liquid is flowing into the high side, a gurgling sound may be heard. If this sound ceases abruptly, it means that the cylinder has been emptied. Use this method only if all the refrigerant has been removed from the system. The amount of refrigerant to be put into a system that is being serviced for lack of sufficient refrigerant must be governed by the serviceman's knowledge concerning the size of the system, the apparent amount of refrigerant in the system, and the kind of refrigerant used. Fig. 15-35 is a table of approximate refrigerant amounts which may be added to the system.

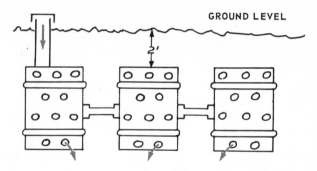

Fig. 15-36. *Method of disposing of used refrigerant and used refrigerant oil.*

	R-12		R-22		R-502	
	Flooded	Dry	Flooded	Dry	Flooded	Dry
1/2 hp Unit	3	1 1/2	3	1 1/2	3	1 1/2
1 hp Unit	6	3	6	3	6	3
1 1/2 hp Unit	9	4 1/2	9	4 1/2	9	4 1/2
2 hp Unit	12	6	12	6	12	6

Fig. 15-35. *Table of approximate number of pounds of refrigerant which may be safely added to system which is low on refrigerant.*

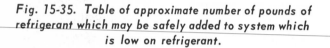

15-19 Discharging System

When it is necessary to discharge a system for repair purposes, the refrigerant if not in excessive quantity, should be discarded, purging it out the nearest window by means of a 1/4 in. flexible line or a copper line. Place an oil trap in the line to make sure the oil in the refrigerant will not damage surrounding property.

This method cannot be used for ammonia (R-717) because of the odor. Most localities forbid purging refrigerant into a sewer system. If the refrigerant is to be put back into the same machine, or if facilities are available for distilling it, it may be temporarily stored in a clean refrigerant cylinder. Remember that the refrigerant will always have an oil content. Some large companies save all refrigerant, redistill, and process it for further use.

To get rid of refrigerants removed from systems stored in service cylinders,

it is possible to purge the refrigerant into perforated containers buried in the ground, as shown in Fig. 15-36. The ground absorbs the oil and the refrigerant.

15-20 Starting a System

You should follow a planned procedure when starting a new system or starting a system which has been shut down for a period of time. Avoid overloading electrical circuits, compressor, and motor.

Make a first check on the electrical characteristics of the power-in circuit.

1. Be sure the phase is correct.
2. Be sure the voltage is correct.
3. Be sure the power leads are large enough. If you have any doubts, the electrical utility company will assist.
4. Connect a voltmeter and an ammeter in the circuit. Recording types are preferred.

By using hand valves, load the compressor with a normal back pressure during start up. Install the gauge manifold to check pressures. If the condensing circuit is water-cooled, be sure the water circuit is turned on. Remember, it is just as hard on the compressor to have too low a given pressure as too high (oil pumping, etc.).

Once the unit is started, check the electrical meters, the pressure gauges, and the water flow as soon as possible. Shut down the unit at the first sign of trouble. If possible, record the electrical characteristics, the pressures and the temperature during the first 24 hours to one week. These charts will serve as a good future reference.

15-21 Starting Flooded System

Enough low side float flooded systems are still in service to warrant an explanation of how to start them.

Inspect the unit:

1. If it is a conventional compressor (electrical power-off) turn flywheel by hand to determine if motor, fan, belt, etc., are free to move.
2. Check compressor and motor mounting.
3. Remove or loosen hold-down bolts.
4. Check electrical circuit for good wiring, proper sized fuses, tight electrical connectors, etc.

Open all liquid line and liquid receiver valves. Start compressor. When starting a completely warm installation of this kind, if the evaporator coil low side pressure is permitted to go into the crankcase of the compressor unreduced, an excessive load may be imposed upon the compressor and motor and serious harm is likely to result. Since the compressor pulls down the low side pressure rapidly, the following procedure is suggested: after starting the unit, open the suction line valve on the various evaporator coils, one at a time at 10 to 15 minute intervals. Open each valve slowly. It should take at least two minutes to open each suction line valve two turns. This procedure gives the compressor time to reduce the pressure on the low side to close to the normal level.

After all evaporator coil valves have been opened and everything is running normally, the serviceman should stay on the premises for at least an hour checking the operation. He should return within 24 hours to determine how the system is performing. Checking of the system should include high and low side pressures, vibration of unit, amount of water flow in case of a water-cooled system, temperature of suction lines at evaporator coils to find out if they are flooding back due to out-of-calibration floats or a leaky needle. Also repeat the leak test. It is recommended that an installation of this kind be checked with a 24-hour thermograph after the unit has settled down to a routine cycle.

15-22 Starting Dry System

Thermostatic expansion valves are open when they are warm. To start the system with the full load of all the coils on it, the compressor may be overloaded, as in the low side float installation. Therefore, all liquid line hand shutoff valves should be closed and the condensing unit started. Liquid line manifold valves may then be opened one at a time, requiring two minutes to turn valves two revolutions. It is an important precaution in refrigeration never to overload the compressor even for short intervals. After one coil has been opened and after a 15-minute interval of operation, the coil has a chance to cool down somewhat, tending to make the expansion valve throttle off the refrigerant. This gives the compressor a chance to gradually reduce its load. The other coils may then be brought into service in the same way.

The serviceman, after starting the unit, should check high and low side pressures, amount of water flow in case it is a water-cooled system, and operation of each individual expansion valve. He should also determine if the adjustment is correct for each coil; that is, frost or sweating on suction line will indicate whether or not the expansion valve is opened too far or not far enough. Another important procedure or routine to be followed at this time is to determine whether or not the system has enough refrigerant. This should be done as described in Par. 15-17.

Test for leaks after the unit has operated for 24 hours. Maintain records for future maintenance or service operations.

15-23 Code Installations

Many localities have definite codes or rules and regulations covering the installation of refrigerating equipment. Domestic units are usually not included because these units are self-contained and use only small quantities of refrigerant.

In commercial installations, where the units are assembled on the premises, or where the hp or refrigerant needs exceed certain maxiums, there are requirements that must be met to insure uniformity of performance, and to make the installation safe. Installation codes also protect the purchaser from careless installations.

Most cities have codes. Some of the high points of these codes are: only licensed refrigeration contractors may install commercial equipment, a permit must be obtained for each installation, each installation must be inspected by civic authorities, lines must be labeled as to refrigerant, certain safety devices must be installed in system, condensing unit must be installed in a safe place, electrical and plumbing work must be according to code and by licensed electricians and plumbers respectively, system must be tested under certain pressures on both high side and low side, and must be free from leaks. See Chapter 27 for National Refrigeration Code.

The National Code and Local Codes are based on experiences with many installations. The codes provide for safety for the installer, owner, user, public and should be carefully followed.

15-24 Installing a Condensing Unit

The condensing unit must be firmly mounted to avoid a sudden shift that would endanger the refrigerant lines. Precautions to be observed vary with the kind of refrigerant, and situation in which unit is to be placed.

The condensing unit must be placed where it cannot be damaged. It should have a protective cage around it (small unit) or be placed in a separate room. The area should be well ventilated to permit escape of refrigerants in case the unit develops a leak (windows for smaller units, forced exhaust for larger units). Also larger units must be protected from fire damage by using fireproof self-closing doors, etc. Electrical work must be done according to code and by a licensed electrical contractor. Plumbing work must be done according to code and by a licensed Master Plumber.

To prevent violent rupturing or an explosion of the condensing unit due to excessive pressure, the code specifies:

1. High pressure cut-outs to stop motor.
2. Pressure relief valves or rupture disks to dissipate discharge slowly. These safety openings are piped to outside by way of copper pipe connected by silver brazed joints. Spring loaded safety valves and/or fuse plugs are used (for those cases where the unit may become overheated because of fire).

All refrigerant lines should be permanently labeled with signs identifying refrigerant.

15-25 Installing an Evaporator Coil

The Code recommends limits of refrigerant for evaporating coils that would expose people to the refrigerant in case of leaks. Coils installed in air ducts must be cooled with a brine rather than refrigerant on some installations.

The evaporator coil should be mounted firmly in the cabinet and it should be protected to avoid injury to the system. Refrigerant lines should be of hard copper pipe (L or K) or should be protected with conduit where there is possibility of injury to the system.

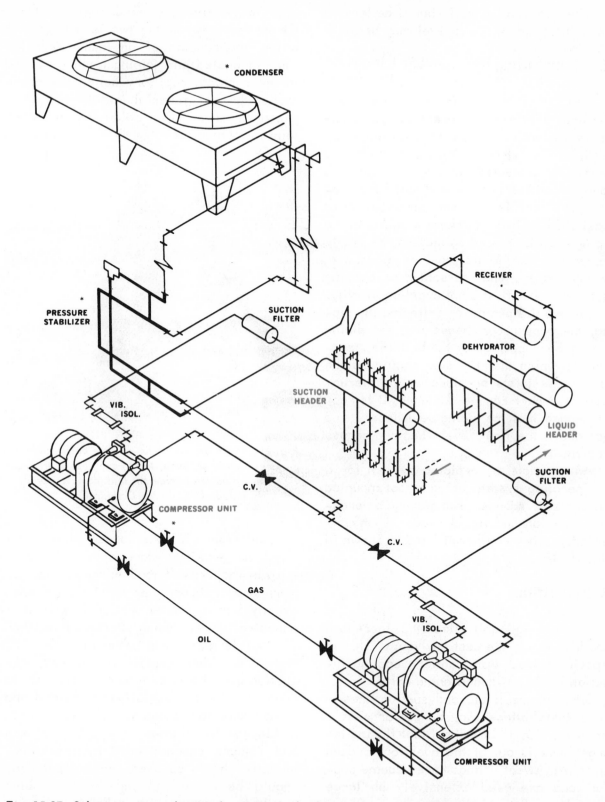

Fig. 15-37. Schematic piping diagram for commercial refrigerating system using roof mounted air-cooled condenser, two motor-compressors and suction and liquid header each connected to six refrigerant lines. (Dunham-Bush, Inc.)

The evaporating coil should be leveled when installed. A spirit level may be used.

15-26 Installing Refrigerant Lines

The codes attempt to specify refrigerant lines that are permanent and safe. The codes recommend that strong piping be used, type K (strongest) or L, and that the piping be protected by adequate guards. Some localities recommend that hard copper pipe that is exposed should have at least .065 in. wall thickness. Joints in the piping must be placed so they can be easily inspected. The joints must be made with strong fittings and the solder or brazing material used must be of excellent quality.

To avoid pinching or crimping the piping, the code recommends that the piping always be supported by the building structure, meaning that the pipe should not be run across joists or studs where the unsupported part can be damaged. It is recommended that the piping be at least 7 1/2 feet above the floor level when run across a room.

An example of a piping system for a refrigerating system using a roof mounted air-cooled condenser, two motor-compressors, suction and liquid header each connected to six refrigerant lines is shown in Fig. 15-37

15-27 Fittings

Commercial unit size has increased steadily during the past few years. This is especially true with comfort cooling installations in air-conditioning units.

Sizes of the liquid and suction lines in these installations may be as large as 2 and 6 in. OD. It is evident that flaring the large lines is out of the question. Brazed joints with sweat fittings have become popular and are used extensively on large units. These fittings, as described in Chapter 2, consist of a drop-forged or extruded copper fitting with a recess of sufficient size to receive the hard copper tubing. Clearance between the two is a matter of a few thousandths of an inch. When the joint is heated and joining material is fed to the surface, capillary action draws the molten joining material into the space between the two. Upon soldifying, a strong joint is formed.

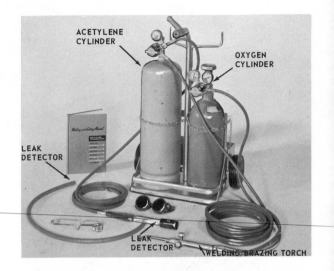

Fig. 15-38. An oxyacetylene welding outfit including pressure regulator, hose, torch, goggles, spark lighter, and a halide refrigerant leak detector torch. (Linde Div., Union Carbide Corp.)

Soldering of hard copper pipe joints must be expertly done or considerable trouble may result (bad joints and leaks). Hard drawn copper pipe which is seamless usually has a greater wall thickness than annealed copper tubing. It comes in 10 or 20 foot lengths rather than in rolls. The ends are either capped or plugged. The suction line should be mounted with a slight drop in the horizontal runs toward the compressor to provide for oil return. When making an installation of this kind, fluxes and solders recommended by the manufacturer should be used. Joining surfaces should be clean and ends of the tubing should be square to prevent flux or joining metal from running into the tubing. See Par. 2-16.

15-28 Special Tubing

Copper tubing normally comes with no special finish provided for the inside or the exterior surface. This permits the copper to become corroded if exposed to certain corrosive elements, such as running the tubing through liquid, food, beverages or through air saturated with acid fumes or corrosive elements. In places where sanitation is of primary importance, tubing with tinned surface may be used.

Where the tubing is used to convey beverages such as beer between kegs and dispensers, soft drinks, carbonated beverages, etc., many local codes require the use of special tubing. One such tubing is block tin tubing. Another is stainless steel.

15-29 Refrigerant Line Connections

There are two common methods of making a multiple installation of tubing.

One method is to have a common liquid line and common suction line and to tap the various evaporator coil liquid and suction lines into it at the most convenient points.

Another method is to use a clustering system where various lines are brought to a common point and connected through a hand valve to a manifold. A larger suction and liquid line is run from the manifolds to the compressor. This method is not strictly adhered to in cases where one coil is at some distance from the box, necessitating a duplication of long runs. The manifold of a code installation is usually mounted in a steel cabinet and is located on a wall near the condensing unit.

AN IMPORTANT ITEM TO BE KEPT IN MIND AT ALL TIMES IS THAT EVERY FITTING USED, AND EVERY BEND PUT INTO THE REFRIGERANT AND SUCTION LINES, DECREASES THE EFFICIENCY OF THE INSTALLATION. THE NUMBER OF BENDS AND FITTINGS SHOULD BE LIMITED AS MUCH AS POSSIBLE.

Remember that inner parts of valves, driers, filters, sight glasses, etc., should be removed while tubing is being brazed to it, or the part wrapped with a wet cloth. Take care not to allow moisture to enter the valve.

15-30 Welding Equipment

Gas welding equipment needed for refrigeration installations consists of an oxygen cylinder, acetylene cylinder, regulators and gauges, hose, and a torch, as shown in Fig. 15-38. This equipment may be used for soldering, brazing, and welding the various parts of refrigeration systems. Before doing any welding the local code on welding should be thoroughly studied and understood. Never operate a welding outfit near flammables. CAUTION: NEVER USE OXYGEN, ACETYLENE, OR ANY OTHER WELDING FUELS, FOR THE PURPOSE OF DEVELOPING PRESSURE IN REFRIGERATION TUBING, PIPING, OR EQUIPMENT. Carbon dioxide, nitrogen and argon are safe gases which may be used for developing pressures in refrigeration lines. A severe explosion may result if welding gases or oxygen (air) are used.

Electric welding equipment may also be used. It may be either AC or DC. AC equipment is popular because small portable units are available. A unit using 240V feed-in can use 1/8 in. electrodes. Steel, copper, cast iron, and aluminum can be welded successfully. Arc welding is a popular way to reweld hermetic domes. CAUTION: THE WELDER SHOULD WEAR APPROVED TYPE ARC WELDING MASK AND GLOVES.

15-31 Soldering Equipment

The refrigeration serviceman uses soldering for many jobs. Acetylene-air torches furnish a clean flame at a temperature of 2500 F. With compressed air, the torch flame temperature is approximately 2500 to 2800 F. Acetylene is supplied in cylinders of 40 cu. ft. capacity and 10 cu. ft. capacity. A 3/16 square valve stem valve is located in the cylinder and a fixed adjustment or variable adjustment regulator is attached to the cylinder valve. A 3/16 in. inside diameter fabric reinforced (red color) hose connects the regulator to the torch. The torch is made of brass, has a wooden handle, and is usually equipped with a shutoff needle valve. Various size tips are available. Although the flame temperature is the same for each type, the amount of heat is greater with some tips as the tip hole or orifice is made larger. See Fig. 15-39. These torches are used for soldering, silver brazing, brass brazing, etc. They do not produce a high enough temperature to do successful welding. It is important to follow the following safety precautions:

1. Always use acetylene at a pressure of 15 lbs. per sq. in. or less as higher pressure may cause an explosion due to the instability of the acetylene at higher pressures.
2. Always use the cylinder in a vertical position because the cylinder has a porous filler wet with acetone in which the acetylene is dissolved. If the cylinder is laying down while in use, some acetone may flow out, causing a dirty flame and the acetone may grease up the regulator and valves.
3. Keep the flame away from any flammable substance such as oil, wood, paper, paint, cleansing fluids, methyl chloride, barrels, or cylinders which may have contained flammable material at one time. Use an asbestos sheet or board to protect surfaces that might be discolored or scorched when using the torch, such as assembling piping along a wall.
4. Always light the torch with a flint lighter, as matches or a cigarette lighter may bring your hand too close to the flame.

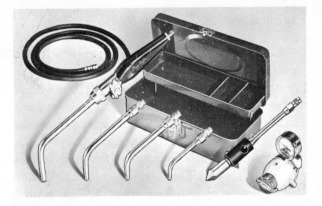

Fig. 15-39. Air-acetylene soldering and brazing outfit. From left to right; hose, large tip and handle, three other tips, soldering copper, and regulator.

15-32 Refrigerant Line Valves

All line valves are to be hand operated. The codes require that these valves be of such construction that anyone may shut them off on short notice without the need of special tools. The valve uses a handwheel mounted permanently on the valve. These valves are provided with brackets whereby they may be attached firmly to a panel. The valves commonly come in two styles:

1. Two-way valves.
2. One-way valve.

One type of two-way valve shuts off just one of the three connections made to the valve. The other two, remaining uncontrolled, permit the passage of refrigerant to the remainder of the system.

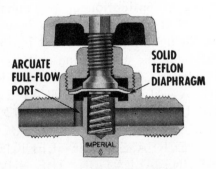

Fig. 15-40. One-way hand valve used with flared connections. (Imperial Eastman Corp.)

The other type valve is a one-way valve and stops the flow of refrigerant when turned in (clockwise). A flared type is shown in Fig. 15-40. Fig. 15-41 shows a brazed type of one-way valve. Older style valves were of the lead and graphite packing type. Packless valves are now used extensively. The operation of the code installed unit, upon starting, to insure long and efficient refrigeration, is the same as described for starting non-code installations.

Fig. 15-41. One-way hand valve designed for brazed connections. (Henry Valve Co.)

15-33 Testing Code Installations

Code authorities require that permits be obtained before an installation can be made or a major service operation performed on commercial units. Specifications of the proposed job are presented. Permits are not issued unless the specifications presented meet code requirements.

On completion of the work an inspector is called, and his sanction must be given before the unit may be run. Some localities require that the refrigeration installation men be licensed.

The inspector upon reaching the premises, checks the installation to see if all the work has been done according to specifications and code, and then proceeds to test the system. His testing primarily consists of checking for leaks and checking the unit for safety. He does this by building up the required pressures in the high and low sides of the system. These pressures vary with the kind of refrigerant used in the system. If no leaks are indicated at the pressures established, the inspector sometimes checks the system further by producing a vacuum on all of the systems. If this vacuum is maintained over a certain period of time the installation is approved.

After the system has been approved, the installation man should make a record of the running behavior of the unit for at least 24 hours. Fig. 15-42 shows a pressure recorder, making a 24 hour record of the low side pressures of an installation. Any variations in cycles reveals needed adjustments.

Fig. 15-42. A 24 hour recording thermometer. Charts should be dated and kept for future reference. (Marshalltown Mfg., Inc.)

15-34 Servicing Commercial Units

Modern commercial refrigerating units are available in a great variety of forms. Chapters 13 and 14 describe the design, construction and operation of various mechanisms.

Small units such as self-contained beverage coolers of hermetic design are serviced in the same manner as the domestic systems. Details are given in Chapter 12.

Some commercial installations use an open system with motors, belts, and open compressors. Many use hermetic condensing units.

The servicing of the larger commercial systems is controlled in most communities by the local Refrigeration Code. Any major repairs or changes to a commercial system can only be done by licensed contractors and the service work done must be checked by the local community refrigeration inspector.

The plumbing and electrical service work should be subcontracted to licensed plumbers and electrical contractors.

The servicing of commercial installations in some respects is similar to that of the domestic units. However, the use of multiple evaporator coils on a single compressor, increased use of the thermostatic expansion valve, rather universal application of water-cooled condensing units, all necessitate a rather detailed study of how these commercial units may be serviced.

The troubles encountered come under various headings such as, no refrigeration, continuous running, excessive cost of operation, poor refrigerating temperatures, frosted suction lines, etc.

15-35 Service Engineers Equipment

Two major items with which a service engineer must be concerned are: 1. Obtaining and using high quality tools. 2. Keeping complete records of each and every job.

Most companies provide a service engineer with a panel truck or pickup truck equipped with major items such as: 1. Refrigerants. 2. Vacuum pumps. 3. Tubing and piping. 4. Combination soldering, brazing, and welding outfit. 5. Supply of replacement parts: a. Controls. b. Fittings. 6. Oil. 7. Leak detectors, especially electronic tester.

The service engineer is usually expected to furnish his own tool kit. Chapter 2 describes many of the tools needed. These tools should be of good to excellent quality. Two operations which will speed up the service engineer's work are:

1. Keep tools clean. This action will result in better work, faster work, and longer life tools.

2. Keep tools in one certain place in a tool kit or in the truck. They should be placed in such a place and position that the service engineer may pick up the desired tool in the correct way without looking.

15-36 Servicing Condensing Units

Condensing units come under several divisions: 1. Open type compressor. 2. Serviceable hermetic motor-compressor (field serviceable compressors). 3. Welded hermetic motor-compressor (non-field serviceable compressors).

Compressor types: 1. Reciprocating, 2. Rotary or 3. Centrifugal. The condensers used may be either: 1. Air-cooled. 2. Water-cooled. The variety of mechanisms and the variety of applications presents a great challenge to the service engineer. Fortunately, in spite of the great variety there are certain basic problems all these condensing units have in common: 1. Compressor efficiency. 2. Condenser efficiency (Air-cooled, Water-cooled). 3. Refrigerant charge. 4. Refrigerant cleanliness. 5. Electric circuit problems. The compressor may be tested for efficiency as described in Chapter 12 but such things as "lack of refrigerant" present new problems.

An air-cooled condenser gives the same symptoms when there is a lack of refrigerant as those explained in Chapter 12 but the water-cooled type presents a different problem. The water flow should be so adjusted that the temperature rise is no more than 15 deg. as the water goes through the condenser.

Because of similar variations throughout the mechanism, the study is divided into individual parts of the condensing unit.

The condensing unit should be cleaned

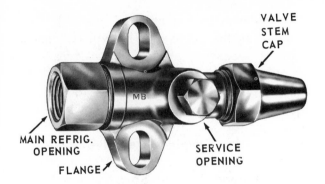

Fig. 15-43. Compressor service valve with slotted flange holes and protective cap over valve stem. (Mueller Brass Co.)

externally as thoroughly as possible, using cleaning cloth and a nonflammable, nontoxic cleaning fluid. Belts should be checked for alignment and tautness.

If there is a decided metallic pounding sound occurring regularly in the compressor, the customer should be informed of this, and a recommendation made that repairs be made as soon as possible.

The amount of refrigerant in the system should be carefully checked according to the methods explained in Chapter 12. The motor control should be inspected to determine whether it trips freely and whether the points, if any, are clean. Dirty or pitted contact points should be replaced.

15-37 Servicing Open Type Units

As all open type compressor units are similar, the general instructions which follow will apply to nearly all of them. There are still many open type units in use. The open type unit is belt driven and is sometimes referred to as the "conventional" type.

15-38 Care of Service Valves

In units equipped with service valves, the valves must be leakproof to obtain a leakproof joint where the valve stem goes

into the valve. The packing is usually made of asbestos, lead, and graphite. Packings differ with different valve designs. When replacing them you must be sure the proper packing is used.

A replacement service valve is shown in Fig. 15-43. It has a slotted flange that enables the serviceman to fit this valve to a great variety of compressor flange sizes.

Practically all service valves have a drop-forged brass body, and are equipped with steel stems, which have a tendency to rust and stick in the valve gland. See Fig. 15-44. A good way to lessen this corrosion, especially in damp locations, is to fill the valve body with refrigerant oil before replacing the plug each time the service valve is used. This oil, of course, should be the specified refrigerant oil for that machine.

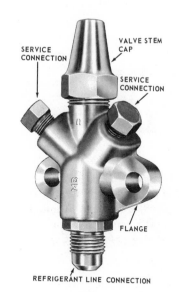

Fig. 15-44. Refrigeration unit service valve having two service openings; two bolt flange and valve stem cap.

Before turning the valve stem it is advisable first to loosen the packing nut that is used as a seal around it. This can be done by loosening the large packing nut a half turn or so. When turning the valve stem, it is always best that a steady pressure be applied to the wrench and that the wrench fit the stem well.

In case a service valve is "frozen," or stuck, it may be loosened by heating the body of the valve with a torch and tapping on the valve stem.

Service valves on commercial installations must be kept in good condition because they are used more frequently than those on a domestic unit. Three things may be noted which will assure good service and valve life: (1) fitting the wrench to the valve stem, (2) maintaining the packing so that the service valve will not leak, (3) oil the threads of the gauge connections each

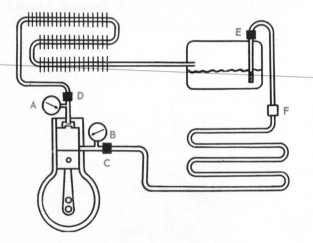

Fig. 15-45. An open-type compression system which shows location of gauges and service valves. A—High pressure gauge. B—Compound gauge. C—Suction service valve. D—Discharge service valve. E—Liquid receiver service valve. F—Expansion valve.

time gauges are used. Occasionally, after a certain period of use, these service valves have to be replaced. After gauges have been mounted in the gauge opening of the valve a number of times, the pipe threads in the valve gauge openings may become worn and leak at this point. If the fittings inserted in these gauge openings are given a thin coat of solder, this trouble can frequently be eliminated.

When cracking the valve, always use a

fixed wrench (not a ratchet wrench). This is done so the valve may be quickly closed again if necessary.

Occasionally a service valve will be found in such bad condition as to be useless. In this case you must remove the refrigerant or isolate it in another part of the system and replace the valve.

15-39 Preparing for Service Work

When evaporator coils or refrigerant controls need service, remove articles that are inside the refrigerator cabinet or put them to one side and cover them with paper or cloth. Spread papers, or a tarpaulin, around and under the mechanism.

Be careful of all surfaces. Porcelain is brittle and any chipping or cracking may necessitate replacing a complete panel. Enamel finishes should not be smeared with oil or grease.

Tools and materials should be placed in a safe place to prevent injury by tripping. Always arrange for good lighting.

15-40 Removing System Part

The general steps to be followed when removing any part of any system are as follows:

1. Remove all refrigerant from part to be opened.
2. Balance pressures in parts just evacuated.
3. Isolate parts to be opened from the rest of the system.
4. Clean and dry joints to be broken.
5. All refrigerant openings should be immediately plugged as soon as they are opened.

Fig. 15-45 shows an elementary unit showing the location of the three main service valves.

This (removal of the refrigerant) is done by installing gauges in the system, the proper manipulation of the service valves, and operation of the compressor.

The removal of any part is usually accomplished by drawing a low pressure or vacuum on that part to be dismantled in order to evaporate the refrigerant from it, and then equalizing the pressure to 0 psig. The vacuum removes the refrigerant, and the equalizing or balancing of the pressure prevents a rush of air into the mechanism, when the system is opened. This last step is very important. The process is performed by closing the inlet service valve to the part to be removed, running the compressor until the gauge shows a 0 psig to a 28 in. vacuum, and then after opening the inlet service valve until the gauge reads zero, closing the inlet service valve to that part, closing the outlet service valve to that part, cleaning and drying the joints and then removing the parts. Always plug openings immediately after removing the part to keep out dirt and moisture.

When servicing a refrigerating mechanism, you must always keep in mind the internal part of the machine must be kept as chemically clean as possible. Moisture causes acids, sludge and even freezes in low temperature passages. Dirt (solids) will abrade control valves, compressor valves and seats, and clog screens.

Some general instructions follow for removing only part of a system. Turn the discharge service valve all the way out and attach a line from a storage cylinder (if one is to be used) to the valve. The storage cylinder may be connected to the center opening if a manifold is used. Purge the line leading from the cylinder by sealing the line at the cylinder; then leaving it loose at the discharge service valve, crack the cylinder valve and the escaping gas will force the air out of the line. Seal the line at the discharge service valve, close the discharge line of the compressor by turning the discharge service valve all the way in, test for leaks, and start the compressor. Place the cylinder in a bucket of water in order to keep it as cool as possible. This action will promote the condensation of the refrigerant in the cylinder. Allow the compressor to run with all but the discharge service valve open. Shut the compressor off after a constant vacuum has been maintained for several minutes. A high pressure gauge should be connected to the refrigerant cylinder to enable the serviceman to observe the head pressure. The pressure should not exceed the normal condensing pressure for the particular refrigerant. Excessive head pressures may be avoided by cooling the refrigerant cylinder with ice, or water, or by running the compressor intermittently. Saving the refrigerant is not recommended in small systems because it may be saturated with dirt and impurities. Never allow the system to pump oil as the hydraulic pressures may cause serious damage to the compressor and lines. Never use the refrigerant in any system but the one it was removed from unless the refrigerant is distilled and dried. The operation may be speeded up by cautiously applying a torch to the liquid receiver and to the evaporating coil. Keep the torch away from fuse plugs and soldered joints. Never allow any part or spot to become too warm to touch with your hand.

The refrigerant is all pumped from the system and placed in a storage cylinder.

Close the cylinder valve and stop the compressor; then after opening the discharge service valve, crack the cylinder valve until a zero pressure is indicated on the compound gauge. This action returns enough gaseous refrigerant to balance the pressure in the entire system. Before opening it to the air, close the liquid receiver service valve and turn the discharge service valve stem, all the way in. Then the condenser and receiver may be removed from the mechanism.

The above method is also used for removing the refrigerant. As mentioned before, clean and dry all the connections to be opened and immediately upon removal of any parts, the refrigerant openings should be carefully plugged. When the serviceman wants to discard the refrigerant, he may either exhaust it to the air or into an approved exhaust system.

A good practice to follow when discarding refrigerant is to attach a purging line made of 1/4 in. copper tubing to the discharge service valve gauge opening. This purging line should have a hand needle valve and a check valve mounted in the compressor end. The hand needle valve should be located between the check valve and the purging line.

The purpose of the hand valve is to control the amount of gas purged while the check valve prevents backing up of air or moisture into the unit after it has been completely purged.

Because all refrigerants being purged have an oil content the purging should be done into an oil trap. Always purge a refrigerant into a well-ventilated space.

Most of the mechanisms used in conventional refrigerating machines may be repaired and used again. However, the use of replacement parts, if available, is usually recommended. Many orphan makes (manufacturers are no longer in business), are still being used and parts are unavailable. With these machines in mind, the following suggestions are offered: there are many things that can go wrong with a refrigerating unit, but only a few cause 90 to 95 percent of the failures. These are (1) leaks, (2) faulty motor, (3) faulty compressor and (4) faulty refrigerant control. The service of the electric motor is covered in Chapter 7. Leaks are discussed in Chapters 9 and 12.

15-41 Checking Open Compressor

Many refrigeration troubles are due to compressor failure. In most cases of refrigeration failure, it is advisable to check the compressor first to determine if it is operating satisfactorily. A good service-

man will also look for other indications of troubles as he performs the check on the compressor. However, he should be certain that the compressor is in satisfactory operating condition before proceeding with other tests.

The amount of oil in the compressor is important and the condition of this oil is also important. Some compressors have an oil level sight glass or port to enable a serviceman to check the oil level. Some compressors have a plug located at the proper oil level. Discolored oil should be tested. This may be done by removing a sample and using an oil test kit as shown in Fig. 15-46. Be careful. Do not get the

Fig. 15-46. Oil sampler which may be used to remove oil from system and test it for acid.
(Henry Valve Co.)

oil on your skin; it may be acidic and cause a severe burn. Fig. 15-47 shows an oil sampler which may be connected into a system to sample and test the oil.

The two most common causes of compressor trouble are faulty valves and seals. Noisy valves may be detected by a sharp clicking noise in the compressor as it operates. Leaky valves may be detected as follows: install both the high pressure and compound gauges on the gauge manifold and test for leaks. Turn the suction service valve stem all the way in to close the suction line, then run the compressor intermittently. That is, turn the power on

SIGHT GLASS

LINE CONNECTION

LINE CONNECTION

Fig. 15-47. Oil sampler which may be connected into system for oil removal and testing.

and off for a few seconds at a time until the danger of pumping oil is stopped; then allow the compressor to run.

Determine the vacuum that the compressor will develop by turning the suction service valve all the way in as shown in Fig. 15-48. Record the best vacuum obtainable against the normal head pressure for the refrigerant being used. Also, record the time. If the compressor cannot produce a vacuum of greater than 20 in. of mercury against the normal head pressure, it should be overhauled.

A worn piston or cylinder is indicated by a clicking noise which is somewhat duller than the noisy valve indication mentioned before.

A compressor should be able to produce at least 28 in. of vacuum against its head pressure (depending on the refrigerant) to be good enough for use. The compressor must pump a specified quantity of gas at a certain pressure difference to do the work necessary. This is difficult to check, so the above methods are used as secondary checks. Some repair shops use a shop mounted tank into which the compressor pumps air while being tested. If the time required by a compressor to pump to 150

psig is noticed for each size compressor, a relative volumetric efficiency check may be made.

Compressor Testing Methods:
1. Vacuum producing ability.
2. High pressure maintaining ability.
3. Being able to hold both vacuum and head pressure.

If the compressor exhaust valve leaks, high head pressure will leak back through the exhaust valve and produce a pressure above atmospheric on the compound gauge; therefore if the compound gauge creeps up, it is a sign that the exhaust valve needs repair. If there is a leak on the low side (seal) of the compressor, the pressure will only rise to approximately 0 psig.

Another way to check efficiency of an exhaust valve of a compressor is to mount the pressure gauges, test for leaks, and

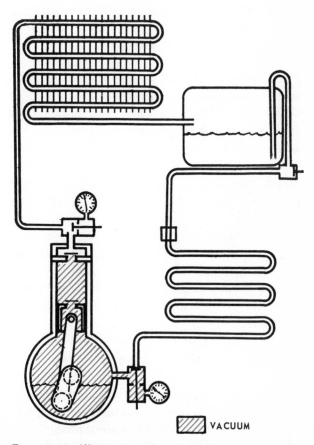

VACUUM

Fig. 15-48. Illustration shows suction service valve stem turned all the way in and compressor evacuated.

603

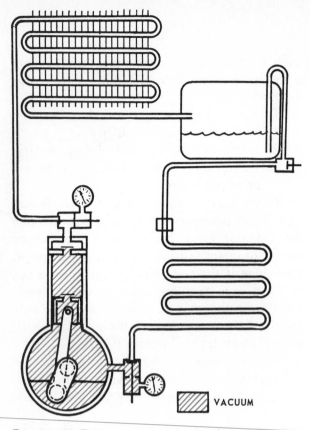

Fig. 15-49. *Testing compressor by determining best vacuum it can create with suction service valve turned all the way in.*

VACUUM

then turn the discharge service valve stem all the way in. TURN THE COMPRESSOR OVER BY HAND. If the discharge valve leaks, the pressure, as indicated on the gauge, will then leak back to its former value as the piston goes down, if the exhaust valve is leaking. That is, if the gauge pressure fluctuates considerably, it is an indication of a leaky exhaust valve, but if the pressure merely increases and does not drop back to any extent, it indicates that the exhaust valve is not leaking.

An intake valve leak is indicated by the inability of the compressor to produce a high vacuum, but vacuum produced is maintained after the compressor is shut off, provided the exhaust valve is holding.

To determine whether the crankshaft seal is leaking, close the suction service valve, pump as high a vacuum as possible on the crankcase of the compressor, and with the discharge service valve and suction service valve turned all the way in, as

shown in Fig. 15-49, keep the compressor running. If there is a low side leak, the head pressure will gradually increase with the running of the compressor, indicating that gas or air is being drawn in on the low side of the compressor.

A seal leak is usually noticeable by the oil trace at the seal or on the floor underneath. Leak detectors may also be used.

15-42 Removing Service Valve

Occasionally a service valve stem will break or the threads will strip, necessitating a replacement of the valve. If it is the suction service valve, you must remove all the refrigerant from the evaporator unit and then balance the pressure, unless the evaporator unit is furnished with valves. To remove a discharge service valve or a liquid receiver service valve, the refrigerant must be removed from the entire system. Do not pinch the lines to replace valves as weakened tubing will shortly cause trouble. Servicemen have successfully replaced these valves by super-cooling the refrigerant in the system by using dry ice. When dry ice is packed around the refrigerant containing parts of the system and when the gauges show atmospheric pressure, the system can be opened. Be sure to wear goggles during this operation.

15-43 Removing Compressor

When removal of a compressor is necessary, the procedure is as follows: Install the gauges, or the manifold, as shown in Fig. 15-50. Carefully test for leaks. Note connection F is for fastening the vacuum pump to the manifold. Opening F has a Schrader valve which closes the opening unless a depressor is connected to the opening.

Turn the suction service valve (D) all the way in, closing off the suction line as shown. Start the compressor, but let it run for only a moment in order to prevent oil pumping, for the oil in the crankcase may bubble vigorously as the refrigerant boils out. Pumping of oil is indicated by a pounding noise in the compressor and usually occurs between a 10 in. and 12 in. vacuum. After starting and stopping the unit two or three times, it may finally be run continuously. Keep the unit running for a few minutes after a constant vacuum is reached on the suction gauge.

Crack the suction service valve (D) until the compound gauge reads zero or 1 psig (equalizing the pressures). Then turn the discharge service valve (C) stem all the way in. Shut off the electric power and lock the switch in the open position. The joints should be cleaned and dried before opening. Unbolt the suction service and discharge service valves from the compressor. (DO NOT REMOVE THE LINES FROM THE VALVE.) Immediately plug all the openings through which refrigerant flows using dry rubber, "cork" stoppers or tape.

Disconnect the compressor base bolts that hold the compressor to the base, remove the belt, and the compressor is ready

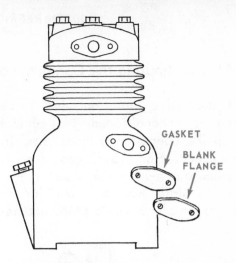

Fig. 15-51. Blank flange used to close compressor valve opening while compressor is being moved.

for removal. The oil should be drained immediately or plug the compressor refrigerant openings (blank flange covers are best). Fig. 15-51 shows a blank flange. Do not use the old oil again if it shows discoloration. To keep the crankshaft seal from being abused, never rest the compressor weight on the flywheel. Always set the compressor on a block in such a way that the flywheel hangs free. If possible, remove the flywheel, before removing the compressor, as any undue strain on the flywheel may injure the crankshaft, and/or the crankshaft seal. The flywheel can be removed by using a universal flywheel puller and by supplying a little heat to the flywheel hub as the wheel puller is drawn up snugly. Fig. 15-52 shows a universal type flywheel puller.

When the compressor from a larger unit must be removed for overhaul, the handling of the compressor, because of its weight, presents a problem. WHEN LIFTING A COMPRESSOR, THE SERVICEMAN SHOULD AVOID STRAINING HIMSELF BY ASSUMING AN AWKWARD POSITION. HE SHOULD BE CAREFUL NOT TO SLIP ON OIL OR LOOSE TOOLS. Carts, small hydraulic hoists, etc., are available that should be used to move heavy compressors.

Compressors are usually reconditioned by companies specializing in this work.

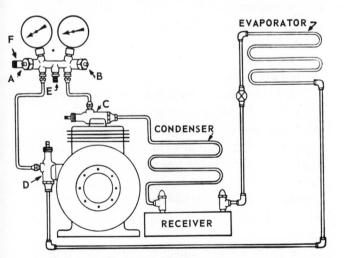

Fig. 15-50. A conventional system with a gauge manifold installed. A—Manifold suction valve. B—Manifold discharge valve. C—Compressor discharge service valve (DSV). D—Compressor suction service valve (SSV). E—Manifold purging and charging connection. F—Vacuum pump connection. (Mueller Brass Co.)

15-44 Overhauling the Compressor

If the valve plate only has to be repaired or reconditioned, the serviceman can do the operation without removing the compressor. Par. 15-47 describes methods used to remove a compressor head and the valve plate, how to recondition a valve seat, assemble a valve plate and test it.

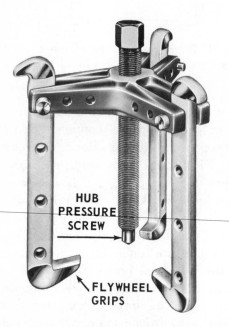

Fig. 15-52. Universal type flywheel puller. (Duro Metal Products Co.)

Crankshaft seals can also be frequently replaced and/or repaired on the premises without removing the compressor. The job consists of removing the flywheel, removing the old seal and replacing it with a crankshaft seal kit as described in Par. 15-46.

In cases where a compressor has been removed and is to be reconditioned, this procedure should be followed:

1. Identify (tag) the compressor.
2. Clean outside of compressor.
3. Prepare work order form.
4. Take compressor apart.
5. Clean all parts - keep parts in tagged trays. Fig. 15-53 shows a cleaning station.

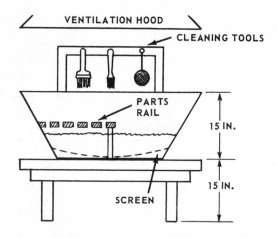

Fig. 15-53. Ventilated cleaning station.

6. Insert the parts - order replacement parts - tag parts needing repairs.

All precision parts must be precision inspected with dial indicators and micrometers, because these parts must fit to tolerances of .001 to .003 in.

7. Recondition parts.
8. Assemble (gasket surfaces must be flat, clean, and free from burrs).
9. Test compressor.

Many means have been used to clean parts of a refrigerator. Each method has its advantages. The cleaner should be a good moisture absorber, it should remove oil and grease quickly. The cleaner should be nontoxic, nonflammable, and should evaporate quickly.

R-11 is a cleaning solvent (refrigerant with a high boiling point, 74.8 F.) which is nontoxic and nonflammable. It is an excellent cleaning solvent for use in flushing systems which have been contaminated due to hermetic motor burn out. It leaves no noncondensible residue and has no reaction with insulation. R-11 can be recleaned and reused.

Also available commercially is Virginia Number 10, a degreasing solvent. Some of its features are low toxicity, noncorrosive, and high flash point, 165 F.

Hand wire brushes and power wire brushes are excellent ways to remove

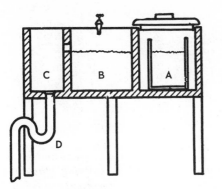

Fig. 15-54. Acid type cleaning station. A—Weak acid. B—Rinsing basin. C—Drain (overflow from B). D—Trap.

scale and crusted dirt, but grease and oil should be removed first. Fig. 15-54 shows another type of cleaning station.

15-45 Replacing Bearings

It is seldom that any work has to be done on connecting rod or crankshaft bearings of compressors. If this should be necessary, it is a replacement and reaming process similar to some automobile work. Old bearing sleeves usually made of brass or bronze are removed by first splitting

them with a cape chisel. The new sleeve is pressed into place and then line reamed to fit.

A bushing pressed into a blind hole can also be removed by using hydraulic pressure. Fill the cavity with grease and then insert a shaft the same size as the ID of the bushing. Cover the shaft with a cloth to protect against flying grease and then hit the shaft a sharp blow. The hydraulic pressure created will usually push out the bushing.

Always measure crankshaft journals for size, taper, out-of-round and/or bent crankshaft. Fig. 15-55 shows a dial indicator used to determine the variation in a crankshaft. A variation of more than .001 in. necessitates reconditioning the journal or replacing the crankshaft. A method of checking shafts for trueness is shown in Fig. 15-56. Close clearances are usually

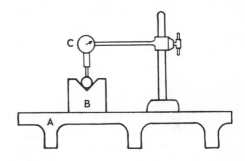

Fig. 15-56. Method of checking shafts, rollers and cylinders for trueness. A—Surface plate. B—Blocks. C—Dial indicator.

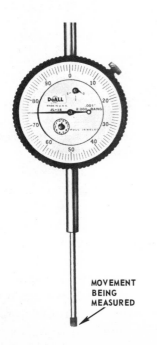

MOVEMENT BEING MEASURED

Fig. 15-55. Dial indicator used to check clearance, roundness and accuracy of surfaces. (DoAll Co.)

held in fitting compressor bearings. One of the most common sources of noise in a compressor is the piston pin. This pin must be replaced in practically all overhauls. Tolerances of .0005 in. are not too small. The fit must be very snug. Adjustable reamers, hand operated, may be used to ream the piston and connecting rod. If the pin itself is badly worn, a new one must be used. Some automobile piston pins are usable in some of the larger refrigerating compressors. Badly scored eccentric connecting rod bearings must be replaced.

15-46 Repairing Crankshaft Seal

Crankshaft seal design and construction is described in Chapter 5. The repair or replacement required depends on the seal design.

In sylphon seals, a squeaky noise may be caused by running the compressor with a dry seal surface. A leaky seal may be caused by a scored seal surface.

A noisy seal will soon become a leaky one if not attended to. The trouble may be remedied by the usual process of replacing the seal or lapping the seal. It may sometimes be repaired by tapping the seal box lightly with a hammer. Another remedy is to wrap the bellows with oil-soaked wool yarn or string. A leaky seal may be detected by the usual test for leaks. Air in the system may be the result of a leaky seal. This may be detected by a high head pressure in systems having a below atmospheric low side pressure. A seal leak will usually cause a lack of refrigerant in systems using an above atmospheric low side pressure. The usual symptoms of this trouble are high power bill, constant running and poor refrigeration.

The contact surfaces of the sylphon and the crankshaft shoulder must be perfectly square and polished. To lap in a sylphon seal properly, the work should be done with a special tool made of case-hardened steel with a ground surface, as shown in Fig. 15-57, using oil-saturated lapping compound of fine texture. The crankshaft surface and the surface of the sylphon that

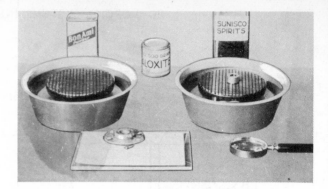

Fig. 15-58. Equipment and supplies needed to lap seals and valve plates. Note magnifying glass used for inspection and checking cleanliness needed for accurate lapping. (Norge Div., Borg-Warner Corp.)

come in contact should not be scratched and should be of a burnished appearance to give satisfactory service.

A scored crankshaft seal shoulder is best repaired by putting the crankshaft in a lathe and polishing the shoulder face with a high speed grinder. The amount ground

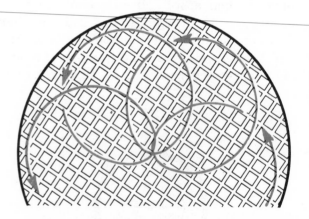

Fig. 15-59. Correct lapping motion when lapping seal faces or valve plates.

away must be small because the case hardening on these shafts is only .015 in. to .030 in. deep. Once this case hardening is ground through, the seal will not wear long. After the shaft is ground, it must be lapped in the lathe, using phosphor bronze or cast-iron lapping blocks and a fine lapping compound with a light, even pressure. The seal ring or the seat may be lapped. Fig. 15-58 shows a kit used for lapping. The use of a lapping block is shown in Fig. 15-59.

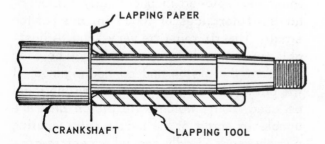

Fig. 15-57. Lapping crankshaft seal shoulder.

Fig. 15-60. Seal alignment tool.

When assembling a new or a rebuilt seal a special tool may be used to align the seal mechanism so it will be located in proper position in relation to the crankshaft and seal housing. Fig. 15-60 illustrates a seal alignment tool.

Many servicemen use replacement seal assemblies. These assemblies eliminate grinding and polishing as the kit replaces both the crankshaft shoulder and the seal ring.

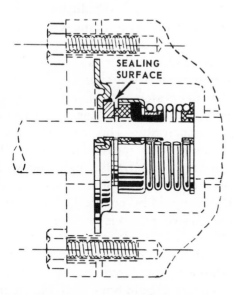

Fig. 15-61. Replacement seal for conventional compressors. Seals of this type are also used on many new compressors.
(Rotary Seal Div., Muskegon Piston Ring Co.)

Fig. 15-61 shows one type of replacement seal. The rotating seal ring is fastened to the crankshaft by a synthetic cir-

cular gasket (neoprene or some flexible oil immune plastic). Another type of seal is shown in Fig. 15-62.

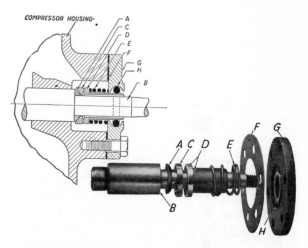

Fig. 15-62. Replacement seal. Such units are available for most conventional type compressors.
(Chicago Valve Plate and Seal Co.)

15-47 Repairing Compressor Valve Plate

The compressor valve plate, especially the exhaust valve does need repair or replacement on occasion.

The complete valve plate is usually replaced if a new one or a reconditioned one is available. Fig. 15-63 shows a replacement type valve. These units are available for most conventional compressors.

Hermetic unit compressors also have valve plates and valve reeds. If facilities are on hand to open these compressors and reweld them, the compressor valve plates can be replaced or repaired.

The valve plate should be carefully cleaned and the valve seal must be resurfaced with great precision. Minor repairs can be made using a lapping block and fine grinding compound. Extensive wear (erosion, pits, etc.) are best removed by grinding the complete valve plate surface until the seal is in good condition and then finishing it by lapping the surface.

It possible, always replace the valve. Chapter 12 describes precautions to follow and testing of these valve plates. Valves are also described in this chapter.

Fig. 15-63. Replacement valve plate. Special valve plates are available for most conventional refrigeration compressors. Valves and valve seats are removable and can be easily repaired. Left picture shows discharge or exhaust valve assembly. Right picture shows plate turned over to reveal intake (suction) valve assembly. Note multiple intake openings and single exhaust port.
(Chicago Valve Plate and Seal Co.)

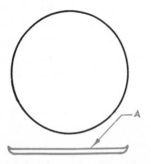

Fig. 15-64. Disk valve used frequently as an exhaust valve in compressor. Surface A should be away from the valve seat otherwise small burr may cause valve leak.

Fig. 15-64 shows a disk valve. In these valves it is important that the burr edge face away from the valve seat.

15-48 Assembling Compressor

Always use new gaskets when assembling a compressor as the old gaskets have lost their compressibility. Lead or special composition gaskets are generally used. Thickness of the lead is usually between .010 and .020 in. Composition gaskets, when used, must be of the same thickness as gaskets removed and must be thoroughly dry (dehydrated).

If you have to make a gasket, remember the gasket must be exactly the same thickness as the original gasket. A gasket that is too thick will reduce the compressor efficiency, and a gasket that is too thin may cause an annoying knock.

If a compressor has been frozen due to a high head pressure or moisture in the refrigerant, it should be carefully cleaned and the piston and cylinder burnished in order to remove all foreign substances.

Whenever a compressor is overhauled, new refrigerant oil should be replaced in the crankcase. The compressor must be thoroughly dehydrated (baked) for 8 to 24 hours at 200 F. while subjected to a high vacuum before it is used.

The precision fit of all parts of the compressor must be checked before and during assembly. The cylinder must be round and neither tapered or barrel shaped. The piston must fit the cylinder with the correct clearance. Manufacturer's specifications should be carefully followed.

The piston pin must fit the piston snugly. It should fit close enough to hold the weight of the connecting rod when the rod is extended horizontally. The connecting rod bearing should have .001 in. clearance on the crank pin.

The main bearing fit should be approximately the same as that of the piston. There should be no appreciable end play (.010 in.) in the crankshaft. See Fig. 15-65. Some have spring loaded end thrust bearings. The main bearings must be in line.

The crankshaft seal must be clean when

assembled. A drop of refrigerant oil should be put on the two sealing surfaces. The parts must be carefully aligned on the shaft, and must be free to move to allow the sealing surfaces to press together.

The cylinder head, end bearing housing, seal plate and crankcase must be fastened to the cylinder evenly. Draw up or tighten each cap screw a little and crisscross over the center of the assembly until all are tightened evenly. Use a torque wrench for final tightening. Careless tightening may warp or break the parts.

All brass and copper parts of a compressor can be cleaned by immersing the parts in a dilute solution of hydrochloric acid (muriatic acid) for 12 to 24 hours. A buffing wheel can also be used to polish the parts. Use goggles for both acid work and when buffing.

15-49 Testing Repaired Compressor

After a compressor has been repaired it should be tested, dehydrated, sealed and painted.

The compressor must be tested for leaks and for pumping efficiency. This may be done in a shop, as shown in Fig. 15-66.

To test for leaks on the low pressure side of a compressor, such as at gaskets, at the suction service valve, or the crankshaft seal, one of these methods may be used: 1. Close the suction service valve and draw as high a vacuum on the com-

pressor as possible. Then turn the discharge service valve all the way in. Keep the compressor running. If the head pressure rises gradually, air is being drawn into the low side of the system. 2. A better way is to balance pressures in the crankcase and turn the discharge service valve

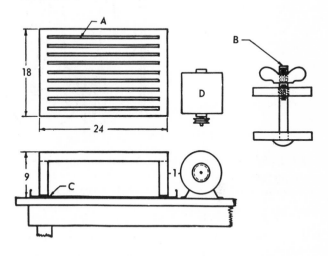

Fig. 15-66. Compressor testing stand. A—Universal clamping plate. B—Clamp down bolts, wing nut and bars. C—Oil pan. D—Motor.

all the way in. Remove the discharge service valve gauge plug and connect a 15 in. length of copper line to this opening or assembly, as shown in A of Fig. 15-67. Then immerse the end of the copper line into a glass bottle partly filled with oil. A gauge manifold can also be used during this test. If the tube discharges continuously as shown by bubbles appearing in the oil, when the compressor is running, air is being admitted to the low side of the compressor. If there are no leaks, the bubbling will stop immediately after the compressor is started. To locate the leak, put refrigeration oil around one joint at a time. If air is leaking in at that point, air bubbles will cease while oil is being drawn in instead of air. Exhaust valve leaks may be located:

    1. By turning the discharge service valve all the way in after mounting the high pressure gauge or a gauge manifold as shown in B, Fig. 15-50.

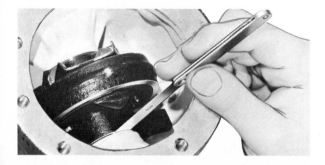

Fig. 15-65. Checking the end play of crankshaft. The thickness gauge is .010 in.

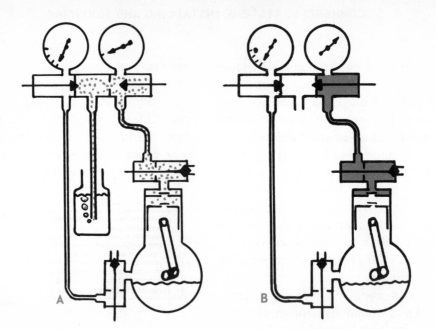

Fig. 15-67. Testing for leaks. A—Testing compressor for low pressure side leaks. Bubbles indicate air is leaking into compressor at seal, gaskets, and/or fittings. B—Testing compressor exhaust valve for leaks. If high pressure gauge reading drops while compressor is idle, vapor is leaking back into compressor low side.

2. When the compressor is turned over (revolved) a few turns, and the head pressure rises rapidly.

3. When the compressor is stopped. If the exhaust valve leaks, the pressure will decrease. Any decrease in pressure will indicate a leaky exhaust valve.

Compressor efficiency (intake valve, piston ring fit, valve action, etc.) are best checked by running the compressor at a constant low side pressure and checking the time required to pump a head pressure in a certain size cylinder. Another efficiency test is the amount of vacuum a compressor will produce against a standard head pressure. If service valves are not available, a universal flange can be bolted to the compressor in place of the service valve, as shown in Fig. 15-68.

15-50 Installing Open Type Compressor

When installing compressor, the condensing unit base should be cleaned. All the hold down bolts should be used, and the bolts should be tightened evenly. Compres-

sor and motor must be carefully aligned. The compressor shaft and motor shaft must be parallel and the flywheel and the pulley must be in line. If difficulty is experienced when installing hold down bolts, masking tape may be used to hold them temporarily, or string may be used to pull the bolts into position. A universal socket is very handy for holding bolts that are not readily accessible. New gaskets should always be used when mounting service valves on a compressor. Belt tension is important. The belt should be tight enough to al-

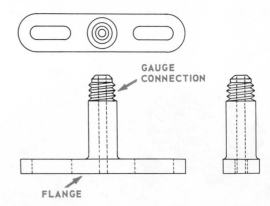

Fig. 15-68. Flange attachment which takes place of service valve on compressor while compressor is being tested.

low only 1 in. deflection of the belt with approximately 25 lb. force on the belt. Multiple belts should all deflect the same amount.

15-51 Servicing Hermetic Compressors

Two types of hermetic compressors used in commercial refrigeration are:
1. Welded motor-compressors.
2. Bolted motor-compressors.

The welded motor-compressors may or may not be equipped with service valves. Bolted units usually have service valves.

Both units eliminate belt service and crankshaft seal service.

The bolted motor-compressor units are tested, removed, overhauled, retested and installed in a manner similar to the conventional compressor. Since the motor is built into the housing, it is usually tested and reconditioned at the same time the compressor is reconditioned.

Welded motor-compressors very seldom have service valves in the smaller units and the valves must be mounted in the system. One method of doing this is to use a line tapping valve, as shown in Fig. 15-69. Larger units usually do have service valves.

Chapter 12 describes the testing, removing, reconditioning and installing of welded hermetics.

15-52 Servicing Condensers

Condensers are used to remove heat from the compressed refrigerant vapor and to return the vapor to liquid form.

Condenser service procedures are dependent on the type of condenser.

In all cases the heat transfer surfaces must be clean, both the surfaces in contact with the refrigerant, and the surfaces in contact with the cooling medium (air or water). There must be enough refrigerant vapor space (area) to remove the heat from

the vapor. For example, if a condenser has liquid refrigerant in it (is overcharged), cooling will be reduced. If the amount of air flowing or water flowing is not enough, the condenser cannot do its job. If the air temperature or the water temperature is above normal, the condenser operation will decrease, the condenser temperature will rise, and the head pressure will increase.

If a noncondensible gas is in the system it will collect in the condenser (it cannot condense and will be held back by the liquid trap in the receiver or at the lower end of the condenser). Each pound pressure of noncondensible gas (usually air) will increase the head pressure by one pound

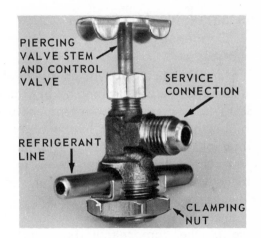

Fig. 15-69. Special valve which can be mounted on suction line and can pierce refrigerant line for pressure testing, charging, and/or discharging purposes. (Mechanical Refrig. Enterprises)

pressure. This increase in pressure will reduce the pumping efficiency of the compressor and will increase the condensing temperatures.

Excess oil in the system will usually collect in the condenser as it is pumped out of the compressor. Because oil is only soluble to a certain extent in the various refrigerants and because oil is lighter than the refrigerant, excess oil will tend to fill part of the condenser and reduce its condensing ability.

Troubles encountered in commercial condensers vary with the type of condenser used. However, air in the system, too much refrigerant, not enough refrigerant, too much oil, or a corroded interior are common to all types.

Whether the condenser is air or water-cooled, too much refrigerant, too much oil, or a corroded interior of the condenser, will produce an excessive head pressure. Air in the system will also produce this condition. Remember that the purpose of the condenser is to remove heat. The condenser will fail to do its job if the heat transfer surfaces are inefficient, or if the heat removing medium (air or water) is not in the correct volume or temperature.

15-53 Servicing Air-Cooled Condensers

The correct pressure in an air-cooled condenser may be determined by first adding 30 F. to 35 F. to the room temperature, to obtain the refrigerant temperature on the interior of the condenser. Then, using this corrected temperature, refer to the refrigerant charts, Chapter 9, for the correct head pressure.

If the pressure is above normal, the outside of the compressor is clean, and there is enough air movement (both air-in passages and air-out passages must be free of obstruction) there is a good chance there is air in the system. There is also a chance that the unit is overcharged.

If the pressure is below normal, it is possible that the unit is undercharged.

Most commercial air-cooled condensers are of the forced convection type. They have from one to several fans for moving the air through the condenser. Some larger fans are belt driven, some are direct driven. The fans, motors, and belts need maintenance and service.

Belt tension must be correct as described in Par. 15-50. These belts must be free from cracks and must be flexible.

Old belts should be replaced. The motor pulley and fan pulley must be in line and the grooves must be in line. Motors should have periodic bearing oiling, (approx. one or two drops every six months). The motors should be clean, inside and out. Some motors have overload relays. If a fan motor equipped with these devices does not work, the overload should be checked for continuity. Multiple fan condensers sometimes have sequenced fans. When more condensing is needed, all fans operate. As the condensing load decreases, first one fan is shut off, then the second, etc.

Sequence controls should be checked if the fans do not operate. Most outdoor air-cooled condensers have thermostat controlled louvers which are powered to partly close or completely close as the outdoor temperature decreases. If the head pressure is too low, the refrigerant control capacity is decreased.

15-54 Removing Air From Condenser

Air in the system will be indicated by an above normal head pressure even after the unit has cooled down. It may be removed by purging the system using the gauge opening on the discharge service valve while the unit is idle.

A tube fastened to the gauge opening should be led out-of-doors to avoid releasing fumes indoors. A purge of 10 to 15 seconds will be of sufficient duration to remove the air if the condenser is cold. This removal is possible because the air is non-condensible. Therefore, it will collect in the top of the condenser as the lower end of the refrigerant passages are sealed with liquid refrigerant. Two or three purges may be necessary.

15-55 Removing Air-Cooled Condenser

If a condenser is leaking or needs replacing for some reason, the condenser usually must be removed from the system.

To remove the condenser, the liquid refrigerant must be removed from the condenser and the pressure in the condenser must be adjusted to atmospheric pressure.

The usual procedure is to close the valve between the condenser and the liquid receiver, purge the condenser by removing the gauge plug from the discharge service valve, then opening the valve (wear goggles) until the condenser pressure is down to atmospheric. Be careful. There may be oil in the condenser and it is best to connect a purge line to the gauge opening of the valve and run the purge line outdoors and into a container to trap the oil.

If there is no shutoff valve between the condenser and the liquid receiver, you may save the refrigerant by pumping the refrigerant into a cylinder, as shown in Fig. 15-70. The refrigerant cylinder usually has to be cooled during this operation or the pressure in the cylinder will quickly rise to dangerous levels. Run the compressor intermittently and put the cylinder in a tub or bucket of running cold water or ice water. Some servicemen put a spare condenser between the compressor and the service cylinder to speed the condensing operation. The operation can be done as follows:

The liquid receiver may need to be heated in order to vaporize the liquid in it. Use warm water. NEVER USE AN OPEN FLAME. To remove a condenser, first clean the condenser as much as possible. Brushes, vacuum cleaner, air or nontoxic refrigerant jets, carbon dioxide and/or nitrogen jets may be used for this purpose.

Most air-cooled condensers are housed in a protective shroud which also serves as an air duct. These sheet metal parts are heavy on some of the larger units and should be handled with care. Gloves and safety shoes are recommended. Be sure to place the sheet metal screws and/or assembly bolts in a container.

Fans, fan brackets, belts and motors

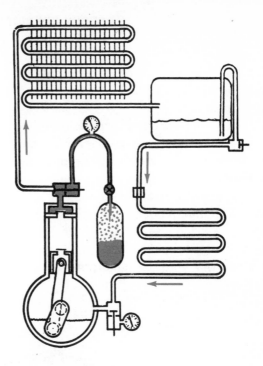

Fig. 15-70. Illustration which shows one way to discharge system.

may need to be removed on some units. These parts should be labeled and stored for reuse. Be sure the fan blades are not nicked or bent as this abuse may put them out of balance and decrease the efficiency.

If electrical connections are removed, label them. Masking tape and a marking pencil should be used.

Always clean the connections before disconnecting the condenser from the unit. Immediately plug the refrigerant openings to keep the internal refrigerant passages clean and to avoid spilling oil as the condenser is moved.

Avoid abusing the condenser fins. Wood or cardboard protectors taped over the corners of the fins will provide protection. Because the fins are sharp, always use gloves when lifting or carrying a condenser.

15-56 Repairing Air-Cooled Condenser

A leaky condenser can be repaired. First clean the condenser and flush the inside of the refrigerant tubes. If a brazed joint is leaking, clean the outside of the joint, put flux on the joint, heat, and take the joint apart.

Clean the brazed surfaces, flux the male part of the joint, assemble, support the joint and braze the joint and remove the flux.

If there is a cracked tube, repair by removing that part of the tube and replace with a new tube section. Silver braze the new part in place.

The fins may be straightened using a fin-comb, as shown in Fig. 15-71.

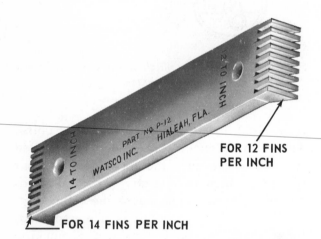
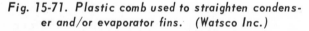

Fig. 15-71. Plastic comb used to straighten condenser and/or evaporator fins. (Watsco Inc.)

To test a condenser, plug one end of the condenser, connect a refrigerant cylinder to the other end. Build up a refrigerant vapor pressure in the condenser, and test for leaks (1. bubble test; 2. halide torch; 3. electronic leak detector; 4. immersing condenser in water).

Inspect the fittings (and the flares, if used). These connections must be in good condition.

15-57 Installing an Air-Cooled Condenser

Protect the condenser fins and the condenser tubing (return binds, etc.) at all times. Mount the condenser securely in its frame. Install it as level as possible. Connect the condenser to the compressor and liquid receiver (if one is used). Flare connectors should be carefully aligned. The fittings should be in line without being under load or forced in any way. If the fittings are out of line or are under strain, threads on the fittings or the flare, may be abused. Brazed connections must also be carefully aligned before brazing. The surface to be brazed should be cleaned with steel wool, wire brush, or dry sandpaper just before assembling the joint. Flux should be put on the outside of the male part of the fitting only. The joint should be supported during the brazing operation. See Chapter 2 for instructions on brazing. When brazing, use asbestos sheets to protect the other parts of the unit from the brazing flame.

After the joint is brazed, remove excess flux by washing the joint with warm water. Then inspect the joint all around (use an inspection mirror if necessary).

Use the refrigerant in the system or a service cylinder to purge the air from the condenser (purge outdoors or out of the room if possible). Build up a pressure of approximately 15 psig in the condenser and test for leaks. If a leak is found, do not attempt to patch the leak, but rather take the joint completely apart and do it over. If no leak is found, increase the pressure to approximately 100 to 200 psig and test for leaks again.

If no leaks are found, install fans, belts, motors, etc., as required. to operate the system. All these parts should be cleaned prior to assembling.

Run the system (be careful of the fan, belts, and pulleys as they can cause serious injuries). Check the refrigerant charge and operation of the unit.

Test for leaks again (shut the unit off to stop air flow). If the unit is OK, install the shroud or casing. These parts should be securely fastened or rattles, inefficient air flow, etc., may result.

15-58 Servicing Water-Cooled Condensers

Water removes heat from the hot compressed vapors about 15 times more rapidly than air. Water-cooled condensers are much smaller than air-cooled condensers. The water is usually colder than air and the condenser temperature can therefore be lower. Usually the condenser is designed to permit a water temperature rise of 10 F. as it goes through the condenser. If the water-in temperature is high, the condenser temperature will be high and vice versa. Care must be taken to avoid freezing the water circuit of water-cooled units.

If the unit is water-cooled, add 10 F. to 15 F. to the temperature of the water as it is leaving the condenser to determine what the refrigerant temperature should be. The correct head pressure may then be obtained from a refrigerant chart. The unit must be running for these conditions to hold true.

If the head pressure exceeds this value by more than 5 lbs., purge the system through the discharge service valve gauge opening for 10 to 15 seconds; then run the condensing unit again. To determine whether the trouble is excess refrigerant, or air in the system, stop the unit and purge as before for 15 to 20 seconds. If the pressure drops somewhat, the trouble was air in the system.

If the pressure does not drop, continue to purge the unit until that part of the condenser and liquid receiver which is full of liquid refrigerant, becomes cold. Do not allow the temperature to go lower than 32 F. or the water tubes may freeze and burst. Some condensing units have small valves that can be used to check liquid levels. A liquid level sight glass is installed in some large units. It is connected to the top and bottom of the receiver. When the pressures are equalized, the liquid level in the sight glass will be the same as that in the receiver. This will quickly reveal the level of the refrigerant in the condenser and liquid receiver, and you may easily judge whether this is the correct amount. An excess amount of oil in a system is indicated by the erratic refrigeration obtained, and a continuous slugging or pumping of oil in the compressor, especially just as it starts after the off-part of the cycle. A common water-cooled condenser problem is formation of deposits from the water on the tubing walls of the condenser. This deposit (carbonate, sulphate, and the like) acts as an insulation. It must be removed or the condenser must be replaced.

A corroded condenser is determined by noting the liquid line temperatures of the refrigerant. If the amount of refrigerant is correct, and if the other troubles just mentioned are not prevalent in the system, a corroded condenser will produce a hot liquid line in a water-cooled condenser. It will produce a temperature in the condenser considerably above that to be expected. If all other possible causes of excessive head pressure are eliminated, a badly corroded or dirty condenser is probably the cause. Scale may be removed from some water-cooled condensers by using a power driven wire brush, as shown in Fig. 15-72. This operation can usually be done without removing the condenser from the system. However, the water circuit must be closed and the unit shut down. Always use new gaskets and tighten assembly cap screws evenly.

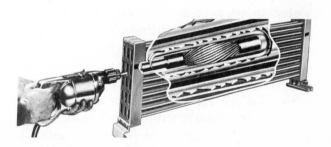

Fig. 15-72. Tube-within-a-tube condenser which is being cleaned with power driven wire brush. (Halstead and Mitchell Co.)

When the condenser water tubes have a small lime or iron deposit, the tubes can be cleaned, as shown in Fig. 15-73. A weak

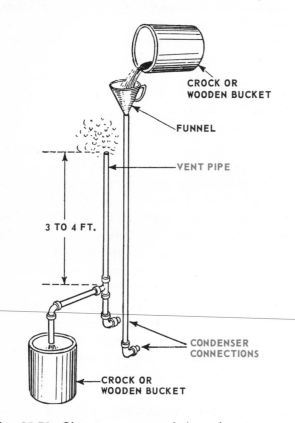

Fig. 15-73. *Cleaning water-cooled condenser water tubes. Using dilute hydrochloride acid solution, connect vent pipe to upper condenser connector as shown. (Copyright, Frigidaire Div., General Motors Corp.)*

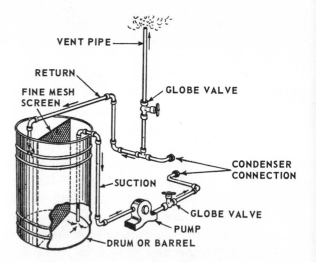

Fig. 15-74. *Condenser water tube cleaning using a forced circulation system for acid solution. Note the screen in drum to keep scale from entering pump. Drum must be acid proof, i.e., do not use galvanized materials and the like. (Copyright, Frigidaire Div., General Motors Corp.)*

acid solution is used (78 percent water, 22 percent commercial hydrochloric acid, sometimes called muriatic acid, of 1.19 sp. gr. + 1/4 oz. inhibitor powder per gallon). To make the mixture, first put the water in an acid-proof container, then add the inhibitor, stir until mixed, then slowly add the acid (the solution will become warm as the acid is added). Wear rubber gloves and goggles during the mixing and when using the solution. Gases are formed as the solution reacts with the deposits. Good ventilation is required to prevent breathing problems and respiratory damage. It takes from 12 to 24 hours for the solution to thoroughly clean the water tubes.

Fig. 15-74 shows cleaning being done with a forced circulation system. The pump must be designed to pump an acid solution. A warm solution will react faster than a cold solution. Do not heat the solution above a warm temperature. Avoid spilling the solution on your skin, clothing or on the floor.

Crocks and barrels used must be made of acid resisting materials (wood, ceramic, or steel materials are acceptable – avoid using galvanized or aluminum containers).

15-59 Removing Water-Cooled Condenser

A leaky condenser should be removed and repaired or replaced. Removing a water-cooled condenser is similar to removing an air-cooled condenser except for the water line disconnections. After removing the refrigerant from the condenser (do not allow freezing temperatures) and isolating the condenser, close off the water circuit, disconnect the water lines and drain as much water as possible from the condenser.

If a pressure operated water valve is used leave it installed in the system if possible.

Clean the outside of the condenser, wipe or mop the water, clean the condenser connections. Dry the connections thoroughly. If the connections are mechanical, be sure to use correct size wrenches. Wear goggles. Plug the refrigerant openings at once using good plugs (synthetic rubber expanding plugs or flared plugs are recommended).

If the condenser is large and heavy, two or more men should handle it or a lifting device should be used.

15-60 Repairing Condensers and Receivers

When trouble is encountered with either a condenser or a receiver, it is usually cheaper to replace the unit than to repair it. Welding or brazing is sometimes used to repair leaks in the system, but it requires careful work. If possible, all joints should be silver brazed to insure a lasting leakproof joint.

A welded shell type condenser can be cut open, a new water coil installed and the shell rewelded but this is done only in an extreme emergency because pressure vessels should be made under well controlled conditions, by a pressure vessel certified welder and tested to at least twice the operating pressure.

The liquid receivers used in most commercial systems serve as refrigerant storage cylinders and are usually constructed of a welded steel shell.

The shell and tube liquid receiver, that has a water coil built into it, sometimes develops leaks. Because of the corrosive action of the water and refrigerant under certain conditions, the copper tubing which is used to carry the water eventually corrodes through; the resultant leak forces the refrigerant from the system into the cooling water. A leak of this kind may be detected by the release of refrigerant at the water drain. Also, leaks occasionally occur at the joints where the water-cooling coil is attached to the liquid receiver and may be due to abuse or to corrosive action. In such a case, the condenser should be replaced with a new one.

If new parts are not obtainable for the machine being repaired, a fairly satisfactory repair may be made as follows: the water tubing, if eaten through within the liquid receiver, must be removed. The liquid receiver should be mounted on a lathe and the end of the receiver cut open. This permits removing the old water coil and putting in a new one. The new one must have the same length of tubing as the one removed, or the capacity of the condenser will be changed materially. The new coil is usually made up by winding it on a drum mounted on a lathe. The tubing is then put in the liquid receiver and the joints are silver brazed. The end of the liquid receiver that was removed may now be replaced after the interior has been cleaned thoroughly.

A bolted condenser can be dismantled quite easily and the water tubing replaced.

All liquid receivers above a certain size must be equipped with safety release valves. The National Refrigeration Code, Chapter 27, specifies the type, location, size, and piping for such relief valves. A receiver repair must be done under the sanction of local inspectors.

15-61 Installing Water-Cooled Condenser

Installing a water-cooled condenser is similar to the installation of an air-cooled unit. The mounting of the condenser, the joints, the leak testing should all be done with the same care. When leak testing a water-cooled unit, the leak detection should include the exhaust water.

Connecting the water lines should be done according to the local plumbing code.

The water circuit should be tested for leaks also. All of the assembled parts should be cleaned before assembly including the assembly devices. Be sure to test for leaks after the unit has run for a few hours and the system is in normal operation.

15-62 Servicing Evaporative Condensers

Evaporative condensers and the cooling towers are subject to deposits from the cooling water. These deposits must be removed periodically or they will act as coil insulation. The deposits can be reduced materially by using water softener chemicals in the water. Such chemicals can be obtained from wholesale supply companies. The treatment of water is a necessity. The chemicals in the water are measured by a pH factor. The scale of pH is from 1 to 14 with 1 through 7 indicating an acid solution and 8 through 14 indicating a basic condition. Chemicals may be added to the water to create a 7 or 8 condition in the water.

pH
Intensity factor (parts per million in quantity)

1	8	
2	9	
3	10	
4	Acid 11	Alkali
5	12	
6	13	
7	14	

Other chemicals may be used to minimize algae, mold, and slime growths. If deposits have formed, they can be removed by scraping or by using a weak acid solution, followed by a soda solution rinse and wash. Water-cooled condensers should not be placed in a location which may be subjected to freezing temperatures.

In the event a water-cooled condensing unit is to be shut down and perhaps subjected to below freezing temperatures, the condenser coils must be completely emptied of water. This may be done by blowing out the coils with air, nitrogen, or carbon dioxide (do not exceed a 50 to 60 psig pressure or the system may be damaged). The water drain valves should be left open to allow drainage of residual water in the piping. Be sure the drain plug of the circulating pump is removed and left loose in its opening.

15-63 Servicing Ice Cube Makers

Ice cube makers have refrigerating systems similar to other applications. However, they do have special water circuits, defrosting devices, and ice cube or flakes moving devices. Fig. 15-75 shows an ice maker piping installation. Many of these

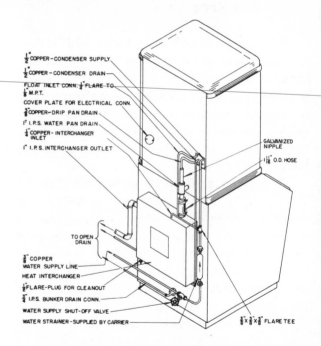

Fig. 15-75. External plumbing installation for automatic ice maker. (Carrier Air Conditioning Co.)

units have a water pump for recirculating the water used for making ice. Fig. 15-76 shows a water pump and motor installed. Just in front and below the motor is the float control for water makeup. Motors, pumps and water level float controls should be checked frequently. Fig. 15-77 shows one type of installation.

PUMP
MOTOR

PUMP-

WATER
IN

Fig. 15-76. Water circulating pump and water float control for ice maker.   (Ross-Temp Inc.)

15-64 Servicing Water Valves

Water-cooled condensers require attention frequently because of incorrect water flow. This trouble is sometimes due to the water valve or to the screens in the water circuit. See Chapter 13 for details of construction of these valves.

The main purpose of the water valve is to provide water when the unit is running and to stop the water flow when the unit is idle. Some of the trouble caused by the water valves are:

1. Too little water flow.
2. Too much water flow.
3. Water flow does not stop when the unit is idle.

A water control valve will only operate correctly if the installation is correctly made and if the water is clean.

15-65 Restricted Water Flow

Some common troubles often encountered with water valves if the water flow is too little are:

1. Leaky valve.
2. Clogged or partially clogged screen.
3. Chattering valve.
4. Adjustment of the valve turned out too far.
5. Sediment-bound valve.
6. Leaky bellows.

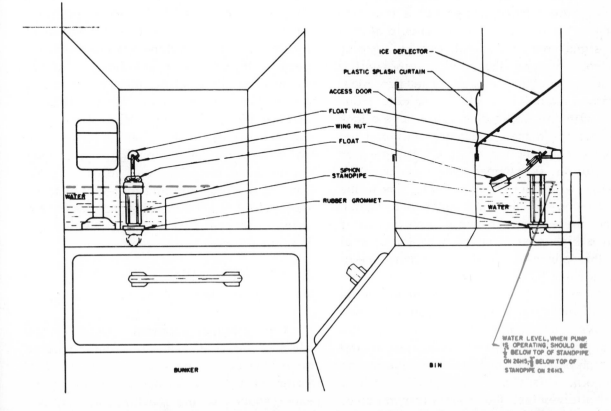

Fig. 15-77. Water pump and water level control for typical automatic ice maker.

In addition to these troubles, the water-cooling system may present the following difficulties: some water-cooled systems use a length of rubber hose connected between the water pipe running along the wall and the condensing unit water lines in order to eliminate transmitting the condensing unit vibration into the plumbing system of the building, and also to eliminate breakage of tubes from this vibration. The cold water inlet hose connection presents no difficulties and this hose will ordinarily give many years of service. However, as the water circulates through the condenser it sometimes becomes quite warm. This warm water, as it passes through the outlet hose connection, tends to deteriorate the inner rubber of the hose, resulting in a blistering of the inner wall. This will eventually clog the hose and restrict or stop the flow of water through the condenser.

Occasionally, someone may partially or completely shut off the water supply by closing the hand-operated valve installed in the system. A serviceman should always put signs near the shutoff valves warning of the effect on the refrigerating unit if these valves are closed. The two most common complaints which indicate troubles with the water circulation, are a lack of cooling in the condensing unit and too great a consumption of water. If the water circulation is stopped, the refrigerating system will start to short cycle, due to the functioning of the high pressure switch since these systems are always provided with a high pressure safety motor control for this purpose. As the head pressure of the machine builds up due to a lack of cooling, pressure is soon reached at which the control will open a switch stopping the motor. As soon as the motor is stopped, the head pressure drops rapidly, permitting the high pressure control to turn the motor on again. This short cycling will continue indefinitely unless the trouble is remedied. Such a condition is a severe strain on the motor in addition to not providing satisfactory refrigeration.

15-66 Too Much Water Flow

Too much water flow will give satisfactory refrigeration, but the amount of water consumed will be in excess of that needed and will increase the cost of operation. Three things which may cause too great a water flow are:
1. Too high water pressure.
2. Leaky water valve.
3. Water valve out of adjustment in such a way as to hold a valve too far open.

The condition of too high water pressure is seldom encountered unless the water supply pressure is uncontrolled. If encountered in one machine, it will perhaps be true for all the machines in that locality.

To determine whether the condition is due to a leaky valve or to a valve open too far, ask questions of the proprietor as to whether anyone has been working on the machine. If the machine has not been tampered with, and the trouble has just started to make itself evident, the trouble is usually a leaky water valve. This will be indicated by a continuous flow of water on the off cycle. Quite often a leaky water valve may be due to foreign matter lodging between the valve and valve seat. You can usually dislodge this material by flushing the valve. The flushing may be done by using a screwdriver to pry the valve open several times.

15-67 Tracing Water Circuit Troubles

The principal problem is to determine whether the water valve is causing trouble, or if it is caused by some other part of the water circulating system. To locate the exact source of the trouble, you may disconnect the joints where the hose is fastened to the rest of the system. By disconnecting the water outlet hose from the machine unit, you can readily determine whether the water is flowing as far as this point. If the water is coming as far as this point, the connection should be resealed and the other end of the hose disconnected from the wall pipe. If the water does not flow up to this point, the trouble is probably in the exhaust rubber hose of the system. You should determine whether the water is coming as far as the water valve by disconnecting the rubber hose used as the inlet connection. If the water flows through the hose, the sources of trouble are the water valve and the condenser proper. To check these sources, reseal the inlet rubber hose from the system and disconnect the water valve from the condenser. If the water flows through the water valve, but does not go through the condenser, the trouble is a major one necessitating replacement or cleaning of the condenser water tubes. However, if the water does not flow through the water valve, the water valve must be disconnected from the system and repaired or replaced.

Water hammer (a very noisy condition) can usually be eliminated by putting a short vertical pipe into the water line just ahead of the water valve to provide a shock absorbing air pocket.

15-68 Removing Water Valve

To remove an electrical solenoid water valve from the system, open the hand switch that controls the circuit to the motor and remove the water valve wires from the motor circuit. These wires are usually soldered and taped, so it will be necessary to unsolder or cut them. Before disconnecting the water valve from the water system, the water supply must be shut off at the hand valve. If the serviceman does not have a replacement valve on hand, the water system may be temporarily connected without a water valve and the water

flow regulated with the hand shutoff valve.

Some pressure operated water valves are difficult to remove from the system because the valve is connected to the high pressure side of the condensing unit. The pressure tube for these valves is usually connected into the cylinder head of the compressor, although some manufacturers connect this tube into the liquid line of the unit. A hand shutoff valve for this tube is sometimes provided, and if so, the removing of the valve is simple.

If the tube is connected to the cylinder head of the compressor, the following procedure is suggested:

1. Install gauge manifold.
2. Turn suction service valve all the way in.
3. In case refrigerant is R-12 or R-22, run compressor until pressure in crankcase reaches 0 psi.

Note: Be very careful of oil pumping which will sometimes occur before the pressure of 0 psi can be reached with R-12 or R-22.

4. Heat the water valve line and the water valve bellows carefully with a torch flame for three or four minutes until both of these become quite warm to the hand. This operation will move the liquid refrigerant, which has condensed in this tube and valve, back into the condensing unit, leaving only a small quantity of high pressure vapor in this tube.
5. Turn discharge service valve all the way in.
6. Clean joints to be opened.
7. Disconnect pressure tube from water valve. Wear goggles.
8. Plug the refrigerant pressure tubing openings immediately.
9. Heat water valve again gently, for often a quantity of liquid refrigerant becomes oil bound within the bellows chamber and releases with explosive force a few minutes after the valve is opened to the atmosphere.

Note: Be very careful not to point the refrigerant openings toward anyone because of the danger of being hit by the refrigerant.

10. Shut off water supply.
11. Disconnect water valve from water line and replace it with a good one or connect water lines directly. The water valve is now ready to be dismantled and repaired.

Some water valves are designed to permit removal of the valve body without disturbing the refrigerant connections (bellows, etc.). To disconnect one of these valves, simply shut off the water, disconnect valve body from water lines and bellows body.

Thermostatic water valves or motorized water valves are easily removed as only electrical connections need to be broken and the water circuit closed.

15-69 Repairing Water Valves

To completely overhaul a water valve, in addition to cleaning it, which may best be done with wire brushes, the valve and valve seat must be repaired. The valve seat, which is made of brass in most cases, may be lapped in a manner similar to lapping a compressor valve seat.

The valve proper usually consists of fiber, rubber, or Bakelite material and it should be replaced. In cases of emergency, however, this valve may be trued up by using a fine grade of sandpaper backed up by a level surface.

Occasionally, where the valve actuating stem passes into the valve body proper, a packing gland is used to seal the joint. This packing is usually the typical asbestos, graphite, and lead packing. If the packing nut has been turned all the way down and this joint still leaks, the packing should be replaced.

Electric water valves may have a faulty electrical coil (either shorted or with an open circuit). Replace with a coil of the same electrical properties (voltage and wattage). Thermostatic water valves may lose the element charge. If so, replace.

15-70 Installing and Adjusting Water Valves

After cleaning and repairing a pressure operated water valve, it should be tested and adjusted before being placed in service. If the maximum temperature of the water supply is 75 F. the valve should be adjusted to open at the following pressures: 87 psi for R-12; 144 psi for R-22; 152 psi R-717; 112 psig for R-500 and 173 psig for R-502.

If the water-in temperature is different from this, you may adjust the valve to its correct opening pressure by referring to Fig. 15-78.

A valve should also be tested for leaks at the same time it is being adjusted. This may be done by connecting an air pressure line to the inlet water opening of the valve. In order to adjust and test the pressure operating bellows, which controls the water flow, connect another air line and a pressure gauge to this fitting. No air should

WATER IN TEMPERATURE F.

REFRIGERANT	50	55	60	65	70	75	80	85	90	95	100
R-12		56	62	68	74	80	87	93	101	108	117	125
R-22		95	104	113	123	133	144	155	158	180	194	208
R-717		98	108	119	130	140.5	152	164	177	191	205	220
R-500		71	78	86	94	103	112	121	131	142	153	165
R-502		116	126	137	148	160	173	186	200	214	230	246

Fig. 15-78. Table of head pressures for systems with various refrigerants at various inlet water temperatures.

flow through the water valve until the correct control bellows pressure has been reached. Necessary adjustments may be made to obtain this condition.

Solenoid water valves are nonadjustable. Thermostatic water valves may be tested by using an adjustable temperature well to change the bulb temperature and air pressure used to check the valve operation.

After installing the water valve it should be checked for leaks (both water and refrigerant). Outlet water temperature, water flow and condensing pressure should also be checked.

15-71 Servicing Direct Expansion Evaporator Coils

"Dry" evaporating coils are coils using either an automatic expansion valve (AEV) or a thermostatic expansion valve (TEV) refrigerant control.

These coils must be clean inside and out for good heat transfer. They must contain just enough liquid refrigerant at the proper vapor pressure to provide the required cooling. Air or water being cooled must flow in and out of the coils efficiently. The coil must be leakproof and must be the proper size.

A serviceman should check these conditions. Ideally, pressure at the inlet of the coil (just after the AEV or TEV) should be measured as well as pressure at the outlet of the coil. However, most servicemen check only the low side pressure at the compressor suction service valve and assume that the coil pressure is close to this pressure. The pressure drop due to friction in the tubing and bends can be checked by reading the low side pressure when the unit is running and then reading it again just as the compressor stops. The rise in pressure is the pressure drop. Normally this pressure drop will be 2 to 3 psi.

Coil temperature should be checked. Thermometers can be mounted on tubing using spring loaded clip-on thermometer

holders. Superheat setting of the thermostatic expansion valve can be checked using thermometers. Location of the liquid in the cooling coil can also be located this way.

Frost accumulation acts as an insulation and also tends to reduce the air flow. Frost near the TEV usually means too great a superheat adjustment along with low suction pressures. Spotty frost usually means uneven air flow over the coil or that some defrosting elements are not working.

Air flow through the coil can be checked with an anemometer, (air velocity meter). If the air outlet or inlet is too small, the coil will be starved. Air-in temperatures and the air-out temperatures can also be checked. The air temperature will usually drop about 15 F. as it passes through the coil.

When checking for leaks, the fan and unit should be shut off. The low side pressure should be at least 15 psig when testing for leaks.

15-72 Removing the Evaporator Unit (Dry System)

If a dry evaporator coil needs to be removed, proceed as follows:

Install the compound gauge, or gauge manifold, and test for leaks. Start the compressor and close the LRSV (liquid receiver service valve). Run the compressor until atmospheric pressure or a constant vacuum has been produced and until the evaporator unit is warm (all the liquid refrigerant removed). To speed up this operation heat the evaporator unit carefully with a torch or hot water. Never allow it to get more than warm to the hand.

After stopping the motor, open the LRSV a little until the compound gauge reads zero (equalizing the pressure); then turn the suction line service valve all the way in, closing the suction line. A balanced pressure (atmosphere) in the evaporator unit may be obtained by either warming the unit, or by bypassing high pressure back through the gauge manifold. Fig. 15-79 shows an evaporator coil being pumped down.

Check the suction line, if it has a suction pressure regulator in it, or a solenoid valve, be sure they are open.

If a "hot gas" injection unit or a liquid injection unit is connected to the suction line, be sure the solenoid control valves for these units are shut off.

If the system has hand shutoff valves for each coil of a multiple installation, use these valves instead of the compressor service valves. Close the liquid line valve first, pump refrigerant out of evaporator coil, be sure there is 0 psig or slightly more in the evaporator coil, close the suction line hand valve, and the coil is ready for removal.

Shut off the electric power to the fan and liquid line solenoid valve (if there is one). Remove the casing or shroud of the coil carefully.

If electric defrost elements are mounted in or on the coil, disconnect them.

Clean and dry the suction line where it is connected to the cooling unit and also the inlet connection. Then unfasten the suction line and liquid line from the evaporator unit and plug the openings with appropriate fittings.

15-73 Repairing Direct Expansion Evaporator Unit

Coil repairs are usually limited to:
1. Repairing leaks.
2. Repairing or replacing fittings.
3. Straightening fins.
4. Replacing defrosting elements.
5. Repairing or replacing coil hangers.
6. Repairing or replacing fins and/or motors.

Where leaks occur, completely dismantle that part and clean the surfaces. If it is a silver brazing repair, follow the correct procedure as explained in Chapter 2.

Always anneal an old tube before flaring it. The fins can be straightened using a fin comb or wide jaw pliers.

Electrical defrosting elements should be checked for continuity and the terminals and insulation should be inspected. Rusty hangers, bent hangers and abused hanger assembly bolts should be replaced.

Check the fan and motor for vibration, tightness of the fan on the motor shaft, motor end play, motor bearing wear, and lubrication. Small faulty motors should be replaced. Larger motors can be reconditioned as explained in Chapter 7.

All the parts should be cleaned before assembly. The assembly of the evaporator coil is usually done on the job. If leaks have been repaired, the coil should be tested for leaks before it is installed.

15-74 Installing Direct Expansion Evaporator Unit

In the event the evaporator unit has been removed, several important things must be remembered during the assembly in order that the apparatus will function properly. After bolting the coil back into the refrigerator and leveling it, remove the plugs on the refrigerant openings and attach the liquid line and suction line to the unit. Be careful during these operations that no moisture enters the lines. It is good practice to dry the surfaces of the lines and evaporator unit before removing these seals.

The expansion valve (TEV) should be installed using a new gasket if it is of the bolted type.

Loosen the compressor end of the suction line and crack the liquid receiver service valve allowing some refrigerant to escape, forcing the air out of the evaporator unit and suction line. The compressor end of the suction line should then be tightened.

Another method is to evacuate the evaporator unit, suction line, and compressor

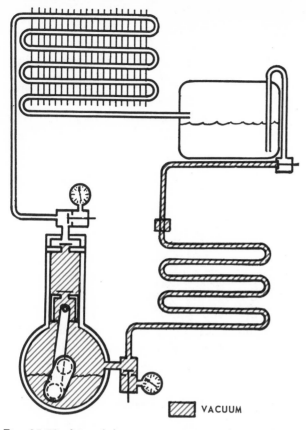

Fig. 15-79. *Liquid line, evaporator, and compressor crankcase being pumped down with refrigerant being pumped into condenser or receiver.*

VACUUM

twice to the air. The trapped air will then be drawn out of the system. The discharge service valve must be turned all the way in during the evacuation, and the gauge plug removed. Test for leaks with 5 to 25 psi pressure, and test for leaks again at ambient refrigerant pressure (high side pressure) before allowing the refrigerant to escape into the unit.

The cooling coil may be dehydrated more completely by heating it to a fairly high temperature of (175-200 F.) as it is evacuated to drive out any moisture that may be present. Heat lamps may be used for this purpose.

After the coil has been installed and tested for leaks, install the electrical connections for the defrost units, install the fan and motor. The electrical connections should be tight and moistureproof. Operate the defrost unit and the fan.

Assemble the casing or shroud. Start the unit and check for normal operation.

15-75 Dry Coil Refrigerant Controls

The installation, operation, and service of refrigerant controls in commercial systems is much the same as described in Chapter 6.

All types of refrigerant controls may be found in commercial systems. If the system has a self-contained hermetic unit, it may be serviced as described in Chapter 12.

The multiple evaporator coil installations, however, and the larger commercial units, do have several other features with which a serviceman should be familiar.

15-76 Servicing Thermostatic Expansion Valves

Dry systems which use the thermostatic expansion valve refrigerant control may be of the single evaporator coil type or multiple coil type. The design and operation of this valve is explained in Chapter 6. The serviceman should check the complete system, install the gauge manifold and check for pressure. Check the amount of refrigerant (sight glass) and check for liquid line solenoid valves, two- temperature valves, "hot gas" or liquid injection systems, driers (both suction line and liquid line) temperature or pressure motor controls, and electrical supply.

The serviceman can check the coil by the appearance of the coil, by the sound, and by the temperature of the expansion valve. If the coil is frosting back so the suction line is frosted, it may be due to the following troubles:

1. Needle may be leaking.
2. Control may be adjusted for too little superheat.
3. Valve may have the incorrect thermal bulb charge.
4. Valve orifice may be too large.
5. The power element may be attached loosely to suction line.

6. Power element may be located in too warm a position.

7. Dirt in system may be holding valve open.

8. An external equalizer valve may be needed.

To determine which of these troubles is the one responsible for the fault in operation is difficult, and the best method is the process of elimination. The location of the power element may be easily checked and its attachment to the suction line noted. It is recommended that the thermostatic bulb be placed on top of the suction line rather than beside or below it in order that the liquid in the bulb will make good thermal contact with the suction line. Fig. 15-80 shows two recommended thermal bulb locations. A thermostatic control in

itself is frosting unevenly or not sweating properly, may be due to the following:

1. Clogged screen in expansion valve which may give no refrigeration.

2. Loss of refrigerant from power element in expansion valve which will give erratic refrigeration.

3. Moisture in the system which may periodically give good refrigeration and then none, as the moisture will freeze in the orifice to expansion valve and close it, then defrost.

4. Wax in valve. This wax is from the oil and its presence means that the oil used was for a different temperature range or was improperly prepared for refrigeration service.

5. Stuck-shut needle (this is a rare occurrence).

6. Under capacity valve orifice.

In case of expansion valve trouble it is usually recommended that a new valve be installed.

A flooded coil will be indicated by a sweating or frosted suction line beyond the thermal bulb position which may be caused by:

1. Thermal bulb loose from suction line.

2. Thermal bulb in warm air flow.

3. Too large TEV orifice.

4. TEV needle stuck open.

5. Undersize cooling coil.

6. Thermal bulb has wrong charge.

7. Pressure drop is too large in coil.

If the bulb is loose, is mounted wrong or is in a warm air stream remove it, clean it and the tubing, remount it firmly and insulate it if necessary.

An oversize TEV should be replaced with one of the correct size.

A stuck-open needle condition is best remedied by replacing the valves.

Only rarely does one find a condition of an undersize coil (replace), a TEV with the wrong charge (replace) or too great a pressure drop (replace coil).

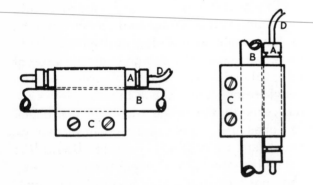

Fig. 15-80. Illustration showing recommended location of thermostatic bulbs on suction lines to obtain best operation. Bulb should be on top of horizontal suction line. It should have closed end on bottom when mounted on vertical suction line. A—Thermal bulb. B—Suction line. C—Clamp. D—Thermal bulb capillary tube.

which the adjustment has been tampered with is rare and you may usually depend on customers not trying to set them; therefore, you should not attempt to readjust the control at first, but rather to check for other troubles. Leaky needles or out-of-adjustment valves cannot be repaired satisfactorily on the premises.

A starved coil, that is, one that is giving poor cabinet temperatures and the coil

15-77 Repairing Clogged Screen

A clogged screen may be easily detected by poor refrigeration, sweating or frosting near the TEV only and no refrigerant sound.

Removing an expansion valve which has a clogged screen necessitates removing both the liquid and vaporized refrigerant from the lines to be opened. The liquid line may be carefully heated, driving the liquid refrigerant back to the nearest shutoff valve, and this valve then closed. The coil is already evacuated (indicated by a.warm coil); after determining that the low side pressure is at atmospheric pressure or higher, the suction line valve may be closed. The screen may then be removed after cleaning and drying the connections.

Clean the screen or replace with a new one.

Install the screen, assemble the TEV, install it in the system, remove the air, test for leaks and return the coil to normal operation by opening the suction and liquid line valves.

15-78 Removing Expansion Valve

The serviceman should remove a faulty expansion valve and replace it with one that is known to be in good condition. The troublesome valve may then be checked in a shop equipped for this purpose and the trouble accurately determined.

Install gauges or gauge manifold and test for leaks. Remove the casing from the evaporator coil. Store all parts carefully. Close the liquid receiver service valve or liquid line and run the compressor until the evaporator coil hand shutoff valve has no liquid refrigerant in it and the pressure is at or slightly above 0 psig. You can equalize the pressure by cracking the liquid receiver service valve or hand valve when the compressor is idle. Turn the suction service valve stem all the way in, or close the suction line hand valve. Dry and clean the expansion valve. An important

factor, inasmuch as many systems are R-12, is to dry thoroughly all connections before breaking them open. Frequently, the thermostatic expansion valve is attached to the coil in such a manner that is difficult. It must be done by using a dry cloth, or one saturated with alcohol, in order to dry thoroughly and prevent future trouble due to moisture and dirt entering the system. Then remove the liquid line and unbolt the valve from the evaporator unit. Larger units may use silver brazed valve connections. Before disconnecting the joints remove the internal parts of the valve and the thermal element assembly.

If it becomes necessary to dismantle a thermostatic expansion valve, the thermostatic element should be removed as a complete assembly and not taken apart. The thermostatic element is charged with refrigerant and the power element bellows is under considerable pressure at normal temperatures. In the assembled condition, this pressure is counteracted by springs or by expansion valve diaphragm pressure. If dismantled and the power element is free to act, the pressure may burst the power element or at least extend it so far its accuracy is destroyed. If the thermostatic bulb is placed in an ice and salt solution and its temperature brought low enough, the power element may then be safely dismantled. In many cases these are the parts that need replacing and the valve body need not be removed. Seal refrigerant openings immediately.

15-79 Repairing Expansion Valves

Four things likely to go wrong with an expansion valve are (1) the needle and seat becoming worn, (2) a dirty screen, leaky bellows, (3) moisture accumulation on the outside of the bellows, (4) loss of charge in thermal element. Occasionally, one finds such trouble as a broken spring, etc., but this is rare and the troubles are easy to locate.

Most of the repairs apply to both AEV's and TEV's. A worn needle and seat is usually due to a lack of refrigerant in the system. Refrigerant does not have a chance to condense before it passes through the expansion valve orifice and this dry, hot gas rapidly cuts or erodes the needle and seat. As there are many models and types of TEV's on the market, only general instructions are given here.

The best repair of a needle seat is to replace it with new parts. If replacements are not available, the needle must be reground or restored in a lathe or drill press until the shoulder that has been worn into the needle surface disappears. It is important that the same taper be kept on the needle point. The seat, which is nearly always made of softer metal than the needle, may usually be filed, with a dead smooth file, until the older surface against which the needle was seated has disappeared. The seat must be filed square at right angles to the center line of the needle. A file guide is best for this purpose.

One may tap the new needle into the new seat during assembly of the valve and get good results.

A leaky bellows may be due either to breaking down of the soldered joint, or to a fracture in the bellows or diaphragm itself. A bellows is a difficult thing to repair, without a special fixture to hold the parts. The correct thing to do is to replace the expansion valve.

The matter of successfully cleaning a screen is quite important. Fine-mesh copper screens may be cleaned fairly successfully by combining air pressure and a safe solvent, too, but, the best way is by heating it. This must be very carefully performed or the screen will be burned. It is important never to allow an expansion valve to go into service without a screen being placed in the liquid line entrance.

Moisture on the outside of the bellows or diaphragm is a result of air leaking into the housing surrounding the bellows and

the natural condensation of the moisture in the air upon the cool surfaces. This moisture, when it freezes, binds the bellows or diagraphm and does not permit the expansion valve to operate at all, or permits erratic operation. Washing this part with a moisture absorber removes the moisture. The serviceman may do three things:

(1) Put a quantity of Vaseline in this space which will not allow moisture to accumulate. (2) Put a quantity of glycerin in this chamber which will combine with any moisture that enters and form a nonfreezing mixture. (3) Place a seal cap over the open end to exclude the air. The seal cap usually is adequate and is the most common practice.

To test an automatic expansion valve after it has been repaired you may use the following system: join the liquid line connection to dry air line and create at least a 90 lb. pressure at the expansion valve, as shown in Fig. 15-81. Turn the adjusting

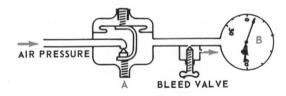

Fig. 15-81. Method used to check expansion valve for leaks and for pressure setting. A—Pressure adjustment. B—Compound gauge.

nut in until the valve is opened and permits the air to come through. Then turn it out again until air ceases to pass by the needle. To accurately test this, pour some refrigerant oil in the evaporator coil connection or low side opening of the expansion valve. If the valve is leaking, bubbles will be formed. No leak of any size should be permitted, except those AEV's which have a bypass to permit the high and low side pressures to balance during the off cycle.

Another way to test an expansion valve is to connect a compound gauge into the low side of the valve and a high pressure line on the liquid line connection.

With air fed into the liquid line opening, an increase of the pressure on the compound gauge will indicate a leaking valve.

If a hand needle valve is used in the low pressure side opening in parallel to the gauge a definite amount of air can be released and you can tell if the expansion valve needle is sticking. Any variation of pressure at the compound gauge will show that the needle valve is leaking.

To test the bellows for leaks at this point, plug the low side opening of the expansion valve, then turn the adjusting screw in until a positive pressure of at least 30 to 40 lbs. is produced on the inside of the bellows. Any leaks in the bellows will be indicated by bubbles coming through the oil placed over the adjusting screw opening of the valve.

Testing and adjusting of a TEV is described in Chapter 6.

15-80 Installing Expansion Valves

Mount the expansion valve and evacuate the liquid line, cooling unit, and suction line. Test for leaks carefully by purging, building up a refrigerant vapor pressure and then evacuate again. Install the fan and motor if used. Open liquid receiver valve or liquid line hand valve, start compressor, and observe the operation.

In multiple systems all dry coils using expansion valves should be installed with individual shutoff valves for both the liquid and suction lines to each coil.

A condition which results in trouble with thermostatic expansion valves is the attempt to adjust these valves in an effort to maintain too great a difference in temperatures in various boxes in the system. This gives rise to erratic operation particularly in the coils which are closed off the most. The remedy for this difficulty is to use, in addition to the thermostatic expansion valve, one or more two-tempera-

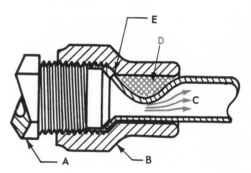

Fig. 15-82. Illustration which shows what happens when moisture freezes between nut and tubing. A—Fitting. B—Flare nut and tubing. C—Restricted refrigerant opening. D—Ice formation. E—Flare being pulled out of place.

ture valves in the suction line in appropriate places.

Gauges and thermometers should be used to check for correct superheat setting.

When the unit is operating correctly, connect the defrost wires, if used, install the casing and shroud.

In multiple commercial installations, in which finned coils are used, the expansion valve is usually attached to the coil by means of an SAE flared connection. The flare nut in such an installation must be shellacked, or sealed from moisture, after the installation has been made and before the unit starts to operate; otherwise, ice may form between the nut and the tubing and in a short time will cause the tube to collapse or break. This condition can also occur at the place where the suction line fastens to the evaporator coil. Fig. 15-82 shows the pinching operation of ice formation between the flare nut and the tubing.

Other methods have been devised to prevent moisture from accumulating behind flare nuts. One method provides a rubber seal at the end of the flare nut. Another method consists of drilling holes through the flare nut, the idea being that moisture will drain out and if ice does form it will release its pressure through the holes in the nut rather than against the tubing. Short shank flare nuts should be used in places where frosting occurs. Fig. 15-83 shows a short flare nut with openings across the threads for moisture escape. As mentioned previously, the best sort of connection for use in the interior of the cabinets is a silver brazed flanged connection. Soft solder is popular but some manufacturers are recommending silver brazing for all such joints, except for expansion valves, as it is stronger and safer.

15-81 Servicing Flooded Coils

Flooded coils use high side floats, low side floats or capillary tube refrigerant controls. High side floats are used mainly with large ammonia systems. Low side floats are used with some beverage coolers. Capillary tube systems are used on single units and the service is explained in Chapter 12.

In low side float systems, a continuous hissing sound in the cooling coil is an indication of trouble and may be due to the following causes:

1. Leaky needle.
2. Lack of refrigerant.
3. Float out of calibration.
4. Cooling coil not being level.
5. Leaky float ball.
6. Leaks in the coil.
7. Clogged screen.

Chapter 13 describes a low side float unit.

The hissing sound is distinctive if there is a lack of refrigerant and, in addition, the liquid line is considerably warmer than the suction line at the evaporator coil. This may be determined by putting your hand over the two lines just as they are going into the coil. The temperature difference will be noted at once. The suction line, although cold, will sweat if there is a lack of refrigerant. If the needle and seat are leaking, the hissing sound is not so distinctive and may be classified as more of a gurgling sound. Also, the suction line will likely sweat back to the opening in the cabinet wall and sometimes all the way back

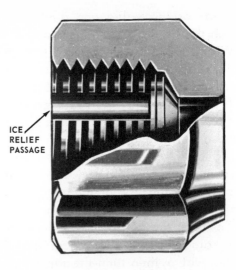

Fig. 15-83. Special flare nut used to prevent ice accumulation between flare nut and tubing. (Superior Valve and Fittings Co.)

to the compressor. This sweating under normal conditions should never be more than 6 in. to 8 in. back along the suction line.

A low side float coil out-of-level may be easily checked with a spirit level. An out-of-calibration float and a leaky float ball are rather difficult to check and necessitate dismantling the evaporator coil to learn the source of the trouble. A float which is calibrated so the refrigerant level is too low when the needle closes will not give a hissing or gurgling sound, but will be indicated by a low sweat line on the coil and inadequate water temperatures. It may tend to become oil bound, since an extra deep layer of oil in the evaporator coil will replace the liquid refrigerant.

In case of a lack of refrigerant, the coil farthest from the condensing unit vertically will be the one to show lack of refrigerant first. Another way to check trouble occurring in the coil is to loosen the evaporator coil from its hanger and rock it back and forth. If it has an out-of-calibration float or a slight lack of refrigerant, you will find the hissing sound stops for short periods of time as the liquid refrigerant moves back and forth in the chamber. If there is a leaky needle, the noise will not change. If the needle is leaking, or one of the other troubles is existent, one way to determine it is to shut off the liquid line valve (normally the one mounted right on the evaporator coil). Then allow the condensing unit to run for several minutes. This will lower the float more than usual. Next, quickly open the valve, permitting a rush of liquid refrigerant to wash past the orifice opening. If a piece of dirt has lodged between the needle and its seat this will be washed away and the sound of hissing or gurgling will stop momentarily, indicating that the trouble has been eliminated.

If the coil has a refrigerant leak, it should be replaced.

Beverage tubes need periodic cleaning. Sanitation laws usually specify what chemicals to use and the procedure. The owner of the equipment is responsible for this operation.

Occasionally poor beverage flow may be found to be the trouble. If cleaning does not remedy the condition, the coil should be replaced.

One trouble sometimes found in multiple systems is clogging of screens located at each individual coil. These screens are located in the inlet to the refrigerant control. On low side float units with the liquid line valve bolted on the header, the screen is inserted in a pocket between the liquid line service valve and the header.

If a service call is made and it is found that all evaporator coils except one connected to a multiple system are operating satisfactorily, and this one coil is not giving any refrigeration whatsoever, the trouble may be due to one of two things, either the needle is stuck closed or the screen is clogged.

To remove the screen, close the suction line valve and, after cleaning and drying the joint between the liquid line service valve and the coil, this valve may be unbolted. When the connection (a gasketed one) is opened, a little liquid refrigerant

may escape, so be sure to wear goggles. The screen is located at this point and is easily accessible for replacement or cleaning. The recommended service practice is to replace the clogged screen with a new one. Replacement screens should be carried on all service calls.

Upon assembling the coil after repairing the trouble, proceed as follows: open the liquid line valve after unit has been assembled and then carefully test for leaks. When starting a coil in this case, you should always wait until you hear the float valve stop the flow of refrigerant. This policy will save many service call-backs.

Some low side floats, when opened to remove a screen, permit a slow seepage of air into the evaporator coil through the needle orifice opening. This amount is negligible if the unit is assembled immediately. However, if the coil has been left open for a number of hours, the coil should be purged of air by loosening the suction service valve from the coil header and then cracking the liquid line valve. The resultant surge of refrigerant will remove most of the air from the coil.

Needless to say, when reassembling the unit, a new gasket should be used and the two gasket surfaces should be perfectly clean and smooth. A scraper made from an old flat file is a good tool for removing the old gasket. If possible, the serviceman should put a little refrigerant oil on the new gasket before installing it. Never use other than Monel or extra heavy cadmium plated bolts and cap screws on evaporator coils. ALWAYS TEST FOR LEAKS.

The screens proper are best cleaned in the repair shop. One excellent method to clean a screen is to heat it very carefully, over an electric plate, then quench it in water. This treatment quickly loosens most of the dirt. A weak solution of hydrochloric acid and water also does a good job. POUR ACID INTO THE WATER, NEVER WATER INTO ACID. Wear goggles when doing this job to protect your eyes from splatter. Be sure to rinse the screen. Thermostatic expansion valve screens may be serviced in much the same way.

Master screens located at the receiver end of the liquid line are also serviced as stated. In some cases, the receiver must be discharged to permit removing the master screen.

15-82 Removing Flooded Coil

The refrigerant may be left in the evaporator unit because the unit is equipped with service valves between the lines and the unit. This method will necessitate leaving both the service valves on the evaporator unit; close the liquid receiver service valve and run the compressor for about 1 minute or until the liquid line becomes warm. In the meantime, heat the liquid line slightly with a torch or by rubbing your hand on it. This action will remove the liquid refrigerant from the liquid line. Then close the liquid line valve located on the cooling unit. It is best to close this valve when the compound gauge is reading zero pounds or slightly above. The liquid line may be disconnected and plugged after the exterior has been carefully cleaned and dried. Turn the evaporator unit suction line valve stem all the way in, and balance the pressures in the suction line by manipulating this valve. Close the nearest suction line hand shutoff valve. Clean and dry this connection, remove, and plug the suction line. By carefully bending suction and liquid lines to prevent buckling, the evaporator unit may be readily unbolted and removed from the cabinet. Many evaporator unit mounting devices become corroded and are difficult to remove. Heat them carefully and tap lightly, or use penetrating oil.

15-83 Repairing Flooded Coils

Four troubles which most commonly occur with low side float valves are: leaky needle and seat, clogged screen, leaky float, float mechanism out of calibration. Screen should be repaired as described for expansion valves. Leaky coils can be repaired. The leaky joint should be completely dismantled, cleaned, repaired, and tested.

Faulty floats and float needle valves are best factory reconditioned.

15-84 Installing Flooded Coils

The clean, repaired evaporator coil, should be installed and bolted in place. It must be mounted level.

Clean and dry the refrigerant connections. Make the refrigerant connections, flared or brazed, carefully. Inspect the joints. Purge, evacuate, and purge the refrigerant lines. Build up a refrigerant pressure in the lines and test for leaks. Open all four of the refrigerant valves (two on the evaporator coil and two on the refrigerant lines). Turn on the beverage valves.

Check operation of the coil (temperature, sound, sweat back, etc.) and do a thorough cleanup before leaving the premises.

15-85 Installing Two-Temperature Valves

Many multiple installations involve several cabinets of different temperatures connected to one condensing unit. This necessitates use of two-temperature valves. The metering type, two-temperature valve is commonly used in ice cream and soda fountain combinations in which the ice cream must be maintained at around 5 F., the beverage coolers must be kept at about 45 F., and the storage chamber kept at a different temperature.

The two-temperature valves used to permit this condition should be installed in the suction line of the warmer coils. This connection may be at any place on the suction line because its operation is usually not affected by the distance from the coil. Frequently this valve may be found located in the soda fountain; some are located near the condensing unit.

This type of installation may be improved considerably by mounting a check valve, as shown in Fig. 15-84, in the suction line of the coldest coil to prevent backing up of the higher pressure gases into it.

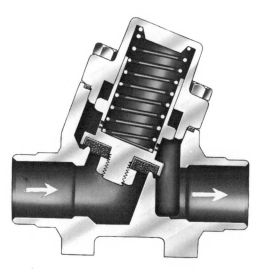

Fig. 15-84. Check valve used to prevent reverse flow of refrigerant in line. Valve should be dismantled before it is brazed into line. Notice valve insert and damper action of valve stem and housing.

Also, a surge tank should be mounted near the condensing unit and connected between the compressor and the main suction line to cut down the rapid fluctuations of the low side pressure.

In most code installations the two-temperature valve and the check valve must be mounted near the condensing unit, and the surge tank must be mounted on the condensing unit base.

15-86 Servicing Two-Temperature Valves

As explained in Chapter 12, the two-temperature valves are automatic valves, which, when installed in the suction line, maintain a higher refrigerant pressure on one or more evaporator coils than that which exists in the remainder of the system. Four types of two-temperature valves are:

1. Metering type.
2. Snap-action type.
3. Thermostatic type.
4. Solenoid valve, which is thermostat controlled.

The metering type, two-temperature valve is used extensively in beverage cooling and ice cream cabinet combinations. It should be located in the suction line of the beverage cooler. It maintains an evaporating pressure in the beverage cooler 10 psi or 15 psi above the pressure needed to maintain ice cream. The four troubles commonly encountered with this valve are:

1. Leaky needle.
2. Stuck-shut valve.
3. Out-of-adjustment.
4. Frost accumulation on bellows.

If the valve is leaky, the warmer evaporator coil will be too cold and there will be danger of freezing. This cold temperature may also be due to the two-temperature valve being adjusted too close and at too low a pressure. To determine which of the two troubles is prevalent, a check should be made to see if the valve has been adjusted recently. If the valve has not been tampered with, the trouble is very likely a leaky needle. If the valve has been tampered with, you must readjust it by using a thermometer to obtain the correct cooling coil temperature. The adjusting nut should not be turned more than 1/2 turn at a time. A 15-minute interval should be allowed between each adjustment to permit the coil to completely respond to the new pressure.

For accuracy in making adjustments on two-temperature valves, a low pressure gauge should be installed in the low pressure side of the evaporator coil. Sometimes such a gauge opening is available, but in many cases it is not. Service work on such valves will be facilitated if the

serviceman, when installing two-temperature valves, will install a shutoff valve with
a gauge opening in the suction line to permit the use of a gauge to check the low
side pressure.

A stuck-shut valve, which will be a rare
occurrence, may be easily checked by a
noncooling condition of the warmer cooling
coil and an adequate refrigerant supply to
the two-temperature valve, but not through
it. This refrigerant supply may be checked
by cracking the flare nuts on the high pressure side of the two-temperature valve.
Some of these two-temperature valves are
provided with screens. A clogged screen
will be indicated by a warmer cooling condition of the coil with symptoms similar
to the stuck needle condition.

Frost accumulation on the bellows will
occur only when the valve is located in or
near a freezing compartment. The valve
should be removed from the freezing compartment and the bellows covered with
Vaseline.

The same troubles are encountered with
the snap-action, two-temperature valve as
with the metering type. However, most
snap-action valves are provided with a
gauge connection in the nature of a one-
way service valve mounted on the two-
temperature valve body. This gauge connection makes adjustment of the valve
simple and is a means whereby you may
determine whether the valve is leaking or
out of adjustment. Occasionally, trouble
is encountered because of the presence of
moisture and its freezing on the exterior
of the valve bellows. This moisture prevents the bellows from working evenly and
will tend to give erratic operation to the
unit. Any frost accumulation on the bellows
should be removed and the bellows coated
with Vaseline to prevent any further accumulation.

Thermostatic two-temperature valves
offer the same troubles, causes, and remedies as the other two. In addition it has
troubles resulting from the thermostatic

element. These troubles are the same as
mentioned in regard to thermostatic expansion valves. They are:
1. Loss of charge from thermostatic
   element.
2. Frost on bellows.
3. Poor power element contact with
   coil.
4. Pinched capillary tube.
5. Wrong adjustment.

These troubles are checked in the manner similar to the method of checking the
thermostatic element in thermostatic expansion valves.

An electric solenoid valve in the liquid
line of the warmer coil and electrically
connected to a thermostat in the fixture
may have the following troubles:
1. Needle stuck open.
2. Needle stuck shut.
3. Thermostat troubles.
   A. Points stuck together.
   B. Open circuit.
   C. Out-of-adjustment.
4. Poor wiring.
5. Open solenoid winding.
6. Burned-out solenoid winding.

The solenoid valve should be replaced
if the needle is not working properly. When
a solenoid coil is replaced, be sure to use
the correct coil (24V, 120V or 240V).

15-87 Suction Line

Suction lines have the following items
that may need service:
1. Fittings.
2. Hand valves.
3. Two-temperature valves.
4. Check valves.
5. Surge or accumulation tanks.
6. Hot gas injection unit.
7. Liquid injection unit.

The fittings are checked as previously
explained. The hand valves are similar in
construction to liquid line hand valves. It
is important to check the suction line size
and to determine, by using the compound

gauge, the pressure drop in the low side of the system. The pressure drop varies but it should not exceed 2 psi. To check the pressure drop, record the low side pressure when the unit is running and then record the pressure just as the unit stops. The difference in the readings is the pressure drop.

15-88 Assembling Refrigerating Unit

When the repairs have been made, and the parts, after rigorous testing are found to be all right, the proper assembling of the apparatus to insure correct operation is very important.

Four fundamentals to be followed when installing part of a refrigerating mechanism are:
1. Clean and dry part to be put into the system.
2. Purge and evacuate that part of the system which has been opened.
3. Test for leaks.
4. Start and adjust the unit.

If an open type compressor overhaul has just been completed, the proper installation of the compressor is very important. Bolt the compressor to the base and line it up with the electric motor so the belt or belts are installed in exact alignment. With the 1 in. movement tightness, bolt the suction service valve and the discharge service valve to the compressor. If it is a motor-compressor unit, mount it on its base and bolt it to the frame. Install suction line connection, condenser line connection, and electrical leads to the motor and controls. Install the gauges or the gauge manifold and exhaust the compressor to the outside until a vacuum of 25 to 28 in. has been drawn upon the crankcase for several minutes using a vacuum pump.

After sufficient vacuum has been drawn, complete the operations of putting the compressor in service. Crack the suction service valve slightly and allow some refrigerant to escape into the crankcase until a

5 to 30 lb. pressure is obtained. Then test carefully for leaks. Close the suction service valve completely and evacuate again to a 25 to 28 in. vacuum. This evacuation should be to the open air of the room or piped to the outside. The discharge service valve is turned all the way in during this operation.

After second vacuum has been drawn, open both the suction service and discharge service valves all the way out, but not far enough to close off the gauge openings. As this is done, it is a good policy to start the compressor; otherwise there might be a flow of liquid refrigerant from the evaporator unit to the crankcase of the compressor. This may cause a freezing condition when starting the compressor. The presence of liquid refrigerant may also cause pumping of oil which may break the compressor valves.

Because it is virtually impossible to assemble a refrigerating mechanism in the field without having some foreign matter (dirt and moisture) get into the system, a filter-drier should be installed in the system.

Leave the gauges attached to the mechanism to check on the condensing pressure. This will help determine whether the unit is working correctly. A service call should be made within the next day or two to check on the operating pressures, and the general condition of the refrigerator. When available, temperature and pressure recorders should be connected into the system for 24 hours to check on unit operation.

15-89 Moisture in System

Many troubles in refrigerating systems may be traced to the presence of moisture in the system. Moisture, as it circulates through the system in the presence of oil and the refrigerant at high temperatures (compressor and condenser) causes many complex actions.

Application	Max Tolerable Moisture, PPM		Moisture in Units, PPM	
	Refrigerant 12	Refrigerant 22	Refrigerant 12	Refrigerant 22
Domestic Refrigerators, Freezers	10,10,10,15	--	5,8,10	--
Food Display Cases	10,15,15,20	15,20	5,10	5
Frozen Food Cases	10,10,10,10,15	10,15,15	10	--
Room Air Conditioners	15,25	25,25,40,55,60,10, 100	10,10	5,15,15,15,20,60
Residential, Package Air Conditioners	10,15,15,25,50	10,15,25,25,35,40, 40,40,60,100,180	7,10,15,40	7,10,15,15,15,20, 25,40,50,55,60
Field-Built Systems	15,20,25	15,40,40,100	--	10,15,60

Fig. 15-85. Maximum allowable moisture in refrigerating system and average amounts found in systems. (ASHRAE Guide and Data Book)

Moisture in the system may freeze at the refrigerant control orifice, eventually clogging it. Moisture in hermetic systems also may cause a chemical breakdown between the oil, the refrigerant and the motor winding insulation and create acids which ruin the motor windings. If immediate action is taken to remove all moisture or to make the moisture harmless, many troubles may be eliminated.

Fig. 15-85 shows the safe limits of moisture allowable in a system using R-12 and R-22.

Many servicemen install large driers in a system on a temporary basis. These units quickly clean the system and remove the moisture. Fig. 15-86 shows such an installation in a liquid line.

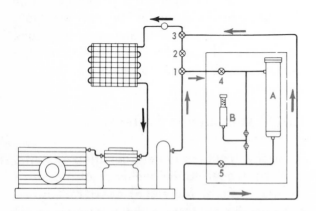

Fig. 15-86. Master drier and filter installed in liquid line of unit. A—Drier. B—Moisture indicator. 1, 2, 3, 4 hand valves.
(McIntire Co., Sub. Superior Valve and Fittings Co.)

To remove the unit, open valve No. 2 and close valve No. 4. Wait until the drier has had most of the refrigerant removed, close valve 3. The system is now back in operation. Then close valves 4 and 5 and the connecting lines may be removed and the openings capped. Be careful, there is high pressure in the lines and there may be some liquid.

15-90 Use of Driers (Dehydrators) and Filters

Surveys show that about 80 percent of all service calls are either directly caused by, or, are traceable to moisture. If moisture is present in large enough quantities, it will form ice in capillary tubes and expansion valves, plugging them.

There are a number of ways of removing moisture from refrigeration equipment. These include high vacuum, slow steady flow of hot dry air, and several alternate moderate vacuums broken with dry refrigerant.

In all commercial systems driers are a standard part of the installation. Drier size is usually based on the horsepower of the system, kind of refrigerant and use of system (air conditioning, commercial or low temperature). A 30 cu. in. drier will serve for a 1 hp R-12 or R-500 air conditioning system. A 100 cu. in. (3 in. dia. x 10 in. long) will serve a 5 hp AC, a

3 hp commercial, or a 3 hp low temp unit having R-12 or R-500 refrigerant. It will also serve a 10 hp AC, a 5 hp commercial or a 5 hp low temp unit using either refrigerant 22 or R-502.

A sight glass with a moisture indicator is a good device for determining whether the system is dry.

The drier must have sufficient capacity based on the size of the equipment or the amount of refrigerant in the system. Fig. 15-87 shows a drier with flared connections and a combination of bead desiccant and solid baked core desiccant. A drier

Fig. 15-89. Suction line filter sealed assembly. (McIntire Co., Sub. Superior Valve and Fittings Co.)

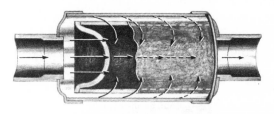

Fig. 15-90. Cross section of suction line filter showing filter element and refrigerant vapor flow.

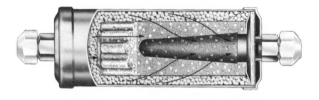

Fig. 15-87. Sealed filter-drier. Has screens, felt filters, desiccant beads and baked dessicant core. (Henry Valve Co.)

with a bolted flange opening to enable a serviceman to replace the desiccant element is shown in Fig. 15-88.

Driers and filters may be installed in the suction line to protect the compressor from burnout after a hermetic motor burnout replacement or after severe oil breakdown. Fig. 15-89 shows a suction line filter and Fig. 15-90 its internal design. Dirt in a system may cause serious damage. The small solid particles act as an abrasive. They will wear the needles and seats and as the suction vapor carries these particles into the motor-compressor they may wear through the motor insulation and cause a burnout. A filter for a large sys-

Fig. 15-88. Drier with a bolted end flange. The baked desiccant core is replaceable in these units without disconnecting the refrigerant lines.

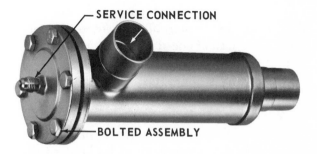

Fig. 15-91. Suction line filter with bolted flange construction permits easy replacement of filter element. Service connection is equipped with Schraeder valve.

tem showing a bolted assembly to permit replacement of filter element is shown in Fig. 15-91. The service connection is to enable a serviceman to check the pressure drop. If this gauge reads more than 2 psi higher than the compressor compound gauge with the unit running, the filter element should be replaced. Fig. 15-92 shows a large suction line filter unit equipped with a gauge connection. In cases of extreme space limitation, driers may be placed in the suction line. All of the common refrigerants can be successfully dried with the drier in either the liquid or suction line.

Fig. 15-92. Large capacity suction line filter equipped with a gauge connection. (Henry Valve Co.)

15-91 Servicing Burnouts

A motor burnout is possible with any system using a welded motor-compressor or a bolted assembly motor-compressor. Moisture, dirt in the system, plus excessive temperature (the warmest spot is usually the motor windings) may cause an acid condition to develop and eventually a motor winding short (burnout).

To prevent this occurrence, the system must be kept moisture free and dirt free. To detect acid formation, the system should be checked regularly.

1. Use a sight glass with moisture indicator.
2. Take an oil sample periodically and test this sample with an oil test kit. The oil sample must be kept sealed until tested.

The test kit consists of an indicator solution. This solution makes the oil sample

change color if acid is present. The kit contains measuring vials, mixing bottles, and other accessories.

If a burnout occurs, the motor-compressor must be replaced. If it is a small hermetic, discard the refrigerant In large systems equipped with shutoff valves it may be possible to save the refrigerant. Purge the motor-compressor. BE CAREFUL. USE GOGGLES, RUBBER GLOVES AND VENTILATE THE SPACE. The oil may cause serious burns – do not get this oil on your skin. In some cases the fumes are toxic.

The system can be reconditioned by:
1. Flushing the complete system with R-11 using CO_2 to circulate the refrigerant or use a separate pump.
2. Installing a suction drier-filter of excessive capacity in the suction line.

In system 1, after cleaning, install the new motor-compressor, test for leaks, evacuate the system to 5 to 100 microns, install a drier in the suction line, charge the system and operate. Make frequent oil acid tests. Replace the driers if the oil sample is discolored or shows an acid trace.

Fig. 15-93. Suction line filter-drier installed on bolted assembly motor-compressor. Pressure drop across filter-drier is being checked with gauge manifold.

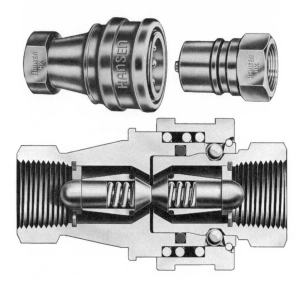

Fig. 15-94. Reusable quick coupler: Above, disconnected. Below, connected. (Hansen Mfg. Co.)

Fig. 15-95. Connecting high capacity filter-drier to suction service valve connector of motor-compressor unit. (Henry Valve Co.)

In system 2, install the new motor-compressor, install an excessive capacity filter-drier in the suction line, test for leaks, evacuate the system to 5 to 100 microns, charge the system and operate. The pressure drop across the filter-drier should be checked frequently and oil samples should be checked frequently. Fig. 15-93 shows such an installation. The installation of the unit can be done permanently, with quick couplers, as shown in Fig. 15-94A and B. Fig. 15-95 shows a bypass or flow diverter block installed be-

tween the suction service valve and the compressor. This may be used to divert the flow of vaporized refrigerant through a high capacity filter-drier.

15-92 Transferring Refrigerants

It is good economy to purchase refrigerants in 50-lb. and 100-lb. quantities. This practice, however, necessitates the transferring of refrigerant from the large cylinders to smaller service cylinders used by servicemen. These large cylinders are equipped with two types of valves:

1. Regular valve which releases vapor only when the cylinder is upright and the valve open. This cylinder must be inverted to remove liquid refrigerant from it.
2. A special valve with two valve stems and handles. The handle marked gas releases vapor. The other handle marked liquid allows liquid to escape from the cylinder when opened.

If the cylinder has the first type valve, liquid refrigerant is removed from it as follows:

Invert the large drum in a special stand and connect it to a small drum with a horizontal tubing or flexible charging line at least four feet long. Purge this line and then open both valves after placing the small cylinder on a weighing scale. When the small cylinder is charged with the correct amount as indicated on the scales, close the valve on the large cylinder and then carefully warm the line. This will force the liquid out of the line. Next, close the valve on the small cylinder. NEVER ALLOW THE LINE TO BECOME MORE THAN WARM TO THE HAND. WEAR GOGGLES.

If the cylinder has the double valve, the same procedure is used except the cylinder is kept upright.

A charging board provides an accurate means of transferring refrigerant. This system uses a glass cylinder or measuring tube to measure the amount of refrigerant. The scale reads in pounds and usually has scales for R-12, R-22, R-500. Fig. 15-96 shows a complete evacuating and charging service station. In many cases, especially

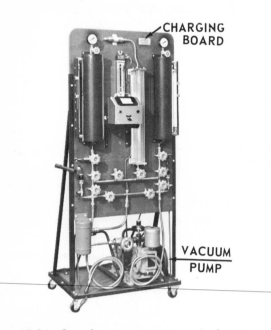

Fig. 15-96. Complete evacuating and charging system. The 3 cfm pump is connected to both high side and low side of system. Large evacuating lines and a vacuum breaker are used. Refrigerant measuring tube measures amount of refrigerant put into system. (Airserco Mfg. Co.)

with small commercial systems, disposable refrigerant cylinders are used, as shown in Fig. 15-97.

WHEN TRANSFERRING REFRIGERANT FROM A STORAGE CYLINDER TO A SERVICE CYLINDER, NEVER FILL A SERVICE CYLINDER COMPLETELY FULL OF LIQUID REFRIGERANT. This is particularly dangerous in cold weather since liquid refrigerant expands and contracts greatly with a change in temperature. If a service cylinder is filled completely full with cold liquid refrigerant and then brought into a warm room, the liquid tends to expand and the resulting increase in hydrostatic pressure may burst the service cylinder with possible serious consequences.

15-93 Adding Oil to System

When a compressor runs too warm or is noisy and it is determined the trouble is due to a lack of refrigerant oil, there are several methods which may be used to add oil. The most rapid method is to attach tubing equipped with a hand valve to the middle opening of the gauge manifold, and after purging the tubing immerse it in a glass (clean, dry) jar nearly filled with refrigerant oil. Then run the compressor, and after drawing a vacuum on the low side by turning the suction service valve all the way in, crack the manifold suction valve. Oil will then be drawn into the crankcase. It is important that some of the oil in the glass container be left in the container so the filling tube is always immersed in the oil, otherwise air will be drawn into the system. The reason a glass container is used is to enable the serviceman to observe how much oil has been added to the unit. It is a safe policy to never add more than a quarter of a pint of oil at a time to smaller units.

Another method of adding oil to the system is to evacuate the crankcase; then equalize the pressures, remove the oil plug of the crankcase housing, and add the oil. Replace the oil plug and evacuate the compressor to the air.

Oil can also be forced into the system by putting the oil in a service cylinder first (draw in by using an evacuated cylinder). Then build up a pressure in the cylinder with refrigerant vapor through the gauge manifold. Invert the cylinder and by using the low side manifold valve the oil can be forced into the compressor.

15-94 Servicing Electrical Circuits

More and more electrical devices are being used on refrigerating units. Electrical defrost systems, solenoid valves, multi-units with electrical coupling devices, crankcase heaters, internal motor winding protectors, and various other accessories make it necessary for a serviceman to be knowledgeable about electrical devices and electrical circuits. Chapters 7 and 8 explain the fundamentals of electricity, electric motors and electric controls.

It is important that the serviceman have a wiring diagram of the system being serviced. Certain items should always be checked:

1. Are the wires large enough?
2. Is there electrical power up to the machine?
3. Is the voltage correct? (Not too low.)

With the power on, the current draw and the voltage at the unit can be checked.

If the unit will not run TURN OFF THE POWER, and check the circuits for continuity. Use an ohmmeter. Locate the open in the circuit by measuring sections of the circuit with the ohmmeter.

1. Controls.
2. Motor (if open and motor is warm, wait for at least an hour to allow the overload points to close).

If the motor hums but will not start, check the starting capacitor with a capacitor tester.

Do not try to start a unit without having overload cutouts in the circuit.

15-95 Servicing Open Type Motors

Motors used on commercial condensing units usually vary in size from 1/2 hp to 15 hp. Air-conditioning systems require motors of 1/3 hp. to 25 hp. These motors are connected to either 115-230V or 230V three-phase lines.

In addition to the condensing unit motors, commercial systems use motors for fans, water pumps, mixers in ice cream machines, and the like.

Many localities require that a licensed electrical contractor, remove, repair and install these motors. However, the refrigeration serviceman must be able to diag-

nose motor troubles, to be able to locate the fault. It is best for the refrigeration serviceman to subcontract motor work.

Motor troubles can be traced to:

1. Mechanical troubles.
2. Electrical troubles.

Mechanical troubles are faults in the bearings, pulleys, out of alignment and excessive end play.

Electrical troubles may be further classified as:

1. Internal troubles.
2. External troubles.

To test the motor, it should be disconnected from the compressor and run without any load. The sound of the motor is indicative of any trouble. Under normal con-

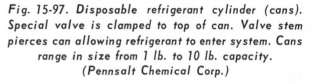

Fig. 15-97. Disposable refrigerant cylinder (cans). Special valve is clamped to top of can. Valve stem pierces can allowing refrigerant to enter system. Cans range in size from 1 lb. to 10 lb. capacity. (Pennsalt Chemical Corp.)

ditions a motor will emit a steady low hum, but in case of worn bearings, rubbing armatures, dry bearings, lack of voltage, etc., erratic beats will be heard in the humming, and the armature may chatter. If one is doubtful as to condition of the motor, it should be thoroughly checked as described in Chapter 7.

With the motor running, make sure the armature position is between the two extremes of the armature end play. If the armature operates against one extreme of end play, it means that it is trying to assume its magnetic center and in not being able to do so is running inefficiently. The end play should never exceed 1/16 in. This may be adjusted by using fiber washers which are obtainable at electrical supply houses.

Adequate lubrication of the motor bearings is necessary. Normally motors should be oiled twice each year. Refrigerant oil should not be used to lubricate motor bearings. Too much oil is just as detrimental as not enough. Most motors are equipped with overflow openings which eliminate most of the danger of too much oil. Bearing temperatures are best checked with a thermometer.

Occasionally the motor should be thoroughly cleaned. Dust, dirt, and grease accumulations should be removed from within the motor and the exterior. Commutators and brushes, if used, should be cleaned. They must make good contact. The brush throw-out mechanism should be free. The brush releasing mechanism of small motors may be checked by mounting a V-belt on the motor pulley and imposing a load on the motor by pulling on the other end of the belt. A torque stand is the best means of determining the real capacity of a motor. A noisy motor may be caused by a loose pulley, loose fan on the pulley, or loose flywheel. These items should be checked when a noise complaint is received.

Fan motors are usually of the shaded-pole type. The most common trouble is worn bearings. The location of these motors usually results in a lack of attention to oiling. Many of these motors are designed to not need lubrication but practice has proven that many do need lubrication periodically.

The pump motors and mixer motors are serviced similar to the methods described.

Always be sure the motor is wired correctly, and that the voltage at the motor is sufficient. Always test a motor for grounds, and ground the motor (single-phase units).

15-96 Removing Open Type Electric Motor

To remove an electric motor, first disconnect the power line, then remove the wires from the motor terminals. Label the terminals to aid assembly later. Next loosen hold-down bolts which attach the motor to the base. Remove the belt from the flywheel first, then the pulley. The motor can then be lifted out. Use care that the fan does not hit the condenser coils or catch on the belt.

Fan motors are sometimes difficult to remove. It is best to loosen and remove the fan. The fan hubs are usually clamped to the motor shaft with Allen setscrews. Fig. 15-98 shows an Allen setscrew with a wrench which is designed to operate on these setscrews in recesses which are hard to reach.

15-97 Repairing and Testing Conventional Electric Motor

Conventional motor troubles are described in Chapter 7.

The motor should be cleaned, completely dismantled and cleaned inside. The motor internal switches should be replaced (capacitor start motors). The bearing walls should be cleaned of oil and the bearings carefully inspected. If they are scored or have more than .001 in. clearance they should be replaced (ream to size in line). If the armature joints are scored, or, are worn they should be resurfaced or new armature installed.

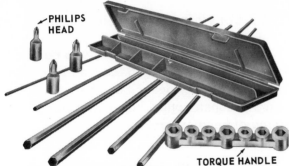

Fig. 15-98. A set of Allen setscrew wrenches and Phillips screwdrivers with turning handle. These tools can reach screw in recess up to 9 in. in depth. (Watsco Inc.)

When assembling the motor do not force the parts. Be sure the end bells fit into place. Keep turning the armature by hand during the assembly to detect any binding before damage is done.

A motor should be tested before being installed.

1. Run under no load.
2. Run under load.

Run the motor, check it for end play (1/16 in. max.), check bearing temperatures and listen for noises other than the normal hum.

Run the motor under load. Fig. 15-99 shows a torque arm and pulley for motor testing. Fig. 15-100 shows a motor being tested. The electrical load of the motor is checked by using meters connected, as shown in Fig. 15-101.

15-98 Installing Open Type Electric Motor

Open type compressor drive motors may drive a compressor directly or by means of a belt. In either case the motor must be carefully aligned when installed. Always lock out the power before starting work.

In the belt drive units the motor shaft and the compressor shaft must be parallel. This is easily checked by putting a straight edge across the compressor flywheel face

and checking the alignment of the pulley with it. The pulley grooves must be in line with the flywheel belt grooves. Make clean, tight electrical connections.

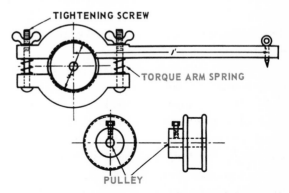

Fig. 15-99. Torque arm and pulley used for testing conventional motors under load.

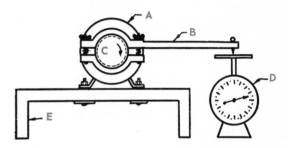

Fig. 15-100. A motor being tested under load. A—Motor. B—Torque arm. C—Motor pulley. D—Torque scale. E—Motor stand.

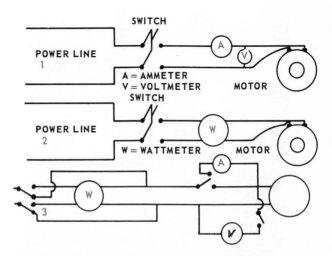

Fig. 15-101. Electric motor testing. 1—Using voltmeter and ammeter. 2—Using wattmeter. 3—Using either voltmeter or combination of voltmeter and ammeter.

Four hold-down bolts are usually used. After installing them loosely, install the belts, use a lever to move the motor until the belts are tight and the motor is in line. While holding the motor in this position tighten at least two of the hold-down bolts. Then tighten the others. Make clean, tight electrical connections.

In the direct drive units, put the motor on its part of the stand, assemble and install the coupling, check the alignment carefully because the motor shaft center must be the same height as the compressor shaft center. The two shafts must be in alignment when looking down on them. (A dial gauge can be used.) Install and tighten the bolts.

Water pump motors require the same care.

Fan motor installations sometimes require installing the fan on the shaft before the motor is installed.

If possible, always turn the motor by hand to determine if the assembly will rotate freely, before unlocking the power and turning it on.

15-99 Servicing Hermetic Motors

Servicing hermetic motors is basically the same as servicing conventional motors. Chapter 7 describes the principles, design, construction, operation, and servicing of hermetic motors.

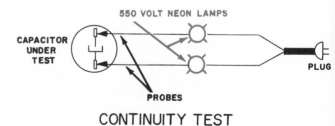

CONTINUITY TEST

Fig. 15-103. Testing continuity of capacitor with neon lamps. Lamps will light to full intensity if capacitor has continuity. Be sure circuit is of same voltage as capacitor; higher voltage may cause capacitor to explode. (Copeland Refrig. Corp.)

As with all energy devices, you should first check to determine if the power has the correct characteristics. Voltmeters, ammeters, demand meters, and wattmeters are used for this purpose. You should check the electrical properties of the motor and then check the power to make sure the motor is receiving:

1. Correct voltage.
2. Correct amount of current.

Voltage must be within 5 percent of the needs of the motor. This voltage should be read with the motor running. Voltage higher than required is not as critical up to a voltage of 20 percent over the rating.

The correct amount of current is vital to good operation. Again, a good instrument is needed. An ammeter of the terminal type (shunt unit) should never be connected across the line (in parallel). It must always be put in series (interrupt one wire only) with the electrical device being checked.

You should carefully check external wiring, and electrical controls for correct operation before assuming the motor is at

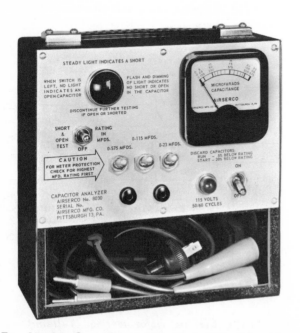

Fig. 15-102. Capacitor tester. 0 to 575 mfds. Also tests for opens and shorts.
(Airserco Mfg. Co.)

fault. An ohmmeter is recommended to check continuity in these circuits. Check each circuit separately. Disconnect if there is a chance of parallel circuits. BE SURE THE POWER IS LOCKED OFF. Capacitors should be checked with a capacitor tester, as shown in Figs. 15-103 and 15-104. Do not test capacitors by shorting after charging as this method is not accurate enough.

The motor should be checked for:

1. Open circuits (motor should be cool or internal overload in open position will give false readings).

2. Shorted windings (ohmmeter readings should be compared to manufacturer's specifications.

3. Grounded windings. First check with ohmmeter and then check with a 500V circuit tester. Insulation breaks can only be checked accurately with this high voltage tester. You must carefully handle this instrument to avoid shocks.

Most companies report that a high percentage of motor-compressors returned

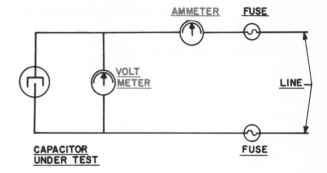

Fig. 15-104. Wiring diagram and formula used for determining capacity (capacitance) of capacitors:

Use this formula for 50 cycle: $mfd = \dfrac{3180 \times Amps.}{Volts}$

Use this formula for 60 cycle: $mfd = \dfrac{2650 \times Amps.}{Volts}$

(Copeland Refrig. Corp.)

labeled "faulty motor" actually have good motors. This false diagnosing indicates the need for careful checking.

The following chart is a list of typical motor and circuit troubles, their cause and their remedy:

HERMETIC COMPRESSOR SERVICE CHART

PROBLEMS AND CAUSE	REMEDY
Compressor Will Not Start—No Hum	
1. Open line circuit.	1. Check wiring, fuses, receptacle.
2. Protector open.	2. Wait for reset—check current.
3. Control contacts open.	3. Check control, check pressures.
4. Open circuit in stator.	4. Replace stator or compressor.
Compressor Will Not Start—Hums Intermittently (Cycling On Protector)	
1. Improperly wired.	1. Check wiring against diagram.
2. Low line voltage.	2. Check main line voltage, determine location of voltage drop.
3. Open starting capacitor.	3. Replace starting capacitor.
4. Relay contacts not closing.	4. Check by operating manually. Replace relay if defective.
5. Open circuit in starting winding.	5. Check stator leads. If leads okay replace compressor.
6. Stator winding grounded (normally will blow fuse).	6. Check stator leads. If leads okay replace compressor.
7. High discharge pressure.	7. Eliminate cause of excessive pressure. Make sure discharge shutoff, and receiver valves are open.
8. Tight compressor.	8. Check oil level—correct binding condition, if possible. If not, replace compressor.
9. Weak starting capacitor or one weak capacitor of a set.	9. Replace.

(Continued on Next Page)

HERMETIC COMPRESSOR SERVICE CHART (Continued)

PROBLEMS AND CAUSE

Compressor Starts, Motor Will Not Get Off Starting Winding.

REMEDY

1. Low line voltage.
2. Improperly wired.
3. Defective relay.
4. Running capacitor shorted.
5. Starting and running windings shorted.

6. Starting capacitor weak or one of a set open.
7. High discharge pressure.
8. Tight compressor.

1. Bring up voltage.
2. Check wiring against diagram.
3. Check operation—replace relay if defective.
4. Check by disconnecting running capacitor.
5. Check resistances. Replace compressor if defective.
6. Check capacitance—replace if defective.
7. Check discharge shutoff valves. Check pressure.
8. Check oil level. Check binding. Replace compressor if necessary.

Compressor Starts And Runs But Cycles On Protector.

1. Low line voltage.
2. Additional current passing thru protector.

3. Suction pressure too high.
4. Discharge pressure too high.
5. Protector weak.
6. Running capacitor defective.
7. Stator partially shorted or grounded.

8. Inadequate motor cooling.
9. Compressor tight.
10. Unbalanced line (3-phase).

11. Discharge valve leaking or broken.

1. Bring up voltage.
2. Check for added fan motors, pumps, etc., connected to wrong side of protector.
3. Check compressor for proper application.
4. Check ventilation, restrictions, and overcharge.
5. Check current—replace protector if defective.
6. Check capacitance. Replace if defective.
7. Check resistances, check for ground. Replace if defective.
8. Correct cooling system.
9. Check oil level. Check for binding condition.
10. Check voltage of each phase. If not equal, correct condition of unbalance.
11. Replace valve plate.

Starting Capacitors Burn Out.

1. Short cycling.
2. Prolonged operation on starting winding.

3. Relay contacts sticking.
4. Improper relay or incorrect relay setting.
5. Improper capacitor.

6. Capacitor voltage rating too low.
7. Capacitor terminals shorted by water.

1. Reduce number of starts to 20 or less per hour.
2. Reduce starting load (install crankcase pressure limit valve), increase voltage if low. Replace relay if defective.
3. Clean contacts or replace relay.
4. Replace relay.
5. Check parts list for proper capacitor rating—mfd. and voltage.
6. Install capacitors with recommended voltage rating.
7. Install capacitors so terminals will not be wet.

Running Capacitors Burn Out.

1. Excessive line voltage.

2. High line voltage and light load.
3. Capacitor voltage rating too low.

4. Capacitor terminals shorted by water.

1. Reduce line voltage to not over 10% above rating of motor.
2. Reduce voltage if over 10% excessive.
3. Install capacitors with recommended voltage rating.
4. Install capacitors so terminals will not be wet.

HERMETIC COMPRESSOR SERVICE CHART (Continued)

PROBLEMS AND CAUSE	REMEDY
Relays Burn Out.	
1. Low line voltage.	1. Increase voltage to not less than 10% under compressor motor rating.
2. Excessive line voltage.	2. Reduce voltage to maximum of 10% above motor rating.
3. Incorrect running capacitor.	3. Replace running capacitor with correct mfd. capacitance.
4. Short cycling.	4. Reduce number of starts per hour.
5. Relay vibrating.	5. Mount relay rigidly.
6. Incorrect relay.	6. Use relay recommended for specific motor compressor.

15-100 Removing Hermetic Motor-Compressor

If you are positive the motor in a hermetic motor-compressor unit is faulty, the removal procedure is:

1. Remove the refrigerant as described in Chapter 12 and as described in this chapter for serviceable hermetics.

2. Open the main circuit switch and LOCK the switch in open position. Tag the switch to inform others why the switch is locked open.

3. Disconnect the wires from the motor-compressor (label them or use color code).

4. Clean outside of motor-compressor.

5. Disconnect lines. (WEAR GOGGLES.) The type of disconnect depends on assembly. Unbolt service valves, open brazed joints by heating or cut the lines (tube cutter only to avoid chips getting into the system).

6. Remove motor-compressor. Do not tilt or oil may be spilled. Avoid lifting over 50 lbs. If it is a large heavy unit use a lifting machine (tripod, fork lift, etc.).

7. Plug refrigerant openings.

15-101 Repairing Hermetic Motor

Removing a hermetic motor, repairing the bearings, replacing the windings is a specialty job. Most servicemen replace the complete assembly by obtaining a replacement unit, either a new unit or a rebuilt unit.

The actual overhaul of a hermetic motor-compressor is described in Chapter 7.

15-102 Installing Hermetic Motor-Compressor

A hermetic motor-compressor is usually furnished without starting relay, capacitors, overload protectors, and other accessories. It has service valve openings and these openings are plugged, or, it is provided with short tubing ends, brazed in place with the ends of the tubing crimped and brazed.

Carefully mount the motor-compressor in place. Use all the safety precautions (lifting, safety shoes, protecting floors, equipment, etc.). Install the mounting bolts. If externally spring mounted, the springs and grommets must be in the correct position and the hold-down bolt or nut must be positioned correctly.

Install the electrical devices (overload, starting relay, etc.) and the electrical wires (all connections must be clean and tight); all wires must be in good condition (insulation, wire terminals, etc.).

Install suction and condenser lines. Units using service valves are installed the same way as described for a conventional compressor. If brazed connections are used, flux the outside of the brazed joints on the compressor dome, heat (wear goggles) and remove the stubs. Clean the outside of the suction line and condenser line, flux the surface, insert the lines in the compressor and dome and silver braze (the area must be well ventilated) the joints. Clean the joints (remove flux).

Install a gauge manifold using charging stub or a valve mounted on the suction line.

Evacuate the system, put some vaporized refrigerant in (enough to build a 15 psig pressure), test for leaks, (repair any, if found), evacuate to a 10 to 100 micron range for several hours.

Charge the system.

Turn on the power, run, check the temperatures, pressures, electrical characteristics. If any detection is made of non-normal operation be sure to diagnose and remedy same before leaving the job.

Clean up the area.

15-103 Servicing Motor Controls

Three main types of motor controls are used in commercial refrigeration, namely, low side pressure motor control, thermostatic motor control, and high side safety motor control. Troubles encountered with these include:

1. Corroded points.
2. Broken "Mercoid" bulb.
3. Out-of-adjustment.
4. Corroded or broken operating springs.
5. Out-of-level.
6. Leaky bellows.

Motor controls normally function year in and year out without giving trouble, but in cases such as unit overloading, the resultant short cycling will rapidly deteriorate the contact points in the control, or will so overload the "Mercoid" contacts that it will crack and be destroyed. Corrosion of the points may be remedied by

cleaning with clean, fine sandpaper (emery cloth must not be used) or a clean fine mill file. A broken Mercoid bulb must be replaced.

An out-of-adjustment switch is often the result of tampering. These causes of trouble are often difficult to overcome. A pressure control may be easily checked by installing the gauge manifold; use the compressor as a vacuum and pressure pump and check the cut-in and cut-out points. Three different methods may be employed to build up pressure in the crankcase after the compressor is run to the cut-out point of the control: (1) the suction line may be cracked open again; (2) a bypass may be run from the discharge service valve of the compressor to the suction service valve (use the gauge manifold); (3) you may use a refrigerant service drum containing the same kind of refrigerant attached to the gauge manifold. Many servicemen carry a hand vacuum and pressure pump in their tool kit for the purpose of testing controls. See Fig. 15-105. This tool enables a rapid check of pressure control.

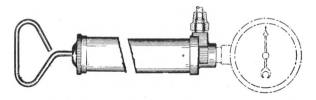

Fig. 15-105. Hand vacuum and pressure pump used for adjusting motor controls.

A thermostatic motor control is more difficult to reset; an approved method is to use an ice bath and thermometer or a temperature bath, as shown in Fig. 15-106. The control may then be set to cut in or out at the temperature desired.

The high pressure motor control presents but few difficulties because it is adjusted to work only under extreme conditions. The most common troubles encountered are the occurrence of leaks in the bellows, or at the joints of the controls. Occasionally, however, you may find that this control is short cycling the refrigerating mechanism, and this short cycling is due to excessive head pressure. To check a high pressure motor control element, connect it to the gauge manifold and turn the discharge service valve all the way in. On running the compressor, a head pressure will be produced sufficient to cut out the control; the high pressure gauge will record the pressure at which the cutting out takes place.

Many large compressors use oil pressure lubrication. If this oil pressure fails or falls below a safe pressure there is danger of injuring the compressor. An oil pressure safety control is used to protect these systems. It will cut out if the oil pressure decreases to a dangerous level.

15-104 Servicing Liquid Line

The liquid line contains several important items needed to be checked by the serviceman, including:

1. Size of the liquid line.
2. Hand shutoff valves.
3. Sight glass.
4. Moisture indicator.
5. Screen filter.
6. Drier or dehydrator.
7. Vibration absorber.
8. Connections.
9. Solenoid valves.
10. Joints.

When diagnosing troubles of a system, the serviceman's first problem is to determine if the various parts of the system are of sufficient capacity. It is important that the liquid line be as large as the condensing unit liquid receiver valve connections. Check to be sure that reducer fittings have not been used. Also see Chapter 16 for recommended liquid line sizes. Many large units use various sizes of liquid lines as the line feeds to various cooling coils. A sight glass should be installed in the liquid line prior to the mounting of the filter screens, and dehydrators.

A SPECIAL PRECAUTION THAT ALL SERVICEMEN MUST REMEMBER IS TO HAVE THE LIQUID LINE VALVES OPEN WHEN SERVICING THE UNIT, OTHERWISE A TEMPERATURE RISE MAY CREATE A VERY HIGH HYDROSTATIC PRESSURE AND THIS PRESSURE MAY BURST THE LINE. You should be especially careful if a solenoid valve or a clogged screen or clogged dehydrator is in the line.

You should check the full length of the line for line condition. The line must be protected from abrasion and from abuse as objects are moved. The line should be well supported along its full length.

When admitting liquid refrigerant into a liquid line by opening the liquid receiver service valve, always open the valve slowly or the sudden rush of liquid may injure the screen and may pack the desiccant in the drier so firmly that it will soon clog.

Test all joints for leaks. Check the temperature of the liquid line. It should be close to room temperature for its full length.

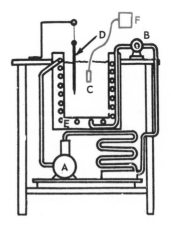

Fig. 15-106. Temperature bath system. Cooling system used to control liquid bath temperature. May be used for checking thermostat cut-out and cut-in temperatures and for checking thermostatic expansion valves. A—Condensing unit. B—Refrigerant control (AEV). C—Temperature bath. D—Thermometer. E—Evaporator. F—Thermostat being tested.

A partially clogged screen or drier is indicated by a lower than normal temperature at the outlet and by an excessive pressure drop (may cause bubbles in the sight glass).

15-105 Servicing the Suction Line

Servicing the suction line is similar to servicing the liquid line. Parts to be inspected are:

1. Size of the suction line.
2. Hand shutoff valves.
3. Vibration absorber.
4. Check valves.
5. Two-temperature valves.
6. Constant pressure valves.
7. Filter-drier.
8. Muffler.
9. Accumulator.
10. Joints.

Suction line size is important. If it is too small, it will cause too much pressure drop and the high gas velocities will cause noise. The line should be the size of the suction service valve connection or the suction line connection on the hermetic dome. On multiple installations, the lines become smaller as each evaporator coil is serviced. For example, the most remote coil may have a 1/2 in. OD size, the next size 5/8 in. OD, the next 1 in. OD, the next 1 1/2 in. OD and the line at the compressor may be 2 in. OD.

The pressure drop should be checked by installing a gauge at the most remote coil and one at the compressor. The pressure drop should be approximately 2 psi. If more, line sizes should be increased.

The pressure change across two-temperature valves and constant pressure valves should be checked. Their pressure drops are separate from the line pressure drops and are not included in the 2 psi pressure drop.

The pressure drop across the suction line filter-drier should be checked. A large pressure drop here indicates a partially clogged filter-drier. This should be replaced.

Test for leaks. Be sure a 15 psig pressure or more is in the lines.

15-106 Service Notes

Pinching lines is a practice to be used in cases of emergency only. Some servicemen follow this practice needlessly and it only leads to future trouble. Almost all systems are provided with sufficient valves to service them. However, pinching lines used to service hermetic units, prior to silver brazing the stub, is common practice. Fig. 15-107 shows one type of pinch-off tool.

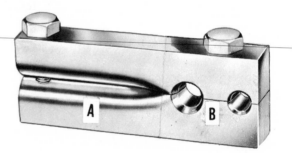

Fig. 15-107. Tubing pinch-off tool. A—This section of tool pinches tube to leakproof condition. B—This section rounds tubing again to permit refrigerant flow. (Duro Metal Products Co.)

Remember that when adding refrigerant to a system some of the oil in the system will be dissolved in the refrigerant. If a unit becomes noisy soon after the refrigerant has been added, some refrigerant oil should be added.

Conventional electric motors, when installed, should have approved electrical connections; the motor must be carefully aligned with the compressor, and the belt tightness should be just right.

Driers, if heated while in the system (such as a refrigerant shortage) will release water to the system. A new drier should be installed if the moisture indicator so indicates or is on a borderline indication.

Crankshaft seals are subject to leaking, if the compressor has been idle for a long time. You should turn the compressor over by hand a few times to allow oil to seep

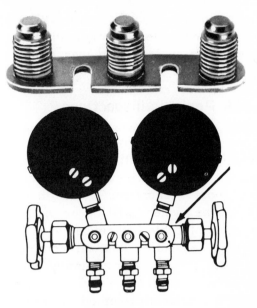

Fig. 15-109. Gauge manifold equipped with three flare plugs. Plugs hold ends of three-gauge manifold flexible lines when not in use. This method is used to keep service lines clean.
(Madden Brass Products Co., Div. of Robinair Corp.)

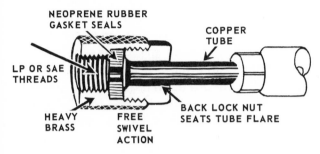

Fig. 15-108. Speed coupling as used on charging and purging lines. Synthetic rubber gasket produces leakproof joint when connection is "finger" tightened. (Wabash Corp.)

between the rubbing metal surfaces. You should also put an ounce of one of the special refrigerant detergent oils into 'the crankcase to help eliminate this problem.

For ease of service operations, it is recommened that the serviceman use a speed coupling on his charging and purging lines to insure a leakproof joint. See Fig. 15-108. A gauge manifold is shown in Fig. 15-109.

15-107 Summary of Refrigerator Mechanism Servicing

If the previous instructions have been studied carefully, the student should recognize the following important things:

1. It is necessary to remove the liquid refrigerant from that part of the mechanism to be overhauled.

2. It is necessary to equalize pressures in the unit before dismantling or there will be a rush of air into the unit or of refrigerant out of the unit upon opening the lines.

3. It is necessary to plug all refrig-

erant openings immediately after dismantling.

4. It is necessary to put in new gaskets wherever gaskets are used.

5. It is necessary, upon reassembling, to remove all the air and moisture from the lines and whatever part that has been open to the air. This may be done both by purging, by evacuating and purging, or by deep evacuating.

6. It is necessary to keep the inside of the system clean.

7. To remove any part of the system necessitates closing the closest valve between that unit and the liquid receiver, and evacuating the unit by means of the compressor into the condenser and liquid receiver.

It is usually advisable to remove a tedious task to the shop to be worked on. In the meantime, replace the unit with a temporary unit so the owners may have the use of the refrigerator.

Where possible, a serviceman should review the wiring diagram and the specific service manual before working on a refrigerating system. Complications of some of the systems requires that a service manual be used.

15-108 Periodic Inspections

The capital investment in a commercial refrigeration installation amounts to hundreds of dollars. The inherent construction of most mechanisms is such that troubles in the system will be accumulative; that is, one trouble will cause others. It is, therefore, essential that all commercial machines should be completely checked over periodically. The serviceman should devise a systematic method of doing this in order that no detail may be overlooked. All inspections should cover such things as:

1. Electrical connections.
2. Motor and safety devices.
3. Compressor noises.
4. Amount of refrigerant.
5. Dryness of refrigerant.
6. Oil level.
7. Water flow.
8. Gas leaks.
9. Coil conditions.
10. Supports for tubing.
11. Coil supports.
12. Cleanliness.

For conventional condensing unit, you should check:

1. Belt condition.
2. Belt alignment.
3. Belt tightness.

For a hermetic condensing unit, you should check:

1. Overload cut-out.
2. Relay.
3. Capacitors.

It establishes goodwill and also builds up a good contact file to prepare a check sheet, one copy of which should be given to the owner. This check sheet is a time-tried system that prevents overlooking important items.

15-109 Locating Troubles

Methods of testing used to locate the sources of trouble are based on the operating principles of the mechanism. By checking the pressures, the temperatures, the running time, etc., the serviceman is soon able to isolate or pick out that part of the system which is giving trouble.

Naturally the serviceman must have a thorough knowledge of the fundamentals of refrigeration and of the cycles before he can become a reliable and competent trouble tracer and repairman. It is obvious that one must locate the trouble in a refrigerator mechanism before dismantling it, in order to keep the cost of servicing at a minimum, and to make sure the repair work is going to enable proper functioning of the mechanism after assembly.

Methods of locating troubles naturally vary with the type of the system, that is, with direct expansion, with low side float, with high side float or with the capillary tube. The call for service should give the first indication of what the trouble will be; the owner will probably say that it costs too much to operate it, that it is not freezing but is running continuously, or it is freezing but running continuously, etc. From these trouble calls the serviceman may usually get a pointer as to what the trouble is, but he should always verify these statements by checking over the refrigerator before attempting any trouble-shooting or service work.

The method of trouble tracing is best learned and is best adapted to practical work by first classifying the type of service call and then determining what caused the trouble named in the service call. Therefore, the following troubleshooting pointers have been prepared to help the serviceman. Naturally, it is impossible to give every detail, but once the serviceman learns the method of trouble tracing he should have no difficulty.

A serviceman should check all of the

following things in a refrigerating mechanism before coming to a conclusion as to the trouble:

1. Low side pressure.
2. High side pressure.
3. Temperature of cooling unit.
4. Temperatures of liquid and suction lines.
5. Amount and dryness of refrigerant.
6. Running time of mechanism.
7. Probability of leaks.
8. Noise.

There are several basic fundamentals that help make locating trouble easier. When there is poor refrigeration, or no refrigeration, either one or both of two things can be wrong:

1. There is no refrigerant, or very little refrigerant.
2. The pump is not moving the refrigerant (the pressures are not correct).

If there is no refrigerant, there will be no liquid refrigerant in the evaporating unit. A lack of refrigerant means that the refrigerant has leaked out, or it is being held in a certain part of the system by clogged needles, clogged screens, pinched lines, etc. This clogging condition will cause a high vacuum reading on the low side. If there is a lack of refrigerant in the complete system there will be a hissing sound at the refrigerant control which will indicate the refrigerant passages are not closed. The sight glass will show bubbles.

A hissing sound at the refrigerant control always indicates a lack of refrigerant because the dry gas going through the restriction will cause the gas noise.

If the pump is not functioning, the low side pressure will be above normal and the condenser and discharge line from the compressor will be below normal temperature.

To determine what is responsible for a poor condensing condition, you should proceed as follows: install the gauge manifold and determine the head pressure. Compare this pressure with what the pressure should be for the refrigerant being used.

15-110 Little or No Refrigeration and Unit Runs Continuously

A. DIRECT EXPANSION SYSTEM (TEV)

If the unit has lost all the refrigerant, there is naturally no refrigeration. To test for this, install gauges and determine evaporating or low side pressure. If this pressure is correct, the unit probably has little or no refrigerant. If the compound gauge indicates a high vacuum, 20 in. or more, it means that the expansion valve is either so adjusted that it draws this vacuum, it is frozen closed, or it has a clogged screen.

A clogged unit can be caused by moisture freezing at the refrigerant control and stopping the flow of refrigerant. The results are the same as a stuck-closed needle, or a clogged screen except that after the system warms above 32 F. at the valve this ice will melt, and normal refrigeration will start again. The only sure cure for the moisture condition is to remove the moisture using a drier. If you suspect that moisture in the valve has caused the clogging, heat the valve with a torch.

This moisture problem occurs with all refrigerants that do not chemically combine with the water; for example: R-12, R-22, and R-500. A high vacuum may also be caused by a suction service valve being shut off or by a clogged or restricted suction line filter. In either case it is not allowing refrigerant to flow through, and there will be no refrigerant on the low side which naturally gives continuous running with little or no refrigeration.

If the compound pressure gauge shows a high pressure on the low side; that is, a pressure which will not allow the refrigerant to evaporate at a low temperature, the trouble may be a stuck-open expansion valve or one that is out of adjustment. This trouble will have an additional indication of a frosted or sweating suction line because it simply means that the refrigerant is going into the low side too fast and the liquid will flood both the evaporator unit and the suction line.

This high pressure may also be due to an inefficient compressor. If the expansion valve is stuck open, it may be due to dirt on the needle. To remedy, one may flush the valve by alternately opening and closing the liquid receiver service valve or liquid line hand shutoff valve, causing surges of liquid past the expansion valve needle, thereby cleaning it.

B. LOW PRESSURE SIDE FLOAT SYSTEM (FLOODED)

If the compound gauge indicates a high vacuum, it may be due either to a frozen-closed needle valve, or to a restricted suction or liquid line (clogged screen). To determine whether it is a frozen needle valve or a lack of refrigerant:

1. Stop the compressor after installing the gauges and notice the action of the compound gauge. If it creeps up rapidly to almost the pressure on the high pressure side, it indicates that the needle valve is open; therefore, there is a lack of refrigerant. If the pressures do not tend to equalize, it means that the needle valve is stuck closed, or the suction line or liquid line has become clogged. The valve will also have a steady hissing sound while the unit is running.

If the needle is stuck closed, a sudden jar may loosen it. Use a rubber hammer or shake the evaporator unit.

In case there is a lack of refrigerant, put enough refrigerant into the system until the hissing sound stops and the head pressure is normal.

2. If the compound gauge indicates a high pressure, it may be due to a slight lack of refrigerant, a stuck-open needle valve, or an inefficient compressor.

It is best first to eliminate the compressor by testing its efficiency and then determine whether there is a stuck-open needle valve or a lack of refrigerant. To do this, flush the needle valve by shutting off the liquid receiver service valve or liquid line shutoff valve and running the unit for a few minutes. Then open the liquid valve rapidly. Allow a rapid flow of refrigerant through the needle valve orifice which may wash out any dirt particles on the needle valve seat. If this does not cure the trouble, charge the refrigerator with some refrigerant and see if that will cure the trouble. If this does not, it means that the evaporator unit must be dismantled.

A rather accurate check as to whether there is a lack of refrigerant or a stuck-open needle valve, is the frosting of the suction line. If the line frosts back excessively it means that there is liquid refrigerant in the suction line caused by too much refrigerant in the evaporating unit, as the result of a leaky needle, etc. If the suction pressure is too high, this indicates an open needle valve. To check for an open needle valve the compound gauge will creep up rapidly as soon as the unit is stopped because the high pressure tends to equalize rapidly through the needle valve.

A lack of refrigerant will not frost the suction line. Both of these troubles will give a continuous hissing sound in the evaporating unit although the lack of refrigerant sound is at a higher pitch. Of course, this may also mean an inefficient compressor, but that is easily checked.

A lack of refrigerant in most systems using low side floats, high side float, or expansion valves, causes the refrigerant to go through the liquid line before it has completely condensed. This vapor is therefore warm and you can detect this condition by feeling the liquid line. If the line is warmer than room temperature, a lack of refrigerant is indicated (air-cooled systems only).

Short cycling of the mechanism, that is, the unit shutting down for only a minute or two at a time is indicative of a rapid pressure rise in the low side. This is particularly true on the older units which use a pressure control.

C. CAPILLARY TUBE

If capillary tube is partially or completely clogged, if there is moisture frozen in the tube, or if the screen is clogged, no refrigerant can pass into the evaporator coil. This stoppage of flow will give a high vacuum reading and a normal or high head pressure. If it is a lack of refrigerant, the capillary tube will be noisy and the low and high side pressures will be below normal.

An inefficient pump will be indicated by an above-normal low side pressure and a normal or below-normal head pressure.

15-111 No Refrigeration: Unit Does Not Run

The trouble is probably somewhere in the electrical circuit. The power may be shut off, which may be easily checked by using a test light; the motor may be burned out or the circuit is open. An ineffective temperature control, such as a leaky power element, which may be checked as described in Chapter 6, may also be a cause of the motor not starting. A manual switch in the circuit may be in the off position or the overload may be in the off position. The internal overload switch may be open. If the motor-compressor is hot, this may well be the trouble and it should be checked with a test light, or an ohmmeter.

Basically, the problem is the motor or the electrical power circuit.

15-112 Motor Running Continuously and Normal or Too Much Refrigeration

This trouble is due, usually, to a faulty motor control which will not cut out at the correct temperature. It must be remembered that there is a relationship between the control cut-out point and the evaporating pressure on the low side. If the con-

trol is adjusted to cut out at a temperature or pressure corresponding to a pressure lower than the evaporating pressure, the control cannot stop the electric motor.

A. DIRECT EXPANSION SYSTEM (TEV)

If there is an undercharge of refrigerant in the system there may be just enough to fill the evaporator or evaporator unit partially, but not enough to operate the temperature control cut-out point and shut down the unit. In this way one may get normal refrigeration, but the unit will never shut down. This trouble may be detected by checking the frost or sweat accumulations on the exhaust tubing of the evaporator unit and seeing if it reaches as far as the temperature control. A shortage of refrigerant is also indicated by a warm liquid receiver and liquid line. The sight glass should show bubbles.

The trouble may also be caused by an overcharge of refrigerant or the presence of air in the condenser, because excessive head pressures decrease the efficiency of the compressor to such an extent that continuous operation is the result.

A leaky expansion valve will sometimes give normal refrigeration, but will not allow the pressure to drop to such an extent that the motor control will cut out the motor. An improperly adjusted expansion valve may also give this trouble. This will result in a frosted or sweating suction line, and an above normal and fluctuating low side pressure.

An inefficient compressor may also be the cause and may be checked by the use of gauges. Expansion valve troubles and the compressor troubles may be checked as mentioned previously.

B. LOW PRESSURE SIDE FLOAT (FLOODED)

An undercharge or overcharge of refrigerant will give the above trouble. A compressor which is inefficient, excessive head pressure due to air in the system, a restricted condenser, an overcharge of refrigerant, or a suction pressure which is not low enough to cut out the control may give refrigeration but run continuously. This may also be due to a leaky needle valve or lack of refrigerant.

A leaky needle will cause a frost or sweat back and it will hiss or gurgle continuously. A lack of refrigerant will hiss continuously, but it will never more than sweat back. Also the liquid line will be warmer than normal in the latter case.

C. CAPILLARY TUBE

If there is too much refrigerant in the system, the excess liquid will collect on the low side and may enter the suction line. This excess may prevent the compressor from producing a low enough pressure to operate the thermostat. Therefore, the unit will run continuously and will produce either a normal refrigeration effect or, more likely it may cause excessive refrigeration. A slight lack of refrigeration will cause only a partially refrigerated evaporator coil and the refrigerated part may not be close enough to the thermostat to cause it to shut the motor off.

15-113 Short Cycling

By short cycling is meant that the unit runs and then stops every few minutes. It is first necessary to locate the control which is turning the system on and off.

1. Temperature control.
2. Overload controls.
3. High pressure safety control.
4. Oil pressure safety control.

This trouble may be due to a rapid pressure rise on the low side of the system caused by a leak at the float valve or expansion valve. This leak will also cause a frosting or sweating of the suction line.

Most units are equipped with an overload device in the electrical unit. If the motor becomes too hot or if the motor consumes too much current, these safety devices will stop the motor and then restart it after they cool.

A temperature control which is out of adjustment, that is, one with a small differential, will also cause a short cycle.

If the refrigerator has a pressure motor control, short cycling may be caused by either a leak in the refrigerant control or poorly seated compressor valves. In either case the pressure on the low side will rise rapidly during the off part of the cycle causing the motor to start.

Machines equipped with a high side pressure safety control will sometimes short cycle if the condensing pressure becomes too high because of a high condensing temperature.

15-114 Noisy Unit

There are three principal sources of noise: compressor, electric motor, and mounting of the complete condensing unit. A compressor is noisy when the valves, the piston pin, the connecting rod, and piston have become worn, or if it pumps oil. Sometimes when the compressor gets very warm, it will develop knocks which are usually rather hard to remedy. Lack of oil in the compressor may cause a noisy unit.

The metal shaft seal used on most of the open type compressors occasionally becomes noisy and emits a shrill squeak. This is indicative of a lack of oil, at the seal, and, if not remedied will soon score the seal and naturally cause a leak at that point.

A conventional electric motor will give noise trouble due to a fan roar, squeaky bearings, or an armature rumble. Occasionally, if the motor is loaded too much, the starting winding does not cut out and will result in a continuous noisy operation. If this trouble is allowed to continue, the motor will burn out. End play in an electric motor is necessary, but an excess will cause a dull knock.

In a conventional unit, belt noise may be due to a dry belt or pulleys that are out of line. It may be remedied by using some dressing recommended for belts and by lining up the pulleys. Do not use oil. Sometimes the whole machine unit will vibrate excessively, producing a rumbling sound as the unit runs and shaking the cabinet disagreeably. This is probably due to improper mounting, such as the wrong rubber suspension or spring suspension; it may be due to not enough movement in the suction and liquid lines, or some obstruction may have been put in the compartment which destroys the action of the shock and the noise absorbing mounting of the condensing unit.

An excessive head pressure will make a unit vibrate more than normal.

A badly worn needle or seat will sometimes make a chattering noise while the unit is in operation.

15-115 Refrigeration Service Contracting

Much has been done during the past few years in respect to contracting for refrigeration service. Many large companies have developed definite policies in this respect, and many of the larger independents are featuring this type of servicing.

The usual contracting plan provides for the charge of a definite monthly or weekly rate, for which the service company agrees to keep the refrigerating mechanism in good condition. This charge may or may not cover parts depending upon how the contract is written.

The success of such a plan depends on a large volume of contracts in order to break even on extremely bad installations. Contracts may be on a time and material basis. Two features of a service contract which appeal to the purchaser are the 24-hour available service clause, and an absolute guarantee of work done.

If one has a service contract, a procedure sheet or record sheet should be used to prove service and to insure complete coverage of checking.

This check sheet should include:
1. Test for leaks.
2. Check refrigerant charge.
3. Check oil charge.
4. Check water valve.
5. Check water drain.
6. Check and lubricate motor.
7. Check belt condition and tension.
8. Clean unit.
9. Clean condenser exterior.
10. Straighten fins.

Service records are absolutely essential if one wishes to establish a permanent business. These records should contain details of the ownership, machine, and what type work was done and material used. This record enables check backs if the unit does not operate correctly, and it establishes sales prospects as units become older.

15-116 Service Estimates

Many organizations operating refrigerating equipment ask for bids when a repair, replacement, or service is required. A service organization bidding on such work should have a man who specializes in estimating work of this kind. This man should be thoroughly acquainted with material costs, service problems, and labor costs. He must be able to judge the time necessary to do the repair. Records kept of service and maintenance work are used as a guide in making estimates.

Needless to say estimates must include overhead expense such as rent, equipment obsolescence, office and shop services, advertising.

A pleasing personality in combination with rapid and accurate estimating ability is essential.

15-117 Review of Safety

A refrigeration service engineer must always be safety alert. Refrigerating units have pressure hazards, electrical hazards, power device hazards, heat hazards, flame hazards, heavy object hazards, climbing hazards, etc.

The safety program must include:

1. Safety for the mechanism.
2. Safety for the items being refrigerated.
3. Safety for the operator, the installation, the serviceman, and lay people who may be near the mechanism.

It is important that all parts in a refrigerating system be absolutely clean prior to installation in the system.

Always know what is inside a pressure vessel and know the pressures. Always wear goggles when working on a pressure vessel (refrigerating unit) and when there is danger of flying particles.

One should never breathe fumes of any kind. Do not neglect the use of the gas mask when working in refrigerant laden atmosphere. This safety device applies to cleansing bath fumes, soldering fumes, brazing fumes, welding fumes, and the like. It is true that one's body can and will dissipate certain amounts of strange chemicals and fumes but some chemicals and fumes accumulate in the body and there may be an effect not felt for years. GOOD VENTILATION IS OF VITAL IMPORTANCE.

Avoid exposing yourself to electrical shocks. Keep open electrical terminals covered. Do not work on electrical circuits in a damp or wet situation.

Avoid spilling liquid refrigerant on any fixture, finished surface, floor and especially on your body or a freeze burn will result.

Put guards on powered moving objects such as flywheels, belts, pulleys, fans, etc.

Lift objects using the leg muscles, not the back.

Before using a flame (halide torch) for leak testing, soldering, brazing or welding; have a fire extinguisher handy, remove all combustibles from the area, and provide good ventilation. When using the flame, protect surrounding objects with sheet metal, asbestos sheet or some other flame resistant shield.

Always test used compressor oil for acid content before allowing any of it to touch your skin or a severe acid burn may result.

Never use oxygen or any fuel gases for developing pressure in a system. If a gas other than a refrigerant is desired use carbon dioxide, nitrogen, helium or argon.

15-118 Test Your Knowledge - Chapter 15

1. Why do code installations require safety release valves on some receivers?
2. Why should hand valves be provided in the refrigerant lines to each individual coil?
3. Why is it necessary to run refrigeration tubing parallel with beams rather than across them?
4. Why is it necessary to mount low side float coils absolutely level?
5. Where are two-temperature valves usually located?
6. Where may soft tubing be used in a code installation?
7. Explain the method whereby air is removed from a multiple dry coil system.
8. Why is it necessary to put a dehydrator on a new system?
9. What would be the purpose of a dehydrator placed in a suction line?
10. Why are hard drawn copper tubing and streamline fittings popular?
11. How is a lack of refrigerant in a low side float multiple installation indicated?
12. What may be wrong if a thermal expansion valve coil suddenly starts to frost or sweat excessively at the expansion valve, but the coil near the suction line connection is dry?
13. How are flare nuts protected so moisture cannot get under them and freeze?

14. Why is it necessary to have an open water drain?
15. What must be done to balance the low side pressures in a multiple coil installation in case the normal low side system pressure is 5 in. vacuum?
16. Are commercial systems normally charged through the high pressure side or low pressure side?
17. What safety precautions should a serviceman follow when charging a system through the low side?
18. Why are brazed flanged fittings recommended for use in making inside cabinet connections?
19. What is the purpose of the felt and fine mesh screen in a dehydrator?
20. Why must a system be very carefully checked for leaks if a lack of refrigerant is discovered in the system?
21. How is a leaky exhaust valve detected in a conventional compressor?
22. What special precautions must be followed when installing a suction line?
23. What will happen if the lowest temperature evaporator coil check valve leaks?
24. What cleaning fluid can be used to clean joints before joints are opened?
25. What may cause a water-cooled condensing unit to short cycle?
26. Of what material are service valve packings made?
27. List the procedure to be followed when lapping an exhaust valve.
28. Why may suction service valves and discharge service valves be called two-way valves?
29. What are four common TEV troubles?
30. What two things can most sight glasses indicate to a serviceman?

31. What should be done to the main switch before one works on the wiring of a unit?
32. Why is a fuse plug used?
33. What is put on a brazed joint before it is taken apart?
34. What may happen if moisture collects on the outside of the bellows of a refrigerant control?
35. What happens if a suction line is undersized?
36. What may cause a capacitor to explode?
37. How should the contaminated hermetic compressor oil be handled?
38. Can a conventional compressor crankshaft seal be repaired without removing the compressor?
39. When should one wear goggles when working on a refrigerating mechanism?
40. What should one do if a leaky refrigerant joint is located?
41. What are two uses for an ohmmeter?
42. Why do some compressors have a sight glass?
43. How may one put oil in a compressor?
44. What may one do if refrigerant lines are noisy?
45. What should one do to evaporative condenser water?
46. What chemical is sometimes used to clean water lines?
47. What causes a hermetic motor-compressor burnout?
48. Why should a suction line have a slight down slope toward the compressor?
49. What is a refrigerant charging tube? How does it indicate the weight of the refrigerant?
50. What voltage should the power line to a motor have?

Chapter 16

COMMERCIAL SYSTEMS, HEAT LOADS AND PIPING

Commercial refrigeration installations must be properly engineered if they are to perform satisfactorily. Four steps required if a refrigeration system is to give good performance are:

1. HEAT LOAD. Determine the total amount of heat that must be removed.

2. CONDENSING UNIT. Determine the condensing unit capacity to handle the heat load.

3. EVAPORATOR. Determine the evaporator unit capacity to handle the heat load.

4. TOTAL SYSTEM. You must consider such factors as water supply, temperature control devices, refrigerator line sizes, air circulation, humidity control, and must correctly install the components according to code.

When determing the heat load, two factors which must be considered are:

1. Heat leakage into the cabinet. The heat leakage is affected by the amount of exposed surface, thickness and kind of insulation, and temperature difference between inside and outside of cabinet.

2. Usage or service heat load of the cabinet. This load is determined by temperature of articles put into the refrigerator, their specific heat, generated heat, and latent heat as the requirements demand. Another consideration is the nature of the service required such as air changes determined by the number of times per day

that doors of the refrigerator are opened and heat generated inside by fans, lights, and other electrical devices.

The total heat load is the sum of:
1. Wall heat transmission load.
2. Air change load.
3. Product load.
4. Miscellaneous loads.

The selection of a condensing unit is usually made from manufacturers' tables of condensing unit capacities.

Evaporators are selected from specifications for capacities, and are selected to balance the capacity of the condensing unit. The capacity of the refrigerant control, the type of temperature control, the arrangement for air circulation, and specific duty also affect the selection of an evaporator.

The installation of all commercial refrigeration equipment involves a technical understanding of the variables and is a determining factor in the successful operation of the system. The following paragraphs on commercial refrigeration describe the fundamentals of equipment selection for commercial refrigeration. Technical installation knowledge is also important to the serviceman. The more the serviceman understands about the refrigerant liquid and vapor behavior inside the system, the more accurately he can diagnose the service problems.

16-1 Heat Load

Total heat load consists of the amount of heat to be removed from a cabinet during a certain period. This is dependent on two main factors:

1. Heat leakage load.
2. Heat usage or service load.

The heat leakage load or heat transfer load is the total amount of heat that leaks through the walls, windows, ceiling, and floor of the cabinet.

The heat usage or service load is the sum of the heat load of cooling the contents to cabinet temperature, cooling of air changes, removing respiration heat from fresh "or live" vegetables, meat, removing heat released by electric lights, electric motors and the like, and heat given off by people entering and/or working in the cabinet.

16-2 Heat Leakage Variables

Research organizations, manufacturers and refrigeration associations have experimented to determine the factors of heat leakage through walls and other heat loads. Charts based on these findings are used by engineers and technicians.

Five factors which affect heat leakage are:

1. TIME. The longer the period of time, the more heat will leak through a certain wall. The standard time unit used for computation is the 24-hour period in refrigeration situations, while the 1-hour period is used in air conditioning situations.

2. TEMPERATURE DIFFERENCE. The difference in temperature is an important factor in the heat leakage into a container. The greater the temperature difference the more heat will leak or transfer through the wall. One might compare this idea to pressure: the more pressure the more water will flow through an opening. The room temperature is usually chosen as the average summer temperature. In this country it varies between 90 and 105 F. See Fig. 16-1.

3. THICKNESS OF INSULATION. The third variable is the thickness of the insulation. The thicker the insulation, the less heat will flow through it. Twice as much heat will ordinarily leak through a wall that is insulated with 1 in. insulation as will flow through a wall having 2 in. insulation.

4. KIND OF INSULATION. The kind of insulation or the material used is an important consideration in the construction of containers. Cork, for instance, will insulate approximately four times better than

SUMMER DESIGN TEMPERATURES

STATE	Design Dry Bulb °F.	STATE	Design Dry Bulb °F.
Alabama	95	Michigan	95
Arizona	105	Minnesota	95
Arkansas	95	Mississippi	95
California		Missouri	100
Lower	105	Montana	95
Middle	90	Nebraska	95
Upper	85	Nevada	95
Colorado	95	New Hampshire	90
Connecticut	95	New Jersey	95
Delaware	95	New Mexico	95
Dist. of Col.	95	New York	95
Florida		North Carolina	95
Upper	95	North Dakota	95
Lower	98	Ohio	95
Georgia	95	Oklahoma	101
Idaho	95	Oregon	90
Illinois		Pennsylvania	95
Upper	95	Rhode Island	93
Lower	98	South Carolina	95
Indiana	95	South Dakota	95
Iowa	95	Tennessee	95
Kansas		Texas	100
Upper	95	Utah	95
Lower	100	Vermont	90
Kentucky	95	Virginia	95
Louisiana	100	Washington	93
Maine	90	West Virginia	95
Maryland	95	Wisconsin	95
Massachusetts	92	Wyoming	95

Fig. 16-1. Table of summer design temperatures which may be used as ambient temperatures when figuring heat leakage loads.

wood and eight or nine times better than brick, etc. On the other hand, some insulations are more costly than others and this must be taken into consideration.

5. EXTERNAL AREA OF CABINET. Just as the size of a pipe determines how much water will flow through it (the bigger the pipe the more water will flow), so the more the area through which heat may leak the greater the heat flow. The common unit used for determining the heat flow is the square foot of area. This area is always measured on the outside of the cabinet.

16-3 Heat Transfer

To bring together the variables just discussed, standards have been developed which are used by refrigerating companies. The variables have been reduced to unit values. Heat leakage of the wall is determined for these unit values. The unit or basic values are the thermal conductance (symbol is K) obtained for an area of insulation one square foot in size, one inch thick, with a temperature difference of 1 F., over a period of time of either 1-hour or 24-hours. The values obtained represent the heat flow through the slab under these conditions. These naturally vary with the

kind of insulation. This material has no air film, or liquid film, on either side. The symbol is K.

If the insulation is less than, or more than 1 in. thick, the heat leakage will be different, and the symbol is K_T.

For example:

$$K_T = \frac{K_1}{\text{thickness}}$$

By definition:

K_T = Conductance, total and

K_1 = Conductance for one in. thickness.

If thickness is 2 in.:

$$K_T = \frac{K_1}{2}$$

$$K_T = \frac{1}{2}K_1$$

If thickness is $\frac{1}{2}$ in.:

$$K_T = \frac{K_1}{\frac{1}{2}}$$

$$K_T = K_1 \div \frac{1}{2}$$

$$K_T = K_1 \times 2$$

$$K_T = 2K_1$$

In order to compute the heat leakage or thermal conductance through a composite wall, such as a wall made out of wood and cork or wood and metal, as shown in Fig. 16-2, the formula for computing the K_T or total heat conductance factor is explained as follows:

Resistance to heat flow is known by the symbol R. If the same heat is flowing through two substances, the total resistance is equal to the resistance of each substance.

$$R_T = R_1 + R_2$$

R_T = Resistance total

R_1 = Resistance of substance 1

R_2 = Resistance of substance 2

R is the opposite, or the reciprocal of K. In the formula it would be:

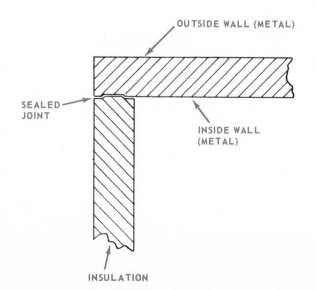

OUTSIDE WALL (METAL)

SEALED JOINT

INSIDE WALL (METAL)

INSULATION

Fig. 16-2. Cross section of a walk-in cooler wall.

$$\frac{1}{K_T} = \frac{1}{K_1} + \frac{1}{K_2}$$

K_T = Conductance, total
K_1 = Conductance, substance 1
K_2 = Conductance, substance 2

Example:

If K_1 = .6 and K_2 = .2

$$\frac{1}{K_T} = \frac{1}{.6} + \frac{1}{.2}$$

$$\frac{1}{K_T} = \frac{1}{\frac{6}{10}} + \frac{1}{\frac{2}{10}}$$

$$\frac{1}{K_T} = \frac{10}{6} + \frac{10}{2}$$

$$\frac{1}{K_T} = \frac{5}{3} + \frac{5}{1}$$

$$\frac{1}{K_T} = \frac{5}{3} + \frac{15}{3}$$

$$\frac{1}{K_T} = \frac{20}{3}$$

$$K_T = \frac{3}{20}$$

$$K_T = .15$$

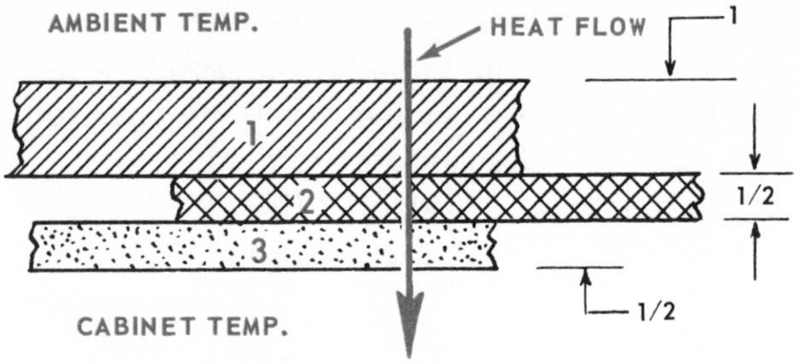

Fig. 16-3. A composite insulated panel or wall. 1, 2, and 3 are different insulating materials of different thickness.

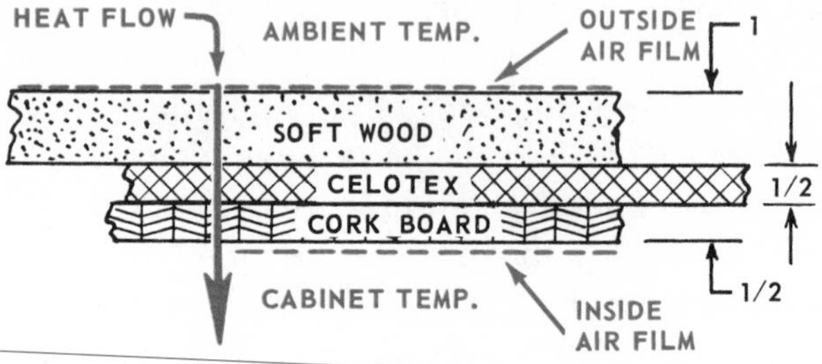

Fig. 16-4. Composite insulating panel composed of various materials at specified thicknesses, with air film on both sides.

If the wall is made up of three different materials, as shown in Fig. 16-3, the overall heat leakage (K) is found as follows:

$$K_T = \frac{1}{\dfrac{\text{thickness of material 1}}{\text{conductivity factor material 1}} + \dfrac{\text{thickness of material 2}}{\text{conductivity factor material 2}} + \dfrac{\text{thickness of material 3}}{\text{conductivity factor material 3}}}$$

where Th_1 = thickness of material 1.
        Th_2 = thickness of material 2.
        Th_3 = thickness of material 3.
and K_1 = conductivity factor for material 1.
        K_2 = conductivity factor for material 2.
        K_3 = conductivity factor for material 3.

then the formula becomes:

$$K_T = \frac{1}{\dfrac{Th_1}{K_1} + \dfrac{Th_2}{K_2} + \dfrac{Th_3}{K_3}}$$

To solve for the conductivity for the panel shown in Fig. 16-3, proceed as follows:

$$K_T = \cfrac{1}{\cfrac{\text{thickness A}}{\text{K for wood}} + \cfrac{\text{thickness B}}{\substack{\text{K for} \\ \text{celotex}}} + \cfrac{\text{thickness C}}{\substack{\text{K for} \\ \text{corkboard}}}}$$

From Chapter 27, we find the K values as follows:
   K for wood = .80 for 1 in. thickness.
   K for celotex = .31 for 1 in. thickness.
   K for corkboard = .285 for 1 in. thickness.

However, in the example the wood is 1/2 in. thick, the celotex is 1/4 in. thick and the corkboard is 1/4 in. thick.

Substituting these values in the above formula we have:

$$K_T = \cfrac{1}{\cfrac{.5}{.80} + \cfrac{.25}{.31} + \cfrac{.25}{.285}} = \cfrac{1}{.625 + .807 + .877} = \cfrac{1}{2.3}$$

   $K_T = .435$ which is the conductivity for the panel.

An air film that clings to the outer and inner surfaces of the cabinet adds to the insulating value of the walls of the cabinet. This added resistance is calculated in the following formula in which the outside air film is considered to have a heat transfer value of 6.00 and the inside wall air film has a value of 1.65.
   K_T = Unit of conductivity for materials of a composite nature.
    U = Unit of conductivity for materials of a composite nature. Plus the effect of the air clinging to both the outside (F_0) and the inside (F_1) walls.
   If the insulating value of the air clinging to the walls is considered the formula becomes:

$$U = \cfrac{1}{\cfrac{1}{F_0} + \cfrac{Th_1}{K_1} + \cfrac{Th_2}{K_2} + \cfrac{Th_3}{K_3} + \cfrac{1}{F_1}}$$

If the value of $F_0 = 6.0$ and the value of $F_1 = 1.65$ then the problem in Fig. 16-4 may be solved as follows:

$$U = \cfrac{1}{\cfrac{1}{6.0} + \cfrac{.5}{.80} + \cfrac{.25}{.31} + \cfrac{.25}{.285} + \cfrac{1}{1.65}} = \cfrac{1}{.166 + .625 + .807 + .877 + .606} = \cfrac{1}{3.081} = .32$$

The value of K as computed in the previous problem equals .435, while the value of U as computed in this problem equals .32, which shows the additional insulating effect of the air films.

This type of computation is complicated and slow as you can see. It is for this reason that standard tables for computing heat leakage are generally used.

16-4 Air Change Heat Load

Air that enters a refrigerated space must be cooled. Air has weight and contains moisture. When it enters the refrigerated space, heat must be removed from it.

By Charles' Law, air which enters and is cooled, reduces in pressure. If the cabinet is not airtight, air will continue to leak in. Also each time a service door or a walk-in door is opened, the cold air inside being heavier, will spill out the bottom of the opening allowing the warmer room air to move into the cabinet. The actions of material moving in or out of the cabinet, a person going into or leaving a cabinet, all result in warm air moving into the space. This action is sometimes called infiltration of air.

VOLUME CU. FT.	AIR CHANGES PER 24 HR.	VOLUME CU. FT.	AIR CHANGES PER 24 HR.
200	44.0	6,000	6.5
300	34.5	8,000	5.5
400	29.5	10,000	4.9
500	26.0	15,000	3.9
600	23.0	20,000	3.5
800	20.0	25,000	3.0
1,000	17.5	30,000	2.7
1,500	14.0	40,000	2.3
2,000	12.0	50,000	2.0
3,000	9.5	75,000	1.6
4,000	8.2	100,000	1.4
5,000	7.2		

NOTE: For heavy usage multiply the above values by 2. For long storage multiply the above values by 0.6.

Fig. 16-5. Average air changes per 24 hours for storage rooms due to door openings and air infiltration. (ASHRAE Guide and Data Book)

Fig. 16-5 shows accepted air change values for refrigerated cabinets of various internal volumes. Fig. 16-6 shows the total heat (sensible + latent) to be removed from this air depending on various outside conditions and refrigerator temperatures.

16-5 Product Heat Load

Any substance placed in a refrigerator, which is warmer than the refrigerator, will lose heat until it cools to the refrigerator temperature.

Three kinds of heat removal may be involved:
1. Specific Heat.
2. Latent Heat.
3. Respiration Heat.

The total product heat load would be the sum of these three heat loads. An example of all three heat loads would be moist head lettuce at 55 F. being put into a 35 F. refrigerator. The lettuce must be cooled to 35 F. (specific heat), some of the moisture on the lettuce will evaporate and collect on the coils (latent heat) and the lettuce, being a live vegetable, would change and release heat energy (live vegetables absorb carbon dioxide and release oxygen). Meats go through a slow bacteriological change and during this action, heat is released.

1. An example of specific heat: bottled beverages at 50 F., if placed in a 35 F. refrigerator will release heat until their temperature reaches 35 F. This action is a specific heat problem. If the bottles were moist or if the bottle carton were moist however, there would be a moisture evaporating problem (latent heat).

2. An example of latent heat: If meat at 50 F. is placed in a refrigerator, and cooled (frozen) to 0 F., the meat cools to about 27 F., freezes, then it cools to 0 F. The latent heat of freezing of the meat is considerable. For fresh beef it is 98 Btu per pound. Fig. 16-7 shows the specific heats and latent heats of various refrigerated products in addition to recommended storage temperatures and relative humidity.

3. An example of respiration heat: If lettuce is stored at 40 F., each pound will release 7.99 Btu/24 hours or 15,990 Btu/ton. Fig. 16-7 also shows the respiration heat of some of the more common vegetables and fruits.

16-6 Miscellaneous Heat Load

All sources of heat not calculated by heat leakage, product cooling, and respiration load are usually listed as miscellaneous heat loads. Some of the more common

HEAT REMOVED IN COOLING AIR TO STORAGE ROOM CONDITIONS
(BTU PER CU. FT.)

TEMPERATURE OF OUTSIDE AIR, F.

STORAGE ROOM TEMP. F.	85		90		95		100	
	RELATIVE HUMIDITY, PERCENT							
	50	60	50	60	50	60	50	60
65	0.65	0.85	0.93	1.17	1.24	1.54	1.58	1.95
60	0.85	1.03	1.13	1.37	1.44	1.74	1.78	2.15
55	1.12	1.34	1.41	1.66	1.72	2.01	2.06	2.44
50	1.32	1.54	1.62	1.87	1.93	2.22	2.28	2.65
45	1.50	1.73	1.80	2.06	2.12	2.42	2.47	2.85
40	1.69	1.92	2.00	2.26	2.31	2.62	2.67	3.06
35	1.86	2.09	2.17	2.43	2.49	2.79	2.85	3.24
30	2.00	2.24	2.26	2.53	2.64	2.94	2.95	3.35

TEMPERATURE OF OUTSIDE AIR, F.

STORAGE ROOM TEMP. F.	40		50		90		100	
	RELATIVE HUMIDITY, PERCENT							
	70	80	70	80	50	60	50	60
30	0.24	0.29	0.58	0.66	2.26	2.53	2.95	3.35
25	0.41	0.45	0.75	0.83	2.44	2.71	3.14	3.54
20	0.56	0.61	0.91	0.99	2.62	2.90	3.33	3.73
15	0.71	0.75	1.06	1.14	2.80	3.07	3.51	3.92
10	0.85	0.89	1.19	1.27	2.93	3.20	3.64	4.04
5	0.98	1.03	1.34	1.42	3.12	3.40	3.84	4.27
0	1.12	1.17	1.48	1.56	3.28	3.56	4.01	4.43
− 5	1.23	1.28	1.59	1.67	3.41	3.69	4.15	4.57
−10	1.35	1.41	1.73	1.81	3.56	3.85	4.31	4.74
−15	1.50	1.53	1.85	1.92	3.67	3.96	4.42	4.86
−20	1.63	1.68	2.01	2.09	3.88	4.18	4.66	5.10
−25	1.77	1.80	2.12	2.21	4.00	4.30	4.78	5.21
−30	1.90	1.95	2.29	2.38	4.21	4.51	4.90	5.44

Fig. 16-6. Heat removed in cooling air to storage room conditions.
(ASHRAE Guide and Data Book)

sources of miscellaneous heat loads are:
1. Lights.
2. Electric motors.
3. People.
4. Defrosting heat sources.
5. Sun (solar) heat.

1. Lights located in the refrigerated space will release heat. For example, a 100 watt lamp will give off 342 Btu in 1 hour or

342 x 24 = 8208 Btu/24 hours.

If the work day was 8 hours (the only time

Product	Quick Freeze Temp.	Storage Temp. Long	Storage Temp. Short	Humidity % R.H.	Specific Heat Above Freezing	Specific Heat Below Freezing	Latent Heat	Freezing Point	Respiration BTU/lb. Per Day
Apples	—15	30-32	38-42	85-88	0.92	0.39	91.5	28.4	0.75
Asparagus	—30	32	40	85-90	0.95	0.44	134.0	29.8	....
Bacon, Fresh		0-5	36-40	80	0.55	0.31	30.0	25.0	....
Bananas		56-72	56-72	85-95	0.81	....	108.0	30.2	4.18
Beans, Green		32-34	40-45	85-90	0.92	0.47	128	29.7	3.3
Beans, Dried		36-40	50-60	70	0.30	0.237	18	....	....
Beef, Fresh, Fat	—15	30-32	38-42	84	0.60	0.35	79	....	....
Beef, Fresh Lean	—15	30-32	38-42	85	0.77	0.40	100	....	....
Beets, Topped		32-35	45-50	95-98	0.90	....	....	26.9	2.0
Blackberries	—15	31-32	42-45	80-85	0.89	0.46	125	28.9	....
Broccoli		32-35	40-45	90-95	0.93	....	....	29.2	....
Butter	+15	....	40-45	....	0.64	0.34	15	15.0	....
Cabbage	—30	32	45	90-95	0.93	0.47	130	31.2	....
Carrots, Topped	—30	32	40-45	95-98	0.87	0.45	120	29.6	1.73
Cauliflower		32	40-45	85-90	0.90	....	....	30.1	....
Celery	—30	31-32	45-50	90-95	0.95	0.48	135	29.7	2.27
Cheese	+15	32-38	39-45	....	0.70	....	....	....	....
Cherries		31-32	40	80-85	0.85	....	118	28.0	6.6
Chocolate Coatings		45-50	....	....	0.3	....	....	....	....
Corn, Green		31-32	45	85-90	0.86	....	....	29.0	4.1
Cranberries		36-40	40-45	85-90	0.91	....	....	27.3	....
Cream		34	40-45	....	0.88	0.37	84	....	....
Cucumbers		45-50	45-50	80-85	0.93	....	....	30.5	....
Dates, Cured		28	55-60	50-60	0.83	0.44	104	....	....
Eggs, Fresh	—10	30-31	38-45	....	0.76	0.40	98	31.0	....
Eggplants		45-50	46-50	85-90	0.88	....	....	30.4	....
Flowers		35-40	....	85-90	....	....	....	....	....
Fish, Fresh, Iced	—15	25	25-30	....	0.82	0.41	105	30.0	....
Fish, Dried		30-40	....	60-70	0.56	0.34	65	....	....
Furs		32-34	40-42	40-60	....	....	....	....	....
Furs, To Shock		15	15						
Grapefruit		32	32	85-90	0.92	....	111	28.4	0.5
Grapes		30-32	35-40	80-85	0.92	....	111	27.0	0.5
Ham, Fresh		28	36-40	80	0.68	0.38	87	....	....
Honey		31-32	45-50	....	0.35	0.26	26	....	....
Ice Cream	—20	....	0-10	....	.5-.8	0.45	96	....	....
Lard		32-34	40-45	80	0.52	0.31	90	....	....
Lemons		55-58	....	80-85	0.91	0.39	190	28.1	0.4
Lettuce		32	45	90-95	0.90	....	....	31.2	8.0
Liver, Fresh		32-34	36-38	83	0.72	0.42	94	....	....
Lobster, Boiled		25	36-40	....	0.81	0.42	105	....	....
Maple Syrup		31-32	45	....	0.24	0.215	7.0	....	....
Meat, Brined		31-32	40-45	....	0.75	0.36	75.0	....	....
Melons		34-40	40-45	75-85	0.92	0.35	115	28.5	1.0
Milk		34-36	40-45	....	0.92	0.46	124	31.0	....
Mushrooms		32-35	55-60	80-85	0.90	....	....	30.2	....
Mutton		32-34	34-42	82	0.81	0.39	96	29.0	....
Nut Meats		32-50	35-40	65-75	0.30	0.24	14	20.0	....
Oleomargarine		34-36	....	....	0.65	0.34	35	15.0	....
Onions		32	50-60	70-75	0.91	0.46	120	30.1	1.0
Oranges		32-34	50	85-90	0.89	0.40	91.0	27.9	0.7
Oysters		....	32-35	....	0.85	0.45	120.0	....	....
Parsnips	—30	32-34	34-40	90-95	0.82	0.45	120.0	28.9	....
Peaches, Fresh		31-32	50	85-90	0.92	0.42	110	29.4	1.0
Pears, Fresh		29-31	40	85-90	0.90	0.43	106	28.0	6.6
Peas, Green		32	40-45	85-90	0.80	0.42	108	30.0	....
Peas, Dried		35-40	50-60	....	0.28	0.22	14	....	....
Peppers		32	40-45	85-90	0.90	....	....	30.1	2.35
Pineapples, Ripe		40-45	50	85-90	0.90	....	127	29.9	....
Plums		31-32	40-45	80-85	0.83	....	115	28.0	....
Pork, Fresh		30	36-40	85	0.60	0.38	66	28.0	....
Potatoes, White	—30	36-50	45-60	85-90	0.77	0.44	105	28.9	0.85
Poultry, Dressed	—10	28-30	29-32	....	0.80	0.41	99	27	....
Pumpkins		50-55	55-60	70-75	0.90	....	....	30.2	....
Quinces		31-32	40-45	80-85	0.90	....	....	28.1	....
Raspberries		31-32	40-45	80-85	0.89	0.46	125	30.0	3.3
Sardines, Canned		....	35-40	....	0.76	0.410	101	....	....
Sausage, Fresh		31-36	36-40	80	0.89	....	....	....	....
Sauerkraut		33-36	36-38	85	0.91	0.47	128	....	....
Squash		50-55	55-60	70-75	0.90	....	....	29.3	....
Spinach		32	45-50	85	0.92	....	....	30.8	....
Strawberries	—15	31-32	42-45	80-85	0.92	0.48	129	30.0	3.3
Tomatoes, ripe		40-50	55-70	85-90	0.95	....	135	30.4	0.5
Turnips		32	40-45	95-98	0.90	....	....	30.5	1.0
Veal	—15	28-30	36-40	....	0.71	0.39	91	29	....

Fig. 16-7. Temperature, specific heat, and latent heat data for more common foods.
(Dunham-Bush Inc.)

the light was on) the heat load would be
342 x 8 = 2736 Btu/24 hours.
2. Electric motors release 2545 Btu/

hp/hour on the average. The heat release depends on motor efficiency, the larger the motor the more efficient the motor. Fig.

16-8 shows the heat given off by motors and devices they drive. Because forced convection evaporator coils usually have motors and fans, it should be noted that the

Whether the defrost heat is electric, hot gas, or water; the defrosting operation adds heat to the interior of the refrigerator. The amount of heat is difficult to determine be-

BTU PER (HP) (HR)

MOTOR HP	CONNECTED LOAD IN REF. SPACE[1]	MOTOR LOSSES OUTSIDE REF. SPACE[2]	CONNECTED LOAD OUTSIDE REF. SPACE[3]
1/8 to 1/2	4,250	2,545	1,700
1/2 to 3	3,700	2,545	1,150
3 to 20	2,950	2,545	400

[1]For use when both useful output and motor losses are dissipated within refrigerated space; motors driving fans for forced circulation unit coolers.
[2]For use when motor losses are dissipated outside refrigerated space and useful work of motor is expended within refrigerated space; pump on a circulating brine or chilled water system, fan motor outside refrigerated space driving fan circulating air within refrigerated space.
[3]For use when motor heat losses are dissipated within refrigerated space and useful work expended outside of refrigerated space; motor in refrigerated space driving pump or fan located outside of space.

Fig. 16-8. Heat equivalent of electric motors.
(ASHRAE Guide and Date Book)

total heat release of such a motor is about 4,250 Btu/hp/hr. for motors of 1/8 to 1/2 hp. Example, a 1/8 hp motor-fan would release:

4250 Btu/hp/hr.
4250 Btu/hr. x 1/8 x 1 =
4250 ÷ 8 = 540 Btu/hour.
540 x 24 = 12,960 Btu/24 hours if the motor runs continuously.

3. When people are inside a refrigerated space they release heat at varying rates depending on what they are wearing (insulation), temperature of cabinet, and on how hard they are working. Fig. 16-9 shows a variation of 720 Btu/hour/person at 50 F. to 1,400 Btu/hour/person at -10 F. For example, if one person worked in a 30 F. refrigerator for eight hours, the heat load would be

950 Btu/hr. x 8 hours = 7600 Btu.

4. Many refrigerating units are equipped with defrosting heat sources, especially if the fixture temperature is 32 F. or lower.

cause most of the defrosting heat is removed in the defrost drain water. Approximately 10 percent of the defrosting heat input should be added as part of the heat load.

5. If part of the refrigerator is exposed to the sun, the heat from this source must be considered. If a dark surface, add approximately 10 F., if a medium colored surface, add 5 F., and if a light surface add 3 F.

HEAT EQUIVALENT OF OCCUPANCY

COOLER TEMPERATURE F.	HEAT EQUIVALENT/ PERSON BTU/HR.
50	720
40	840
30	950
20	1,050
10	1,200
0	1,300
-10	1,400

Fig. 16-9. Heat equivalent of occupancy.
(ASHRAE Guide and Data Book)

16-7 Total Heat Load

The use of the information from the previous pargraphs can be illustrated by the following problem.

If a metal sheathed walk-in cabinet 16 ft. long x 20 ft. wide x 9 ft. high with 4 in. cork insulation is in a 90 F. 50% RH room, and it cools 2,000 lbs. of beef from 60 F. to 35 F. each day and the evaporator coil has two 1/10 hp motors and the cabinet has two 40 watt lamps (8 hours), what is the total heat load?

Heat leakage = External area x Btu/ sq. ft./hr. for above conditions, Fig. 16-10.

Heat leakage = 1288 x 99 = 127,512 Btu per day.

Air change = Volume x Air changes/24 hours x Btu/cu. ft.
(Heat to be removed, cooling air from 90 F. 50% RH to 35 F., Fig. 16-6.)

Air change = 2280 x 11.4 x 2.17 = 56,403 Btu per day.

Product load = weight x spec. heat x temp. diff., Fig. 16-7.

Product load 2000 lbs. x .77 spec. heat x 25 F. temp. diff. = 38,500 Btu per day.

The two motor's load (continuous operation) = No. of motors x Btu/hp/hr. x hp x hrs., Fig. 16-8,

2 x 4250 x 1/10 x 24 = 20,400 Btu.

The two lamps load = No. of lamps x watts x hrs. of operation x 3.42 Btu/watt

2 x 40 x 8 x 3.42 = 2,189.0 Btu

Therefore, the total heat load = 127,512 + 56,403 + 35,500 + 20,400 + 2,189 = 245,004 Btu/24 hrs.

$$\text{Per 16 hours} = \frac{245,004}{16\,hr.} = 15,313 \text{ Btu per}$$

hour based on 16 hours of unit operation.

16-8 Determining Heat Leakage Using Tables (Short Method)

A method of determining heat leakage into a cabinet, such as used by some refrigeration manufacturers, is shown by Fig. 16-10. The values are based on actual experiments and investigations, and practice has shown them to be accurate.

You will note that tables for the heat leakage of glass are also included in Fig. 16-10. Many refrigerator cabinets are equipped with windows. The tables show

Heat Gain Factors (Walls, Floor and Ceiling)
Btu per (sq ft) (24 hr)

Insulation Cork or equivalent in.	Temp difference (ambient temp minus storage temp), F deg																		
	1	40	45	50	55	60	65	70	75	80	85	90	95	100	105	110	115	120
3	2.4	96	108	120	132	144	156	168	180	192	204	216	228	240	252	264	276	288
4	1.8	72	81	90	99	108	117	126	135	144	153	162	171	180	189	198	207	216
5	1.44	58	65	72	79	87	94	101	108	115	122	130	137	144	151	159	166	173
6	1.2	48	54	60	66	72	78	84	90	96	102	108	114	120	126	132	138	144
7	1.03	41	46	52	57	62	67	72	77	82	88	93	98	103	108	113	118	124
8	0.90	36	41	45	50	54	59	63	68	72	77	81	86	90	95	99	104	108
9	0.80	32	36	40	44	48	52	56	60	64	68	72	76	80	84	88	92	96
10	0.72	29	32	36	40	43	47	50	54	58	61	65	68	72	76	79	83	86
11	0.66	26	30	33	36	40	43	46	50	53	56	60	63	66	69	73	76	79
12	0.60	24	27	30	33	36	39	42	45	48	51	54	57	60	63	66	69	72
13	0.55	22	25	28	30	33	36	39	41	44	47	50	52	55	58	61	63	66
14	0.51	20	23	26	28	31	33	36	38	41	43	46	49	51	54	56	59	61
Single glass	27.0	1080	1220	1350	1490	1620	1760	1890	2030	2160	2290	2440	2560	2700	2840	2970	3100	3240
Double glass	11.0	440	500	550	610	660	715	770	825	880	936	990	1050	1100	1160	1210	1270	1320
Triple glass	7.0	280	320	350	390	420	454	490	525	560	595	630	665	700	740	770	810	840

Note: Where wood studs are used multiply the above values by 1.1

Fig. 16-10. Heat gain factors (walls, floor, and ceiling).
(ASHRAE Guide and Data Book)

REFRIGERATION SALES ENGINEERS DATA SHEET

Name _____ Type of Business _____ Date _____

Address _____ City _____ Zone _____ State _____

Person Contacted _____ Title _____

Fixture No. 1-Make _____   Fixture No. 2-Make _____   Fixture No. 3-Make _____

Use _____ Model _____   Use _____ Model _____   Use _____ Model _____

Temperature _____   _____   _____

Humidity _____   _____   _____

Width _____   _____   _____

Length _____   _____   _____

Height _____   _____   _____

Construction _____   _____   _____

Insulation:
   Kind _____   _____   _____

   Thickness _____   _____   _____

Glass:
   Area _____   _____   _____

   No. of Panes _____   _____   _____

Produce _____   _____   _____

Lights _____   _____   _____

Motors _____   _____   _____

Sun Load _____   _____   _____

No. of People in Refrigerator ____   _____   _____

Unusual Temperatures _____   _____   _____

Unusual Service _____   _____   _____

Remarks _____   _____   _____

Use Reverse Side for Sketch of Installation

Salesman _____

Fig. 16-11. Sample data sheet which may be used by sales engineers in recording data for refrigeration installation.

that heat leakage through windows is high compared to leakage through walls.

To use the tables, proceed as follows (using a walk-in refrigerator box as a sample problem): The sales engineer visits the establishment and obtains all the data possible concerning the cabinet and the service. For instance, he must determine exterior dimensions of the box, dimensions of windows, dimensions of wall, thickness of

the data needed to select the proper equipment. Fig. 16-11, is a sample of this type of data sheet.

16-9 Cabinet Areas

The area of a cabinet is the outside area. There are six surfaces: The four walls, the ceiling, and the floor. Usually the floor and ceiling are the same area, and the

Box		8' HIGH CAPACITY (CU. FT.)								10' HIGH CAPACITY (CU. FT.)						
Lg. & Wd.	Outside Sq. Ft.	2" Cork	2½" Cork	3" Cork	4" Cork	5" Cork	6" Cork	8" Cork	Outside Sq. Ft.	2" Cork	2½" Cork	3" Cork	4" Cork	5" Cork	6" Cork	8" Cork
5x 5	210	137	131	124	112	101	90	71	250	174	167	159	144	131	117	93
5x 6	236	169	161	154	140	127	114	91	280	215	206	197	180	164	148	120
5x 7	262	201	194	184	168	153	138	111	310	256	248	236	216	198	179	146
5x 8	288	233	224	214	196	179	162	131	340	296	286	274	252	232	210	172
6x 6	264	209	201	193	175	160	145	119	312	266	256	247	225	207	188	156
6x 7	292	248	238	228	210	193	176	146	344	316	304	292	270	249	228	192
6x 8	320	286	277	267	245	226	207	173	376	364	353	342	315	292	269	228
6x 9	348	325	315	305	280	259	238	200	408	414	402	390	360	335	309	263
6x10	376	364	353	343	315	292	269	227	440	463	451	439	405	378	350	299
6x12	432	444	432	419	385	358	331	281	504	555	546	536	495	463	430	370
7x 7	322	294	283	272	254	234	214	180	378	374	361	348	326	302	278	237
7x 8	352	341	329	317	294	273	252	214	412	434	420	406	378	353	328	281
7x 9	382	386	374	362	334	312	290	248	446	492	477	463	430	403	377	326
7x10	412	433	420	407	374	346	318	282	480	551	536	521	481	448	413	371
7x12	472	527	512	497	454	414	374	348	548	670	653	635	583	535	486	458
8x 8	384	394	382	369	343	320	296	253	448	501	487	473	441	413	385	333
8x 9	416	448	434	420	392	367	341	294	484	570	553	538	504	474	443	386
8x10	448	503	587	471	441	413	385	335	520	641	748	603	567	534	500	441
8x12	512	610	591	573	539	506	473	417	592	776	755	734	692	653	615	548
8x14	576	718	697	675	637	594	561	499	664	914	889	864	818	768	730	656
9x 9	450	510	489	469	448	420	392	341	522	649	623	600	576	543	510	449
9x10	484	570	554	537	504	473	443	386	560	725	706	686	647	612	575	508
9x12	552	694	674	654	616	581	545	476	636	883	859	836	792	752	708	626
9x14	620	814	793	771	728	687	647	566	712	1035	1011	987	935	888	840	745
10x10	520	638	620	602	567	534	500	440	600	870	790	770	729	680	650	579
10x12	592	776	755	734	693	655	617	547	680	988	962	939	890	847	802	720
10x14	664	912	889	866	818	775	733	654	760	1158	1132	1110	1050	1005	954	860
12x12	672	946	919	893	848	804	760	680	768	1203	1172	1144	1090	1038	988	895
12x14	752	1110	1086	1052	1001	951	900	809	856	1411	1382	1348	1289	1230	1170	1060
14x14	840	1304	1269	1235	1180	1126	1072	968	952	1660	1619	1568	1518	1458	1394	1272

Fig. 16-12. Table of cabinet external areas and internal volumes (capacity).

insulation, kind of insulation, number of panes in windows, how much business user does, what temperatures user desires in cabinet, what the average summer temperature is for the locality, and the highest possible water temperature, if a water-cooled installation is to be made.

Specification or data sheets are available that help the sales engineer obtain all

opposite walls are the same area. To determine the total outside area you may proceed as follows:

(1) Width and length are multiplied together and then multiplied by two; these areas represent floor and ceiling of the cabinet; (2) Width and height are then multiplied together, and multiplied by two, to determine area of ends of the cabinet; (3)

Length and height are multiplied together, and multiplied by two, to determine area of sides of box. Add these three values and you will have the total external area of the box. By formula:

L = Length   W = Width   H = Height

(1) W x L x 2 = Area of ceiling and floor.

(2) W x H x 2 = Area of ends.

(3) L x H x 2 = Area of sides.

Total external area = Sum of (1), (2) and (3).

The reason most companies base their computations on the external area of the box rather than the interior area or a medium area is that the results are on the safe side.

Tables can be used to obtain the external area of a cabinet and also its internal volum. See Fig. 16-12.

After obtaining the external area of the box, you must subtract the window area, to obtain the area of the insulated surface. Window areas are calculated from the measurements of the outside edges of the window frame and must be considered separately.

Total external area - the window area = insulated area.

From the table, Fig. 16-10, you may find the amount of heat that will leak through the insulation per square foot of area per 24 hours for that particular type of wall construction for the temperature difference. For example, if the wall is made of steel paneling on both sides and there is 4 in. of slab cork between, the tables will reveal that at a temperature difference of 50 F., (85 F. -35 F.) 108 Btu will leak through per square foot during the period of 24 hours. The glass leakage table will similarly give values for the heat leakage through 1 square foot of glass. If the cabinet has double glass, 550 Btu will leak through at a temperature difference of 50 F. Adding the two will give the total heat leakage into the cabinet.

A typical example is a 6 ft. x 7 ft. x 9 ft. high walk-in cooler with two windows 1 1/2 ft. x 2 ft. The box is kept at 36 F. in a room with a summer design temperature of 96 F. The wall construction consists of 4 in. cork with metal on each side. The windows are of the double-pane construction. The temperature difference is 96 -36 = 60 F.

Solution.

Total surface.

Walls: 6 x 7 x 2 = 84 sq. ft. (ceiling and floor)

6 x 9 x 2 = 108 sq. ft. (ends)

7 x 9 x 2 = 126 sq. ft. (sides)

318 sq. ft. total area

Windows: 1 1/2 x 2 x 2 = 6 sq. ft. of window

318 -6 = 312 sq. ft. of insulated wall

From table Fig. 16-10:

1 sq. ft. of the wall allows 108 Btu per 24 hours.

108 x 312 sq. ft. = 33,696 Btu per 24 hours through the walls.

From table Fig. 16-10:

1 sq. ft. of the windows allows 550 Btu per 24 hours.

550 x 6 sq. ft. = 3,330 Btu per 24 hours through the windows.

Or a total heat leakage of:

33,696 + 3,300 = 36,996 Btu per 24 hours.

16-10 Determining Usage Load Using Tables (Short Method)

The total heat load of the refrigerator cabinet in addition to being dependent upon the heat leaking through the walls and windows is also affected by the heat to be removed from articles in the cabinet, the air change and other sources of heat. This heat is called heat usage, or service load, and it is caused by changes of air in the cabinet, by produce to be cooled, by lights and motors which may be used inside the box, and by the occupancy of the box.

Refrigeration equipment manufacturers have developed a standard whereby you may

Fig. 16-13.

USAGE HEAT GAIN, BTU PER 24 HR. FOR ONE CU. FT. INTERIOR CAPACITY

Volume Cu. Ft.	Service*	Temperature Difference (Ambient Temp. Minus Storage Room Temp. F. Deg.										
		1	40	50	55	60	65	70	75	80	90	100
20	Average	4.68	187.	234.	258.	281.	305.	328.	351.	374.	421.	468.
	Heavy	5.51	220.	276.	303.	331.	358.	386.	413.	441.	496.	551.
30	Average	3.30	132.	165.	182.	198.	215.	231.	248.	264.	297.	330.
	Heavy	4.56	182.	228.	251.	274.	297.	319.	342.	365.	410.	456.
50	Average	2.28	91.	114.	126.	137.	148.	160.	171.	182.	205.	228.
	Heavy	3.55	142.	177.	196.	213.	231.	249.	267.	284.	320.	355.
75	Average	1.85	74.	93.	102.	111.	120.	130.	139.	148.	167.	185.
	Heavy	2.88	115.	144.	158.	173.	188.	202.	216.	230.	259.	288.
100	Average	1.61	64.	81.	84.	97.	105.	113.	121.	129.	145.	161.
	Heavy	2.52	101.	126.	139.	151.	164.	176.	189.	202.	227.	252.
200	Average	1.38	55.	69.	76.	83.	90.	97.	103.	110.	124.	138.
	Heavy	2.22	90.	111.	122.	133.	144.	155.	166.	178.	200.	222.
300	Average	1.30	52.0	65.	71.5	78.	84.5	91.	97.5	104.	117.	130.
	Heavy	2.08	83.2	104.	114.	125.	135.	146.	156.	166.	187.	208.
400	Average	1.24	49.6	62.	68.2	74.4	80.6	86.8	93.	99.2	112.	124.
	Heavy	1.96	78.4	98.	108.	118.	128.	137.	147.	157.	176.	196.
500	Average	1.21	48.4	60.5	66.6	72.6	78.7	84.7	90.7	96.8	109.	121.
	Heavy	1.87	74.8	93.5	103.	112.	122.	131.	140.	150.	168.	187.
600	Average	1.17	46.8	58.5	64.	70.	76.	82.	88.	94.	105.	117.
	Heavy	1.85	74.0	92.5	102.	111.	120.	130.	139.	148.	167.	185.
800	Average	1.11	44.4	55.5	61.1	66.6	72.2	77.7	83.3	88.8	100.	111.
	Heavy	1.76	70.4	88.0	96.8	106.	115.	123.	132.	141.	158.	176.
1,000	Average	1.10	44.0	55.0	60.5	66.	71.5	77.	82.5	88.	99.	110.
	Heavy	1.67	66.8	83.5	91.9	100.	108.	117.	125.	134.	150.	167.
1,200	Average	.995	39.8	49.8	54.7	59.7	64.7	69.7	74.7	79.6	89.6	99.5
	Heavy	1.58	63.2	79.0	86.9	94.8	103.	111.	119.	126.	142.	158.
1,500	Average	.920	36.8	46.0	50.6	55.2	59.8	64.4	69.	73.6	82.8	92.
	Heavy	1.50	60.0	75.0	82.5	90.0	97.5	105.	113.	120.	135.	150.
2,000	Average	.835	33.4	41.8	45.9	50.1	54.3	58.5	62.7	66.8	75.2	83.5
	Long storage	.775	31.0	38.8	42.6	46.5	50.4	54.3	58.1	62.	69.8	77.5
3,000	Average	.750	30.0	37.5	41.3	45.0	48.8	52.5	56.2	60.0	67.5	75.0
	Long storage	.576	23.0	28.8	31.7	34.6	37.3	40.3	43.2	46.1	51.8	57.6
5,000	Long storage	.403	16.1	20.2	22.2	24.2	26.2	28.2	30.2	32.2	36.3	40.3
7,500	Long storage	.305	12.2	15.3	16.8	18.3	19.8	21.4	22.9	24.4	27.5	30.5
10,000	Long storage	.240	9.6	12.0	13.2	14.4	15.6	16.8	18.0	19.2	21.6	24.0
20,000	Long storage	.187	7.48	9.35	10.3	11.2	12.2	13.1	14.0	15.0	16.8	18.7
50,000	Long storage	.178	7.12	8.90	9.79	10.7	11.6	12.5	13.4	14.2	16.0	17.8
75,000	Long storage	.176	7.04	8.80	9.68	10.6	11.5	12.3	13.2	14.1	15.8	17.6
100,000	Long storage	.173	6.92	8.65	9.52	10.4	11.2	12.1	13.0	13.8	15.6	17.3

* For average and heavy service, product load is based on product entering at 10 deg. above the refrigerator temperature; for long storage the entering temperature is approximately equal to the refrigerator temperature. Where the product load is unusual, do not use this table.

USE OF REFRIGERATOR

TEMPERATURE DIFFERENCE IN DEGREES FAHRENHEIT	FLORIST	GROCERY OR NORMAL MARKET	MARKET WITH HEAVIER SERVICE OR FRESHLY KILLED MEATS	RESTAURANT SHORT ORDER
40°	40.0	65.0	95.0	120.0
50°	50.0	80.0	120.0	150.0
60°	60.0	95.0	145.0	180.0
70°	70.0	114.0	167.0	210.0
80°	80.0	130.0	190.0	240.0
90°	90.0	146.0	214.0	270.0

Fig. 16-13A. Usage heat gain, Btu per 24 hours for one cu. ft. interior capacity.
(ASHRAE Guide and Data Book)

obtain a fairly accurate estimate of the usage heat load. The method is as follows: the cabinet is classified as the type of service to be performed. Under this classification come florist's cabinets, grocery boxes, normal market coolers, fresh meat cabinets, and restaurant short order boxes. From experience these companies have found that such boxes used for the same general line of business hold rather consistently to the same usage heat load. This load depends in detail upon the following basic factors:

1. Temperature difference between exterior and interior of cabinet.
2. Volume of cabinet (internal).
3. Type of service.
4. Time.

It is possible to calculate, using a typical installation and determine the amount of food put into the refrigerator, how many times the door is opened, and for how long a period of time the employees are inside the cabinet. This is a laborious process and, unless carefully performed, discrepancies are bound to appear in the results.

The data in the tables are based on 1 cu. ft. content at various temperature differences. The usual procedure to determine the usage heat load is as follows:

1. The temperature difference is the same value as that used for heat leakage into the cabinet.
2. Volume of the cabinet is computed from inside dimensions.

3. Next determine under what type service the cabinet is being used, such as average, heavy or long storage. The service load is also dependent on cabinet size, the smaller the cabinet the more heat load is caused by service. A meat market, for instance, may be one in either a small neighborhood store or it may be in a supermarket.

4. Time, 24 hours. There would, of course, be considerable variation in the amount of heat to be removed from the cabinet content. Fig. 16-13 gives the load for three conditions.

After the total volume of the box has been calculated, the load for each cubic foot is determined by referring to the table, Fig. 16-13. If the cabinet appears to have average service with a temperature difference of 60 F., and has a volume of 300 cu. ft. the amount of heat to be removed from each cubic foot will be 78 Btu per 24 hours. Multiply this value by the total volume in cubic feet, as shown in Fig. 16-12, and a fairly accurate estimate of the service load may be obtained. The table, Fig. 16-13, gives the heat usage over a period of 24 hours as this time is the established standard.

Heat usage = usage Btu x volume in cu. ft.

Using the above example:

In the sample cabinet which is 6 x 7 x 9 the walls are 4 in. thick. Therefore the internal or inside width is 6 feet minus 4 inches minus 4 inches (there is a wall at each end).

6 ft. - (4 in. + 4 in.) = inside width.
6 ft. 8 in. = inside width.
5 ft. 4 in. = inside width.
5 1/3 ft. = inside width.

The same method is used to calculate the other internal dimensions.

The internal dimensions are:

Width 5 1/3 ft., length 6 1/3 ft., height 8 1/3 ft.

The inside volume =

$$5 \ 1/3 \times 6 \ 1/3 \times 8 \ 1/3 = \frac{(5 \times 3) + 1}{3} \times$$

$$\frac{(6 \times 3) + 1}{3} \times \frac{(8 \times 3) + 1}{3} =$$

$$5 \ 1/3 \times \frac{3}{3} = \frac{5 \times 3 \times 1}{3} = \frac{15 + 1}{3} \times \frac{18 + 1}{3}$$

$$\times \frac{24 + 1}{3} = \frac{16}{3} \times \frac{19}{3} \times \frac{25}{3}$$

16 × 19 × 25 = 7600 = 281.5 cu. ft.

Heat usage under the above conditions from Fig. 16-13 at 60 F. temperature difference and for approximately 300 cu. ft. the value is 78 Btu per 24 hrs. for 1 cu. ft.

Heat usage = 281.5 cu. ft. × 78 Btu cu. ft./24 hours =

Heat usage = 281.5 × 78 = 21,957 Btu per 24 hours.

Fig. 16-13A is another heat usage table.

16-11 Total Heat Load Using Tables

The total heat load is the sum of the heat leakage load and the heat usage load.

Total Heat Load = Heat Leakage + Heat usage.

From the previous example.

Total Heat Load = 36,996 (Par. 16-9) + 21,957 (Par. 16-10).

Total Heat Load = 58,953 Btu/24 hours.

The addition of the heat leakage and usage will give the total heat load upon the cabinet for a certain set period of time.

This value may be listed either as Btu's per 24 hours, or Btu's per 1 hour.

Btu/1 hr. = Btu/24 hours ÷ 24.
= 58,953 ÷ 24.
= 2456.4 Btu/hr.

However, in refrigeration applications, the unit to be installed to remove this heat should do so in less than 24 hours. This extra capacity permits reserve refrigeration for unusual loads, times for defrost operations, provides reserve if there is some wear in the unit, etc.

For fixtures above 32 F. it is generally understood that the unit should operate 16 hours out of 24 (two-thirds of the time) and for fixtures below 32 F., the unit should operate 18 hours out of 24 (three-fourths of the time).

A. Example: If the unit were to operate 16 hrs./day the serviceman would divide the total Btu load 24/hr. period by 16.

For 16 hour running:

$$\frac{58953}{16} = 3685 \text{ Btu/hr. of running.}$$

For 18 hour running:

$$\frac{58953}{18} = 3275 \text{ Btu/hr. of running.}$$

16-12 Evaporator and Condensing Unit Capacities

After calculating the heat load, it is necessary to determine the size of the evaporator and condensing unit required to furnish the refrigeration.

Some important things to remember are:

1. Evaporator removes heat from the cabinet only when the condensing unit is running.
2. Refrigerating unit usually runs from 14 to 20 hours out of each 24 hours. This means that the unit must have a refrigerating capacity in 14 hours of operation equal to the total heat load in 24 hours.

The evaporators capacity depends upon three conditions:

1. Cabinet temperature.

CONDENSING UNIT		EVAPORATOR COIL	
LOW SIDE TEMP.	BTU/HR.	TEMP. DIFF.	BTU/HR.
40	6650	1	400
35	6100	10	4000
30	5600	12	4800
25	5100	15	6000
20	4650		
15	4200	300 sq. ft. surface	
10	3800	natural convection	
5	3400	evaporator coil.	
0	3000		
- 5	2600		
-10	2250		
-15	1900		
-20	1550		
-25	1250		
-30	950		

90°F. ambient air.
Add 6% for 10°F. drop in air temperature, subtract 6% for each 10°F. rise in ambient temperature.
Liquid line 1/4 in.
Suction line 5/8 in.
Approximately one hp.

Fig. 16-14. Tables of condensing unit and evaporator coil capacity variations with temperature and pressure.

2. Refrigerant temperature.
3. Space allowed for the evaporator.
Condensing unit capacity depends on:
1. Low side pressure.
2. Condensing medium.

It is more important to balance the capacity of the evaporator to the capacity of the condensing unit than to balance either one to the heat load of the cabinet. When balancing the capacity of the condensing unit and the evaporator, all calculations for each must be based on the same low side pressure. This is because the capacity of the evaporator increases as the temperature decreases, while the capacity of the condensing unit decreases as the low side pressure decreases, Fig. 16-14.

Capacity of the evaporator increases as the evaporator coil temperature drops (as the low side pressure decreases) providing the cabinet temperature stays the same.

The capacity of a condensing unit increases as the low side pressure increases, Fig. 16-15.

From the figure you can see that this particular evaporator unit matches the condensing unit at a low side pressure of 31 psig and the combination will remove 12,500 Btu per hour when the coil refrigerant temperature is 32 F. and the pressure is 31 psig. The temperature difference for a 42 F. cabinet in this case is 10 F.

The manufacturers of evaporators and condensers list the capacities of their products in Btu for either one hour of operation, 16 hours of operation or 18 hours

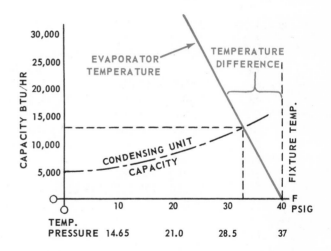

Fig. 16-15. Graph which shows relative effect on evaporator and unit capacity at different temperatures inside evaporator coil.

of operation. Before making a choice of models, it is important that the above items be considered carefully. Fig. 16-16 lists some typical condensing unit capacities at two condensing temperatures of 110 F. and 120 F. and at four evaporating temperatures of -30F., -15 F., 20 F. and 40 F.

16-13 Evaporator Installations

Practically all refrigerator cabinets are built to be used with mechanical refrigeration. These cabinets are specially designed to facilitate cooling of the cabinet with evaporator coils. The refrigeration service engineer should know the theory of air circulation in the cabinet, and what is

The colder air coming from the coil is made to flow down the center of the cabinet, while the warmer air is directed up the walls back to the evaporator coils. The

AVERAGE COMPRESSOR CAPACITIES

EVAPORATING TEMPERATURES °F.

	−30°		−15°		+20°		+40°	
CONDENSING TEMPERATURE °F.								
HP	110°	120°	110°	120°	110°	120°	110°	120°
2	5,200	4,500	9,100	8,200	18,000	16,800	22,800	21,200
3	9,000	8,300	14,300	13,200	22,100	20,800	36,300	34,200
5	14,200	12,500	24,800	22,400	41,700	39,300	62,400	58,500
7 1/2	25,000	20,000	31,000	28,000	53,000	48,000	87,000	81,700
10	31,000	26,000	43,600	44,800	81,000	75,000	120,000	112,000
15	42,600	37,500	74,400	67,200	111,000	102,000	171,600	160,000
20	56,000	44,700	82,000	71,000	154,000	142,000	235,000	218,000
25	70,000	56,000	96,000	85,000	188,000	174,000	283,000	263,000
30	80,000	67,000	116,500	102,500	225,000	210,000	349,000	324,000
40	94,000	75,000	155,000	135,000	325,000	306,000	439,000	406,000
50	122,000	100,000	188,500	159,500	375,000	350,000	585,000	550,000
60	168,000	134,000	240,000	220,000	450,000	420,000	710,000	670,000
70	196,000	156,000	272,000	239,000	571,000	534,000	800,000	742,000
75	210,000	167,000	291,000	256,000	582,000	542,000	855,000	795,000
80	224,000	178,000	310,000	273,000	622,000	578,000	900,000	842,000
90	252,000	201,000	349,000	307,000	750,000	700,000	1,027,000	955,000
100	280,000	223,000	388,000	341,000	777,000	723,000	1,170,000	1,100,000

NOTE: The above figures are only approximate and based on catalog ratings of leading compressor manufacturers. For precise figures, refer to catalog of your compressor manufacturer.

Fig. 16-16. Table of condensing unit capacities in Btu per hour at various evaporator temperatures and two condensing temperatures.

supposed to happen during the operation of the unit. The following deals with the study of efficient baffling and correct air circulation in cabinets.

Baffles are surfaces, or air ducts, which increase the efficiency of the air flow around the coil and throughout the cabinet. They direct the air flow in such a manner that it is speeded up and carried all around the interior of the box, leaving no dead or warm air spots. A typical evaporator and baffle are shown in Fig. 16-17.

design must be scientifically proportioned to insure that air circulation is unrestricted and that there will be no contrary influences to impede the air flow. Any horizontal baffle or coil deck must be insulated because the top surface may be in contact with cold air while the under part of the baffle may be in contact with relatively warm air. If it were not insulated, this temperature difference would not be maintained and eddy currents of air would result (small circular flows of air) disturb-

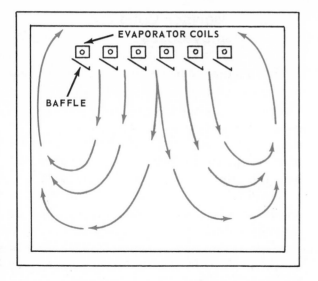

Fig. 16-17. *Natural convection air flow inside fixture.*

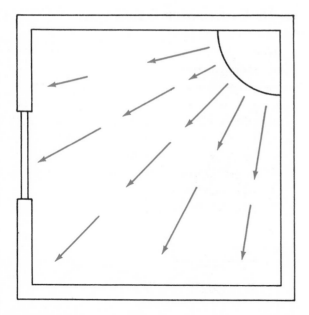

Fig. 16-18. *Blower evaporator mounted in upper corner of walk-in cooler. Note air distribution relative to door.*

ing the air flow in the cabinet. Multiple baffled evaporator coils of the natural convection type are frequently used and the air flows around the cabinet because of the relative weights of the cold air and the warm air (density). Warm air is lighter per cubic foot of volume and, therefore, rises in the box. This natural circulation must not be

hindered or the box temperature will not be constant. Baffling the coils tends to promote this natural circulation of the air and to speed it up.

16-14 Evaporator Coil Locations

Many cabinets do not have room to mount overhead coils such as one type of walk-in cooler which is constructed with an exterior height of approximately 7 1/2 feet. This height necessitates some other coil mounting. Two common types of mountings are:

1. The coil is placed in the upper corner of the cabinet as far as possible from the entrance door, Fig. 16-18.
2. Wall coil mounted against the wall opposite the windows or the reach-in doors of the cabinet, Fig. 16-19.

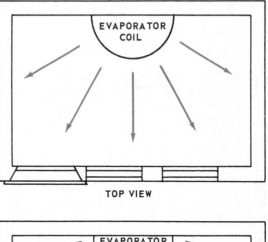

TOP VIEW

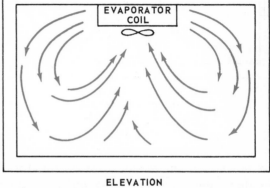

ELEVATION

Fig. 16-19. *Blower evaporator mounted on center back wall of walk-in cooler.*

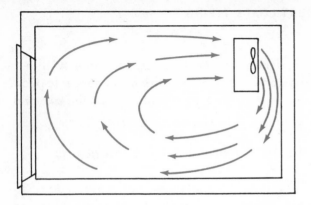

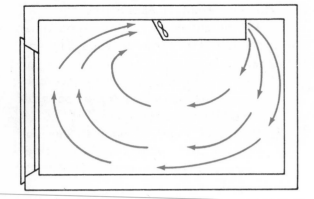

Fig. 16-20. *Two blower evaporator installations for walk-in refrigerator.*

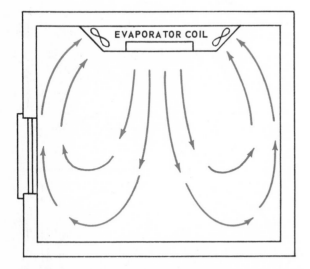

Fig. 16-21. *Two motor-driven fans reduce distance air circulates in cabinet.*

The coils are shrouded, have motor-fan to circulate the air and have built-in drain pans. See also Figs. 16-20, 16-21, and 16-22.

16-15 Evaporator Coils for Display Cases

Evaporator coil designs for closed and open type display cases have a difficult air circulation problem to overcome. The cases are narrow, there is less room for the evaporator coil, and many cases are open. Fig. 16-23 shows a dual evaporator coil installation for a double duty case.

A display case using a blower coil is shown in Fig. 16-24. Note the location of the motor-fan.

The design for an open display case is shown in Fig. 16-25. Notice how ducting is used to control the flow of the refrigerated air.

16-16 Evaporator Coil Types

Many kinds of evaporator coils have been used in mechanical refrigeration, but there have been in use two basic types. One type of coil is used to cool the air within the cabinet directly, while the other type of coil is used to cool a liquid which may then be either consumed or used to cool other substances. These are called:

1. Air-cooling evaporator.
2. Liquid-cooling evaporators.

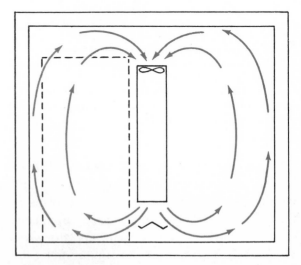

Fig. 16-22. *Reach-in cabinet with blower evaporator coil mounted behind mullion or door frame.*

The air-cooling evaporators are classified as the dry type, and may be either of the frosting, defrosting, or nonfrosting type. Some of these coils are forced circulation coils.

Liquid evaporating coils may be subdivided into the submerged evaporator and the tube-within-a-tube evaporator.

In commercial refrigeration certain kinds of coils are tending to become more popular than others. Among these are the dry nonfrosting air-cooling evaporators, forced circulation dry evaporators, and submerged flooded or dry evaporator. See Chapter 13.

16-17 Air-Cooling Evaporator Theory

The theory involved in the transfer of heat from the air circulating over the evaporator to the refrigerant is that, as the warmer air comes in contact with the evaporator, air molecules striking the fins release some of their energy to the fin (transfer some heat to it). This heat in turn travels through the fins, then through the tubing of the coil, and comes in contact with the

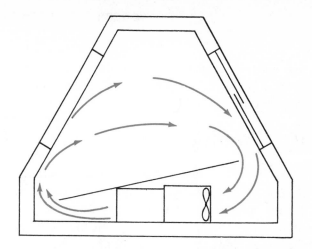

Fig. 16-24. *Closed display case with a blower evaporator coil located below display shelf.*

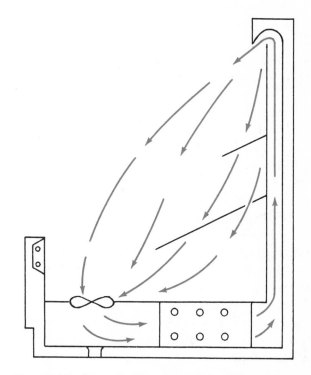

Fig. 16-25. *Open display case with a blower evaporator coil located in base of cabinet.*

liquid refrigerant on the inside, transfers this heat energy to it.

The greater heat transfer problem in this case is that of moving the heat in the air to the fin due to the low density of air. After reaching the metal, the heat travels efficiently and rapidly, but upon reaching the interior surface of the tubing, it again has difficulty in reaching the refrigerant in

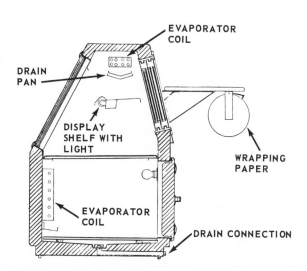

Fig. 16-23. *A cross section of a double-duty display case showing two evaporator coils. Note combination drain pans and baffles.*
(ASHRAE Guide and Data Book)

the system due to such things as gas bubbles clinging to the internal surface and an oil film on it.

16-18 Evaporator Coil Capacities

One of the laws of thermodynamics (heat in action) is that heat always flows from an object at a higher temperature to an object at a lower temperature. As in the case of the heat leakage, the amount of the heat leakage depends on four variables:

1. Area.
2. Temperature difference.
3. Thickness of material.
4. Time.

The kind of material used in evaporator coils is of utmost importance since the materials used must be good heat conductors.

The heat transmission may be through various materials. For air evaporator coils, the heat must pass through an air film on the metal surface, through the metal and then through an oil or liquid refrigerant film on the inside of the coil, as shown in Fig. 16-26.

If the air is moved rapidly, the heat flow is greater because more air contacts the metal per unit of time and the air film is thinner and therefore the heat conductivity is greater.

If the oil or refrigerant film is moved faster, or if it is thinner due to greater movement, this also will increase the rate of heat flow.

Generally speaking, the denser the fluid the greater the heat flow, and the faster the fluid motion, the greater the heat flow.

The U factor or heat transfer for natural convection coils is approximately:

1 Btu/sq. ft./F./hr.

The U factor for blower coils is approximately:

3 Btu/sq. ft./F./hr.

The U factor for liquid cooling coils is approximately:

15 Btu/sq. ft./F./hr.

These values are fairly accurate if the temperature difference is taken as the average air or liquid temperature and the refrigerant temperature.

For natural convection coils the temperature is usually selected as 10 F. For example, a 45 F. cabinet would have a refrigerant temperature in the evaporator coil of 35 F.

The smaller the temperature difference, the higher the relative humidity can be kept. For example, 10 F. to 12 F. temperature difference will keep a 75 to 90 percent RH while a 20 F. to 30 F. temperature difference will keep a 50 to 70 percent RH.

If the evaporator coil refrigerant temperature goes below 28 F., frost will form on the coil. The cycle off time must be long enough to permit defrosting (air is at 35 F.). If refrigerant temperature goes below 28 F., a defrost system must be used.

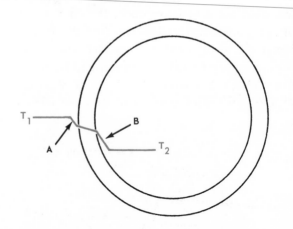

Fig. 16-26. Heat transfer from air surrounding an evaporator, to evaporator, through coil and to refrigerant inside. T_1 is cabinet air temperature; T_2 is refrigerant temperature.

16-19 Evaporator Coil Area

It is best when calculating or determining the capacity of evaporators to rely on the manufacturer's specifications inasmuch as they obtain their heat capacity values from actual experimental investigation. Such things as poor circulation, frosted fin condition, air turbulence around the coil, and even the amount of moisture in the air will affect the capacity of the evaporator.

To calculate the external surface area of an evaporator, care must be taken to consider such things as both surfaces of the fin, the outside surface of the tubing (neglect the area where it comes in contact with the fins) and the external surface of the tubing bends. For example, to find the area of a coil, as shown in Fig. 16-27, with 6 in. x 8 in. fins .025 in. thick, 10 ft. long, having 1/2 in. fin spacings and using two 5/8 in. tubes 4 in. apart, proceed as follows:

1. Area of one fin:
   Each fin is 8 in. x 6 in.
   8 in. x 6 in. = 48 sq. in.
   There are two sides to each fin.
   48 in. x 2 in. = 96 sq. in.
   However, there are two holes in each
   fin 5/8 in. diameter.

2. The total number of fins:
   10 ft. x 12 in./ft. = 120 in. long.
   2 fins per in. = 120 x 2 = 240 fins.
   240 fins + 1 extra fin at end = 241 fins.
   Fin area = area of each side of fin
   minus area replaced by tubing.
   Area of a circle = πR^2
   (R = radius and π = 3.1416)
   2R = Diameter = D

$$\pi \left(\frac{D}{2}\right)^2 = \pi \frac{D^2}{4} = \pi \frac{D^2}{4}$$

$$\text{Area} = \frac{\pi \times D^2}{4} = \frac{\pi \times \left(\frac{5}{8}\right)^2}{4}$$

$$= \frac{\pi \times \frac{25}{64}}{4} = \frac{\pi \times 25}{4 \times 64} = \frac{3.1416 \times 25}{4 \times 64}$$

$$= \frac{78.54}{256} = .307 \text{ sq. in.}$$

   However, each hole takes out two fin
   surfaces this size.
   .307 x 2 = .614 sq. in.
   There are two holes in each fin
   .614 sq. in. x 2 = 1.228
   Heat removing area for one fin =
   96 sq. in. - 1.228 = 94.772 sq. in.

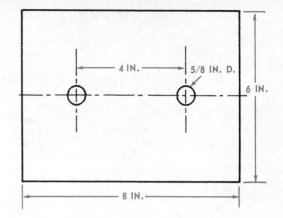

Fig. 16-27. Evaporator coil fin specifications for sample problem. Fin is .025 in. thick.

3. Total fin area = 94.72 x 241 =
   22,840 sq. in.

4. Area of 2 tubes 5/8 in. D; 10 ft. long:
   10 ft. x 12 in./ft. = 120 in.
   There are two tubes
   120 in. x 2 = 240 in.
   The circumference of the tube is
   Cir. = π x diameter
   = π x 5/8 in.
   = 3.1416 x 5/8 in.
   = 1.9635 in.
   The area = length x circumference
   = 240 in. x 1.9635 in.
   = 471.24 sq. in.

5. The actual tube area is decreased by the thickness of the fins, i.e., the following amount:
   Fin contact area = $\pi 5/8$ x .025 x 241 =
   1.9635 x .025 x 241 = 473.2035 x
   .025 sq. in.
   Actual tube area 471.24 - 11.83 =
   459.41 sq. in.

6. Tube bend area = length of bend x circumference length x number of bends (1)
   (2 in. radius)
   Length = π x D.
   = π x 4 in.
   = 3.1416 x 4 in.
   = 12.5664
   but it is only 1/2 of a circle so
   12.5664 ÷ 2 = 6.2832
   Circumference of tube = 5/8 in. x
   Area = 6.2832 x   5/8 = 6.2832 x
   1.9635 = 12.34 sq. in.

Fig. 16-28. Section through tubes and fins of evaporating unit. (McQuay Inc.)

7. Total area 22,840.
459.41
12.33
_____
23,311.74 sq. in.
or in sq. ft. 23,311.74 ÷ 144 =
161.9 sq. ft.

The evaporator is unable to remove heat from the cabinet when the compressor is not running. Therefore, the heat removing capacity of a coil is calculated on the same running time as that of the compressor. The allowable calculated time for the condensing unit to run and, therefore, the allowable time for the evaporator to remove heat from the cabinet during a 24 hour period, varies between 16 and 18 hours in commercial applications (16 for nonfrost coils, 18 hours for coils that need energy defrosting).

An example of heat transfer ability is as follows: What is the capacity of a natural convection evaporator having an external area of 15 sq. ft. with a refrigerant temperature of 22 F., if the average box temperature is 42 F.?

Solution: First, it is known that 1 sq. ft. will handle 1 Btu per F. per hr. The refrigerant temperature is 22 F.; with the air temperature passing over the coil at 42 F., the temperature difference is 20 F. If 1 F. temperature difference will handle 1 Btu., 20 F. temperature difference will handle 20 Btu, then multiply this value by the number of sq. ft., and we have the total capaci-

ty of the coil per hr. difference. In this case Btu = 15 x 20 = 3,000 Btu per hr.

It is claimed that the maximum effective distance that the fin should extend from the coil should not exceed 3 in. for a natural convection cooling coil.

Fig. 16-28 shows an evaporator coil constructed of rippled fin surfaces and with a flange contact between the prime surface (tubing) and the fin.

16-20 Frosting Evaporator

A frosting evaporator is one which frosts continuously when in use, operating at evaporator surface temperatures always below 32 F. The machine must be manually or automatically shut down periodically to rid the system of frost. If the evaporator has refrigerant temperatures of 28 F. or higher, the coil will usually defrost during the off part of the cycle. This is called a defrosting evaporator and is described in Par. 16-21.

If the refrigerant temperature is below 28 F., the coil needs heat energy of some kind to defrost the evaporator or the evaporator must be on the off cycle for a longer time than the normal cycle.

Some evaporator coils run at extremely low temperatures to keep the fixture cool, which results in an accumulation of frost and ice. As the accumulation of frost grows thicker, it decreases the cooling efficiency of the coil. These coils are used in low temperature and frozen food fixtures.

Blower evaporators operated at low refrigerant temperatures need special defrosting care. The fin spacing is small, the evaporator surface is small, and frost and ice will interfere drastically with heat transfer.

16-21 Defrosting Evaporator

Many evaporators run on what is called a defrosting cycle, that is, when the condensing unit is running, the temperature of

BOX SIZE	BTU HR 15 TD	SQ. FT SURF.	NO. COILS	COIL AND PAN COMBINATIONS				COILS ONLY			
				MODEL NO.	D	W	L	MODEL NO.	D	W	L
5 x 4	2496	161	1	548P	13	24	46	C548	7	21	40
5 x 5	3094	199	1	558P	13	27	48	C558	7	24	42
6 x 4	3120	201	1	648P	13	24	54	C648	7	21	48
6 x 5	3225	206	1	658P	10½	38	57	C658	3	35	50
6 x 6	4160	234	1	668P	13	32	54	C668	7	28	48
7 x 4	2808	178	1	748P	10½	32	68	C748	3	28	62
7 x 5	3600	229	1	758P	10½	38	62	C758	3	35	55
7 x 6	3975	253	1	768P	10½	38	67	C768	3	35	60
7 x 7	4568	276	2	778P*	10½	24	70	C778*	3	21	64
8 x 5	3848	249	1	858P	10½	38	73	C858	3	35	66
8 x 6	4425	283	1	868P	10½	38	73	C868	3	35	66
8 x 7	4815	292	1	878P	10½	38	75	C878	3	35	68
8 x 8	5513	342	2	888P*	10½	24	75	C888*	3	21	68
9 x 6	4725	295	1	968P	10½	38	87	C968	3	35	80
9 x 7	5205	329	1	978P	10½	38	83	C978	3	35	76
9 x 8	5928	372	2	988P*	10½	24	90	C988*	3	21	84
10 x 6	5250	327	1	1068P	10½	38	95	C1068	3	35	88
10 x 7	5700	350	1	1078P	10½	38	101	C1078	3	35	94
10 x 8	6075	385	2	1088P*	10½	24	95	C1088*	3	21	88
10 x 10	7500	465	2	1008P*	10½	24	97	C1008*	3	21	90
11 x 6	6500	406	1	1168P	10½	38	114	C1168	3	35	108
11 x 7	6240	392	2	1178P*	10½	24	95	C1178*	3	21	88
11 x 8	7020	429	2	1188P*	10½	24	105	C1188*	3	21	98
12 x 6	6368	387	1	1268P	10½	38	112	C1268	3	35	105
12 x 7	7020	429	2	1278P*	10½	24	105	C1278*	3	21	98
12 x 8	7410	458	2	1288P*	10½	24	109	C1288*	3	21	102
12 x 10	8400	516	2	1208P*	10½	24	122	C1208*	3	21	115
12 x 12	9113	534	2	1228P*	10½	32	119	C1228*	3	28	112
14 x 8	8580	521	2	1488P*	10½	24	136	C1488*	3	28	128
14 x 10	9750	606	2	1408P*	10½	24	140	C1408*	3	21	133
14 x 12	10500	614	2	1428*	10½	32	135	C1428*	3	28	128
14 x 14	12075	710	2	1448P*	10½	38	126	C1448*	3	35	119
16 x 8	9240	535	2	1688P*	10½	24	154	C1688*	3	21	148
16 x 10	10692	618	2	1608P*	10½	24	176	C1608*	3	21	170
16 x 12	12636	783	2	1628P*	10½	24	176	C1628*	3	21	170
16 x 14	14256	825	2	1648P*	10½	24	176	C1648*	3	28	170

Note: All dimensions above are for one coil and one pan in combination or one coil only.

Asterisk (*) appearing after model number denotes that 2 coils and 2 pans or 2 coils without pans are supplied by specifying designated model number.

BOX SIZE	BTU HR 15 TD	SQ. FT SURF.	NO. COILS	COIL AND PAN COMBINATIONS				COILS ONLY			
				MODEL NO.	D	W	L	MODEL NO.	D	W	L
5 x 4	2925	192	1	541P	13	35	40	C541	7	31½	33
5 x 5	3861	249	1	551P	13	35	47	C551	7	31½	41
6 x 4	3432	220	1	641P	13	24	58	C641	7	21	52
6 x 5	3780	242	1	651P	13	24	57	C651	7	21	50
6 x 6	4570	292	1	661P	13	32	58	C661	7	28	52
7 x 4	3900	248	1	741P	13	24	64	C741	7	21	58
7 x 5	4140	269	1	751P	13	24	62	C751	7	21	55
7 x 6	4410	286	1	761P	13	24	65	C761	7	21	58
7 x 7	5824	369	1	771P	13	32	70	C771	7	28	64
8 x 5	4613	286	1	851P	13	24	73	C851	7	21	64
8 x 6	5025	310	1	861P	13	24	78	C861	7	21	71
8 x 7	5325	348	1	871P	13	24	75	C871	7	21	68
8 x 8	5850	359	2	881P*	10½	24	78	C881*	3½	21	71
9 x 6	5513	386	1	961P	10½	38	87	C961	3½	35	80
9 x 7	6000	390	1	971P	13	27	83	C971	7	24½	76
9 x 8	6512	383	2	981P*	10½	32	88	C981*	3½	28	82
0 x 6	6113	386	1	1061P	10½	38	95	C1061	3½	35	88
10 x 7	6593	412	1	1071P	10½	38	101	C1071	3½	35	94
10 x 8	7275	453	2	1081P*	10½	24	95	C1081*	3½	21	88
10 x 10	8400	622	2	1011P*	10½	32	95	C1011*	3½	28	88
11 x 6	6370	391	1	1161P	10½	38	112	C1161	3½	35	106
11 x 7	7254	453	1	1171P	10½	46	107	C1171	3½	42	101
11 x 8	7800	486	2	1181P*	10½	24	114	C1181*	3½	21	108
12 x 6	6900	426	1	1261P	10½	38	120	C1261	3½	35	113
12 x 7	7392	429	1	1271P	10½	46	126	C1271	3½	42	120
12 x 8	7650	472	2	1281P*	10½	24	112	C1281*	3½	21	105
12 x 10	9375	546	2	1211P*	10½	32	122	C1211*	3½	28	115
12 x 12	10500	616	2	1221P*	10½	38	111	C1221*	3½	35	104
14 x 8	9672	601	2	1481P*	10½	24	138	C1481*	3½	21	132
14 x 10	10648	619	2	1411P*	10½	32	135	C1411*	3½	28	129
14 x 12	12480	777	2	1421P*	10½	32	134	C1421*	3½	28	128
14 x 14	13125	766	2	1441P*	10½	38	135	C1441*	3½	35	119
16 x 8	11544	716	2	1681P*	10½	24	154	C1681*	3½	21	154
16 x 10	11880	689	2	1611P*	10½	32	149	C1611*	3½	28	143

These recommendations are for refrigerators constructed with 4" cork or equivalent, and are based on 55 degrees temperature difference (box to room temperature) with normal service.

Fig. 16-29. Table of capacities for nonfrost evaporator coils.
(Tenney Engineering Inc.)

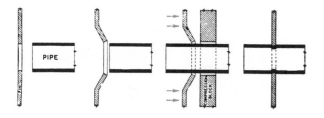

Fig. 16-30. An illustration which shows mechanical means of bonding evaporator fins to tubing. Fin is dished to expand tube hole and tubing is inserted. When mandrel flattens fin, it is firmly pressed into tubing. (Peerless of America, Inc.)

the evaporating coil is such that frost accumulates on it, but after the compressor shuts off, the coil must warm up above 32 F. before the condensing unit will start again. The frost accumulation melts off

during the off cycle. This keeps the fin surfaces clear and provides consistent and efficient heat transfer. It also keeps a high humidity (approximately 90-95% RH). This is done, however, at a sacrifice of temperature differences between the evaporator refrigerant temperature and the air in the cabinet and a greater evaporator area is needed. The basic calculations are the same, the only change being a smaller temperature difference.

16-22 Nonfrosting Evaporator

The nonfrosting coils serve the same heat transfer purpose as the ones already mentioned with the exception that they operate at a refrigerant temperature which is never below 31 F. This temperature permits only a slight formation of frost which disappears immediately when the condensing unit stops.

A nonfrosting evaporator operating with natural convection (gravity) and placed at the top of a cabinet is often referred to as a "flash" coil. These evaporator coils are shallow in depth and are usually provided with a drain pan to collect condensation.

A typical evaporator coil capacity table for nonfrosting coils is given in Fig. 16-29.

16-23 Evaporator Coil Design

Many types of evaporator coils are available which use the following combinations: copper tubing and aluminum fins, copper tubing and copper fins and steel tubing and aluminum fins (for ammonia R-717). The fins are usually securely bonded to the tubing. Some manufacturers construct the fin to fit the tubing with a drive fit, others use some mechanical devices to attach the fins firmly to the tubing. Some expand the tubing with a mandrel or by hydraulic pressure to force it against the fin. See Fig. 16-30. A method of bonding tubing to off center fins is shown in Fig. 16-31. Another method of mounting fins on tubing and spacing them at the same time is shown in Fig. 16-32. The fin spacings vary between 1/2 and 1 1/2 in. This spacing is a means of varying the capacity of the evaporator and is also used to compensate for the depth of the evaporator coil. The deeper the evaporator, the greater the fin spacing to minimize air restriction. Evaporators which have 6 in. to 8 in. depth coils usually have 1 in. spacings, whereas the 18 in. or 20 in. coils will have 1 1/2 in. spacings. Fin spacings of 1 in. or less are said to decrease air turbulence. The tubing used in the coil is usually 5/8 in. OD, although 3/4 in. OD tubing is used in the large evaporators. Some companies use one continuous piece of tubing for the complete coil; others have all bends made separately. The bends are silver brazed or

brazed to the straight lengths. Some companies use devices inside the tubing to swirl the refrigerant to improve heat transfer to the boiling refrigerant. Fittings to the evaporator are usually 1/2 in. OD tubing brazed to the 5/8 in. tubing and are then flared with an external nut mounted on it. Some manufacturers use a 1/2 in. male flare fitting, brazed to the end fin.

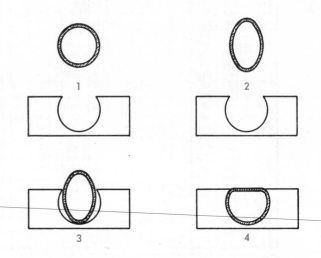

Fig. 16-31. Method of mechanically bonding tubing to off-center fins. Original tubing and fin are shown at (1). Tubing is formed into elliptical shape (2), inserted into fin opening (3). Fixture holds fins while tube is pressed into fin opening shape (4). (Peerless of America, Inc.)

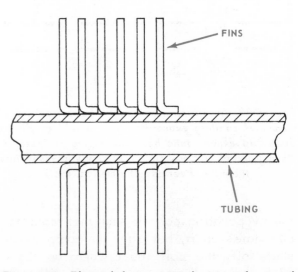

Fig. 16-32. Flanged fins mounted on a tubing with flanges determining fin spacing.

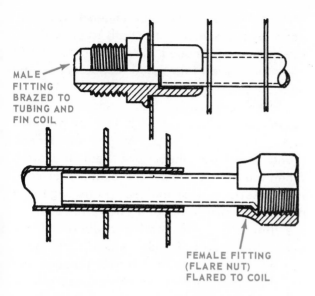

FEMALE FITTING
(FLARE NUT)
FLARED TO COIL

Fig. 16-33. Illustration which shows construction of coupling devices used in attaching refrigeration lines to evaporator coils.

Fig. 16-33 shows two types. The corners of the fins should be braced or reinforced using some method to eliminate bending while the coil is being installed. This often consists of right angle strips clamped or soldered to the fins. Some concerns fit a strip of metal into a slot cut in the corner of each fin.

16-24 Evaporator Coil Mounting

The evaporators are mounted in the cabinet either by suspending them from the ceiling, by mounting them on pipe, which is fastened to the vertical baffle and the wall of the cabinet, or by mounting them on stands fastened to the horizontal baffle. The thermostatic expansion valve may be mounted to the top of the coil, allowing the refrigerant and oil to flow by gravity to the suction line down to the compressor, or the expansion valve may be connected to a horizontal run of coil tubing of the evaporator making the refrigerant pass horizontally to come to the suction line as shown in Fig. 16-34. If the expansion valve is fastened to the upper part of the coil permit-

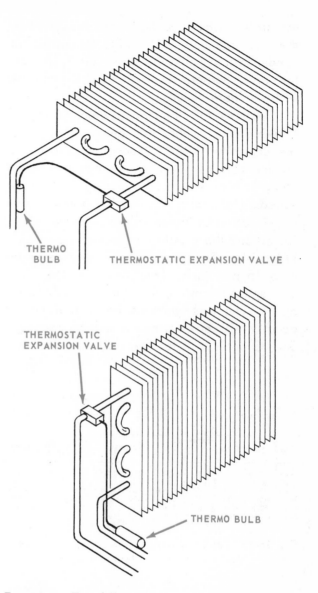

THERMO
BULB

THERMOSTATIC EXPANSION VALVE

THERMOSTATIC
EXPANSION VALVE

THERMO BULB

Fig. 16-34. Two different evaporator installations and recommended expansion valve mounting for each.

ting a gravity flow, oil binding will be negligible, but the fins will be coldest at the top in contact with the warm air.

16-25 Forced Circulation Air-Cooling Evaporator Coil Capacities

A forced circulation evaporator is one having an electric fan mounted in conjunction with it in order to produce a flow of air past the coil. Velocities of 44 feet per minute to 2,000 feet per minute are permissible with 1,000 feet per minute being the average value. Draining facilities for condensation removal must be built into the unit. Sometimes motors are provided with variable speeds.

Because of the large amount of air striking the evaporator per unit of time, the capacity of the evaporator in Btu per square foot per deg. F. hour is increased remarkably. The values vary with the air speed. The table, Fig. 16-35, gives an approximation of these values. The coils are finned and the spacing of the fins vary considerably. The fin spacings may be from 4 to 15 per inch. This means that the fins are spaced from 1/4 in. apart to 1/15 in. apart. The fins must be kept straight and equally spaced or air flow will be reduced. See Chapter 15 for service instructions.

tion problems. Many submerged evaporator coils use a sweet water bath to provide an ice holdover around the evaporator coils and thus maintain good capacity during peak loads.

The capacity of the evaporator coils varies depending upon whether or not they are of the frosting type. As you can understand from the theory of heat transfer, When ice forms around the evaporator coil, it necessitates that the heat go through this extra material in order to be removed from the liquid and the cooling capacity of the evaporator coil is decreased. Furthermore, it makes the heat travel through one extra contact surface which reduces efficiency. Liquid cooling coil evaporators are used for beverage cooling for water, chillers for air conditioning, and for cooling brines.

Surface in Sq Ft.			Paral- lel Paths	Cooling Capacities B.T.U. per Hour		Motor		Fan	
Tube	Fin	Total		15° F. T.D.	25° F. T.D.	H.P.	Speed R.P.M.	Di- ameter	C.F.M.
2.94	32.39	35	3	2200	4500	1/80	1800	12″	620
5.88	63.0	68	5	4100	7200	1/80	1800	12″	465
7.94	70.06	78	3	5200	9000	1/10	1140	15½″	1200
13.2	116.8	130	5	8300	12300	1/10	1140	15½″	1000
14.7	83.3	98	3	6500	10500	⅛	1140	17″	2020
17.2	145.8	163	5	10000	14000	⅛	1140	17″	1715

Fig. 16-35. Table of forced circulation evaporator coil capacities. (McCord Corp.)

16-26 Liquid Evaporator Coil Capacities

Liquid evaporator coils, regardless of the type, may be calculated for capacity on the basis of a factor of approximately 10 to 120 Btu per square foot per deg. F. per hour. However, the U factor varies with the fluid velocity, coil construction and the total temperature difference. Fig. 16-36 shows the average values for a certain evaporator coil.

Some of the coils are used to cool brine solution. This is a nonfreeze solution and does not provide any frost accumula-

16-27 Special Evaporator Capacities

A considerable variation of evaporator coil types may still be found in use including: cast metal coils, iron pipe coils, brine spray coils, and intermediate refrigerant coils. The problems incurred with these will be the same as the ones discussed previously. The metal used as the refrigerant carrying device does not have much effect upon the heat transfer capacity of the evaporator coil, because its conductivity is relatively so much greater than the contact between the coil and the air that it may be neglected. The capacity of the cast

WATER VELOCITY FT./MIN.	TOTAL TEMPERATURE DIFFERENCE				
	6	8	10	12	15
150	67	76	83	90	97
200	83	95	103	110	118
250	97	109	115	122	129
300	103	115	123	130	138

Fig. 16-36. Heat transfer in Btu per sq. ft. per hr. for typical flooded liquid evaporator using 5/8 in. OD tubes. (Btu sq. ft. hr. F.)

USAGE	FINAL TEMP. REQUIRED °F.	TOTAL AMOUNT OF WATER USED AND WASTED
1. Office Building—Employees	50	1/8 gallon per hour per person
2. Office Building—Transients	50	1/2 gallon per hour for each 250 persons per day
3. Light Manufacturing	50 to 55	1/5 gallon per hour per person
4. Heavy Manufacturing.....	50 to 55	1/4 gallon per hour per person
5. Restaurant................	45 to 50	1/10 gallon per hour per person
6. Cafeteria.................	45 to 50	1/12 gallon per hour per person
7. Hotels...................	50	1/2 gallon per day per room (14 hr. day)
8. Theaters.................	50	1 gallon per hour per 75 seats
9. Stores	50	1 gallon per hour per 100 customers per hour
10. Schools.................	50 to 55	1/5 gallon per hour per student
11. Hospitals...............	45 to 50	1/12 gallon per day per bed

NOTE—Total amount of water used and wasted varies with type of installation and kind of service This table will serve as a basis for determining cooler capacity required.

Fig. 16-37. Drinking water-cooling table giving values of various applications. (Temprite Products Corp.)

metal coil and the iron pipe coil may be calculated exactly the same as the method described in Par. 16-19.

Some installations use brine spray. In this system the brine is forced through a pipe extending into the cooling chamber, and the pipe is perforated with a number of fine holes. The brine sprays out of these holes and mixes with the air flowing over the baffle removing the heat. The capacity of these systems is calculated upon the temperature difference between the air in the box and the temperature of the brine. It is safe to assume a high efficiency of heat transfer for brine spray installations.

The Baudelot Cooler (milk cooler) runs water or the liquid to be cooled over refrigerant cooled pipes or plates. The liquid being cooled is in the open and can be easily controlled. Icing is not critical and therefore the liquid can be cooled close to its freezing temperature.

16-28 Water-Cooling Loads

The problem of determining the refrigeration load of a water-cooled installation is basically a specific heat and heat leakage problem combination. The water is cooled to temperatures which vary upward from 35 F., and the amount of heat removed from the water to cool it to a predetermined temperature is a simple specific

heat problem. The water, being maintained at these low temperatures, results in a heat leakage from the room into the water, and this part involves the heat leakage portion of the installation.

The two major factors to be solved in a water-cooling installation are determining how much water is to be consumed at the temperature difference desired. Fig. 16-37 is a table giving the values of these two variables. The temperature of the water should be regulated according to the type of work the consumers are performing, the heavier the work or the warmer the room temperature the warmer the water must be. The amount of water consumed varies extensively in the different applications. By using this table for obtaining initial values, the exact heat load is easily determined after a small amount of investigation. For example, item No. 4 in the table points out that for heavy manufacturing the water to be consumed should be kept within 50 to 55 F., and that 1/4 gallon per hour per person will be consumed. A production foundry may be classed as heavy manufacturing.

If a foundry employs 50 men for a period of 8 hours, the water load per day would be 50 x 8 x 1/4, which would represent 100 gallons quantity of water to be cooled per 8 hours. If the city water is at a temperature of 75 F. in the pipes it must be cooled 20 F. to reach the temperature of 55 F. There are 8.34 pounds of water in 1 gallon and the specific heat load would therefore be as follows:

Btu = specific heat x weight x temperature difference, therefore,

Btu = 1 x 100 x 8.34 x 20 = 16,680 Btu per 100 gal. water.

The heat leakage for this particular problem is determined by the external area of the insulated parts of the system. One to three inches of cork are common thickness for water-cooling insulations with ice water thickness insulation being standard at 1 1/2 in. The heat leakage is calculated identically with that of the heat leakage for cabinets. The example, just described, deals only with a unit installation.

Many water-cooling installations involve the circulation of the refrigerated water to the various fountains. The heat leakage load in a case of this kind is calculated on the basis of gallons of water per hour to be circulated through the system to maintain satisfactory temperatures.

The table, Fig. 16-38, illustrates the tabular method of computing this load.

Gallons per Hour To Be Circulated per 100 Feet of Pipe to Hold Temperature Rise Within 5° F. Add This Amount to Usage Fig. 21-36

PIPE SIZE	TEMPERATURE DIFFERENCE BETWEEN ROOM AND CIRCULATING WATER							
	20°	25°	30°	35°	40°	45°	50°	55°
¼"	4.8	6.3	7.3	3.2	9.7	10.9	12.3	13.6
⅜"	5.5	6.8	8.2	9.6	11.0	12.3	13.7	15.0
½"	6.3	8.0	9.5	11.2	12.7	14.3	16.0	17.6
¾"	6.7	8.4	10.1	11.8	13.5	15.2	16.9	18.6
1"	7.3	9.1	10.9	12.8	14.6	16.5	18.5	20.6
1¼"	8.6	10.4	12.5	14.6	16.6	18.7	20.4	22.1
1½"	9.0	11.2	13.5	15.7	18.0	20.2	22.5	24.7

Fig. 16-38. Table showing heat gain through insulated cold water pipes. (Temprite Products Corp.)

16-29 Ice Cream Cooling Load

Ice cream is manufactured from milk, solids, fat, sugar, gelatin, and water and, after mixing, the product is cooled to about 27 F. and is frozen. It is then cooled rapidly to approximately -20 F. It is maintained between 0 to 5 F. if brick; or 5 to 12 F. if bulk; until it is dispensed. The heat values of the various ice creams vary, but the average values are: the specific heat of the mix before freezing is 0.80 and the latent heat at 27 F. is about 90 Btu per pound. The specific heat of the frozen ice cream is 0.45. The weight of the original mix is about 9 pounds per gallon; but on freezing it expands and comes to a density of 5 pounds per gallon if simply flavored, and to 6 pounds per gallon, if it contains fruits or nuts.

Next determine the size of unit to maintain ice cream in its cabinet during the dispensing of the cream. Normally an ice cream cabinet is designed to hold brick ice cream and flavored ice creams next to the evaporator coil; but many cabinets, especially the dry coil models, need separate evaporators for the two types. Fig. 16-39 shows an ice cream display cabinet. It is 4.6 cu. ft. cabinet with a 1/4 hp condensing unit. Metal finished cabinets with 3 in. to 4 in. of slab cork well sealed from moisture are used.

The ice cream is delivered at the correct temperature, and the heat load is, therefore, composed only of leakage and air entering when the covers are removed. The tables, Figs. 16-5 and 16-6, may be used to calculate heat leakage. Use the external area and add 20 percent to take care of the cover openings.

Fig. 16-39. Ice cream display cabinet. Used to merchandise ice cream novelties. (Bally Case and Cooler Inc.)

16-30 Condensing Unit Capacities

After the heat load has been determined for a refrigerator, and after an evaporator coil has been selected for this cabinet, a condensing unit must be chosen to balance the evaporator coil capacity.

The condensing unit must match the evaporator coil capacity in two ways:

1. It must operate at the same low side pressure that corresponds to the refrigerant temperature in the evaporator coil.
2. It must remove heat that the evaporator coil removes in the same running time as was determined calculating the capacity of the evaporator coil. For example, 16 hours or 18 hours.

When choosing a condensing unit you must decide if the condensing unit is to be water-cooled or air-cooled, whether it is to be a hermetic unit or an open unit and what the available electric power is (such as 115, 208 or 230 volt, single-phase or 220 or 440 volt, three-phase).

Fig. 16-40 is a table of data on a typical open type condensing unit. This is an air-cooled unit with a 1 hp motor and it has a 2 cylinder compressor with a 2 in. bore and a 2 in. stroke.

COMPRESSOR RPM	REFRIGERANT (EVAPORATOR COIL) TEMPERATURE	BTU/HR.
	45	11,000
	40	10,200
475	35	9,370
	30	8,530
	25	7,740
	25	8,700
	20	7,960
540	15	7,200
	10	6,430
	5	5,740
	0	5,100
	0	5,780
	−5	5,700
665	−10	4,430
	−15	3,820
	−20	3,280
	−25	2,800

Fig. 16-40. Capacity table for a one horsepower condensing unit, air-cooled, 90 F. ambient temperature.

If the evaporator coil was selected on the basis of a 15 F. temperature difference and a 16 hour running time, this means that if the cabinet is to operate at 38 F. the refrigerant temperature will be 38-15 or 23 F. If it is an R-12 refrigerant unit, the condensing unit capacity must be matched to a low side pressure of 23.2 psi.

The table, Fig. 16-16, lists the average hourly capacity of various horsepower capacity condensing units. This clearly shows the increase in capacity of a condensing unit as the low side pressure (and temperature) increases providing the head pressure remains fairly constant. It also shows the effect of condensing temperature (and pressure) on the capacity of a condensing unit.

The capacity of hermetic condensing units can also be found in tables provided by manufacturers.

16-31 Refrigerant Properties

To understand the operation of the condensing unit in relationship to the evaporator coil, compressor capacity, motor capacity, and refrigerant lines capacities, it is necessary to have a good understanding of the physical properties of refrigerants and how the refrigerant does its work.

The refrigerant vapor is taken up by the compressor, and a pressure is imposed upon it to convert it to a high pressure, high temperature condition. This action introduces a small amount of heat energy to the refrigerant from the motor heat of compression and puts the refrigerant in a condition so that it may be converted from a vapor to a liquid again. It is necessary to determine how large a compressor is needed to produce a certain amount of refrigeration, and how large a motor is needed to drive this compressor.

To understand how these values are determined you must understand the heat behavior of the refrigerant.

The refrigerant cycle is simple. The

refrigerant is admitted into the evaporating coil in the liquid state and at near room temperatures. The vaporizing of some of it under the low pressure in the evaporator coil cools the remainder of the refrigerant to the desired refrigerating temperature, and then as the remainder of the refrigerant evaporates, it removes heat from the evaporating coil and therefore from the cabinet. The total amount of heat absorbed is the LATENT HEAT of vaporization, while the amount of heat absorbed from the cabinet and coil is the EFFECTIVE LATENT HEAT.

The refrigerant vapor formed on evaporation passes down the suction line. As the vapor does so, it decreases a little (usually 2 psi) in pressure and it usually increases in temperature a little (about 10 F.). The condition of a vapor warming up or increasing in temperature after it has vaporized is called superheating of the vapor. The degree of superheat is the temperature difference between the temperature of the vapor at the compressor, and its corresponding evaporating temperature.

The compressor then takes the slightly superheated vapor and converts (compresses) it to a high temperature, high pressure vapor. This condensing temperature sometimes becomes as high as 180 F depending upon the refrigerant and the conditions.

The superheated vapor passes to the condenser and if its temperature is higher than the ambient temperature (water or air) it loses its heat to the air or water and cools down to its vapor-pressure temperature. If the vapor pressure-temperature is above that of the water or air ambient temperature, the refrigerant vapor starts losing some latent heat of evaporation; and the quantity of heat it loses determines the amount of the vapor that will condense into a liquid. After it has liquefied, the liquid refrigerant cools down close to the water or air temperature.

It then goes on to the refrigerant control where the pressure is reduced, it is cooled, and vaporized, and thus the cycle is repeated. Fig. 16-41 shows this cycle taking place and the corresponding temperatures through the refrigerating unit.

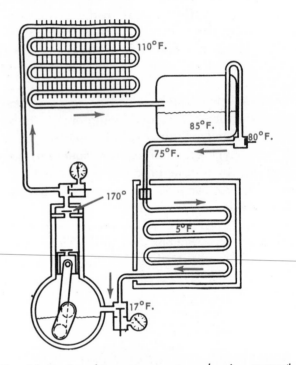

Fig. 16-41. A refrigerating system showing approximate temperatures of refrigerant in various parts of system.

16-32 Pressure--Heat Diagram

To study refrigerant behavior more accurately, we will base our discussions on one pound of the refrigerant regardless of its state, (liquid or vapor). The discussion will deal only with the pure refrigerant, neglecting the effect of lubricating oils and other influences. The chart, Fig. 16-42, shows the behavior of one pound refrigerant in a refrigerating machine. The horizontal scale shows the amount of heat present in one pound of refrigerant at all times and under all conditions; whereas the vertical scale shows the pressure imposed upon it. This graph is commonly

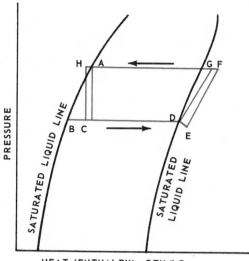

Fig. 16-42. Pressure-heat diagram for a refrigerant. Saturated liquid curve represents heat in liquid at various pressures before it will start vaporizing. Saturated vapor curve represents division between superheated gas and where gas starts condensing into liquid.

called a pressure-heat chart. It is also called a pressure-enthalpy chart. The heat (Btu) in the pound of refrigerant is usually measured from saturated liquid refrigerant at -40 F. The pressures will be different for each kind of refrigerant. Using this chart as a basis for our study, we note that as the refrigerant vaporizes at a constant pressure it passes horizontally from B to D. This line indicates the vaporization of the refrigerant from a liquid into a vapor in the evaporating coil. The distance D to E represents the heating of this vapor into a superheated condition as it passes down the suction line. Note that only a few Btu of heat have been added and that the pressure has decreased a little. Point E is the condition of the vapor when it is taken into the compressor and compressed. Note how the pressure increases rapidly and how a few Btu of heat are added to the vapor as the vapor is compressed from E to F. The vapor is now considerably superheated.

Point F represents the condition of the vapor as it leaves the exhaust valve of the compressor. The distance between F and G is the cooling of this superheated vapor down to the point where it starts to condense. At G the vapor has no superheat and is 100 percent saturated vapor. The line G to A represents the condensation of the refrigerant in the condenser from a vapor into a liquid. Point A represents the amount of heat in the liquid and the pressure imposed on the liquid as it forms in the condenser. From A to H is the loss of heat from the liquid as it passes along the liquid line to the refrigerant control. Point H to C represents the throttling of the liquid upon passing through the refrigerant control orifice, and the cycle is ready to be repeated for one pound of refrigerant.

Note that the distance C to D does not represent the total LATENT HEAT of the liquid at the low side pressure condition. This means that R-12 which has a latent heat of 70 Btu per pound at 5 F. will not remove all of the heat from the evaporating coil because some of it (approximately 19 Btu) is used to cool down the liquid refrigerant to the 5 F. temperature before the remainder can vaporize. The 51 Btu remaining is called the EFFECTIVE LATENT HEAT or the EFFECTIVE REFRIGERATING CAPACITY. This means that 19/51 of the pound or 37 percent of the R-12 flashes into gas at the refrigerant control.

This pressure-heat chart is an important graph of the physical property changes of a pound of a refrigerant as it passes around the refrigerating cycle.

A thorough knowledge of this chart is helpful to the engineer, the technician, and to the serviceman.

16-33 Pressure--Heat Areas

The pressure-heat chart, Fig. 16-43, is divided into three main areas. As shown in Fig. 16-43, to the left of the saturated liquid line, all of the one pound of refrigerant is liquid. Between the saturated liquid line and the saturated vapor line the refrigerant is a mixture of liquid and vapor, as shown in the squares on the drawing. Close

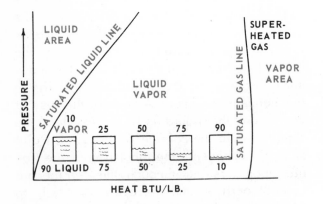

Fig. 16-43. Pressure-heat diagram. It should be noted that as heat is subtracted refrigerant becomes a liquid and as heat is added refrigerant becomes a vapor.

to the saturated liquid line, the refrigerant is almost all liquid and close to the saturated vapor line the one pound of refrigerant is almost all vapor.

16-34 Constant Value Lines of Pressure--Heat Chart

Many facts can be read from the chart, Fig. 16-44. Along any vertical line (A) the heat in one pound of refrigerant is the same or constant. Along any horizontal line (B) the refrigerant has the same or constant pressure. The line along which the temperature reading is the same or constant (C) is almost vertical in the liquid area, is horizontal in the liquid vapor area, and slants down and to the right in the superheated vapor area. Refrigerant quality means how much of the one pound of refrigerant is liquid and how much is vapor. Ten percent (10%) quality means the one pound is 10 percent vapor and 90 percent liquid. A line showing the same or constant quality is shown at (D).

16-35 Latent Heat

The value of the latent heat of the refrigerant when vaporizing or when condensing in a refrigerating machine is different. At the lower pressure (vaporizing), as you may see from Fig. 16-45, the total latent heat to be added to the liquid (to be absorbed by the liquid) to vaporize it, is more than that needed to be subtracted or removed from the refrigerant to condense it into a liquid at the higher pressure. The explanation for this is that the liquid, when formed, is at a higher temperature than the liquid at the vaporizing pressure. This difference is represented by the specific heat of the refrigerant multiplied by the temperature difference for the two conditions.

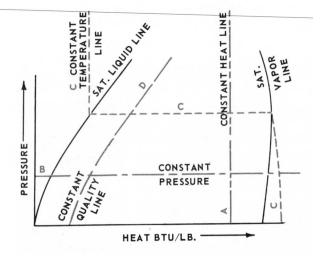

Fig. 16-44. Pressure-heat diagram. Line A indicates constant heat condition with pressure change. Line B indicates constant pressure line and condition of refrigerant with changing heat content. Constant temperature, line C, indicates conditions of equal temperature with changing pressure and heat.

The actual cooling or amount of heat removed is not equal to the total latent heat of the refrigerant at the lower pressure but is somewhat less, and the actual heat removing ability is called the EFFECTIVE LATENT HEAT.

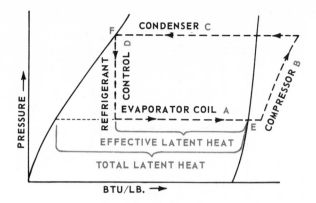

Fig. 16-45. Pressure-heat diagram. A—Liquid boiling is in evaporator coil and pressure and temperature are constant as heat is being added to refrigerant. B—Compressor raises pressure to condensing pressure, heat of compression is added and temperature rises. C—Condenser cools hot vapor to saturated vapor line and then condenses vapor into a liquid. Pressure is constant and heat is removed. D—Refrigerant control reduces pressure quickly to evaporating or low side pressure, temperature drops as some of liquid refrigerant "flashes" into vapor.

The effective latent heat of the refrigerant, when vaporizing, is the total latent heat at the low pressure minus the difference in the heat content of the liquid at the high (condensing) pressure, minus the heat content of the liquid at the low (evaporating) pressure. This is because the high pressure liquid, when throttled in the refrigerant control, must be cooled down to the low pressure temperature liquid before it can vaporize and remove heat from the surrounding substances. Part of the liquid vaporizes in order to cool the remaining liquid to the lower temperature. The vapor formed during this operation is called "flash gas."

The effective latent heat is the total heat at (E) minus the heat of the liquid at (F). The effective latent heat is an average value because the low side pressure varies somewhat during the operation of the system. Other conditions such as oil in the system, and system efficiencies affect the ideal cycle. For R-12 the latent heat of vaporization at 5 F. is 79 Btu per pound

but its actual heat absorbing ability is only approximately 51 Btu per pound during the standard operating cycle of 5 F. evaporization and 86 F. condensation.

16-36 Saturated Vapor

A saturated vapor is a vapor in such a condition that if a little heat is removed from it, some of the vapor will condense. Another definition is that saturated vapor is a substance in a vapor form in the presence of some of its own liquid. An example of a saturated vapor is a refrigerant cylinder half full of liquid refrigerant. The vapor in this space is saturated vapor. When the refrigerant vaporizes in the evaporator, it is saturated vapor at first; but as this vapor passes down the suction line to the compressor, it usually becomes warmer by 5 F. to 15 F. This additional heat and increase in temperature is called superheating the vapor; that is, it is raising the vapor above its saturated condition for this pressure, and the vapor will now obey Charles' and Boyle's Laws. See Chapter I.

In Fig. 16-43, any vapor in the space marked liquid and vapor area is saturated vapor.

16-37 Superheated Vapor

A superheated vapor is vapor in such a condition that if some heat is removed from it, the volume and/or pressure of the vapor will decrease, but there will be no condensation. The vapor that the compressor handles is always superheated unless a condition arises where the last drop of liquid refrigerant evaporates just as the refrigerant travels past the intake valve of the compressor.

Normally, the low pressure superheated vapor, when it enters the compressor, is compressed; the energy, put into it by the compressor, increases the temperature and pressure on this gas tremendously and and the amount of superheat is increased.

Superheating of the vapor lowers the efficiency of a machine. The less the superheating, the more efficient the machine will be. The heat added to the vapor is the mechanical energy of the compressor being converted into heat energy. By knowing how much heat has been added, you may calculate the size of the motor necessary to drive the compressor.

There are two places in the refrigeration cycle where superheating usually takes place. One place is in the suction line (a low-temperature superheat). The other place is in the compressor and top part of condenser (a high-temperature superheat). These two conditions are shown in Fig. 16-46.

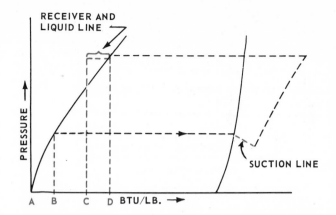

Fig. 16-47. *Pressure-heat diagram. By using heat exchanger or installing liquid and suction lines together, heat increase in suction line vapor comes from heat decrease in liquid line. Note gain in effective latent heat.*

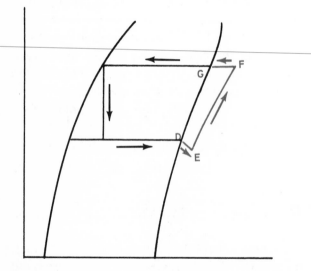

Fig. 16-46. *Superheated vapor sections of refrigeration cycle. D to E is superheat added to one pound of refrigerant vapor as it travels from evaporator to intake valve of compressor. E to F is superheat added as vapor is compressed (F is condition of exhaust valve). F to G is superheat removed in top portion of condenser.*

16-38 Specific Heat

The specific heat of a substance is the amount of heat necessary to raise the temperature of one pound of that substance 1 F.

Substances may exist in three different states (solid, liquid, and vapor). Every substance has three different values for its specific heat, depending on whether it is a solid, a liquid, or a vapor. The specific heat of the vapor may be found subdivided into the specific heat when under a constant pressure, or the specific heat when confined to a constant volume. The specific heat of a vapor under constant pressure is more than that of the same vapor under constant volume, because when a vapor is heated with a constant pressure being maintained upon it, the vapor expands and does external work (such as increasing the size of a balloon). This external work naturally necessitates an additional quantity of heat.

When a compressor compresses one pound of the refrigerant vapor, it does not add heat to it under a constant pressure or constant temperature condition. This state of affairs in the compressor is called adiabatic compression, meaning that no heat has been removed from the vapor as it was compressed. Actually, a refrigeration compressor operates almost adiabatically because the compression takes place so rapidly.

The specific heat of liquid refrigerants

varies considerably, depending on pressure imposed upon them. As shown in Fig. 16-47, the pressure to which the liquid refrigerant is subjected in the condenser, after it has condensed, (D) must be determined before calculating how much heat must be removed from one pound of the liquid at this temperature to further cool it to room temperature (C).

After the refrigerant passes through the throttling valve, it is subjected to a lower (or evaporating) pressure. The specific heat of liquid under the evaporating pressure (B) must be determined to find out how much heat must be removed to cool it down to vaporizing temperature.

If refrigerant goes through the refrigerant control while at condensing temperature, it will have A-D specific heat/lb.

16-39 Cascade System

To obtain extremely low temperatures efficiently, two refrigerating systems may be used instead of one. The two systems are connected in series (cascade system). That is, the evaporators of the higher pressure cycle removes the heat from the condenser of the lower pressure cycle. Fig. 16-48 shows the principle of this type system on a pressure-heat diagram.

16-40 Two-Stage Compressor

Some refrigerating systems, especially ultra-low temperature systems, use two compressors connected in series to pump the very low pressure suction line vapor up to the condensing pressure and temperature condition. The first stage, usually a large cylinder, pumps the vapor up to a midpoint on the compression curve, then the compressed vapor is cooled but kept in the vapor condition. The second cylinder then compresses the cooled intermediate vapor to the final pressure--temperature condition. Fig. 16-49 shows an approximate cycle.

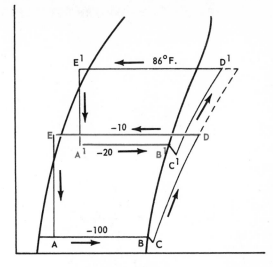

Fig. 16-48. Pressure-heat diagram for cascade system used to obtain ultra-low temperatures. Evaporator coil $A^1 - B^1$ removes heat from condenser $D - E$.

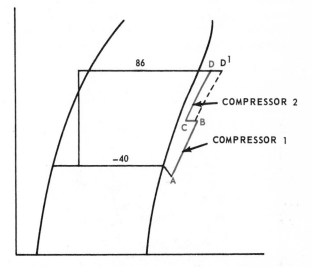

Fig. 16-49. Cycle of a two-stage compressor system. Compressor number 1 (A – B) or the first stage, compresses vapor from A to B. Vapor is cooled in heat exchanger (air or water) from B to C. Compressor 2 (C – D) then compresses vapor to condensing pressure D. This action reduces amount of heat of compression at final stage (D – D^1) and reduces superheat temperature at compressor number 2 exhaust valve considerably.

16-41 Bypass Cycle

Many refrigerating systems use an automatic bypass system. Two types are:
1. "Hot gas" bypass.
2. Liquid bypass.

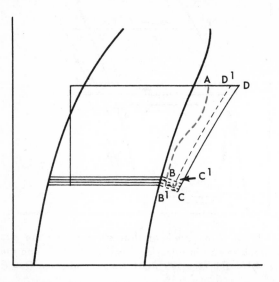

Fig. 16-50. *"Hot gas" bypass system allows low side to maintain normal low side pressure. If pressure tends to drop to point B^1, bypass circuit (A to B) opens and brings low side pressure up to normal (C^1). Without bypass low side pressure would tend to operate at C.*

The bypass line (controlled by a solenoid valve and a pressure valve) is piped from the "hot gas" part of the condenser into the suction line near the compressor. The bypass circuit is controlled by a pressure control connected to the suction line. The bypass action will return the compression line to approximately C^1 - D^1.

A liquid bypass cycle is shown in Fig. 16-51. If the low side pressure drops to B^1 the suction pressure control will open a solenoid valve and liquid refrigerant bypasses the refrigerant control and the evaporator, and is fed into the suction line (B). The liquid evaporates quickly and maintains a definite low side pressure.

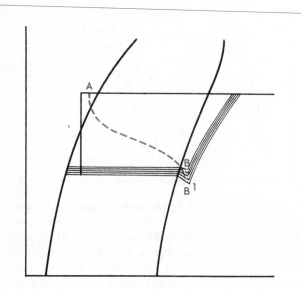

Fig. 16-51. *Liquid refrigerant bypass (A – B) used to maintain normal low side pressures.*

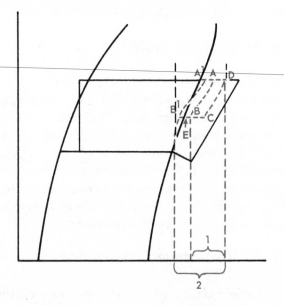

Fig. 16-52. *Hot gas defrosting cycle. Heat lost (D to B) as shown at 1 is heat used to defrost evaporating coil. If defrost hot gas is cooled too much (B^1) it will become partly liquid and may cause liquid to enter compressor. To prevent this action, an accumulator is put at E to insure that only vapor can reach compressor. Defrost cycle is A to B to C to D. Maximum heat for defrosting is shown at 2.*

The "hot gas" bypass may be used for either of two purposes:
1. Defrost evaporators.
2. Prevent suction pressure from going too low.

The cycle for "hot gas" bypass for low pressure control is shown in Fig. 16-50.

The "hot gas" bypass cycle used to defrost an evaporator is shown in Fig. 16-52. The "hot gas" is traveling through the evaporator as it travels from A to B to C.

16-42 Practical Pressure-Heat Cycle

The refrigeration cycles described in previous paragraphs are based on 5 F. evaporating temperature and 86 F. condensing temperature.

Practical cycles for various other refrigerating systems are somewhat different. For example, in an air-cooled unit for frozen foods, the evaporator refrigerant temperature will be -10 F. and with summer design ambient temperatures of 95 F., the condensing temperature will be 95 F. + 30 F. or 125 F., as shown in Fig. 16-53.

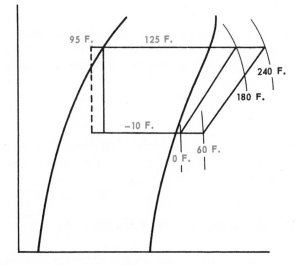

Fig. 16-53. A typical cycle of an air-cooled frozen foods refrigerating unit. Cabinet is kept at 0 F. (Refrig. -10 F.) and air temperature is 95 F. Note effect of the temperature change of suction vapor entering the compressor.

Note the difference in compressor performance and refrigerant temperatures between suction line refrigerant temperatures entering the compressor at 0 F. and 60 F. (The surface of the suction line must be above the dew point temperature of the air or the suction line will sweat, collect moisture, and/or collect frost.)

An air conditioning (comfort cooling) cycle is shown in Fig. 16-54.

A water-cooled unit with 70 F. water and therefore 80-90 F. refrigerant condensing temperature is similar to the standard cycle.

16-43 Refrigeration Troubleshooting

To locate trouble, the serviceman must be able to accurately determine what is going on inside a refrigerating system. The system is sealed; the serviceman has gauges to check the pressure, thermometers to measure evaporator, line, and condenser temperatures, a sight glass to check the amount of refrigerant and its dryness.

Much of the investigation has to be by logic. The serviceman needs to know what is supposed to be going on inside the system. He must be able to visualize the behavior of the refrigerant and what each part of the system is supposed to do. The pressure heat diagram provides considerable aid in this area.

The following paragraphs show the effect of some of the more common troubles on the pressure-heat cycle.

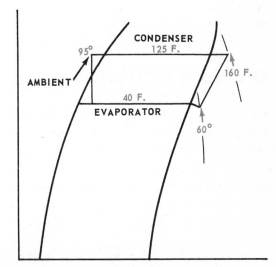

Fig. 16-54. Typical air conditioning, comfort cooling cycle with an evaporator temperature of 40 F. and an ambient temperature of 95 F.

16-44 Effect of Lack of Refrigerant

If the system is undercharged, each pound of refrigerant does not completely liquefy before it passes through the refrigerant control, as shown at part A, Fig. 16-55. The result is three fold. (1) The effective latent heat is reduced by the amount indicated by the "loss," (2) some vapor now passes through the refrigerant control reducing the refrigerant control capacity, and (3) this vapor as it passes between the needle and seat at a high velocity increases the wear on the refrigerant control needle and seat.

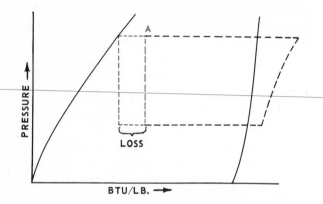

Fig. 16-55. *Pressure-heat diagram showing effect of insufficient refrigerant in system. Note loss of effective latent heat. This loss means unit will have to run longer to remove same amount of heat.*

16-45 Effect of Air in System

Air in the system increases the total head pressure. The total head pressure will equal the refrigerant condensing pressure plus the pressure of the air in the condenser. The refrigerant will condense at the temperature and pressure as if it were in the condenser alone (Dalton's Law).

Because total head pressure is higher, the compressor has to pump the vapor to a higher temperature and pressure. The extra work performed by the compressor

is illustrated in Fig. 16-56. The additional heat added to do this is a "loss." The cylinder head, (especially the exhaust valve) and the top tube of the condenser will be

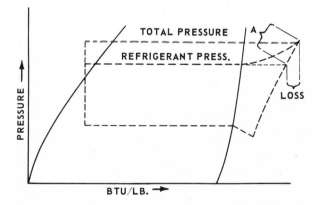

Fig. 16-56. *Pressure-heat diagram showing effect of air in system. A indicates increase in cylinder head and exhaust valve temperature. The "loss" is heat energy put into the vapor by compressor and is electric motor energy waste.*

at above normal condensing temperatures which may also tend to cause the oil to deteriorate.

16-46 Effect of Heat Exchanger

The suction line vapor after it leaves the evaporator, travels down the suction line and into the compressor, during this time it usually warms up somewhat. Part A, Fig. 16-57, shows the heat gain. Because the low pressure vapor picks up the heat in most cycles, it is more efficient to remove the heat from some part of the cycle. This heat exchange is done by putting the suction line in thermal contact with the liquid refrigerant line just before the liquid goes into the refrigerant control.

This action removes the heat at (B) and the result is a gain in effective latent heat and a reduction in "flash gas" which will increase the life of the refrigerant control.

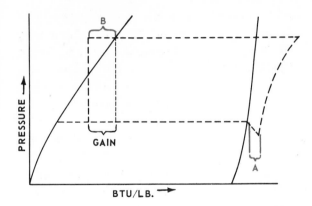

Fig. 16-57. *Pressure-heat diagram showing effect of use of heat exchanger. A shows slight amount of decrease in intake pressure and an increase in temperature. B shows amount of effective heat gain. In addition to heat gain, there is a reduction of flash gas, which improves operation of refrigerant control. Heat exchanger also minimizes chance of liquid refrigerant in suction line reaching compressor.*

16-47 Excessive Condensing Pressure

If the condenser is dirty (internally or externally) or if the condenser is under-size, the head pressure and condensing temperature will be above normal. Fig. 16-58 shows a cycle diagram in which condensing pressure is above normal. The

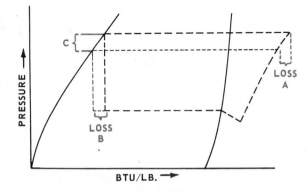

Fig. 16-58. *Pressure-heat diagram showing effect of a dirty or undersize condenser or above average room temperature. A indicates the loss due to unnecessary added heat of compression. B indicates loss in effective latent heat of liquid. C indicates loss due to work done to compress gas at higher pressure.*

higher temperature conditions will cause the compressor to pump to this higher pressure and temperature and the extra heat of compression added is a "loss" (A). If the liquid does not subcool to room tem-

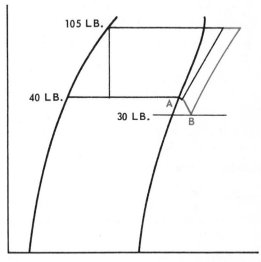

Fig. 16-59. *Typical cycle except there is an excessive pressure drop in suction line A–B. Pressure drop causes an excessive head temperature and reduces capacity of unit.*

perature an additional loss is encountered in a decrease in effective latent heat and an increase in flash gas (B).

16-48 Excessive Pressure Drop

If the pressure of the vapor going into the compressor decreases, the compressor will pump less weight of vapor per stroke and therefore per minute. The less vapor pumped, the lower the capacity of the system.

Fig. 16-59 shows the effect of excessive suction line pressure drop on the cycle. Note that as the volume of the vapor increases, there is more volume per pound of vapor, the vapor picks up heat, its temperature increases and therefore the exhaust valve temperature increases and the condenser must remove more heat from each pound of vapor.

The effect of a partially clogged filter-drier in the suction line is shown in Fig. 16-60.

16-49 Compressor Capacities

As mentioned previously, the compressor is the heart of the refrigerating machine. It is the means whereby mechanical energy, produced by an electric motor, is used to pump the refrigerant through the cycle which picks up heat at one place and discards or dissipates it at another place.

The most efficient construction possible is to have a compressor built just large enough to handle the amount of refrigeration necessary. If the compressor is too large, energy is lost in excess friction, starting energies, etc. If the compressor is too small, it will not produce the amount of refrigeration required.

Basically, the compressor must remove the vapor sufficiently fast from the evaporator to enable the refrigerant to vaporize at the correct low pressure. To do this it must remove the refrigerant vapor as fast as heat goes into the evaporator and vaporizes the refrigerant.

The method of determining the compressor size may be simply stated as follows: an evaporator is designed to remove a certain amount of heat over a 16 hour or 18 hour running period; this amount of time being dependent upon the factors described in previous paragraphs.

Let us say that the effective heat removing ability of the refrigerant is 60 Btu per pound, meaning that as each pound of refrigerant vaporizes in the evaporator it picks up exactly 60 Btu of heat from the coil itself.

To remove this amount of heat from the evaporator, the compressor must handle all the vapor formed. Refrigerant tables give us values called specific volumes. The specific volume values mean that at certain pressures one pound of refrigerant as it is vaporizing will form a certain number of cubic feet of vapor. For example, if one pound of R-12 vaporizing at 9.17 psig pressure and 0 F. and forms 1.637 cu. ft. of vapor in 10 minutes, the compressor, in order to remove the same amount of heat from the evaporator during the period that the evaporator removes its heat from the cabinet, must remove the 1.637 cu. ft. of vapor in 10 minutes.

The size of the compressor needed to do this depends on: the volume pumped per revolution of the compressor, which is dependent upon the bore, stroke, and the number of cylinders. The speed of the compressor in revolutions per minute, and the volumetric efficiency.

As the crankshaft of the compressor completes one revolution, the piston reaches the lower dead center of its travel, and the low pressure vapor fills up the space between the top of the piston and the head of the cylinder. As the crankshaft completes its revolution, the piston compresses this vapor and pushes it through the exhaust valve into the high pressure side of the system. The volume handled in each case is the volume displaced by the piston as it moves from upper dead center to lower dead center. This volume may be calculated by the following formula:

$$V = \frac{\pi \times D^2 \times S \times N \times R}{4}$$

V = Volume in cu. in.
S = Length of stroke in inches.
D = Diameter of cylinder in inches.
N = Number of cylinders.
R = Rpm (revolutions per minute)

This formula simply calculates the area of the piston head $\left(\frac{\pi D^2}{4}\right)$ and then multiplies it by the length of the stroke producing the displacement volume in cubic inches. Now, if this is multiplied by the number of cylinders used, and the revolutions per minute of the compressor, the total volume in cubic inches pumped per minute will be obtained.

Example: how much vapor will a 2 cylinder compressor pump if it has a 2 in. bore, a 2 in. stroke and operates at 400 rpm? Using the formula:

$$V = \frac{\pi \times D^2 \times 2 \times 2 \times R}{4}$$

$$= \frac{3.1416 \times 4 \times 4 \times 400}{4} = 3.1416 \times 4 \times 400$$

$$= 3.1416 \times 1600 = 5026.56 \text{ cu. in./min.}$$

The volume in cu. ft. will be

$$V = \frac{5026.56}{1728} = 2.95$$

Because 1728 cu. in. = 1 cu. ft.

$$= 2.95 \text{ cu. ft./min.}$$

Illustration problem:

Calculate the bore and stroke of a two cylinder compressor which, operating at 1750 rpm, will compress the refrigerant vapor formed by vaporizing 10 pounds of R-22 at 5 F. (28.2 psig) 1.2434 cu. ft./lb. in 10 minutes.

Solution:

V = 12.434 cu. ft. = 12.434 x 1728 cu. in. per cu. ft. = 21,485.95 cu. in.

Volume pumped per min. $= \dfrac{21,485.95}{10} =$

2,148.6 cu. in. per minute.

Using the formula:

$$V = \frac{\pi D^2 \times S \times N \times R}{4} = 2148.6 \text{ cu. in.}$$

Compressors are usually designed with a bore equal to the stroke. So the formula becomes:

$$V = \frac{\pi D^3 \times N \times R}{4} = 2148.6 \text{ cu. in.}$$

$$D^3 = \frac{V \times 4}{\pi \times N \times R}$$

$$D^3 = \frac{2148.6 \times 4}{1750 \times 2 \times \pi} = \frac{2148.6 \times 2}{1750 \times \pi}$$

$$= \frac{2148.6}{875 \times \pi}$$

$$= .8 \text{ cu. in.}$$

D = .93 in. approx. Therefore, this compressor has a bore of .93 in. and a stroke of .93 in.

However, this value obtained is the theoretical amount of vapor pumped by the compressor. The actual amount will be less and will depend on the volumetric efficiency of the compressor. See next paragraph.

16-50 Volumetric Efficiency

The term, VOLUMETRIC EFFICIENCY, IS DEFINED AS THE RATIO BETWEEN THE VOLUME ACTUALLY PUMPED PER REVOLUTION, DIVIDED BY THE VOLUME CALCULATED FROM THE BORE AND STROKE AND RPM.

If the refrigerating unit is maintaining a 150 psig head pressure and a 0 psig low side pressure, the following things are evident: when the piston is on its upward

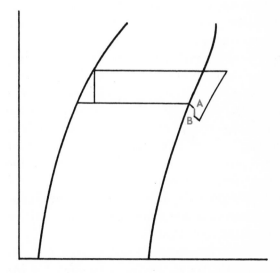

Fig. 16-60. Effect of partially clogged suction filter and/or drier. Drastic pressure drop occurs as shown at A-B.

stroke, it compresses this 0 psig vapor until the pressure of the vapor in the cylinder reaches 150 psig. When this pressure is reached, the vapor should start passing through the exhaust valve into the condenser. However, in addition to reaching this high side pressure, it must overcome the exhaust valve spring tension or weight. This means an additional slight increase in pressure is required.

Further, after the piston reaches upper dead center, there is still a little volume of the vapor at a high pressure between it and the exhaust valve. This space is necessary because if no clearance were left between the two, when the piston came up it would pound against the cylinder head. This little volume of vapor is under a high pressure of 150 psig or more, and as the piston goes down to receive a new charge of vapor this high pressure vapor expands and partially fills the cylinder chamber. This residue vapor decreases the amount of vapor that may come into this chamber from the low pressure side of the system. This necessary space is called clearance volume. This volume varies between 4 and 9 percent of the piston displacement.

Also at speeds of 300 to 3400 rpm or more, the piston is traveling so fast that the inertia or the inability of the vapor to move fast enough prevents it from filling the cylinder chamber completely and losses are encountered in this manner. The difficulty vapor encounters going through small openings, etc., is called "wire-drawing." The pressure in the cylinder never gets as high as the pressure in the suction line during the suction stroke. You can see from this that the higher the speed of the compressor, the less vapor will be pumped per stroke.

Just as the exhaust valve offers a restriction to the vapor flow, so does the intake valve with its tension and the weight of the valve parts.

The compressor runs at a warm temperature. Some of the head warms the vapor as it enters the cylinder, causing an expansion which also interferes with a complete load of vapor entering the cylinder.

Other losses, such as the leaking of the vapor past the piston and rings into the crankcase, etc., also explains why com-

pressors cannot pump the amount of vapor as calculated by using the bore and stroke formula.

For small compressors used in domestic refrigeration, having bores and strokes of 1 1/2 in. or thereabouts, the volumetric efficiency varies from between 40 percent and 75 percent with 60 percent being a fair value. The larger commercial compressors depending on their size and speed have volumetric efficiencies between 50 percent and 80 percent with 70 percent being a fair value. The 60 percent to 65 percent volumetric efficiency should be used if the unit is air-cooled.

If the compressor, explained in Par. 16-49, has a volumetric efficiency of 60 percent, the size of the compressor would be increased as follows:

As calculated in Par. 16-49, $D^3 = .8$.

$$D^3 \text{ corrected} = \frac{.8}{.60} = 1.33 \text{ cu. in.}$$

D corrected = 1.1 in.

or a bore and stroke of 1.1 in. x 1.1 in. would be required. Note that the correction for volumetric efficiency was made on the displacement volume of the cylinder, and not on the calculated bore and stroke.

The volumetric efficiency of a compressor is dependent on the relative difference between the low side pressure and the high side pressure of the machine. For instance, in an R-12 machine being used for domestic purposes, the compressor will be more efficient than if it were converted over into an ice cream system, because the decrease in low side pressure from 40 psig down to 0 psig with the same head pressure, reduces the actual pumping capacity of the compressor. The low pressure vapor is expanded so that when the cylinder is filled at the low side pressure, only a small amount, by weight, is represented. It may be judged from the various items affecting efficiency that increasing the head pressure, increasing the speed, using thicker gaskets, and overheating the compressor will all reduce pumping ability of the compressor.

16-51 Coefficient of Performance (C.O.P.)

The cooling effect of one pound of refrigerant in a cycle compared to the heat equivalent of the energy put into the refrigerant by the compressor pumping is called the coefficient of performance.

For example, if the one pound of refrigerant has an effective latent heat of 50 Btu and the compressor pumping energy is equivalent to 10 Btu, the coefficient of performance is 50 to 10 or 5 : 1.

The heat input by the compressor is less than the electrical energy put into the motor because the motor is not 100 percent efficient and there are also compressor friction losses. The overall coefficient of performance will usually be approximately 60 percent of the theoretical. The actual coefficient is therefore more near 3 : 1 than 6 : 1.

16-52 Motor Sizes

The size of an electric motor necessary to drive a compressor in a refrigerating machine may be calculated on two basically different methods:

The first method is called the mean effective pressure method.

1. The hp of the motor may be calculated by determining the hp put into the compressor. This hp is based upon the speed of the compressor and the mean effective pressure (mep) of the vapor in the compressor.

The second method is called the heat input method.

2. The size of the motor may be determined by using the amount of heat added to the vapor in the compressor as the energy taken out of the motor.

16-53 Motor Size-Mean Effective Pressure Method

The mean effective pressure (mep) of the gas is the median (average) pressure bearing down on the piston head, and it is the pressure to be overcome by the electric motor when driving the compressor. The mep is determined by a formula which uses as the basic variables the low side pressure, the high side pressure, and the ratio of the specific heat of constant pressure to the specific heat of constant volume $\dfrac{C_p}{C_v}$ for the refrigerant used. This formula and the solution will be found in Chapter 27 – Technical Characteristics.

16-54 Motor Size-Heat Input Method

From the pressure heat charts, you can readily determine the amount of heat (Btu) added to a vapor when compressed by the compressor. Referring to the R-12 pressure heat chart, Chapter 9, one will notice that approximately 10 Btu are added to the one pound of gas if the low side pressure is 10.81 psig and the high side pressure is 93.2 psig.

It is known that 2545.7 Btu per hour is equal to 1 hp and is also equal to 746 watts.

For example:

Calculate the hp required to drive the above compressor.

10.0 Btu are added per pound.

Suppose 1 pound of refrigerant is compressed in 2 minutes.

The Btu rate per hour $= \dfrac{10.0}{2} \times 60 = 300$ Btu per hour.

The hp required (Btu method) =

$\dfrac{300}{2546} = .117$

hp = 1/9 hp.

This is the mechanical equivalent of the heat energy put into the vapor; if the compressor friction were 0 and the belt drive were 100 percent efficient, this would be the size of the motor necessary to drive the compressor. However, one must add about 50 percent to this value to allow for compressor friction and belt efficiency. This system would therefore require about 1/6 hp.

16-55 Motor Efficiency

Theoretically, an electric motor should produce 1 hp of mechanical energy for every 746 watts of electrical energy put into it; that is, a 1 hp electric motor on a 115V circuit should only consume 6.8 amperes. This situation, however, is not encountered because of bearing friction, magnetic eddies, magnetic air gaps, and power factor. The efficiency of the motor is the mechanical energy delivered at the motor shaft divided by the power input to the motor. For small domestic motors of approximately 1/6 hp, the efficiency of the motor is only 40 percent to 60 percent, and for 1 hp to 2 hp the motor efficiency increases to from 75 percent ot 80 percent. As the size of the motor increases, the efficiency increases; this is due to the fact that friction losses and air gap losses remain practically constant regardless of the size of the motor. Motors with an efficiency of 90 to 95 percent are usual in the large sizes.

16-56 Condenser Capacities

The calculation of the capacity of a condenser is similar in many ways to the problem of figuring the capacity of an evaporator. The condenser must take the heat from the vapor fast enough so that just as much vapor condenses in the condenser as is being pumped into the condenser by the compressor in a given unit of time. When this condition is reached the head pressure will build up until the temperature rises to the point where the heat removed will equal the heat put into the condenser. The problem of figuring the ca-

pacity of the condenser varies according to the type of condenser being used. Condensers may be divided under the following headings:

1. Air-cooled:
   (a) Plain tubing.
   (b) Finned tubing.
      1. Natural convection.
      2. Forced convection.
2. Water-cooled:
   (a) Tube and shell type.
   (b) Tube-within-a-tube type.

The method of calculating condenser capacities is explained in Par. 16-57 and Par. 16-58.

16-57 Air-Cooled Condenser Capacities

The capacity of an air-cooled condenser may be calculated using one of two basic methods:

1. Using the total external area of the condenser to compute its heat dissipating ability.
2. Computations based upon what is called the frontal area of the condenser.

Using the total external area of the condenser for dissipating heat depends upon the following variables:

1. External area.
2. Temperature difference.
3. Time.
4. Air velocity.

Using these values, the capacity of an air-cooled condenser varies between 1 and 4 Btu per square foot per deg. F. per hour. The effect of air velocity is to increase the condenser's capacity as the air speed is increased. The fans used to do ,this work are generally mounted on the motor shaft, and drive air through the condenser at speeds between 400 to 1,000 feet per minute. When an air speed of 400 feet per minute is used, a 2.5 Btu per square foot per deg. F. per hour value will be found satisfactory. This value will increase up to approximately 4 Btu with a 1,000 feet per minute air velocity. The calculation of the area of the condenser is identical to that for a finned evaporator (Par. 16-19). A single tube condenser has a total area of approximately 20 times its frontal area. For example: if a condenser has 60 square feet of surface with a heat removal of 2.5 Btu/sq.ft./hr./deg.F., what must be the refrigerant temperature to dissipate 5,000 Btu per hour if the room temperature is 75 F.?

The formula is:

Area x Btu/sq. ft./hr./F. x temperature difference = Btu/hr.

$$60 \times 2.5 \times \text{temp. difference} = 5,000$$
$$150 \times \text{temp. difference} = 5,000$$
$$\text{temp. difference} = \frac{5,000}{150}$$
$$\text{temp. difference} = 33.3 \text{ F.}$$

Assuming an ambient temperature of 75 F., the refrigerant temperature = 33.3 + 75 = 108.3 F.

The same problem using a 75 sq. ft. condenser:

$$75 \times 2.5 \times \text{temp. difference} = 5,000$$
$$\text{temp. difference} = \frac{5,000}{187.5}$$
$$\text{temp. difference} = 26.7 \text{ F.}$$

Therefore, the refrigerant temperature = 26.7 + 75 = 101.7 F.

The heat to be removed by the condenser for each pound of vapor is the heat content of the vapor, as it leaves the compressor, minus the heat of the liquid at the condensing pressure.

From an understanding of the refrigeration cycle, you may realize that if a condenser is under capacity, the compressor head pressure will rise in proportion in order to dissipate the required amount of heat; therefore one may put condensers of various sizes on the same compressor. If too small a condenser is used, a decrease in compressor efficiency, an increase in motor load, and a decrease in the life of the unit will result. The examples above illustrate this principle.

When the capacity of the condenser is based upon frontal area, it is claimed that the air being blown through the condenser is removing heat only from the surface which it strikes directly, and that the turbulent flow against the rear surfaces makes the heat removal from these surfaces negligible. The capacity per square foot of frontal area naturally is greater than the value stated above, and is between 6 to 10 Btu per square foot per deg. F. per hour, depending on the air speed. For air-cooling the dry bulb temperature of the room should be used.

16-58 Water-Cooled Condenser Capacities

The capacity of a water-cooled condenser is high due to good thermal contact between the cooling medium and the refrigerant for either the tube and shell type or tube-within-a-tube type. The capacity will vary some with the type of water-cooled condenser used. See Fig. 16-61.

The heat transfer varies directly as the amount of water passed through the condenser. If the flow is fast, more heat will be removed, and if the water flow is slow, the heat removal will be less. At 50 feet per minute, water will remove about 185 Btu/sq.ft./hr./deg. F. At 200 feet per minute, the water will remove about 330 Btu/sq.ft./hr./deg. F. The heat removing capacity of these varies between 30 and 50 Btu per square foot per deg. F. per hour in the smaller machines. For machines of one ton capacity or more, this value may be increased up to 90 Btu per square foot per deg. F. per hour.

In addition to this heat removal, you must also calculate the air-cooling surface of the condenser, such as the external area of the shell, or the external area of the refrigerant tubing in the tube-within-a-tube type, to reach the correct capacity.

The method of determining the temperature difference between the cooling medium and the refrigerant is to use, as the refrigerant temperature, the saturation temperature of the refrigerant according to the head pressure obtained. Water tempera-

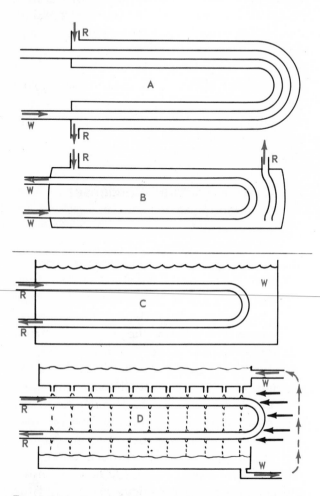

Fig. 16-61. Types of heat exchangers using liquids (water) as one of liquids. A—Tube-within-a-tube. B—Shell and tube. C—Tank. D—Baudelot. R = Refrigerant. W = Water.

tures should be taken as the average between the water-in and water-out temperature. For example:

A shell and tube type water-cooled condenser is required to remove 5,000 Btu per hour. How much tubing 3/8 OD must be put into the receiver to remove this heat if the water supply is 70 F. and the outlet water is 80 F.? How many gallons of water per hour must be circulated? Consider the re-

frigerant temperature at 100 F. Assume the heat removing capacity of the condenser to be 40 Btu per square foot per deg. F. per hour. Tube area = Condenser capacity = area (sq. ft.) x temp. diff. deg. F. x Btu rate x time.

Area = Circumference x length

Area = πD x length

$$\text{Area in square feet} = \frac{\pi D \times \text{length (in.)}}{144}$$

$$\text{Temp. difference} = 100 \text{ F.} - \left(\frac{80-70}{2}\right)$$

$$= 100 - 75$$

$$= 25$$

Btu = Area x temp. difference x Btu/sq.ft./hr. deg. F. x hr.

$$5,000 = \frac{\pi 3/8 \times \text{length (in.)}}{144} \times 25 \times 40 \times 1$$

$$\frac{5,000}{25 \times 40} = \frac{\pi 3/8 \times \text{length (in.)}}{144}$$

$$\frac{5,000 \times 144}{25 \times 40} = \pi 3/8 \times \text{length}$$

$$\text{or length} = \frac{5,000 \times 144}{25 \times 40 \times \pi 3/8} = \frac{720}{\pi 3/8} =$$

$$\frac{720}{3.1416 \times .375} =$$

$$\frac{1920}{3.1416} = 611 \text{ in.}$$

$$= 51 \text{ ft. approximately}$$

The amount of water circulated =
Specific heat x wt. x temperature difference = Btu
Specific heat of water = 1
1 x wt. x 10 = 5,000

wt. = 500 lbs./hr.

1 gal. of water weighs 8 1/3 lbs.

$$\frac{500}{8\ 1/3} = 60 \text{ gal. of water per hr.}$$

16-59 Liquid Receiver Sizes

Liquid receivers for a commercial system should be large enough to hold all the refrigerant in the system. This practice is recommended for service operations and as a safety measure should the refrigerant circuit become restricted (clogged filter or screen).

Fig. 16-62 shows recommended minimum sizes of receivers based on horsepower capacity of the system. The receivers may have to be larger than this depending on the refrigerant, piping lengths, and other factors.

Hp	Volume Cu In.	Weight—Lb	
		Refrigerant	
		R–12	R–22
½	150	6.8	6.2
¾	225	10.3	9.3
1	300	13.7	12.4
1½	450	20.5	18.6
2	600	27.4	24.8
3	750	35	32
5	900	41	37
7½	1500	70	64

Fig. 16-62. Minimum net recommended liquid receiver volume for two refrigerants, R–12 and R–22. (ASHRAE Guide and Data Book)

16-60 Refrigerant Lines

The liquid and suction lines on refrigerating machines must be of sufficient size to handle the amount of the liquid or vapor required. The method of calculating the capacities of these lines as to determine the maximum velocity allowed in the line and then, knowing the amount of vapor or liquid to be handled, the internal cross section of the line may be easily calculated.

16-61 Refrigerant Line Capacities (Liquid)

Velocities in the liquid line of a unit vary with the density of the liquid and with its viscosity. These velocities may vary between 50 to 200 feet per minute, depending on the refrigerant used, (R–12 should have velocities no greater than 100 feet per minute).

For example: if 75 cu. in. of liquid were used a minute, the internal cross section area of the liquid line to keep the liquid line velocity at 100 ft. per minute or below would be:

$$\text{Cross section area} = \frac{\text{volume in cu. in.}}{\text{velocity in in./min.}} = \frac{75}{100 \times 12}$$

Cross section area = .063 sq. in.

$$\text{Area} = \frac{\pi D^2}{4} \quad D^2 = \frac{\text{area} \times 4}{\pi} \quad D = \sqrt{\frac{\text{area} \times 4}{\pi}}$$

The inside diameter $= \sqrt{\frac{.063 \times 4}{\pi}} = .285$ in.

Use 3/8 in. OD tubing.

It is important that these refrigerant carrying lines be of sufficient capacity; the cost of increasing the tubing size is so small in comparison to the total cost of the machine, that there is no real necessity for calculating the size of these tubings to too close limits. At least 50 percent oversize of the tube is therefore recommended.

If the liquid line is too small or if there are too many restrictions in the liquid line, the pressure drop may be enough to reduce the capacity of the refrigerant control below the capacity of the evaporator coil. Extremes of this condition are revealed by sweating or frosting liquid lines when excessive pressure drops occur due to partially clogged driers, strainers, or pinched lines.

The pressure drop in a liquid line carrying R–12, is shown in Fig. 16-63. Note that if one tried to use a 1/4 OD liquid line for a 12,000 Btu/hr. or one ton load, that the pressure drop would be .42 psi per foot. A 100 foot equivalent length liquid line would then have a total pressure drop of 42 psi. Equivalent length is the actual length of the piping, plus the pressure drop in the bends and fittings, as expressed in feet. See Fig. 16-70.

If the normal head pressure were 125 psig the pressure in the liquid line near the thermostatic expansion valve would be 125–42 or 83 psig. At 83 psig, the boiling

Load Btu/hr.	¼"	⅜"	½"	⅝"	¾"	⅞"	1⅛"
3,000	.035						
6,000	.120	.011					
9,000	.250	.021					
12,000	.420	.036					
18,000		.075	.010				
24,000		.127	.016				
36,000		.260	.033	.012			
48,000		.450	.054	.020	.010		
60,000			.080	.030	.014	.009	
84,000			.150	.054	.025	.015	
120,000			.280	.100	.049	.028	.009
240,000				.350	.160	.095	.029
360,000					.340	.200	.058
480,000						.340	.100

Fig. 16-63. Pressure drop in R–12 liquid lines based on refrigerating load and size of line (OD). Value is to be multiplied by equivalent length.
(Dunham-Bush Inc.)

temperature is 79 F. and sweating might occur in a humid 90 F. room.

In large systems, one must take into account the amount of refrigerant stored in the liquid line. This amount also affects

pressure based on weight of the liquid (static head), as shown in Fig. 16-64.

Bends and fittings increase the resistance to the fluid flow. It is claimed that there is as much friction to flow in a 90

¼"	⅜"	½"	⅝"	¾"	⅞"	1⅛"
.015	.043	.086	.134	.202	.269	.458

Fig. 16-64. Refrigerant charge in pounds per foot of liquid line. (Dunham-Bush Inc.)

deg. elbow as there is in 5 ft. of straight tubing of the same size. The friction in bends, fittings, and the normal friction of fluid flow through the tubing must be calculated when figuring fluid velocities.

In multiple installations which use a series connected evaporator coil installation, as shown in Fig. 16-65, the liquid line is usually variable in diameter as the number of coils it feeds changes. Note that

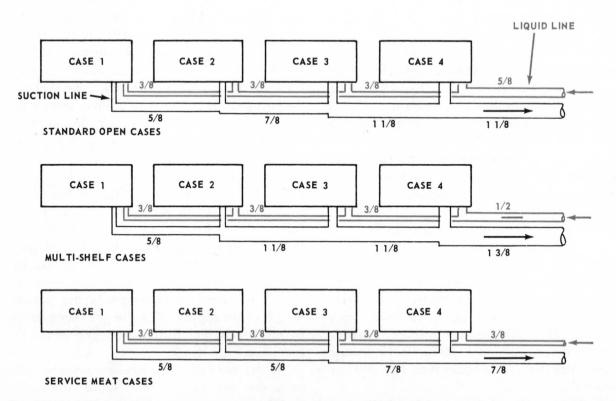

Fig. 16-65. As number of evaporators serviced increases, size of liquid line must also increase. The line sizes shown are for normal temperature refrigeration installations. Note change in diameter of liquid lines.

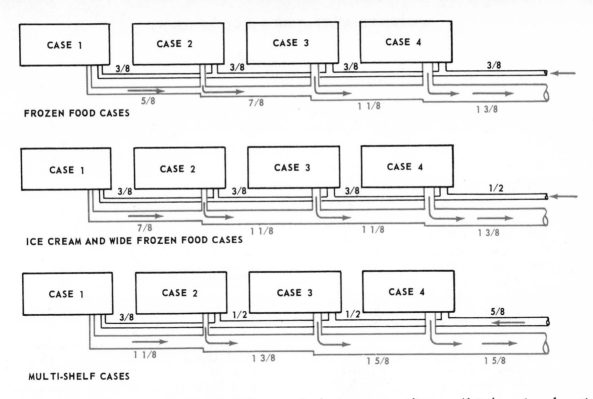

Fig. 16-66. Three typical supermarket piping diagrams for low-temperature fixtures. Note how size of suction lines increases as vapor accumulates from each case.

two 1/2 in. OD liquid lines do not feed from a 1 in. OD line. The cross-sectional areas are added. Line 1 area + Line 2 area = Line 3 area. The wall thickness is neglected.

$$\frac{\pi D_1^2}{4} + \frac{\pi D_2^2}{4} = \frac{\pi D_3^2}{4}$$

$$D_1^2 + D_2^2 = D_3^2$$

$$\sqrt{D_1^2 + D_2^2} = D_3$$

$$\sqrt{\frac{1^2}{2} + \frac{1^2}{2}} = D_3$$

$$\sqrt{\frac{1}{4} + \frac{1}{4}} = D_3$$

$$\sqrt{\frac{2}{4}} = D_3$$

$$\sqrt{\frac{1}{2}} = D_3$$

$$\sqrt{.5} = D_3$$

$$.70 = D_3$$

Use one size larger = 3/4 in. OD.

Fig. 16-66 shows some typical piping diagrams for low-temperature installations.

16-62 Orifice Sizes

The size of the orifice opening, controlled by a needle, which is usually located in the thermal expansion valve, must be carefully calculated. Its size depends on the shape of the opening, viscosity of liquid passing through it, and upon the pressure difference as the fluid passes through the orifice. These orifice sizes, however, become fairly standard for domestic and commercial machinery with orifice openings of 0.93 in. and .156 in. being adopted as most popular. If larger orifices are needed multiple installations of expansion valves are used. See Fig. 16-67 for a table of orifice sizes and capacities.

If the orifice is undersize (too small) the amount of refrigerant that can pass through the valve will not be sufficient and the coil will be starved. Also the evaporator pressure will reduce too fast.

If the orifice size is too large, the valve will feed too much refrigerant too fast causing a "sweat back" or "frost back" down the suction line. The result will be a

ORIFICE DIAMETER

NORMAL CAPACITY	R–12	R–22
1/2 ton	.0625 to .109	.03125
1 ton	.078 to .109	.0625
1 1/2 ton	.125	.109
2 ton	.156	.125
3 ton	.209	.15625
5 ton		.209
10 ton	.2812	.219
15 ton		

Fig. 16-67. Table of expansion valve orifice sizes and capacities.

"searching or hunting" action causing alternate flooding and then starving of the evaporator.

The pressure difference is important. As the difference increases the valve capacity increases. Therefore, if there is a high head pressure the valve may feed refrigerant too fast and cause a sweat or frost back. If the pressure is too low (low head pressure or the liquid line is too long or has too many bends or fittings or is too

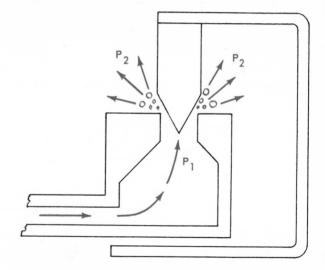

Fig. 16-68. Action of refrigerant as it passes through orifice of AEV or TEV valve. Liquid refrigerant at P_1 (high side pressure) is forced through orifice and almost at once reaches P_2 (low side pressure). As liquid changes in pressure some of liquid instantly changes (about 30%) into vapor (flashes) and this vaporizing cools rest of liquid to evaporator coil refrigerant temperatures.

16-63 Refrigerant Line Capacities (Suction)

The gas velocity in the suction line depends on the low side pressure of the system and, therefore, in its application the velocities usually used are between 800

ALLOWABLE VELOCITIES IN FEET PER MINUTE

REFRIGERANT	SUCTION LINE (GAS)	CONDENSER VEL. (GAS)	LIQUID LINE VEL. (LIQUID)
Ammonia	4000–5000	5000–6000	100–250
R–12	800–1800	1800–2250	80–100
Water	30–50 (Liquid)	. . . .	100–250

Fig. 16-69. Table of allowable refrigerant liquid and suction line velocities.

small or if the TEV is too high above the liquid receiver) the valve will feed too little refrigerant and the evaporator will starve. Fig. 16-68 shows the operation of a refrigerant orifice.

and 5,000 feet per minute, as shown in Fig. 16-69. As the refrigerant evaporates in the evaporator, its pressure must be somewhat higher than the vapor pressure at the suction side of the compressor before it will go down the suction line. There must be a pressure difference before a fluid will flow. The compound gauge, mounted on the compressor, can be used to show that the pressure is lower at the compressor than it is in the evaporator while the unit is running. Stop the compressor and the pressure will rise to the evaporator pressure. The rise indicates the pressure difference in the low side of the system.

The correct size of liquid and suction lines is important in refrigerating units. An excessive pressure drop in a suction line is similar to operating the compressor at a lower pressure thereby reducing its capacity. For example, a pressure drop of 2 psi at low temperatures, -15 F. is the same as trying to operate at -20 F. and the condensing unit capacity is lowered approximately 12 percent. The oil return should be taken care of by slanting the

For Each	¼	⅜	½	⅝	¾	⅞	1⅛	1⅜	1⅝	2⅛	2⅝	3⅛	3⅝	4⅛
Valve	1.5	1.5	2	2	2.5	3.0	4.0	5.0	6.0	7.5	9.0	11.0	13.0	15.0
Elbow (90°)	.75	.75	1	1	1.5	1.5	2	2.5	3	4.0	5.0	5.5	6.5	7.5
Tee	1.5	1.5	2	2	2.5	3.0	4.0	5.0	6.0	7.5	9.0	11.0	13.0	15.0

Fig. 16-70. Table of amount of resistance of valves, elbows, and tees over straight length pipe. Values for each fitting shown in above table should be added to length of pipe in order to obtain equivalent length. Note that valve has as much resistance as 2 ft. of 1/2 in. pipe. (Dunham-Bush Inc.)

The suction line involves two additional problems in the understanding of the pressure drop within the line. One additional complication is due to the necessity of returning oil to the compressor by means of the suction line. Also, when two or more coils are connected to one compressor, the resistances to flow in the different lines may cause the pressure on the surface of the refrigerant in the various evaporators to vary as much as 2 to 3 lbs. per sq. in. The friction in a 1/2 in. OD suction line is approximately .25 in. mercury (Hg) per 10 ft. of length with a gas velocity of 1,000 ft. per minute. This results in a problem of balancing evaporator capacities. The amount of pressure drop becomes greater as the length of the suction line increases, as the cross-sectional area of the tubing decreases, or is in proportion to the number of bends and fittings in the suction line. Fig. 16-70 shows the values to be added to the actual length of the pipe in order to obtain the equivalent length.

suction line consistently downward from the evaporator to the compressor to permit the oil to drain naturally into the compressor. If a low spot is constructed into the suction line, the oil will accumulate there and decrease the cross-sectional area of the tubing, causing an orifice action which also decreases the efficiency of the gas flow, as shown in Fig. 16-71. Furthermore, when this low spot eventually becomes filled with oil, the pressure difference builds up and the oil is slugged into the compressor. The slugging of the oil in the crankcase of the compressor accel-

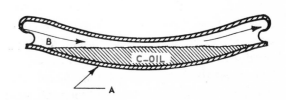

Fig. 16-71. Illustrating restricting of vapor flow due to oil collecting in low spot in suction line. A—Suction line. B—Refrigerant vapor. C—Oil.

erates oil pumping momentarily and may damage the compressor.

Fig. 16-72 shows the capacity of various size suction lines using R–12 refrigerant. Note that a 1 in. nominal or 1 1/8 in.

calculating the equivalent length of pipe from Fig. 16-70, and correcting for temperature using Fig. 16-73.

For example: to determine the suction line size for a 5 ton system at 0 F., allow

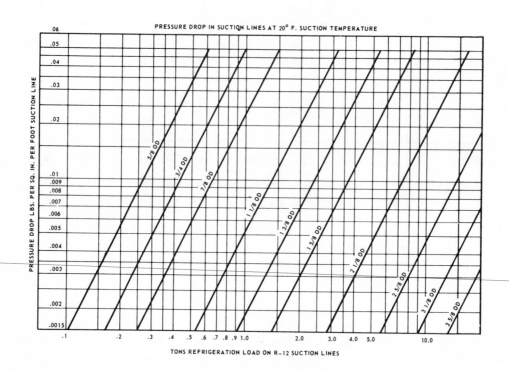

Fig. 16-72. *Graph of suction line capacities for R–12 refrigerant. Suction line size should be chosen using a pressure drop of .02 to .03 psi per ft. Chart is based on 20 F. If lower temperatures are used, larger suction lines are needed and vice versa.*

OD suction line can carry from 1/2 ton to 3 tons of capacity depending on the pressure drop. However, the best choice would probably be between .02 and .03 psi pressure drop and this pipe should be used for 2 to 2 1/2 ton units. If the suction temperatures are lower or higher than 20 F., the pressure drops must be corrected because the denser vapor should have lower velocities and vice versa, as shown in Fig. 16-73.

One usually knows the capacity of the installation in Btu/hour or in tons of refrigeration. He can then estimate the correct suction line size by first getting an approximate size from Fig. 16-72, and

for a total 2 psi pressure drop. The suction line has 30 ft. of straight run, 6-90 deg. elbows, 1-tee, and 1-valve, at 0 F. Assume that 1 1/8 OD suction is to be used.

Suction line	30 feet
6 elbows x 2	12 feet
1 tee x 4	4 feet
1 valve x 4	4 feet
The equivalent length	50 feet

If a total of 2 psi pressure drop is desired then, 2 ÷ 50 = .04 psi per foot.

However, this line operates at 0 F. instead of 20 F. Therefore, .04 ÷ 1.38 = .029 psi per foot of length.

Suction Temp	—40	—30	—20	—10	0	10	20	30	40	50
Correction Factor	2.70	2.28	1.90	1.62	1.38	1.18	1.00	0.88	0.75	0.64

Fig. 16-73. Table of correction values for pressure drops in a suction line. If suction temperatures exceed 20 F., pressure drop is decreased, and if temperatures are below 20 F., pressure drop increases because vapor is less dense. Equivalent length is to be multiplied by correction factor.

Now referring back to Fig. 16-72, a 5 ton load with a .029 psi per foot pressure drop needs a 1 5/8 OD pipe for the suction line.

It is important to always use piping as large as the fittings that are on the evaporator unit and on the compressor. If a compressor suction line connection is 1 in. OD, it is advisable to use this size piping. If the liquid receiver liquid line connection is 1/2 in. OD, use this size.

16-64 Review of Safety

Because excessive temperatures and excessive pressures are dangerous, the refrigeration serviceman must be aware of the danger of guessing at piping sizes, condenser sizes, evaporator sizes, and motor sizes to be used on a refrigeration system.

Carefully compute the sizes of each of the above items according to the methods described in this chapter. Improper sizing of the unit or any part of the unit may create a damaging or dangerous condition.

16-65 Test Your Knowledge - Chapter 16

1. What is a Btu?
2. What is the Btu equivalent of a hp?
3. What is sensible heat?
4. What is latent heat?
5. What is specific heat?
6. Why is it important when calculating the heat load of a cabinet to know what the cabinet is used for?
7. Why is the heat leakage into a cabinet based upon the external area?
8. What is the purpose of a baffle?
9. What is usage heat load?
10. What materials were used for the interior walls of the newer cabinets?
11. What is the purpose of the ice hold-over in the sweet water bath?
12. Why must a pressure type water cooler never be allowed to accumulate too much ice?
13. What is the specific heat of ice cream?
14. At what temperature should brick ice cream be maintained?
15. What is meant by the superheating of the gas in the suction line?
16. What is the "effective latent heat" of a refrigerant? Why is it different from latent heat?
17. What causes the superheating of gas as it passes through the compressor?
18. Why may one use the Btu added to the gas as it goes through the compressor to calculate the size of the motor to drive the unit?
19. What is meant by volumetric efficiency and what variables influence it?
20. What factors must be considered when determining the type of compressor drive?
21. What is meant by motor efficiency and what are the usual efficiencies?
22. Explain how heat travels from one carrying medium to the next, starting with the refrigerated cabinet and continuing to the suction line vapor, describing the ease of transfer from one medium to the other.
23. What is the product heat load?

24. Explain conductance.
25. How many heat leakage surfaces does a cabinet have?
26. How does an evaporator capacity vary as the refrigerant temperature decreases?

27. If an evaporator capacity is rated at a temperature difference of 10 F., what two temperatures is it the difference of?
28. What is a nonfrost evaporator?
29. What is the coefficient of performance?

Chapter 17

ABSORPTION SYSTEMS, PRINCIPLES AND APPLICATIONS

The absorption system differs from the compression system in that it uses heat energy instead of mechanical energy to make a change in the conditions necessary to complete a refrigeration cycle. The absorption system may use gas, kerosene, or an electric heating element as a source of heat supply.

The system has a minimum of moving parts. The smaller units have moving parts only in the valves and controls which are used. Some of the larger units use circulating pumps and fans in addition to valves and controls.

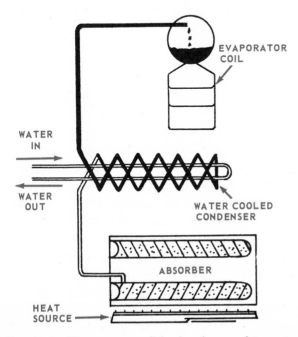

Fig. 17-1. Elementary solid absorbent refrigeration unit. Note water-cooled condenser.

Absorption systems are quiet in operation. They are used in commercial installations and in domestic installations as well. In recent years absorption units have been used extensively in recreation vehicles, campers, trailers and boats. The fact an absorption unit can be operated from a small gas cylinder has increased its use in portable refrigerators.

17-1 The Absorption System

Fig. 17-1 illustrates fundamentals of a basic absorption system. This diagram shows the solid absorbent type and is included for the purpose of comparison with mechanical types of refrigerators.

The condensing coil, receiver, and evaporator (cooling coil) are quite similar to those used in the compression system. The compressor has been replaced by a heater or generator. The system has been simplified by leaving out the various controls. These will be covered later.

Fig. 17-2 illustrates a basic absorption system of the liquid absorbent type. This unit uses a water-cooled condenser.

17-2 Types of Absorption Systems

There are several combinations of substances which have an unusual property; one substance will absorb the other without any chemical action taking place. One substance will absorb the other substance when cool, and will release it when heated.

If the substance is a solid, the process is sometimes called absorbing; if the substance is a liquid, the process is called absorbing.

There are two main types of absorption refrigerators: one utilizing a solid absorbent material, the other using a liquid absorbent.

These two type of absorption refrigerators are best typified by the Faraday, which is a solid absorbent type; and by the Electrolux, which uses a liquid absorbent.

Another classification of absorption systems is:

1. Intermittent system.
2. Continuous system.

Absorption systems have had several applications as follows:

1. Domestic.
2. Industrial.
3. Air Conditioning.

The absorption systems are also identified by the type of heat used, as follows:

1. Kerosene.
2. Natural or artificial gas.
3. Electric heat.

Some absorption units used in family trailers and mobile homes may be electrically heated, or LP fuel heated. These systems are explained in this chapter.

17-3 Principles of Solid Absorption System

Michael Faraday, in 1824, performed a series of experiments to liquefy certain "fixed" gases--gases which certain scientists believed could exist only in vapor form. Among them was ammonia (R-717) which had always been regarded as a "fixed" gas. Faraday knew that silver chloride, a white powder, had the peculiar property of absorbing large quantities of ammonia vapor. He exposed silver chloride to dry ammonia vapor. When the powder had absorbed all of the vapor it would take, he sealed the ammonia-silver chloride compound in a

test tube which was bent to form an inverted V. He then heated the end of the tube containing the powder and at the same time cooled the opposite end of the tube with water as shown in Chapter 3, Fig. 3-10. The heat released ammonia vapor, and drops of colorless liquid soon began to appear in the cool end of the tube. Thus liquid ammonia was produced.

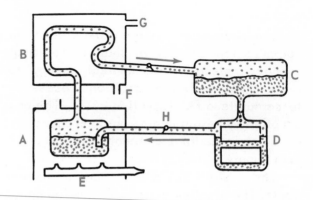

Fig. 17-2. Elementary liquid absorbent refrigerating unit: A—Generator. B—Condenser. C—Receiver. D—Evaporator. E—Burner. F—Water in. G—Water out. H—Check valve.

Faraday continued the heating process until sufficient liquid ammonia had been produced for his purpose. When this was accomplished, he extinguished the flame under the powder and proceeded to observe the characteristics of the newly discovered substance.

A few moments after the flame had been extinguished, Faraday began to note a most unusual occurrence. The liquid ammonia instead of remaining quietly in the sealed test tube, began to bubble and then to boil violently. It was rapidly changing back into a vapor, and the vapor was being reabsorbed by the silver chloride powder. Upon touching the end of the tube containing the boiling liquid, Faraday was astonished to find it was cold. Ammonia, in changing from liquid to vapor form, extracted heat. It took this heat from the nearest thing at hand, which was the test tube itself.

17-4 Principles of Continuous Absorption System

The liquid absorbent system possesses some desirable characteristics. Water at ordinary pressures and temperatures will absorb great quantities of ammonia (R-717). Ammonia absorbed in water may be easily driven from the water by the addition of heat. Also, liquid ammonia has such a high latent heat of vaporization, that is, it absorbs a large amount of heat when changing from a liquid to a vapor.

The Servel is a domestic refrigerator which is designed to operate in a continuous cycle. It has no moving parts or valves other than those used to control the burner flame. The refrigerant is ammonia with water used as the absorbent; hydrogen gas is utilized to create a low partial ammonia pressure (Dalton's Law, Par. 1-53) to allow the ammonia to evaporate at a low pressure.

In Fig. 17-3, A represents ammonia, and H is the hydrogen.

When the burner at (1) is lighted and its heat applied through the center of the generator (1), ammonia vapor is released from the solution. This hot vapor in part (1b) passes upward through the percolator tube (10), and as the hot ammonia vapor rises through this tube, it carries the solution to the upper level of the separator (11).

Most of the liquid solution settles in the bottom of (11) and flows through the liquid heat exchanger (9) into the absorber (4). The hot ammonia vapor being light, rises to the top of tube (11). The hot ammonia vapor then passes downward through the center tube, into the analyzer (6). Here any water vapor is removed while the hot ammonia vapor rises into the rectifier (7).

The rectifier (7) consists of a series of small baffle plates, surrounding the tube. If the hot ammonia vapor still contains traces of water vapor, it must be removed to insure pure ammonia vapor.

The heat has at this point completed its work. For the remainder of the cycle, the natural force of gravity is depended on to create circulation.

The pure hot ammonia vapor continues into the condenser (2).

The ambient air, passing through the fins, removes heat from the ammonia vapor, thus condensing some of the vapor into a liquid in (2a). This ammonia is now in a pure state, and it flows by gravity into the evaporator (3a).

The ammonia gas that does not condense rises into (2b) where it is condensed and drains to the upper tube or trap.

The U-tube is the receiving and storage compartment in the cycle where the liquid ammonia is allowed to build up to a predetermined level. When it reaches this level it flows into the evaporator (3a). Because a liquid will always seek its own level, the liquid ammonia flows by gravity through the liquid ammonia tube and spills into the evaporator.

As the liquid ammonia falls into the evaporator, (3a and 3b) it forms in large shallow pools on a series of horizontal baffle plates. The hydrogen gas that is being fed to the evaporator in large quantities permits the liquid ammonia to evaporate, (Dalton's principle) at a low temperature. During this process of evaporation, the ammonia absorbs heat from the food compartment of the refrigerator and causes the water in the ice cube containers to freeze. The more hydrogen and less ammonia, the lower the temperature. The evaporated vapor formed by the evaporating of the liquid ammonia, mixes with the hydrogen gas. This mixture is heavier than hydrogen and moves downward through the middle of the gas heat exchanger (8) into the absorber (4). This circulation is continuous in the evaporator. The mixed hydrogen gas and ammonia vapor that pass through the gas heat exchanger cools the hydrogen gas rising in the outer tube.

During this time a weak solution of am-

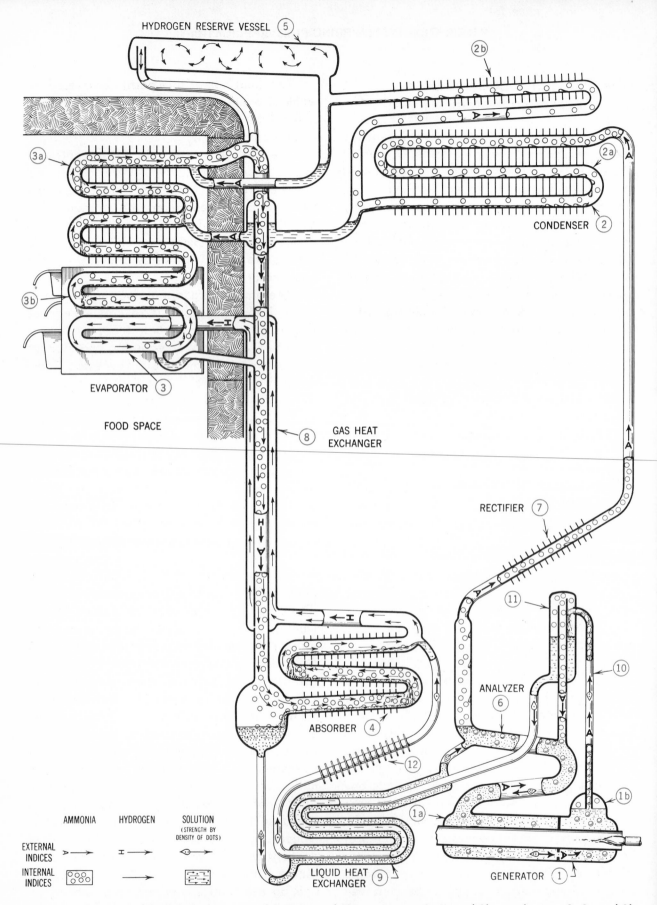

Fig. 17-3. Diagram of Servel absorption cycle. 1—1a and 1b, generator. 2—2a and 2b, condenser. 3—3a and 3b, evaporator. 4—Absorber. 5—Hydrogen reserve. 6—Analyzer. 7—Rectifier. 8—Gas heat exchanger. 9—Liquid heat exchanger. 10—Percolator tube. 11—Separator. 12—Precooler.

monia and water is flowing by gravity from the generator (1) down to the top of the absorber (4) by way of the liquid heat exchanger (9). Here it meets the mixture of hydrogen gas and ammonia vapor coming from the evaporator by way of the gas heat exchanger. The weak and fairly cool solution absorbs the ammonia vapor. The hydrogen gas is left free since hydrogen is insoluble in water. Because it is also very light, it now rises to the top of the absorber and returns to the evaporator by way of the gas heat exchanger (8).

The absorber (4) has fins and is air-cooled. The cooling of the weak solution helps it to absorb the ammonia gas out of

mixture, back to the analyzer (6) and to the generator where it again starts its cycle.

The apparatus is a welded assembly. There are no moving parts to wear out and get out of adjustment. The total pressure throughout the cycle is about 400 psig at a room (ambient temperature of 100 F.) necessitating a rugged construction which insures a long life.

To produce a temperature of 0 F. in the evaporator the ammonia must boil at 15.7 psig, which means that the hydrogen must make up the remainder of the pressure (384.3 psig), if the total pressure is 400 psig. This refrigerator is considered to be unique among domestic refrigerators. A more detailed study is made of the Servel in Par. 17-8.

17-5 Principles of Intermittent Absorption System

A convenient refrigerator cycle for localities not furnished with gas or electricity is the Superfex and Trukold cycle. The Superfex cycle is basically the Faraday principle, but incorporates features which warrant a description.

As shown in Fig. 17-4, ammonia is mixed with water in a sealed tank or generator (A) under which is located a kerosene burner (M). The burner is lighted and the heat produced drives the ammonia in vapor form, out of the mixture. This ammonia vapor is forced up a pipe (D) and through a coil (E) which is immersed in water contained in a tank (B) on the top of the refrigerator.

The water cooling causes the ammonia vapor to change back into a liquid at the high generating pressure. This liquid ammonia drops through a pipe into the liquid receiver (C) and from here it passes to the evaporator (K) which is surrounded by a brine (H). The liquid receiver is insulated (F) to prevent this container from overcooling the food compartment by acting as the evaporating coil.

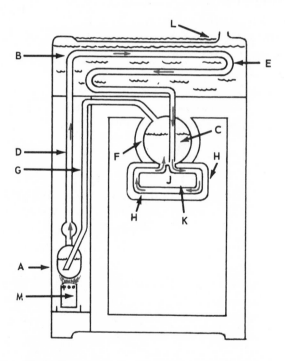

Fig. 17-4. Generation or heating interval in typical intermittent type absorption refrigerator.

the mixture of ammonia vapor and hydrogen gas. Also when the weak water solution absorbs the ammonia vapor, considerable heat is liberated and the air-cooled fins remove this heat to permit refrigeration to continue.

The liquid heat exchanger carries the strong liquid, or ammonia liquid and water

This process continues for a relatively short time until the kerosene is consumed and the burner automatically goes out.

As the absorber cools to room temperature, the ammonia will evaporate at a low temperature in the evaporator because, as the generator cools, it tends to reabsorb the ammonia gas, thereby reducing the pressure and permitting the liquid ammonia in the evaporator to boil at a low temperature. This evaporation causes the cooling effect or refrigeration required to preserve the contents of the food compartment.

The water in the generator (A) cools to room temperature quite quickly after the burners have gone out, and as cool water has a strong affinity for ammonia, the ammonia vaporized in the evaporator passes back to the generator through a connecting pipe (G) and is reabsorbed by the water in the generator maintaining a low pressure in the evaporator unit as shown in Fig. 17-5.

In other words, heat from the oil burner drives the ammonia from the generator (A) to the cooling unit (K) in a short time; the ammonia in the evaporator vaporizes and passes back to the generator slowly over a period of twenty-four to thirty-six hours. The vaporization of the ammonia in the evaporator produces a refrigerating effect.

For additional efficiency in unusually hot climates or for handling extra large loads, a depression (L) in the top of the condenser tank may be filled with water which will evaporate rapidly and aid the cooling of the tank.

This refrigerator is also explained in Par. 17-7 along with the Trukold refrigerator which is fundamentally similar.

Absorption mechanisms are provided with a fuse plug which will release the charge from the mechanism if the temperature of the unit becomes excessive 175-200 F., as might be experienced in a fire. This prevents any possibility of exploding the complete mechanism.

17-6 Superfex System

The Superfex refrigerator was designed to produce refrigeration using kerosene as the source of energy. The system had the generator on the left side of the cabinet with the kerosene burners mounted on racks and accessible through a small door on the lower left side. The condenser was immersed in a tank of water mounted on the top of the cabinet.

The system used ammonia as the refrigerant and water as the absorbent. The evaporator was surrounded by a cold retainer which served to keep the refrigerator cold during the heating portion of the cycle.

With this unit, two precautions were to be observed: the water-cooled condenser was immersed in a nonflowing water tank located in the top of the box. This water level had to be kept up to the indicated level, especially just before lighting. The ker-

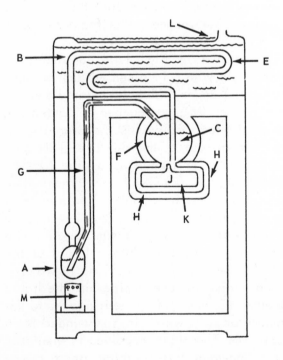

Fig. 17-5. Refrigerating part of cycle in intermittent type absorption refrigerator.

osene burners had to be clean, dry, and in good condition. They had to be filled to the correct level and kept level when burning to prevent improper flame.

17-7 Trukold System

Another kerosene-fired absorption refrigerator· was distributed by Montgomery Ward. This refrigerator was intermittent in operation; it used ammonia and water as the refrigerant and absorbent. A kerosene burner was located under the cabinet and the heating flue was behind the cabinet as shown in Fig. 17-6.

Note the location of the liquid ammonia receiver inside the insulation of the cabinet behind and above the evaporator. This location prevented the receiver from acting as the evaporating coil. The burners and tank were mounted on a rack to make moving for refilling simple. The water reservoir was kept filled to the correct depth.

17-8 Servel System

As explained in Par. 17-4, the Servel system operates on the principle of Dalton's Law of partial pressures. The Servel has been manufactured in three basic styles. The original unit used water to cool the condenser and the absorber. In Europe, an electric heating element was used, while in the United States all the units were heated with artificial or natural gas. The water-cooled units were produced between 1927 and 1933.

In 1934 and 1935, a secondary cooling system was used in place of water cooling. The ammonia condenser was air-cooled and the absorber was cooled by a methyl chloride coil and the hot methyl chloride was in turn cooled by an air-cooled condenser located just beneath the ammonia condenser.

Starting in 1936, the secondary system was discontinued and both the ammonia

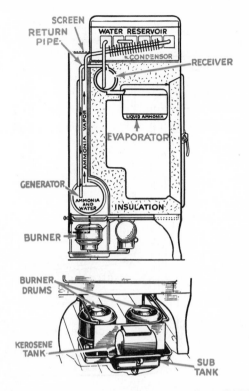

Fig. 17-6. Trukold cycle and burners. Note two kerosene burners mounted on the slide out track. (Montgomery Ward)

condenser and the absorber are now directly air-cooled as shown in Fig. 17-7.

17-9 Electrolux System

Servel, Inc. announced their secondary system air-cooled unit in 1933 and has continued this model with refinements.

The Servel air-cooled unit is charged with a small quantity of aqua-ammonia (distilled water and ammonia) and hydrogen. The charge distributes naturally in the unit; the liquid seeks the lowest levels and the hydrogen gas and ammonia vapor fill the remaining space.

Referring to Fig. 17-7, with the application of heat (about 365 F.) at the generator, ammonia vapor is driven from the strong solution, and is raised through the pump tube to the weak liquid separator. Ammonia vapor with traces of water vapor, is driven off in the separator, leaving the aqua-ammonia solution comparatively weak

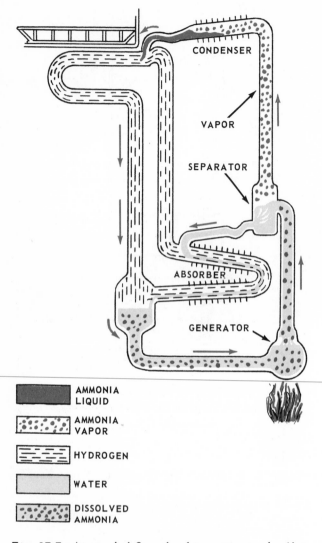

evaporation at a low partial pressure. The ammonia vapor thus formed in the evaporator mixes with hydrogen gas, and the mixture flows by gravity through the evaporator. The long column of heavy gas, rich in ammonia vapor (ammonia vapor and hydrogen gas mixture) readily overbalances the short column of heavy gas in the evaporator, thereby causing the desired flow in the evaporator.

AMMONIA LIQUID

AMMONIA VAPOR

HYDROGEN

WATER

DISSOLVED AMMONIA

Fig. 17-7. Air-cooled Servel refrigeration cycle. Note water circuit, ammonia flow and hydrogen circuit.

in ammonia (weak solution). The hot ammonia vapor then passes from the separator to the condenser. When the hot ammonia vapor reaches the condenser it is liquefied by cooling. The condenser is finned, and natural convection produces a steady flow of air over it. The liquid ammonia maintains a level in the condenser, causing the liquid ammonia to flow into the cabinet evaporator.

An atmosphere of hydrogen gas, continually sweeping the surface of liquid ammonia in the evaporator keeps removing the ammonia vapor and causes continued

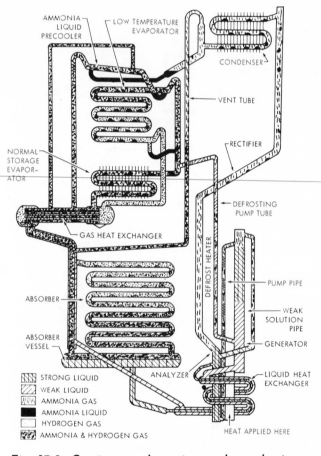

STRONG LIQUID
WEAK LIQUID
AMMONIA GAS
AMMONIA LIQUID
HYDROGEN GAS
AMMONIA & HYDROGEN GAS

Fig. 17-8. Continuous absorption cycle mechanism. Note two evaporators and defrost pump tube. (Norge Div., Borg-Warner Corp.)

A flow of weak solution, being returned from the generator, (to temperatures about 350 F.) contacts the ammonia and hydrogen gas mixture entering the absorber, and the ammonia is dissolved. The hydrogen being lighter returns to the evaporator. The hydrogen temperature as it leaves the ab-

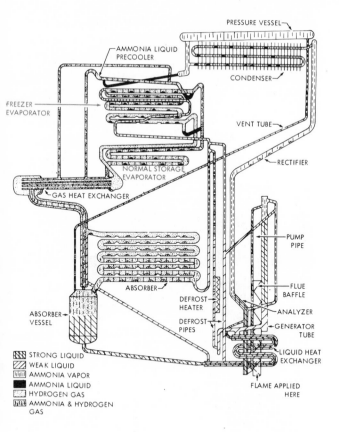

Another system designed for no-frost operation is shown in Fig. 17-9. This system has a precooler to further cool the liquid ammonia before it enters the freezing evaporator. The freezer evaporator also has two liquid traps and two vapor traps. This system pumps weak solution into the evaporator using electric heaters to activate the defrost percolator tube (pump pipes) during defrost.

In Fig. 17-10 nonfrost conditions are obtained by using a high flame and pumping hot gas into the freezer evaporator. The

Fig. 17-9. Refrigerating cycle of nonfrost absorption household refrigerator. Defrost heater is not in operation during part of cycle as shown.
(Norge Div., Borg-Warner Corp.)

sorber, is about 130 F. to 135 F., if the ambient temperature is 100 F.

The heat, which is liberated by absorption of ammonia in the absorber, is carried away by air cooling. From the absorber, the strong solution is returned by gravity to the generator. Continued refrigeration is merely a repetition of this cycle.

The refrigeration mechanism that contains the ammonia is usually made of welded steel. The fins on the ammonia condensers are made of copper, although the tubing is steel. The gas controls are almost identical with those used in the water-cooled unit (Par. 17-4).

The unit used in a recent model gas absorption unit is shown in Fig. 17-8. It has a defrost cycle using a hot solution percolator type pump.

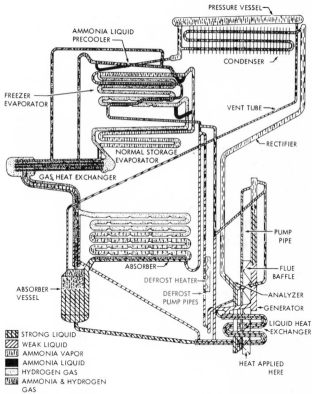

Fig. 17-10. Defrost cycle portion of continuous absorption system. Note action of refrigerant in defrost tubes in freezer evaporator.

electric heater on the defrost pump pipe percolates warm aqua-ammonia through the freezer evaporator section when the thermostat-timer closes the defrost heater circuit. Fig. 17-11 shows the unit installed in a cabinet.

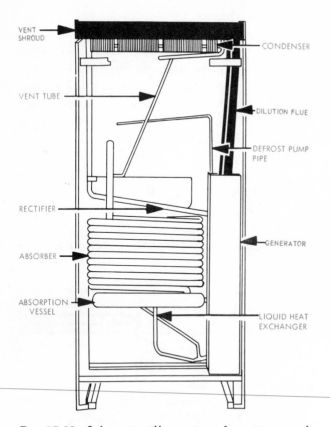

Fig. 17-11. Schematic illustration of continuous absorption unit installed in cabinet. This shows rear of cabinet.

17-10 Installing and Servicing Absorption Systems

The absorption refrigerator, like all refrigerator mechanisms, is a device to move heat from the interior of the cabinet to the outside of the cabinet. This outside

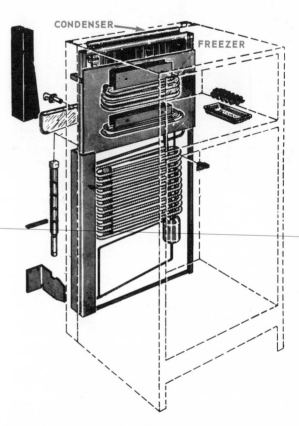

Fig. 17-12. Phantom view of continuous absorption refrigerating mechanism installed in combination refrigerator freezer cabinet.

A phantom view of an absorption refrigerator with a flue is shown in Fig. 17-12.

Electrical circuits for recent Servel units are shown in Fig. 17-13. Note the defrost circuit and devices and also note the wiring circuit for the ice maker.

The wiring harness installed in a late model absorption cabinet is shown in Fig. 17-14. Note the use of timers, fans, and heaters.

A small amount of sodium chromate is put into the system to prevent corrosion of the steel parts, especially at the welds.

Typical operating conditions for this system with a normal ambient air temperature are as follows:

Freezer section	0 to 15 F.
Cabinet Air	39 to 40 F.
Condenser	140 F.
Absorber	145 F.
Generator	365 F.

heat is transmitted to the air, and this air must be removed from the vicinity of the cabinet to allow cooler air to receive heat from the condensers, as shown in Fig. 17-15.

Kerosene piped gas, or bottled gas, when burned forms carbon dioxide gas (harmless) and steam vapor (harmless). However, to provide good air flow past the burner, these products of combustion must be moved away from the cabinet. Because warm gas-

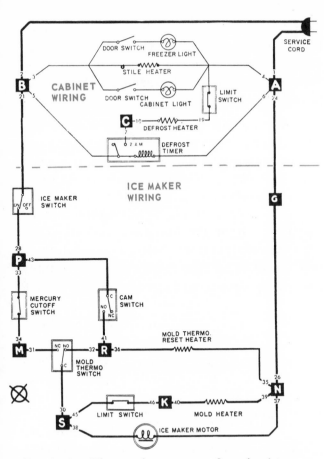

Fig. 17-13. Electrical circuits on Servel refrigerator. This model has automatic defrost and automatic ice cube maker.

es rise, the absorption cabinets must have proper air flow space beneath, in back, and over the top of the cabinet.

Inside the mechanism, the liquids flow by gravity, and the mechanism must be properly leveled or the movement of the liquids and gases inside the unit will be uncertain.

The condensers and flues of the unit must be kept clean to allow proper air flow and flue gas flow. It is recommended that the condensers be cleaned at least twice each year; more often if necessary.

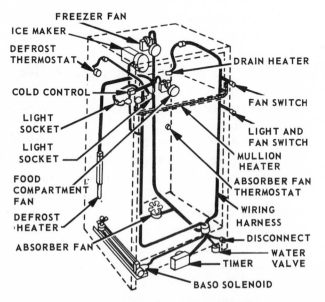

Fig. 17-14. Electrical circuits for continuous cycle absorption refrigerator. (Norge Div., Borg-Warner Corp.)

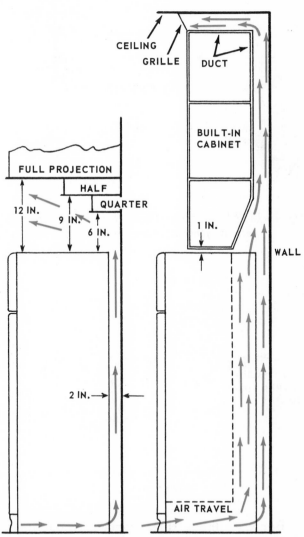

Fig. 17-15. Diagram which shows proper provision for air circulation under, in back of and over top of absorption refrigerator.

17-11 Flues

Heat from the burners must be efficiently transmitted into the generator. The kerosene flame gases and the natural gas hot gases are conducted along a flue that extends around the generator or through it. These flues sometimes have spiral metal fins inside to make the hot gases give up their heat more efficiently to the flue walls as shown in Fig. 17-16.

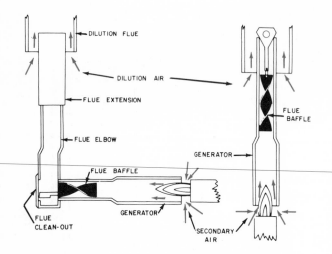

Fig. 17-16. Flue construction for both horizontal and vertical generator type Servel units.

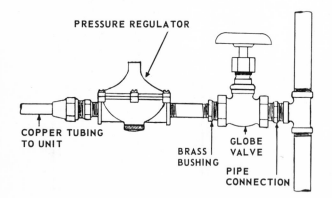

Fig. 17-17. Gas line installation for early model Servel refrigerator.

Because these flues carry combustion gases they must be kept open or the combustion will not be complete. The flues must also be kept clean or much of the

heat will be lost by poor heat transmission into the generator. The flue should be cleaned at least twice each year. Special flue brushes should be used for this purpose.

17-12 Intermittent Systems

Intermittent systems that use a kerosene burner, ordinarily require but little servicing. They are manual in operation, and eliminate controls by having the owner refill and light the kerosene burner. The previous instructions about air circulation and location of the cabinet also pertain equally to the kerosene heated units.

17-13 Continuous System Gas Supply

The fuel most commonly used for absorption system refrigerators is natural or LP gas, although electrical heating elements are sometimes used. Using clean fuel such as gas prevents the formation of carbon monoxide or carbon deposits on the burner. The cleaner the fuel the less frequently the burners have to be cleaned.

Piped gas refrigerators should be supplied with gas under a steady pressure. The burner should be designed for the type of gas being used. The gas must be strained before being admitted to the burners. It must have a pressure regulator to provide unvarying pressure on the burner. Fig. 17-17 shows gas connections to an absorption system.

It is important to become acquainted with local rules concerning installation of these refrigerators before attempting to install them. Fig. 17-18 shows a complete gas burner installation.

In case of burner difficulty, a check should be made to make sure the burner is the correct one for the gas used.

Four different gases in use as a fuel for the gas refrigerator units are:

Artificial gas (425 to 600 Btu per cu. ft.).

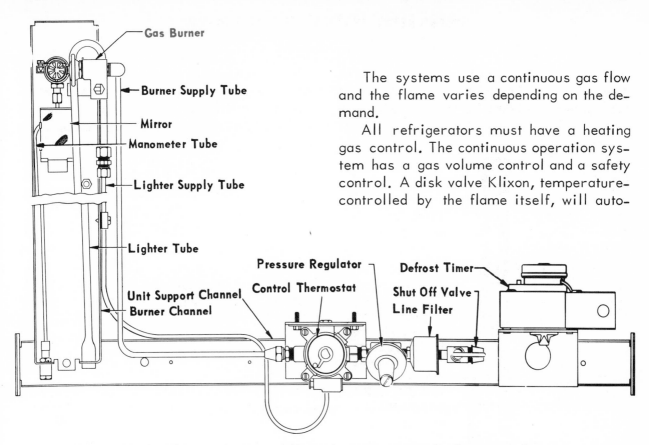

Gas Burner

Burner Supply Tube

Mirror

Manometer Tube

Lighter Supply Tube

Lighter Tube

Unit Support Channel
Burner Channel

Pressure Regulator

Control Thermostat

Defrost Timer

Shut Off Valve
Line Filter

The systems use a continuous gas flow and the flame varies depending on the demand.

All refrigerators must have a heating gas control. The continuous operation system has a gas volume control and a safety control. A disk valve Klixon, temperature-controlled by the flame itself, will auto-

Fig. 17-18. Complete gas burner installation for continuous cycle absorption refrigerator. (Norge Div., Borg-Warner Corp.)

Natural gas (600 to 1600 Btu per cu. ft.).

Liquid petroleum (LP) gas (1600 Btu per cu. ft.).

Propane gas (1600 Btu per cu. ft.).

Butane gas (1600 Btu per cu. ft.).

These fuels are discussed in more detail in Chapter 20.

17-14 Continuous System Controls

Aside from cabinet care and cleaning, the service (outside the factory) that may be needed on the absorption refrigerator is generally limited to the heating controls and air circulating equipment. The adjustments determine the efficiency of the unit to such an extent they must be made carefully.

Heating gas valves are used in the absorption system to enable the automatic control of the amount of the heating gas burned.

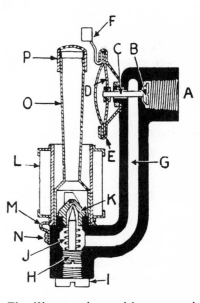

Fig. 17-19. The Klixon valve and burner used on the older model Servel units: A—Gas in. B—Poppet valve. C—Poppet valve stem. D—Klixon snap button. E—Housing. F—Klixon disk heater. G—Gas passage to burner. H—Manual adjusting screw for maximum gas flame. I—Seat cap. J—Spring. K—Gas nozzle. L—Screen. M—Screen retainer. N—Screen retainer screw. O—Burner venturi. P—Burner cap.

matically close the gas supply if the flame goes out, Fig. 17-19. An exploded view of the burner is shown in Fig. 17-20. A bulb

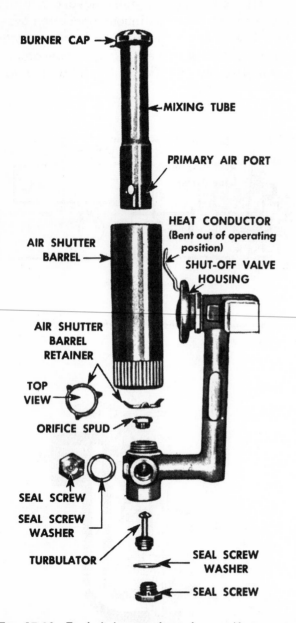

Fig. 17-20. Exploded view of gas burner. Notice primary air port and burner cap.

BURNER CAP

MIXING TUBE

PRIMARY AIR PORT

HEAT CONDUCTOR (Bent out of operating position)

SHUT-OFF VALVE HOUSING

AIR SHUTTER BARREL

AIR SHUTTER BARREL RETAINER

TOP VIEW

ORIFICE SPUD

SEAL SCREW

SEAL SCREW WASHER

TURBULATOR

SEAL SCREW WASHER

SEAL SCREW

pressure-temperature control located at the evaporator unit controls the amount of gas burned according to the needs of the refrigerator, as shown in Fig. 17-21. The temperature of the evaporator controls the size of the flame.

A great deal of the successful operation of domestic refrigerators is dependent on the functioning of the automatic control valves. It is obvious the serviceman must be thoroughly familiar with the operation and servicing of the valves.

The continuous operation absorption unit generally has its heat energy supplied by a gas burner. Several different methods have been devised for the regulation and control of this gas. In this refrigerator, between the gas main and the operating controls of the refrigerator, are placed a manual shutoff valve, a strainer, and a pressure-regulating valve. As explained previously, the unit operates on the continous cycle, and gas is continually being consumed. However, to take care of variations of demand on the refrigerator itself, the amount of gas fired must be automatically controlled. This is done by the use of a pressure control valve operated by a power element located at the evaporator. As the refrigerator warms up, gases in the power element expand, and press on a diaphragm in the control valve to open the gas control, and allow more gas to flow to the burner.

The larger flame speeds up the cycle in the mechanism and continues to speed it up until the evaporator has cooled.

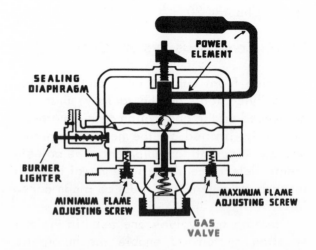

POWER ELEMENT

SEALING DIAPHRAGM

BURNER LIGHTER

MINIMUM FLAME ADJUSTING SCREW

MAXIMUM FLAME ADJUSTING SCREW

GAS VALVE

Fig. 17-21. A thermostatically controlled gas valve. (Norge Div., Borg-Warner Corp.)

As the evaporator cools, the power element located on the evaporator will cool, reducing the pressure on the gas valve diaphragm. This reduction closes the heating gas opening and reduces the size of the flame. Turning the adjustment clockwise or in, increases the gas supply.

A unique valve is used to close off the gas in case the flame must be extinguished. This valve is of the dished-button type and is thermostatically controlled. See Fig. 17-22. Since it is located adjacent to the flame it remains hot as long as the gas is ignited. If the flame is extinguished, the disk will become cold. On cooling, it snaps and becomes dished in the other direction. This movement closes a valve in the gas line, completely shutting off the supply of the gas. If this happens, the only method possible of reigniting the gas is to heat up the Klixon disk so it will open the safety valve. A burner push button mounted on the thermostat body is provided for the purpose.

Each refrigerator has an automatic pressure control for maintaining a constant gas pressure. This valve reduces the fluctuation in pressures from the gas mains to a minimum. The supply of gas must be constant to insure proper operation.

17-15 Pressure Regulating Valves

The purpose of the pressure regulating valve is to supply a steady flow of gas to the burner. Without a regulating valve, if the burner gas pressure should change, the flame would change and might be extinguished.

Fig. 17-22. *Safety shutoff valve in open position. This valve will shut off gas supply if gas flame is extinguished accidentally.*

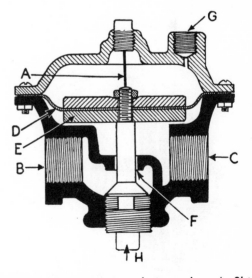

Fig. 17-23. *A pressure regulating valve. A—Shipping pin (this is removed when valve is placed in operation). B—Gas in. C—Gas connection to thermostatic control. D—Flexible diaphram. E—Weights. F—Valve and seat. G—Bleeder connection. H—Valve cap.*

The pressure regulator both reduces the pressure and provides a constant gas pressure. See Fig. 17-23.

Liquid petroleum (LP) gases do not need a pressure regulator at the refrigerator because the pressure regulator mounted on the LP cylinder performs the same duty.

The pressure regulator operates much the same as an expansion valve. The outlet pressure presses against a diaphragm (synthetic rubber, fabric reinforced). If the pressure begins to drop the diaphragm will move, opening the gas valve allowing more gas to flow. The increased gas flow will press the diaphragm up, tending to close the valve. The pressure regulator should be accurate to approximately 1/100 of an inch water pressure. Pressures the regulator must maintain vary from 1.6 to 3.9 in. of water. The pressure needed varies with gas flow in cu. ft. per hour. This gas flow is controlled by the orifice size in the burner. The pressure also varies with the density or specific gravity of the gas. The greater the gas flow the greater the

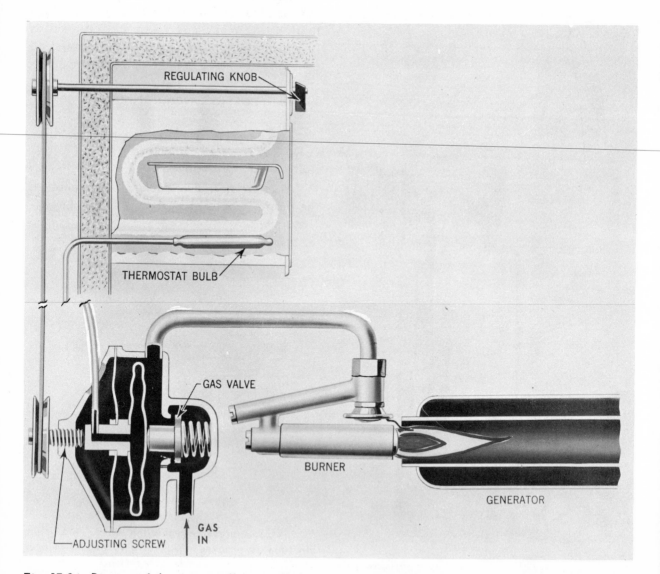

Fig. 17-24. Diagram of thermostatically controlled gas flame. Note that control bulb is attached to evaporator coil. An increase in pressure in control bulb will result in increase in flame size.

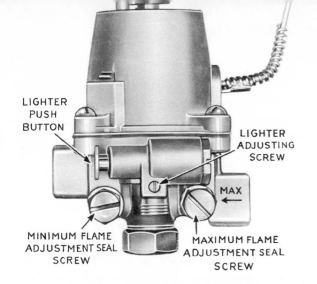

Fig. 17-25. Servel thermostat showing adjustments and lighter push button.

pressure needed. Pressures must be adjusted to within .1 in. water pressure for good results.

17-16 Thermostats

The thermostat mechanism varies the amount of cooling by varying the amount of heat. The more heat fed to the generator, the cooler the evaporator will become. A thermostat is used to perform this job. A thermal bulb clamped to the evaporator will create pressure if the evaporator becomes warmer. This pressure is carried to a diaphragm by a capillary tube. An increase of pressure in the diaphragm opens the gas valve and more gas flows to the burner. See Fig. 17-24.

Increased cooling resulting from the added heat will cool the thermal bulb and the diaphragm pressure will decrease, closing the valve. Note the capillary tube, the temperature adjusting knob on the top of the body, and the minimum and maximum devices located on the body, Fig. 17-25.

The inner working of the thermostat is shown in Fig. 17-21. This shows the construction of the minimum and maximum flame adjustments, and also details of the burner lighter mechanism.

The amount of primary air is adjustable. The outer casing of the burner, called the air shutter barrel, can be turned to adjust the air flow. It should be carefully adjusted to give a flame that is all blue just as the yellow disappears from the flame. Too much primary air will also give a blue flame but the flame cone will be sharp and the flames will hiss more sharply.

17-17 Burners

The burner is the mechanism used to carefully mix the air with gas in the proper proportion and burn the mixture to provide the most efficient heat. The burner used is basically a Bunsen type burner, Fig. 17-26.

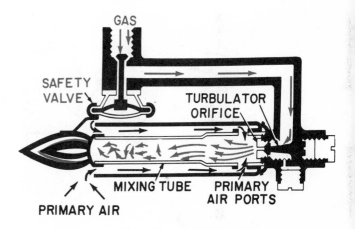

Fig. 17-26. Sectional view of horizontal type burner. Note the safety valve.

Gas enters at the top, travels past the safety valve and passes through the turbulator, through the carefully sized orifice, mixes with the primary air, and burns at the end of the mixing tube where the secondary air and the heat enters the generator tube and flue. The fitting at the lower right (at the bottom) is the opening that may be connected to a manometer to check the gas pressure.

Different types of burners are available. Type A is for fast burning gases; Type D is for liquefied petroleum (LP) (bottled) gas.

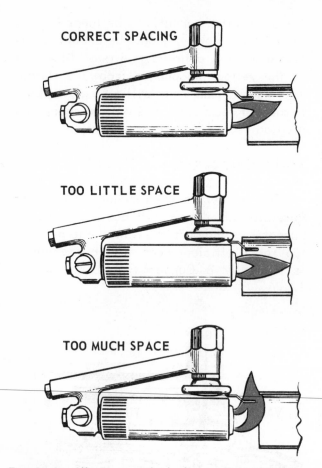

CORRECT SPACING

TOO LITTLE SPACE

TOO MUCH SPACE

Fig. 17-27. Illustration which shows effect of burner spacing.

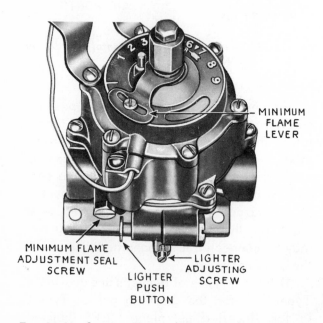

MINIMUM FLAME LEVER

MINIMUM FLAME ADJUSTMENT SEAL SCREW

LIGHTER PUSH BUTTON

LIGHTER ADJUSTING SCREW

Fig. 17-28. Semiautomatic defrosting thermostat for Servel refrigerator.

The turbulator is available in two different models; one-groove type for LP gases; two-groove type is for fast burning gases.

The burner must be exactly the right distance from the generator flue to obtain the correct amount of secondary air, as shown in Fig. 17-27.

The burner can be adjusted to the distance it is mounted from the generator flue. It can be moved to center the flame in the center of the generator flue. The flame must never be adjusted so it touches the flue. Use a mirror if it is difficult to see the flame location.

The products of combustion are harmless and there is no odor.

17-18 Burner Safety Valve

It is unlikely the burner flame will be snuffed out. If someone should shut off the gas and then turn it on, or if someone accidentally puts out the flame, the positive safety device on the burner will prevent unburned gas from escaping.

The safety valve is operated by the flame. A metal plate which touches the flame becomes hot. The heat is transmitted to a bimetal disk which when hot will move with a snap action and open the gas valve. If the disk cools, the bimetal disk will dish the other way pulling the valve shut and stopping the gas flow.

It is important that the heat conductor strip be kept against the outer edge of the flame, as shown in Fig. 17-27.

17-19 Automatic Defroster

Several models of the Servel continuous system have defrosting devices.

The semiautomatic defroster is used to set the thermostat to a minimum flame (or defrost position), and when the evaporating coil has defrosted, the thermostat will automatically start normal operation, Fig. 17-28.

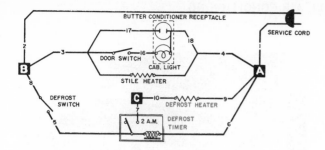

Fig. 17-29. A wiring diagram for automatic defrost system.

The automatic defroster is controlled by an electric timer. At the time the owner prefers, usually in the early morning hours (1 a.m.), the electric clock stops the operation of the thermostat and sends electrical energy through resistance wires located under the evaporating coil. Heat from these wires quickly defrosts the outer portion of the coil without disturbing the frozen foods within the coil. When the coil is defrosted, the system automatically returns to normal operation. The wiring diagram for this device is shown in Fig. 17-29.

A nonfrosting system has also been developed. This system uses an electric heater to percolate hot aqua ammonia into the evaporator.

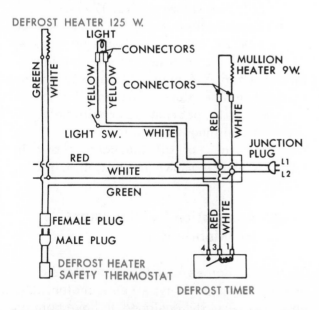

Fig. 17-30. Wiring diagram for continuous operation absorption refrigerator. Note 125-watt defrost heater. (Norge Div., Borg-Warner Corp.)

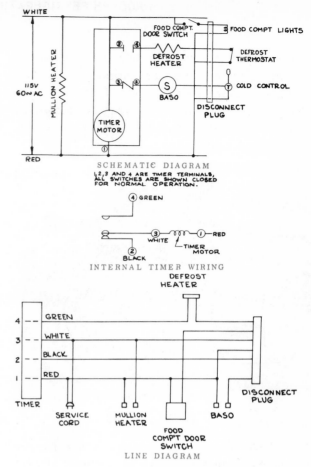

Fig. 17-31. Wiring diagram for defrost timer; schematic diagram, internal timer wiring, and line diagram.

17-20 Electrical Circuits

Electrical circuits of the absorption refrigerator are used to provide lighting, power system cooling fans, power evaporator fans, operate defrost timers and heaters, and mullion heaters. These circuits are similar to the circuits for the compression system refrigerator except for the circuit to the motor-compressor and its safety devices. Fig. 17-30 shows a typical absorption unit electrical circuit. Note the safety thermostat in series with the defrost heater.

The defrosting timer and the defrost heater that it controls are shown in more detail in Fig. 17-31. The defrost thermostat opens the electric heater circuit at the end of about 20 min. when the temperature reaches about 60 F. Some of these units have an extra electric defrost heater mounted on the freezer evaporator to insure complete defrost. The freezer compartment evaporator blower is shown in Fig. 17-32. The freezer evaporator has a

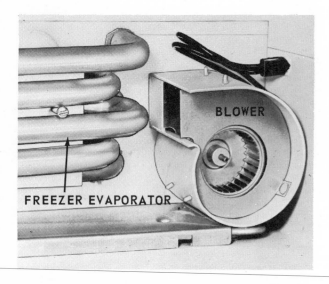

Fig. 17-32. *The absorption system freezer evaporator blower. Note "plug in" connection. Blower is stopped during defrosting.*

thermostat capillary tube clamped to it. The thermostat controls a solenoid gas valve. This opens on temperature rise and the deenergized solenoid valve permits a high flame. As the temperature drops, the points will close and the energized solenoid valve will reduce the flame to a low flame.

The care and service of electric circuits is covered in Chapter 8.

17-21 Portable Absorption Refrigerators

A portable refrigerator (Polar-Fridge), which is completely portable, developed by the Bernz O Matic Corporation, is shown in Fig. 17-33. The unit holds 1.1 cu. ft. of food and weighs only 42 lbs. The cabinet is made of plastic and its uses a foam insulation.

The refrigeration system is the self-contained continuous absorption type, using

Fig. 17-33. *A portable absorption refrigerator which can use propane gas cylinder or electric heating element as energy source. (Bernz O Matic Corp.)*

bottled gas, 115V AC or 12V DC, as a source of power to the generator.

The Polar-Fridge is built in four styles. It may be fitted to operate on:
1. Electric--115V.
2. Gas--Propane gas cylinder.
3. Electric--Gas combination which can be used with 115V or propane cylinder as shown in Fig. 17-34.
4. Combination electric 115V AC or 12V DC for use on boats or in cars.

The pull-down time for this refrigerator is from 2-6 hours, dependent on the ambient temperature. The small propane cylinder will provide approximately 70 hours of continuous operation.

The names of all the parts shown in Fig. 17-34 are shown in the table in Fig. 17-35.

17-22 Absorption Refrigerators for Mobile Homes

Mobile homes and travel trailers often use an absorption type refrigerator. The units are usually designed to have both an electric heating element and a gas burner to heat the generator of the continuous unit.

Gas heat is used when electricity is not available. It is essential that the refrigerator be mounted level. If this is not done the gravity controlled flow of the fluids will not operate efficiently.

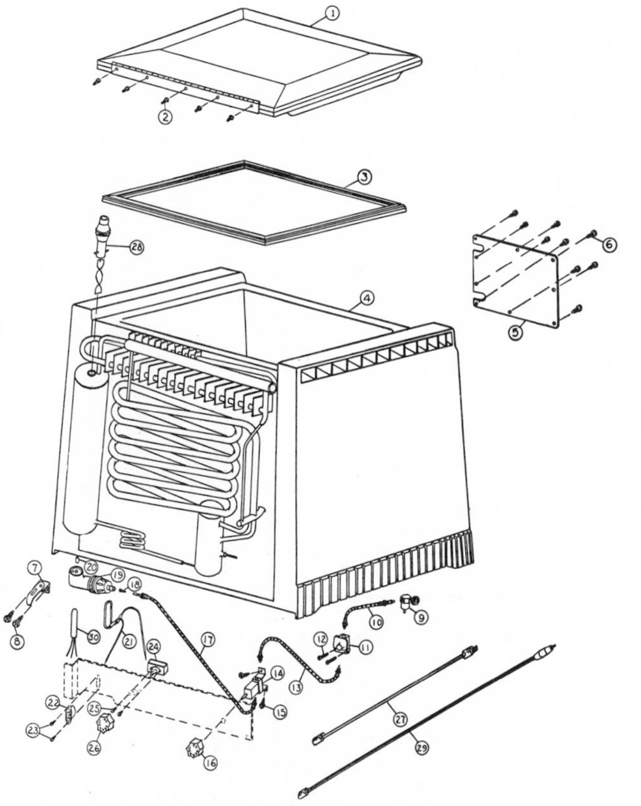

Fig. 17-34. *Schematic drawing of portable absorption refrigerator which shows generator, condenser and absorber. See Fig. 17-35 for part identification.*

The installations must be carefully designed with air ventilation to cool the condenser, and to provide air for the flame and outside exhaust for combustion gases.

17-23 Commercial Absorption Systems

Absorption systems are used successfully for air conditioning comfort cooling installations. The systems are also used for heating.

Some units use the ammonia-water-hydrogen continuous cycle. Other systems use water as the refrigerant and various chemicals as the absorber. One system uses water as the refrigerant and lithium bromide as the absorber. Steam heat applied to the generator percolates water vapor (red dots) and weak solution up to the

NO.	PART NAME
1	Cover Assembly
2	Pan Head, Tapping Screw
3	Closure Gasket
4	Refrigerator Case
5	Plastic Case Closure
6	No. 7-16 "Tapit" Screw, 1/2 in. Long
7	Burner Bracket Assembly
8	No. 6-18 "Tapit" Screw, 3/8 in. Long
9	Valve Assembly
10	Hose Assembly
11	Gas Regulator
12	Pan Head, Self Tapping Screw
13	Hose Assembly
14	Gas Thermostat
15	No. 6-18 "Tapit" Screw, 3/8 in. Long
16	Knob—Gas Thermostat
17	Hose Assembly
18	Orifice (.008)
19	Burner Assembly
20	Burner Tip
21	Heating Element
22	Service Cord Receptacle
23	Pan Head, Tapping Screw
24	Electric Thermostat
25	Round Head Machine Screw
26	Knob—Electric Thermostat
27	Service Cord, 115V
28	Windshield, Spiral Assembly
29	Service Cord, 12V
30	Combination Cartridge Heater

Fig. 17-35. *Table which identifies parts in Fig. 17-34.*

separator, as shown in Fig. 17-36. The liquid lithium bromide (shown in black) then flows by gravity through the heat exchanger to the absorber where the lithium bromide absorbs the evaporated water. The strong solution (black dots) settles to the bottom of the absorber, and returns to the generator after passing through the heat exchanger. The pressure difference is maintained by the pressure head of the lithium bromide liquid.

The hot steam (red) in the separator rises up the condenser where it is condensed and turned into water. The condensed water flows by gravity through an orifice into the evaporator. The water evaporates at a low temperature due to the almost perfect vacuum and the steam (water vapor) formed is absorbed by the lithium bromide (black). Note that the absorber and the condenser are both cooled by water coils. The condenser water is then taken to a cooling tower where it is cooled. A typical cooling tower is shown in Fig.

17-37. The condensing pressure is about 50 to 60 millimeters of Hg (about 3 psia) and the evaporating pressure is 8 to 10 millimeters of Hg (about .5 psia).

17-24 Absorption Units for Air Conditioning

A growing application of absorption refrigerating systems is in comfort cooling air conditioning. The system has a unique feature in that the source of heat and the steam used to operate the absorption sys-

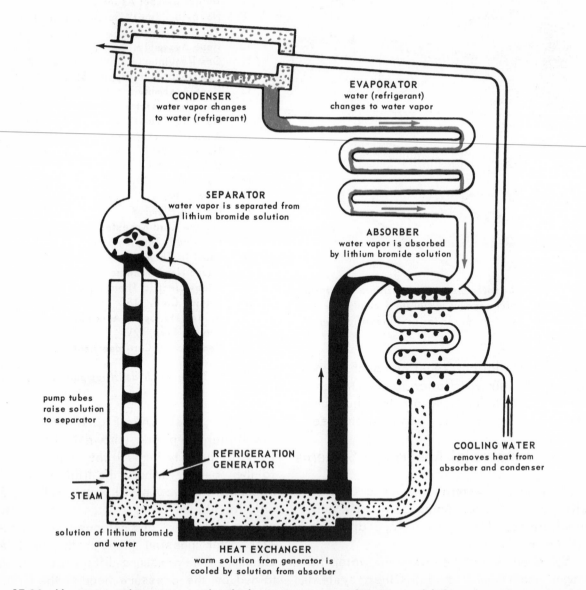

Fig. 17-36. Absorption refrigeration cycle which uses water as refrigerant and lithium bromide as absorbent.

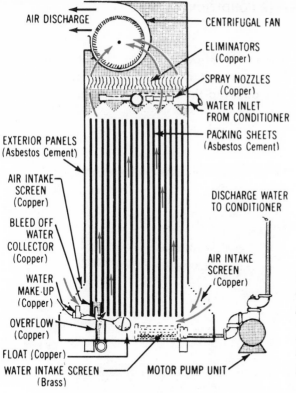

AIR DISCHARGE

CENTRIFUGAL FAN

ELIMINATORS (Copper)

SPRAY NOZZLES (Copper)

WATER INLET FROM CONDITIONER

EXTERIOR PANELS (Asbestos Cement)

PACKING SHEETS (Asbestos Cement)

AIR INTAKE SCREEN (Copper)

DISCHARGE WATER TO CONDITIONER

BLEED OFF WATER COLLECTOR (Copper)

AIR INTAKE SCREEN (Copper)

WATER MAKE·UP (Copper)

OVERFLOW (Copper)

FLOAT (Copper)

WATER INTAKE SCREEN (Brass)

MOTOR PUMP UNIT

tem during warm weather can also be used to provide some of the heating during cool weather.

A year round Servel air conditioner (both heating and cooling) is shown in Fig. 17-38. The heating section is on the left and the cooling mechanism is on the right, (1) steam line to heating coil, (2) steam condensate return pipe, (3) steam line to generator, (4) steam condensate return line from generator, (5) separator, (6) pipe to

Fig. 17-37. Cooling tower used to cool condenser and absorber cooling water. Tower evaporates about 15 percent of condenser water and in so doing cools rest of water down to wet bulb temperature of air. It consists of water sprays, asbestos sheets, overflow tubes, make up water float valve, water pump. Eliminator plates keep water from being drawn into fan. Air enters at bottom and leaves at top.

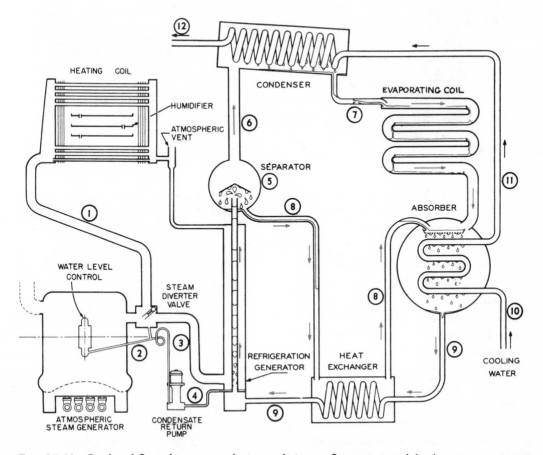

Fig. 17-38. Cycle of Servel year-round air conditioner. Steam is used for heating section and to heat generator of cooling system.

condenser, (7) reducing orifice, (8) pipe feeding lithium bromide to absorber (9) return pipe from absorber, (10) condenser

system is shown in Fig. 17-40. The condenser water first cools the absorber before passing through the condenser.

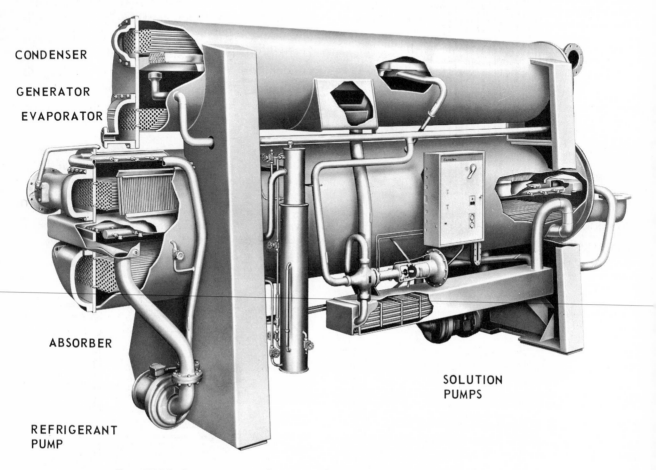

Fig. 17-39. Large capacity hermetic absorption system designed to cool water. (Carrier Air Conditioning Co.)

water into system (11) condenser water pipe from absorber to condenser, and (12) condenser water to cooling tower.

These systems are also used to produce chilled water. The chilled water in turn is used for a multitude of processes such as quenching baths, drinking water, cooling welding tips, etc.

A hermetic absorption system for chilling water is shown in Fig. 17-39. The top cylinder is the generator and condenser while the lower cylinder encloses the evaporator and the absorber. The cycle of this

17-25 Installing Absorption Refrigerator

Absorption types of refrigerators involve a number of installation requirements. A lead must be made from the gas line which will probably require the sanctioning of the company. Some city codes specify that the fuse plug opening in the refrigerant system must be vented to the outside to prevent any chance of discharging the refrigerant into the house.

The absorption unit must be carefully

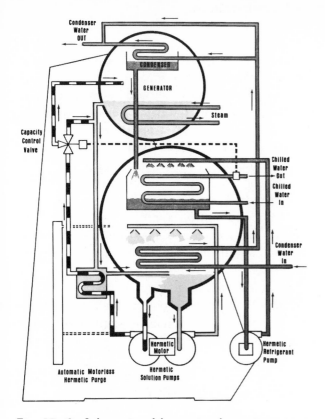

Fig. 17-40. Schematic of hermetic absorption system used to cool water. Chilled water is then used for air conditioning, or other cooling purposes.

leveled to operate correctly. The gas pressure must be carefully adjusted. A water column manometer is usually used. The domestic units have electric controls and solenoid valves. The electrical service must be carefully checked. The minimum flame and maximum flame adjustments must be made.

Be careful to provide enough air inlet and exhaust to provide for proper combustion, condenser, and absorber cooling.

17-26 Servicing Absorption Refrigerator

An important servicing operation for gas fired absorption refrigerator is to determine that the gas furnished the refrigerator is supplied in the correct amounts and at the proper pressure.

The amount of gas fed to the refrigerator may be checked by the size of the flame and may be adjusted by the use of the automatic temperature controlled gas valve which has a manual minimum and maximum flame adjustment. Always check gas pressure using water-filled manometer. The temperature control valve body has a manometer connection. The flue must be kept clean to allow good transfer of heat. Brushes should be used to clean the flue.

Fins on the ammonia condenser, and/or the absorber must be cleaned periodically to insure good heat removal from these surfaces.

If a service call is received which reports the refrigerator is too cold, the following steps should be followed:

1. First, check the temperature control dial. It may be set too cold.
2. The temperature of the evaporator unit may be lower than that indicated by the temperature control dial setting. A time temperature graph should be taken of such a unit.

Perhaps the most common service call will be "little or no refrigeration." Following are some possible causes of this trouble:

1. Overloaded cabinet.
2. Improper condensing temperatures.
3. Little or no heating of the generating unit.
4. The gas supply has been turned off or restricted. If the line has become clogged, resulting in a small consumption of gas, there is naturally little or no refrigeration. This trouble may be traced by checking the pressures at the burner.
5. Restricted or dirty gas flue.

If the condenser or absorber are dirt and lint covered, poor refrigeration will result, due to high temperature of these two parts.

After a certain period of use the flue of the generator may become coated with a soot deposit, preventing a rapid transfer of heat from the gas flame to the generator body. This soot deposit should be removed periodically (every 1-2 months) to insure proper refrigeration and to reduce gas consumption.

When scraping the flue of a generator or when removing the soot from any surface of the generator, considerable care should be taken to prevent injury to the surface. Always put papers or a cloth under the refrigerator when cleaning flues. The gas fired and kerosene fired refrigerators are equipped with flues to direct the hot gases around and away from the generating units. Occasionally, these flues may be restricted by placing the refrigerator too close to the wall, by placing objects over the opening, or by having some obstruction fall into it. These flues must be kept clean to insure proper functioning of the refrigerator.

A Servel unit which has not been used for a period of time may refuse to freeze when started. To remedy this trouble, invert the refrigerator for approximately 1/2 to 1 hour. Right the refrigerator and it should be ready for operation. Some servicemen prefer to remove the unit and invert the unit only. This permits cleaning the unit while it is out of the cabinet.

17-27 Review of Safety

The refrigerant most commonly used in the small absorption refrigerating units is ammonia. This refrigerant is pungent and tends to restrict breathing. It is toxic. It is injurious to the skin and eyes. You should be careful to avoid puncturing the system or creating too high a pressure in the system or a leak may result.

CAUTION: NEVER CUT OR DRILL INTO AN ABSORPTION REFRIGERATING MECHANISM. THE HIGH PRESSURE AMMONIA SOLUTIONS ARE DANGEROUS AND MAY CAUSE BLINDNESS IF THE FLUID GETS INTO YOUR EYES.

Many of the absorption units are heated with LP gas or natural gas. The gas piping system must be leakproof. Always use soapsuds to check for leaks. NEVER USE AN OPEN FLAME SUCH AS A MATCH, or an explosion may occur. The burner flues should be cleaned periodically or poor flame action may occur.

The flame safety should be checked. To do this, smother the pilot flame and check to determine if the safety valve closes.

The condenser duct system and the condenser should be cleaned at least each six months or excessive condenser pressures may result.

Most absorption systems use electrical current as well as a fuel gas. Usual precaution should be used in handling these circuits.

It is advisable to ground these refrigerators to eliminate any danger of receiving a shock if a circuit should become grounded to the frame of a cabinet or part of the mechanism.

17-28 Test Your Knowledge – Chapter 17

1. Who discovered the absorption principle?
2. What localities would probably need kerosene-fired intermittent absorption refrigerators?
3. Name three substances which have been used in absorption refrigerators to absorb refrigerant gas.
4. In absorption refrigerators, does the liquefication of the refrigerant depend upon compression?
5. Why is the ammonia and water combination popular?
6. What purpose does the hydrogen serve in the Electrolux?
7. Why is the storage cylinder or receiver in the Superfex refrigerator insulated?
8. Why are the mechanisms provided with a fuse plug?
9. How can burning more gas in the Servel cycle produce more cold?
10. What three fluids are used inside a Servel mechanism?
11. What precautions must be taken with kerosene in intermittent units?

12. How is the cabinet temperature adjusted in the Servel refrigerator?
13. Why was the liquid receiver in the Trukold placed above the evaporator coil?
14. What was the purpose of the tank on the top of the Superfex refrigerator?
15. Why must the absorption unit be leveled?
16. Is kerosene sometimes used as the fuel for continuous systems?
17. How is the gas pressure in a piped gas system measured?
18. Why is a pressure regulator not required in the base of the cabinet for LP systems?
19. How is the temperature regulated in a piped gas continuous system?
20. Why doesn't the flame go out when the cabinet is cold enough on the continuous piped gas systems?

21. What are two basic causes for insufficient refrigeration in a continuous system?
22. How are some of Servel units automatically defrosted?
23. What is the purpose of lithium bromide in an absorption system?
24. Do any absorption systems operate under a vacuum?
25. Are solenoid valves used in domestic absorption units? If so, how?
26. What causes the liquid refrigerant to flow in a domestic absorption system?
27. What does the fan in the base of some absorption refrigerators do?
28. Does the generator percolate a weak solution or a strong solution?
29. Can weak solution be used to defrost the freezer evaporator?
30. Is hot ammonia vapor used to defrost the freezer evaporator?

Fig. 18-1. A 9 cu. ft. thermoelectric refrigerator. Note freezer compartment in upper left-hand corner. (Norge Div., Borg-Warner Corp.)

Chapter 18

SPECIAL REFRIGERATION DEVICES AND APPLICATIONS

This chapter covers briefly, special refrigeration devices and systems including:

1. Thermoelectric heating and cooling. A process in which electrical energy is used as a carrier instead of a refrigerant.
2. Use of an expendable refrigerant, such as liquid nitrogen or liquid carbon dioxide.
3. Cryogenics, a branch of physics relating to the production of extremely cold temperatures (range of –250 F. to 0 F.).
4. Vortex tube cooling and heating. A system which uses compressed air as its source of energy.

5. Steam jet cooling. A system which makes use of the principle that water under a partial vacuum boils at a relatively low temperature.
6. Air-cycle conditioning. Air becomes a refrigerant and is used for cooling.
7. Free-piston compressor. Unit which uses an internal combustion unit for power, and a piston refrigeration compressor, in a single unit.

18-1 Thermoelectric Processes

The thermoelectric process is one of the latest advances in the field of refrigeration. It is a means of removing heat from one area and depositing it in another area using electrical energy as a carrier instead of a refrigerant. Its major growth has been in the area of portable refrigerators and luxury type stationary domestic refrigerators, water coolers, and in the cooling of scientific apparatus used in space explorations. A typical thermoelectrc refrigerator is shown in Fig. 18-1.

In the thermoelectric process cooling is produced without the use of conventional equipment necessary in a vapor system (compressor, evaporator, condenser, and refrigerant, etc.). Outstanding features of the thermoelectric unit are: it has no moving parts, is silent, compact, and requires little service.

Since electric current is the only requirement and there are no refrigerant lines, cooling in several different locations can be provided by one source of power through the use of several thermoelectric modules. This unit can operate in any position or even when the unit is being transported.

The overall size occupied by the refrigeration unit to provide a given amount of cooling is far less than that which is required for conventional refrigerators of equal cooling capacity.

Because electrical flow can be precisely controlled with solid state controls, thermoelectric refrigeration provides extremely accurate and narrow tolerance temperatures. Some systems use vapor systems for absorbing major cooling load and thermoelectric units to produce the more accurate temperatures and changes in temperatures in various parts of a fixture.

18-2 History of Thermoelectric Refrigeration

The discovery of the basic principle of thermoelectric refrigeration can be traced to a German physicist, Thomas J. Seebeck. In 1820 Seebeck made the discovery that

if a closed circuit was made through two different metals in contact with each other an electrical current flowed in the circuit when heat was applied at one of the junctions, Fig. 18-2.

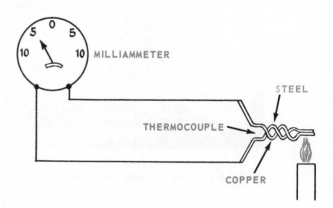

Fig. 18-2. The principle of thermoelectric refrigeration is shown in Seebeck effect. Heat is applied to junction of copper and steel wire (A) thermocouple; and electrical energy is formed, as shown by the milliammeter (B).

This should have suggested to Seebeck that a current was flowing through the circuit; however, he did not interpret it in this manner and his discovery laid dormant for many years.

In 1834 Jean Peltier discovered that when a direct current passed through a junction of two dissimilar metals, as shown in Fig. 18-3, the junction became either hot or cold. Peltier, like Seebeck, failed to see the significance of this find in relationship to thermoelectric cooling.

In 1838 Emil Lenz clearly showed the importance of both Peltier's and Seebeck's discovery by placing a drop of water on a junction of two dissimilar metals and passing a direct current through the circuit. When the current flowed in one direction, the water froze. When he reversed the directional flow of electricity through the metals, the ice melted. However, Lenz, like his predecessors, failed to realize the significance of his findings and the knowledge remained dormant for over 100 years, mainly due to the unavailability of materials (semiconductors) which could produce wide temperature differences.

It was not until the early 30's that available materials (semiconductors) were developed that made the application of See-

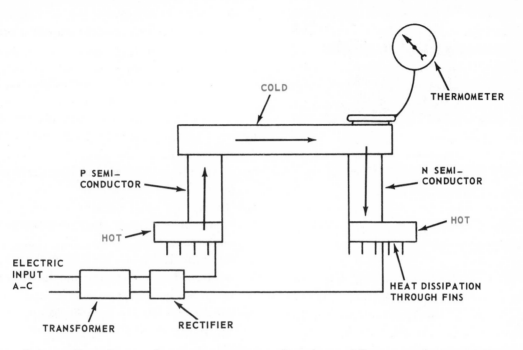

Fig. 18-3. Peltier effect shows a direct current passing through two different metals, causing junctions to become either hot or cold.

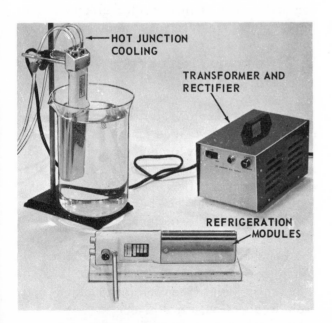

Fig. 18-4. Thermoelectric immersion cooler, used in laboratory work for cooling small beakers or tanks of chemicals. Note size of overall unit in foreground. (Whirlpool Corp.)

beck's and Peltier's discovery applicable to spot cooling. In the period of the 30's and 40's thermoelectric progress was limited mostly to scientific laboratories. In the early 60's many companies began an intense drive to manufacture refrigeration equipment based on the thermoelectric principle. In the period 1960 through the present, we have seen the production of full-size refrigerators, water coolers, portable coolers and spot appliance coolers for both domestic and industrial use. Fig. 18-4 shows an experimental immersion cooler which may be used to either cool or heat a liquid.

It should be noted that the direction of flow of the DC current determines which junction will be cooled and which junction will be warmed. Reversing the flow of current will reverse the cold and warm junctions.

Fig. 18-5. Portable two cubic foot refrigerator using thermoelectric principle.

18-3 Basic System of Thermoelectric Refrigeration

The basic principles previously outlined are utilized to their fullest extent in the design of a thermoelectric cooling mechanism, as shown in Fig. 18-5.

As was seen in the Peltier effect, when a direct current is passed through two dissimilar semiconductors (P and N), heat is liberated at one junction (hot) and heat is absorbed at the other junction (cold). Par. 18-6 describes semiconductor materials and their properties.

As the electrons pass from P to N they absorb energy making the upper surface cold. As the electrons pass from P to N the energy which has been absorbed at the

cold plate is released making this surface hot. This is an example of a single thermoelectric couple which alone has very little cooling capacity.

In order to achieve a larger cooling capacity it is necessary to connect a number of thermoelectric couples in series, as shown in Fig. 18-6. When this is done, thermoelements are imbedded in the walls of the unit between an insulating material and the cold plate and are separated from the thermoelectric couples by the use of electrical insulation. By reversing the flow of current, the cold and hot junctions will be reversed and heat will be produced in the cavity which was formerly cooled. This reversal of electron flow enables the unit to become a heat pump. Fig. 18-7 shows a unit installed in a refrigerator wall.

It should be noted that the letters P and N as used in thermoelectric applications as used here DO NOT refer to current polarity positive (+) and negative (-), but rather refer to the characteristics of the semiconductor materials which are also designated as positive or negative depending on how the semiconductor electrons behave under the influence of current flow.

18-4 Removing Heat From Hot Junction

The temperature difference which is obtained at the various junctions is dependent on properties of the materials used, number of thermocouples used, and the rate of current flow. To obtain the best temperature difference between the hot and cold junctions, the materials must have a low thermal conductivity and high electrical conductivity. One semiconductor metal which meets these requirements is bismuth-telluride. (See Semiconductors and their Properties, Par. 18-6.)

As the characteristics of the material are known, it is possible to determine the temperature difference between the junctions. Because of the great quantity of heat

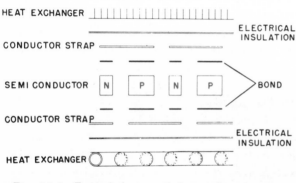

Fig. 18-6. Exploded view of thermoelectric unit. (Carrier Air Conditioning Co.)

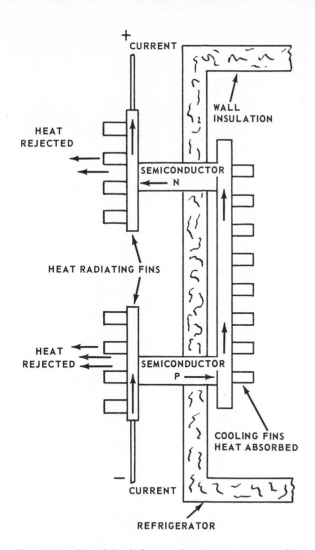

Fig. 18-7. Simplified thermoelectric system used in cooling small areas. Note flow of current to produce cooling within box.

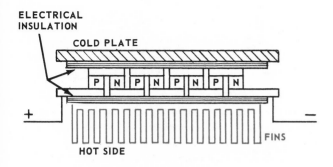

Fig. 18-8. Assembled thermoelectric module. Note use of fins (hot side) to speed up removal of heat which has been absorbed from surface of cold plate.

collected at the hot junction, it is often necessary to provide a series of fins, a tan, or water cooling to the hot side to re-

Fig. 18-9. Thermoelectric cooling unit using fan to remove heat from hot junction. Unit is designed for cooling low pumping loads to −50 C. (−58 F.) from an ambient of 24 C. (75 F.). (Westinghouse Electric Corp., Air Conditioning-Sturtevant Div.)

move the absorbed heat, as shown in Fig. 18-8.

The absorption of heat at the hot junction will help produce a lower temperature at the cold junction.

Fig. 18-9 shows a thermoelectric unit using a fan to remove heat from the hot junction.

18-5 Thermoelectric Compared to a Compressor System

The thermoelectric refrigeration system may be compared to a vapor compression system, to obtain a better understanding of the principle of operation of the thermoelectric system. Fig. 18-10 shows a thermoelectric system used to cool air. It is complete with blowers and water-cooled hot junction (heat sink).

The main objective in both vapor and thermoelectric cooling is to provide a means of obtaining a change in energy level at the hot and cold junctions of the system. In the thermoelectric system this is accomplished through the use of two different materials and a direct current. If the P and N materials were the same, the energy level would be the same and there would be no energy change. There would, therefore, be no cooling or heating. Fig. 18-11 shows the similarities between the vapor system and the thermoelectric. Note

that there is considerable similarity between the two systems. In each, heat is absorbed at one place and released at another.

In the vapor system the refrigerant
control valve alters the pressure and enthalpy of the refrigerant allowing it to ab-

18-6 Semiconductors

Ordinary metals which are good conductors of electricity are poor insulators.
The P and N type materials used in the
thermoelectric refrigerating systems are
known as semiconductors of materials.

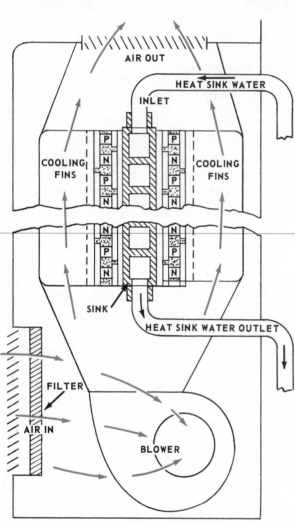

Fig. 18-10. *Thermoelectric unit using water as the heat removing medium instead of air. Unit is being used to cool air.*

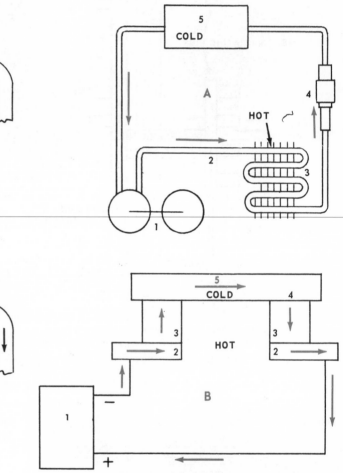

Fig. 18-11. *A—Vapor compression system using: 1—Compressor. 2—Refrigerant. 3—Condenser. 4—Refrigerant control. 5—Evaporator. B—Thermoelectric unit using: 1—Power supply. 2—Hot junction. 3—Semiconductors. 4—Cold junction. 5—Electron flow.*

sorb heat from the evaporator (cold junction) and eject it through the condenser (hot
junction). Without the use of the refrigerant control the refrigerant would be at a
constant pressure throughout the system,
and no heat pumping would occur.

These materials have the qualities of both
ordinary metals and insulators. The ideal
semiconductor is a material which is a
poor conductor of heat because heat is absorbed at one end and rejected at the other
end. However, the semiconductor must al-

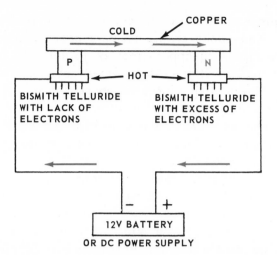

Fig. 18-12. Thermoelectric unit using bismuth-tellu-ride as semiconductors. The N pole has been "doped" to provide an excess of electrons.

temperature at the opposite end. This is due to the increase of kinetic energy of the electrons at the hot end and a consequent flow of electrons toward the cold end. The movement of the electrons also transports heat toward the cold end. Because the heat laden electrons also carry an electrical charge the flow of heat will be accompanied by a flow of electrons. This is the basis of the operation in a thermoelectric unit. The electron flow transports both heat and electricity, it is therefore possible to transport heat directly through electric current.

18-7 Operation of Thermoelectric Units

Due to the assembly of electrons in the structure of the molecule, positive (P) and negative (N), current passing through the P junction of the thermoelectric module into the N material requires energy. The electrons, therefore, pick up this energy and leaves the interface material cooler (removes heat)

When this occurs in a thermoelectric module the cold side removes heat from the section to be cooled and releases its heat in the hot side of the module, as shown in Fig. 18-13.

When a battery or electrical current DC is applied with the negative terminal attached to the P type material (lack of electrons) the copper plate will become cold and absorb heat from the atmosphere. (See basic system of thermoelectric refrigeration.) Electron flow is from the battery through P where there is lack of electrons and will pick up heat on top cold surface and reject this heat at the bottom plates.

18-8 Power Supply and Transformer

As has been indicated, the thermoelectric process is dependent on a direct current supply as opposed to the alternating

so be a good conductor of electricity in order to minimize the voltage drop. It must also have a high coefficient of voltage temperature relationship.

A favorable material for semiconductors is bismuth-telluride. This bismuth-telluride N type material is treated ("doped") in such a manner that it will have an excess of electrons. The P type semiconductor is treated ("doped") to have a structure which is not completely filled with electrons. Fig. 18-12 shows a circuit using these treated semiconductors. The two materials are connected by a good electrical conductor material such as copper.

The terminals P and N contain a certain distribution of electrons which are free to move in either direction. Movement of the electrons is dependent on either temperature or electrical potential difference. (See Seebeck effect.)

The cooling effect of a semiconductor comes from energy absorption by the electrons as they flow from the P material into the N material. If the electron flow is reversed, the electrons release heat as the flow from the N material into the P material.

An example of this is to heat a piece of metal at one end and notice the increase in

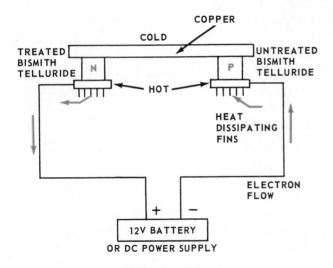

Fig. 18-13. Basic thermoelectric unit. The N pole which has been doped will allow electrons to flow through it at different rate of speed than P pole.

densers are used, as shown in Fig. 18-14.

The choke on the power supply reduces the ripple to approximately 10 percent. In normal unfiltered full wave rectification the amount of ripple is approximately 48 percent. A comparison of the filtered and unfiltered wave is shown in Fig. 18-15. The amount of ripple flow will determine the cooling capacity of the module.

The P type material is connected to the negative side of the current flow and has a great capacity for electron flow (because of its physical structure). If there is a large ripple in the direct current, there will be a reduction in cooling. A reduction in the cooling rate can vary from 2 percent of capacity when the ripple is 10 to 75 percent of capacity when the ripple is at 48 percent (or unfiltered).

18-9 Voltage and Amperage Range

A low voltage is necessary because it has been found that if a voltage level of above 20V is maintained or required, the insulation in the thermocouple must be quite heavy. The heat transfer then becomes a problem because the base of the power pack in most cases is used as a heat sink or dissipater. Therefore (as of 1968) it is undesirable to operate above 20V in most systems.

Most direct current loads for thermo-

current (AC) which is normally found in most buildings. The direct current should have a high current, low voltage, and a low ripple (as steady a flow as possible).

The input for most domestic appliances is usually 120V single-phase, which is a standard line voltage. To produce low voltage and high current a step down transformer and two silicon diodes are used to convert the AC to DC.

Direct rectification of single-phase current usually results in a high ripple. To smooth out this ripple in the DC to the allowable 5-10 percent, chokes and/or con-

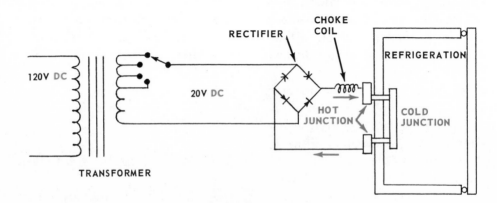

Fig. 18-14. To provide necessary low voltage DC current, transformer and diodes are used which will produce low ripple direct current. Note choke which reduces ripple to allowable 5-10 percent. Note hot and cold junctions.

couples are in the 30 ampere range because of two factors. The first is basically economics. Most automotive type recti-

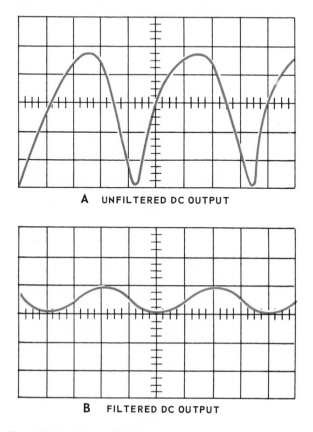

A   UNFILTERED DC OUTPUT

B   FILTERED DC OUTPUT

Fig. 18-15. Wave length as shown on oscilloscope recordings: A—Unfiltered DC output. B—Filtered DC output through use of choke or condenser.

Fig. 18-16. External view of power supply. This may be used with separate thermocouples for spot cooling. (Joseph Kaye and Co., Inc.)

fiers are in the 30 ampere range, consequently rectifiers in this category are mass produced and are obtainable at a fraction of the cost which would be necessary for rectifiers above 30 amperes.

The second factor is that a higher current rating would require a larger heat sink than is needed with a 30 ampere rectifier and transformer. A manufacturer would need two heat sinks or more which would increase the cost and the size of the power pack.

18-10 Selection of Power Supply

Both the voltage applied to the thermocouples and the maximum current must be selected for the specific thermocouple. These will depend on the cooling capacity required. A small spot cooling unit would use approximately 4V DC while a 3/4 ton thermoelectric air conditioner unit would require approximately 100V. A large system of approximately 200 tons capacity would require several thousand volts. Therefore, it is normal to use several parallel circuits on a large system with each circuit operating at a designated voltage.

An example of a commercial power supply used with separate thermocouples for spot cooling or incorporated into a thermoelectric cooling unit is shown in Fig. 18-16. The wiring diagram is shown in Fig. 18-17.

18-11 Thermomodule Construction

Fig. 18-18 shows a thermoelectric module which is soldered to a thin metallized ceramic plate on both sides of the heat exchange surfaces. It is a 31-couple type module which measures 1.17 in. sq. x .22 in. thick, and is capable of producing 70 C. (126 F.) temperature differential heat pumping of 68 Btu/per hour using a current of 9 amperes. The construction of a thermoelectric module containing 20

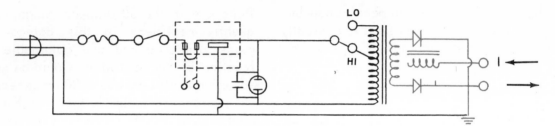

Fig. 18-17. *Wiring diagram of DC power supply.*

couples is shown in Fig. 18-19. In normal installation the thermocouple is soldered to a cold plate and a heat sink. The cooling ability is rated as the temperature difference between the cold plate of the heat sink

Fig. 18-18. *A 31-couple type module. Note small size in comparison to the coin (quarter). (Materials Electronic Products Corp.)*

and the hot plate. A heat sink temperature of 27 C. (48.6 F.) is standard. Fig. 18-20 shows a method of measuring the temperature difference of a couple.

18-12 Servicing of Thermoelectric Units

The exterior appearance and the cabinet construction of the thermoelectric refrigerator unit differs but little from the cabinets described in Chapter 11.

The servicing of thermoelectric refrigeration mechanisms is dependent on the method of assembly of the unit. If the part or parts which require replacement are brazed or welded together or is part of the thermomodule, it is considered good practice to remove the unit and take it to the shop for servicing.

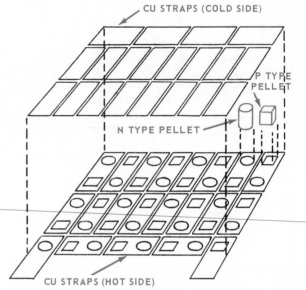

Fig. 18-19. *Construction of thermoelectric module which contains 20 couples (one P and one N pellet per couple). Copper (Cu) connecting straps are used. (Westinghouse Electric Corp., Air Conditioning-- Sturtevant Div.)*

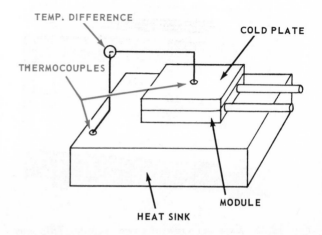

Fig. 18-20. *Thermoelectric module with thermocouples used to measure temperature differences.*

Servicing of thermoelectric refrigerators may be divided into two major divisions:

A. Cabinet repairs.
B. Thermoelectric unit repairs.

18-13 Cabinet Servicing

External servicing means service operations which are concerned with the repair and maintenance of the refrigerator cabinet which do not involve direct servicing of the thermoelectric unit.

The serviceman will find some of the more common external complaints to be the same as those of compression refrigeration units.

A. Noise (rattles).
B. Cabinet hardware (replacement and adjustment).
C. Cabinet finish.
D. Gasket repairs.
E. Condensation on the inside or outside walls.
F. Interior light and switch.
G. Thermostat.

Most of these service operations are similar to those described in Chapter 12.

18-14 Servicing Thermoelectric Systems

Servicing the thermoelectric unit consists mainly of checking the following:

1. Power pack electrical system.
2. Thermoelectric unit electrical system.

To successfully check a thermoelectric refrigeration system it is recommended that the serviceman have an ohmmeter and an AC, DC voltmeter which will check the range of from 4 to 125V. Or, a milliohmmeter may be used.

A combination volt-ohm-milliammeter, as described in Chapters 7, 8, and 12, will simplify servicing. Two jumper wires with alligator clips on both ends can be used to good advantage.

Prior to checking the system, locate the wiring diagram for the unit, Fig. 18-21. This is usually found on the service plate at the rear of the unit. If it is not there, obtain a wiring diagram of the unit from the manufacturer.

Before checking the internal power supply unit and wiring make certain the malfunction is not due to: blown power supply fuse, house fuse, faulty power supply cord, selector switch, thermostat, etc. It is also desirable to check all wiring connections to make certain there is no break (open circuit). An ohmmeter should be used to check for continuity. The use of lights or ammeters may allow enough voltage or current to ruin the modules, the diodes, and/or the transistors.

If after all the above external operations have been checked, and there is still no cooling, check the internal power supply system (transformers, etc.) and determine if the refrigerator is receiving proper AC input and DC output. The use of an AC and then a DC voltmeter across the terminals with power on is a common check.

18-15 Checking Diodes and Chokes

If, after checking the transformer, there is still a malfunction, it is recommended that the diode be checked with the use of an ohmmeter. The leads must be disconnected for this check. It is important also, that the power supply be disconnected. A diode will allow current flow in one direction (0 ohms) and not in the other direction (infinite ohms).

To test the diode, the positive lead from the ohmmeter is connected to one of the diode terminals and the negative lead to the heat sink. If the diode is open, no current will flow, and the ohms reading will be infinite. If the diode is good, there will be a 0 ohms reading.

The ohmmeter leads are then reversed, and because current should pass through a good diode in one direction only, the nee-

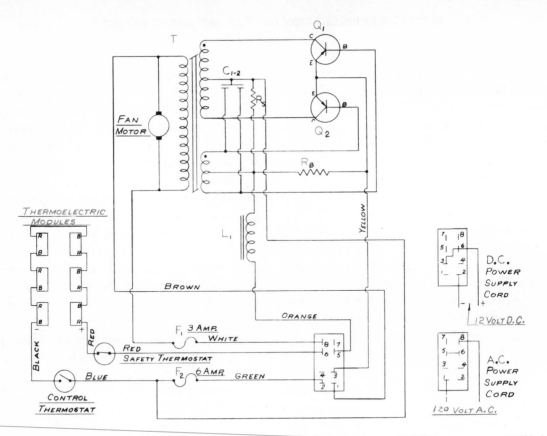

Fig. 18-21. Wiring diagram of thermoelectric cooling unit which operates on 12V DC system, or 120V AC. T—Transformer. Q—Transistors. L—Choke coil. F—Fuse. R—Resistance. (Whirlpool Corp.)

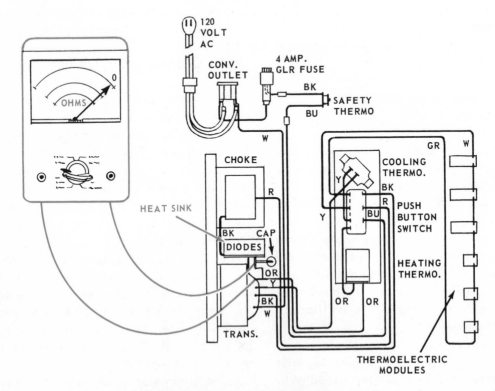

Fig. 18-22. Ohmmeter being used to check diodes on thermoelectric unit. One lead is connected to one of the diode terminals and one to heat sink for ground.

dle should show an infinite reading. If the diode is shorted, it will allow current to flow through in both directions and the needle will have a zero ohms reading on the resistance scale when the meter leads are connected either way.

Fig. 18-23. Mobile thermoelectric unit which can be used as refrigerator or as warming oven simply by reversing flow of electrons.

If the diode is open, the meter will read infinite ohms both ways.

If the diode is good, the ohmmeter will read 0 ohms with one lead hooked-up and infinite ohms with the ohmmeter leads reversed. Fig. 18-22 shows an ohmmeter being used to check a diode.

The choke coil may be checked using the same procedure. Disconnect the choke coil leads to eliminate the possibility of other parts of the system furnishing an electrical path and therefore causing false reading. An open circuit in the choke will indicate a need for replacement. A grounded or shorted coil will also require replacing the choke coil.

Transistors, if used, are checked by a trial replacement procedure.

Capacitors may be checked as described in Chapters 7 and 8.

18-16 Checking Modules

If after all of the above operations have been performed and the trouble has not been found, the serviceman may conclude that the problem lies in the thermomodule.

The thermomodule may develop unwanted resistance, if moisture gets through the seal of the module and deteriorates the insulation. Check the resistance of the thermomodule with a milliohmmeter (the normal resistance could be less than one ohm and would not show with the use of an ohmmeter).

If the trouble is diagnosed as being in the thermomodule, it should be removed and replaced. The removed thermomodule should be sent to the factory for servicing.

18-17 Thermoelectric Applications

Thermoelectric cooling is used for refrigeration equipment for domestic use, and spot cooling in industrial, military, medical and space flight applications.

An example of a thermoelectric domestic refrigerator is shown in Fig. 18-23. This unit has a cabinet capacity of 2 cu. ft. and can maintain temperatures in the range of 40 F. in the refrigerator cabinet. It can produce two trays of ice cubes. The unit operates on normal line voltage of 120V 60 cycles AC. A secondary voltage of 16V 60 cycle AC is supplied from the transformer to the rectifier diodes, and through the choke which delivers 5.3V DC to the cooling module.

This cabinet can also function as a warming oven by reversing flow of electricity through the thermoelectric modules by the use of a heating thermostat. Fig. 18-24 shows a wiring diagram for the unit shown in Fig. 18-23. When the cabinet is being used as a warming oven, the transformer produces 13V at 60 cycle AC to the diode and choke, which in turn produces· 4.3V DC to the thermoelectric module.

Another example of a thermoelectric

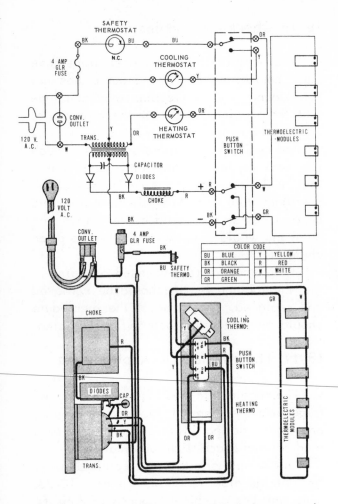

Fig. 18-24. Wiring diagram for thermoelectric cooling-heating unit. Note individual heating and cooling thermostats. (Whirlpool Corp.)

Fig. 18-25. Small portable thermoelectric refrigerator which operates from normal 120V household current or from a 12V battery.

application is shown in Fig. 18-25. This is a compact lightweight portable refrigerator. It is insulated with polyurethane foam insulation and has a storage capacity of .22 cu. ft. The power source may be 110V AC or a 12V DC automobile or boat battery.

Thermoelectric units have been used for ice cube makers; thermoelectric-modules of 3.5 tons capacity (42,000 Btu per hour) have been placed into a one cubic foot space.

Thermoelectric cooling has been successfully adapted to large cooling applications for the government. However, present application has been limited mostly to sea-going vessels where heat transfer does not present a problem. Fig. 18-26 shows a unit which supplies approximately 8 tons of refrigeration to a frozen food storeroom. The unit consists of water heat exchangers (external), thermoelectric heat pump modules and air heat exchangers. The panels are mounted in a support frame so the air heat exchangers face each other and form the chilled air duct. The entire refrigeration system is external to the storage room which provides increased storage volume within the room plus ease of installation and maintenance of the system.

Fig. 18-27, shows one panel removed from the unit for maintenance. The finned surfaces are the air heat exchangers of the opposing panel. Each of the four air heat exchangers on each panel can be removed to provide access to the nine heat pump modules located beneath. Fig. 18-28 shows the air heat exchanger and modules removed. The "holes" appearing on the exposed water heat exchanger surface hold the relay type contacts which provide electrical connections for each heat pump module.

The electrical circuitry of the entire system is quite simple. Each complete panel assembly consists of four separate series circuits (one per each air heat exchanger). These are connected in series at a junction box located on the end of the mounting frame. Each panel circuit (10 panels for the larger unit) is connected to a parallel branch of a laboratory type power supply. The power supply shown in Fig. 18-26 is used only for testing and does not represent a shipboard design.

18-18 Expendable Refrigerant Cycles

The use of liquid nitrogen and liquid carbon dioxide for cooling transportation vehicles (truck bodies) is rapidly increasing. The basic system, using a liquid non-toxic low temperature refrigerant as a cooling medium, is the same as any vapor

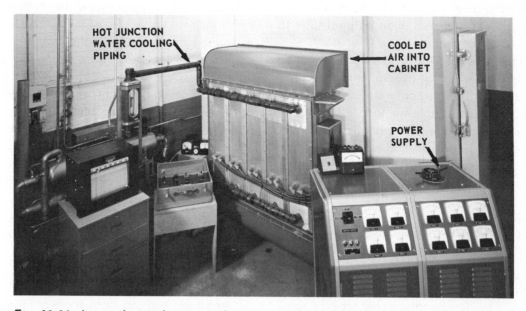

Fig. 18-26. Large thermoelectric cooling unit used in nuclear submarine which will provide 8 tons of refrigeration effect. (Whirlpool Corp.)

Fig. 18-27. Panel being removed from the thermoelectric unit in preparation for servicing operations. (Whirlpool Corp.)

Fig. 18-28. This photo shows one air heat exchanger removed to provide access to heat pump modules.

system without using a condensing unit. The cost of the liquid being rather low, it can be used as a refrigerant and then released to the atmosphere. This system is sometimes called chemical refrigeration. Expendable refrigerant systems are also used in the cooling of railroad cars that are used to transport perishable items.

Two basic systems are:

1. Passing of liquid nitrogen through a cold plate and then releasing it to the atmosphere.
2. The use of liquid nitrogen sprayed through a spray header into the compartment to be cooled.

The most popular expendable refrigerant is liquid nitrogen. Carbon dioxide has also been used to a limited extent.

18-19 Cold Plate Cooling System

In this system the liquid refrigerant is pumped into an insulated container in the front of the cargo vehicle, as shown in Fig. 18-29. Each unit has a temperature control which allows for a setting of -20 F. to 60 F. The temperature control is con-

Fig. 18-29. Liquid nitrogen storage cylinders located inside refrigerated truck body. Two nitrogen cylinders are connected by manifold to regulators, temperature control solenoid valves and to cold plates.
(National Cylinder Gas, Div. Chemetron Corp.)

nected to a temperature sensor much the same as a standard thermostatic motor control. As the temperature rises, the switch operating the control valve is opened and liquid refrigerant flows into the vaporizers or cold plates. As the liquid refrigerant passes through the plates it vaporizes. The vapor is forced through the plates by the difference in pressure. When the desired temperature is reached, the refrigerant valve is closed. The used or expended vapor leaves the cargo space at approximately the same temperature as vapor in the cargo area. With this method the interior of the vehicle has no refrigerant vapor mixed with the air in the truck body. A form of this type of cooling is shown in Fig. 18-30. The expendable refrigerant passes between the inside wall and the insulation. Temperatures of -20 F. to 60 F. are possible without any of the refrigerant entering the storage port of the truck or vehicle space being refrigerated.

18-20 Spray Cooling System

Another way to cool transportation vehicles is through the use of liquid nitrogen sprayed into the refrigerated space. The nitrogen turns into vapor inside the cargo area. This method is primarily designed for truck units which are converted to liquid nitrogen cooling after construction. The cold plate method is commonly used for original construction. The liquid-vapor spray method has many of the same parts as the cold plate method--liquid containers, control box, fill box, etc. See Fig. 18-31. However, it also contains additional devices not necessary in the plate method, such as spray headers, emergency switches, safety vents, etc.

The system operates as follows: liquid nitrogen is pumped into the storage cylinders by way of the fill box. Some units have two or more containers, primary container, and secondary container which are filled in series. As the first or pri-

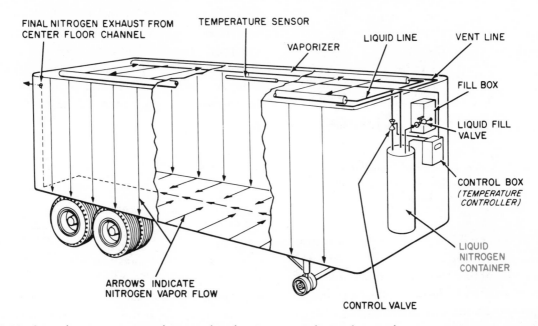

Fig. 18-30. *Liquid nitrogen, carried in insulated container at front of van, changes to gaseous state in vaporizers and passes through channels in insulation in ceiling, walls, and floor. It exhausts through vents in floor.*

mary container is filled, liquid nitrogen will overflow into the second container and so forth. When the containers are filled and the cargo space is loaded, the desired

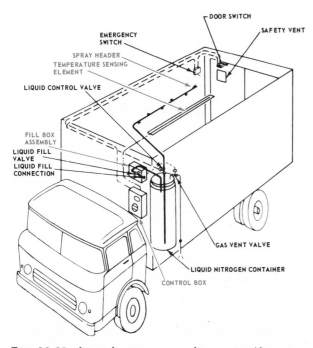

Fig. 18-31. *Liquid nitrogen cooling unit. Note temperature sensing element connected to control box.*

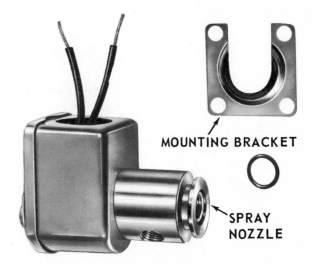

Fig. 18-32. *Solenoid valve used to control liquid nitrogen flow in spray type expendable system. (Automatic Switch Co.)*

temperature is selected at the main control. This temperature sensing device anticipates temperature changes in the cargo space. When the cargo temperature rises above the setting, the temperature controller opens the liquid line solenoid valve as shown in Fig. 18-32. This allows liquid nitrogen to enter into the spray header

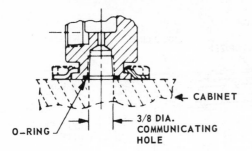

Fig. 18-33. Cut-away drawing of installation of sole-noid valve mounted directly to mobile vehicle. (Automatic Switch Co.)

rated pipe usually mounted along the center of the cargo compartment ceiling. The nitrogen tanks are equipped with safety valves which will vent nitrogen to the outside of the trailer if the pressure in the containers rises above 22 psig. All units

where it becomes a vapor and maintains the desired temperature. The solenoid valve is mounted directly on the truck body as shown in Fig. 18-33. Both remote and direct installations are shown in Fig. 18-34.

The spray header system is a perfo-

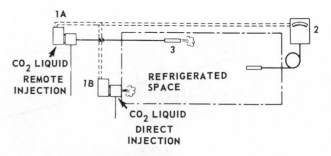

Fig. 18-34. Diagram showing a CO_2 liquid remote injection (1A) and a CO_2 direct injection installation (1B). 2—Thermostat. 3—Remote injector tube.

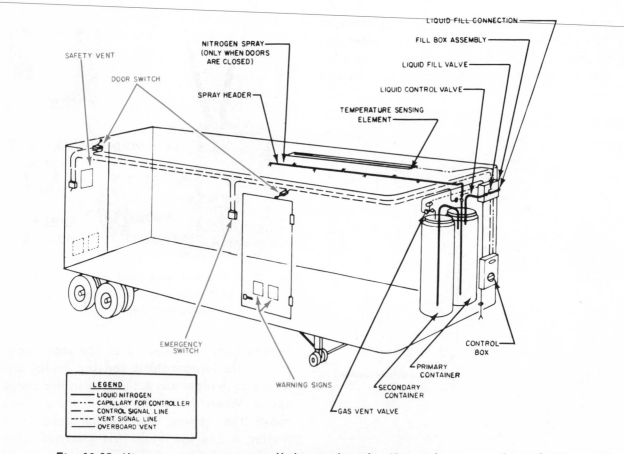

Fig. 18-35. Nitrogen spray system installed in truck trailer. Note safety vent and switches. (National Cylinder Gas, Div. Chemetron Corp.)

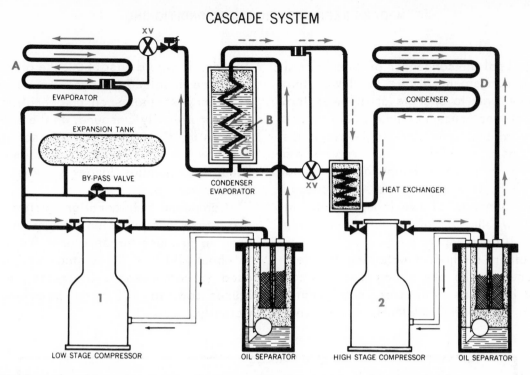

Fig. 18-36. Cascade refrigerating system. Condenser (B) of system 1, is being cooled by evaporator coil (C) of system 2. This arrangement provides ultralow temperature in evaporator (A). D. Condenser of system 2; XV. refrigerant controls. Note use of oil separators to minimize oil in circulating refrigerant. (Temprite Products Corp.)

are equipped with a safety vent which allows gas to exhaust to the atmosphere when the inside carge space pressure increases above atmospheric. This safety vent is a spring-loaded device, which will close when the excess pressure has been expelled. In addition, each door has a safety switch connected to it which will automatically shut down the unit when a door is opened and before one can enter. You should always read the warning signs on refrigerated vehicles before entering them. Fig. 18-35 shows the safety devices installed in a truck using an expendable refrigerant system. Caution: the temperature of the liquid nitrogen as it sprays from the spray nozzles, depending on the thermostat setting, may be much below 0 F. If any of this liquid were to hit any part of a human body, the flesh would be frozen instantly. Be sure that no living animal or human is in the refrigerated space when the doors are closed.

The spray cooling system which uses nitrogen or carbon dioxide has some other advantages as well as the ease in providing necessary refrigerating temperatures. Fruits, vegetables, meats and fish, either in transit or in storage, are preserved by inert atmosphere of these gases since they exclude oxygen from the storage space.

18-21 Multistage Systems

Multistage systems are used where ultralow temperatures are desired but cannot be obtained economically through the use of a single-stage system, because of the evaporating and condensing vapor temperatures which require high compression ratios.

A refrigeration system which contains more than one stage of compression is generally called a multistage system. There are two general types of multistage systems; cascade, and compound.

The cascade system, as shown in Fig. 18-36, is a multistage system in which two separate refrigerant systems are interconnected so that the cooling from one is used to cool the condenser of the other unit. This arrangement allows the lower temperature unit to operate at a lower temperature and pressures than would be possible with the same size single-stage system. Cascade refrigeration systems may be used to produce temperatures as low as -250 F. (see cryogenics). The cascade system consists of two independent units and allows the use of two different refrigerants, if desired.

Another method of obtaining low temperatures is the use of compressors connected in series in the same refrigeration system (compound system), as shown in

speeds. It would also, because of the temperature involved, reduce the volumetric efficiency so that such an operation would be economically unsound. In the compound system the first stage compressor is larger than the secondary stage compressor, because it handles larger volumes of low density vapors.

Compound refrigeration systems using two stage compression equipment can be used to produce temperatures from -20 F. to about -80 F. If three stage equipment is used (3 compressors in series), temperatures down to -135 F. can be achieved efficiently.

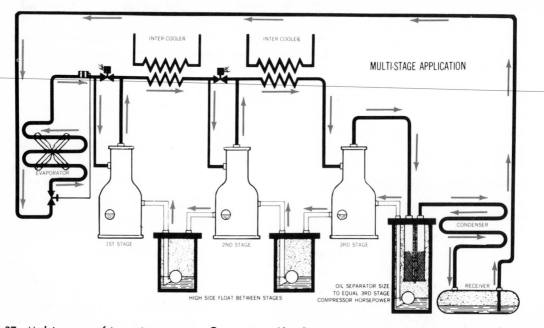

Fig. 18-37. Multistage refrigerating system. Compressor No. 1 pumps vapor into inter-cooler and then into intake of compressor No. 2. This operation is repeated between the 2nd and 3rd stages. In 3rd stage refrigerant vapor is further cooled and travels to evaporator for use in specific cooling operation.

Fig. 18-37. Through the use of compound units, it is possible to increase the performance and efficiency of low-temperature refrigeration systems. In a low-temperature system the vapor in the evaporator has a high specific volume at a low temperature. In a single-stage system this would require a longer than normal compressor piston stroke operating at high

18-22 Cascade Systems

One of the means used to obtain low temperatures is to place two or more refrigerating systems in series (cascade system). This method uses the evaporator coil of one system to cool the condenser of the other system, as shown in Fig. 18-36. Usually two different refrigerants are used, each being adapted to the temperature-pressure conditions under which it operates. For example, system 1 would use Refrigerant 13, while system 2 would use Refrigerant 22.

In the system shown, the unit (2) cools the evaporator (C), and condenses the refrigerant in condenser (D), either air or water-cooled. From here the refrigerant goes through a heat exchanger to the refrigerant control (XV).

The evaporator (C) removes the heat from the condenser (B) of the low-temperature system. This condensed refrigerant (it may be as low as 0 F. to -100 F.) goes through the refrigerant control XV and evaporates in evaporator (A). The refrigerant in A may be evaporating at temperatures as low as -100 F. to -400 F. This low temperature may be used for a number of purposes (heat treatment, research, condensing rare gases, etc.).

18-23 Cryogenics

Cryogenics is a branch of physics that relates to producing very cold temperatures. It covers refrigeration in the range of -250 F. to absolute 0 F. (Kelvin 0). It is used to liquefy and separate gases such as the atmosphere's gases (oxygen, nitrogen, argon, etc.). It is also used to liquefy hydrogen and helium. Because of the ultralow temperatures, special materials of construction must be used; lubrication of moving parts is a special problem and electrical devices must be specially designed and constructed.

Methods used to create these low temperatures are:

1. Expansion process with heat exchangers (Joule-Thompson process).
2. Expansion process with heat exchangers and with gases performing work.
3. Multiple cascade system.

Cryogenics is being used to condense and solidify obnoxious and harmful gases from exhaust products of industrial processes. One example is removing sulphur and ammonia gases from coke making exhaust gases. One plant solidifies 120 tons of sulphur per day using cryogenic equipment.

Special care must be taken when operating and servicing cryogenic equipment. The liquids are ultracold and will severely injure anyone coming in contact with them. Certain parts of the system are also ultracold and will injure one in the same manner.

Either no lubricant is used in moving parts or a dry lubricant such as molybdenum sulphide is used.

Nickel steels (stainless steels), copper alloys, and aluminum metals have been used in cryogenic units.

18-24 Vortex Tube Cooling and Heating

The vortex tube is an interesting device which is capable of providing both cooling and heating. Its source of energy is compressed air.

The three elements of the device are shown in Fig. 18-38. Compressed air at about 150 psig enters through tube A. This tube enters the larger tube B at a tangent to the outer surface and at a position at the end of the tube B, which connects to

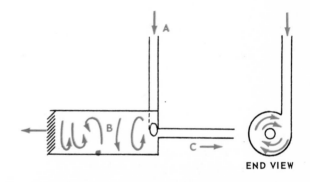

Fig. 18-38. Vortex tube. Compressed air enters through tube A. Cooled air leaves tube C. The remainder (warmer) air leaves at B.

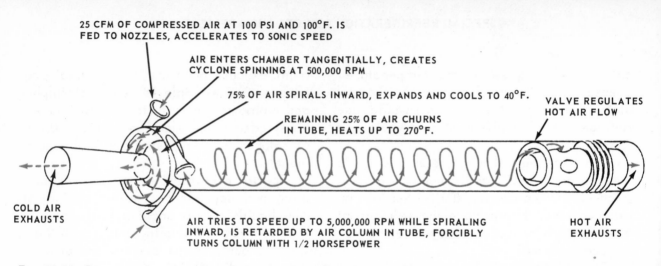

25 CFM OF COMPRESSED AIR AT 100 PSI AND 100°F. IS
FED TO NOZZLES, ACCELERATES TO SONIC SPEED

AIR ENTERS CHAMBER TANGENTIALLY, CREATES
CYCLONE SPINNING AT 500,000 RPM

75% OF AIR SPIRALS INWARD, EXPANDS AND COOLS TO 40°F.

VALVE REGULATES
HOT AIR FLOW

REMAINING 25% OF AIR CHURNS
IN TUBE, HEATS UP TO 270°F.

COLD AIR
EXHAUSTS

AIR TRIES TO SPEED UP TO 5,000,000 RPM WHILE SPIRALING
INWARD, IS RETARDED BY AIR COLUMN IN TUBE, FORCIBLY
TURNS COLUMN WITH 1/2 HORSEPOWER

HOT AIR
EXHAUSTS

Fig. 18-39. Diagrammatic view of a vortex tube. Note flow of air at 100 psig at 100 F. into nozzles. Air is exhausted at temperature of 40 F. at cold end. The cold air is shown by the broken arrow line.
(Fulton Cryogenics Inc.)

tube C. Tube C leaves tube B at the center of their joining ends, as shown in Fig. 18-38. The cold air leaves the device through tube C.

In operation, the high pressure compressed air entering through tube A causes a very rapid whirling motion in tube B.

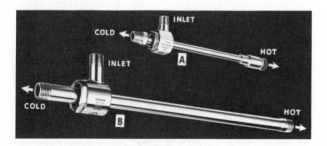

Fig. 18-40. Two vortex tubes. Above—Tube which is 6 1/2 in. long and weighs 2 1/2 oz. Below—Tube 10 in. long and weighs 6 oz.
(Fulton Cryogenics Inc.)

Some work is done by the compressed air as it expands and this causes the cooling (adiabatic expansion).

The internal operation of the vortex tube is similar to that of a turbine in which compressed air acts as a rotor. The compressed air moving at supersonic velocities rapidly expands in the vortex tube into hot and cold fractions (portions).

The cooled air collects at the center of the whirl and escapes through tube C. The

remainder of the air, which is warmer, will escape through the open end of tube B.

Fig. 18-39 shows diagrammatic sketch of the air flow inside a vortex tube which is used for cooling purposes. Note that there are four nozzles for the compressed air to enter.

Fig. 18-40 shows a small vortex tube. (A) which has a variable capacity of from 2 to 8 cfm at 100 psig. It is used for small instrument cooling, for cooling of safety helmets, and the like. The lower picture

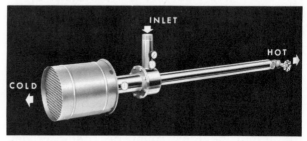

Fig. 18-41. Large capacity vortex tube. Muffler (cold end) is 10 in. in diameter. Amount of warm air exhaust is controlled by hand valve. Inlet tube has a dial thermometer and pressure gauge while both cold end and hot ends have dial thermometers.

(B) shows a larger vortex tube which has a capacity of from 15 or 25 cfm at 100 psig. This unit is used extensively for cooling or heating of small spaces or air conditioned suits.

Fig. 18-41 shows a vortex tube which is used for pressurized room air conditioning. It has a capacity of 500 cfm at 100 psig. Note the use of a 10 in. diameter muffler on the cold end. The complete unit weighs 45 lbs. and is 4 ft. 6 in. in length.

The vortex tube cooling is particularly desirable in locations where both ventilation and cooling are needed. A common application is the cooling of miners clothing for use in mines which are too warm for normal comfort. Fig. 18-42 illustrates a vortex tube installation inside a miner's clothing. The cooled air is carried by flex-

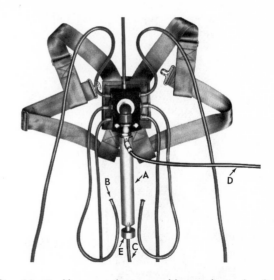

Fig. 18-43. Vortex tube assembly ready to be fitted to miner's clothing. A—Vortex tube device. B—Cooled air outlet (seven). C—Exhaust warm air. D—Compressed air lines. E—Temperature adjustment valve (manual).

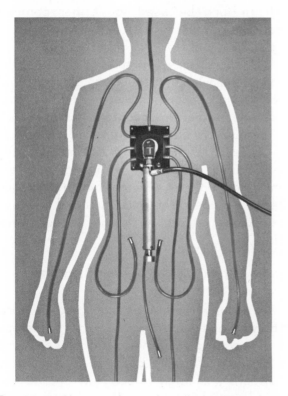

Fig. 18-42. Vortex tube cooling device fitted inside miner's clothing. Note distribution tubes which carry cooled air to various parts of wearer's body. (Mine Safety Appliances Co.)

ible tubes to various parts of the miner's suit and in this way gives a general cooling effect to his whole body. The exhaust air from the tube B aids in providing necessary ventilation. Fig. 18-43 shows the device ready to be fitted to a wearer's

clothing. The vortex tube is insulated so it will not be uncomfortable to the wearer. The control valve E shown in Fig. 18-43 is manually adjustable and regulates the rate of air flowing out the opening C. This also regulates the flow through the tubing B since if the air is restricted from flowing out of C, it will be forced to leave through the tube B. Fig. 18-44 illustrates a garment and hood fitted with a vortex tube cooling and heating device. The adjusting valve is controlled manually. Opening this valve allows a greater portion of the air to flow out of the exhaust outlet; however, the temperature of the air flowing from the cooling tube will be decreased. Fig. 18-45 is a table showing the performance of the vortex tube application.

The complete mechanism, less the carrying harness, weighs about 1 1/2 lbs. It is recommended that an air line filter be installed in the compressed air line to remove dirt and petroleum vapors from the compressor lubrication.

This unit can easily reduce the temperature within the operator's garment 40 F. to 50 F. below the ambient temperature and at the same time provide fresh air for

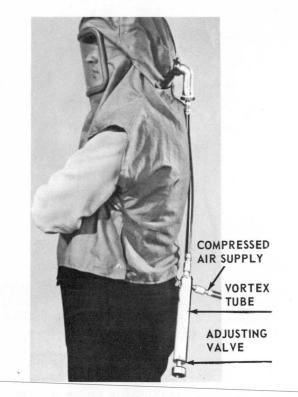

Fig. 18-44. Garment and hood fitted with vortex tube cooling and heating device. Adjusting valve controls rate of air flow through both cooling and heating tubes.

COMPRESSED
AIR SUPPLY

VORTEX
TUBE

ADJUSTING
VALVE

breathing. This unit consumes about 19 cfm of compressed air.

In addition to the above applications, the vortex tube may be used for cooling machine tools and in other applications where a small spot cooling effect is desired, and where an ample supply of compressed air at the desired pressures is available. The vortex tube is also being used to cool drinking water aboard trains. Vortex tubes may be used in parallel in order to obtain greater capacity.

18-25 Steam Jet Cooling System

The steam jet system consists of a steam jet ejecter assembly, condenser, evaporator or flash chamber, chilled water circulating pump and condensate pump.

The principle of operation is based on the fact that water under a partial vacuum boils at a relatively low temperature. This

causes evaporation to occur at a fast rate and reduces the temperature in relationship to the pressure created. Fig. 3-17A shows a table of water boiling temperatures under varying vacuum pressures. However, since water is the refrigerant used in steam jet applications, only temperatures down to approaching 32 F. are obtainable.

The steam jet refrigeration system is used extensively in air conditioning, cold water gas absorption in chemical plants, beverage cooling in distilleries and many others. The steam jet system is used primarily as a means of cooling water which will in turn be used for either comfort cooling or upper range temperature cooling.

Its operation is normally limited to installations where there is an abundance of steam and condensing water at a low cost and where the desired temperatures are in the 40 F. to 50 F. range.

Since a relatively low steam pressure is required, steam jet refrigeration is often used in plants which use high pressure steam for operating machines and then use the exhaust steam for steam jet refrigeration.

18-26 Air-Cycle Air Conditioning

A popular method of producing air conditioning and cooling in aircraft is the use of air-cycling equipment. It has been found to be very effective because of the ready availability of high velocity air and its low overall weight. In a cooling system using the open air-cycle principle, air becomes the refrigerant and is used directly to cool the required space.

Open air-cycle system refrigeration is done in three basic steps:

1. Compression.
2. Transfer of heat.
3. Work, accompanied by expansion.

The operation is as follows: air is compressed in a centrifugal compressor to a

PERCENT THRU COLD TUBE CONTROL VALVE	40	50	60	70	80	90	100
TURNS OPEN	OUT	4	2.10	1.40	.89	.42	0
INLET PRESSURE psig							
60	93	84	73	59	44	28	2
	58	80	104	132	168	236	346
80	102	92	80	65	49	31	3
	63	86	113	143	181	249	360
100	110	99	86	70	53	33	4
	66	91	119	151	192	257	365
120	116	104	90	74	55	34	5
	69	94	123	156	195	256	363
140	121	109	94	76	56	35	6
	70	96	124	156	193	250	354

Temperature drop through cooling tube, degrees F. – Black type.
Temperature rise from exhaust warm air, degrees F. – Red type.

Fig. 18-45. Table of the cooling and heating capacities for a vortex tube installation used in miner's clothing. The values are for dry inlet air of 40 to 100 F.   (Mine Safety Appliances Co.)

pressure which is higher than the pressure of the area to be cooled, as shown in Fig. 18-46. Heat which is added to the air by compression is removed by the use of a heat exchanger. This may be the ambient air. Next, the air is further cooled by removing work energy "causing it to do work" as it expands through a turbine which operates a fan. If the air is passed through a normal throttling valve, the air temperature will not be reduced enough. Therefore, work energy must be removed from the expanding air. To do this, the turbine must have some type of load imposed upon it. Normally, this is a fan. The amount of cooling obtained will be in proportion to the amount of work done by the turbine. The fan draws cool air through the heat exchanger located upstream from the turbine. The cold air which the turbine expels is used for cooling.

18-27 Free-Piston Compressor

A recent development in the area of refrigeration compressor designs is the free-piston compressor. This type of unit uses the basic principles of the conventional internal combustion engine as a source of power and the basic piston type refrigeration compressor in a single unit. The internal combustion engine may operate on either bottled gas, natural gas, or gasoline. With the exception of the reed valves, the only moving part is the piston which receives its power and movement from the combustion chamber and in turn compresses the refrigerant gas. Because of the unique design of the piston, close tolerances are not required, except for the oil seal.

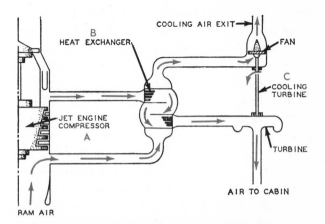

Fig. 18-46. Basic air-cycle refrigeration system used on aircraft. A–Jet engine compressor. B–Heat exchanger. C–Cooling turbine.
(ASHRAE Guide and Data Book)

The free-piston compressor has a two stroke-cycle combustion chamber on the top end (similar to the common gasoline lawn mower engine) and the conventional refrigeration piston intake and discharge valves and cylinder, on the bottom end. The diameters of both the refrigerant compression cylinder and the power cylinder are the same. There are no complicated mechanical links from the piston to its source of power. The exhaust gases from the combustion engine are passed through a muffler which decreases the noise and temperature of the gases.

Sealing of the refrigerant within the compression end to prevent its passage to the power end of the piston is accomplished by maintaining a fluid in a gland around the compression piston. One of the most common methods of accomplishing this is to maintain oil at a pressure in the gland higher than in the compressor. The oil is prevented from escaping by the use of hydraulic sealing rings. Oil to the sealing gland is supplied directly from the oil separator at 150 psig.

The operation of the free-piston compressor is as follows: fuel is injected into the upper chamber and is ignited by means of a high voltage electrode. This causes the combustion pressure to drive the piston downward and compress the refrigerant vapor in the bottom of the cylinder. Compression will continue until the discharge port opens and the high pressure vapor is forced into the condenser. The operation of the refrigerant vapor compression side of the free-piston compressor is identical to the compression in a reciprocating compressor, piston intake and exhaust valves and the like. The exhaust reed valve prevents the refrigerant from reentering the compression chamber. However, the area between the piston and head of the compressor (compressor clearance pocket) remains filled with high pressure refrigerant vapor. These vapors produce a force on the piston and this force will push the

piston away from the cylinder head, thus starting a compression stroke in the internal combustion end of the unit.

When the refrigerant cylinder pressure decreases enough, the intake valve will open to allow refrigerant from the evaporator coil to enter the chamber. This flow of refrigerant causes the piston to continue its travel until ignition occurs in the combustion chamber of the combustion cylinder and the cycle repeats itself. Because of the greater power created by the combustion engine, the downward drive of the piston takes only half the time that is required for the upward stroke which is dependent upon the clearance volume and the low side pressure. The refrigeration compression cycle can use any of the available refrigerant controls or coils.

18-28 Review of Safety

In working with electrical equipment it is always recommended that the equipment being tested be fully grounded through either the use of a polarity plug or through the use of a ground wire.

The local and national refrigeration and electrical code should be followed when servicing and installing all units.

Before checking a thermoelectric system obtain a wiring diagram of the system to be certain that the polarity is not reversed. Avoid imposing voltages and current above the ratings at the diodes, transistors and thermal modules.

In checking expendable refrigerant systems, always make certain that the safety doors are opened and the truck body vented.

Before entering a unit that is being cooled, make certain there is no refrigerant passing through the system. As has been repeated throughout the text, a serviceman should always wear goggles when checking a unit which uses a refrigerant.

It is not safe to work on any part of an expendable refrigerant system unless one knows the required pressures and the nature of the safety valves and controls used in the system.

As indicated in Par. 18-23, temperatures in the cryogenic range are -250 F. and below. These temperatures are dangerous, since the rate that heat will be removed from the surface of the body at these temperatures is so great that the flesh may be severely frozen before the person feels the cold.

18-29 Test Your Knowledge - Chapter 18

1. What are the advantages of a thermoelectric system as compared to a compression system?
2. Does a thermoelectric system use alternating current throughout the system?
3. Were two dissimilar metals used by Emil Lenz to show the basic system of thermoelectric refrigeration?
4. Is it necessary to connect a number of thermoelectric elements in series in order to achieve a low temperature in large areas?
5. How can a thermoelectric module used for cooling be converted into a heating unit?
6. Must the material used in thermoelectric modules have a high thermal conductivity and a low electrical conductivity in order to obtain the best temperature difference between the hot and cold junctions?
7. Name three methods of removing heat from the hot junction.
8. How is the change in energy at the hot and cold junctions accomplished in a thermoelectric system?
9. May semiconductors be poor conductors of heat and still be excellent conductors of electricity?
10. Is bismuth-telluride a popular semiconductor material?
11. Why is the N type material treated or doped in a thermoelectric unit?
12. Is it possible to transfer heat directly through electrical current?
13. What is the allowable ripple when direct current is flowing?
14. Most power pack systems do not operate above 20V. Why?
15. What type of meter is needed to successfully check a thermoelectric unit?
16. What type refrigerant is predominately used in an expendable refrigerant cycle?
17. Name the two basic types of expendable refrigerant systems available today.
18. What is the purpose of the safety vent in an expendable refrigerant system?
19. What is one application of a cascade system?
20. What is the most popular means of comfort cooling aircraft?

Chapter 19

AIR CONDITIONING SYSTEMS, FUNDAMENTALS

19-1 Introduction

People are continually endeavoring to improve their surroundings and to make living conditions more comfortable. Air conditioning is one of the important recent developments in this area. Air conditioning provides a comforting effect, health effect, and psychological or emotional effect on human beings.

19-2 What Air Conditioning Includes

Important factors involved in a complete air conditioning installation include:
1. Temperature control.
2. Humidity control.
3. Air movement and circulation.
4. Air filtering, cleaning and purification.

Complete air conditioning provides automatic control of these factors for both summer and winter.

In addition to the comfort phases of air conditioning, many industries have found that air conditioning of their plants make possible more complete control of manufacturing processes and material and improves the quality of the finished product.

An early step toward modern air conditioning was the development of the central heating plant. Another step was the development of automatic controls for regulating the heating plant and providing the proper humidity. A third step was the development of automatic refrigeration devices which could be employed for summer cooling and dehumidifying the air.

The complete system must heat or cool the air, increase or decrease the humidity, control the air movement, and clean the air. All these functions must be accurately controlled and are preferably done automatically.

19-3 Air

To understand air conditioning, it is important that you have a knowledge of the structure and properties of air. Air is an invisible, odorless and tasteless mixture of gases which surrounds the earth.

Air surrounding the earth is about 400 miles thick. Air is divided into several identifiable layers. The ionosphere is the outer layer. The stratosphere is the layer between 50,000 ft. (10 miles) and up to 200 miles. The air we are most interested in is the layer between sea level and 50,000 ft. This includes cooling of aircraft. Air from about 30,000 to 50,000 ft. is called the troposphere layer; air from sea level to 30,000 ft. is called atmosphere. The atmosphere consists of a mixture of gases. Each of these gases behaves as though it occupied the space alone (Dalton's law). See Fig. 9-1.

Because Oxygen (O_2) is a heavier gas, it has a higher percentage by weight than by volume. Hydrogen (H_2) is a very light gas, and it therefore does not show in weight percentage but is shown in the volume column.

Water and dust are so variable in the air that they cannot be given any definite value in a table. However, these two sub-

Name	Chemical Symbol	DRY AIR		AVERAGE AIR	
		Amount by Weight %	Amount by Volume %	Amount by Weight %	Amount by Volume %
Nitrogen	N₂	75.47	78.03		
Oxygen	O₂	23.19	20.99		
Carbon Dioxide	CO₂	.04	.03		
Hydrogen	H₂	.00	.01		
Water	H₂O			X*	X*
Dust				X*	X*
Rare Gases		1.30	.94		

* Variable

Fig. 19-1. Table showing gases and substances that make up normal air.

stances in the air are of considerable importance in air conditioning.

Water exists in air under all temperature conditions. It is in vapor form. It is present in the air even at temperatures below freezing, because it behaves as though it occupied the space alone, and it is operating under extremely low pressure. For example, at .013 in. Hg (very close to perfect vacuum) steam can be made at -20 F., at 50 F. the pressure is .3624 in. Hg, and at 100 F. the pressure is 1.9 in. Hg. The amount of water (steam or vapor) in air is relatively small. For example, air at 72 F., which is one half saturated with water vapor, has 58 grains of water for each pound of dry air. As it takes 7,000 grains to equal one pound, you can see that water vapor accounts for less than one percent of the air. Also, dry air at 72 F. has a volume of about 13.34 cu. ft. per lb. which, if this same air is saturated (filled) to its maximum weight of water vapor, the volume will increase to 13.8 cu. ft. per lb. of dry air. In a 50 percent saturated case, the volume will be 13.51 cu. ft. per lb. of dry air.

Therefore, the 58 grains of water vapor form 13.6 - 13.4 = .2 cu. ft. of volume. This vapor will weigh $\frac{58}{7000}$ of a lb. or .0083 lbs.

The impurities in the air come in a great variety of forms. Some of the impurities are:

1. Dust (solid particles 1 to 150 microns in diameter).

2. Fumes (.2 to 1 microns in diameter).
3. Smoke (less than .3 microns in diameter).
4. Bacteria (measured by culturing an exposed plate for 48 hours at 98 F.).

See Par. 19-23 for more information on air contaminates. To appreciate the size of a micron, the following compares the micron to other units of measure.

1 micron = .00003936 in. or approximately $\frac{4}{100,000}$ of an in. = .00004 in. = approximately 1/2 of $\frac{1}{10,000}$. The average human hair is $\frac{4}{1,000}$, therefore 1 micron = $\frac{1}{100}$ of a human hair diameter.

1 micron = $\frac{1}{1,000}$ of a millimeter.

1 millimeter = $\frac{1}{1,000}$ of a meter.

1 micron = $\frac{1}{1,000,000}$ of a meter.

1 meter = 39.36 in.

1 micron = $\frac{1}{25,400}$ in.

Air has weight, and density. It presses against the earth at sea level with a pressure of 14.7 psi. It has a density of .0725 lbs. per cu. ft. and it occupies a space of 14 cu. ft. per lb.

Because of the mass of the air, it requires energy to move it, and it can exert pressure above atmospheric pressure. Also it requires energy to make air change its direction of motion.

19-4 Air Temperature

Air temperatures in the United States vary from a low of about -55 F., to a high of around 120 F. The normal, desirable temperature is considered to be 72 F.

The human body temperature is normally 98.6 F. In temperate zones the average atmospheric temperatures are below the body temperature, so clothing is required to help conserve the body heat.

In the summer the human body loses heat when the air temperature exceeds 98.6 F., by evaporation of perspiration from the body. As can be readily seen, heating the air in some instances and cooling the air in other instances is necessary in order to maintain temperatures that are comfortable. The specific heat of dry air is .24 Btu per lb., and energy is therefore needed to bring about these changes.

19-5 Dry Bulb Temperature

Human comfort and health depend not only on the air temperature, but also on the humidity and the dust content in the air. In air conditioning the air temperature indicated is the dry bulb temperature (db) which is taken with the sensitive element of the thermometer in a dry condition, unless otherwise specifically noted.

If a moist wick is placed over a thermometer bulb the evaporation of moisture from the wick will lower the thermometer (temperature) reading. This temperature is known as "wet bulb" temperature, Par. 19-8. If the air surrounding a wet bulb thermometer is dry, evaporation from the moist wick will be more rapid than would be the case if the air is quite moist. The difference between the dry bulb temperature and the wet bulb temperature indicates the relative humidity of the air.

19-6 Air Moisture

The atmosphere we live in always has a water vapor content. Because the human body releases considerable moisture through its pores and by breathing (respiratory system), it is important that we know how air can absorb this moisture, and how the moisture in the air affects the release of moisture from our breathing mechanism and our pores.

Moisture in the air is in a water vapor (gaseous) form. Snow, sleet, hail, clouds,

fog, and rain are forms of water vapor in condensed form. It is important to remember that this vapor can exist in the air at below freezing temperatures without freezing.

The vapor behaves as if it existed or occupied the atmosphere by itself. Therefore, it has a temperature pressure table like other volatiles. See Fig. 19-2.

As indicated in the table, the heat in the vapor is considerable, especially that amount of heat necessary to change the water or ice to steam and vice versa. The amount of heat is measured from 0 F. If we take, as an example, 72 F., the air when dry has only 17.31 Btu/lb., but if the air is saturated with vapor, the total heat is 17.31 + heat in the water vapor (sensible + latent). From the table, Fig. 19-2, at 72 F. the total heat after vaporization is 1092.6 Btu per lb. However, there are only 118.4 grains of moisture per lb. of dry air. The vapor heat is therefore $1092.6 \times \dfrac{118.4}{7,000} = 18.48$ Btu per lb. of dry air. The total heat is 17.31 + 18.48 = 35.79 Btu/lb. Note that there is more heat in the vapor than there is in the dry air.

Air is seldom completely saturated with water vapor. If this condition did exist, the human body would not lose heat by evaporation of moisture. Vapor in the air would condense when it contacted any material lower in temperature. Moisture would collect (condense) on clothing, on walls and other surfaces.

19-7 Dew Point

To find out how much moisture is in the air, or how close it is to being saturated with water vapor, we may use one of several methods.

One simple method is to use a polished or shiny surface that can be cooled slowly. As this surface is cooled, it finally reaches a temperature at which a film of moisture appears on the surface (dew). The temper-

		ICE, WATER, WATER VAPOR			DRY AIR		
Temp.	Sat. Press. in Hg.	Heat in Liquid Btu/lb.	Total Heat after Vaporization Btu/lb.	Vol. of Water Vapor cu.ft./lb.	Volume cu.ft./lb.	Specific Heat Btu/lb.	Amount of Water Vapor Saturate Grains
−40	3.790(10)−3	−177.1	1043.4	1.343(10)5	10.567	−9.61	.5508
−30	7.503(10)−3	−172.7	1047.8	7.441(10)4	10.820	−7.21	1.018
−20	1.259(10)−2	−168.2	1052.3	4.237(10)4	11.073	−4.81	1.830
−10	2.203(10)−2	−163.6	1056.7	2.475(10)4	11.326	−2.40	3.206
0	3.764(10)−2	−159.0	1061.1	1.481(10)4	11.579	0.00	5.480
10	6.286(10)−2	−154.2	1065.5	9060	11.832	2.40	9.161
20	.1027	−149.4	1069.9	5662	12.085	4.81	14.99
30	.1645	−144.4	1074.3	3608	12.338	7.21	24.07
32	.1803	−143.4	1075.2	3305	12.389	7.69	26.40
35	.2034	0.0	1076.5	2948	12.464	8.41	29.80
40	.2477	8.0	1078.7	2445	12.591	9.61	36.34
45	.3002	13.1	1080.9	2037	12.717	10.82	44.14
50	.3624	18.1	1083.1	1704	12.844	12.02	53.40
55	.4356	23.1	1085.2	1431	12.970	13.22	64.36
60	.5216	28.1	1087.4	1207	13.096	14.42	77.29
65	.6221	33.1	1089.6	1022	13.223	15.62	92.51
70	.7392	38.1	1091.8	868.0	13.349	16.83	110.4
72	.7911	40.1	1092.6	814.0	13.399	17.31	118.4
75	.8751	43.1	1093.9	740.0	13.475	18.03	131.3
80	1.0323	48.1	1096.1	633.0	13.602	19.23	155.8
85	1.2136	53.1	1098.3	543.3	13.738	20.43	184.4
90	1.4219	58.0	1100.4	467.9	13.854	21.64	217.6
95	1.6607	63.0	1102.6	404.2	13.981	22.84	256.4
100	1.9334	68.0	1104.7	350.2	14.107	24.04	301.5
120	3.4477	88.0	1113.3	203.2	14.612	28.85	569.0
140	5.8842	108.0	1121.7	123.0	15.117	33.67	1071.
160	9.6556	128.0	1129.9	77.27	15.622	38.48	2090.
180	15.295	148.0	1137.9	50.22	16.128	43.30	4598.
200	23.468	168.1	1145.8	33.64	16.632	48.12	16052.
212	29.921	180.1	1150.4	26.80	16.900	50.00	− − −

Fig. 19-2. Air water vapor table. This table gives characteristics of a mixture of air and water vapor for various temperatures from 40 F. to 212 F. Note large volume occupied by one cubic foot of water vapor at lower temperature.

ature at which the surface "fogs" is the saturation temperature for the air sample.

Dew point temperature can also be measured or determined fairly accurately by placing a volatile fluid in a bright metal container, and stirring the fluid with an air aspirator. A thermometer is used to determine the temperature at which a mist or fog appears on the outside of the metal container. The slower the temperature is lowered, the more accurate the reading. Flammable or toxic volatile fluids must not be used for this experiment.

Dew point temperatures may be obtained more accurately by using instruments made especially for this purpose. Such an instrument is shown in Fig. 19-3. This instrument can measure dew point temperatures from room temperature to as low as -80 F. The principle of operation

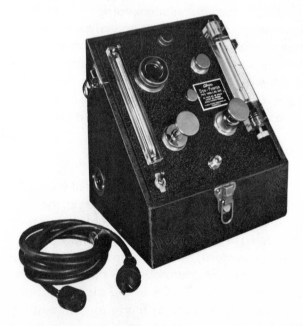

Fig. 19-3. An instrument for determining dew point temperature. (Alnor Instrument Co., Illinois Testing Laboratories, Inc.)

is to pump a sample of the gas into the observation chamber of the instrument. The pressure is above atmospheric.

The pressure ratio gauge on the right adjusts for this pressure. Then the valve is manipulated to exhaust the air. The lighted observation window will indicate a fog when the gas sample is cooled to its dew point. This window is lighted and a "sunbeam" effect is noted if any fog exists. The pressure ratio determines the dew point temperature by formulation. Such an instrument is quite accurate.

19-8 Wet Bulb Temperature

Another way to determine moisture content of air is to use a wet bulb thermometer, as mentioned previously. This is a regular or standard thermometer except that its sensitive element (bulb) is covered with a clean white cloth (wick), and the wick is wet with pure distilled water. See Fig. 19-4.

When the air is saturated with moisture, no water will evaporate from the cloth wick, and its temperature will be the same as a dry bulb thermometer near it.

However, if the air is not saturated, water will evaporate from the wick, and in doing so it will lower the wick temperature. Heat will flow from the air to the wet bulb which it surrounds.

The heat change is adiabatic; that is, no heat is gained or lost from outside sources (radiation losses must be kept to a minimum). The total heat at saturation, (wet bulb temperature) therefore, equals the total heat in the original sample. $H_1 = H_2$.

The accuracy of the wet bulb reading depends on how fast the air passes over the bulb, speeds up to 5,000 ft./min. or 60 mi./hr. are best but dangerous if the thermometer is moved at this speed. Also the wet bulb should be protected from above normal heat radiation surfaces (radiator, sun, electric heater, etc.). Errors as high as 15 percent may be made if the air movement is too low, or if too much radiant heat is present.

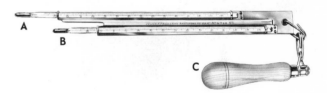

Fig. 19-5. A sling psychrometer. Wet bulb wick is mounted on thermometer (A) at left.
(Bendix Corp., Friez Instrument Div.)

Relative air movement is usually obtained by whirling the thermometers on a handle provided for this purpose. Fig. 19-5 illustrates a pair of thermometers (wet and dry bulb) called a psychrometer. The wick of the wet bulb thermometer should be clean and white. Sling psychrometers come in a variety of sizes.

There are certain conditions in which it is difficult to spin the psychrometer such as narrow passages, etc. To obtain accurate results in these places an aspi-

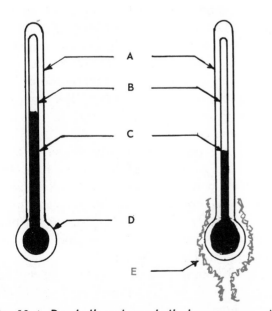

Fig. 19-4. Dry bulb and wet bulb thermometers. A—Thermometers. B—Mercury column. C—Wet bulb column distance below dry bulb reading. D—Dry bulb. E—Wick over wet bulb.

rating psychrometer is used, as shown in Fig. 19-6. In this instrument the air sample is blown over the wet and dry bulb thermometer by suction created by an air pump.

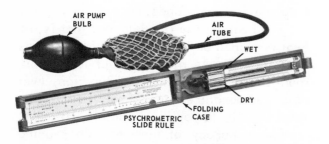
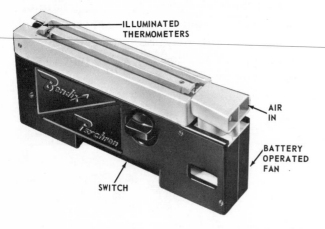
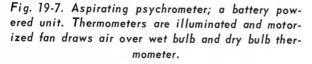

Fig. 19-6. Aspirating psychrometer. Air samples are drawn over thermometer bulbs by air pump. Note handy calculating slide rule incorporated in case. (Bendix Corp., Friez Instrument Div.)

Fig. 19-8. Seven day recorder for both temperature and humidity. These records are important as a means of checking on efficiency of air conditioning system. (Bristol Co.)

Fig. 19-7. Aspirating psychrometer; a battery powered unit. Thermometers are illuminated and motorized fan draws air over wet bulb and dry bulb thermometer.

Another type of aspirating psychrometer is shown in Fig. 19-7. This unit is battery operated. It has illuminated thermometers and a fan which draws air over the thermometer sensitive bulbs.

19-9 Humidity

Humidity is a term used to describe the presence of moisture or water vapor in the air. The amount of moisture that the air will hold depends upon the temperature of the air. Warm air will hold more moisture than cold air. The amount of humidity in the air affects the rate of evaporation of perspiration from the body. Dry air causes rapid evaporation, which cools the surface and makes it feel cool. Moist (humid) air prevents rapid evaporation of perspiration; thus one feels warm, although the temperatures as indicated by a thermometer may be the same. It is important to remember that this moisture (humidity) is in vapor form, and it is invisible.

On all air conditioning systems there should be a record of the controlled temperature and humidity. Fig. 19-8 shows a seven day recorder for both temperature and humidity. Fig. 19-9 shows a 24 hour record of the temperature and humidity taken by a 24 hour recorder.

A different type of temperature and humidity recorder is shown in Fig. 19-10. The charts printed on stiff paper move down as the recording proceeds. The humidity sensitive element is made of multiple strands of human hair.

Fig. 19-11 shows a portable temperature and relative humidity recorder. This unit records both the dry bulb temperature and relative humidity. It can be set to record for one day or for one week.

Instruments other than wet and dry bulb thermometers may also be used for mea-

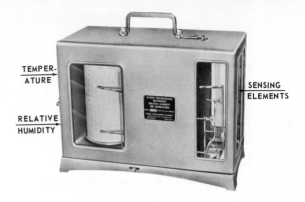

Fig. 19-11. Portable temperature and relative humidity recorder. Temperature sensing element is Bourdon tube while humidity sensing element is several strands of human hair.
(Bendix Corp., Friez Instrument Div.)

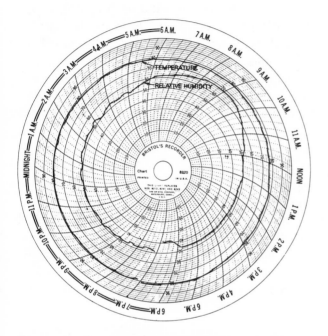

Fig. 19-9. Chart from 24 hour temperature and humidity recorder. Note how relative humidity increased from 5 to 10.

Fig. 19-10. Temperature-humidity ten or thirty hour recorder.

suring relative humidity. Substances such as dry wood, human hair, and certain vegetable fibers change size with varying moisture content. If these substances are arranged in such a way air may circulate past them freely, they will absorb moisture from the air and respond to the atmospheric humidity. By connecting these substances to certain mechanisms, and by calibrating the mechanisms, we are able to develop accurate hygrometers (humidity indicators).

Humidity may be measured in two ways:
1. Absolute humidity.
2. Relative humidity.

19-10 Absolute (Specific) Humidity

Absolute humidity is the actual amount of moisture in the air. The amount of moisture is measured as that amount which is contained in each pound of dry air. The amount of humidity is measured in grains. One grain is 1/7000 of a pound. It can also be measured in terms of vapor pressure such as in inches of Hg. (mercury) or in pounds per square inch absolute.

19-11 Relative Humidity

Relative humidity is a term used to express the amount of moisture in a given sample of air in comparison with the amount of moisture the air would hold if

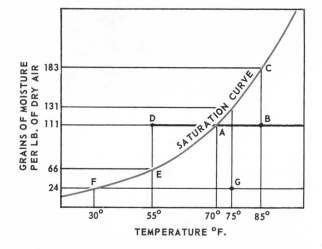

Fig. 19-12. Typical water vapor saturation curve for air. As temperature increases, amount of moisture that air will hold also increases.

totally saturated at the temperature of the sample. Relative humidity is expressed in percentage as 30 percent, 75 percent, 85 percent, etc.

Referring to Fig. 19-12, (Point B) contains 111 grains of moisture per pound of dry air. The saturated condition (Point C) for the corresponding temperature (85 F.) is 183 grains of moisture per pound of air. The relative humidity for Point B is therefore 111/185 x 100 = 60 percent.

Line A to B represents what happens when saturated air is warmed. Point D represents what happens when saturated air is cooled. The moisture represented by the distance D to E is condensed out of the air, since air at the temperature corresponding to Point D (55 F.) will hold only 66 grains of moisture. The amount condensed is 111 - 66 = 45 grains.

A typical winter condition. is represented by Point F. Saturated air is taken indoors at 30 F. and 100 percent relative humidity. It holds 24 grains of moisture. If this air is heated to 75 F. and no moisture is added, its new condition will be represented by Point G. The saturated condition for Point G would be 131 grains. Since the original air had only 24 grains, the relative humidity is 24/131 = 18.3 per-

cent. This is too dry for comfort, as evaporation will take place too rapidly from the body and nasal passages. Moisture will also be removed from hydroscopic materials in the home. For example, if there is a shortage of humidity, the woodwork and wood furniture will shrink, and the joints will probably separate.

Air movement is also an important factor affecting comfort. If cool dry air is circulated past a warm body, the heat flow from the body will be increased and evaporation will increase which tends to cool the body. In the winter, when a considerable difference in temperature exists indoors and outdoors, if there is no air movement within a room, the air may tend to stratify; that is, the cold air will sink to the floor and the warmer air rise to the ceiling. By providing a certain amount of air movement in the room the air will be stirred up so that a more uniform temperature will exist throughout the room. Air movement is usually accomplished by means of fans located in air conditioners or in air ducts.

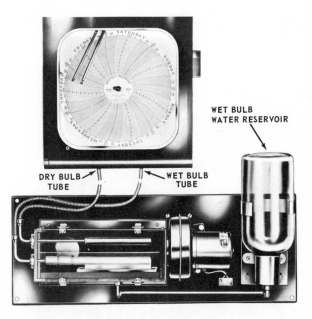

Fig. 19-13. Seven day recording hygrometer. Small motor forces air over dry and wet bulbs. Note bottle on right, used to supply distilled water to wet bulb wick. (Bristol Co.)

19-12 Humidity Measurement

As mentioned before, relative humidity is measured by an instrument called a hygrometer. The simplest form of hygrometer consists of a wet and dry bulb thermometer, as shown in Fig. 19-5. Fig. 19-13 shows an electrically powered hygrometer using a remote power element thermometer connected to a recorder. The wet bulb thermometer is an ordinary thermometer having a wick which encloses the thermometer bulb and extending into a small water reservoir. As the wick soaks up water from the reservoir, it moistens the bulb of the thermometer, and evaporation of this moisture takes place. The evaporation removes heat from the thermometer bulb and cools it. This bulb is called a wet bulb. The wet bulb temperature, except in cases of 1.00 percent relative humidity, will be lower for a given set of conditions than the dry bulb temperature. It is evident that under conditions of low humidity, evaporation takes place rapidly from the surface of the wet bulb. This will result in a much lower wet bulb temperature. Under conditions of 100 percent humidity, the wet and dry bulbs will read the same.

Tables and charts have been worked out using the wet bulb and dry bulb temperatures to indicate the relative humidity for the conditions measured.

19-13 Psychrometric Properties of Air

Psychrometry is the science and practice of dealing with air mixtures and their control. The science deals mainly with dry air and water vapor mixtures. Fig. 19-14 shows the control panel used to determine and control the condition of the air in a large building complex.

Psychrometry deals with the specific heat of dry air and its volume. It deals also with the heat of water, liquid, heat of vaporization or condensation, and the specific heat of steam in reference to moisture mixed with dry air.

Tables and graphs have been developed to show the pressure, temperature, heat content (enthalpy), and volume of air and its steam content. The tables and charts are based on one pound of dry air plus the water vapor to produce the air conditions being studied.

Fig. 19-14. Modern control panel being used to determine and control environmental conditions throughout building. A—Recorder. B—Direct reading instruments. C—Master control panel.
(Johnson Service Co.)

A standard pressure of 29.92 in. of mercury (29.92 in. Hg.) is used as the standard atmospheric pressure, because the volumes of these vapors vary rapidly with pressure changes.

The charts and tables are properties of steam values with the specific heat of air added. The main curve of the chart is actually the pressure-temperature curve (saturation curve) for low pressure steam. See Figs. 19-2 and 19-15.

19-14 Psychrometric Chart

The psychrometric chart is a graph of the temperature-pressure relationship of steam (water vapor). The horizontal scale (abcissa) is the temperature, while the vertical side (ordinate) is the water vapor pressure scale.

Several types of psychrometric charts are available. Fig. 19-15 shows a type of chart used frequently. Fig. 19-16 is a special chart which shows the vapor pressure values on the left side. The area bounded by A, B, C, and D is the area in which most of people feel comfortable either in winter or summer.

The chart should be studied extensively, because it is a means for showing air at various conditions and can be used to determine the results of mixing air of various properties. Various constant value lines are shown in Fig. 19-17.

Many of the air conditioning problems in the text will involve the use of a psy-

chrometric chart. Some examples of the use of the graph, Fig. 19-15, are included in the following paragraphs.

The values along the horizontal scale represent dry bulb temperatures in F. The values along the vertical scale represent grains of moisture per pound of dry air. The 100 percent humidity line or the line of saturation is indicated. The wet bulb temperatures are also indicated along this same line. This psychrometric chart may be used in connection with the wet and dry bulb thermometers to determine the relative humidity under various conditions.

Example: given the dry bulb temperatures of 75 F. If the wet bulb temperature is 60 F., what is the relative humidity?

Refer to the psychrometric chart: the vertical line corresponding to the 75 F. dry

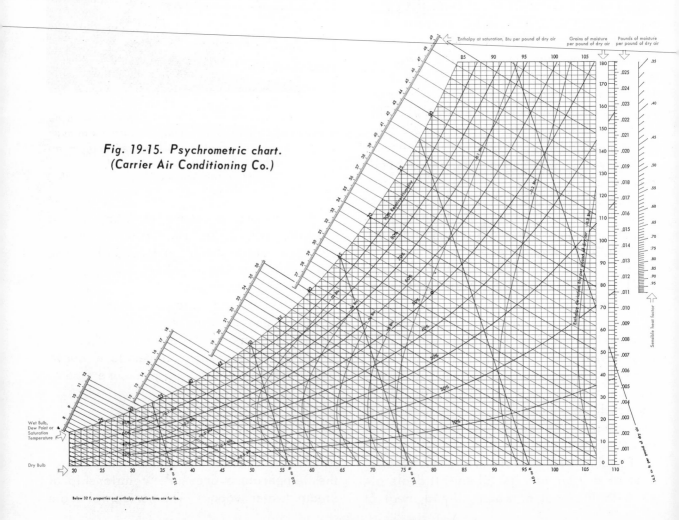

Fig. 19-15. Psychrometric chart.
(Carrier Air Conditioning Co.)

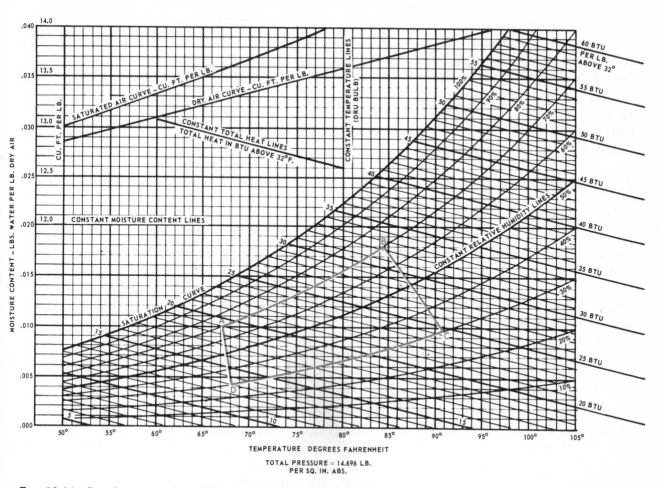

Fig. 19-16. Psychrometric chart showing different variables based on one pound of dry air. Space marked A B C D is temperature-humidity range which is most comfortable for majority of people. (Kelvinator Div., American Motors Corp.)

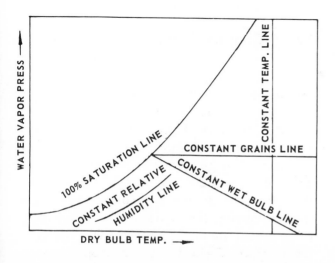

Fig. 19-17. Psychrometric chart line nomenclature. The 100% saturation line is the pressure-temperature curve for water.

bulb temperature crosses the oblique line corresponding to the 60 F. wet bulb temperature just above the 40 percent humidity line, approximately 41 percent.

The dew point is also indicated on the psychrometric chart. This is the temperature below which, if a quantity of air is cooled, moisture will start to condense. It is also the 100 percent humidity point.

Problem: What is the dew point for a sample of air in which the temperature is 80 F. and the relative humidity 60 percent? Referring to the psychrometric chart, the point where the 80 F. line intersects the 60 percent humidity line represents the quantity of moisture contained in each pound of air. If this air is cooled without a change in its moisture content, as represented by the horizontal line going through this point, it will be found that the horizontal line intersects the dew point line at a temperature of approximately 64 F. This is the dew point for a sample of air in which the temperature is 80 F. and the relative humidity is 60 percent.

19-15 Heating Cycle

Heating a certain space means to warm the air to the correct conditions. Let us assume the outdoor conditions are 30 F. and 90 percent RH. Fig. 19-18 shows that the outdoor air as it comes into the building is from 30 F. to 72 F. No moisture is added, and therefore the heating is along a constant vapor pressure of grains of moisture line. This is a typical heating path for air that filters into a house. The volume is increased from 12.4 cu. ft. to 13.45 cu. ft./lb. dry air. The amount of heat increases from 10.6 Btu to 20.8 Btu/lb. of dry air, or an increase of 10.2 Btu.

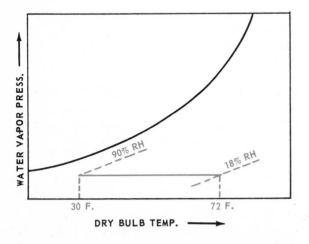

Fig. 19-18. Graph showing decrease in relative humidity as an air sample is heated from 30 F. (90% RH) to 72 F. (18% RH) without any water vapor being added to air sample.

In a warm air heating device, assuming that the return to the furnace is 60 F. and is 25 percent RH, that the furnace heats

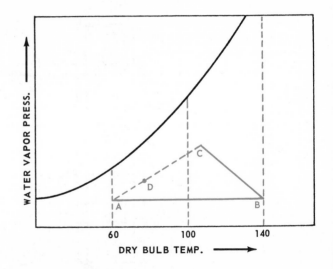

Fig. 19-19. Air recirculating warm air heating cycle on the psychrometric chart. A—Cold air return. A to B—Heating in furnace. B to C—Humidifying air. C to A—Mixing of air with room air. D—Final conditions after mixing.

the air to 140 F., that a humidifier adds moisture to the warmed air, and finally that this heated air mixes with the air in the room. In Fig. 19-19, A to B air is being heated, B to C this warm air is passing over the humidifier (total heat is constant). Between C and A the heated and the humidified air are mixed. D indicates the final condition of the air as it is delivered to the conditioned space.

19-16 Cooling Cycle

In a cooling cycle the dry bulb (db) temperature of the air is lowered. When this happens, as shown in Fig. 19-20, A to B, the relative humidity increases and some moisture should be removed. This moisture can be removed by using chemicals to dehydrate the air, or by cooling the air down to the saturation curve and then removing the moisture by condensing it on a cool surface (B to C to D). The distance from C to D is the drop in vapor pressure or grains of moisture removed. Reheating along a horizontal line to E will decrease the humidity. However, what often happens is the air leaving at D is mixed with the room air which is at some intermediate condition between 85 F. and 100 F. The mixture meets on the line between D and A. If one third of the air by weight is passed through the evaporator, the mixed air temperatures will be one third of the way from D to A, that is to F. Some systems mix the air inside the air conditioner and also introduce fresh air into the air conditioner to obtain results, as shown in Fig. 19-21.

19-17 Psychrometric Tables

The table values permit much more accurate results because the values are accurate to four and five places. However, considerable arithmetic must be used to determine humidity values and other values for air that is not saturated.

You should become familiar with the use of charts and tables.

19-18 Comfort Zone

As has been indicated, comfortable conditions result from a desirable combination of temperature, humidity, air movement,

and air cleanliness. However, we may have comfort under varying values of these factors. For instance, the high relative hu-

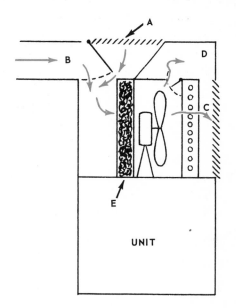

Fig. 19-21. Air circulation in console comfort cooling air conditioner. A—Recirculated air. B—Fresh air. C—Cooled air. D—Recirculated untreated air. E—Filter.

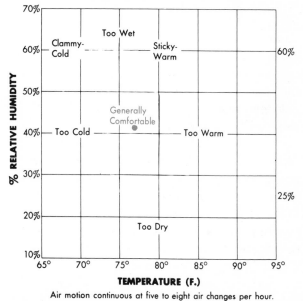

Air motion continuous at five to eight air changes per hour.

Fig. 19-22. Indoor comfort chart. Most people would feel comfortable at points marked generally comfortable. (Lennox Industries Inc.)

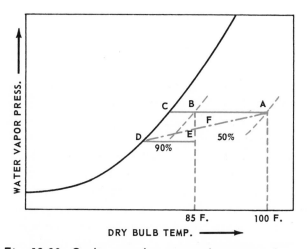

Fig. 19-20. Cooling cycle on psychrometric chart. A—Condition of outside air. B—Partly cooled air. C—Air cooled to saturation. D—Air cooled to remove some moisture. E—Dehydrated air reheated. F—Result of mixing treated and untreated air.

midity, which would tend to be oppressive, may be counteracted by a relatively low temperature; rapid air movement, or as is in the case of many homes in the winter time, a low relative humidity is compensated for by an increase in room temperature and slight air movement. Fig. 19-22 illustrates what is commonly accepted as the comfort zone for the various conditions. It will be noticed that this comfort zone represents a considerable area. However, experiments have indicated that any point in this area gives approximately equal comfort under equal conditions of clothing and work.

Fig. 19-23 is a more technical graph showing the comfort zones for both winter and summer.

19-19 Effective Temperature

While the studies so far would indicate that one should establish certain comfort zones of effective temperature in residences and places of work, this is not entirely true due to the fact that all outdooors cannot be air conditioned, and that a certain portion of the time most people spend outdoors. The human body is able to accustom itself only to certain changes in a given length of time. Therefore, it becomes necessary to regulate air conditioning equipment so that it will produce a certain degree of air conditioning. While this will be comfortable in itself, it will not subject the person to too great a shock on entering this conditioned space, or when going out into the normal outdoor atmosphere. It may, therefore, be said that air conditioning is, to some extent, a compromise between the actual atmospheric conditions and the ideal conditions as indicated in the comfort zone.

Some of these changes are compensated for by the clothing people wear. For example, in the winter time an attempt is made to maintain temperatures of approximately 70 F. to 75 F. indoors, although the

temperature outside may be 0 F., which is a temperature difference of 70 F. This is because it is usually considered more comfortable to put on additional clothing when going outdoors under such conditions than to remain indoors with sufficient clothing to be comfortable at a temperature only a few degrees above zero. However, in the summer, the reverse of this is not true. People do not dress warmer when they enter a space conditioned to 70 F. when the outside temperature is 90 F. to 100 F. Instead of feeling comfortable on entering such a conditioned space, they feel chilled and too cold. It is, therefore, important that a compromise condition be maintained which corresponds to some extent with outdoor temperature.

Fig. 19-23 indicates that in the summer most people are comfortable between 72 F. db and 100 percent RH up to 85 F. db and 10 percent RH. During the winter most people feel equally comfortable between 66 F. db and 100 percent RH and 74 F. db and 10 percent RH.

19-20 Air Movement

Air movement has a distinct effect on our comfort. If we reside in still air, we soon build up the surrounding air to a higher temperature and a higher humidity. Likewise, if there is too great an air movement, over 15-20 ft./min., the wiping action of the wind produces an effective temperature below the actual conditions.

Air conditioning attempts to produce the right amount of air movement in spaces occupied by people. However, the apparatus is designed to move the air as fast as practical in the air cycle before it reaches the people. This air speed increase is due to reducing the size of the air passageways (ducts and machine air passages), and to throwing the air out into the conditioned space (to reduce the number and size of the air openings in the room).

Air passage velocities are limited however, because if the velocity is too high, an air turbulence noise becomes disturbing, and also the energy needed to move the air at high velocities (friction losses) becomes excessive.

The subject of air distribution is covered in more detail in Chapter 22.

use, air passages must be built. These air passages are called ducts.

Ducts are made of many materials. Pressure in the ducts is light so the use of materials with a great deal of strength is unnecessary. Originally, air ducts were thin tinned sheet steel (hot air ducts). La-

11

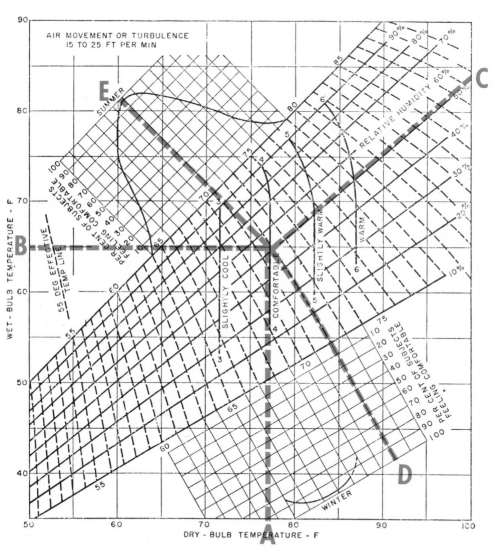

Fig. 19-23. *A graphical representation of comfort zone.* **A—***Constant dry bulb temperature line.* **B—***Constant wet bulb temperature line.* **C—***Constant relative humidity line.* **D—***Constant winter effective temperature line.* **E—***Constant summer effective temperature line.* *(ASHRAE Guide and Data Book)*

19-21 Ducts

To carry air through an air conditioning unit, and to deliver it to the place of

ter galvanized sheet steel, aluminum sheet, and finally insulated ducts made from materials such as asbestos and fiberboard, were developed. Passageways, as formed

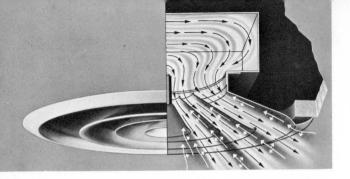

Fig. 19-24. Ceiling grille with specially designed outlets that produce air diffusion in grille. (Anemostat Products Div.)

by studs or joists, are sometimes used where a fire hazard does not exist.

Three common classifications of ducts are:

1. Conditioned air ducts.
2. Recirculating air ducts.
3. Fresh air ducts.

Round ducts are the more efficient but square and rectangular ducts are used extensively because they conform better to the design of building structures.

Chapter 22 covers ducts in more detail.

19-22 Grilles

The end of a duct is usually covered with and concealed by a perforated covering called a grille. This type covering is also usually placed over the intake of a recirculated air duct or a fresh air duct.

The grille prevents large objects from getting into the duct, provides control for the direction of flow of the air into the room, and a pleasing appearance to the duct end.

Grilles provide resistance to air flow. Grille cross section pieces block the air passage by approximately 30 percent. For this reason, and also because they must use slow air movement to reduce noise, the duct cross section is usually enlarged at the grilles.

Many forms of grilles have been designed. Some are fixed and direct the air only in one direction. Others are adjustable and can be arranged to direct the air in different directions. Fig. 19-24 shows a grille with circular segments, designed to

serve as an air diffuser. Air from the duct flows along the upper surface of the truncated cone. This action reduces the pressure under the cone and causes room air to enter and mix with duct air.

19-23 Air Cleaning

In air conditioning air cleanliness is an important consideration. Air contaminants, as all foreign matter is called, very considerably in size and in material. Efficient air conditioning systems will remove 75 to 95 percent of these contaminants.

Three general classes of impurities are:

1. Solid.
2. Liquid.
3. Gases and Vapors.
1. Solid particles, kept in suspension in the air by air currents, may be classified into three general groups:
   A. Dust is the result of wind, a sudden earth disturbance, or by mechanical work on some solid. Dust can have as its origin -- animal, vegetable, or mineral.

Dust particles are usually over 600 microns in size (about .004 in. in dia.).

   B. Fumes are solids formed by condensation and solidification of materials that are ordinarily solids but have been put into a gaseous state (usually an industrial or chemical process). These particles are about 1 micron in in size.
   C. Smoke is the result of incomplete combustion. Solid particles are carried into the atmosphere by the gaseous products of combustion. These particles vary in size from .1 to 13 microns.
2. There are also liquid impurities in the air. Two of the most common are known as:
   A. Mists.
   B. Fogs.

Mists are small liquid particles, mechanically ejected into the air by splashing, mixing, atomizing, etc.

Fogs are small liquid particles formed by condensation. Fogs indicate that the atmosphere has reached the saturation state for that particular chemical.

3. The third general classification of air impurities consists of the impurities that act as true gases:
   A. Vapors.
   B. Gases.

There is little difference between these two impurities. Vapors are gases that have condensing temperatures and pressures close to normal conditions.

Not all impurities are objectionable or harmful. Perfumes and deodorizers have been used for years to either make air more pleasant to smell and to conceal objectionable odors.

Special applications for air cleaning may be provided for:
1. Pollen.
2. Bacteria.

The best air conditioning practice is to clean the air.

Pollen grains come from vegetation growth such as weeds, grasses and trees. Their presence in the air is usually responsible for hay fever, rose fever, and other respiratory conditions. Removal of these pollen from the air has been an important contribution of air conditioning. These particles vary in size from 10 to 50 microns.

Bacteria are microorganisms and are responsible for the transfer of many diseases. Many manufacturing processes require the removal of these bacteria. Hospital rooms and some refrigerators use bacteria removing devices.

19-24 Air Cleaning Devices

Many methods have been developed to clean the air. Solid impurities should be removed as completely as possible be-cause these particles settle from the air and cover furniture, carpeting, drapes, floors, etc. with dust.

Methods of removing dust particles include:
1. Centrifugal devices.
2. Air washers.
3. Adhesive impregnated filters.
4. Electrostatic precipitators.

An adhesive impregnated filter is shown in Fig. 19-25.

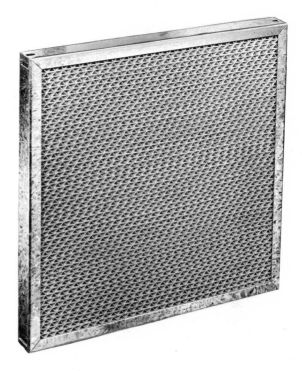

Fig. 19-25. An adhesive impregnated filter which is cleanable. After cleaning, filter adhesive is sprayed on both sides. (Air Filter Corp.)

Mists or fogs are usually eliminated by the use of heat which raises the temperature and turns the small water particles into vapor making them invisible.

A condensation process may be used to remove vapors and gases.

Pollen grains may be removed by filters, or by using a wet surface to which the particles will adhere.

Bacteria can be removed either by filter chemicals or by using a sterilizing light such as an ultraviolet light. See Fig. 19-26. These lamps are usually locked in position to shine upward. If they are turned

downward, they should be below eye level. They must be located or controlled in such a manner that the rays cannot hit any personnel. Ultraviolet lamps are used extensively in meat packing house storage rooms to retard the growth of bacteria.

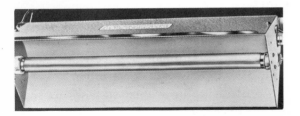

Fig. 19-26. *Ultraviolet lamp for elimination of bacteria and mold spores from air.*

19-25 Adhesive Filters

Adhesive filters are those made of various fibers (glass-wool, and the like). The fibers are coated with adhesive liquid or oil. Air changes direction and speed as it passes through the filter with the result that particles of lint and dust contact the adhesive surfaces and are trapped.

These filters will remove as much as 90 percent of the dirt if they do not become "loaded," or if the air velocity is not too high. The more common filters are of the throw away or disposable type. See Fig. 19-27. These filters should be renewed twice each year or more frequently if the dust conditions are high. The frames are usually made of cardboard with wire reinforcement or of rustproof steel. Fig. 19-28 shows a fiber filter being installed in a window air conditioner.

Fig. 19-27. *Typical throw-away filter. Metal frames are reusable. Filter or media is a glass or fiber material. (Farr Co.)*

Another method used to determine if a filter needs replacement is to use a water manometer with the two manometer openings connected to the air flow on the two opposite sides of the filter. The filter should be replaced if the pressure drop exceeds .5 in. of water.

19-26 Water Filters

Water may be used as a filtering agent. It may be used as a spray; this method provides some humidity control. The finely divided spray will remove most of the dirt, but it cannot remove soot dirt particles (carbon), as this type of dirt cannot be wetted. Spray systems are usually found in larger units.

A second method uses water to wet a loosely woven cloth (cotten). This cloth is

Fig. 19-28. *Fiberglas filter being installed in a window unit. (Owens-Corning Fiberglas Corp.)*

usually stretched over wire frames and the air is drawn through or over the cloth. The cloth is kept wet by wick action or by using slowly dripping water.

A third method is incidental to the use of a moisture condensing coil. An evaporator coil operating below the dew point temperature will collect considerable water. Air passing over this water will lose much of its dirt.

Naturally any type of water filter will require plumbing connections both for the water to the unit and for the drain connections.

19-27 Carbon Filters

A filter made of activated carbon will remove solid particles and will also remove odor-causing gases and bacteria. This type filter is used in air conditioners and in refrigerators with considerable success. Fig. 19-29 shows an activated carbon filter assembly. The carbon in activated charcoal form, is commonly made from coconut shells. This charcoal will absorb as much as 50 percent of its weight in foreign gases. The filter may be reactivated or rejuvenated by baking at 1,000 F. to drive out the absorbed gases.

19-28 Electrostatic Cleaning

A filter that eliminates practically all dust, is the electrostatic filter. Basically it puts a static electrical charge on all particles that pass through it. Usually the air is first passed through regular filters to remove most of the larger particles of dirt and the air is then fed through the electrostatic filter. In the filter the air first passes through a highly ionized field. A wire with a high positive voltage is suspended between ground wires. Electrons passing through the air space put a positive electrical charge on any particle that attempts to pass through the ionized field. This particle is then drawn to the grounded

Fig. 19-29. Activated carbon filter and air purifier. (Conner Engineering Corp.)

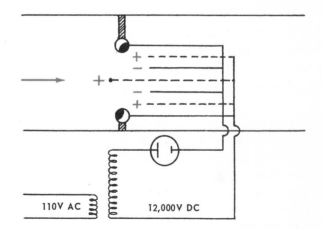

Fig. 19-30. Electrical circuit and air flow in simple electrostatic type air filter.

plates (negative potential). Potentials of as high as 12,000V are used. Fig. 19-30 shows a diagrammatic view of an electrostatic filter.

Because of the high voltages used, the electrostatic filter may be dangerous. The units should be so designed that when the service doors are opened to gain excess to the units, the power is automatically shut off.

Filters which carry small static electricity charges are also available. These filters remove dirt particles by attracting them to surfaces charged with static electricity. Such filters are cleanable, by washing in water.

19-29 Ozone

Ozone has been extensively studied as a means to improve conditioned air.

Tests have proven that ozone will improve air, but its use above 0.01 to 0.05 parts per million of air may cause an unpleasant odor and may cause breathing difficulties.

19-30 Discomfort Index

A discomfort index is a numerical method used to indicate the possibility of human discomfort. This measurement is also called a Temperature-Humidity Index (THI). It is determined by adding the wb and db temperatures, multiplying by .4 and then adding 15.

Example: 90db + 80wb = 170 x .4 =
68.0 + 15 = 83

According to the U. S. Weather Bureau Discomfort Index, a certain percent of people will be uncomfortable at some common temperature-humidity index numbers. The following table indicates the percent who will be uncomfortable at the indicated THI numbers:

THI	%
70	10
75	50
79	100

Also see Temperature-Humidity Index, (Par. 1-61).

19-31 Review of Safety

Air we breathe should be as clean as possible and have the correct oxygen content. When wood, gas or oil furnaces are used, it is absolutely essential that none of the fumes (products of combustion) be-

come mixed with the air being sent to the rooms.

It is important that air conditioners provide enough fresh air to the rooms being conditioned to keep the oxygen content of the air within allowable limits.

It is extremely important that the serviceman makes certain an electronic filter is disconnected before servicing the unit. Ultraviolet rays should be shielded.

19-32 Test Your Knowledge - Chapter 19

1. What four factors are involved in a complete air conditioning system?
2. Is air conditioning used only for human comfort?
3. Of what materials is the living portion of the atmosphere made?
4. In what form does water exist in the air?
5. What is fog?
6. What is a grain?
7. What is a micron?
8. List at least two temperatures one should know about any particular air sample?
9. Define psychrometry.
10. How does air movement affect one's comfort?
11. What is the boiling or evaporating temperature of water at 1 in. Hg pressure?
12. List two ways to remove moisture from the air.
13. What happens to the moisture absorption properties of air as the temperature decreases?
14. How should a psychrometer be used?
15. What values are constant along a horizontal line of the psychrometric chart?
16. Does air contain moisture at temperatures below 32 F.?
17. When air is heated, what happens to the relative humidity?
18. Under what conditions are most people comfortable in the summer?

19. List three uses for air ducts.
20. What is the purpose of a grille?
21. How large are dust particles?
22. What are fumes?
23. Describe the difference between a vapor and a gas.
24. How can oil be used to remove impurities from air?
25. How does an ultraviolet ray help clean air?
26. Describe how a cooling coil helps clean the air.
27. What is the principal impurity removed by an activated carbon filter?
28. How is electricity used to remove dust from the air?

Chapter 20

AIR CONDITIONING SYSTEMS, HEATING AND HUMIDIFYING

Air conditioning systems for heating and humidifying are dependent on heat sources, heat distribution, heat control, filtering devices and facilities for control of humidity.

The fundamentals of purpose, design and operation of the heat and humidifying sources and their control are explained in this chapter. Filtering devices are explained in Chapter 22.

20-1 Types of Systems

A complete automatic air conditioning system that satisfactorily performs all the functions of air conditioning is difficult to achieve. Most of the systems available today are compromises in one form or another. The two most difficult results to obtain are air cleaning and proper humidity.

Fig. 20-1. Four types of heat sources used for space heating purposes: coal, oil, gas and electricity.

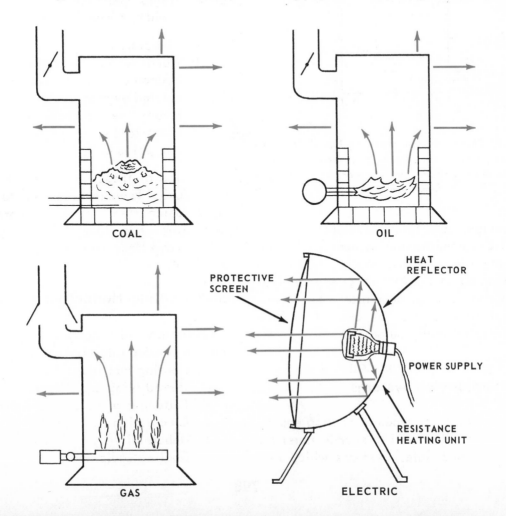

COAL

OIL

GAS

PROTECTIVE SCREEN

HEAT REFLECTOR

POWER SUPPLY

RESISTANCE HEATING UNIT

ELECTRIC

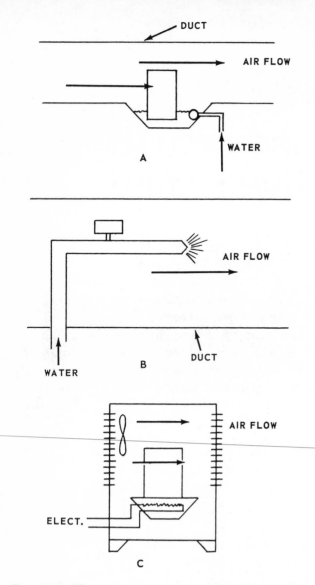

Fig. 20-2. Three common types of humidifiers: A—Open water tray in warm air duct. B—Spray nozzle in warm air duct. C—Freestanding room or space type humidifier.

Most air conditioning systems are only partial air conditioning systems. That is, the system is for either heating, humidifying, cleaning, and distributing; or, the system is for cooling, dehumidifying, cleaning, and distributing. The operation of the systems is normally automatic.

20-2 Types of Heating and Humidifying Systems

There are many types of heating equipment in use. The heating source must be economical and safe. Systems which re-

quire a minimum of attention by the user are most desirable.

Sources of heat may be classified by fuels: wood, peat, antracite coal (hard), and bituminous (soft), oil, gas, electric including: resistance, light (radiant), heat pump (see Chapter 26).

Principles as applied to space heaters are shown in Fig. 20-1.

Sources of humidifying provide a means of turning water into water vapor and mixing this vapor with air in the occupied space. Fig. 20-2 shows three methods: (A) Exposing a large surface of water to air being humidified, (B) Spraying atomized water into air being humidified. Illustration (C) shows an electrically heated room humidifier. On rare occasions, during heating operations, moisture must be removed from the air. Chemicals or a cooled condensing surface may be used to perform this operation.

Heat energy may be distributed by:

A. Circulated air through ducts.
B. Warm water thermal circulation.
C. Hydronic systems, warm water circulated by means of a pump.
D. Steam lines and radiation.
E. Electric heat radiation from electric grids or infrared lights.

Basics of these systems are shown in Fig. 20-3. Transferring heat to occupied space using steam or warm water heating is shown in Fig. 20-4. All heating furnaces should have Underwriter's Laboratory (UL) approval.

20-3 Heating-Humidifying Equipment

Complete air conditioning equipment may be divided into six headings:
1. Heating facilities.
2. Humidifying equipment.
3. Filtering and cleaning equipment.
4. Circulating equipment.
5. Dehumidifying equipment.
6. Cooling equipment.

798

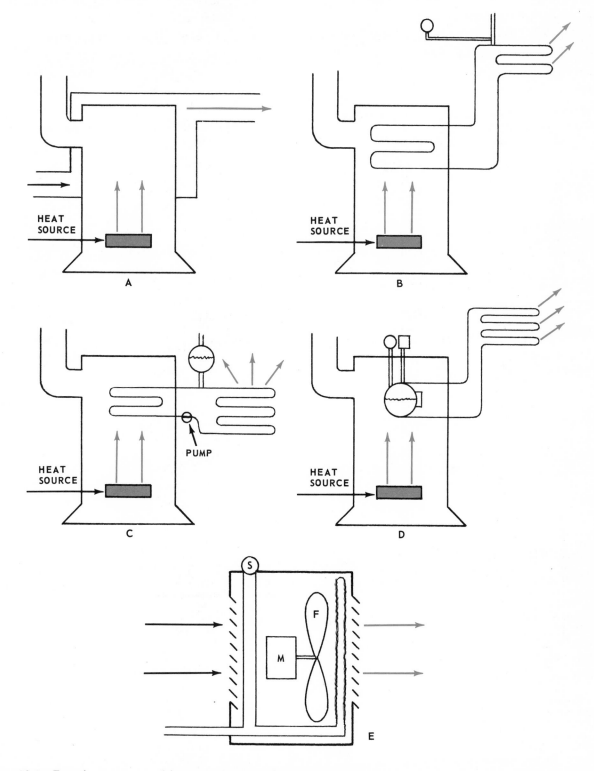

Fig. 20-3. Five basic types of heating systems: A—Natural convection warm air. Fuel may be coal, gas, or oil. B—Natural convection warm water. Fuel may be coal, gas, or oil. C—Forced convection warm water. Fuel is usually oil or gas. D—Low pressure steam. Fuel may be coal, gas, or oil. E—Electric resistance space heater. M—Motor. S—Switch. F—Fan.

During the winter or heating season, heating and humidifying equipment is usually used. The other equipment such as filtering, cleaning equipment, and circulating equipment is used the year round.

Complete air conditioning equipment may be of three different types:

1. Entire air conditioning plant may be located in a remote area and conditioned air circulated throughout

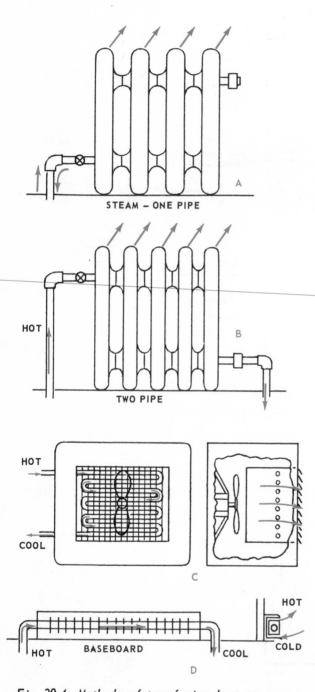

Fig. 20-4. Methods of transferring heat to an occupied space using steam or warm water as the heating medium: A—One pipe radiator. B—Two pipe radiator. C—Forced air heating coil. D—Baseboard convector.

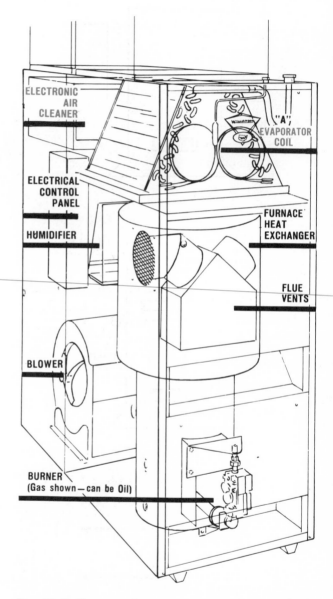

Fig. 20-5. Warm air furnace using gas burner, which has evaporator coil for summer cooling. Note electronic air filter. (Williamson Co.)

the building. Such a plant is shown in Fig. 20-5. A warm air furnace using an oil burner is shown in Fig. 20-6.

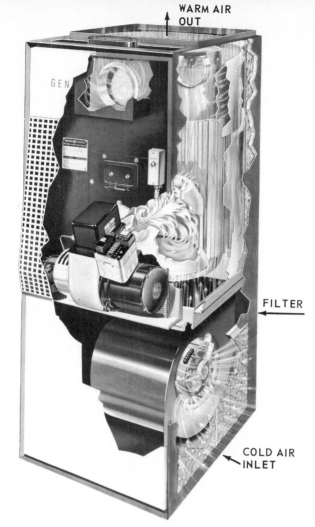

Fig. 20-6. Sectional view of warm air furnace using an oil burner. Note blower at cold air entrance at base of furnace. (General Electric Co.)

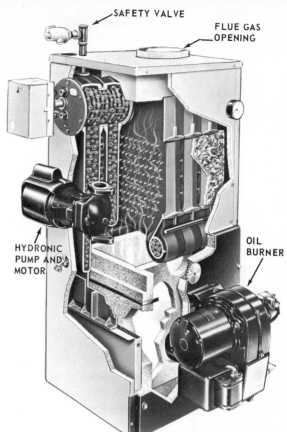

Fig. 20-7. Gun type oil burner used in a furnace which is part of a hydronic heating system.

2. Heating may be located in a remote place but pipe lines are used throughout the building to carry the heating medium to the various rooms. Small ducts in this case usually provide ample ventilation and air circulation. The heat source may also be outside the room if the installation uses steam or hot water for its heating medium. Fig. 20-7 shows a hydronic (see Par. 20-19) furnace using a gun type oil burner.

3. Unit installations have a complete heating unit located in each room. Such plants usually contain humidifying equipment, as well as heating, and air circulating equipment.

20-4 Heating Equipment

Most heating equipment is automatic in operation. The source of the heat may be coal, oil, gas, electricity, or heat pump. The choice will be governed largely by the location and equipment available.

In systems in which a central plant is located in a remote place such as a basement, heat is circulated throughout the structure. With steam or water heating plants, radiators or heating coils are usually incorporated in room air conditioning units and the necessary humidifying, air circulating, and filtering is done by each room unit.

The furnace in which the fuel is burned must be of safe design. Products of combustion must be vented outside the building to prevent health hazards. The assembly must be equipped with devices to close the unit down (1) if combustion is delayed or ceases, (2) if the furnace overheats, (3) if air, steam, or water ceases to circulate, (4) when the heated space becomes warm enough.

20-5 Coal Furnaces

One of the oldest fuels used for heating is coal. There are two main kinds of coal, bituminous (soft) and anthracite (hard). The soft coals are more commonly used. When completely burned, this coal will release between 12,000 to 15,300 Btu/lb. The heat is formed by the oxidation of carbon and hydrogen in the coal. Most coal has an ash content. The ash varies from 6 to 10 percent. Coals have a variable sulphur content. This sulphur is corrosive. Soft coal sulphur content varies between 1.2 and 2.1 percent. Anthracite coal has a heat value of 13,000 to 14,000 Btu/lb. It has an ash content of about 10 percent and a sulphur content of approximately 0.7 percent.

Coke is a solid product of the distillation of the volatile matter of coal. It has approximately the same heating value as bituminous coal.

Coal furnaces use two sources of air to support combustion:

1. Primary air which passes through the grate and through the coal bed. This is air which is mixed with fuel before it burns.
2. Secondary air, is the air which surrounds the flame and supports combustion of the outer envelope of the flame.

Hand fired coal furnaces are not very efficient. Their efficiency is 25 to 50 percent. Stoker fired furnace efficiency varies from 50 to 80 percent.

A stoker is a machine which automatically feeds coal into a furnace firepot as needed. It is electrically controlled by a thermostat, a limit control, and a controller which keeps the fire alive in mild weather. Small pebble size coal pieces (usually bituminous) are placed in a hopper. The coal feeds by gravity to a slowly revolving screw which feeds the coal to the firepot. The motor which drives the feed screw usually also drives a fan which provides a forced draft through the coal bed and supports combustion. When the space being heated reaches the correct temperature the thermostat responds to the temperature. The stoker shuts off and the fire automatically is reduced to a banking fire.

The ash has to be removed periodically. Some stokers do this operation automatically. One advantage of the stoker fired coal furnace is even, steady heat. There are many models and types of stokers in use. Stokers are rated in four classes:

Class 1, 10 to 100 lbs. of coal/hr.
Class 2, 100 to 300 lbs. of coal/hr.
Class 3, 300 to 1,200 lbs. of coal/hr.
Class 4, over 1,200 lbs. of coal/hr.

Class 1, is the stoker most commonly used in domestic heating.

20-6 Fuel Oils

Fuel oils vary considerably. They contain about 85 percent carbon, 12 percent hydrogen and various other elements in the remaining 3 percent. Fuel oil grades which are established by the U.S. Department of Commerce conform to ASTM specifications.

Grades 1 and 2, are used in domestic and small commercial furnaces; Grade 1 is also used in pot type oil burners; Grade 2 is the most popular domestic fuel oil. Grades 4, 5, and 6 are used in industrial applications. Grade 2 is the most popular domestic fuel (about 140,000 Btu/gal.). It has a flash point of 100 F., a Sayboldt viscosity of 40 (compared to Grade 4 of 125). The heavier oils 3, 4, 5, and 6 provide slightly more heat per gallon, as shown in Fig. 20-8.

Products of combustion are carbon dioxide, and water in vapor form. About 106 lbs. of air are required for each gallon of Grade 2 fuel oil consumed. Multiplying

COMMERCIAL GRADE NO.	BTU PER GALLON	GRAVITY RANGE DEG. API	AVERAGE WEIGHT PER GALLON LBS.
1	137,000	45–38	6.8
2	140,000	40–30	7.1
3	140,000 *		
4	141,000 *	32–12	7.7
5	148,000	20–8	8.1
6	152,400	18–6	8.2

* not in common use.

Fig. 20-8. Table of heating values of fuel oils. Numbers 5 and 6 are high viscosity oils and require preheating before use. Note API denotes American Petroleum Institute.

106 x 14 (cu. ft. per lb.) equals about 1,500 cu. ft., the quantity of air which must be fed to a furnace for each gallon of fuel oil consumed. Combustion gases vary. For good combustion, excess air must be used, so considerable nitrogen (from the air), some oxygen, carbon dioxide, steam, and impurities go up the stack. These gases may be moved up the stack by natural convection (common in domestic and small commercial units), by forcing with a fan or blower (forced draft) or by drawing them up the chimney (induced draft). It is important to keep flue gases warm, otherwise condensation will take place in the stack and flue causing severe corrosion. One corrosion agent will be sulphurous acid (H_2SO_3) which corrodes steel rapidly.

An oil furnace in good condition should not release visible smoke from the flue, chimney or stack. However, there may be soot deposits which should be removed annually. The soot may be removed by using air pressure, mechanical cleaning, vacuum cleaning, or chemicals such as chlorides.

20-7 Oil Furnaces

The three most common types of oil burners are the gun type, rotary type, and pot type.

The gun type burner forces oil under pressure through definite size orifices. Oil is broken into finely divided particles (atomized), mixed with air, and forced into the combustion chamber by a blower. Fig. 20-9 shows a gun type oil burner.

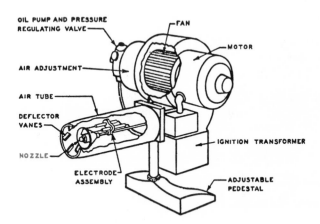

Fig. 20-9. Gun type oil burner. Oil is atomized as it leaves nozzle of burner.
(ASHRAE Guide and Data Book)

In the rotary type burner, oil is thrown by centrifugal force from a motor driven rotary disk or slinger, against red-hot stainless steel plates which vaporizes the oil. The combustion takes place at the point of vaporization and a clean flame results. See Fig. 20-10.

Space type oil burners use a "pot" type burner. The level of oil in the burner pot is controlled by a float and needle valve sim-

Fig. 20-10. Rotary type oil burner.

ilar to the float and needle in an automobile carburetor. Vaporization takes place from the heated surface of the oil in the pot.

Oil has a heating value of approximately 140,000 Btu/gal.

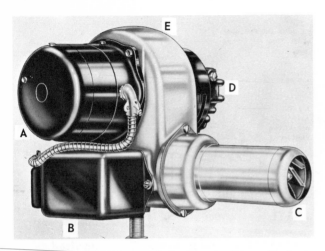

Fig. 20-11. Gun type oil burner. A—Motor. B—Ignition transformer. C—Air and oil nozzles. D—Pump. E—Blower housing. (Fedders Corp.)

It is important to remember that oil will not burn while it is in the liquid form. It must be vaporized and turned into a gas. To vaporize oil, heat must be added to the oil (latent heat of vaporization). The oil will turn into a gas quicker and easier if it is finely divided (sprayed). This spraying process is called atomizing. Gun type oil burners accomplish the atomizing by forcing oil into a twisting, spiralling, and turbulent air stream. A small amount of heat (electric spark) will turn a few of the finely divided particles into gas and the burning will start.

Some large industrial furnaces use combination oil and gas burners.

20-8 Gun Type Oil Burner

Gun type oil burners are available in two types (1) high pressure type (2) low pressure type. In the high pressure type, oil is fed under pressure, 80 to 100 psig,

to a nozzle. Air is forced into the furnace through a tube that surrounds this nozzle. The air is usually twisted in one direction and the oil is given a twist in the opposite direction. See Fig. 20-11. The nozzle should be carefully centered in the housing. The ignition transformer furnishes a high tension spark between two electrodes located near the front of the nozzle. The burner shown in Fig. 20-11, has a two-stage oil pump. Note that the same electric motor drives the pump and the air blower. Fig. 20-12 shows the construction of an air blower gun type oil burner. The low pressure type burner uses oil at 1 to 4 psi. Oil is mixed with air before it reaches the nozzle.

The main parts of a gun type burner are: motor, oil pump, fans, nozzle, air tube, and ignition system.

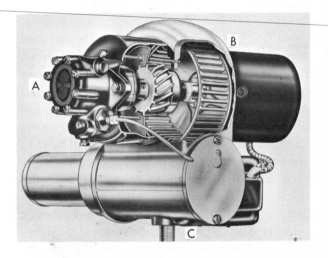

Fig. 20-12. Sectional view of gun type oil burner. A—Two-stage fuel oil pump. B—Air blower. C—Adjustable stand.

The motor is usually a split-phase 1/6 hp motor that provides power for both the fan and the fuel pump. The blower delivers approximately 1,500 cu. ft. of air for each gallon burned. The motor is electrically connected to the master oil burner control and uses 120V 60 cycle electricity.

The fan is usually the radial flow type

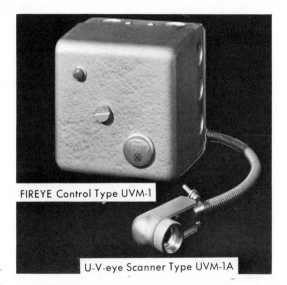

Fig. 20-13. *Safety control for use with large oil or gas burners, operated by ultraviolet light rays. If combustion is delayed or furnace flame goes out, unit safely shuts down heating system.*
(Electronics Corp. of America)

with air inlet openings which are adjustable. The openings are adjusted until the flame burns a yellow color.

To avoid spraying unburned oil into a furnace (DANGEROUS) and to prevent continuous operation of the oil burner in case of ignition failure or the oil flame is extinguished, safety devices are installed. Fig. 20-13 shows a light sensitive safety device which will shut off the system af-

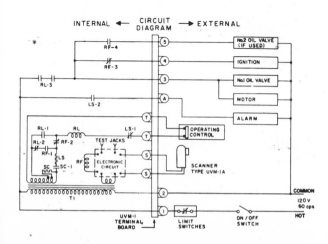

Fig. 20-14. *Wiring diagram of ultraviolet sensitive safety device for large oil burners.*

ter 12 seconds if combustion does not occur, and will shut down the system in 0.8 of second if the flame goes out. The wiring diagram for this device is shown in Fig. 20-14.

20-9 Gun Type Oil Burner Pumps

Several types of oil pumps are used in gun oil burners including the gear type, and the rotary type. These pumps come in either single-stage or two-stage models. The single-stage pump is used in the single-pipe system and is shown in Fig. 20-15.

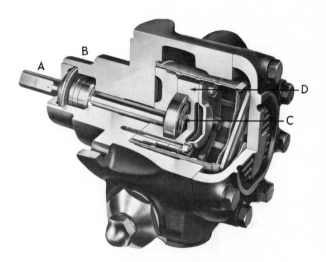

Fig. 20-15. *Single-stage rotary fuel pump for gun type oil burners. A—Shaft. B—Shaft seal. C—Pump rotor. D—Pump housing.*
(Hydraulic Div., Sunstrand Corp.)

This system carries fuel oil from the tank through a filter in the line, the inlet screen in the oil burner, the pump and into the pressure regulator and relief valve. The pump rotates counterclockwise and the oil flow is from left to right. The oil leaves the upper center of the pressure regulator and passes to the gun nozzle, as shown in Fig. 20-16.

Many systems use the two-stage fuel oil pump. This type is necessary when the two-pipe system is used and part of the oil is returned to the fuel tank. This unit

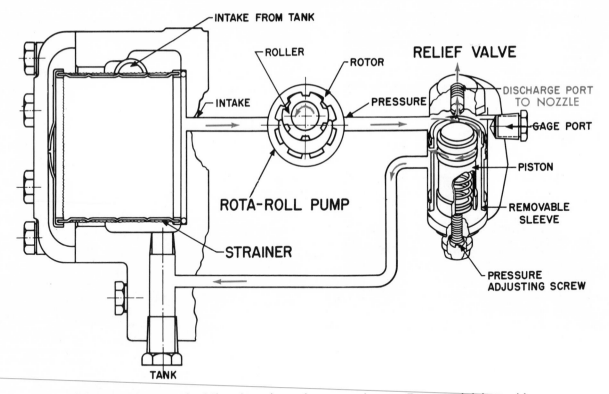

Fig. 20-16. *Schematic diagram of oil flow through single-stage oil pump. Excess oil delivered by pump escapes past pressure controlling piston and returns to pump through intake strainer.*

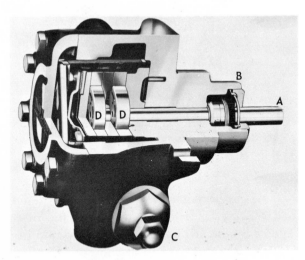

Fig. 20-17. *Two-stage fuel oil pump for oil burners. This is used with two-pipe system from storage tank. A—Shaft. B—Shaft seal. C—Pressure regulator. D— The two rotor stages.*
(Hydraulic Div., Sunstrand Corp.)

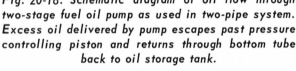

Fig. 20-18. *Schematic diagram of oil flow through two-stage fuel oil pump as used in two-pipe system. Excess oil delivered by pump escapes past pressure controlling piston and returns through bottom tube back to oil storage tank.*

is necessary where the pump lifts oil above the bottom of the fuel tank. Fig. 20-17 shows a two-stage oil pump. Its principle

of operation is shown in Fig. 20-18. The intake from the tank is at the top. Oil passes through the first stage of the pump, into the regulator and back to the tank. The second stage removes only oil from the strainer chamber and pumps it into the nozzle. Excess oil is returned to the strainer chamber.

Details of the relief valve are shown in Fig. 20-19. Oil pressure creates a force against the piston. When this force equals the compression spring force, the piston moves down and permits oil to flow back into the pump inlet.

The gear type oil pump is available in both single-stage and two-stage models. Fig. 20-20 shows the external appearance of a single-stage gear pump. The operation of this single-stage pump is shown in Fig. 20-21. Fuel oil passes through the

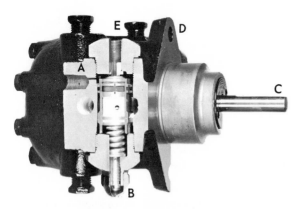

Fig. 20-19. Cutaway of relief valve for fuel oil pump. A—Outlet to nozzle. B—Pressure regulating screw. C—Pump shaft. D—Mounting flange. E—Oil pressure release line.

Fig. 20-20. Single-stage gear pump for gun type oil burners. (Webster Electric Co.)

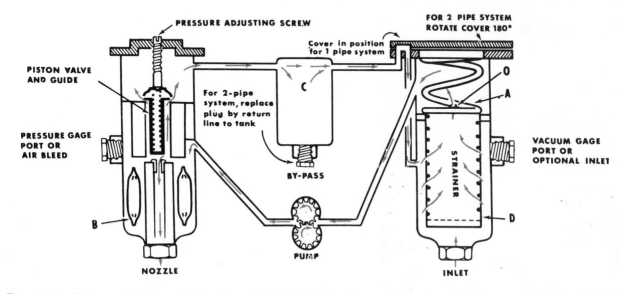

Fig. 20-21. Diagram showing oil flow through single-stage gear type fuel oil pump. Oil enters through inlet into strainer D. It flows upward through silencer orifice O into vacuum chamber A, through gear pump and into pressure equalizing chamber at left. In this chamber, oil pressure cushions provide a uniform pressure flow to nozzle. The pressure regulating piston valve controls pressure of oil entering nozzle. Excess oil is released through bypass system C. (Webster Electric Co.)

Fig. 20-22. Six main items to be checked at the start of each heating season: 1—Shutoff valve and line filter. Replace filter cartridge. 2—Check and clean nozzle assembly. Follow manufacturer's recommendations. 3—Clean strainer using clean fuel oil or kerosene. 4—Check connections for tightness. 5—Insert pressure gauge into pressure port. Start burner and adjust pressure setting to manufacturer's specifications, usually about 100 psi. 6—Pressure gauge reading for correct pressure setting.
(Hydraulic Div., Sunstrand Corp.)

strainer (D) out through the silencer orifice (O) into the vacuum chamber (A). It passes into the gear pump, then enters the pressure regulator from which oil flows to the nozzle. The pressure regulating piston valve opens to allow excess oil to flow into the bypass. In this way a constant pressure is maintained on the burner nozzle. Cushions are used to insure more even oil flow (B).

The gun type oil burner is an efficient heating unit. However, it must be properly maintained to give peak performance. An experienced serviceman should check, clean and adjust the system each year. Some of the important items to check are shown in Fig. 20-22.

Gun type oil burners are also available in low pressure models. In these units oil is mixed with air before it reaches the nozzle, or, the oil is aided in its atomizing by a slinger arrangement. The viscosity of the oil used (ease of flow) is important. Important considerations are the impurities and the quantity of heavy carbons in the oil. Impurities such as sulphur form corrosive chemicals in the stack. Heavy carbons form soot in the stack and tend to retard stack gas flow.

20-10 Electrical Ignition

Gun type oil burners generally use electrical ignition. The system includes a transformer and two electrodes. The transformer is mounted on the oil burner. It transforms 120V AC to about 10,000V. The ignition system must raise the oil to 700 deg. F. for burning to take place. The electrodes made of stainless steel are mounted in ceramic insulators. No part of the electrodes should be less than 1/4 in. away from metal parts. The electrode ends are positioned in front and above the nozzle. As the atomized oil swirls out of the nozzle and mixes with the turbulent air, a spark jumping between the electrode ends ignites the mixture. The ignition may be continuous while the oil burner is in operation or may operate only until the fuel ignites.

The electrode gap should be between 1/8 in. and 3/16 in. The electrode ends should be approximately 1/2 to 5/8 in. above the nozzle and 5/16 to 1/2 in. in front of the nozzle. For over 45 deg. noz-

zles this last dimension should be approximately 1/2 for 45 deg., 5/16 for 30 deg. You should refer to the service manual for exact setting specifications. The porcelain insulators must be kept clean or the high voltage will short. The ignition should be powerful enough to jump a 1 in. gap without the blower being turned on.

A flame mirror can be used to observe the ignition action and spray action to determine if operation is normal.

Weak ignition, improper placement of the electrodes, poor insulation, may cause delayed ignition and a puffback. A puffback is the ignition of a large amount of vaporized oil in the firepot. It will sometimes blow soot into the furnace room and into the living quarters and make a major cleaning job necessary. In no case should the electrode ends be touching the oil spray or the electrodes will become carbon coated.

Moisture in oil tends to retard combustion and may even cause a flame out. A flame out is when combustion stops but the fuel continues to feed into the combustion chamber. If moisture is causing erratic combustion, continuous ignition is usually recommended.

20-11 Gun Type Burner Installation

Oil burners must be installed with great care. A complete installation includes a 200 to 1,000 gal. tank, hand shutoff valve, filter and trap combination, and copper tubing oil line. Fig. 20-23 shows an installation for a one-pipe system with the storage tank located in the room with the furnace. REMEMBER THAT THE STORAGE TANK SHOULD BE AT LEAST 7 FT. AWAY FROM THE FURNACE. In this installation, oil feeds by gravity to the oil burner. This storage should be less than 25 ft. elevation above the burner to keep the feed line pressure below 10 psi. There is danger of corrosion if a copper feed line is installed in a cement floor slab.

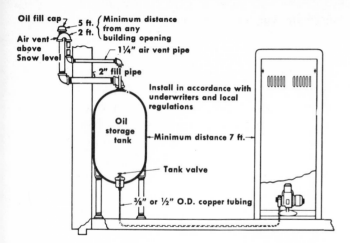

Fig. 20-23. *Typical gun type oil burner installation. Note fill pipe, vent pipe and oil line installation. (Webster Electric Co.)*

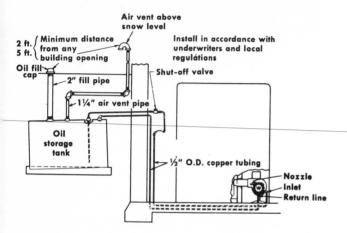

Fig. 20-24. *Gun type oil burner installation with storage tank installed underground but above oil burner. Note two oil lines.*

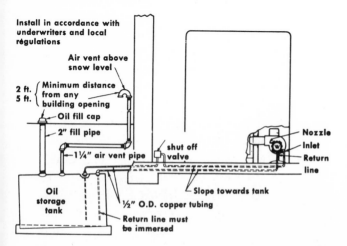

Fig. 20-25. *Gun type oil burner installation which has oil storage tank underground and below level of oil burner. Note special precautions to be observed with oil lines. (Webster Electric Co.)*

In some installations the fuel tank is placed outside the building underground. The two most common installations are (1) with the tank above the oil burner, as shown in Fig. 20-24, as in a residence with a basement, (2) with the tank below the level of the oil burner, as shown in Fig. 20-25, as in a home without a basement. These installations should have the tank located within a reasonable distance of the oil burner. On runs of 50 to 100 ft., 3/8 in. tubing should be used. For runs of 200 to 300 ft., 1/2 in. tubing should be used. The manufacturer's specifications should be checked if the oil must be raised above the tank.

Oil tanks should be installed with a slight down slant away from the oil line connections to provide a low spot in the tank for dirt and water to accumulate. The vent pipe is very important. It provides atmospheric pressure inside the tank and permits volatiles to escape. The vent pipe must be designed with a 360 deg. bend (to keep out dirt and rain) and the opening should be above the highest possible snowfall or other blockage. The oil fill cap should always be in place except when filling the tank.

Always use a pipe thread compound on the pipe threads. This compound should be of the oil-resistant, nonhardening type. The 3/8 or 1/2 in. OD copper tubing is attached to the fittings with standard SAE 45 flares. Flaring techniques are described in Chapter 2. Tight, leakproof connections are essential.

When first starting the unit, air should be removed from the pump. A vent plug (air bleeder fitting) is mounted on the top of the pump housing. Usually this same plug seals the port used to install the pressure gauge.

Always check the fuel oil nozzle, to be sure it is the correct size and that it is in the center of the air duct. The electrodes must be in correct relation to the nozzle and kept clean. Fig. 20-26 shows a typical

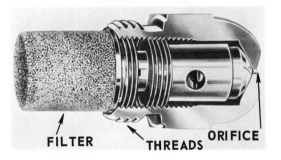

FILTER THREADS ORIFICE

Fig. 20-26. Stainless steel nozzle used with gun type oil burners. Note fine filter at entrance to nozzle. (Monarch Mfg. Works, Inc.)

oil burner nozzle. These nozzles come in various capacities, all based on gallons per hour (gph) at 100 psig (.40 to 28). Some are as large as 100. It should be remembered that a 1 gph nozzle delivers 140,000 Btu/hr. If the overall efficiency is 60 percent, the useful heat would be 84,000 Btu/hr. Poor oil delivery may be the result of the main filter, the pump screen, or the nozzle screen being partially clogged. Check all three filtering devices when checking the unit.

Proper flame appearance is luminous (mainly yellow). If there is insufficient air the flame turns dull orange or red in color and there may be smoky tips to the flame.

The draft in the firepot should measure about 0.02 to 0.05 in. of water (use an inclined water tube manometer). This check will also help determine if the automatic draft is working satisfactorily.

Some oil burner motors are reversible. Fig. 20-27 shows the method of reversing one type of oil burner motor. Controls for oil burners and testing instruments are described in Chapter 23.

20-12 Gas Furnaces

Gas is being used at an ever increasing rate as a heating fuel. The gas is piped into the building. It is usually fed to the furnace at a pressure of 4 to 6 in. water column (approximately 27 in. equals 1 psi). A pressure regulator reduces the pressure

to approximately 2 in. water column pressure. These furnaces usually operate at approximately 80 percent efficiency.

A solenoid valve turns the main gas flow to the furnace burners on and off. This solenoid valve may be operated by electrical current from a power line direct or through a transformer operating at a re-

Fig. 20-27. Method of reversing direction of rotation of oil burner motor. This is accomplished by reconnecting two wires as shown by broken lines.

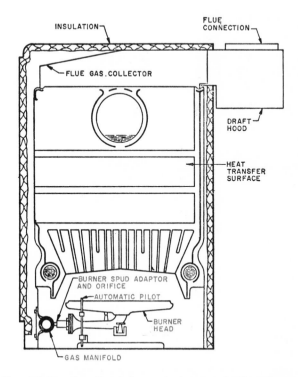

Fig. 20-28. Gas fired domestic heating boiler. Automatic pilot is electrically or pressure connected to safety controls and will shut off gas flow to the burner if it is extinguished. (ASHRAE Guide and Data Book)

duced voltage (24 volts). Some solenoid valves are operated by current generated by a thermocouple located near the pilot light; these do not require any connection to the house current.

The burner may be made of steel pipe or a casting. It may be either of the multiple jet or orifice type, or it may be the one opening type with a deflector plate. These units usually operate on the Bunsen burner principle. Fig. 20-28 shows a gas-fired boiler. Note the gas manifold, burner head, automatic pilot, and burner spud (nozzle) adaptor and orifice combination.

Fig. 20-30. Diverter designed for use on gas furnace stack. (Excelsior Steel Furnace Co.)

Fig. 20-29. Complete gas fired boiler. Note burners, pilot light and safety control.

A complete gas steam furnace is shown in Fig. 20-29. Note the four burners, control valve, pilot light gas line, safety tube and diverter on the flue. The diverter arrests back pressure in the chimney caused by wind gusts which might blow out the gas flame in the furnace. Fig. 20-30 shows a diverter for a round stack.

20-13 Gas Burners

Gas burners are usually of simple design. Gas is fed through an orifice and is mixed with a certain amount of air (primary air). The mixture passes to the burner head where combustion takes place and where the gas mixes with the secondary air. As much as 35 percent excess air is fed to the burner to insure thorough combustion.

The burner system consists of a manual shutoff valve, pressure regulator, automatic shutoff valve, control valve, manifold, burner spuds (nozzles) and adaptors, orifices, primary air inlet, burner head and pilot valve.

The size of the burner should be carefully matched with the furnace capacity. The burner flames should be carefully positioned in relation to the heat exchange surfaces for maximum efficiency. The primary air and the secondary air should be carefully adjusted to insure maximum combustion.

Fig. 20-31 shows a warm air furnace with a gas burner. Note the two primary air mixers, the pilot light and the combination main gas control and pressure regulator. This unit has a maximum output of 132,000 Btu/hr. using natural gas.

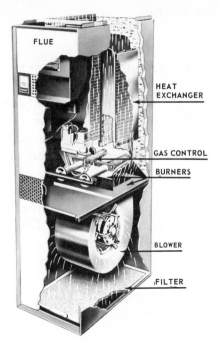

FLUE

HEAT EXCHANGER

GAS CONTROL

BURNERS

BLOWER

FILTER

Fig. 20-31. Sectioned warm air furnace. Heat exchanger is designed to increase heating efficiency. (General Electric Co.)

20-14 Fuel Gases

Fuel gases are generally classified into three types:

1. Natural.
2. Manufactured.
3. Liquefied petroleum (LP).

Natural gas is obtained from gas deposits in the ground. Manufactured gas is made by distilling or cracking coal or oil, and by other processes. Liquefied petroleum (LP) is usually propane and butane which can be easily liquefied, stored and transported in cylinders or tanks. It vaporizes easily and is used in its gas form.

Natural gas commonly used has a heating value varying between 900 Btu/cu. ft. to 1,400 Btu/cu. ft. but the most common heat value varies between 1,000 and 1,050 Btu/cu. ft. This gas contains approximately 55 to 98 percent methane, up to .5 percent carbon dioxide and from .1 percent up to 14 percent nitrogen.

Manufactured gas has a heating value of approximately 500 to 600 Btu/cu. ft.

Liquefied petroleum has a heating val-

ue varying between 2,500 and 3,200 Btu/cu. ft. Propane boils at -40 F. at atmospheric pressure and is stored in cylinders. Butane boils at 32 F. at atmospheric pressure.

20-15 Pilot Lights

A gas furnace is designed to heat a building to a comfortable temperature regardless of the outdoor temperature. Usually the gas furnace must be shut off some of the time to prevent overheating. The controls required are explained in Chapter 23. When the controls shut off the main gas flame, these pilot lights keep burning and then, when the thermostat turns on the heating system, the pilot light is used to ignite the gas. Electric ignition may also be used, or a small flame at the burner (pilot light) may be used. The pilot light obtains its fuel gas from a tube attached to the combination pressure regulator and gas control valve, as shown in Fig. 20-32.

The pilot light is also equipped with a safety device. This safety device may be a thermal fluid bulb or a thermocouple.

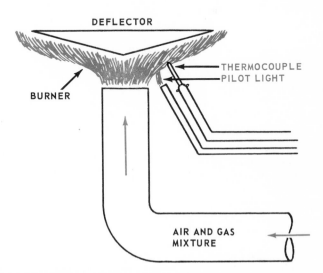

DEFLECTOR

THERMOCOUPLE
PILOT LIGHT

BURNER

AIR AND GAS MIXTURE

Fig. 20-32. Schematic drawing of safety thermocouple and pilot light for gas furnace. Thermocouple generates small electric current which actuates a control which will shut off gas supply to furnace if pilot light is extinguished.

The thermal bulb type allows the main valve to open only if the pressure is high enough (heated by the pilot flame). This type safety device is usually connected to the main gas regulator. The thermocouple unit is operated by its generation of electricity. When a thermocouple is heated by the pilot flame, enough millivolts (about 25 millivolts) are generated to operate a pilot solenoid valve. Only when the thermocouple is heated will the solenoid valve open and allow the main gas valve to open. Some thermocouple assemblies consist of several thermocouples electrically connected in series. These units will generate about 125 to 150 millivolts. This electricity is powerful enough to operate a main solenoid valve and the furnace is therefore independent of the regular electrical circuit in the building. In large systems, the thermocouple operates only a small pilot solenoid valve in the main gas valve. The thermocouple current holds the valve open. The valve will close if the pilot is out or if the pilot flame is low. A pilot flame should be blue color. If it is a yellow color, the primary air inlet to the pilot is probably dirty (partially blocked) and should be cleaned.

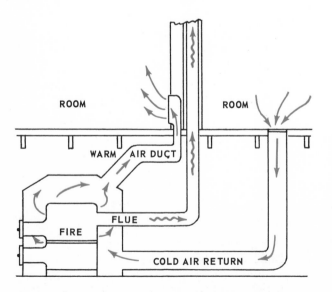

Fig. 20-33. Diagram which shows both heat and air flow in "gravity" type warm air furnace.

20-16 Gas Pressure Regulators

It is important that a constant fuel gas supply be provided in a fuel gas furnace. The air-fuel gas ratio must be carefully maintained. A pressure regulator is usually mounted in the inlet of the gas manifold. It operates much like an expansion valve. It opens and closes a valve in response to the outlet pressure. This pressure is measured in inches of water column. Most of these regulators are adjustable but should be adjusted only when a water column manometer is connected to the outlet. Chapter 23 describes these controls.

20-17 Gas Burner Installations

Because both oil and gas contain small amounts of sulphur and because one of the products of combustion is water (steam) the stack or chimney must be kept warm enough to prevent condensation. If condensation takes place sulphurous acid is formed causing corrosion.

Most cities have code requirements covering the installation of heating equipment. It is important that this code be known and carefully followed; otherwise unsafe conditions may exist.

Furnace capacities are certified by the American Gas Association. This information is given on furnace nameplates.

Furnace capacities decrease at about 4 percent for each 1,000 ft. of elevation above sea level due to the decrease in atmospheric pressure (air becomes less dense). This rating change is effective above 2,000 ft. elevation.

Gas burners burn with a blue flame when the primary and secondary air adjustments are correct. A yellowish flame indicates a lack of primary air and perhaps secondary air. A collection of soot usually indicates a lack of secondary air.

Flame propagation is important. The primary air and gas mixture must flow slightly faster than the flame burns or flashback will occur and burning will take place at the primary inlet (spud). Flashback occurs if too much primary air is used or there is not enough fuel gas pressure. If the fuel gas primary air is too fast, the flame will lift off the burner (called lifting).

The primary air inlet, fuel gas speed and burners should be checked annually.

Incomplete combustion may be the result of:

1. Poor mixing of fuel gas and air.
2. Partial lack of air.
3. Temperature too low to produce ignition, or keep combustion going.

Flue gas temperatures must be maintained above the condensation temperature (dew point) of the flue gas.

For natural gas, the recommended stack temperature is 300 F. to 900 F., depending on the length of the chimney. The values for LP gas are approximately the same.

Excessive temperatures in any part of the heating system will also quickly erode the unit. It is recommended that no part of the system exceed 830 to 1,230 F.

In all cases there must be sufficient air supply to the furnace for combustion. Approximately 1 sq. in. of opening is needed for each 1,000 Btu per hour capacity of the furnace.

Special gas heaters for tents, cabins, etc. should be installed with a stack and a safety pilot light which will shut off the fuel gas flow in case the pilot flame is extinguished.

Testing for leaks should be done with soapsuds. If a leak is suspected do not use open flames. Turn off the electric power. Use an explosion-proof flashlight only.

20-18 Warm Air Heating System

One medium used to carry furnace heat to occupied spaces is air. Heated air which circulates around the firepot can be moved

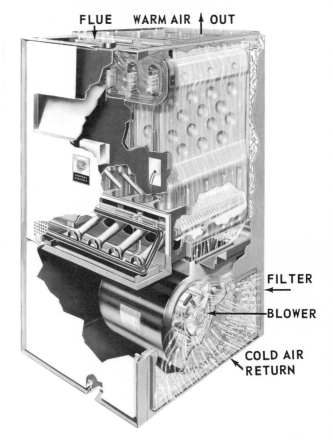

Fig. 20-34. Gas-fired forced warm air furnace. This furnace has a capacity of up to 180,000 Btu per hr. (General Electric Co.)

to the areas needing heat. Two systems are in use:

1. Gravity warm air system.
2. Forced warm air system.

The gravity furnace uses the principle of thermal convection. When air is heated, it rises and as the air cools it settles.

A jacket is placed around the furnace combustion chamber. Ducts are installed to carry the hot air from the top of the furnace to the rooms. Other ducts, called cold air returns, return the cooler air back to the furnace. See Fig. 20-33.

The forced warm air or mechanical warm air system uses a motor blower to increase the flow of heated air to the needed areas. This system usually includes an air filter. Fig. 20-34 shows a forced warm air furnace with a gas fuel heating unit.

20-19 Hot Water Heating System

Hot water systems for carrying heat to occupied spaces have been in use for many years. In some systems, the hot water circulates by thermal convection. The circulating water is under atmospheric pressure and changes in volume are provided

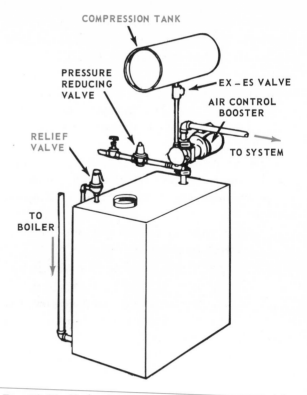

Fig. 20-37. Hydronic system showing piping and location of the pump, compression tank and relief valve.

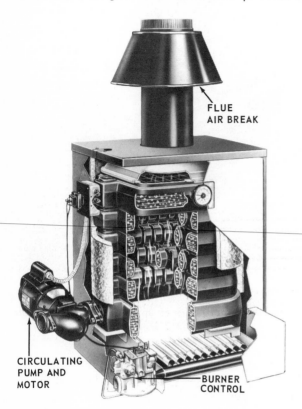

Fig. 20-35. Cross section view of a gas-fired furnace used with a hydronic home heating system.

for by an expansion tank. Many hot water systems now use a circulating pump. This pump increases the water flow, carries more heat per unit of time to the room heat transfer units, and permits smaller furnaces. Fig. 20-35 shows a cross section of a gas-fired furnace for a hydronic installation.

A hydronic heating system uses forced circulated hot water, heated by a boiler and pumped to radiators of various types. Fig. 20-36 shows a circulating pump, Fig. 20-37 piping arrangement when one pump is used. A system with three zones is shown in Fig. 20-38.

The system in Fig. 20-38, has several temperature control devices:

1. Single control which starts and stops the pump.
2. Zone control using two or more controls to operate two or more pumps.
3. Individual radiator controls for individual room control.

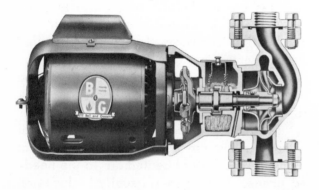

Fig. 20-36. Cross section of a hydronic system pump. (Bell and Gossett ITT)

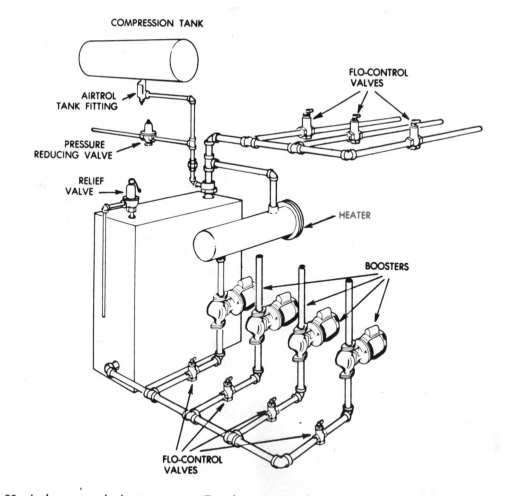

Fig. 20-38. A three zone hydronic system. Fourth pump circulates water through heater to provide hot water.

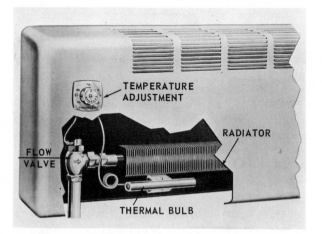

Fig. 20-39. A thermal control valve mounted on convector heating system. This control provides individual room temperature control with either circulating hot water (hydronic) or steam as heat source.
(Danfoss Inc.)

Fig. 20-39 illustrates a hydraulic type radiator control. The temperature sensitive element is adjustable. Note that the control operates the flow valve, and the sensitive bulb is located in the cold air entrance to the radiator. This control can be used for either steam systems or hot water systems (hydronic). It is a modulating control (variable volume flow).

A hot water system using a flow switch control system is shown in Fig. 20-40. The main circuit is shown in solid lines. If the water ceases to flow, the flow switch will open the electrical circuit and shut off the burner. Some systems use a recirculating system within the boiler as shown in the broken line piping diagram. This recirculation of water maintains a more con-

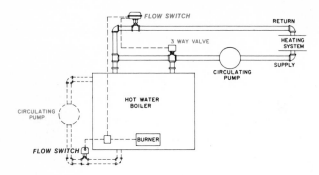

Fig. 20-40. Schematic diagram of hot water system using a circulating pump, three-way valve and flow switch. (McDonnell & Miller, Inc.)

stant water temperature within the boiler. If water flow stops in this water circuit, the flow switch will shut the system down.

Fig. 20-41 shows a hot water system used to heat the air of a ventilating system.

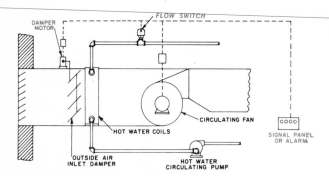

Fig. 20-41. Hot water heating system used to heat incoming air of ventilating system. Note motorized damper control, flow switch and signal panel. (McDonnell & Miller, Inc.)

A system which mixes outside air with return air is shown in Fig. 20-42. The air exhaust, recirculated air, and fresh air intake are controlled together to insure proper air conditions in the occupied space.

20-20 Steam Heating Systems

Steam heating is also a means of distributing heat to the occupied areas. Steam is generated in a boiler. By displacement

it travels to the upper parts of the piping circuit. This steam is at 212 F. or higher. As it releases its heat to the occupied area, it condenses. By gravity, condensed water returns to the furnace boiler.

The steam releases about 1,000 Btu for each pound that condenses. The heat exchange devices located in the room are usually called radiators.

Two basic systems are in use. The single-pipe system uses the same pipe to carry steam to the radiators and return the condensate. The two-pipe system uses one pipe to carry the steam to the radiator and another pipe to return the condensate.

For domestic purposes these systems operate at low pressures or at a partial vacuum. The units are tested at 50 psi for safety purposes. Commercial and industrial systems are progressively higher pressures up to pressures approaching 1,000 psi.

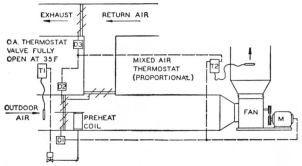

Fig. 20-42. Schematic diagram of controlled air system. Exhaust air, fresh air intake and recirculated air are proportionally mixed to obtain correct atmosphere for occupied space. (ASHRAE Guide and Data Book)

A steam boiler must have pressure safety valves, water level gauge, pressure and temperature gauges. Fig. 20-43 shows a steam boiler with a fuel gas unit. It includes, also, a hot water heater.

A hot water heating unit is shown in Fig. 20-44.

20-21 Humidifiers

When air is heated, it can absorb more water vapor. Human comfort requires a relative humidity of approximately 40 percent. When outside air at 0 deg. F., 100 percent relative humidity, is heated to 70 F. its relative humidity drops to approximately 5 percent. The result is a dry atmosphere which causes dry skin, respiratory dryness, loss of moisture from hydroscopic materials such as wood natural fibers and most foods. This condition also creates static electricity conditions. To change the humidity condition of the air, moisture must be added to it. Moisture comes from plumbing devices, cooking, perspiration, etc. It can be increased and controlled by using humidifiers.

Humidifiers are devices for adding water vapor (low temperature steam) to the air. An important point to remember is that it requires about 1,000 Btu to vaporize each pound of water (7,000 grains). Most humidifiers in warm air systems are part of the furnace or the duct work. Fig. 20-45 shows some basic designs.

Humidistats are used to control the level of humidity. Excessive humidity may cause swelling of hydroscopic materials (wood, etc.) and may cause condensation on cold surfaces such as windows, frames, and walls.

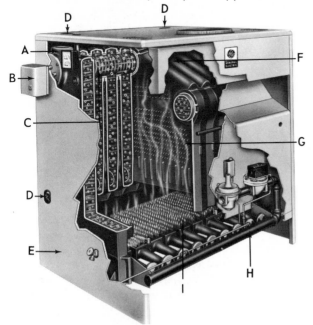

Fig. 20-43. Steam boiler burning gas as a fuel. A—Air eliminator separates air from water. B—Control. C—Water heater which supplies domestic hot water. D—Pipe connections. E—Insulated jacket. F—Draft hood. G—Cast iron boiler sections. H—Manifold and controls. I—Burners.
(General Electric Co.)

Fig. 20-44. Hot water heater which may be mounted in hot water or steam furnace.

20-22 Electric Heat

The use of electricity to heat homes, stores, commercial buildings, and factories is steadily growing in popularity.

Some advantages of electric heat are:
1. Low first cost.
2. Electric heating devices need no oxygen and therefore need no air supply.
3. Highest temperatures needed are below the ignition temperature of most fuels and therefore the system is safe.
4. Because of the absence of combustion and combustion gases there is less danger of toxic conditions arising.
5. Equipment normally requires less space.
6. Individual room temperature control is easily obtained.

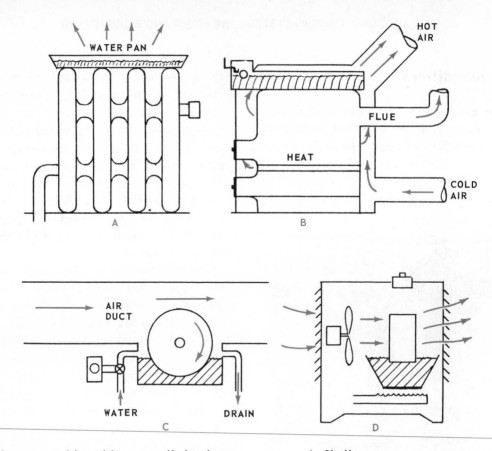

Fig. 20-45. Some typical humidifiers installed in heating systems. A—Shallow pan on warm water or steam radiator. B—Shallow pan in top of warm air furnace. Float keeps level of water in pan constant. C—Revolving wick arrangement in warm air duct. A float maintains constant water level. D—Space humidifier not a part of heating system. Water is vaporized by electric heat. A fan circulates the moist air through the room.

The process has some disadvantages:
1. Cost per unit of heat may be higher than for some of the other fuels.
2. Humidity control problems may occur.

20-23 Principles of Electric Heating

Electricity is a form of energy and because energies can be converted to other forms of energy, electrical energy can be changed to heat energy.

Heating with electricity can be done either directly or indirectly.
1. Heating by directly turning electricity into heat is done in two ways:
   A. Resistance heating. Resistance heating is used either to heat by passing a fluid over an electrically heated element (usually air is the fluid although some units use water), or to heat by raising the temperature of the heating element to a temperature which creates radiant heat.
   B. Thermoelectric heating. Thermoelectric heating is explained in another part of this same chapter.

2. Heating by indirectly turning electricity into heat is done by using the heat pump. The heat pump is described in Chapter 26.

20-24 Applications of Electric Heating

Electric heating has a wide range of applications. It may be used for heating in industrial processes such as fast drying of paints, melting low temperature metals, metal alloys and the like.

It has been used extensively for domestic and commercial cooking and baking.

It is used extensively for providing hot water.

For residential use, it has a growing application for use as:

1. The only source of heat.
2. Supplementary heat; that is, it may be used to provide heat even though some other system provides much of the heat in the residence. Heat pump systems may use electric resistance heating in climates where the heating energy required during cold weather is more than the heat pump can supply.
3. Resistance heating is also used to provide heat in parts of a building which are unsatisfactorily heated by the standard system. It also may be used to heat additions to buildings where the present system does not have enough capacity to heat the addition or where the extension of the present system would be too costly.

20-25 Principles of Electric Resistance Heating

Practically all materials resist the movement of electrons through them. If this resistance is low, the material is called a conductor. Most metals are good conductors of electricity.

If this resistance is high, the material is known as an insulator.

The resistance of the material is reflected by the increased action of the molecules of a material and this action is heat energy. How much agitation takes place depends on the voltage applied, length of material, cross section area, and temperature of the material.

For example:

1. When the cross section of the conductor increases, there is less resistance to electron flow.

2. When the material becomes longer, there is an increase in resistance to electron flow.
3. When the material becomes warmer, there is an increase in resistance to electron flow.

In electric resistance heating, metals are generally used as heating elements. The metals are designed to permit a certain current to flow at either the 120V setting or 240V setting to provide the heat required. Some units are designed to operate at incandescent temperatures. Some are units mounted in well protected cabinets. Systems used are baseboard units, wires installed in floors, in walls, and/or in ceilings and are described as nonincandescent temperature units.

Basically, the higher the temperature of the heating element, the smaller the space it needs to occupy. Some units are also designed with high temperature heating elements to create both air heating energy and radiant energy.

Electrical energy is converted into heat energy in the following ratios:

$$1 \text{ watt} = 3.415 \text{ Btu}$$
$$100 \text{ watts} = 341.5 \text{ Btu}$$
$$1000 \text{ watts} = 3415 \text{ Btu}$$

The voltage multiplied by the amperage flow in a circuit equals the watts.

At 20 amperes maximum input, a 120V circuit will provide 2,400 watts or 7,683 Btu.

A home with a need for 50,000 Btu/hr. for heating therefore requires about 60 amperes service at 240 volts or 14,000 watts or 14.4 kilowatts or 14.4 kwh (kilowatt hours).

20-26 Building Design for Electric Resistance Heating

In some cases, converting a coal, oil, or gas fired heating system building into an electric resistance heating system is possible and practical if the building is modified to reduce heat transfer and air infiltration. The walls and ceiling should be insulated as thoroughly as possible. Windows should be double glazed. Wood or plastic window and door frames are preferable to metal.

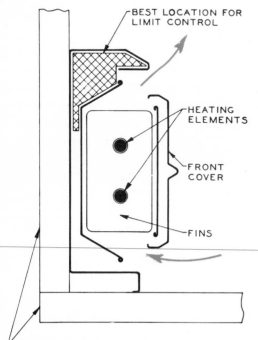

Fig. 20-46. *Basic principle of baseboard natural convection electric resistance heating.*
(White-Rodgers Div., Emerson Electric)

Where electric resistance heating is desired, the building should be designed to minimize heat losses and thereby reduce the operating cost to a minimum.

When possible, advantage should be taken of solar heat as it contacts the east, south, and west exposures. Walls and ceiling should be fully insulated, following latest specifications available from manufacturers.

The building can be designed for individual heat control for each room. Humidity control may require dehumidification rather than humidification. Air cleanliness should be considered. An electrostatic precipitator or activated charcoal filter may be needed to control dust and odors.

20-27 Natural Convection Electric Resistance Heating

This form of heating has the electrical resistance heating unit mounted in a casing which is designed to efficiently move air over the heating element by natural convection. See Fig. 40-46. Warmed air is lighter (air expands when heated) and rises. The colder air, being heavier, settles to the lower opening and enters the unit to replace the rising heated air.

20-28 Baseboard Electric Resistance Heating

A popular form of natural convection heating is baseboard heating. The units used are shaped much like a regular baseboard, are mounted on the wall close to the floor and are usually installed under windows. Fig. 20-47 shows a section of a baseboard heater. Internal construction of

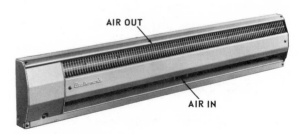

Fig. 20-47. *Section of a baseboard electric resistance heating unit. The covered left end may be used to house junction box and thermostat.*
(Electromode Div., Friden Inc.)

a baseboard heater is shown in Fig. 20-49.

In most cases a baseboard heating unit should be mounted on the wall. If built into the wall, dust in the heated air coming from the unit may streak the wall and necessitate frequent cleaning. Fig. 20-50 shows a unit being installed. It is important to keep the air passages clear to prevent poor air flow. The temperature of the heating element may become too high if the air passages are blocked.

Each unit may be thermostatically operated which permits individual room temperature control. The units are easy to install, take up a minimum of space, and since there are no moving parts, they are noiseless. It is strongly recommended that a safety (limit) switch be installed in each unit, which will open the electrical circuit if any part of the heater reaches an above normal temperature. See Par. 20-36.

Baseboard units are available in lengths from approximately 36 in. to 100 in. Some

units have only one heating element; others have two or more heating elements connected in parallel.

On most installations, it is good practice to keep the current load to 20 amperes or less per circuit. Because twice as much heat (kwh) is obtained at any specified amperage by using 240 volts rather than 120 volts (watts = volts x amperes) the use of 240V circuits where practical, is desirable.

20-29 Forced Convection Resistance Heating

Spaces can be heated efficiently, using either remote or self-contained forced convection electric resistance heaters.

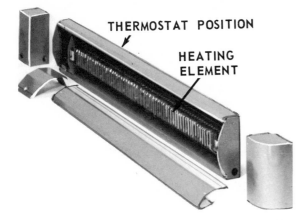

Fig. 20-49. Baseboard electric resistance heating unit with the front cover removed. Note thermostat location, corner block and end piece.

Fig. 20-51. Electric heating unit being installed in roof duct. (H. W. Tuttle and Co.)

These units may be placed either in air distribution ducts of a heating system, as shown in Fig. 20-51, or they may be self-contained units having their own fan and motor, as shown in Fig. 20-52.

20-30 Radiant Electric Heating (Infrared)

Radiant heat is usually the impact of the infrared band of light energy waves against an object. The object absorbs the rays and becomes warmer. When you open a furnace door, even if you stand back from the door, the heat impact which is felt is usually an infrared ray impact. This principle can be used for comfort heating.

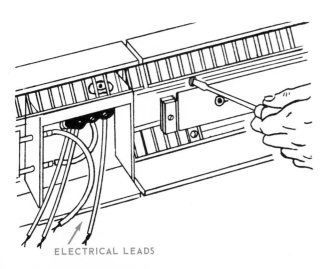

Fig. 20-50. Baseboard electric resistance heating unit with decorative panel removed showing mounting screw. (General Electric Co.)

Fig. 20-52. A forced convection electric resistance heating unit. (Electromode Div., Friden Inc.)

Fig. 20-53. Wall mounted electric heater which may be used for either primary heating or supplementary heating. It has a thermostat, off and on switch and fan switch. (Electromode Div., Friden Inc.)

The energy source may be any fuel although gas-fired and electrically-heated elements are the chief sources.

If radiant heat rays are focused on a person, and this person has several square feet of surface to absorb the rays, he can be kept quite comfortable even though the ambient temperature is below the comfort range. A large warehouse with a few small areas where employees work is a typical example of where radiant heat is often used to good advantage.

Radiant heat dissipates as the square of the distance. That is, an object twice as far away from the radiant heat source will receive only one fourth as much heat.

Radiant heat may be used as the only heat source for a building. Radiant heat fixtures are usually mounted 12 to 14 feet above the space to be served. Two or more fixtures are used to provide radiant heat impact on the person from two or more sides.

Gas-fired radiant heat is usually provided by heating ceramic elements to incandescence and using a reflector to focus this heat. These units first came into use about 1946. In gas-fired units about 50 percent of the heat energy is converted into radiant heat. These units operate about 700 F. to 1,600 F.

Some electrically-heated fixtures use quartz lamps; Vycor or metal sheathed. Some use open resistance wire or ribbon. Quartz lamps are usually of 800 to 2,500 watts power consumption. The lamps and wires reach temperatures of approximately 1,200 F.

A useful application for radiant heat in the temperate zones is for snow melting. 100 to 200 watts are usually needed for each sq. ft. of surface to be serviced.

20-31 Electric Heating Coils

Three types of electric resistance heating wires are:
1. Open wire.
2. Open ribbon.
3. Tubular cased wire.

The open wire type consists usually of nickel chromium resistance wire mounted on ceramic or mica insulation. These wires must be carefully protected from being contacted by metal objects and/or by humans or animals to avoid the danger of burns or electrical shock. See Fig. 20-53.

Ribbon type resistance heating is made of the same material, and is mounted in the same general way. It too, must be carefully covered by a grid to prevent burns or shock. The ribbon design provides more surface exposure for air contact.

The tubular heating element is similar to the heating elements used in electric stoves. Nickel chromium resistance wire is usually surrounded by a magnesium oxide powder. The wire and powder are enclosed in a heat and corrosion resistant steel tube.

This design protects against electrical shock, however the element may reach rather high temperatures. To increase the heating surface, and to reduce dangerous high temperatures, tubular covered elements are sometimes imbedded in fin type aluminum castings.

20-32 Supplementary Electric Heating

Electricity is often used to heat building additions which have a heating plant of insufficient capacity to carry the extra load, or where the problem of extending the present system is difficult.

Radiant heat panels built into the wall, baseboard heaters and resistance heating wire imbedded in the ceiling or wall plaster may be used for this purpose.

Fig. 20-54. Illustration which shows parts of electric resistance space heater. A—Frame. B—Front cover. C—Heating element and fan. D—Back case.

Added bedrooms, family rooms, utility rooms, and the like may all be successfully heated in this manner.

Fig. 20-54 shows a unit which may be used either as a primary heating source or as a supplementary heating source. Air enters at the top and a fan forces the air down over the electrically heated aluminum element. Air leaves the unit through the lower part of the grill. Fig. 20-55 shows a schematic wiring diagram for the unit shown in Fig. 5-54.

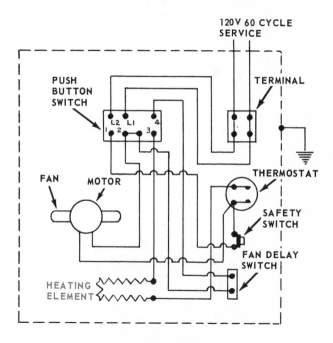

Fig. 20-55. A wiring diagram of a wall mounted heater. (Electromode Div., Friden Inc.)

Another type of supplementary electric heating unit is a panel which gives off infrared heat. Fig. 20-56 shows such a unit.

20-33 Controls

Electric heating units generally use thermostats for temperature control. The units are equipped with safety controls such as temperature limit switches. Large capacity units use a relay in conjunction with low voltage thermostats to control high wattage loads. Another control sometimes used is the sequence control. This control is a block of relays. Each relay controls a separate heating circuit. The

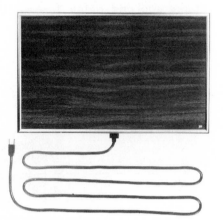

Fig. 20-56. Plug-in type of electric heating panel. (Minnesota Mining and Mfg. Co., Electrical Products Div.)

Fig. 20-57. Wall thermostat used for controlling an electric heating circuit. (Honeywell)

relays are activated one at a time. This sequence timing prevents imposing the full electrical load on the main building circuit at one time.

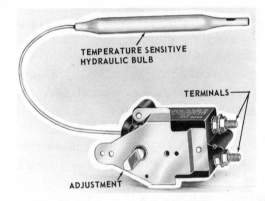

Fig. 20-58. Hydraulic type thermostat used on electric resistance heating units. Rated at 240 to 277 volts and can control up to 5000 watts. Its 1 1/2 deg. differential provides uniform temperature control. (White-Rodgers Div., Emerson Electric)

Controls used with electric heating apparatus include:

1. Thermostats.
2. Relays.
3. Sequence relays.
4. Limit switches.

20-34 Thermostats

Two types of electric heating thermostats are:

1. Line voltage thermostats.
2. Low voltage thermostats.

Line voltage thermostats are usually designed to carry approximately 5,000 watts at 240 volts AC and are used directly in the electrical heating circuit. Fig. 20-57 shows a line voltage thermostat as used for directly controlling electric heating circuits. The thermostats are designed to be mounted on the baseboard or on the wall 4 to 5 ft. above the floor. The thermostats usually have an "off" position.

Since the thermostats must handle 120V or 240V circuits, the contact action and design must be sturdy and fast acting. The controls operate at approximately 2 deg. F. differential. Many wall connected thermostats have a small resistance heater or anticipator which will open the circuit before the actual room temperature reaches the desired temperature. The anticipator heat opens the thermostat points and shuts off the electrical flow. Residual heat in the heating coils continues to heat the room until the unit cools. These thermostats have points that open on temperature rise and close on temperature drop.

Bimetal strips, gas filled bellows, and/or liquid filled bellows are devices which provide movement to open and close the points. Fig. 20-58 shows a liquid filled sensitive bulb thermostat. This thermostat is available in several temperature ranges from 35 F. to 75 F. up to 145 F. to 205 F. It is important to select the correct thermostat for the application.

Low voltage thermostats are located in a low voltage circuit which is connected to a solenoid coil of a relay switch. These thermostats will be damaged if connected into a 120V line circuit. They are used with a step-down transformer.

Some localities require that both leads to the heating element be opened by thermostat control. Fig. 20-59 shows such a thermostat. Terminals on the right are line connection terminals (L); terminals on the left are heater element terminals (H).

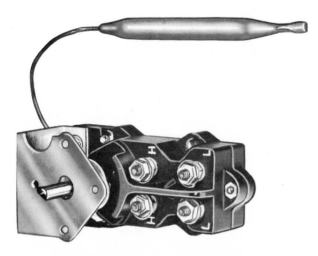

Fig. 20-59. Hydraulic type thermostat used on electric resistance heating which controls both electrical leads to heating unit.
(White-Rodgers Div., Emerson Electric)

Thermostats which are mounted on baseboard heaters are usually encased in attractive covers and have a calibrated dial mounted on the adjustment knob. Fig. 20-60 shows such an installation.

Fig. 20-60. Thermostat designed to be mounted on electric resistance baseboard heater casing. Note "no heat" or off position.

20-35 Relays

A relay is a device which eliminates the need for electric current used for heating energy to flow through the thermostat. Thus the main circuit can be made as short and as direct as possible.

The solenoid which creates magnetism to close the points in the heating circuit or circuits may be energized by either 24V, 120V or 240V. The thermostat voltage and the solenoid coil voltage must be the same. Fig. 20-61 shows a schematic wiring diagram of a relay which controls four separate heating circuits, and one fan motor circuit. When the solenoid is energized, it actuates a lever which operates all of the snap switches. The snap switches are calibrated to make and break (close and open) in sequence. The snap switch controlling the fan motor makes (closes) first and breaks (opens) last.

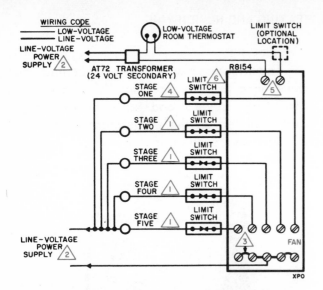

Fig. 20-61. Wiring diagram for relay circuit controlling five electric resistance heaters. In upper left,
the 2 indicates the power supply, also step-down transformer. In the lower left, 2 indicates the line-voltage
power supply. The solenoid coil connections are shown
at 5. (Honeywell)

20-36 Limit Controls

Electrical heating devices, in a manner
similar to all energy sources for heating,
must have safety devices to limit the maximum temperature the device may reach.
If the thermostat points stick closed, if the
air circulation becomes blocked by drapes
or furniture, or if for any other reason the
electric heating baseboard chamber or fur-

nace plenum chamber reaches a temperature of from 190 to 300 F., pressures created in the limit switch element will open
the switch points and protect the equipment and the building. Fig. 20-62 shows
a wiring diagram of a heating element,
thermostat, and limit control circuit.

One type limit control has the temperature sensitive element mounted the full
length of the baseboard chamber. Fig.
20-63 shows such a safety switch. The
limit control is usually set to open the circuit approximately 20 to 40 F. above the
highest thermostat setting.

20-37 Sequence Controls

To avoid imposing a sudden high kilowatt load on electrical service lines which
might cause a voltage drop and flickering
lights, radio interference, TV flicker and
the like, large electrical resistance heating units usually consist of several heating
coils. When heat is called for, a control
system closes the circuit to one heating
element or grid at a time until all of the
heating circuits are functioning. This arrangement is called sequencing.

Methods used to sequence separate
multiple heating elements are:

1. Thermal element switches which
   close as one element heats up and
   which then close the circuit for the
   next element until all the circuits
   are operating.
2. Relays which, as each one closes,
   also activate the relay for the next
   heating element.
3. Timers which rotate and close a
   series of contacts closing the circuit
   for one heating element at a time.

20-38 Heating Coil Installation

Electric heating elements must be installed in accordance with both the electrical codes and the manufacturer's recommendations.

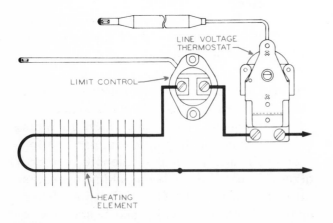

Fig. 20-62. Diagram of electric resistance heating
circuit. Note that thermostat and limit control are
connected in series with power line.

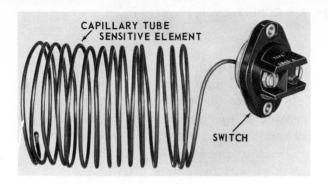

Fig. 20-63. *Safety limit switch which may be connected in series in heater circuit. If temperature exceeds safe limit, this switch will open circuit.*

The installation must be checked to be sure it is safe in reference to fires, safe in reference to humans and animals, and it must be an efficient heating unit.

Baseboard heaters must be provided with unhampered air circulation. The unit heaters must be mounted installed in a way that they are not dangerously close to flammables. Furnace units must be shielded electrically and heat protected.

All metal parts of the units must be grounded.

The electrical service must use wire sizes according to the voltage and amperage of the circuit. The circuit must be properly fused and provided with adequate limit and safety controls. All controls must

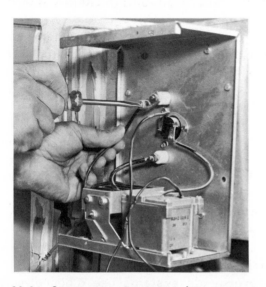

Fig. 20-64. *Serviceman connecting line to terminals of duct mounted electric resistance heating unit. (H. W. Tuttle and Co.)*

be for correct voltage and current. Fig. 20-64 shows electrical connections being made to an open wire supplementary heating coil which has been installed in a duct.

20-39 Electric Heat Humidifiers

When a house or business facility is electrically heated, there is a tendency to have too much humidity. Water vapor sources include:

1. Cooking.
2. Wash basins.
3. Lavatories.
4. Respiration.
5. Perspiration.
6. Laundry.
7. Showers and/or bathing.

A humidistat and a water vapor creating device is usually needed during the winter season in the temperate zones.

This is because infiltered air during the heating season, when heated to room temperature, has a relative humidity of approximately 5 to 10 percent, and because comfort requires about 30 to 40 percent relative humidity, moisture must be added to the air.

An electric humidifier may be used for this purpose. Facilities which use steam heated, hydronic heated, or warm air heated equipment are examples of installations which can use this type of humidifier. Warm air heating units sometimes incorporate a humidifier that uses the warm air as a source of heat. However, if the humidifier water may be separately heated, the amount of humidification can be more accurately controlled.

The electric humidifier has the advantage of ease of installation, flexibility of location and accurate humidity control. Fig. 20-65 shows an electric humidifier designed for use in a duct or plenum chamber installation. This unit has an 800 watt heating coil which is controlled by an adjustable humidistat. Water level is con-

Fig. 20-65. Electric humidifier designed for installation in warm air heating duct.
(Mueller Climatrol Div.,
Worthington Air Conditioning Co.)

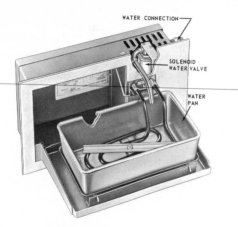

WATER CONNECTION

SOLENOID WATER VALVE

WATER PAN

Fig. 20-66. Details of construction of electric humidifier shown in Fig. 20-65.

trolled by a pan type float which operates a switch in the solenoid water valve circuit. Fig. 20-66 shows the construction of the electric humidifier shown in Fig. 20-65.

20-40 Heating Coil Service

Electric resistance heating requires a minimum of service. Air passages over the heating units must be kept clean. Grills, ducts, heating coils and fins should be cleaned at least once each year. Brushing and vacuuming are recommended. It is extremely dangerous to use flammable fluids for this type cleaning.

The serviceman should check the terminals for tightness and cleanliness. A voltmeter or ohmmeter may be used to determine if there are loose connections or corroded connections. The ohmmeter is preferable because it may be used for checking with the power off.

The thermostat, limit control, relay, are possible service problems' locations. If the circuit does not function, the following typical electrical circuit diagnosis is recommended:

1. Is there power to the fuse or circuit breaker box?
2. Is the fuse in good condition and are the connections electrically good?
3. Is the thermostat operating (open and closed temperatures should be checked)?
4. Is the limit switch operating (open and closed temperatures should be checked)?
5. Are the relay coils in good condition and operating?
6. Are the relay contact points clean and operating?
7. Does the electrical heating coil have continuity?

20-41 Heating Controls and Circuits

Automatic furnaces and other heating devices are controlled by devices which turn the system on and off, and which stop the system if abnormal conditions arise (safety devices).

These devices are mainly electric controls, activated by temperature, pressure, or time. Relays are often used either to control full voltages by low voltage signals or to interlock signal devices for safe operation.

All systems use room thermostats.

If automatic humidity is desired, humidistats are used.

Warm air systems use a bonnet safety thermostat to shut off the system if the plenum chamber overheats.

Oil burners use a stack thermostat which will shut off the burner if the stack temperature does not rise within a few seconds after the oil burner starts.

Pressurestats are used in steam systems to shut off the system if the pressure becomes dangerously high. Each different type heating system has its own special automatic devices.

The wiring diagram of a gun type oil burner system is shown in Fig. 20-67. Note

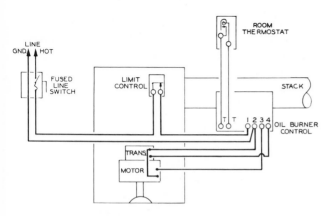

Fig. 20-67. Wiring diagram for gun type oil burner. (White-Rodgers Div., Emerson Electric)

the thermostat, oil burner control, and limit control. An oil burner circuit which has a circulation pump (hydronic system) is shown in Fig. 20-68. The heavy wires are high voltage (120V) lines and the light wires are 24V lines. Note that the circu-

lator control has its own separate control.

A wiring diagram of a gun type oil burner installation that is a bit different is shown in Fig. 20-69. This system operates

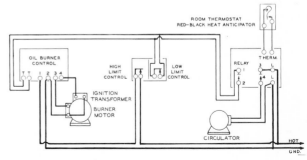

Fig. 20-69. Wiring diagram for gun type oil burner, hydronic installation using motor driven circulator pump. Room temperature controls hydronic pump operation. Temperature of water in furnace controls burner operation.

the circulator motor when the room thermostat calls for heat. The temperature of the water in the boiler controls the burner operation.

Gas furnaces use many varieties of electrical devices. Some operate on 120 volts, some on 24 volts and some on current generated by a thermocouple (25 to 700 millivolts).

A wiring diagram of a solenoid operated gas line valve is shown in Fig. 20-70.

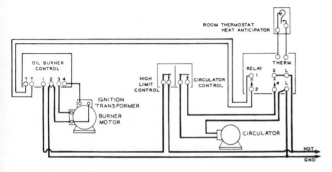

Fig. 20-68. Wiring diagram for gun type oil burner, hydronic installation. Room thermostat controls both the pump motor and the burner.

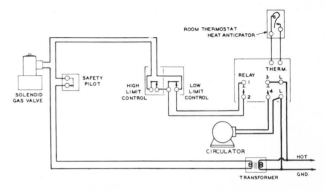

Fig. 20-70. Solenoid operated gas line valve. This is a low voltage type valve. Note step-down transformer at lower right-hand corner.

A diaphragm type gas valve wiring diagram is shown in Fig. 20-71. It has a circulator motor that operates all the time the burner is operating. Fig. 20-72 shows a circulator motor wiring diagram.

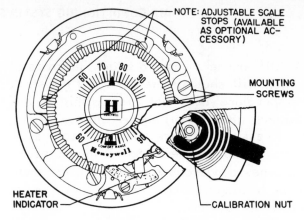

Fig. 20-73. Heating thermostat which uses a mercury switch. (Honeywell)

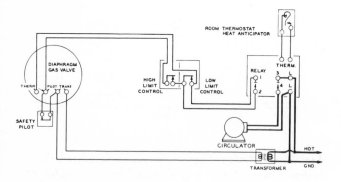

Fig. 20-71. Wiring diagram for diaphragm type control on gas-fired furnace. Note room thermostat controls operation of water circulating pump. The gas valve controls the water temperature. (White-Rodgers Div., Emerson Electric)

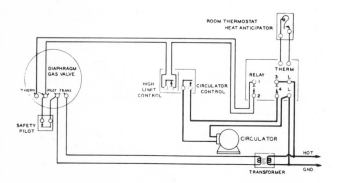

Fig. 20-72. Wiring diagram of diaphragm type gas valve heating plant control. Heavy lines represent line voltage; light lines represent low voltage from step-down transformer.

20-42 Heating Thermostats

The heating thermostats which have been most used in domestic service are what is known as series 10, series 20, series 80 etc. thermostats.

The series 10 thermostat is being replaced by a high voltage thermostat, se-

ries 20. The series 10 is a 24V unit with three wires. The wires are used to make a contact on temperature drop and to close a holding circuit. This thermostat must be used with a relay. The relay contacts control the 120V circuit for the oil burner, gas burner, or stoker.

The series 20 thermostat is a 120V two wire system, and may be used on gas burners, oil burners, or stokers.

The series 80 thermostat is a two wire 24V thermostat that controls furnace devices directly.

A control which can be used either as a series 80 (2 wire 24V) or a series 10 (3 wire 24V) thermostat is shown in Fig. 20-73. Its wiring circuit is shown in Fig. 20-74. This control uses a mercury bulb contact device.

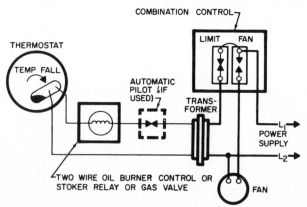

Fig. 20-74. Wiring circuit of a heating thermostat. Note that the automatic pilot and the fuel control are in the low voltage (24V) circuit.

WIRING DIAGRAMS

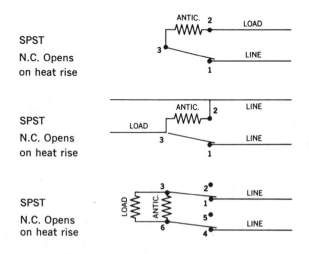

SPST
N.C. Opens
on heat rise

SPST
N.C. Opens
on heat rise

SPST
N.C. Opens
on heat rise

Fig. 20-75. Thermostat used in electrical heating systems. Above—External view of thermostat. Below—Wiring diagrams for thermostat. Note that it is equipped with an anticipator. The SPST indicates that the control has a single pole, single throw switch.
(Controls Co. of America)

An interesting problem in room heating thermostats is brought about by the fact temperatures always tend to rise above the thermostat setting after the thermostat points have opened and the burner has stopped. This action is the result of the residual heat in the furnace. To correct this overheating, manufacturers have placed a small heating coil in the thermostat. During the heating cycle, the thermostat is always about 1 deg. F. warmer than the room. If the thermostat is set for 74 F. the thermostat will open when the room temperature is actually 73 F. Then the room temperature will rise to 74 F. because of the heat in the already

heated furnace. These small resistance coils are usually called anticipator coils. Fig. 20-75 shows an electric heating thermostat equipped with an anticipator.

For heating purposes the thermostat is designed to close the contacts when cooled and open when the thermostat warms.

Thermostats must be located carefully. They must not be exposed to drafts, to hot or cold walls, to sunlight, etc. They must be located in an average temperature location. An inner wall is a popular place. Thermostats should be mounted about five feet above the floor. If placed closer to the floor the temperature control will be more uniform, however it is more likely to be disturbed by children or furniture. These thermostats should be kept as clean as possible inside.

If lint should lodge between the points, an open circuit will result. The contact points should be cleaned using a piece of clean paper. If a mercury tube is used instead of contact points, the thermostat must be installed in a level position (use a plumb line or spirit level).

Another style thermostat has been developed for air conditioning systems. These units have easily manipulated settings. They are designed with all the various types of electrical bases to enable the thermostat to control either:

1. Heating system.
2. Cooling systems.
3. Combination heating and cooling systems.

Some heating-cooling systems use a clock operated thermostat to change the temperature range during the night and reset the adjustment back to normal during the day. Fig. 20-76 shows a clock operated thermostat.

20-43 Furnace Controls

Thermostats send an electrical signal to electrical devices such as solenoid valves, relays, magnetic starters, etc.

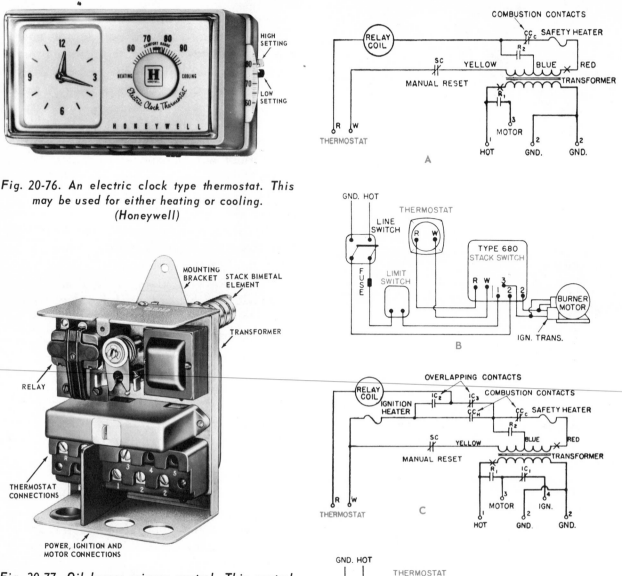

Fig. 20-76. An electric clock type thermostat. This may be used for either heating or cooling. (Honeywell)

Fig. 20-77. Oil burner primary control. This control will cycle the burner, operate electric ignition system, shut off unit if ignition fails and scavenge unit after each cycle. (Penn Controls Inc.)

One such control is shown in Fig. 20-77. It is commonly known as an oil burner primary control. It mounts on the furnace stack and responds to the thermostat and to a bimetal strip suspended in the stack. The control operates the burner motor and also the ignition. However, if the oil does not ignite and if therefore the stack does not heat in a very few seconds, the safety bimetal will shut off the current to the motor and ignition. The unit must be man-

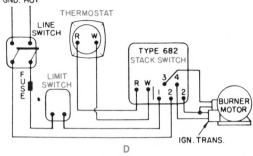

Fig. 20-78. Internal and external wiring diagrams of two types of oil burner controls (stack controls). A—Internal wiring diagram for continuous ignition. B—External wiring diagram for continuous ignition control. C—Schematic wiring diagram for intermittent ignition stack control. D—External wiring diagram for intermittent ignition stack control. (Penn Controls Inc.)

ually reset before it will operate. The control shown has wiring diagrams as illustrated in Fig. 20-78. Note the series connection of the power, limit switch and primary control (stack switch). The thermostat wires are low voltage; the others are 120 volts.

20-44 Humidistats

A humidistat is a device which responds to humidity changes and in doing so opens or closes an electric circuit. Humidistats are connected to a solenoid valve (directly or by means of a relay) or to the heating coils and fan motors of a humidifier.

The element of the humidistat which changes its shape as the humidity changes is called a hygroscopic element. The most commonly used element is a multiple strand of human hair. Wood elements have been used as well as other hygroscopic materials. The humidistat can be designed to activate the system as humidity decreases (heating systems) or designed to activate the system as the humidity increases (cooling systems).The hygroscopic material increases in size (or stretches) when the humidity increases and vice versa. Fig. 20-79 shows a humidistat with a multiple hair element. The control should be kept dust free and the cover must permit free air circulation over the element.

20-45 Review of Heating Safety

Safety must be strongly emphasized when installing and operating heating systems. Coal, oil, fuel gas furnaces are fires in a confined area. The fuel must be stored safely; it must be fed in a safe manner to the firepot of the furnace; means must be taken to shut down the unit, if fuel flow ceases, if any part of the system overheats, or if the products of combustion are restrained from safe exit from the building.

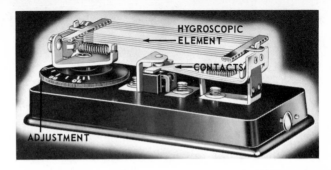

Fig. 20-79. A humidity control showing operating mechanism.

Always remember, that if fuel is in the presence of air and an ignition source exists, fire will result.

Always know exactly what you are doing. Follow manufacturers' specifications carefully. Always follow the building and safety codes in effect in the locality.

Electric heating is considered to be a safe heating method. The elimination of flames, pilot flames, electric spark ignition, and sparks reduces many sources of danger.

There is, however, possible danger from electrical shock, and the chance of burns or of combustion from the heating elements.

All electrical devices must be installed according to the local, state, and national electrical codes. The equipment should have Underwriters Laboratory (UL) approval. The installation should be made by a licensed electrician.

All nonelectrical metal parts of the unit must be safely grounded. Combustibles must not come in contact with heating elements. The heating elements must be mounted to eliminate the chance of persons or animals contacting the heating grids or elements.

20-46 Test Your Knowledge - Chapter 20

1. Name three types of air conditioning plants.
2. What is the most economical way to use electricity for heating?
3. How does a bypass air system operate?

4. List four most common sources of energy for heating?

5. What is the heating value of bituminous coal?

6. Name the types of oil burners.

7. What is one advantage of gas as a fuel?

8. Why must stack temperatures be kept over 300 F.?

9. What is a bimetal thermostat?

10. Name three heating systems which do not use a flame.

11. Why is humidifying needed during the heating season?

12. What is a hydronic heating system?

13. Name three types of electric resistance heating elements.

14. What is primary air?

15. How much heat is obtained from one 1 watt hour?

16. Where is carbon dioxide found in a fuel oil heating system?

17. What is the advantage of a 240V electric resistance heating circuit over a 120V circuit?

18. What grade fuel oil is used in most domestic gun type oil burners?

19. What does a low voltage thermostat control?

20. What is induced draft?

21. Why is a limit control needed?

22. How much air is needed to burn one gallon of domestic fuel oil?

23. Where should an electric resistance heating thermostat be located in the home?

24. What is the main cause of stack corrosion?

25. Why does excess humidity sometimes occur when electric resistance heating is used?

26. What chemicals can be used to remove soot from a flue?

27. What is meant by supplementary electric resistance heating?

28. How does a gun type oil burner obtain combustion air?

29. Why is a manometer used to measure natural gas pressure?

30. What is the color of the combustion of a well adjusted gun type oil burner?

31. How many oil filters or screens does a gun type oil burner system use?

32. What safety device is part of a pilot light?

33. Where is a thermocouple used in a fuel gas system?

34. What is the color of a correctly adjusted fuel gas flame?

Chapter 21

AIR CONDITIONING SYSTEMS, COOLING AND DEHUMIDIFYING

A refrigerating system is the heart of the comfort cooling phase of air conditioning. Comfort cooling machines use one of the standard refrigerating cycles, standard refrigerants, usual types of compressors, condensers, piping, refrigerant controls, motor controls, and evaporators. The refrigerant evaporating temperature of most comfort cooling systems is approximately 40 to 50 F. This chapter describes most of the designs in use today which use mechanical refrigeration for cooling. The use of absorption systems for comfort cooling purposes is also increasing. These units are described in Chapter 17.

Most air conditioning installations involve engineering problems. Adequate calculations must be made and specifications provided, otherwise the system will not function satisfactorily.

21-1 Principles of Atmosphere Cooling

As explained in Chapter 19, man's comfort and certain industrial processes (dealing with hydroscopic materials and processes) are dependent on the condition of the temperature and humidity.

The first mechanical atmosphere cooling and humidity control took place when cooled water was used both to cool air and dehumidify it. The air to be conditioned was passed over cooled coils or through cooled water sprays.

The application of refrigerating systems to condition the air was gradual but steady. Fig. 21-1 shows the basic principle of operation. Air coming from the evaporator coil is at 100 percent relative humidity. This saturated air must be mixed with air in the conditioned space, as it leaves the air conditioner or by a duct system which bypasses some of the returning air to the outlet duct and mixes with the cooled air before the air enters the room.

21-2 Comfort Cooling Systems

Several types of comfort cooling systems are in common use. They may be classified by arrangement of the mechanism:

1. Self-contained or unit coolers.
2. Remote.

The self-contained system may be further described as:
1. Window units.
2. Through-the-wall units.
3. Cabinet units.

Remote units are of two types:
1. The condensing unit is remote and the evaporator coil is installed in the room to be conditioned or in the main duct.
2. The central air conditioning plant. The condensing unit and evaporator unit are installed in a remote place and a cooled brine or water is circulated to heat exchangers in the various spaces to be conditioned.

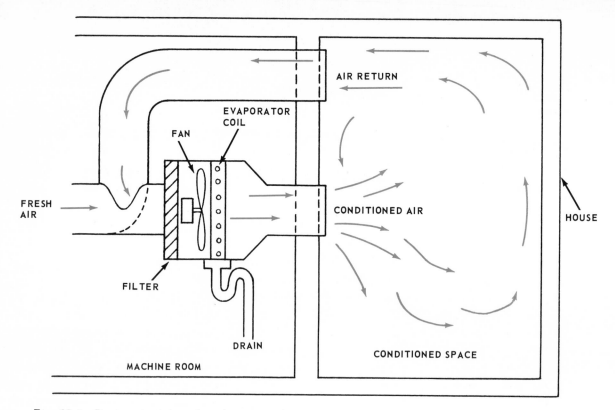

Fig. 21-1. Basic principles of cooling air and removing moisture from fresh air and recirculated air.

21-3 Cooling Equipment for Air Conditioning Purposes

The cooling equipment usually consists of refrigeration coils. The coils are maintained at refrigerant temperatures of 40 to 50 F. and air to be conditioned is blown through them.

There are several systems used to cool the air:

1. Mechanical refrigeration.
2. Absorption refrigeration. Absorption system air conditioning is described in Chapter 17.
3. Ice.

Refrigeration coils also serve as dehumidifiers for the air circulating past them (if the humidity is high), since some of the air will be cooled below its dew point temperature and the excess moisture will be condensed out on the coils. This leaves the conditioned air both cooler and with less moisture. However, the cooled air is at 100 percent relative humidity for the temperature at which it leaves the coil,

and the cooled air must be mixed with other air to reduce the total relative humidity and eliminate the damp feeling. Adequate drains must be provided to carry away the moisture condensed on the evaporators.

Some air conditioning plants use ice for the cooling medium, particularly if cooling is only needed for a comparatively few days of the year. Cold water from streams or wells may also be used for the cooling coils. The water should be 50 F. or cooler, however, to produce satisfactory dehumidification.

Most air conditioning installations use automatic mechanical or absorption refrigeration as the cooling means.

The mechanical system consists principally of:

1. Condensing unit.
2. Evaporator coil.
3. Motor-fans.
4. Filters.
5. Ducts and air flow controls.
6. Motor controls.
7. Temperature and humidity controls.

21-4 Unit Comfort Coolers

Unit or self-contained air conditioners are of two types: (1) one type provides only comfort cooling for summer; (2) the other type provides both summer cooling and winter heating.

Both types have a complete refrigeration plant included, i.e., condensing unit, refrigerant valves, and evaporator coils. Individual room thermostats control the units. Filtering equipment is also a part of the system. These units may also be classified as window or in-the-wall units, or console units.

The window units are air-cooled units, easily mounted and operate from 120V or 240V single-phase circuits. These units vary in capacity from 4000 Btu/hr. to 40,000 Btu/hr.

The console units may be either air-cooled or water-cooled units. They are installed in the room to be conditioned or in an adjacent room with short ducts to deliver air and provide for return air.

21-5 Window Units

The window mounted, or wall mounted comfort cooler is very popular. This unit mounts on a windowsill and the installation is relatively easy. The condenser is located in that part of the cabinet that is outside the building. Outside air is forced over the condenser coil by a fan. Inside the room another fan draws air in through a filter and forces it over the evaporator coil. The two air flow fans may be driven by the same motor or each may have its own motor. Fig. 21-2 shows air circuits of a window air conditioner.

The principle of operation of a window comfort cooler is shown in Fig. 21-3. A more detailed schematic is shown in Fig. 21-4.

Window units are available in several models. One model cools the air, filters the air, and has a fresh air intake. Another model has these same devices but in addition has an electrical resistance heating unit to furnish heat. A third type uses

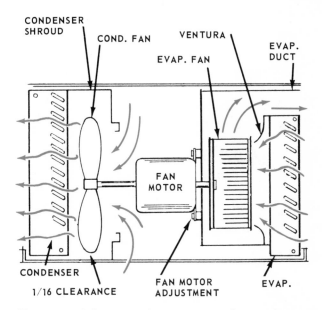

Fig. 21-2. Schematic of air circuits of a window air conditioner. An axial type fan is used at the condenser. The evaporator air circuit uses a radial flow fan. The same motor drives both fans.
(Gibson Refrigerator Sales Corp., Hupp Corp.)

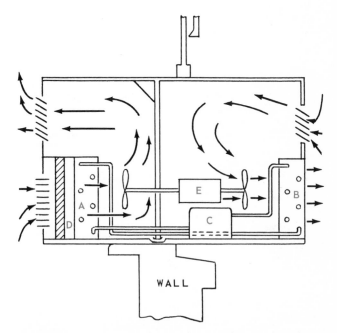

Fig. 21-3. Schematic of a window comfort cooler. A—Evaporator coil. B—Condenser. C—Motor-compressor. D—Filter. E—Fan motor.

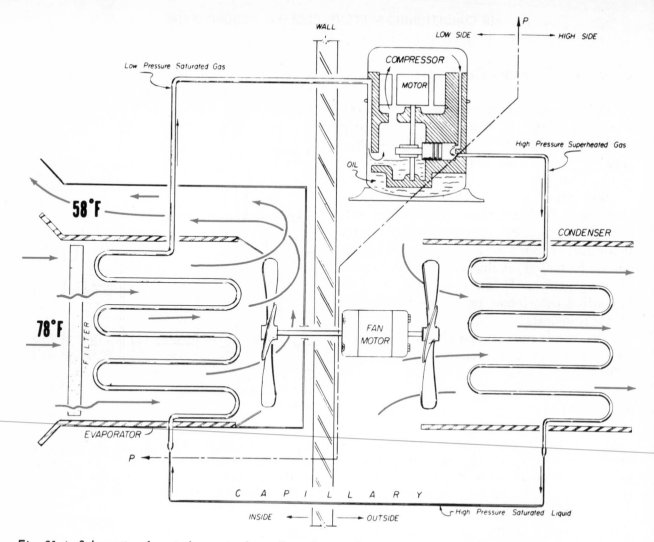

Fig. 21-4. Schematic of a window or in-the-wall comfort cooling unit. Note conditioned air flow and separate condenser air flow.

Fig. 21-5. Window unit showing necessary parts to safely mount unit in window and seal openings. (Kelvinator Div., American Motors Corp.)

Fig. 21-6. Bracing used to hold window air conditioner on a sill. (Remington Air Conditioning Div., Singer Co.)

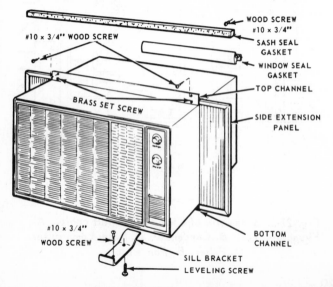

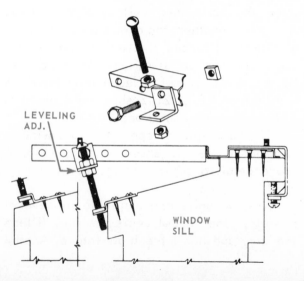

a reverse cycle system (heat pump) to permit the use of the refrigerating units as a comfort cooling unit and a heating unit. Chapter 26 covers heat pumps.

Window units may be obtained to fit double hung windows, casement windows, or can be installed in special wall openings.

The condensate from the evaporator coil is drained to the base of the motor-compressor and the condenser where its evaporation helps to cool these parts. A capillary tube or a bypass type AEV refrigerant control is usually used.

21-6 Installing Window Units

Window units must be installed level (for condensate drain), securely fastened in place (to prevent the unit falling out of the window), sealed to minimize air infiltration, and the window must be secured in the proper position.

When units are installed in windows, metal plates, rubber gaskets, and sealing compounds are used to seal the unit into the window. The unit and the parts needed to install it are shown in Fig. 21-5. Fig. 21-6 shows a windowsill with leveling bracket and security bracket mounted in place. Another method of bracing and leveling a comfort cooling unit is shown in Fig. 21-7. The unit housing should be adjusted to tilt downward about 1/4 in. on the outside of the window to provide condensate drainage. A sponge rubber or plastic strip is usually placed between the housing and the windowsill to help make a leakproof joint. After the sill brackets are installed, and the unit housing installed, the rubber seal strips and the filler boards are installed, as shown in Fig. 21-8.

Most manufacturers have a slightly different design for mounting window units.

Where the lower sash is raised to make room for the air conditioner, an air gap will exist between the two sashes. This opening may be sealed with a sponge rub-

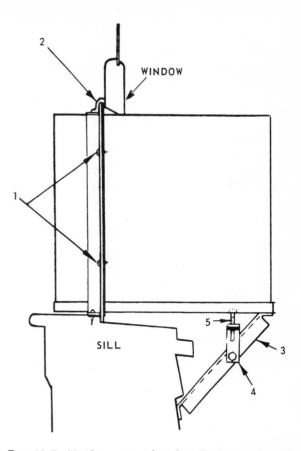

Fig. 21-7. Window unit with indoor flush mounting. 1—Sheet metal screws to hold side closure panels. 2—Gasket. 3—Bracket. 4—Clamp pivot. 5—Clamp adjustment.

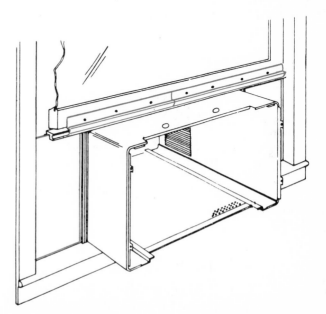

Fig. 21-8. Window air conditioning casing installed, showing rubber seal strips and filler boards.

ber strip, as shown in Fig. 21-9. The sash bracket is fastened to the upper sash if possible, as this position locks both of the windows.

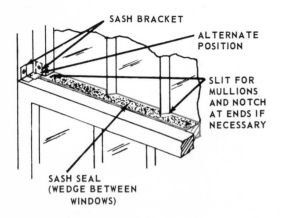

Fig. 21-9. Sponge rubber seal placed between upper edge of lower sash and upper sash of double hung window. The sash bracket keeps lower sash locked. (Philco Corp., Sub. of Ford Motor Co.)

The unit housing must be securely fastened in place before the unit is put in place. The filler boards (between the unit housing and the side of the window) are usually sealed with sponge rubber strips and held in place with sheet metal screws and with spring clips. Fig. 21-10 shows one method of installing them.

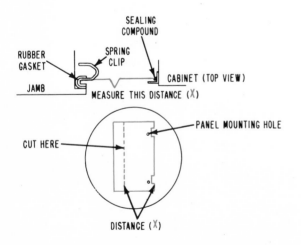

Fig. 21-10. Installing filler panel between unit housing and window joint.

A typical installation of a window unit in a casement window is shown in Fig. 21-11. The inside mechanism is heavy. It should be moved using a dolly or special carrier. Avoid moving or lifting the unit and using the tubing or coils as hand grips. Carry the unit by holding onto the bottom pan.

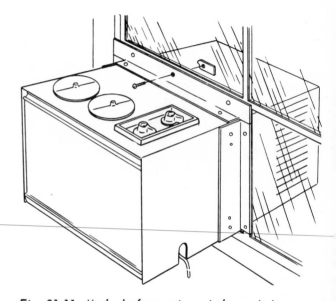

Fig. 21-11. Method of mounting window unit in casement window. (Kelvinator Div., American Motors Corp.)

Avoid forcing the unit into the casing. Check to be sure the refrigerant lines and the wiring are free and clear as the unit moves into the casing. The front grille, the filter and the control knobs are easily installed.

The final step is to check all joints for tightness and to caulk seams which reveal light leaks or which you suspect may not be airtight.

In making the electrical hookup, a separate circuit should be used, if possible. A polarized plug (one with a ground wire) should be used. Fig. 21-12 shows some wall outlet designs.

Thermostats are used with most window units. They are adjustable to cut-out between 56 F. and 60 F. and cut-in be-

VOLTAGE	TYPE OF POWER CORD PLUG USED	DESCRIPTION
115 Volt 15 Ampere	Parallel	
230 Volt 15 Ampere	Tandem	
230 Volt 20 Ampere		

Fig. 21-12. Extension cord male plug and wall out-let designs recommended for window air conditioners. (Philco Corp., Sub. of Ford Motor Co.)

tween 77 F. and 80 F. Their differentials vary between 3 F. to 8 F. If a thermostat fails, the unit will not start. To test the operation of a thermostat, cover the air-out and air-in with a cloth. The air will now recirculate into the unit and the tem-perature will quickly drop to the cut-out temperature (use a thermometer).

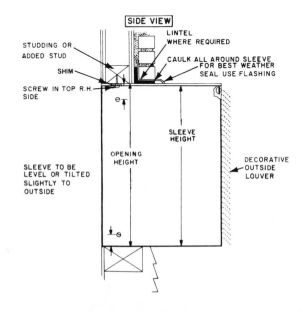

Fig. 21-13. Typical through-the-wall unit air condi-tioning installation.

Units which are mounted through the wall are popular in new apartment con-struction units. There is no interference with windows, and comfort cooling can be provided as desired. Fig. 21-13 shows a typical installation.

21-7 Servicing Window Units

Servicing window units is similar to the servicing of hermetic refrigerating units. Chapters 12 and 15 describe most of the servicing operations.

Some of the external service operations are as follows:

1. Semiannual cleaning or replacement of the filter (usually done by the owner). Fig. 21-14 shows a filter design.

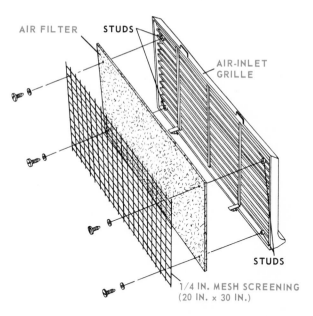

Fig. 21-14. A typical filter design and installation for a window air conditioner. (Philco Corp., Sub. of Ford Motor Co.)

2. Annual cleaning of the evaporator coil, condenser, fan blades, fan motor, mo-tor-compressor, and casing. The unit may be removed for these operations, as shown in Fig. 21-15. A tarpaulin or newspapers should be placed on the floor and the

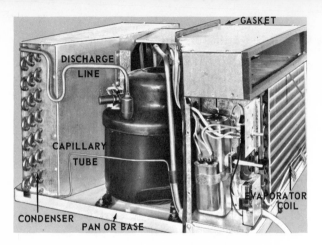

Fig. 21-15. *Window air conditioner unit. (Frigidaire Div., General Motors Corp.)*

drapes or curtains should be removed or tied back during this operation. Taking the unit outside for cleaning is desirable. It is necessary to clean the coils thoroughly. The fins, if bent, should be straightened.

3. The fan motor or motors should be lubricated unless they have sealed-for-life bearings. The fans should be tight on the shaft and the fans should be positioned in the fan shroud for efficient air movement. Carefully avoid bending the fan blades or

Fig. 21-16. *Wiring diagram of 7000 Btu/hr. - 115V window air conditioner. Note two-speed fan motor. (Norge Div., Borg-Warner Corp.)*

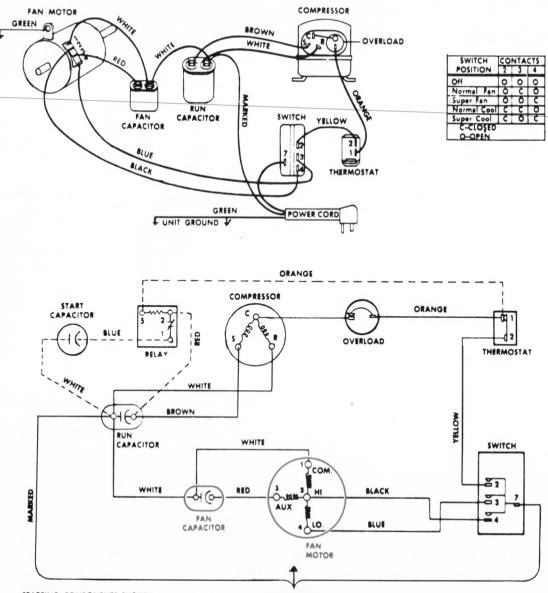

SWITCH POSITION	CONTACTS		
	2	3	4
Off	O	O	O
Normal Fan	O	C	O
Super Fan	O	O	C
Normal Cool	C	C	O
Super Cool	C	O	C

C-CLOSED
O-OPEN

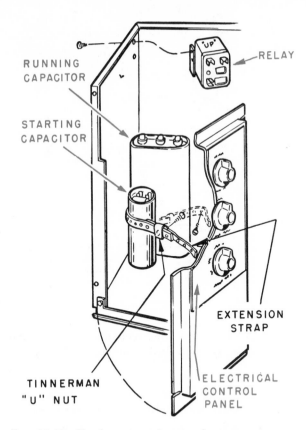

Fig. 21-17. Window unit showing location of capacitors, control panel, and relay.
(Kelvinator Div., American Motors Corp.)

twisting them. An off-balance fan will soon wear out the motor bearings and will be noisy (vibrate). Replace an abused fan.

The wiring of a window unit is very similar to other refrigerating units. See Fig. 21-16.

External electrical servicing procedures are usually the same as for domestic and commercial units except:

1. Fan motors are usually two or three speeds.
2. There are usually three capacitors: starting capacitor, running capacitor, fan motor capacitor.

A unit with a starting capacitor and a running capacitor is shown in Fig. 21-17. Another arrangement of the three capacitors is shown in Fig. 21-18. The position of the fan control switch, thermostat, capacitors, and wiring are shown in Fig. 21-19.

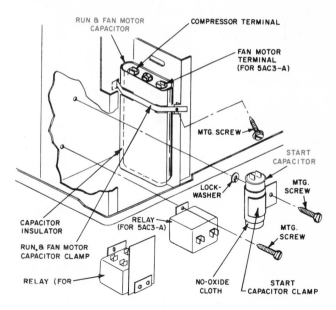

Fig. 21-18. An arrangement of the start, run, and fan motor capacitors. Note that the fan motor run capacitor and the compressor motor run capacitor are in the same container.

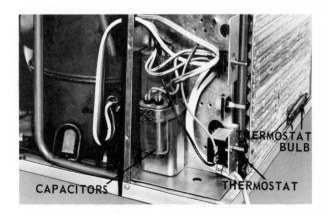

Fig. 21-19. Window unit showing location of capacitors and thermostat.
(Frigidaire Div., General Motors Corp.)

The wiring diagram for a window unit with a variable speed fan motor, a thermostat, etc., is shown in Fig. 21-20. A wiring diagram for a three-speed fan motor system of 21,000 Btu/hr. capacity using a 240V circuit is shown in Fig. 21-21.

Testing of external electrical parts is described in Chapters 7 and 8, and testing of fan and compressor motors is described in Chapter 7. All but the motor-compres-

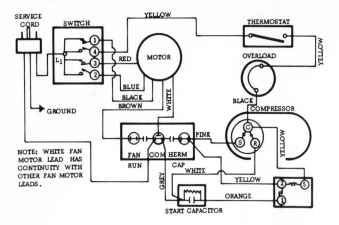

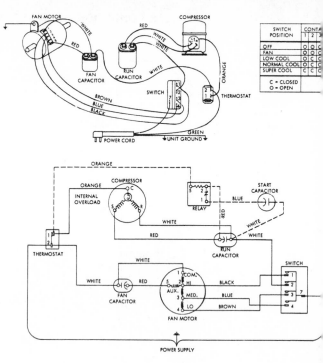

Fig. 21-20. Wiring diagram of window unit which uses R-22. It draws approximately 11.7 amperes at a power factor of 90%.

sor can be checked on the job. Before doing internal service work on the unit be sure the malfunction is not in the external circuit. Test for power in. Check the thermostat, the relay, the capacitors, and the overload protectors (both electrical and temperature).

Fig. 21-21. The wiring diagram of a system of 21,000 Btu/hr. capacity. Notice use of three-speed fan motor.

Internal troubles may be:
1. Lack of refrigerant.
2. Stuck compressor.
3. Inefficient compressor.
4. Clogged refrigerant circuit.
5. Shorted, open circuit, or grounded motor windings.

The motor condition can be checked with a continuity light or with an ohmmeter. To check for lack of refrigerant or clogged refrigerant lines, install a gauge manifold, as shown in Fig. 21-22. Trouble diagnosis is similar to the explanations in Chapters 12 and 15. The unit should be

Fig. 21-22. Air conditioning unit cycle showing gauge manifold installed. (American Standard Air Conditioning Div., American Radiator and Standard Sanitary Corp.)

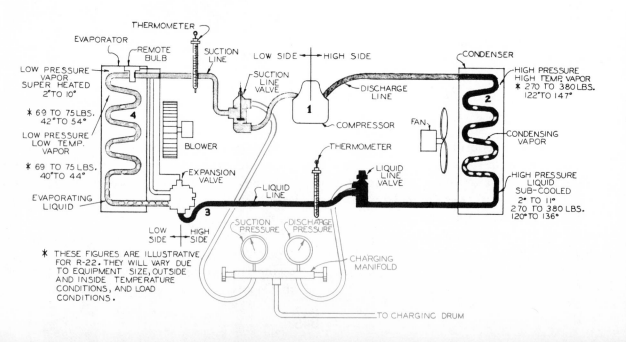

moved to the shop for major repairs. If a lack of refrigerant exists, locate the leak and repair it before charging.

21-8 Residential Central Systems

Central air conditioning systems provide an ideal means for providing residential air conditioning. Three methods used to install central air conditioning in warm air furnaces are as follows: the first method is to purchase the necessary condensing unit, evaporator coil, controls, tubing, and the like, and assemble the conditioner on the customer's premises. Fig. 21-23 is a schematic of such an installation. These units vary in capacity from 1 1/2 hp (approximately 12,000 Btu/hr.) to 7 1/2 hp (60,000 Btu/hr.).

coil, necessary controls, and tubing. The complete assembly is shipped as a single package. The necessary tubing is usually carefully wrapped around the evaporator coil. Work required at the customer's premises includes uncrating, carefully unwinding the tubing from the evaporator, installing the condensing unit and evaporator in their proper places, and making the necessary electrical and control connections. This type of system requires some very careful handling, since the condensing unit is charged with refrigerant and the serviceman must be very careful in uncrating the tubing to eliminate any possibility of kinks which might later crack and make a leak. Fig. 21-24 shows an assembled air conditioner of this type being moved into place in a furnace room.

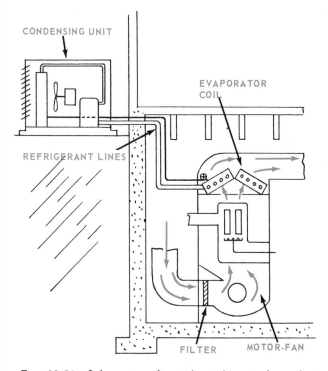

Fig. 21-23. Schematic of residential central comfort cooling system, installed in a forced warm air furnace. The condensing unit is mounted outdoors.

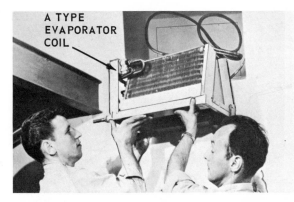

Fig. 21-24. Installing A-type evaporator coil. Refrigerant lines are connected to the coil. (Fedders Corp.)

The second method is to obtain a completely assembled and charged mechanism including the condensing unit, evaporator

The third and perhaps the most popular system consists of completely charged evaporator coil, condensing unit and lines. However, the condensing unit, evaporator coil, and necessary connecting tubing are shipped as separate items. The parts are connected by means of "quick couplers." This is an easy to assemble system, since the quick couplers may be connected and disconnected without loss of refrigerant or without allowing air to enter the system. A condensing unit of this type is shown in

Fig. 21-25 as it is being installed in a wall opening. The precharged condensing unit, evaporator coil, and refrigerant lines required to make this installation are shown in Fig. 21-26.

Fig. 21-25. Condensing unit being installed in wall opening.

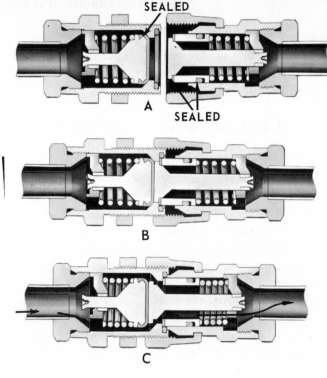

Fig. 21-27. Quick connect and disconnect coupling showing three types of assembly. A—Disconnected. B—Partially assembled. C—Connected and refrigerant passage opened. (Aeroquip Corp.)

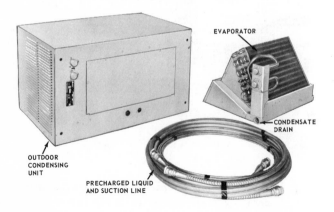

Fig. 21-26. A residential remote comfort cooler system. Note the quick couplers on the ends of the refrigerant lines and the matching fittings on condensing unit and evaporator coil.

21-9 Quick Connect Couplings

Self-sealing couplings enable manufacturers to produce precharged refrigeration and air conditioning units, along with the necessary tubing, in separate packages. These separate units may be assembled at the installation site and are ready to operate without evacuating, charging or cleaning service operations.

The self-sealing coupling fittings are brazed directly to the tubing, thereby eliminating flared joints. There are two types of quick connect fittings:

1. Can be connected and disconnected many times with very little loss of refrigerant.

2. Can only be quick connected once. This latter type uses diaphragms and, when the fittings are attached, the diaphragms are punctured to allow a refrigerant passage. These couplings cannot be disconnected unless the refrigerant is removed from the system first.

In the No. 1 type, when the couplings are separated, independent springs force valves in both halves of the coupling to close, thus preventing the escape of refrigerant. To assemble a quick connect fitting, align the couplings and tighten the coupling nut. Tightening the coupling nut

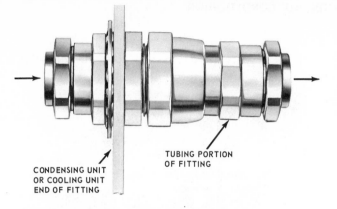

Fig. 21-28. An assembled quick connect and disconnect fitting.

CONDENSING UNIT
OR COOLING UNIT
END OF FITTING

TUBING PORTION
OF FITTING

draws the coupling together and opens the two valves of the coupling internally so the refrigerant can flow. Fig. 21-27 shows a quick connect coupling disconnected, partially connected and fully connected. Fig. 21-28 shows an exterior view of an assembled quick connect as it would appear on an installation.

Quick connect fittings are used primarily on precharged residential air conditioning systems and precharged transpor-

tation units. The units are usually charged at the factory with the condensing unit, the refrigerant lines and the evaporator charged separately.

It is recommended that the gasket which joins the quick connect and disconnect fittings (often made of neoprene and asbestos) be covered with clean, dry oil just prior to assembly. Care should also be taken that excessive wrench pressure is not used because distortion of the fitting may result in a leak. Most quick connects and disconnects will reseal themselves several times.

21-10 Installing Residential Central Systems

These units are installed in four steps:
1. Install condensing unit.
2. Install evaporator coil.
3. Install suction and liquid lines.
4. Install electrical wiring.

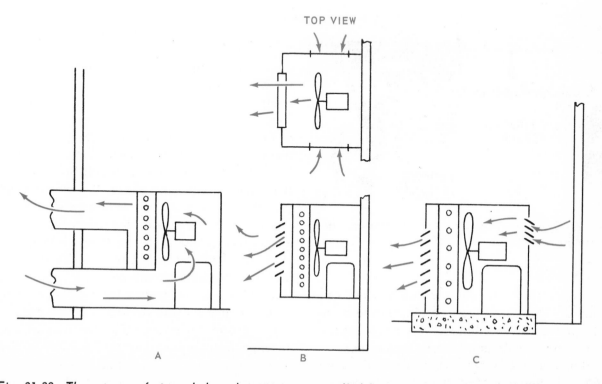

TOP VIEW

A   B   C

Fig. 21-29. Three types of air-cooled condensing units installed for a residential central comfort cooling installation. A—Condensing unit in the wall. B—On the outer wall. C—On a concrete slab.

The condensing unit is mounted to use outdoor air to cool the condenser. Many installation methods have been used. Some are mounted inside the building with ducts to bring the outdoor air to the condenser and to discharge the air. Some units have been mounted on the exterior wall of the building. A popular system is to mount the unit on a concrete slab a short distance from the building (12 to 24 in.). A concrete slab at least 4 in. thick and reinforced with steel mesh is recommended. Fig. 21-29 shows various methods. It is desirable for the outlet air from the condensing unit to move in the same direction as the prevailing summer winds.

The evaporator or cooling coil is mounted in the bonnet or plenum chamber of the furnace. The design of the evaporator and its condensate drain depend on the type of furnace, i.e., upflow, downflow, or horizontal flow type. The evaporator should be as level as possible. It should be mounted firmly, and it must be accessible for

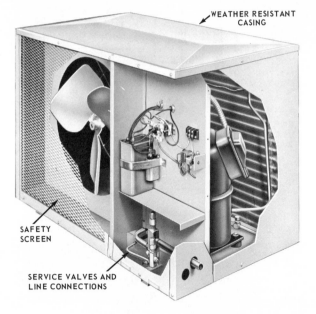

Fig. 21-31. Condensing unit of residential central comfort cooling system. (Williamson Co.)

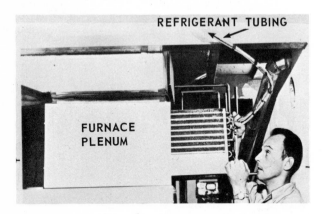

Fig. 21-30. An A-type evaporator coil being installed in the plenum chamber of an upflow warm air furnace. (Fedders Corp.)

periodic cleaning and servicing when required. The condensate drain should be to an open drain and have an air break at the drain. The drain pan is built into the evaporator coil as is the drain connection. An "A" coil being installed in a furnace plenum chamber is shown in Fig. 21-30.

The suction and liquid line connections may be:

1. Flared connections
2. Brazed connections.
3. Quick connect and disconnect couplings.

An installation using flared or brazed tubing connections has a condensing unit equipped with service valves, as shown in Fig. 21-31, and the refrigerant control is a thermostatic expansion valve. The unit would be installed as described in Chapter 15. Many of these installations have the condensing unit above the evaporator and therefore a U bend should be put in the suction line (to assist the oil return). The suction line should slope down slightly toward the condensing unit. A filter-drier and a sight glass should be put in the liquid line. Many servicemen also place a filter-drier in the suction line to prevent motor-compressor burnouts. The portion of the suction line which is installed inside the building should be insulated (1/2 in. thickness for hot humid conditions, 1/4 to 3/8 in. for normal conditions). Without insulation, moisture from the air will form on the suction line and drip. The lines should be supported, should be free of kinks, and the openings in the furnace duct and the wall should be sealed with weatherproof, nonhardening sealing compound.

One company which uses flared connections puts an extra amount of refrigerant in the condensing unit. A timed purging device, connected to the suction service valves, times the purge and at the end of 30 seconds to 105 seconds (depending on the size of the unit) the purging is stopped. The lines are then clean and clear and the correct amount of refrigerant is left in the system.

The quick connect system is growing in popularity. The lines are installed (the correct length of prefabricated line should be used). The quick connects are made and the unit is ready to operate.

In all cases the system should be thoroughly tested for leaks while the pressures inside the system are near ambient temperature pressure conditions.

The electrical circuit must conform to the National Electrical and local codes. Consult with the local electrical utility concerning the primary service capacity. The use of 230 or 240V circuits will enable the use of smaller wires.

21-11 Servicing Residential Central Systems

Servicing procedures and troubleshooting diagnosis for residential central systems are similar to those described in Chapters 12 and 15.

In addition to checking for leaks, proper refrigerant charge, malfunctioning refrigerant controls and motor controls, moisture in the system, etc., there are some service procedures peculiar to these systems.

The system uses the furnace blower, motor, filter and duct system. It is essential that the blower be cleaned once a year,

that the motor be lubricated (a few drops of 30 SAE oil) once or twice a year, that the filter be replaced or cleaned twice a year (beginning of heating season and beginning of cooling season). More often if necessary. The motor-blower speed should be increased for summer comfort cooling (see Chapter 22). The belts on belt driven blowers should be inspected and replaced if glazed or cracked.

The condensing unit should be cleaned once each year. The condenser especially should be blown clean of lint and the fins straightened. A carbon dioxide blower and/or a vacuum cleaner may be used for cleaning the unit.

The "A" style evaporator coil should be cleaned of any lint and its fins straightened, if bent.

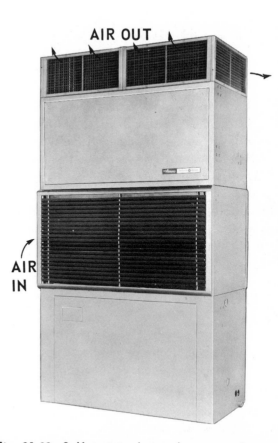

Fig. 21-32. *Self-contained console type comfort cooling air conditioner of Airtemp Div., Chrysler Corp. The air intake is in middle and conditioned air is discharged out top grilles.*

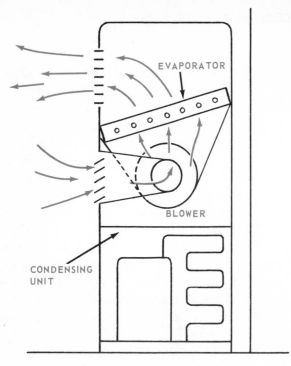

Fig. 21-33. A schematic of a console type air conditioner.

21-12 Console Air Conditioners

In console air conditioners a complete system is mounted in a cabinet. The system is usually water-cooled. The systems vary in capacity from 2 hp to 10 hp. Such units are often used in small commercial establishments such as restaurants, stores, banks, etc.

The console models may have either water-cooled or air-cooled condensing units. Air-cooled models must be used in some localities because of water restrictions. An air-cooled unit must have air ducts to the outdoors for condenser cooling. Fig. 21-32 shows a water-cooled console unit. The return air enters the lower grille. Cooled air is discharged at the upper grilles. Ducts can be connected to portions or all of the upper section for use when partitions interfere with cooled air distribution. The condensing unit is mounted in the bottom of the console, air blowers in the middle, and the evaporator coil in the top of the cabinet.

Most of the console models have a complete refrigerating system, a filtering system and an evaporating coil. Fig. 21-33 shows a schematic of a console unit.

A large self-contained comfort cooler with provisions to add a heating coil if the user desires is shown in Fig. 21-34. The thermostatic expansion valves are of the distributor tube type.

The condenser may be either water-cooled or air-cooled. If air-cooled, a duct is used to bring in outside air and to discharge this air outdoors again.

The water-cooled units require plumbing connections to both fresh water and a drain. The drain is also used to take care of the moisture condensed out of the air by the evaporator coil in the summer. One company has developed a special three openings in one rubber hose for this purpose, which permits moving the unit quickly from room to room. Such units usually do not provide for winter conditioning facilities.

21-13 Installing Console Air Conditioners

Console units are factory assembled. After physically moving the unit into place, plumbing and electrical connections are required. Both the plumbing and the electrical work must conform to codes in force in the locality.

The unit should be mounted level.

The motor-compressor is usually hermetic, the refrigerant control is generally a thermostatic expansion valve. The unit should be thoroughly checked. The air temperature both in and out, the electrical load, and the operating pressures should be checked and recorded for future reference.

21-14 Servicing Console Air Conditioners

Access to internal parts of the unit is obtained by removing panels.

Periodic maintenance duties include

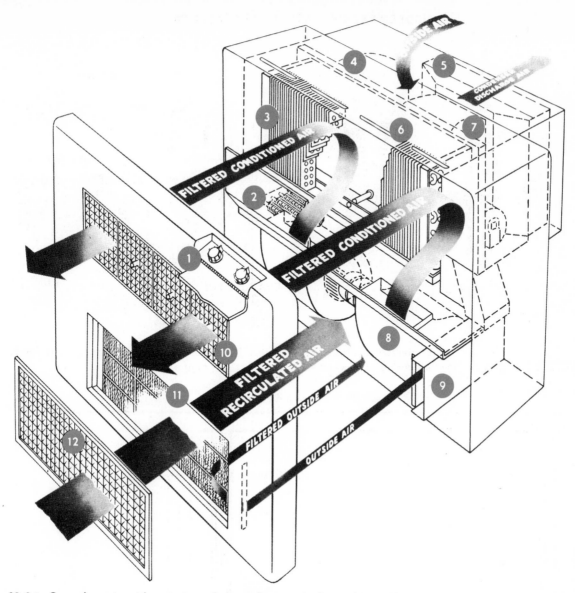

Fig. 21-34. Console unit with an air-cooled condenser. 1—Controls. 2—Heating coil. 3—Evaporator coil. 4—Compressor. 5—Air-cooled condenser. 6—Draft diverters. 7—Condenser fan. 8—Evaporator fan. 9—Ventilating air duct. 10—Discharge grilles. 11—Air filter. 12—Return air grille.
(Remington Air Conditioning Div., Singer Co.)

replacing the filter or cleaning it, cleaning the evaporator coil and fins, cleaning the fan motor and oiling it unless it has sealed bearings, cleaning the drain pan and drain tube. The inner lining of the cabinet sometimes accumulates lint and should be removed by vacuuming.

Servicing the refrigerating unit and the condenser water circuit is as explained in Chapter 15. It is important to check the refrigerant charge, the operation of the thermostatic expansion valve, the water flow, etc.

Fig. 21-35. Air-cooled refrigerating unit for duct distribution of comfort cooled air.
(Fedders Corp.)

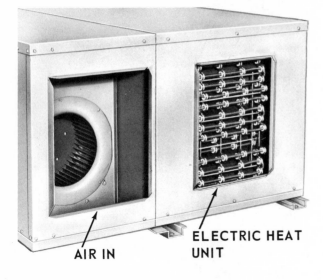

AIR IN

ELECTRIC HEAT UNIT

Fig. 21-36. Central or remote comfort cooling unit with electric heat added for use during cold weather.

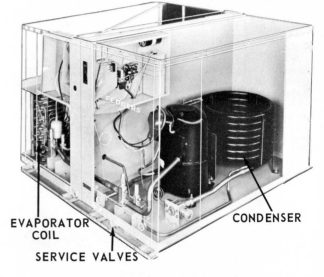

EVAPORATOR COIL

CONDENSER

SERVICE VALVES

Fig. 21-37. Water-cooled condensing unit for central comfort cooling installation.

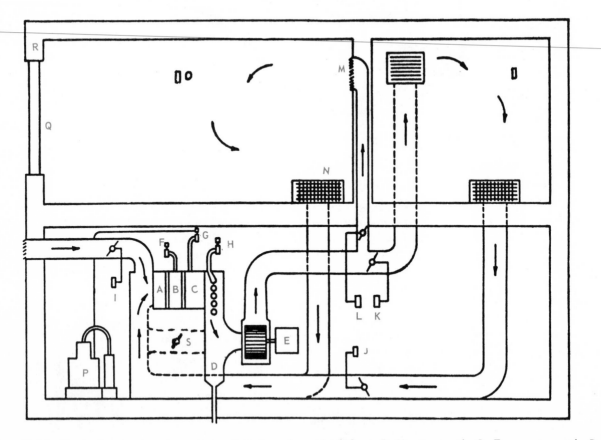

Fig. 21-38. Typical central or duct air conditioning plant. A—Filter. B—Heating coil. C—Evaporator coil. D—Eliminator plates and moisture drain. E—Centrifugal fan and motor. F—Heat control and shutoff. G—Refrigerant control and shutoff. H—Water spray control and shutoff. I—Fresh air control. J—Return air control and damper. K and L—Conditioned air dampers and controls. M—Conditioned air inlet. N—Return air register. O—Room control. P—Refrigerating unit. Q—Double window. R—Insulated wall. S—Bypass and control.

21-15 Remote Comfort Systems

In remote air conditioning systems the refrigerating equipment is located away from the space to be conditioned. These duct distribution system is shown in Fig. 21-40. A schematic of a complete comfort cooling system using chilled water to cool interior zones and perimeter zones is shown in Fig. 21-41.

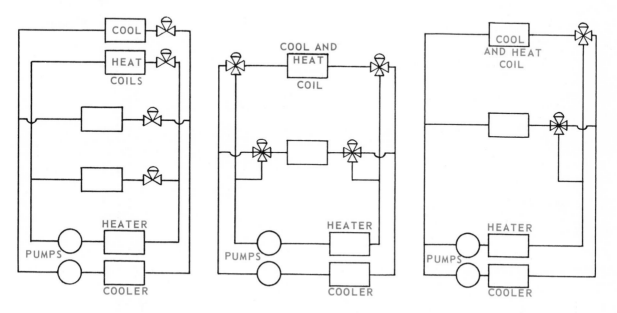

Fig. 21-39. *Several piping methods of distributing either hot water or chilled water to individual coils in spaces to be conditioned.*

units vary in capacity from 2 tons to thousands of tons. Some units condition the air which is then distributed by ducts to the space or spaces, as shown in Fig. 21-35. A similar unit which has an electric heating coil for heating purposes during cool weather is shown in Fig. 21-36. These systems are also water-cooled. A water-cooled system which has service valves, a tube within a tube condenser, and a water valve is shown in Fig. 21-37. A schematic of such an installation is shown in Fig. 21-38. Large systems use chilled water to cool a remote space or a number of spaces. A heat exchanger is located in each space to be cooled and a thermostat controls solenoid valves to allow the flow of cold (chilled water) or hot water (hydronic) to the room units. Fig. 21-39 shows several types of these systems. A chilled water system used in combination with a

The heating and refrigeration lines are run to air conditioning units in each room to be air conditioned. Individual thermostats are connected in each room to each air conditioning room unit. A solenoid valve usually controls the flow to each unit.

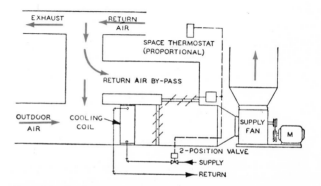

Fig. 21-40. *Control of chilled water coil from space temperature using return bypass damper and valve.* (ASHRAE *Guide and Data Book*)

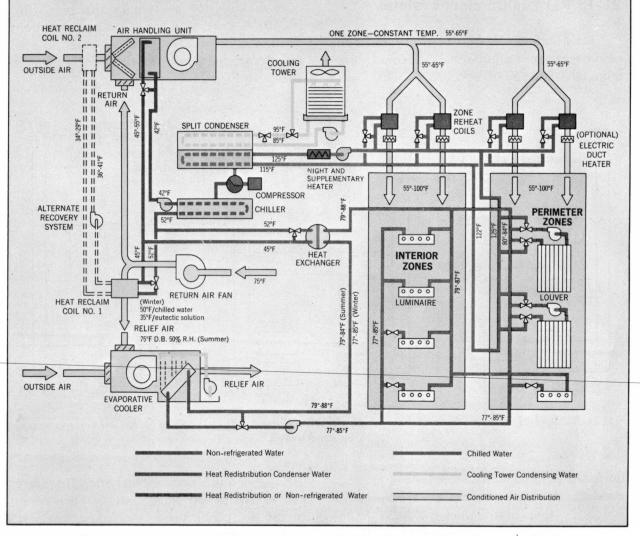

INDIRECT TRANSFER SYSTEM

HEAT RECLAIM COIL NO. 2

OUTSIDE AIR

AIR HANDLING UNIT

ONE ZONE—CONSTANT TEMP. 55°-65°F

55°-65°F

55°-65°F

RETURN AIR

COOLING TOWER

ZONE REHEAT COILS

(OPTIONAL) ELECTRIC DUCT HEATER

34°-29°F

36°-41°F

45°-55°F

42°F

SPLIT CONDENSER

95°F
85°F

125°F

115°F

NIGHT AND SUPPLEMENTARY HEATER

ALTERNATE RECOVERY SYSTEM

42°F

52°F

COMPRESSOR

CHILLER

79°-88°F

55°-100°F

55°-100°F

PERIMETER ZONES

45°F
52°F

52°F

45°F

HEAT EXCHANGER

122°F

125°F

80°-84°F

INTERIOR ZONES

79°-87°F

HEAT RECLAIM COIL NO. 1

RETURN AIR FAN

75°F

(Winter)
50°F/chilled water
35°F/eutectic solution

LUMINAIRE

LOUVER

RELIEF AIR
75°F D.B. 50% R.H. (Summer)

79°-84°F (Summer)

79°-88°F (Winter)

77°-85°F (Summer)

77°-85°F (Winter)

OUTSIDE AIR

EVAPORATIVE COOLER

RELIEF AIR

79°-88°F

77°-85°F

77°-85°F

77°-85°F

Non-refrigerated Water | Chilled Water
Heat Redistribution Condenser Water | Cooling Tower Condensing Water
Heat Redistribution or Non-refrigerated Water | Conditioned Air Distribution

Fig. 21-41. Comfort cooling system for interior spaces and perimeter spaces. Note how ventilation air is coupled to cooling system. (Airtemp Div., Chrysler Corp.)

This valve is connected to the room temperature control, which controls both a fan and the solenoid refrigerant valve in the room unit in such a manner that hot or chilled water to the room unit is turned on when the fan starts in the unit and is shut off when the fan stops.

Air filters should be provided in these units.

21-16 Large Comfort Cooling Systems

Central station comfort cooling systems are available in many styles. One

Fig. 21-42. Complete water chiller unit.

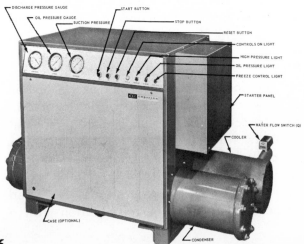

DISCHARGE PRESSURE GAUGE
OIL PRESSURE GAUGE
SUCTION PRESSURE
START BUTTON
STOP BUTTON
RESET BUTTON
CONTROLS ON LIGHT
HIGH PRESSURE LIGHT
OIL PRESSURE LIGHT
FREEZE CONTROL LIGHT
STARTER PANEL
WATER FLOW SWITCH (Q)
COOLER
CASE (OPTIONAL)
CONDENSER

unit has a shell-and-tube water-cooled condenser and a shell-and-tube water chiller evaporator. This unit has a variable capacity system operated by unloading cylinders when the load decreases. Hydraulic controls unload the compressor to minimize the starting load.

freeze protection. The motor-compressor is a six cylinder unit with two cylinders in each bank. Fig. 21-45 shows the internal construction of this compressor. Many large comfort cooling installations use centrifugal type compressors.

The large centrifugal units are fre-

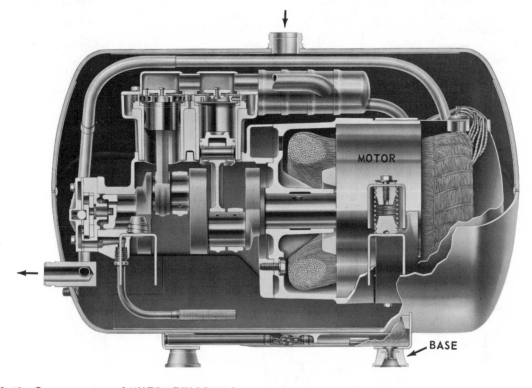

Fig. 21-43. Cross section of "HERMETICOM" hermetic compressor. It is for use in units ranging from 10 tons to 15 tons capacity. (Airtemp Div., Chrysler Corp.)

Another air conditioning system circulates chilled water to the various cooling coils in the multiple installation. This chilled water system is also used for many industrial processing installations. Such a unit is shown in Fig. 21-42. The three gauges shown are for suction pressure, oil pressure and high pressure.

A compressor of 10 to 15 ton capacity is shown in Fig. 21-43.

A water chiller using a serviceable hermetic compressor of the W design is shown in Fig. 21-44. The design permits movement of unit through regular doors. The chilled water evaporator has built-in

Fig. 21-44. A water chiller using serviceable hermetic compressor.

Fig. 21-45. *Cut-a-way of a six cylinder serviceable hermetic compressor motor.* *(Westinghouse Electric Corp., Air Conditioning Div.)*

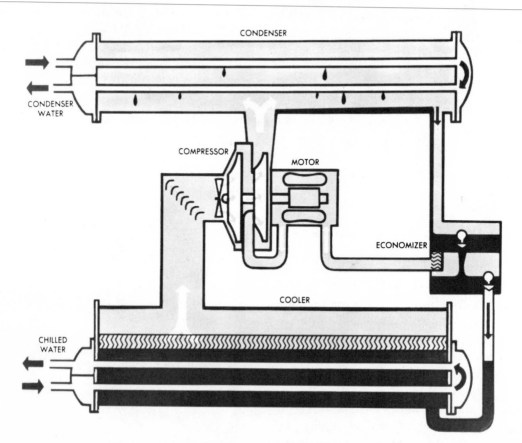

Fig. 21-46. *Centrifugal compressor, hermetic chilled water system.* *(Carrier Air Conditioning Co.)*

858

quently designed to have capacities ranging from 100 tons through 2,000 tons. The basic design of the system is shown in Fig. 21-46. The system uses low pressure refrigerants and the evaporator operates at below atmospheric pressures. Both the condenser and the evaporator are the shell-and-tube type. The water lines vary in size from 6 ips to 14 ips (internal pipe size). The compressor is a two-stage centrifugal pump, driven by a hermetically sealed motor. The capacity of the unit is controlled by inlet vanes to the two-stage centrifugal compressor. The vanes are either electronically or pneumatically controlled and hydraulically operated. These vanes are closed during starting to reduce the starting load. Fig. 21-47 shows the construction of the compressor. This com-

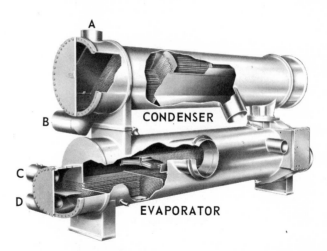

Fig. 21-48. The condenser and evaporator of a large chilled water system which uses a centrifugal compressor. A—Condenser water in. B—Condenser water out. C—Chilled water out. D—Water in. (Carrier Air Conditioning Co.)

Details of this design and construction of the condenser and the evaporator are shown in Fig. 21-48. Capacity of these units necessitates thorough, accurate control. Persons responsible for the operation of these units should receive thorough training in their correct operation. The complete schematic of the wiring and piping of one of these units is shown in Fig. 21-49. These units are also used to cool process liquids. The evaporator, the compressor suction line, and chilled liquid lines are always insulated.

21-17 Dehumidifying Equipment

A mechanism which performs a dehumidifying function is known as a dehumidifier. Dehumidifying equipment may consist of cold coil surfaces over which air is blown and the moisture is condensed out by coming in contact with the cold coils. When coil surfaces are at a temperature below the dew point temperature of the air, moisture will condense out of the air. The coil surface temperature must be kept above the freezing temperature to prevent frost or ice formation which would block the air flow.

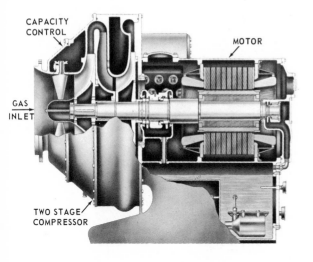

Fig. 21-47. Two-stage centrifugal compressor.

pressor has a forced lubrication system. A separate motor is used to drive the oil pump. The compressor motor is a 3-phase unit of 208, 240, 440, 480, 550, 2300 or 4160 volts. Note the bolted construction for service purposes.

These systems have an automatic purging device for removing noncondensible gases.

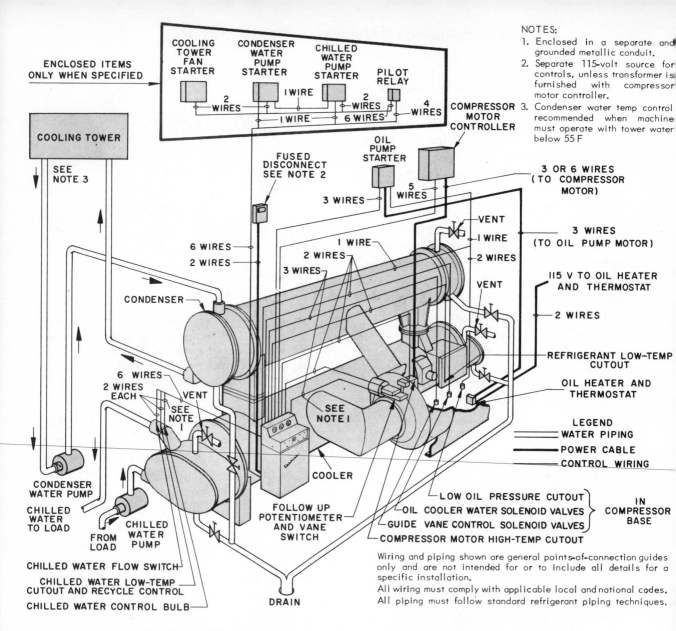

NOTES:

1. Enclosed in a separate and grounded metallic conduit.
2. Separate 115-volt source for controls, unless transformer is furnished with compressor motor controller.
3. Condenser water temp control recommended when machine must operate with tower water below 55 F

ENCLOSED ITEMS ONLY WHEN SPECIFIED

COOLING TOWER FAN STARTER

CONDENSER WATER PUMP STARTER

CHILLED WATER PUMP STARTER

PILOT RELAY

2 WIRES

1 WIRE

2 WIRES

4 WIRES

1 WIRE

6 WIRES

COMPRESSOR MOTOR CONTROLLER

COOLING TOWER

SEE NOTE 3

FUSED DISCONNECT SEE NOTE 2

OIL PUMP STARTER

3 WIRES

5 WIRES

3 OR 6 WIRES (TO COMPRESSOR MOTOR)

VENT

1 WIRE

3 WIRES (TO OIL PUMP MOTOR)

6 WIRES

2 WIRES

2 WIRES

3 WIRES

1 WIRE

2 WIRES

2 WIRES

VENT

CONDENSER

115 V TO OIL HEATER AND THERMOSTAT

2 WIRES

REFRIGERANT LOW–TEMP CUTOUT

OIL HEATER AND THERMOSTAT

6 WIRES

2 WIRES EACH

VENT

SEE NOTE 1

SEE NOTE 1

LEGEND

WATER PIPING

POWER CABLE

CONTROL WIRING

COOLER

CONDENSER WATER PUMP

CHILLED WATER TO LOAD

FROM LOAD

CHILLED WATER PUMP

FOLLOW UP POTENTIOMETER AND VANE SWITCH

LOW OIL PRESSURE CUTOUT

OIL COOLER WATER SOLENOID VALVES

GUIDE VANE CONTROL SOLENOID VALVES

COMPRESSOR MOTOR HIGH-TEMP CUTOUT

IN COMPRESSOR BASE

CHILLED WATER FLOW SWITCH

CHILLED WATER LOW-TEMP CUTOUT AND RECYCLE CONTROL

CHILLED WATER CONTROL BULB

DRAIN

Wiring and piping shown are general points-of-connection guides only and are not intended for or to include all details for a specific installation.
All wiring must comply with applicable local and national codes.
All piping must follow standard refrigerant piping techniques.

Fig. 21-49. Schematic of wiring and piping of large capacity water chiller.

Fig. 21-50. Dehumidifier installed in basement.

The design of a dehumidifier is shown in Fig. 21-50. This unit is usually a small hermetic refrigerating system that has both the condenser and evaporator coil enclosed in a cabinet. The air is drawn over the evaporator coil and after it is cooled below its dew point temperature, the cooled air is moved over the condenser to reheat it to a reasonable relative humidity. The device is used to reduce moisture content in the air. It is useful in basements and other damp places. Fig. 21-51 shows a sectioned view of such a unit. These units are sometimes equipped with a humidistat, as shown in Fig. 21-52. A container is used to collect the condensate or a drain tube is provided.

In some installations, certain chemicals are used which have the property of absorbing moisture from the air. In case chemicals are used, the chemicals are usually cycled in such a way that first the moisture from the air is absorbed into the chemical. Then the chemicals are heated, and the moisture is driven out-of-doors to put the chemicals in a condition to absorb moisture again.

21-18 Review of Safety

All of the safety practices described in Chapters 12 and 15 also apply to comfort cooling units.

Window units should be handled with care. Heavy units should be handled with

hand trucks and lifts. When removing mechanisms be careful not to drop them (they may be slippery). Safety shoes are recommended. Carefully follow installation instructions supplied by the manufacturer.

Fig. 21-52. A dehumidifier equipped with a humidistat. The humidistat automatically stops the dehumidifier when the desired humidity has been reached. (Fedders Corp.)

Remote systems should be sturdily mounted. Suction lines and liquid lines should be protected from abuse.

Always review instructions on larger units before performing any service work or installation work on them.

21-19 Test Your Knowledge - Chapter 21

1. What refrigerant controls are usually used on air conditioning evaporator coils?
2. Why are solenoid refrigerant control valves necessary on air conditioning evaporator coils?

Fig. 21-51. Section view of a dehumidifier. The first pass of the finned coil near the fan is the cooling and dehumidifying coil while the next pass is the condenser. Either a pail or a direct drain can be used to remove the condensate. (International Harvester Co.)

3. Why is air leaving an evaporator coil considered to be damp air?

4. Can air be dehumidified by any other method than by cooling?

5. How is condensate handled in a unit comfort cooler?

6. What air is used to cool the condenser of an air-cooled comfort cooler?

7. What is the relative humidity of the air just as it leaves the evaporator coil?

8. How many fan motors does a window type comfort cooler have?

9. How many coils does air pass through in a dehumidifier?

10. What device varies the capacity of centrifugal compressor?

11. Do window comfort coolers have different types of electrical extension plugs? Why?

12. How are the installation joints sealed?

13. Why is a window comfort cooler slanted down toward the outside of the home?

14. What is the normal cut-out setting of a window unit thermostat?

15. Is it possible to use a 2300V service to an air conditioner?

16. Why is the dew point reading important when using a dehumidifier?

17. What is a three-pipe air conditioning system?

18. Is it possible to have a hydronic comfort cooling system?

19. How many types of quick connects are in use?

20. What is an "A" coil? Where is it used?

21. What portions of a warm air furnace are used with a central comfort cooling system?

22. If the window comfort cooling unit will not start, what should one check first?

23. Why should one avoid bending or twisting the fan blades?

24. How many capacitors maximum does a window comfort cooler have?

25. How can a console air conditioner be installed for condenser air cooling?

26. What are the three ways to install the condensing unit of a residential central system?

27. Describe the three methods used to install residential central systems.

28. What chamber is usually located in the upper part of a console air conditioner?

29. Why is a drain necessary on an air-cooled comfort cooling unit?

30. May one use a duct system with a chilled water system? Explain.

Chapter 22

AIR CONDITIONING SYSTEMS, DISTRIBUTING AND CLEANING

Air conditioning mechanisms are designed to condition the air within the mechanism and then to distribute this treated air to the proper place, in the proper amounts, and with the least possible annoyance to the consumer of the conditioned air.

When a radiator system or a room convector system, such as a steam heating plant or a hot water plant, is used, the distribution of air is simple. The units are located along the outside walls and during the heating season the heated air rising from the radiator along the wall mixes with the cold air adjacent to the cold wall, and the mixture is then distributed by natural convection throughout the room. During the cooling season, chilled water is circulated in the convectors and a blower moves air over the coils and distributes this cool air through the room.

The gravity warm air furnace causes more complicated problems in air distribution. The air is still circulated by natural convection, but the air passages have to be proportioned, which means that the longer run ducts are made larger and that the larger rooms need larger ducts. Means also have to be devised for the air from the rooms to be returned to the furnace. The advancement from the simple one duct cold air return to the complicated multiple cold air returns from each conditioned room is a typical example of why you should study air distribution carefully. Many installations are combinations of a hot water (hydronic) system and a warm air duct system.

An important function of a good air conditioning system is to deliver clean air to the space being conditioned. Chapter 19 describes the impurities present in air and the methods of removal of most of these impurities.

22-1 Use of Air

In air conditioning practice, as air is passed through the mechanism it is heated or cooled, humidified or dehumidified, cleaned, and then distributed to places where it is needed. An air conditioning unit, regardless of its efficiency, and its size, would be handicapped if the air could not be properly distributed. It is important that the air distribution be accurately proportioned to the need and adapted to the apparatus in which it is to be used. The distributed air must be clean, provide the proper amount of ventilation, and must carry enough heat to keep the conditioned spaces warm or must be able to absorb enough heat to cool the conditioned spaces.

22-2 Weight of Air

Air has definite weight. Although it is invisible, its gases have a definite mass, and it takes energy to move air. Fig. 22-1 illustrates the weight of air under various temperature and humidity conditions. At 70 F., 13.34 cu. ft. of dry air weighs one pound, and if this is 50 percent saturated with moisture, 13.51 cu. ft. of the air and moisture mixture weighs one pound. Because air is a gas, it responds closely to

Boyle's and Charles' Laws. Therefore, as the temperature rises, it takes more cubic feet to weigh one pound and as the pressure decreases, it takes more cubic feet to weigh one pound.

change water to water vapor, each grain of water changed to vapor requires a latent heat of 1000/7000 or .143 Btu/grain. If condensation takes place in a cooled air duct or on the outside surface, the heat re-

Air Temp. F.	Cu.ft./lb. Dry Air	Lb./cu.ft. Dry Air	Cu.ft./lb. 50% Saturated	Lb./cu.ft. 50% Saturated	Cu.ft./lb. 100% Saturated	Lb./cu.ft. 100% Saturated
0	11.58	.08635	11.585	.08632	11.59	.08628
50	12.84	.0778	12.915	.0774	12.99	.0769
70	13.34	.075	13.51	.074	13.68	.0731
100	14.10	.0709	14.585	.06856	15.07	.06635
120	14.60	.0685	15.55	.0643	16.50	.0606
150	15.3	.0652	17.7	.0565		
200	16.7	.0600				

Fig. 22-1. Weight of air at various temperatures and humidities.

22-3 Heat in Air

Because air is a physical substance, it has heat carrying capacity. Air can be used to transport heat, either removing it from the space or carrying it to the space. The psychrometric properties already studied in Chapter 19 showed the varying heat content due to temperature changes and to humidity changes. The specific heat of dry air is .24 Btu/lb. The additional heat due to the moisture in the air varies considerably, depending on the amount of saturation. For example, at 100 F. there are 24 Btu in one pound of dry air. There may be .04293 lbs. of moisture added to this one pound of dry air to saturate it (see Chapter 19), but the heat in this moisture is 47.40 Btu (latent heat and sensible heat). The total heat in 1.04293 lbs. is 71.40 Btu. However, as far as distributing the air is concerned, only sensible heat need be taken into account unless vaporizing or condensing of water takes place in the ducts, or in the room being conditioned.

There are 7000 grains to a pound, and, because it requires about 1000 Btu/lb. to

leased is considerable and the temperature of the air delivered to the conditioned space can be changed drastically and may cause a failure in equipment operation. Only sensible heat changes should take place outside of the apparatus itself.

22-4 Basic Ventilation Requirements

As noted before, air is a mixture of gases, and normally the air contains about 21 percent oxygen. A human system requires that a certain oxygen content be contained in the air: (1) to maintain life, and (2) to be comfortable. If a room is tightly sealed, any human in that room would slowly consume the oxygen and increase the carbon dioxide content, the water vapor content, and various small amounts of impurities, and this could cause drowsiness and even death.

One must remember that a space for human habitation must have air with a good oxygen content and that this air must be at a reasonable temperature. It is of utmost importance that fresh air be admitted to these spaces to provide the oxygen. In the past, this fresh air entered the space by infiltration from the outside due to door and window openings with their associated cracks. However, modern construction is reducing this air leakage to a minimum, necessitating the use of air conditioning apparatus to furnish fresh air. Modern units have a controlled fresh air intake; this fresh air is conditioned and mixed with the recirculated air before it reaches the room.

The amount of fresh air required depends on the use of the space and the amount of fresh air admitted by infiltration. One basic rule is to provide at least 4 cfm per person to provide enough oxygen and to remove carbon dioxide. One must remember that the air can be handled either to produce an above atmospheric pressure (positive pressure) in a building or below atmospheric pressure (negative pressure) in an occupied space. A positive pressure will eliminate infiltration and is done by using special air intakes to the blowers. A positive pressure assures that all air entering a building can be filtered and cleaned before reaching the occupied space. Negative pressure increases the infiltration at windows and doors. Residential homes normally use fuel burning furnaces, which consume air from inside the home. This leaves the interior of the house under a slight negative pressure. Fig. 22-2 shows a basic diagram of pressure conditions in a home.

If the amount of impurities in the air, such as odor, smoke, bacteria, and the like, are at a level which requires alteration, the remedy may be either ventilation using fresh air, or improved air cleaning.

Ventilation is usually based on air changes per hour for the conditioned space. If the space is 1000 cu. ft., for example, three changes per hour would mean 3000 cu. ft. per hour or 50 cu. ft./min. Three changes/hr. is the minimum for residences that are only heated. As high as 12

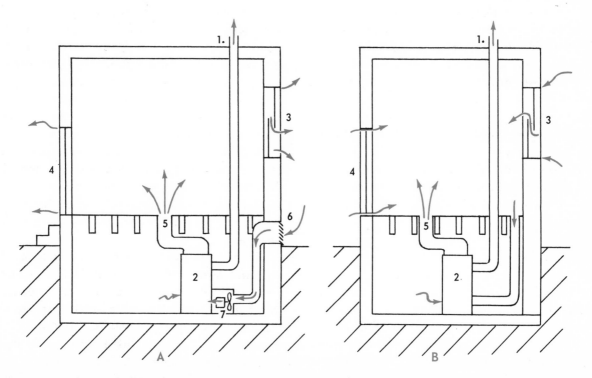

Fig. 22-2. Simplified diagram of air flow into and out of a building during heating season. A—Positive air pressure. B—Negative air pressure. 1—Chimney. 2—Furnace. 3—Window. 4—Door. 5—Warm air grille. 6—Fresh air intake. 7—Fresh air fan.

changes per hour (in the above case 200 cu. ft./min.) are recommended for cooling. Fig. 22-3 shows typical air changes for both the heating season and the cooling season.

Use	Air Changes/Hour	
	Heating	Cooling
Homes	3–6	6–9
Offices Stores	5–8	6–12
Public Assembly	5–10	6–12

Fig. 22-3. Recommended air changes for various types of occupancies.

In general, 80 F. is a good effective temperature. An adequate air supply is the best way to control the thermal atmosphere. Because the body is controlled by evaporation-convection-radiation, one must not only control the walls, floor, or ceilings to make sure they are not too warm or cold (radiation) but enough air should be supplied to promote good evaporation and convection. If the specific conditions are not known, it is best to design for 2 cfm/sq. ft. and/or 12 changes/hr. It is also very important to remember that people occupying a closed space give off considerable heat. A person radiates about 200 Btu/hr. while sleeping, and a man doing heavy work gives off up to 2400 Btu/hr. minimum.

22-5 Noise

The air distributing system must be designed for handling both load and the fresh air required, but it must do these functions in a manner that will not be annoying to the occupants. Two causes of annoyance are objectionable noise and drafts.

Complaints of unpleasant noise connected with air conditioning and refrigeration equipment are often directed to equipment vendors and servicemen.

The noise problem can be divided into three types:

1. Noise source.
2. Noise carriers.
3. Noise amplifiers or reflectors.

The noise source is an audible vibration. This vibration may originate in the heating unit, cooling unit, fan mechanism, air turbulence, duct panels or hangers, or grilles.

Sound or noise is produced by movement or vibration of an object. This movement may be caused by vibration of an object or by the movement of air against an object, as in air conditioning ducts.

An example of how sound is generated is provided by the movement of the wing of a bee. As the wing moves up and down it causes the gas molecules (air) toward the top of the wing to be compressed, thus transferring energy to molecules in an upward direction. At the same time gas molecules under the wing expand into the space left behind as the wing moves upward, and become rarefied, thereby creating less pressure under the wing. This procedure, compression and rarefaction alternates from one side of the wing to another; first the top compresses and then the bottom. This compression and rarefaction of the atmosphere causes waves of pressure (sound) to be transmitted through the air. A vibrating duct panel will create alternate waves of low pressure and high pressure air and produce sound in a similar manner.

In measuring the loudness of sound, the unit used for measurement is the decibel. Decibel meters are available for measuring noise level. Decibels (db) refer to the frequency of the pressure fluctuations in the air and the amplitude or size of these vibrations. Airborne sound is usually expressed in cycles per second (cps). Fans are noise sources; high velocity air is a noise source; the AC hum of a motor is a

Decibels	Typical Condition
0	
10	
20	
30	Residential area at night
40	Average residence
50	Private business office
60	Industrial area
70	Heavy traffic
80	
90	
100	
110	Woodworking shop
120	Boiler shop

Fig. 22-4. Decibel levels of typical sounds. (General Radio Co.)

noise source; compressors are a noise source, and high velocity refrigerant flows (especially at a sharp pipe turn) are noise sources. Fig. 22-4 lists some typical noise levels.

Another common complaint is noise caused by high speed air traveling through the ducts and causing air turbulence. This is often the result of an undersize unit or duct and the blower has been speeded up in an attempt to compensate for the inadequacy.

Noise or vibration carriers are rigid structures that carry vibrations to places where they may be annoying. Floors, ceilings, ducts, doors, pipes--all may carry these vibrations.

Noise amplifiers or reflectors are usually hard, smooth surfaces in conditioned space. Walls, ceilings, floors, and furnishings may pick up a small vibration and reflect it at such a frequency and in such a direction that all or certain parts of the space may be made uncomfortable. Problems involving acoustics and maintenance of a low decibel noise level are constantly being studied and improved.

Soft fabrics such as drapes and curtains and fabric covered furniture are noise absorbers. Felt lined, or soft insulation lined ducts also absorb noise.

Some communities have codes regulating how noisy a mechanism may be. For example, one city is requiring that the decibel level of a window unit or outdoor condensing unit be not over 50 decibels at a 10 foot distance. Drastic sound-deadening devices may be needed to meet this level.

The air velocity (feet/minute) permissible is somewhat dependent on the type of building being air conditioned; hospital, church, hall, residential, etc. Where noise is a factor the velocity should be kept to a minimum. If the velocity cannot be decreased noise may be reduced by using acoustical discharge chambers, or lining the ducts with sound absorbing material such as felt or other soft material.

22-6 Drafts

It is a relatively simple matter to provide ducts large enough and fans large enough to provide a room with the correct amount of air for conditioning. However, the problem of getting the air into the room, distributing it to all parts of the room without short circuiting the air to the air return, without objectionable drafts and noise, is a complicated task.

When air moves past people at a velocity that exceeds 25 fpm (about 1/3 mph), most people feel an annoying draft. This means that, if the air flows faster than 1/3 mph through the length of a 25 foot living room, an uncomfortable feeling results.

To have a grille outlet designed to throw the air into the room a distance of 8 to 13 feet, a velocity of 500 fpm (6 mph) is needed. Therefore, to keep that part of the space occupied by humans at a 25 fpm velocity, the location of the grilles or outlets must be carefully designed to prevent high velocity air from contacting the people.

To move air across a long space at a reasonable velocity the location of the air returns is important. The air returns

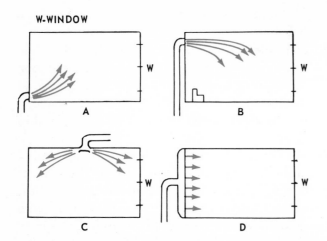

Fig. 22-5. *Location of grilles to minimize drafts in living portions of room. A—People are exposed to drafts. B—High velocity air is above living level. C—Center location permits lower grille velocity; higher velocity is above living level. D—An ideal large grille opening.*

should be located on the opposite side of the space from the air entrance. The air returns should be located high on the wall if warm air return is desired (cooling season) and low on the wall (or in the floor) if cold air return is desired (heating season). Fig. 22-5 shows some typical air flow patterns. The return air openings often used are shown in Fig. 22-6.

22-7 Stratification of Air

Air in an occupied space must be kept moving, or stagnation or stratification results. Warm air tends to rise, cold air tends to settle. In a room where the air is not deliberately moved, the air will assume levels according to its temperature, as shown in Fig. 22-7.

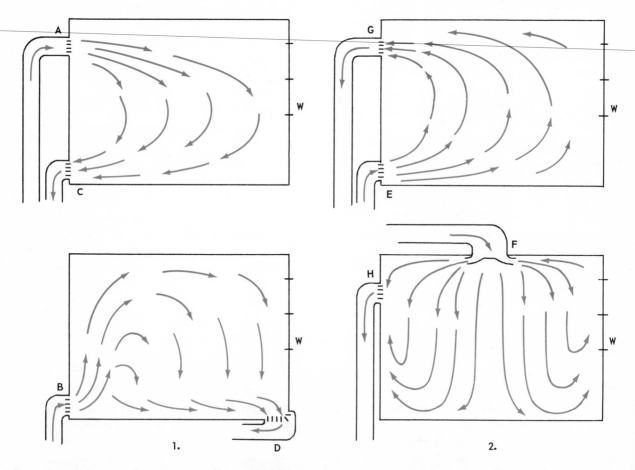

Fig. 22-6. *Location of return air grilles in residential installation. 1—Heating A and B warm air in, C and D cold air return. 2—Cooling E and F cold air in, G and H warm air return.*

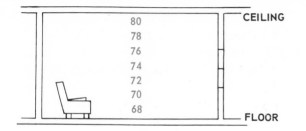

Fig. 22-7. *Various temperature levels found in a room with little or no air circulation.*

It is important to locate all automatic thermostats and humidistats at the proper level because of this stratification. Also, stratification tends to make smoke haze hover in layers.

Unfortunately, some grilles are so located that the air will be moved only in certain parts of the room and the air will become stagnant in other parts. There is also the problem of the obstruction to air movement caused by the furnishings of the room. For this reason, and to enable higher grille velocities, some grilles are located high in the room (6 ft. or more), and some located in ceilings. These high grille locations necessitate that the grilles be attractive in appearance or concealed. See Fig. 22-8. This is called a diffusion grille because its design promotes mixing of some of the room air with the entering air. The mixing principle is shown in Fig. 22-9.

22-8 Air Ducts

To deliver air to the conditioned space, air carriers are needed. These carriers are called ducts. The ducts are made of sheet metal or some noncombustible structural material.

The ducts work on the principle of air pressure difference. If a pressure difference exists, air will move from the higher pressure area to the lower pressure places. The greater this pressure difference, the faster the air will flow.

Two shapes of ducts commonly used for carrying air are: (1) round duct, (2) square or rectangular duct. See Fig. 22-10.

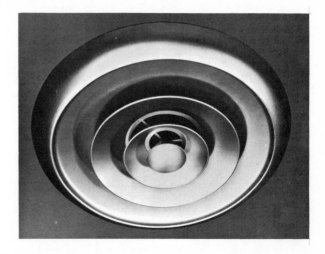

Fig. 22-8. *Ceiling grille which distributes air in all directions (360°) in occupied space.*

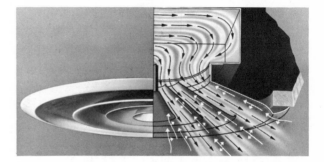

Fig. 22-9. *Air flow and air mix of a ceiling grille. (Anemostat Products Div.)*

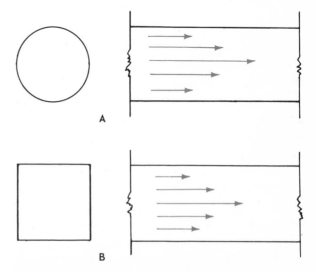

Fig. 22-10. *Round (A) and rectangular (B) ducts. Arrows indicate the closer the air is to the inside surfaces of the duct the slower the flow.*

The round duct is the more efficient based on volume of air handled per perimeter distance (distance around). That is, less duct material is needed to make a large enough duct to carry the necessary air.

The square or rectangular duct harmonizes with building construction and fits into walls and ceilings better than round

A rectangular duct of equal capacity is 17 x 16 in. It has a perimeter of W + W + D + D = perimeter.

17 + 17 + 16 + 16 = perimeter.

34 + 32 = 66 in.

66 in. – 56.55 = 9.45 more in. of duct material per unit of duct length.

ONE SIDE OF RECTANGULAR DUCT—INCHES

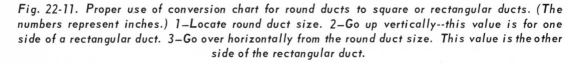

0	6	7	8	9	10	11	12	13	14	15	16	17	18
6						②							
10													
15													
20									18.2				
25						18.1							
30				18.3									
35			18.2										
40		18.2											

(OTHER SIDE OF RECTANGULAR DUCT—INCHES)

Fig. 22-11. Proper use of conversion chart for round ducts to square or rectangular ducts. (The numbers represent inches.) 1–Locate round duct size. 2–Go up vertically--this value is for one side of a rectangular duct. 3–Go over horizontally from the round duct size. This value is the other side of the rectangular duct.

ducts. It is easier to install rectangular ducts between joists and studs.

Tables have been developed which compare carrying capacities of rectangular and round ducts. See Figs. 22-11, and 22-12. There are several round duct equivalent sizes to choose from. The one selected depends on the one side dimension desired. For example, ducts 11 inches high may be wanted to improve appearance, or to fit in between joists (a 14 in. distance). Fig. 22-12 shows the equivalents.

An 18 in. round duct has a perimeter (distance around) of:

diameter x π = circumference (perimeter).

18 x 3.1416 = 56.55 in.

This means 9.45 in. more of duct material is necessary for a rectangular duct, and for each inch length of duct or 12 in. x 9.45 = 113.4 sq. in. per foot of length.

22-9 Duct Sizes

To determine the size duct that should be used to carry air to a room, it is necessary to first find the volume of air that is to be delivered to the room.

This volume of air depends on the amount of heat the air must deliver to the room during the heating season, or the amount of heat to be removed during the cooling season.

Side Rectangular Duct	4.0	4.5	5.0	5.5	6.0	6.5	7.0	7.5	8.0	9.0	10.0	11.0	12.0	13.0	14.0	15.0	16.0
3.0	3.8	4.0	4.2	4.4	4.6	4.8	4.9	5.1	5.2	5.5	5.7	6.0	6.2	6.4	6.6	6.8	7.0
3.5	4.1	4.3	4.6	4.8	5.0	5.2	5.3	5.5	5.7	6.0	6.3	6.5	6.8	7.0	7.2	7.4	7.6
4.0	4.4	4.6	4.9	5.1	5.3	5.5	5.7	5.9	6.1	6.4	6.8	7.1	7.3	7.6	7.8	8.1	8.3
4.5	4.6	4.9	5.2	5.4	5.6	5.9	6.1	6.3	6.5	6.9	7.2	7.5	7.8	8.1	8.4	8.6	8.9
5.0	4.9	5.2	5.5	5.7	6.0	6.2	6.4	6.7	6.9	7.3	7.6	8.0	8.3	8.6	8.9	9.1	9.4
5.5	5.1	5.4	5.7	6.0	6.3	6.5	6.8	7.0	7.2	7.6	8.0	8.4	8.7	9.0	9.4	9.6	9.8

Side Rectangular Duct	6	7	8	9	10	11	12	13	14	15	16	17	18	19	20	22	24	26	28	30	Side Rectangular Duct
6	6.6																				6
7	7.1	7.7																			7
8	7.5	8.2	8.8																		8
9	8.0	8.6	9.3	9.9																	9
10	8.4	9.1	9.8	10.4	10.9																10
11	8.8	9.5	10.2	10.8	11.4	12.0															11
12	9.1	9.9	10.7	11.3	11.9	12.5	13.1														12
13	9.5	10.3	11.1	11.8	12.4	13.0	13.6	14.2													13
14	9.8	10.7	11.5	12.2	12.9	13.5	14.2	14.7	15.3												14
15	10.1	11.0	11.8	12.6	13.3	14.0	14.6	15.3	15.8	16.4											15
16	10.4	11.4	12.2	13.0	13.7	14.4	15.1	15.7	16.3	16.9	17.5										16
17	10.7	11.7	12.5	13.4	14.1	14.9	15.5	16.1	16.8	17.4	18.0	18.6									17
18	11.0	11.9	12.9	13.7	14.5	15.3	16.0	16.6	17.3	17.9	18.5	19.1	19.7								18
19	11.2	12.2	13.2	14.1	14.9	15.6	16.4	17.1	17.8	18.4	19.0	19.6	20.2	20.8							19
20	11.5	12.5	13.5	14.4	15.2	15.9	16.8	17.5	18.2	18.8	19.5	20.1	20.7	21.3	21.9						20
22	12.0	13.1	14.1	15.0	15.9	16.7	17.6	18.3	19.1	19.7	20.4	21.0	21.7	22.3	22.9	24.1					22
24	12.4	13.6	14.6	15.6	16.6	17.5	18.3	19.1	19.8	20.6	21.3	21.9	22.6	23.2	23.9	25.1	26.2				24
26	12.8	14.1	15.2	16.2	17.2	18.1	19.0	19.8	20.6	21.4	22.1	22.8	23.5	24.1	24.8	26.1	27.2	28.4			26
28	13.2	14.5	15.6	16.7	17.7	18.7	19.6	20.5	21.3	22.1	22.9	23.6	24.4	25.0	25.7	27.1	28.2	29.5	30.6		28
30	13.6	14.9	16.1	17.2	18.3	19.3	20.2	21.1	22.0	22.9	23.7	24.4	25.2	25.9	26.7	28.0	29.3	30.5	31.6	32.8	30
32	14.0	15.3	16.5	17.7	18.8	19.8	20.8	21.8	22.7	23.6	24.4	25.2	26.0	26.7	27.5	28.9	30.1	31.4	32.6	33.8	32
34	14.4	15.7	17.0	18.2	19.3	20.4	21.4	22.4	23.3	24.2	25.1	25.9	26.7	27.5	28.3	29.7	31.0	32.3	33.6	34.8	34
36	14.7	16.1	17.4	18.6	19.8	20.9	21.9	23.0	23.9	24.8	25.8	26.6	27.4	28.3	29.0	30.5	32.0	33.0	34.6	35.8	36
38	15.0	16.4	17.8	19.0	20.3	21.4	22.5	23.5	24.5	25.4	26.4	27.3	28.1	29.0	29.8	31.4	32.8	34.2	35.5	36.7	38
40	15.3	16.8	18.2	19.4	20.7	21.9	23.0	24.0	25.1	26.0	27.0	27.9	28.8	29.7	30.5	32.1	33.6	35.1	36.4	37.6	40
42	15.6	17.1	18.5	19.8	21.1	22.3	23.4	24.5	25.6	26.6	27.6	28.5	29.4	30.4	31.2	32.8	34.4	35.9	37.3	38.6	42
44	15.9	17.5	18.9	20.2	21.5	22.7	23.9	25.0	26.1	27.2	28.2	29.1	30.0	31.0	31.9	33.5	35.2	36.7	38.1	39.5	44
46	16.2	17.8	19.2	20.6	21.9	23.2	24.3	25.5	26.7	27.7	28.7	29.7	30.6	31.6	32.5	34.2	35.9	37.4	38.9	40.3	46
48	16.5	18.1	19.6	20.9	22.3	23.6	24.8	26.0	27.2	28.2	29.2	30.2	31.2	32.2	33.1	34.9	36.6	38.2	39.7	41.2	48
50	16.8	18.4	19.9	21.3	22.7	24.0	25.2	26.4	27.6	28.7	29.8	30.8	31.8	32.8	33.7	35.5	37.3	38.9	40.4	42.0	50
52	17.0	18.7	20.2	21.6	23.1	24.4	25.6	26.8	28.1	29.2	30.3	31.4	32.4	33.4	34.3	36.2	38.0	39.6	41.2	42.8	52
54	17.3	19.0	20.5	22.0	23.4	24.8	26.1	27.3	28.5	29.7	30.8	31.9	32.9	33.9	34.9	36.8	38.7	40.3	42.0	43.6	54
56	17.6	19.3	20.9	22.4	23.8	25.2	26.5	27.7	28.9	30.1	31.2	32.4	33.4	34.5	35.5	37.4	39.3	41.0	42.7	44.3	56
58	17.8	19.5	21.1	22.7	24.2	25.5	26.9	28.2	29.3	30.5	31.7	32.9	33.9	35.0	36.0	38.0	39.8	41.7	43.4	45.0	58
60	18.1	19.8	21.4	23.0	24.5	25.8	27.3	28.7	29.8	31.0	32.2	33.4	34.5	35.5	36.5	38.6	40.4	42.3	44.0	45.8	60
62	18.3	20.1	21.7	23.3	24.8	26.2	27.6	29.0	30.2	31.4	32.6	33.8	35.0	36.0	37.1	39.2	41.0	42.9	44.7	46.5	62
64	18.6	20.3	22.0	23.6	25.2	26.5	27.9	29.3	30.6	31.8	33.1	34.2	35.5	36.5	37.6	39.7	41.6	43.5	45.4	47.2	64
66	18.8	20.6	22.3	23.9	25.5	26.9	28.3	29.7	31.0	32.2	33.5	34.7	35.9	37.0	38.1	40.2	42.2	44.1	46.0	47.8	66
68	19.0	20.8	22.5	24.2	25.8	27.3	28.7	30.1	31.4	32.6	33.9	35.1	36.3	37.5	38.6	40.7	42.8	44.7	46.6	48.4	68
70	19.2	21.	22.8	24.5	26.1	27.6	29.1	30.4	31.8	33.1	34.3	35.6	36.8		39.1	41.3	43.3	45.3	47.2	49.0	70
72															39.6	41.8	43.8	45.9	47.8	49.7	72
74															40.0	42.3	44.4	46.4	48.4	50.3	74
76															40.5	42.8	44.9	47.0	49.0	50.8	76
78															40.9	43.3	45.5	47.5	49.5	51.5	78
80															41.3	43.8	46.0	48.0	50.1	52.0	80
82															41.8	44.2	46.4	48.6	50.6	52.6	82
84															42.2	44.6	46.9	49.2	51.1	53.2	84
86															42.6	45.0	47.4	49.6	51.6	53.7	86
88															43.0	45.4	47.9	50.1	52.2	54.3	88
90															43.4	45.9	48.3	50.6	52.8	54.8	90
92															43.8	46.3	48.7	51.1	53.4	55.4	92
96															44.6	47.2	49.5	52.0	54.4	56.3	96

Equation for Circular Equivalent of a Rectangular Duct:[5]

$$d_c = 1.30 \frac{(ab)^{0.625}}{(a+b)^{0.250}} = 1.30 \sqrt[8]{\frac{(ab)^5}{(a+b)^2}}$$

where

a = length of one side of rectangular duct, inches.

b = length of adjacent side of rectangular duct, inches.

d_c = circular equivalent of a rectangular duct for equal friction and capacity, inches.

Fig. 22-12. Various sizes of rectangular ducts necessary to equal carrying capacity of round ducts. (ASHRAE Guide and Data Book)

These calculations are not complicated in most cases, but situations using split heating systems, etc., make the problem more complicated.

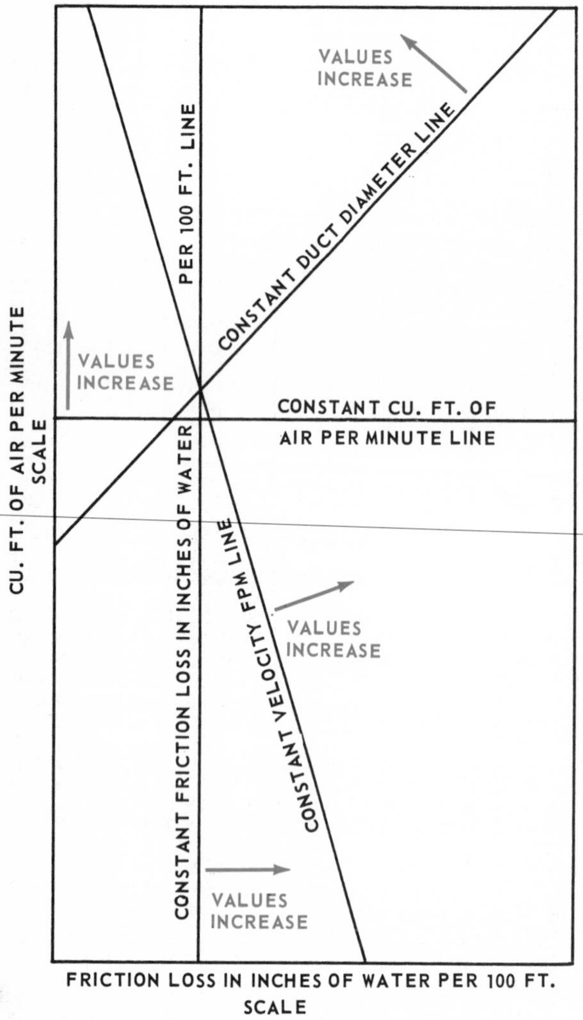
VALUES INCREASE
PER 100 FT. LINE
CONSTANT DUCT DIAMETER LINE
VALUES INCREASE
CONSTANT CU. FT. OF AIR PER MINUTE LINE
CU. FT. OF AIR PER MINUTE SCALE
CONSTANT FRICTION LOSS IN INCHES OF WATER
CONSTANT VELOCITY FPM LINE
VALUES INCREASE
VALUES INCREASE
FRICTION LOSS IN INCHES OF WATER PER 100 FT. SCALE

Fig. 22-13. Value lines for friction of air in straight round ducts.

The amount of air delivered to a room must always be equal to or exceed the minimum fresh air ventilation requirements.

22-10 Air Volumes for Heating

If the heated air is furnishing all the heat for a room, three things must be known to be able to calculate the air volume:

1. Heat load.
2. Room temperature.
3. Duct temperature.

The heat load can be determined by using methods described in Chapter 24. The room temperature is decided by the designer. Normally it is 72 F. dry bulb temperature (dbt). The duct air temperature is more difficult to decide. If a low duct temperature is used, large air volumes will be necessary to carry enough heat. If high duct temperatures are used, the furnace will have to operate with higher chimney (stack) temperatures, and the ducts themselves may have to be insulated.

Engineers recommend that the grille temperatures be at least 125 F., and that duct temperatures be near 140 F. The lowest temperature needed to obtain these results depends on the duct lengths. Knowing that the specific heat of air is .24 Btu/lb., the weight of air needed is easily found by using the specific heat equation.

Room heat load = .24 x wt. of air x the temperature difference. For example:

What is the air weight if a room has a heat load of 20,000 Btu/hr.?

With a room temperature of 72 F. and a duct temperature of 140 F., the temperature difference is 68 F.

$$20{,}000 = .24 \times \text{wt. of air} \times 68$$

$$\frac{20{,}000}{.24 \times 68} = \text{wt. of air}$$

$$\frac{20{,}000}{16.32} = \text{wt. of air}$$

1225.5 lbs. = wt. of air per hour
Divide by 60 to obtain lbs./min.
20.435 lbs. = wt. of air per min.

To obtain the volume, we must first find the volume of one pound of air at the duct temperatures. This value is obtained from the psychrometric chart, Fig. 19-15.

One pound of air = 17.1 cu. ft. If the chart does not read as high as 140 F., we may calculate for this volume by using

Charles' Law (see Chapter 1) and knowing the volume at 72 F. dbt. and 50 percent RH (13.55 cu. ft.)

$$\frac{13.55}{\text{Vol.}} = \frac{460 + 72}{460 + 140} = \frac{532}{600}$$

$$13.55 \times 600 = \text{Vol.} \times 532$$

$$\frac{13.55 \times 600}{532} = \text{Vol.}$$

$$\frac{8130}{532} = \text{Vol.}$$

$$17.16 = \text{Vol.}$$

The volume of air/min. is 20.435 lbs./min. x 17.16 cu. ft.

Vol. = 350.7 cu. ft./min.

We must now determine the duct size. Two separate items must be considered. If the space is limited, the area of the duct is already fixed. For example, if the duct is to run between studs in a partition, the space available is 14 x 3 1/4 in. maximum (2 x 4 studding on 16 in. centers). This duct has an area of

$$14 \times 3\ 1/4 = 45.5 \text{ sq. in.}$$

$$\frac{45.5}{144} = .316 \text{ sq. ft.}$$

Using the above volume

The velocity in ft./min. x .316 sq. ft. = 350.7 cu. ft./min.

$$\text{Velocity} = \frac{350.7}{.316}$$

$$= 1110 \text{ ft./min.}$$

This velocity would produce air turbulence noise and one must therefore use two ducts of 14 x 3 1/4 in. size.

The velocity will now be 555 ft./min. which should be satisfactory.

22-11 Air Volume for Cooling

Air volume for cooling is calculated in much the same way as for heating.

We use the same specific heat equation (see Chapter 1).

Btu = Sp. Ht. of Air x Wt. of Air x (Temp. Difference).

Knowing the heat load, the specific heat of air and the temperature difference, we can determine the weight of air needed.

If the weight is known, the air volume can be determined, and the duct sizes selected.

For example, using a heat load of one ton of cooling (12,000 Btu/hr.), a specific heat value of .24 Btu/lb., we must determine the air temperature in the duct and the air temperature in the room. If the designer desires 75 F. in the room and the comfort cooling unit is designed for 65 F. duct air temperature:

12,000 Btu/hr. = .24 x wt. of air x (75 F. – 65 F.)

12,000 Btu/hr. = .24 x wt. of air x 10

$$\frac{12,000}{24 \times 10} = \text{wt. of air}$$

$$\frac{12,000}{2.4} = \text{wt. of air}$$

5,000 lbs./hr. = wt. of air

$$\frac{5,000}{60} = 86.7 \text{ lbs./min.}$$

At 60 F. db and 50 percent RH (from the psychrometric chart) 13.4 cu. ft. of air weighs 1 lb.

Changing 86.7 lbs./min. to cfm:

The cu. ft. per min. = 86.7 x 13.4 = 1,161.78 cu. ft./min.

To determine the duct size for this volume to the room at 500 ft./min. velocity, use Fig. 22-13 and Fig. 22-14. Where the 1,161 cu. ft./min. line crosses the 500 ft./min. velocity line, a 21 in. round duct would be needed at .018 in. of friction loss, or by conversion through the use of the table shown in Fig. 22-12, a 22 x 17 in. rectangular duct or a 30 x 13 in. duct could be used.

22-12 Air Circulation

Warm air heating systems use three basic systems to circulate the air:

1. Gravity.
2. Intermittent forced air.
3. Continuous forced air.

The gravity system is decreasing in popularity. A Standard Code for Installation of Gravity Warm Air Heating Systems

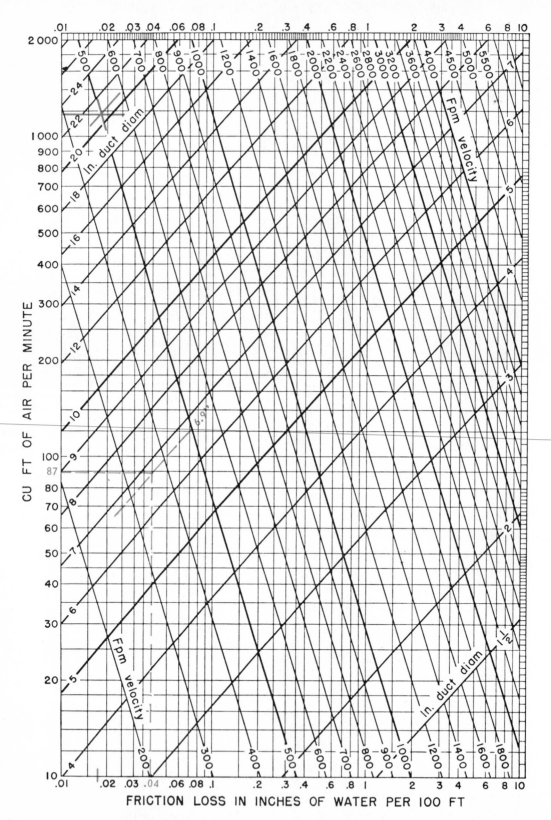

Fig. 22-14. Friction chart for volumes of 10 to 2,000 cfm air flow in ducts.
(ASHRAE Guide and Data Book)

is published by the National Warm Air Heating and Air Conditioning Association.

This code recommends register or grille temperatures of 175 F. It has tables that indicate the Btu carrying capacity of five different duct combinations for either first or second floor registers.

The same association has developed a code for mechanical warm air systems.

The continuous blower operation system is increasing in popularity. This system provides a more constant temperature in rooms.

Many warm air systems are being designed for use with cooling systems. However, the air volume to be circulated must be increased, because during the cooling season each cu. ft. of air can do less cooling (smaller temperature differences); this is somewhat offset by the lower cooling load. In average conditions a 30 to 50 percent air flow increase is needed. Either two-speed blower motors should be used (for directly-driven blowers) or a two-speed pulley is used on the motor if a belt driven unit is used.

A method of controlling air flow into various ducts is to use a duct damper. These dampers are used to balance air flows and are also used to shut off and open certain ducts for zone control purposes. Fig. 22-15 shows a damper with four adjustable vanes.

22-13 Duct Calculations

If a heating system or cooling system which uses a duct system serves more than one room, the duct design must be such that each room being served, receives the correct amount of air. If the distribution is not balanced, one room will be too warm while the other will be too cold.

Two methods which may be used to calculate the proper size plenum chambers, main ducts, branch ducts and grilles are:

1. Unit pressure drop system.
2. Total pressure drop system.

22-14 Unit Pressure Drop System

When air is forced through a duct, it follows the path of least resistance. Many air conditioning duct systems have several openings (grilles) for the air to escape from the duct. A duct with a low air flow resistance will allow most of the air to flow through it, and the other ducts will not obtain their correct amount of air.

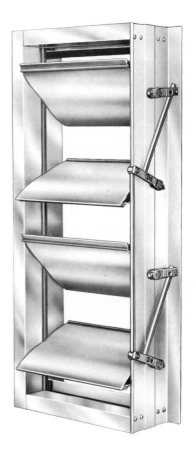

Fig. 22-15. Four-vane adjustable damper used to control air flow in duct. These dampers may be either manually or automatically operated.
(Arrow Louver and Damper Corp.)

In the past, many duct installations were made that fed too much air to some rooms and did not heat or cool other rooms sufficiently.

The unit pressure drop calculating system, uses the same pressure drop for each length of duct throughout the system.

For example, if the total heat load during the heating season is 80,000 Btu/hr., and there are six rooms with heat loads as follows:

1. Living Room   = 25,000 Btu/hr.
2. Dining Room   = 15,000 Btu/hr.
3. Kitchen   = 5,000 Btu/hr.
4. Bathroom   = 8,000 Btu/hr.
5. Bedroom No. 1 = 15,000 Btu/hr.
6. Bedroom No. 2 = 12,000 Btu/hr.

Based on the previous problem in Par. 22-10

Btu/cu. ft./hr. for a 68 F. change =
$\dfrac{.24 \times 68}{17.16}$ = .95 Btu/cu. ft./hr.

= .0158 Btu/cu. ft./min.

the air volumes required per min. for each room equals:

1. Living Room   25,000 × .0158 = 438.6 cu. ft./min.
2. Dining Room   15,000 × .0158 = 263.2 cu. ft./min.
3. Kitchen   5,000 × .0158 = 87.73 cu. ft./min.
4. Bathroom   8,000 × .0158 = 140.3 cu. ft./min.
5. Bedroom No. 1 15,000 × .0158 = 263.2 cu. ft./min.
6. Bedroom No. 2 12,000 × .0158 = 210.5 cu. ft./min.

The total air volume is 1403.53 cu. ft./min.

To determine the duct sizes to handle the air volumes specified above, data must be obtained about air flow. Figs. 22-14 and 22-16 are friction air charts for straight ducts. These values were obtained by research. These charts have four variables: (1) friction loss in inches of water on the horizontal scale (equal value lines are vertical), (2) cu. ft. of air/min. on the vertical scale (equal value lines are horizontal), (3) velocity on scale lines that slant down to the right and, (4) a round duct diameter scale lines that slant down to the left.

In the problem above, the main duct must handle 1403.53 cu. ft./min. To keep the velocity to a low noise level, a friction loss of .04 in water column per 100 ft. should be used On the chart, these two values meet and show that the velocity will be 730 ft./min., and the round duct will be 18 1/2 in. in diameter.

Using this same friction loss for the branch ducts, one may obtain the following round duct sizes:

1. Living Room   = 550 ft./min. and 12.1 in. diameter
2. Dining Room   = 480 ft./min. and 9.8 in. diameter
3. Kitchen   = 370 ft./min. and 6.9 in. diameter
4. Bathroom   = 410 ft./min. and 7.9 in. diameter
5. Bedroom No. 1 = 480 ft./min. and 9.8 in. diameter
6. Bedroom No. 2 = 460 ft./min. and 9.2 in. diameter

These velocities are reasonably low, and the system would work. However, a more accurate system is the total pressure drop system; see Par. 22-15.

The round duct diameters may be changed to rectangular duct sizes using the table shown in Fig. 22-12.

When changing round duct sizes to rectangular duct sizes, it is important to remember that partition ducts cannot exceed 3 1/4 in. in depth and 14 in. in width. Also, all the ducts in the basement should have the same depth for appearance purposes and to enable easy concealment of the ducts in cases where the basement is used as a recreation space or living quarters. In most installations the basement ducts should not exceed 8 in. in depth.

22-15 Total Pressure Drop System

The unit pressure drop system is accurate enough for simple duct installations that do not have long duct runs or great differences in duct sizes.

A more accurate system is based on having the same total pressure drop from the fan to each outlet. Fig. 22-17 shows the

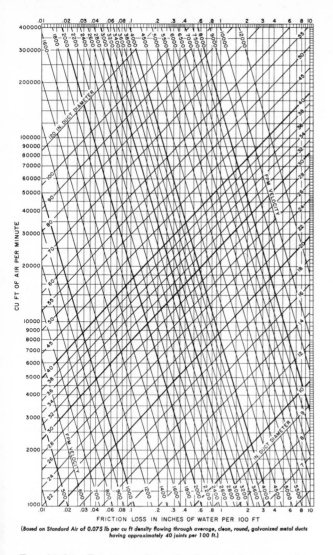

Fig. 22-16. Friction chart for high volume air flow in ducts. (ASHRAE Guide and Data Book)

duct system used with the rooms as calculated in Par. 22-14. To keep the various ducts identified, it is good practice to letter each different size duct.

In the illustration, Fig. 22-17, the following air volumes must be carried:

Duct	Air Volumes cu. ft./min.
A	1404
B	930
C	790
D	526
E	439
F	220
G	220
H	474
I	211

To be sure that the correct air volume leaves each outlet, it is necessary to have each outlet produce the correct equal amount of air resistance.

The method followed is to determine the longest and most complicated duct. This combination is obviously A, B, C, D, E, and F.

If we were to assume a total pressure drop of .04 in. of water, this total means that the pressure drop to each room outlet must be .04 in. For example, the opening

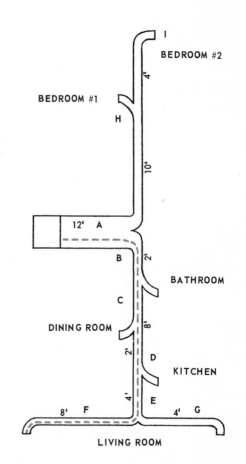

Fig. 22-17. A typical duct installation. Longest air path is shown in red.

to the bathroom is the shortest overall distance. It must have the same total pressure drop as the longest run through F.

An important part of this duct design is that the bends and elbows must be considered when determining pressure drop.

Generally speaking, the pressure drop of one elbow is equal to 10 diameters of the duct. Assuming there is one large bend above the furnace and that the grilles are located at the 7 ft. level in the room, the total length of duct A, B, C, D, E, F, is approximately:

Elbow (18 x 10)	15 ft.
A	12 ft.
Elbow (16 x 10)	13 ft.
B	2 ft.
C	8 ft.
D	2 ft.
E	4 ft.
Elbow (9 1/2 x 10)	8 ft.
F	8 ft.
Elbow	8 ft.
Vertical Rise	7 ft.
Elbow	8 ft.
Total	95 ft.

The total length (equivalent) is 95 ft. Because the .04 in. pressure drop was for 100 ft., the new pressure drop for each actual foot of duct is:

$$\frac{100}{95} \times .04 = \frac{20}{19} \times .04 = \frac{.8}{19} = .042 \text{ in.}$$

water/100 ft.

However, more important than this factor is the pressure drop in each section of the longest duct:

$$\text{Elbow (18 in. x 10)} = .04 \times \frac{15}{95} = .0063$$

$$A = .04 \times \frac{12}{95} = .0050$$

$$\text{Elbow (16 in. x 10)} = .04 \times \frac{13}{95} = .0055$$

$$B = .04 \times \frac{2}{95} = .0008$$

$$C = .04 \times \frac{8}{95} = .0034$$

$$D = .04 \times \frac{2}{95} = .0008$$

$$E = .04 \times \frac{4}{95} = .0016$$

$$\text{Elbow (9 1/2 x 10)} = .04 \times \frac{8}{95} = .0034$$

$$F = .04 \times \frac{8}{95} = .0034$$

$$\text{Elbow} = .04 \times \frac{8}{95} = .0034$$

$$\text{Vertical Rise} = .04 \times \frac{7}{95} = .0029$$

$$\text{Elbow} = .04 \times \frac{8}{95} = \underline{.0034}$$

Total = .0399 = .04 in. of water column pressure drop.

Knowing the pressure drop in each part of the longest duct, we can now determine the pressure loss up to each branch duct, and then from this value and the length of the branch duct determine the pressure loss per 100 ft. for the branch duct.

For example: the kitchen duct.

The pressure loss up to the kitchen branch duct is .0063 + .0050 + .0055 + .0008 + .0034 + .0008 = .0218.

If the total pressure drop to the outlet at the kitchen must equal .04 in. water, therefore, .0400 − .0218 = .0182 as the pressure drop in the kitchen branch.

The kitchen branch has an equivalent length of (assuming 87 cu. ft./min. and .04 in. pressure drop from Fig. 22-14):

Elbow (6.9 in. x 10)	= 6 ft.
Riser	= 7 ft.
Elbow (6.9 in. x 10)	= 6 ft.
Total	19 ft.

If the pressure drop in 19 ft. is .0182, the pressure drop per 100 ft. = .0182 × $\frac{100}{19} = \frac{1.82}{19} = .096$ in. water/100 ft. From the graph, using 87.73 cu. ft./min. volume and the resistance of .096 in., the following data are obtained: Size = 5.8 in. dia. Velocity = 530 cu. ft./min.

Notice how these values differ from the unit pressure drop values.

The method used to calculate comfort cooling air is essentially the same. However, if the cold air duct is exposed to warm, moist air, condensation will take place on the outside surface of the duct causing corrosion, and wetting of structural parts, also dripping which may damage adjacent parts.

22-16 Return Air Ducts

The importance of return air ducts has already been emphasized. The flow through these ducts is almost always by induced action (on the intake side of the fan or blower). If the return air duct is not matched with the air flow into a room, the flow of air in cu. ft. per minute will not be properly balanced.

If the return air exceeds the air in, there will be a tendency to maintain a negative pressure in that room and more air in will then be used by this room and this action may starve other rooms of air.

22-17 Elbows

Air has inertia. That is, air has weight and it obeys the Newton Laws of motion. In addition, air is compressible and, because of these laws, air in motion has the following characteristics.

It takes energy to make air flow change its direction. The air wants to flow in a straight line, and it therefore crowds against the outside on turns, as shown in Fig. 22-18. (A) represents a typical elbow.

It has a short radius of bend. The pressure drop through the elbow is about 10 times an equal length of duct. (C) is a better air flow duct, but its cost and room for installation make it impractical for many installations. (B) is a turbulent air duct design, and (D) is the type of duct with a much better air flow design. (E) is a duct elbow with vanes located at the bend. These vanes (F) considerably reduce the pressure drop.

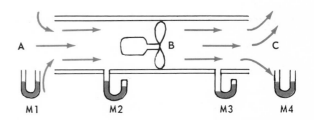

Fig. 22-19. Pressure conditions in simple duct and fan installation. A—Intake. B—Fan and motor. C—Exhaust. M-1. Atmospheric pressure. M-2. Negative pressure. M-3. Positive pressure. M-4. Atmospheric pressure.

22-18 Fans

Air movement is usually produced by some type of fan. These fans are usually located at the inlet of the air conditioner. Air movement can be produced by either creating an above atmosphere pressure (positive pressure) or by creating a below atmosphere pressure (negative pressure). Actually, all fans produce both conditions; the air inlet to a fan is below atmosphere condition, the exhaust of the fan is above atmosphere condition, as shown in Fig. 22-19. The air feed into a fan is called INDUCED DRAFT and the air exhaust from a fan is called FORCED DRAFT.

There are several types of fans, but the two most popular are:

1. Axial flow fan (propeller).
2. Radial flow fan (squirrel cage).

The basic construction shows that the type of fan is named after the direction the air flows. If air flows along the axle, it is

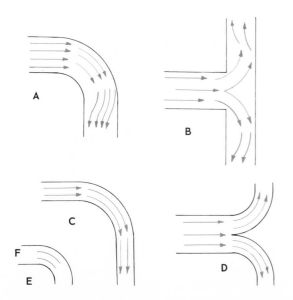

Fig. 22-18. Air flow in duct bends and elbows.

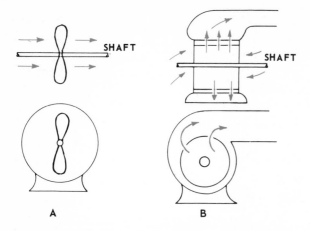

Fig. 22-20. Principal types of fans. A—Axial flow.
B—Radial flow.

called axial flow. If the flow is perpendicular to the axle (radius), it is called radial
flow, as shown in Fig. 22-20.

A four blade axial flow fan is shown in
Fig. 22-21. The rotation is clockwise.
These fan blades should be handled carefully. If they are bent or twisted, the fan
should be replaced.

Fig. 22-21. Blade for axial flow fan.
(Torrington Mfg. Co.)

A radial flow fan is shown in Fig. 22-22.
A radial flow fan assembly is shown in
Fig. 22-23. A motor with an adjustable
mounting drives the fan through a belt. If
possible, the belt tension should be on the
lower belt section to provide more effi-

cient belt drive, as shown in Fig. 22-24.
Proper belt tension is when the belt can be
pushed out of line a distance of its width.
It is often desirable to change fan speeds
to obtain more or less air flow in cfm's.
One way to vary the speed is to use adjustable pulleys. An adjustable pulley (variable
pitch) for a two-belt drive is shown in Fig.
22-25.

Fig. 22-22. Rotor for radial flow fan.

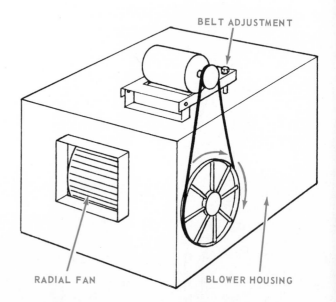

Fig. 22-23. Typical blower housing using radial flow
fan. Note direction of rotation of fan pulley and belt
adjustment.

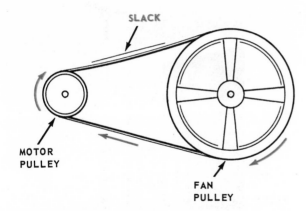

Fig. 22-24. Motor pulley and fan pulley. Note tension on lower part of belt and slack at upper.

22-19 Air Cleaning

Air should contain close to its normal amount of oxygen and it should have a minimum of contaminants. The contaminants may be solids, liquids and/or gases. Chap-

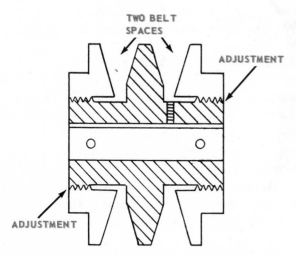

Fig. 22-25. Variable pitch pulley. Note location of set-screws. Pulley is used on a dual belt system and can provide a variation of 100 rpm through its adjustment.

ter 19 describes properties of air including contaminants. Air pollution is becoming an increasing problem as urban areas increase in population and industries increase. Cleaning the air has become an important part of air conditioning.

Air may be cleaned in many ways depending on the foreign matter in the air.

1. To remove solids (dust, soot, smoke, etc.).
   - 1-1. Centrifugal force (for large particles).
   - 1-2. Washing the air (for particles that are wettable).
   - 1-3. Screens (to block the larger particles).
   - 1-4. Adhesives (the air impinges or strikes against a tacky or sticky surface). Fig. 22-26 shows a filter which has adhesive material on the honeycomb surfaces.
   - 1-5. Electrostatic (electric charging the particles and adhering these particles to an opposite charge surface). Fig. 22-27 shows an electronic air cleaner. It has a screen to trap large particles, an electronic unit to remove particles as small as $\frac{1}{100}$ micron, and a mat to trap the electron treated particles. It is equipped with a pressure drop indicator and controls.
2. To remove liquids.
   - 2-1. Liquid absorbents (chemicals to absorb the liquid or to react with the liquid).
   - 2-2. Deflector plates.
   - 2-3. Settlement chambers.
3. To remove gases and vapors (these are molecular size impurities).
   - 3-1. Condensation (cool the gas to its dew point and remove as a liquid).
   - 3-2. Chemical reaction (to react with the gas).
   - 3-3. Dilution.

It is possible to remove almost 100% of the contaminants in the air, but to do so is expensive. Practical removal of 90 to 95% of the contaminants is much more common.

22-20 Water Sprays

Large air conditioners use water sprays to remove wettable solid contaminants, liquid contaminants, and water soluble gas contaminants from the air. The water is usually sprayed in a pattern which produces 100 percent duct cross section coverage. A drain pan catches the water, eliminator plates in the duct collect any water droplets which tend to travel down the duct. The water drain pan is usually equipped with a float controlled makeup water connection. Water in the drain pan is recirculated using a centrifugal pump. A screen is located at the pump inlet to prevent dirt

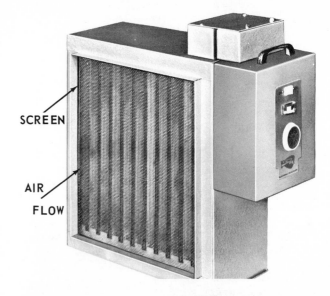

SCREEN

AIR FLOW

Fig. 22-27. Electronic air cleaner used to remove dust particles as small as 1/100 of a micron. Note screen which catches large particles of airborne material such as feathers, lint, etc.
(Electro-Air Cleaner Co., Inc.)

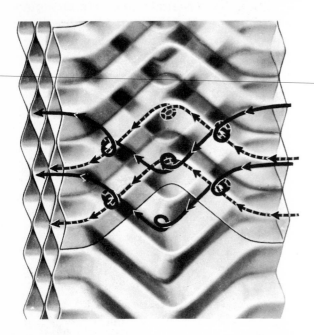

Fig. 22-26. A washable aluminum corrugated filter used to remove dust from forced air system. Aluminum is coated with an adhesive material so dust particles will adhere to surface. Note air flow caused by honeycomb type filters to provide an air turbulence to insure trapping of dust particles.
(Continental Air Filters, Inc.)

particles from clogging the spray nozzles. These air washers are popular during the heating season. Care must be taken to avoid freezing temperatures in the spray chamber. A preheat coil is usually used

to keep the temperatures above freezing. The water spray, in addition to cleaning the air, also serves as a humidifier.

22-21 Review of Safety

It is especially important that you remember that the conditioned air contains sufficient oxygen to support life. The carbon dioxide content must be kept to a minimum.

Always be careful when working with or handling metal duct material. Use gloves with metal inserts when handling the material.

Fans, motors, and belts are potential safety hazards. When these units are operating, protective shields or guards should be provided for protection. When adjusting these units, be sure the main power switch is off and locked in the off position before handling these parts.

Electrostatic air filters require a high voltage to charge the dust particles. Be sure that the current is turned off before servicing them.

22-22 Test Your Knowledge - Chapter 22

1. Is it possible to have a hydronic system and duct system combination?
2. What is meant by negative pressure?
3. What type of air contaminant is molecular in size?
4. What is the volume of 70 F. air at atmospheric pressure if it has 50 percent relative humidity?
5. Does air have specific heat?
6. How is latent heat removed during the cooling season?
7. Is increasing the relative humidity at a constant db temperature an evaporation process?
8. When a comfort cooling air duct has condensation on its outer surface, does the duct air become warmer?
9. How much fresh air should each person receive?
10. What three methods cool a person?
11. What is noise?
12. What is the unit for measuring noise level?
13. Why is an air velocity of 25 ft. per minute important?
14. Does air have inertia?
15. List two ways smaller ducts may be used to distribute heated air and still maintain good heating season temperatures.

Chapter 23

AIR CONDITIONING SYSTEMS, CONTROLS AND INSTRUMENTS

Two important improvements in heating and cooling systems have been:

1. Automatic controls developed to operate systems.
2. Instruments for use by the installation and serviceman to aid him in checking correct operation of system.

It is important to understand the principles, design, construction, operation, and correct use of these controls and instruments. Unless the serviceman has a thorough understanding of the proper use of instrumentation, many wasted hours may be spent trying to diagnose the problem.

23-1 Controls and Instruments

Controls used on heating systems, cooling systems, humidifying systems, dehumidifying systems, airflow, filter operation, combustion and flue systems are of the following main types:

1. Responsive to temperature change.
2. Responsive to pressure change.
3. Responsive to liquid flow and/or gas flow.
4. Responsive to liquid level.
5. Responsive to time.

These controls have made it possible to develop safe, automatic systems.

The basic principles of many of these controls have been described in previous chapters in the text, such as Chapters 6, 8, 13, and 15.

The instruments are important to both the installer and to the serviceman. Elec-

trical instruments, pressure instruments, temperature instruments, and airflow instruments must be used to obtain accurate information. These instruments must therefore give accurate readings. These instruments must be handled with great care. They must be checked periodically with master instruments. If one is dropped it should be recalibrated before using. Never strain the mechanism of an instrument. You should be careful to use an instrument which has a scale which will not be used for more than 1/2 to 2/3 of its maximum reading.

23-2 Air Conditioning Controls

The chief value of complete air conditioning lies in its accurate automatic operation. This operation necessitates many controls such as:

1. Temperature controls.
   A. Heating controls.
      (a) Coal heat.
      (b) Oil heat.
      (c) Gas heat.
      (d) Electric heat.
      (e) Steam controls.
      (f) Water controls.
      (g) Limit controls.
   B. Cooling controls.
2. Humidifying controls.
3. Dehumidifying controls.
4. Air flow controls.
5. Filter controls.
6. Safety controls.

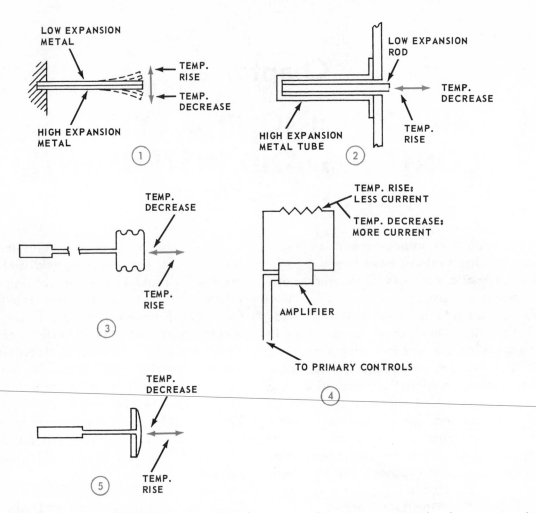

Fig. 23-1. Five basic types of thermostat operating elements. 1—Operates on principle of expansion of metal with heat. 2—Operates on principle of expansion of metal with heat. 3—Operates on principle of expansion of gas with heat. 4—Operates on principle of change of resistance in conductor or semiconductor with change in temperature. 5—Hydraulically operated diaphragm (100% liquid).

There are three basic groups of controls:

1. Operating controls.
2. Primary controls.
3. Limit controls.

The operating controls are usually the thermostats which signal the start or the stop of a heating or cooling system.

The primary controls are those controls which insure a safe start and safe operation of the system.

The limit controls are safety controls which will permit a system to operate if all the safety conditions are in correct order.

The operating controls start and stop a system through the primary controls when the limit controls permit these actions.

23-3 Temperature Controls

Because heating systems and cooling systems control temperatures, they need an operating control which starts and stops the system when the correct temperature conditions are reached.

There are two basic types:

1. Heating thermostat.
2. Cooling thermostat.

These two thermostats may be combined into one unit, called a heating-cooling thermostat. Some of the units change over manually, while some do it automatically.

Some thermostats are time operated. A clock mechanism will change the off-on settings for night and reset again for day. Some units will also change the on-off settings for different days of the week (for example, Saturdays and Sundays).

The device in the thermostat which reacts to temperature change may be one of several types:

1. Bimetal strip.
2. Rod and tube.
3. Bellows or diaphragm.
4. Electrical resistance.
5. Hydraulic.

Fig. 23-1 shows the elements of these five types.

23-4 Heating Thermostats

Heating controls used in air conditioning plants vary somewhat from the types used on refrigeration installations. These thermostats are known as the operating controls of an automatic system. They close the electrical circuit as the room temperature falls, and open the circuit when the room temperature rises to the desired temperature. Several different types of controls are used.

The type used on smaller heating systems is usually the open contact point unit which controls either a 24V or a 120V circuit to the primary controls.

Fig. 23-2 shows a typical room thermostat which is designed to mount on a wall, and has a coiled bimetal strip which reacts to the temperature change.

These thermostats usually operate on a 1/2 F. to 2 F. differential or smaller, which results in close temperature control.

The sensitive element is usually a bimetal strip. A small magnet is sometimes used to produce snap action of the points. A range adjustment is usually a direct force on the bimetal while the differential usually consists of moving the small magnet either closer or farther away from the bimetal strip.

Fig. 23-2. *An internal view of a thermostat showing the coiled bimetal element.*
(Penn Controls Inc.)

Some thermostats are hydraulically operated. Fig. 23-3 shows a diaphragm mechanism with diaphragm movement caused by expansion and contraction of a liquid. Note the adjustment and the small magnet used to obtain snap action in the thermostat.

Electronic measurement of an electric resistance element may be used for temperature control. It is possible to obtain differentials of .01 of a degree using this method.

Thermostats are rated by the voltage they carry and also by the controls to which they are electrically connected. Some thermostats have a time clock mechanism which will change the thermostat setting automatically at certain set time intervals.

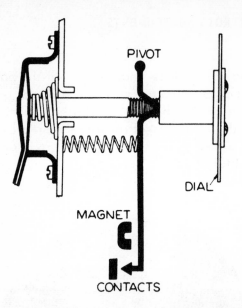

Fig. 23-3. Schematic diagram of hydraulically operated thermostat.
(White-Rodgers Div. of Emerson Electric)

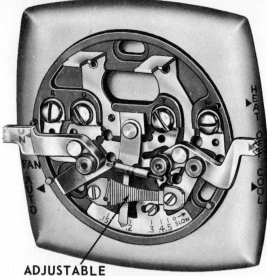

ADJUSTABLE
HEAT ANTICIPATOR

Fig. 23-5. Internal view of thermostat, shown in Fig. 23-4. Variable heat anticipator is shown.
(Penn Controls Inc.)

Fig. 23-4. Combination heating and cooling thermostat which has a heat anticipator. Note fan operation switch and heating-cooling switch.

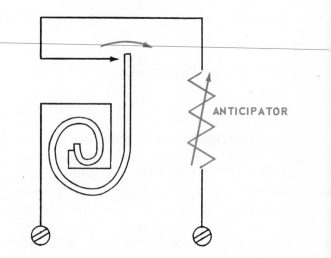

ANTICIPATOR

Fig. 23-6. Schematic wiring diagram of heating thermostat equipped with an anticipator.

One example is the use of a clock for obtaining lower night temperatures, and normal day temperatures. See Par. 23-7.

Heating thermostats usually have a heat anticipator. This unit is a small heating resistor which warms the thermostat a little faster than the room air heats up. The thermostat will then shut off the heating system before the room comes to the propper temperature. The heating unit is still warm and will continue to heat the room to the correct temperature even though the unit is shut off. Different or variable anticipator heaters are used depending on the system. Fig. 23-4 shows the outside of a combination thermostat which has a heat anticipator. The mechanism of this thermostat is shown in Fig. 23-5. The more residual heat in the heating system, the larger the capacity of the anticipator. Fig. 23-6 shows a heating thermostat wiring schematic diagram.

23-5 Cooling Thermostats

Comfort cooling thermostats are similar in design to heating thermostats except that the contacts open as the room cools and close as the room warms up.

The popular bimetal thermostats usually have a 1 F. differential. Both the 24V and 120V controls are available. Some of these units have cold anticipators. These small electric resistance elements are in parallel with the bimetal strip and tend to open the bimetal controlled points just a little before the unit reaches the room cutoff temperature. Fig. 23-7 shows a simplified wiring diagram of a cooling thermostat. The cold anticipator warms the bimetal strip during the off cycle but is bypassed on the on cycle. This lack of heat during the on cycle tends to turn the unit off just a little ahead of normal.

23-6 Combination Thermostats

Some thermostats have both heating control and cooling control mechanisms. These thermostats are used with heat pumps or with other installations which have both a heating system and a cooling system. Fig. 23-8 shows a simplified wiring diagram of a combination thermostat using a bimetal strip, heat anticipator, and cold anticipator.

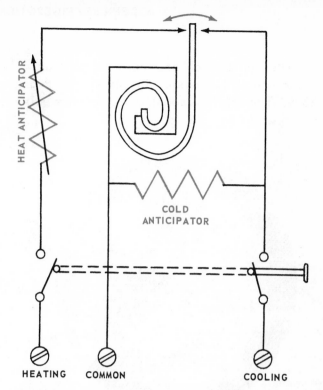

Fig. 23-8. Schematic of bimetal heating-cooling thermostat, which is equipped with heat anticipator and cold anticipator.

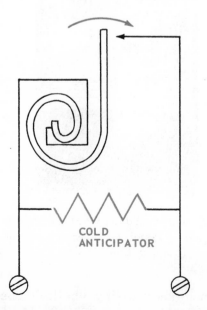

Fig. 23-7. Schematic wiring diagram of a cooling thermostat equipped with cold anticipator.

Fig. 23-9. A thermostat which may be used for both heating and cooling. It also has a fan control switch. Range adjustment is the upper temperature scale. Bottom scale is the room temperature.

The appearance of a combination heating-cooling thermostat is shown in Fig. 23-9. The internal construction of this unit is shown in Fig. 23-10.

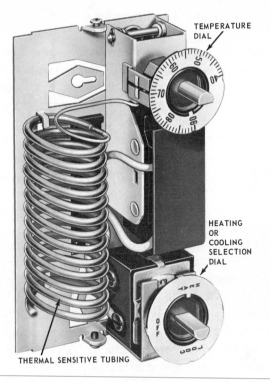

Fig. 23-10. Internal construction of the combination heating-cooling thermostat, shown in Fig. 23-9. (Honeywell)

Fig. 23-12. Internal construction of cooling-heating thermostat.

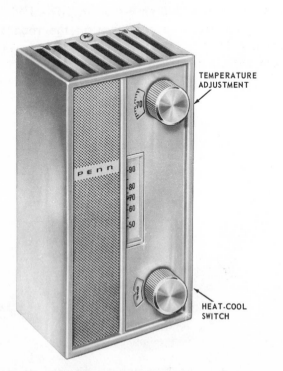

Fig. 23-11. Combination thermostat used for controlling both heating units and cooling units. (Penn Controls Inc.)

Fig. 23-13. Timer used to control operation of heating or cooling system on seven day schedule. (Paragon Electric Co., Inc.)

A thermostat using a bellows operating mechanism is shown in Fig. 23-11. The internal construction is shown in Fig. 23-12.

23-7 Timer-Thermostats

There are many air conditioning installations that can be automatically timed for operation. For example, systems installed in offices need not run at normal temperatures on Saturdays and Sundays. Also, they need not run at normal temperatures during nonworking hours.

Many users of air conditioners want the units to start functioning at a certain time before the premises are used.

Fig. 23-13 illustrates an automatic timer that operates on a seven (7) day schedule. The "buttons" on the periphery of the time disk can be set to turn on the air conditioner at any set time, and shut it off at any set time each day. Note that on this unit there are no on and off buttons for Saturday afternoon and Sunday. Therefore, the unit will not run during this time.

23-8 Electrical Circuits

Four types of electrical circuits used in the heating and cooling systems are:

1. 120 volt (in a few cases 240V up through several voltages and phases for large commercial and industrial systems).
2. 24 volt (these circuits operate relays which in turn control the main electrical circuits).
3. Thermocouple circuits (a few milliamps) used in some pilot light safety devices.
4. Electronic circuits (use of diodes and transistors).

These circuits must have overload safety devices such as fuses and/or circuit breakers.

Smaller motors usually have built-in overload devices, while larger motors use external overloads usually located in the magnetic starter.

In all cases, the wiring and the devices must conform to the local electrical code.

23-9 Primary Controls

Primary controls are the devices in an automatic system which safely turn on and operate the system on command from the operating controls (thermostats in most cases). These primary controls differ depending on the type of heating and/or cooling system used.

The controls depend on the type of heat energy used:

1. Gas.
2. Coal.
3. Oil.
4. Electrical.

The type of controls used also depends on the heat distribution system:

1. Steam.
2. Water.
3. Air.

23-10 Gas Furnace Primary Controls

Gas furnaces have primary controls to insure safe starting and safe operation of gas burners. These controls will allow gas flow only if the pilot light is burning. A thermal element located near the pilot light must either generate thermocouple electrical energy or develop a sensitive bulb pressure to open valves to allow main gas flow. This unit will also shut off the system if the pilot light ceases to operate during the on cycle of the unit. If a blower or pump motor is used in the system, it is operated by a relay, either instantly or after a short delay.

These primary controls operate on the basis of electric interlocks. All conditions must be safe, before all the interlocks are in the correct position to allow the system to operate. Mechanical or thermal sensors are usually considered adequate for the smaller capacity domestic burners.

Commercial and industrial systems use much more elaborate controls due to the larger flow of fuel. Flame sensors are generally used which shut off the system by reacting very fast (in part of a second), in case of flame failure. The sensors are electronic in design and use a flame rod, a photocell (there are two kinds (1) sensitive to radiant energy of flame, (2) sensitive to ultraviolet rays of flame), or a lead sulphite cell which responds to the infrared rays from either the gas or oil flame.

23-11 Stoker Primary Controls

Stokers use a control to feed small amounts of coal to the fire during long "off" periods to keep the fire going. Some controls have a sensor which will stop the fuel feed in case the fire should go out.

23-12 Oil Furnace Primary Controls

Pot type, or vaporizing type furnaces, usually have controls to feed enough oil to keep the pilot burning. A control is also used to feed the correct amount of oil for various size flames. Another control will shut off the oil flow in case the flame goes out.

The gun type oil burner usually has a primary control mounted in the flue. Upon a signal from the thermostat for heat (closing of points) the primary control will start the pump motor and turn on the ignition. This control has a temperature sensing element which will shut down the unit if a fast temperature rise in the flue is not reached in a few seconds (indicating that the oil is not burning). This same sensor will constantly check for flame temperatures and will shut off the system if the flame goes out. This control will shut off the system if the thermostat, or if any one of the limit controls, opens the circuit.

23-13 Electric Heat Primary Controls

Controls used in electric heat systems are covered in Chapter 20.

Baseboard units usually use individual thermostats and the primary controls are usually relays and limit controls. Units using blowers or fans have fan controls which may operate from a separate thermostat, or may be in parallel with the heating elements.

Central systems usually use sequence relays as primary controls. The blowers operate as stated. In addition, a safety control is usually provided which will shut off the heating elements if the blower fails to operate, or if the air ceases to circulate.

23-14 Heat Distribution Controls

Controls must be provided to insure that the steam, water or air is properly circulating to insure the heat is being carried from the furnace to the spaces to be heated.

In steam systems, the zone control valves are either electrically, pneumatically or hydraulically operated upon a signal from a thermostat.

In hot water systems (hydronic), pumps and valves must function in the proper sequence upon command from the operating controls.

In warm air systems, the movement of the air by blowers may be controlled by separate thermostats or as part of the furnace primary controls.

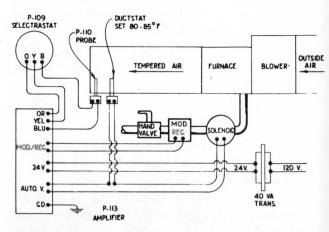

Fig. 23-14. Wiring diagram for remote sensing electronic modulating system. Note modulator regulator valve which controls operation of solenoid and in turn intensity of heat. (Maxitrol Co.)

23-15 Electronic Control System for Gas Fuel

Electronic circuits are also used to control heating systems. One outstanding feature of this type control system is that it can modulate or vary the size of the gas flame. Fig. 23-14 illustrates the wiring circuit for a modulating control. The 120V AC power is reduced to 24V AC using a transformer. This current is then changed to DC in the amplifier. Three control devices are used: (1) the thermostat (selectrostat), (2) the probe (for safety), and (3) the ductstat.

These controls in turn control the sole-

Fig. 23-16. Selectrostat used as component part of an electronic modulation system. Its signals in combination with probe and ductstat is fed to amplifier.

Fig. 23-17. An electronic modulating control system probe. Probe is mounted on main outlet duct (warm air) of furnace. It in combination with electrostat and ducstat, controls gas flame. (Maxitrol Co.)

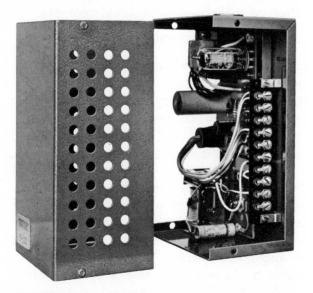

Fig. 23-15. Amplifier of electronic modulating gas flame control system. Unit amplifies and directs electrostat, probe, and ductstat signals to gas line controls.

noid on the main gas line and the modulating regulator on the main gas burner line.

Fig. 23-15 shows the amplifier unit which contains the rectifiers and the transistors for the control circuits. It also contains a potentiometer (adjustable). The thermostat (selectrostat) is shown in Fig. 23-16. This unit contains the thermistor sensing unit which works in conjunction with the probe shown in Fig. 23-17.

The modulator-regulator valve is shown in Fig. 23-18. This is the automatic valve

for varying the gas flow. To combine the varying of the size of the gas flame and also shut off the fuel supply, a modulating (varying) regulating valve and a solenoid shutoff valve are combined, as shown in Fig. 23-19. Direct current flow to this modulator varies to control the amount of gas flow. The less the current flow, the higher the flame. The ductstat is connected in series with the solenoid valve and is used as a safety device in case too high duct temperatures are reached.

23-16 Water Level Controls

Water level controls are especially important on steam heating systems. The control usually consists of a switch oper-

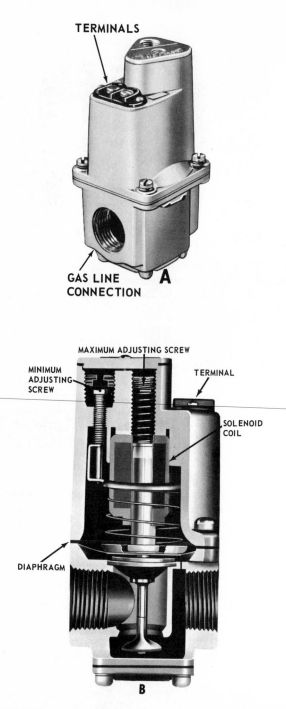

TERMINALS

GAS LINE
CONNECTION

A

MAXIMUM ADJUSTING SCREW

MINIMUM
ADJUSTING
SCREW

TERMINAL

SOLENOID
COIL

DIAPHRAGM

B

Fig. 23-18. Modulator regulator valve as part of electronic control circuit for gas heating system. A—External view. Note gas line connection and electrical terminals. B—Cutaway of same modulator regulator valve. Note adjusting screws used to vary amount of pressure required to operate valve.

ated by a float. If the water level drops near the dangerous level, the float drops and cuts out the electrical circuit to the

system and stops the furnace. The switch usually operates in two stages. The first lowering of the float will actuate a switch to turn on the feed water pump, or feed water solenoid valve. If the float drops more, the system is shut off.

Some water level controls are of the probe type. This type immerses two electrodes in the water. As long as water covers both electrodes, a small current flowing in the water between the two will energize a holding relay and allow the system to run. If the water level falls below the upper probe, the current flow will cease and the system will shut down.

Fig. 23-20 shows the principle of operation of these two water level controls.

23-17 Duct Controls

The safe distribution of conditioned air to the occupied spaces is of great importance in warm air systems. This air must be distributed in the proper amounts to condition the space. It must not be too cold or too hot. You must be sure air is flowing.

Many warm air units are zone controlled. These systems have dampers to control the flow of air to the zones. The dampers open and close upon command of a thermostat. Some dampers are powered by motorized valves, some by pneumatics, some by hydraulics, others by solenoids.

Fig. 23-21 shows a typical duct damper and four ways to control the damper action.

23-18 Fan Controls

Many forced air heating systems use a thermostat in the plenum chamber to start and stop the fan motor (blower). The fan starts only when the plenum chamber reaches a certain temperature. The blower continues to run when the heating unit shuts off until the plenum chamber temperature drops to the fan thermostat cutout temperature.

In some cases the fan control and the limit control are in the same control casing.

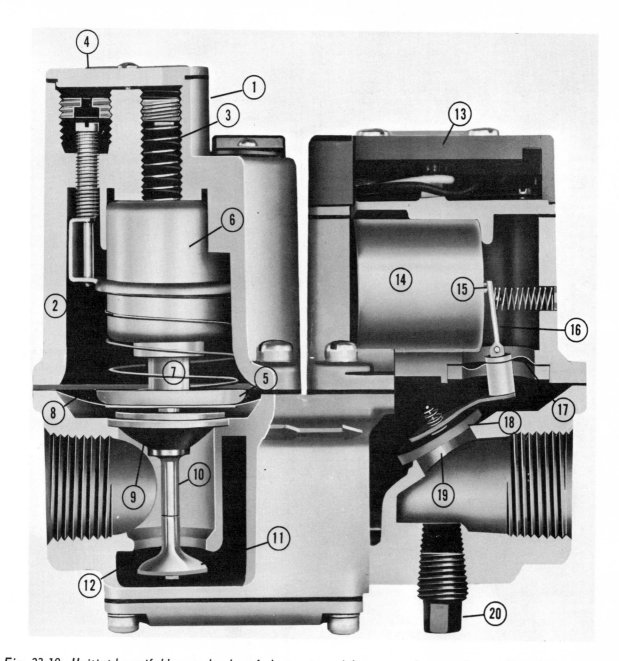

Fig. 23-19. Unitized manifold control valve of electronic modulator control system for gas flame furnace. Flame is modulated from full flame to 20 percent of full flame. Control is combination of modulator-regulator valve and solenoid shut-off valve. 1—Body. 2—Body. 3—Max. adj. 4—Cover. 5—Diaphragm attachment. 6—Solenoid coil. 7—Solenoid core. 8—Diaphragm. 9—Valve guide. 10—Modulating valve. 11—Gas passageway. 12—Valve port. 13—Cover. 14—Solenoid. 15—Solenoid plunger. 16—Lever. 17—Diaphragm. 18—Valve. 19—Valve port. 20—Pipe plug (service connection) (Maxitrol Co.)

23-19 Split System Controls

More and more air conditioning systems are designed to provide either hot or cold water to the heat exchange unit in the space to be conditioned, or, are designed to provide either hot or cold air to the space to be conditioned.

The three-pipe system, for example, will pipe both hot and cold water to a heat

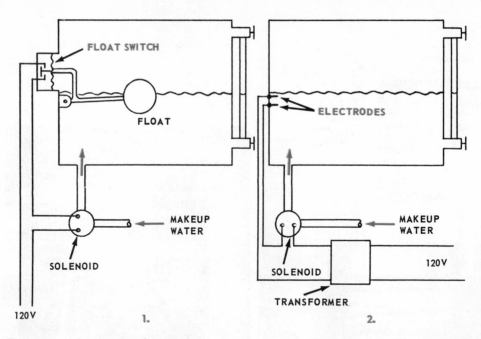

Fig. 23-20. *Two types of water level controls in common use. 1—Float control. Float valve will open make-up water valve when water level drops. Some are connected to electric switch which will shut off unit if water level is too low. 2—Probe type water level control.*

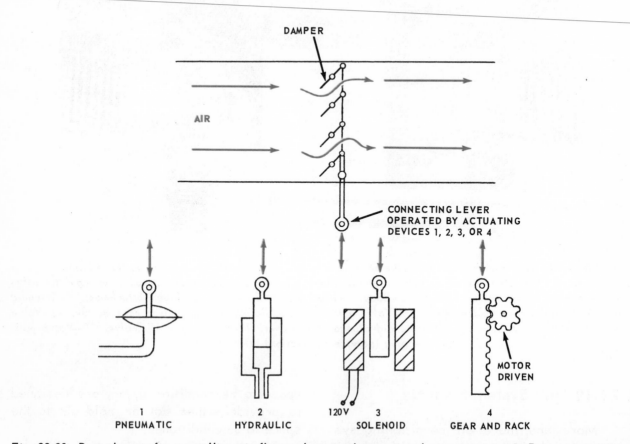

Fig. 23-21. *Duct damper for controlling air flow and power devices used to operate it. 1—Pneumatic motor. 2—Hydraulic motor. 3—Solenoid. 4—Motorized gear and rack.*

exchanger, and the third pipe is a return line for either. A diagrammatic sketch of a thermostat connected to the two valves of a split system is shown in Fig. 23-22.

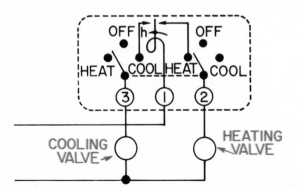

Fig. 23-22. Combination thermostat connected to two valves of split-system, one for cooling and one for heating. (Penn Controls Inc.)

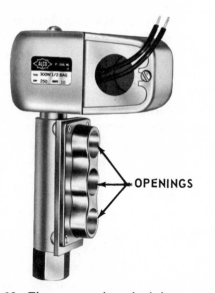

Fig. 23-23. Three-way valve which bypasses cold or hot water when desired. (Alco Valve Co.)

Many water heating or cooling systems utilize a bypass flow of the heat exchange coil when no heating or cooling is needed. This action is obtained through bypassing the hot or cold water unless the thermostat calls for heating or cooling. Fig. 23-23 shows such a valve. The internal construction of this solenoid valve is shown in Fig. 23-24.

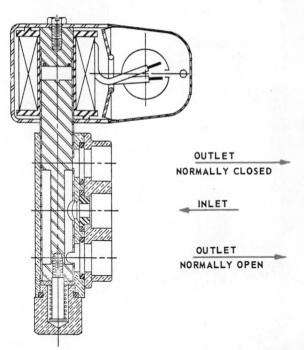

Fig. 23-24. Internal construction of a solenoid operated three-way water valve.

23-20 Draft Controls

Efficient and safe combustion in a furnace requires accurate draft control (flue gas movement). The flue gas flow is dependent on the density of this gas versus the density of the air, and is also dependent on the pressure difference between the inside of the building and the outside of the building.

A draft gauge is usually used to determine the efficiency of flue gas (combustion gas) flow. Fig. 23-25 shows a draft gauge being used. The stack temperature is also an indicator of draft efficiency. Stack temperatures vary from 300 F. to 900 F. Fig. 23-26 shows a stack thermometer being used to determine the temperature of the flue gas.

A popular method of maintaining a constant draft is to install a draft control on the stack. This control is a weighted butterfly valve which opens and allows cool air into the stack to reduce the draft when the draft tends to increase, (pressure dif-

through the combustion chamber. Fig. 23-27 is a schematic of a weighted balance type butterfly draft control.

Gas fired furnaces use an air break system. This is a constant air inlet into the flue. Its most important function is to prevent a chimney pressure pulse (down-draft) back into the furnace which might blow out the gas flames. Fig. 23-28 shows a diagrammatic view of such a device. The draft can be as low as .02 in. of water for a gas furnace flue, while the stack temperature will average about 500 F. Some large commercial and industrial units have motor driven stack controls to control the draft. Others use blowers to either create a definite forced draft or an induced draft.

Fig. 23-25. Draft indicator being used to determine combustion gas flow. Note use of protector over vent in furnace door to prevent inaccurate reading which would occur if room air could enter combustion chamber. (Bacharach Industrial Instrument Co., Sub. of American Bosch Arma Corp.)

23-21 Limit Controls

Limit controls guard against an abnormal condition in a heating system. They will stop the operation of the system if the temperature in a heating system becomes excessive, if the water level is too low in a steam heating system, if the bonnet or plenum chamber temperature is too high in a warm air system, or if the flue temperature in any system becomes excessive.

These controls will shut off the system at some point beyond the operating controls setting.

In warm air furnaces, the limit control is usually a coiled bimetal strip which is in series with the fuel controls and is located in the plenum chamber. It is usually adjusted to open the circuit if the furnace bonnet or plenum chamber reaches 200 F. to 250 F. and cuts back in again after a drop of approximately 25 F. (it usually has a fixed differential).

Fig. 23-26. Stack thermometer used to determine flue gas temperature. Note small hole which is made for insertion of instrument.

23-22 Comfort Cooling Controls

The controls on a comfort cooling unit are of the same basic types as those in heating units. There are operating con-

ference increases), and tends to close the opening when the draft decreases. It, therefore maintains a fairly constant draft

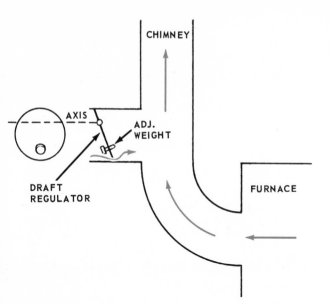

Fig. 23-27. Schematic of draft regulator as used on coal, coke, and/or oil furnaces. Valve will open if draft tends to increase and will close as flue stack draft decreases.

trols, primary controls, and limit controls.

The operating controls are thermostats, pressurestats, humidistats, etc.

The primary controls are motor starters, starting relays, etc.

The limit controls are overload circuit

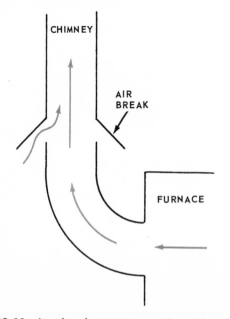

Fig. 23-28. Air break system used on gas furnace flues (stacks).

breakers, thermal overloads, internal motor overloads, refrigerant pressure limit controls, and oil pressure limit controls. Most of these controls are described in Chapters 8 and 13.

The two most popular refrigerant controls are the thermostatic expansion valve and the capillary tube. These controls are described in Chapters 6 and 13.

The complete wiring of a comfort cooling unit is shown in Fig. 23-29. This system uses a low voltage, two-wire thermostat. The thermostat controls a relay which

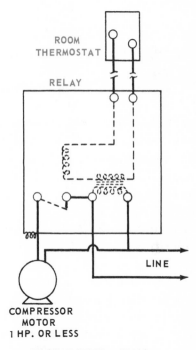

DIAGRAM USING A SMALL
REFRIGERATION UNIT.

Fig. 23-29. Wiring diagram of thermostat relay combination for small comfort cooling units.

will close the motor circuit. If the motor cannot be connected directly to the line, and if pressure safety devices are to be put in the system, the wiring will be somewhat similar to that shown in Fig. 23-30. The high pressure safety cut-out is in series with the starter coil and it will open the circuit if the unit pressures become excessive.

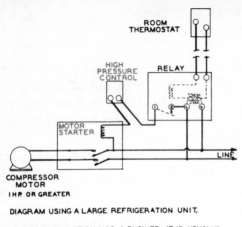

DIAGRAM USING A LARGE REFRIGERATION UNIT.

IF THE INSTALLATION HAS A BLOWER, IT IS USUALLY WIRED TO RUN CONTINUOUSLY DURING THE COOLING SEASON.

Fig. 23-30. Wiring diagram of comfort cooling unit which uses high pressure safety cutout and motor starter. (White-Rodgers Div., Emerson Electric)

Some units cycle on the basis of a low side pressure control. The thermostat operates a solenoid valve mounted in the liquid or suction line. When the thermostat is satisfied the solenoid valve will close and when the low side pressure drops enough, the motor circuit will be opened by means of the pressure control connected to a magnetic starter, as shown in Fig. 23-31, and the unit will stop.

23-23 Comfort Cooling Refrigerant Controls

Large air conditioning evaporator coils usually use the thermostatic expansion valve refrigerant control. Some installations use several such expansion valves on one large coil, in order to get maximum efficiency from the coil. Self-contained systems, especially the hermetically built ones, may use the capillary tube refrigerant control. These controls are described in Chapter 6.

In addition to the refrigerant control used on automatic refrigeration systems, a solenoid refrigerant valve is sometimes placed in the liquid line. This automatically stops the flow of refrigerant to the coil the instant the condensing unit stops. It is necessary in order that the evaporator coil will not become flooded with refrigerant

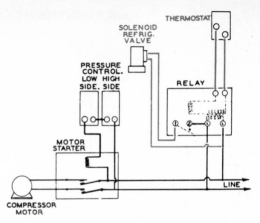

Fig. 23-31. Comfort cooling system wiring diagram. This system has the thermostat operate the solenoid valve. The system cycles as low side pressures vary.

while the condensing unit is idle. Fig. 23-32 illustrates a typical solenoid refrigerant control valve.

This valve uses 5 watts at 120V AC. It has a .100 in. diameter orifice. It has a refrigerating capacity, at a 5 lbs. pressure drop across the orifice, of 1.3 tons for R-12, 2.1 tons for R-22, and 1.62 tons for R-500.

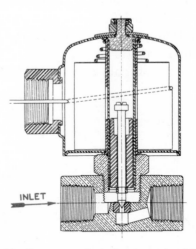

Fig. 23-32. Cross section of solenoid refrigerant control valve used on air conditioning coils. (Controls Co. of America)

23-24 Comfort Cooling Motor Controls

In addition to the operating controls (thermostats), the comfort cooling system has primary controls and limit controls.

The larger refrigerating units are usually equipped with pressure controls. These low and high pressure controls are usually designed to lock the circuit open if any unusual pressures occur. The operator must then manually turn the system on. This action insures careful checking of the unit for any fault.

Fig. 23-33 shows a combination low and high pressure control. The internal construction of this control is shown in Fig. 23-34.

23-25 Comfort Cooling Limit Controls

There are several types of limit controls used in comfort cooling systems:
1. Motor limit controls.
2. Pressure limit controls.
3. Temperature limit controls.
4. Fluid flow limit controls.

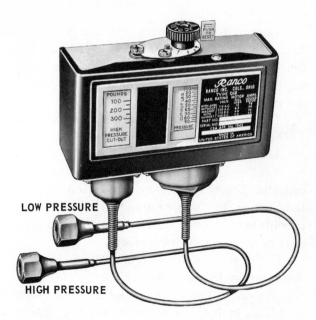

LOW PRESSURE

HIGH PRESSURE

Fig. 23-33. Dual pressure control for air conditioning units. This control will stay open if excessive head pressure or below normal low side pressures are encountered in system. A manual reset is provided and, therefore, the trouble should be detected early.

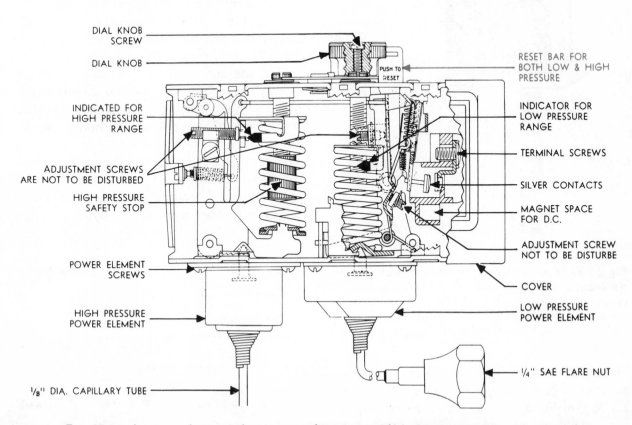

Fig. 23-34. Inner mechanism of an air conditioning condensing unit pressure motor control. (Ranco Inc.)

Motor limit controls are described in Chapter 7. These controls will stop the unit if the current draw becomes too high or if the motor temperature rises to dangerous levels.

The pressure limit control is described in the previous chapter.

Another type of temperature limit control (other than the motor thermistor or bimetal protector) is an anti-icing control located on the evaporator coil. If ice accumulates on the coil, then this control will open and stop the system.

Fluid flow controls are used to stop the system in case the chilled water flow ceases or if the conditioned airflow stops or slows to inefficient amounts. Fig. 23-35 shows an airflow signal switch or shutoff switch or both. If the airflow is not up to

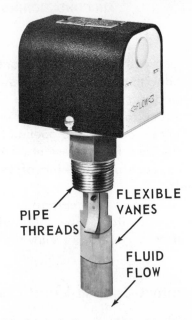

Fig. 23-36. *Liquid flow switch. If chilled water or condenser water flow is not sufficient, this unit will close a signal circuit or will shut off unit, or both.*

23-26 Humidity Controls

Humidity controls are important in keeping the relative humidity of the air conditioned rooms at a satisfactory level. These controls determine the hygrometric state of the air.

Humidity controls operate during periods of winter heating season to add moisture to the air, and keep the humidity approximately constant.

Humidity controls operate in the summer to remove moisture from the air. For the removal of moisture the humidity control usually operates an air bypass to put

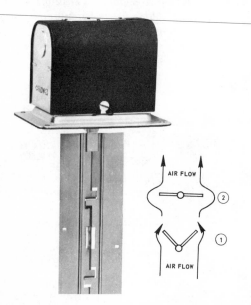

Fig. 23-35. *Airflow switch. 1—Vanes deflected by air movement-operating position. 2—If airflow ceases or is restricted, vane position will be as shown and will either signal trouble or shut off machine, or both. (McDonnell and Miller Inc.)*

standard, the two wings will move into the position shown and operate the switch. Fig. 23-36 shows a similar switch for liquid flow such as chilled water or condenser water.

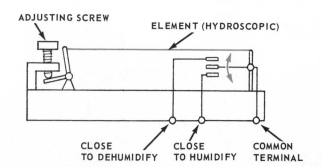

Fig. 23-37. *A humidity control showing the operating mechanism.*

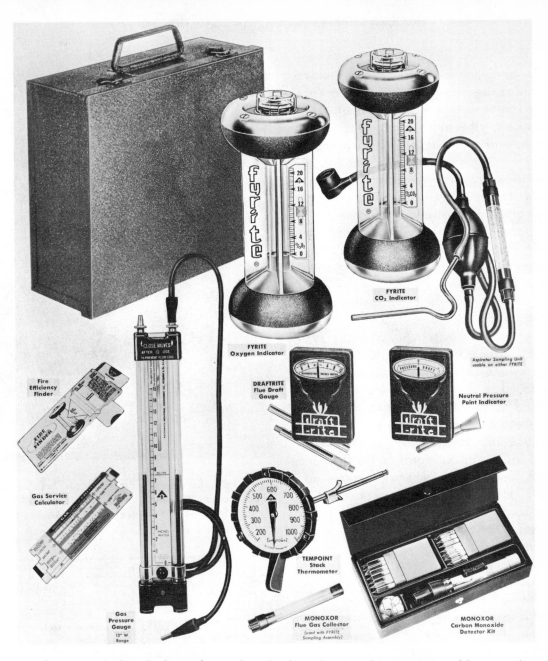

Fig. 23-38. Serviceman's kit which may be used to check combustion characteristics of burner and combustion chamber. Note calculator charts which may be used to aid in interpreting instrument readings. (Bacharach Indus. Inst. Co., Sub. of American Bosch Arma Corp.)

more air over the evaporators. Such controls usually operate electrically to regulate solenoid valves or dampers. The control element may be wood or human hair; both are sensitive to the amount of moisture in the air. Fig. 23-37 illustrates the interior construction of a popular humidity control device. Health studies indicate that humidity control is an important factor in air conditioning.

23-27 Instruments

Instruments are all important to a refrigeration, heating, and air conditioning installation and serviceman. It is virtually impossible to check on the electrical characteristics of a unit without using ammeters, voltmeters, test lights, ohmmeters, etc. These instruments are discussed in Chapters 7 and 8.

In a similar way, the events taking place inside a refrigerating system are virtually impossible to check without pressure gauges, thermometers, etc. These instruments are discussed in Chapters 2, 12, and 15.

In heating systems, the combustion process and the flue gas properties can only be accurately determined by the use of instruments. A set of these instruments are shown in Fig. 23-38. These are described in Chapter 20 as well as in following paragraphs of this chapter.

The flow of liquids should be checked as carefully as possible. The velocity and amount of water flowing in hot water systems, chilled water systems, condensers, cooling towers, etc., should be accurately measured. The amount and velocity of refrigerant liquids is important to know during maintenance and repair work.

Because air is invisible, instruments are also important to measure its flow and pressure conditions. Thermometers and pressure gauges have already been discussed. Some different instruments especially useful for airflow study are:

1. Manometer.
2. Barometer.
3. Pitot tube.
4. Anemometer.
5. Smoke as a velocity indicator.
6. Kata thermometer (see Chapter 27).
7. Hot wire anemometer.

23-28 Combustion Efficiency Instruments

Combustion efficiency is usually determined by measuring the amount of carbon dioxide (CO_2) in the flue gas. A sample of the combustion gas is exposed to a chemical which absorbs carbon dioxide only. Fig. 23-39 shows a CO_2 indicator being used. If 10 cc of the flue gas reduces to 9 cc of gas after exposure to the chemical, the flue gas contained 1 cc or 10 percent of carbon dioxide. If the gas cools during this

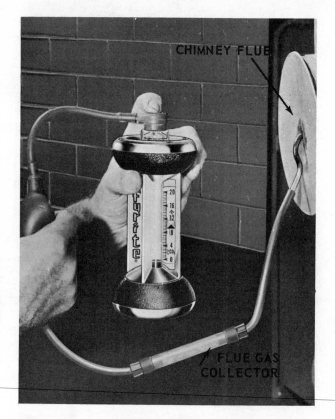

Fig. 23-39. Carbon dioxide analyzer being used to check carbon dioxide content of flue gas. Note flue gas collector and connection into chimney.

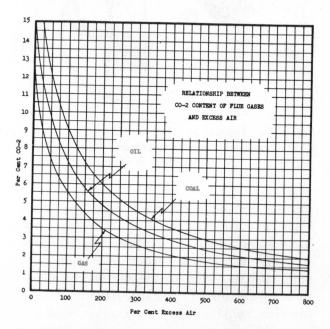

Fig. 23-40. Graph showing change in stack gas carbon dioxide content for coal, oil, and gas fuels as amount of excess air changes from 0 to 800%.

operation, Charles' Law will affect the answer. When the gas cools, its volume reduces, and the serviceman will get a too high reading. The flue gas temperature before and after must be known and a correction must be made to obtain accurate common types of fuel. When the amount of CO_2 has been determined the serviceman can next find the stack temperature and then can determine the combustion efficiency of the furnace through the use of a chart, as shown in Fig. 23-41.

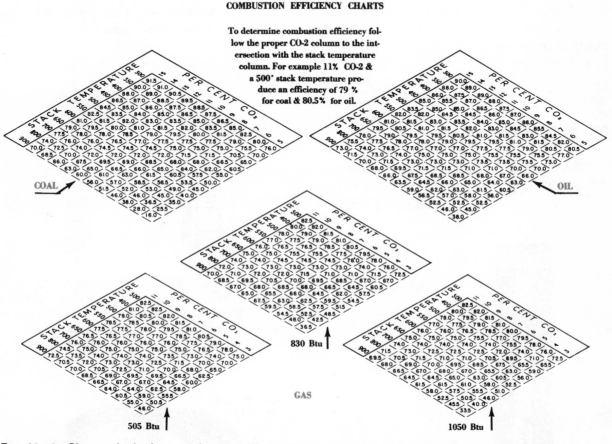

COMBUSTION EFFICIENCY CHARTS

To determine combustion efficiency follow the proper CO-2 column to the intersection with the stack temperature column. For example 11% CO-2 & a 500° stack temperature produce an efficiency of 79 % for coal & 80.5% for oil.

Fig. 23-41. Charts which show combustion efficiencies at various stack temperatures and carbon dioxide percentages. Note that chart gives efficiencies for coal, oil, and three different Btu gas qualities.
(F. W. Dwyer Mfg. Co., Inc.)

results. Tables are provided for this purpose by equipment manufacturers.

Systems will vary in CO_2 content. Some are operating correctly with as low as 8 percent CO_2, some as high as 12 percent CO_2. The manufacturer's service manual will give the correct amount for the particular system. Remember, a clean flame is essential together with the correct CO_2 reading. Fig. 23-40 shows the CO_2 content of the flue gases and excess air for three

23-29 Smoke Test

A smoke test is an excellent way to check combustion efficiency such as air-fuel ratio, primary air, secondary air, and draft.

The test is an empirical test (one which depends on experience and observation) rather than a scientific comparison test. A white filter paper is inserted in the flue and the smoke deposit on the filter paper is compared with a sample chart. Another method inserts a tube in the flue and an aspirator bulb is used to force flue gas samples through a filter mounted in a fixture (about 30 aspirator bulb squeezes are made). The smoke deposit on the filter is then compared to a master comparison scale. This scale (the Ringelmann Scale) specifies smoke by numbers from 1 to 4.

Photoelectric cells may be used to check smoke density in large systems or in laboratories.

In all cases there should be no smoke appearing at the chimney exit.

23-30 Manometers

The manometer is a U-shaped tube, filled with a liquid (mercury or water) as shown in Fig. 23-42. If there is a pressure

will equal the higher pressure in the other tube. Fig. 23-43 shows a simple manometer. Mercury is used for large pressure differences and water for low pressure differences. Duct pressures usually call for water manometers. Scale B is usually movable to make it easier to adjust for the neutral point. Sudden pressure changes must be avoided, or the liquid may be forced out of the manometer.

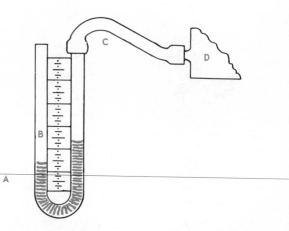

Fig. 23-43. Simple manometer in operation. A—Glass tube. B—Scale. C—Rubber connecting tube. D—Pressure being measured. Pressure is indicated by difference in level of liquid in two sides of manometer and is usually measured in inches.

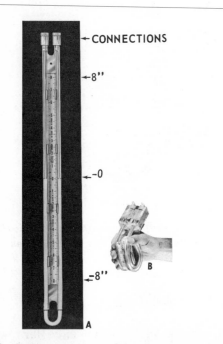

Fig. 23-42. Manometer used for measuring air flow in ducts and also for checking drafts. A—Open ready for use. B—The flexible tube permits easy storing.

difference on the two openings, the column of liquid will move until the liquid level in the low pressure side will be high enough so that its weight and the low pressure

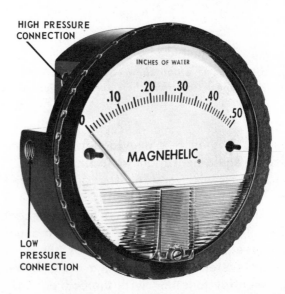

Fig. 23-44. Dial type manometer. Note that calibration is in inches of water.

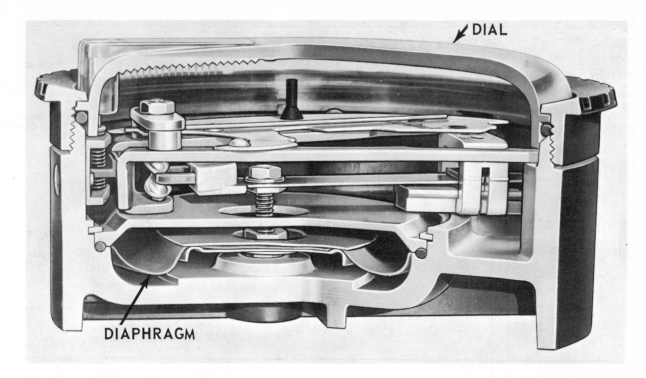

Fig. 23-45. Cross section of a dial type manometer. Moving magnet moves permanent magnet which rotates helix fastened to needle. Diaphragm separates two pressure chambers. (F. W. Dwyer Mfg. Co., Inc.)

Some manometers measure the pressure difference between atmospheric pressure and the pressure of a fluid. Some measure the pressure difference between two different places of the same fluid container (differential manometers). An example, is a manometer used to measure the pressure drop across a filter in an airflow system.

Manometer scales are based on the following data:

14.7 psi = 29.9 in Hg = 34 ft. water
1 in. Hg = .492 psi
1 psi = 2.034 in. Hg
1 psi = 2.31 ft. water
1 ft. water = .432 psi
1 in. water = .036 psi

Dial type manometers are also available. See Fig. 23-44. These gauges have scales to indicate pressures from 0 to 5 in. of water up to 0-5 psi.

The inside of the gauge is shown in Fig. 23-45. Fig. 23-46 shows a dial type manometer in use.

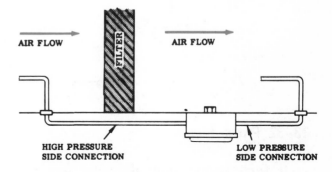

Fig. 23-46. One of many applications of the dial type manometer. The greater the pressure difference in this case, the more resistance (clogging) is indicated at filter.

23-31 Barometers

The barometer is a special form of a manometer. It is sealed at one end and uses mercury as the liquid. Because the pressure height is indendent of the diameter, a single tube can be used, as shown in Fig. 23-47. There is a vacuum in the upper end of the glass tube and the atmospheric pressure operating on the surface of the mercury in the open cup pushes the mercury up in the glass tube until the weight of the mercury column equals the atmospheric pressure.

This instrument may be used to determine the pressure of the atmosphere at any place or time.

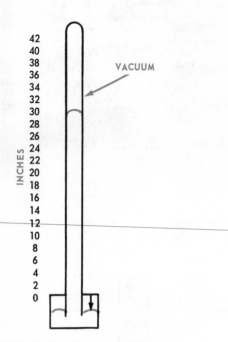

Fig. 23-47. Simple mercury barometer.

23-32 Pitot Tubes

It is essential that air velocities be measured accurately in air conditioning. We must be able to measure duct velocities to determine the air volume and also, to know if the system is operating close to its design conditions.

When measuring air velocities, we should always be sure that the airflow is smooth, not turbulent. A honeycomb structure will tend to smooth airflow. If possible, avoid measuring near obstructions, bends, dampers, or where duct sizes change.

One of the best ways to determine air velocities is to use a pitot tube, as shown

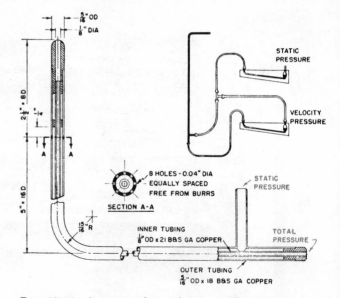

Fig. 23-48. A pitot tube and its connections to two inclined manometers.
(ASHRAE Guide and Data Book)

in Fig. 23-48. Air contacting the nose of the pitot tube creates a total pressure, and the outer tube with the holes on the side measures the static pressure. When these two pressures are connected to the end of a manometer, the difference in the pressures is the velocity pressure. An inclined manometer is used with the pitot tube to measure the velocity pressure, as shown in Fig. 23-49.

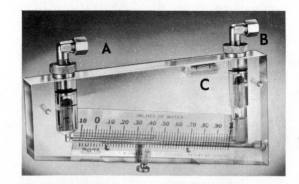

Fig. 23-49. Inclined gauge for use with pitot tube. A—Total pressure connection. B—Static pressure connection. This gauge may also be used for measuring filter, pressure drops. Unit must be carefully leveled; note built-in spirit level. C—Liquid level is easily adjusted to zero reading.
(F. W. Dwyer Mfg. Co., Inc.)

This pressure difference is measured in inches of water. Using the formula:

Velocity = 4050 x square root of velocity pressure in inches of water.

Example:

If the velocity pressure is 1 in. of water, the velocity will be:

Velocity = $4050\sqrt{1 \text{ in.}}$

Velocity = 4050 x 1

Velocity = 4050 ft./min.

If the velocity pressure is .25 in. of water:

Velocity = $4050\sqrt{.25}$

Velocity = 4050 x .5

Velocity = 2025. ft./min.

The constant 4050 is for approximately 80 F. at a 500 ft. altitude. Other values are shown in Fig. 23-50. It is essential that the manometer be mounted level to obtain accurate readings.

Volume Cu.ft./lb.*	Velocity Constant
11.5	3720
12.1	3818
13.2	3980
**13.4	4010
14.1	4118
15.1	4260
16.2	4410
17.1	4530

*Values for any conditions may be read from the psychrometric chart.
**Standard.

Fig. 23-50. Change in velocity correction factor with a change in air density (effect of temperature and altitude).

To obtain correct velocity readings in a duct, several readings in various parts of the duct should be taken and the readings averaged. The recommended method to use is shown in Fig. 23-51. The rectangular duct is divided into equal areas, and the pitot tube is put in the center of each small area. The sixteen velocities are averaged to obtain the overall average

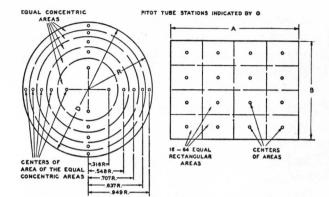

Fig. 23-51. Locations for velocity readings in duct. Average of readings will produce average duct velocity. (ASHRAE Guide and Data Book)

velocity. The round duct is more difficult to measure, because it must be divided into equal circular areas. The location of each of the structure points is as recommended by the Society of Heating, Refrigerating and Air Conditioning Engineers.

23-33 Velocimeters

Velocity measuring instruments have been developed that directly indicate the velocity. Servicemen often use these instruments to avoid the arithmetic which

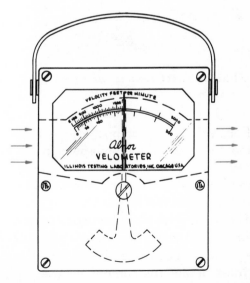

Fig. 23-52. Direct reading air velocity meter. Note air flow is through instrument from left to right. (Alnor Inst. Co., Illinois Testing Laboratories, Inc.)

is necessary when they use pitot tubes and to obtain quicker results. Such instruments, as shown in Fig. 23-52, are being used extensively.

Some impinge the air on a small vane that tilts at different angles as the air pressure increases. The instrument is put directly in the airstream with the left side facing the airflow. The instrument shown has two velocity scales 0-400 and 0-1600 feet per minute. The dotted lines show the airflow through the instrument proper. This instrument can be used to measure air velocities in a great variety of situations.

Some of the instruments are based on the cooling effect of the airflow on an electrical resistance, as shown in Fig. 23-53.

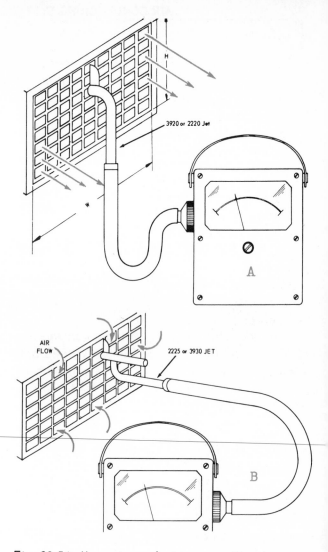

Fig. 23-54. *Measuring velocities at grille. An average of several readings over grille face should be taken. A—Indicates instruments used at discharge grille. B—Indicates intake opening application.* (Alnor Inst. Co., Illinois Testing Laboratories, Inc.)

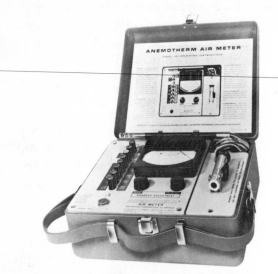

Fig. 23-53. *A direct reading air velocity indicating instrument.* (Anemostat Products Div.)

For velocity readings where it is inadvisable to put the instrument in the airstream or if the instrument cannot be placed in the airstream, special jets are available to get the readings.

The instrument can be used to measure grille air velocities, as shown in Fig. 23-54. Note that a special jet is attached to the air inlet of the instrument by means of a flexible tube.

An important use of the instrument is shown in Fig. 23-55, measuring velocities in main ducts and branch ducts. An instrument of this type is necessary to balance air distribution systems.

The readings are accurate. However, for extreme temperatures, the correct

$$fpm = \frac{460 + T}{460 + 68} \times \text{instrument reading, where}$$

T = temperature of air in duct.

23-34 Anemometers

If a small propeller is put in an airstream, it will revolve as the air flows past the blades. Correctly designed, the

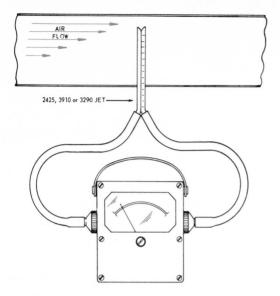

Fig. 23-55. Direct reading air flow meter being used to determine air velocity inside duct.

Fig. 23-56. Anemometer used for measuring air flow. Large dial reads to 100 ft., lower left dial in 100 ft. increments, and lower right dial in 1,000 ft. increments. (Taylor Instrument Companies)

propeller will be practically frictionless. If the propeller is connected to a dial calibrated in feet, it will indicate the feet of flow. Fig. 23-56 shows such an instrument. These devices have a start lever and also a return to zero lever. To use the instrument, carefully place it in the airstream,

allow it to reach a constant speed, this will take approximately one minute, then trip the registering mechanism. At the same time start a stopwatch. Record the reading and the time. From this data the velocity of the air in feet per minute may be readily computed. For example, if the reading is 236 for 1/2 minute, the velocity will be 472 ft./min.

It is advisable to average several readings to insure greater accuracy.

Another type of anemometer is shown in Fig. 23-57. This unit is used mainly for measuring discharge air velocities at

Fig. 23-57. A Velocity-Aire anemometer. This instrument directly reads air velocity in fpm of discharge grilles. (Thermal Industries of Florida, Inc.)

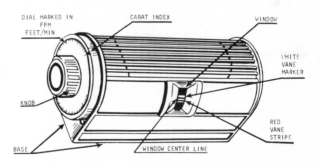

Fig. 23-58. Names of the parts of a Velocity-Aire anemometer.

grilles. Names of the parts are shown in Fig. 23-58. To use the unit, the base is placed against the grille, the knob is turned until the white vane marker is in the center of the window, then the knob is turned until the red vane is just under the center line. The dial will indicate the fpm. For

Fig. 23-59. Velocity-Aire anemometer in use on a rectangular grille.

Fig. 23-60. Velocity-Aire anemometer being used to measure the discharge velocity from a circular grille. (Thermal Industries of Florida, Inc.)

rectangular grilles the unit is used, as shown in Fig. 23-59; for circular grilles the unit should be positioned on the radius of the grille, as shown in Fig. 23-60.

The pitot tube, the direct reading velocimeter, and the anemometer are not accurate at low air velocities.

23-35 Draft Indicators

Drafts of 15 to 25 ft./min. are allowable for most installations. If the air movement is less than this, air stagnation results. If it is more, persons exposed to the draft are uncomfortable.

To determine the amount of the draft and the direction, the most successful method has been to use smoke (visible vapor). Smoke generators release small puffs of smoke into the space being tested, and

the distance they move in 1/2 or 1 minute, is observed. Several readings must be taken and averaged to obtain a degree of accuracy.

One type of smoke generator is shown in Fig. 23-61. Each of the two bottles contains a liquid. The aspirator forces the vapors from the two bottles to mix at the nozzle. The mixing of the two gases forms a white smoke that has a density not much greater than the density of air. The liquids used are hydrochloric acid and aqua ammonia. The smoke formed is ammonium chloride.

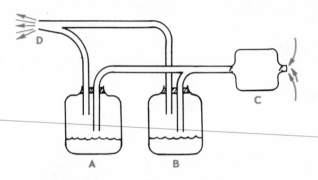

Fig. 23-61. A smoke generator. A—Hydrochloric acid container. B—Aqueous ammonia. C—Rubber aspirator bulb. Smoke is released at nozzle D.

23-36 Flow Meters

Flow meters of many different designs and for many purposes are in use. The gas meter and the water meter are the most common. Both are used to determine consumption.

Fig. 23-62 shows a flow meter that measures water flow. This type flow meter is available to measure water flow from 1/4 gallon per minute up to 5 gallons per minute.

23-37 Thermometers

In many air conditioning installations, it is necessary to know the temperatures of the heat exchange surfaces, the ducts,

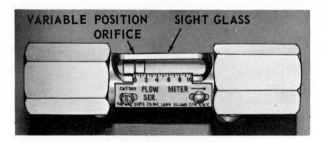

Fig. 23-62. Flow meter for indicating water flow and for measuring volume of water flow. (Henry G. Dietz Co., Inc.)

etc. Almost all temperature indicating instruments may be used for these purposes.

A complete and accurate installation and/or service job cannot be done until you know the in and out temperatures of all the fluids used in the system.

A dial type thermometer is shown in Fig. 23-63. This unit, which may be wall mounted, will register temperatures of a room or conditioned space.

Fig. 23-63. Wall mounted dial type thermometer. (Abrax Instrument Corp.)

Another dial thermometer type is shown in Fig. 23-64. The dial units (2 1/2 in. dia.) fasten by spring clips to pipes up to 3 1/2 in. in diameter and will give the surface temperature of the pipe. There are types

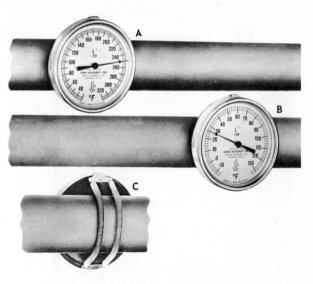

Fig. 23-64. Dial type thermometers for determining surface temperatures of pipe. A—Steam pipe. B—Refrigeration pipe. C—Spring clip mounting.

available for measuring the temperature of steam, water, gas, or refrigeration pipes.

Stem type dial thermometers are used to measure duct air temperatures, flue gas temperatures, liquid temperatures, etc. A quick reading instrument is shown in Fig. 23-65. This instrument has a scale from 0 to 600 F. and it operates on the thermocouple principle. Other temperature scales are also available. To use the thermometer, place the end of the adjustable probe against the surface where the temperature is to be measured.

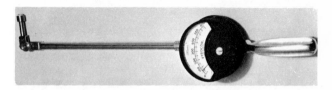

Fig. 23-65. Temperature measuring instrument for obtaining air and surface temperatures. (Alnor Inst. Co., Illinois Testing Laboratories, Inc.)

An electric thermometer is shown in Fig. 23-66. These units are either battery operated or 120V AC powered. The probe

easily located by making 24 hour recordings or 7 day recordings of temperatures. Fig. 23-67 shows such a unit.

23-38 Hygrometers

Hygrometers are used to measure humidity. In many operations both for comfort and for industrial processing, it is important to know the humidity of the air.

Hygrometers are available in many types. Fig. 23-68 is a dial type hygrometer designed for a wall mounting. This instrument is 6 in. in diameter and has a calibration adjustment.

Fig. 23-66. An electric thermometer. Note calibration setting on switch and jack for connecting recorder.

reacts quickly and accurately. The scale is calibrated in both Fahrenheit and Centigrade degrees.

A very useful thermometer is the recording type. Many malfunctions have been

Fig. 23-68. Wall type hygrometer. (Abrax Inst. Corp.)

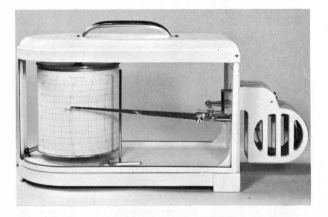

Fig. 23-67. Recording thermometer. Sensing element is at right of cabinet.

An electric hygrometer is shown in Fig. 23-69.

As in pressure and temperature measuring, it is important to have a 24 hour or 7 day record of the humidity in a controlled space. Fig. 23-70 shows such an instrument.

Fig. 23-69. Electric hygrometer. Switch has a calibration position.

SWITCH   ADJ.

SENSITIVE ELEMENT

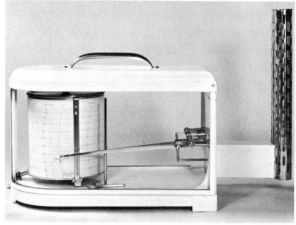

Fig. 23-70. Humidity recorder. Sensing element is at the right.

23-39 Review of Safety

If an instrument is dropped, it should be checked with a master instrument and repaired if necessary before it is used. Safety controls for a heating system or a cooling system should never be removed and bypassed to keep a system operating because dangerous conditions or damage to the system may result.

You should always determine the pressure in the part of a system on which you intend to work. Always measure the temperature of the parts of the system which you intend to repair, adjust, or touch. Do not guess as to the pressure, or temperature in a system. Use instruments to check electrical circuits rather than guess that the power is off.

The handling and use of instruments usually does not present any great hazard to the serviceman. However, if he does not read or interpret the instrument readings correctly, and as a result faulty installations are made, great damage may be done to the equipment and persons within the structure may be seriously injured.

23-40 Test Your Knowledge - Chapter 23

1. What refrigerant controls are usually used on air conditioning evaporator coils?
2. Why are solenoid refrigerant control valves necessary on air conditioning evaporator coils?
3. What is a bimetal thermostat?
4. How fast must air be moved to produce a noticeable draft?
5. Why is water used as a pressure indicating liquid in manometers?
6. What is a differential manometer?
7. How do we find velocity pressure?
8. Why must we take careful readings when measuring duct velocities?
9. What is a hygrometer?
10. Why do oil fired furnace flues have a draft control?
11. What is a limit control?
12. How does a rod and tube thermostat operate?
13. In what controls may a bimetal strip be used?
14. What is the usual bonnet or plenum chamber limit control cut-out temperature setting?
15. Describe a cold anticipator.
16. Describe a heat anticipator.

17. Is there such a control as a combination heating and cooling thermostat?
18. If a flow switch has two sets of contact points, describe the use of each set of points.
19. Is there such a device as an electronic thermostat?
20. Where does the CO_2 come from in flue gas?
21. What is the average CO_2 content of an oil furnace flue gas?
22. How does a smoke tester operate?
23. How many inches of water column equal 1 psi?
24. What three pressures can be determined by a pitot tube system?
25. How does a hydraulic thermostat operate?

Chapter 24

AIR CONDITIONING SYSTEMS, HEAT LOADS

In heating systems, the correct installation is a system that will give enough heat to keep the occupied space at a comfortable temperature even at record low temperatures for that locality. Chapter 20 lists some of the design conditions. In much of the United States the conditions are: a 70 F. inside temperature when it is 0 F. outside and there is a 15 mph wind blowing.

Comfort cooling installations have the same challenge as heating installations. The unit must have sufficient capacity to cool the desired area on the warmest day of the season.

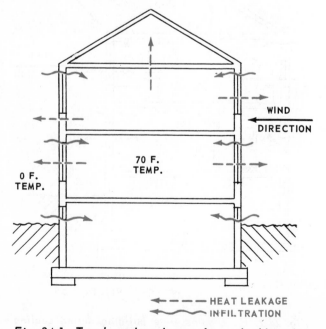

Fig. 24-1. Two large heat losses from a building during the heating season.

24-1 Heat Loads

An air conditioning system must put enough heat into a space to make up for the heat losses (heating); for cooling, it must remove as much heat as the space accumulates (cooling).

Whenever a temperature difference exists, heat energy will flow from the higher temperature to the lower temperature level. It is necessary to retard this heat flow as much as possible, because the amount of heat lost must be replaced in the case of heating, or the amount of heat gained must be removed in the case of cooling.

The most common method is to determine the maximum heat load (lost or gained) for a period of one hour.

24-2 Types of Heat Loads

Heat loads consist partly of heat that is transmitted through the walls, ceilings, and floors (conduction).

1. From the inside to the outdoors (heating).
2. From the outside to the inside (cooling).

The heat load also involves the heat necessary to control moisture content in the air.

1. Adding moisture (humidifying requires additional heat).
2. Removing moisture (dehumidifying requires removal of heat).

The heat load also consists of conditioning the air that enters the building by leakage and for ventilation.

The sun also produces heat in buildings directly through the windows, and by heating the surfaces it strikes (a cooling load).

Any energy device in the building produces heat. Such items as light fixtures, electric motors, electric stoves or gas stoves; all produce heat. People, too, release a considerable amount of heat.

In all cases, the heat load can be described as either sensible heat load (temperature change) or latent heat load (moisture).

24-3 Heat Loads for Heating

Heat loads for heating consist of all those means by which heat will be lost from a building or to the warming of cooler substances that are brought into the building. This heat transfer is usually called heat loss.

The two main heat losses are:
1. Heat lost by conduction through the walls, ceilings, and floors of the structure.
2. Heat lost by the air that leaks out of the building and that which leaks into the building (exfiltration and infiltration).

Fig. 24-1 shows the two main causes of heat loss.

Normally all other heat losses are ignored, because they are relatively too small to affect the size of the unit to be installed.

Humidification requires heat. It requires about 1000 Btu per lb. to vaporize water.

Heat gain from lights, motors, appliances and people are often taken into account in commercial and industrial structures but usually not in domestic heating calculations.

For most of the United States (upper two thirds) the design conditions are 0 F. outside, 70 F. inside, with a 15 mph wind.

24-4 Heat Loads for Cooling

There are definite sources of heat gain in warm weather:
1. Heat leakage into the building.
2. Air leakage into the building or ventilation air.
3. Sun load.
4. Heat from appliances including lights.
5. Heat gain from occupants.

Heat gain is the term applied to heat gained by a space that is being cooled, and the heat must be removed to keep the temperature and humidity at the values desired.

This heat gain is produced by heat conduction through the walls, ceilings, floors, windows, and doors of the enclosure. Also heat moves into the room by way of infiltrated air. The people or any animals in the room also give off heat.

Miscellaneous sources of heat are electrical devices (lights and motors), gas

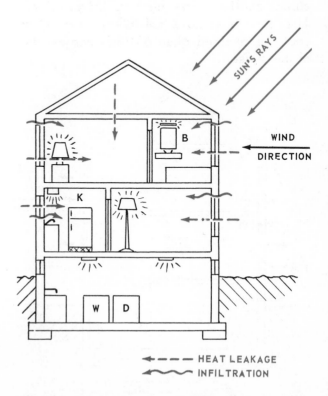

Fig. 24-2. Heat gains in a building during cooling season. Note heat leakage, air infiltration, sun load, lights, appliances, moisture sources.

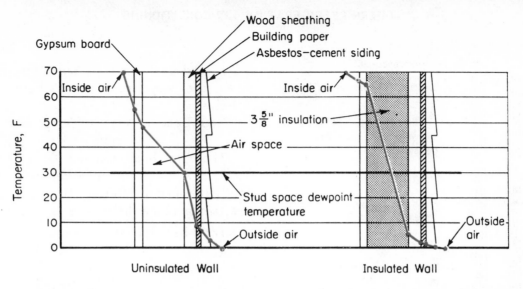

Fig. 24-3. *Temperature change through uninsulated wall and an insulated wall.*

burning devices, steam tables, etc. Another source of heat that may be considerable in some cases is heat from the sun or sun effect. Fig. 24-2 illustrates some of the heat sources during the comfort cooling season.

24-5 Heat Leakage

Heat leakage is that heat that is conducted through the walls, ceilings, and floors of the building. If we determine how much heat will pass from the air, through a wall and into the air for each sq. ft., for each degree F. temperature difference, and for each hour (commonly called U), it will then only be necessary to find the area of each type of surface through which the heat is leaking, and by simple multiplication to find the total heat leakage.

Another method of determining heat leakage is to determine the thermal resistance of the structure and to use this value to determine the amount of leakage. Thermal resistance is known by the letter R. It is the reciprocal of conductance or the overall heat transfer (U). U is the symbol for heat leakage, air to air, through a complex structure.

All building materials have been carefully tested in laboratores. From these data we can obtain the amount of heat that

will transfer through almost any enclosure surface being used today. Fig. 24-3 shows how the temperature changes during the heating season for a typical wood siding residence wall, both noninsulated and insulated. This heat transfer is called conductivity. As there are three general conditions, the following terms are used.

The letter K represents the Btu that will be transmitted through one sq. ft. of the wall or surface in one hour if there is a temperature difference of one degree Fahrenheit, if the material is 1 in. thick.

1. Thus the units of K are Btu/sq.ft./F./hr./1in. thickness.

2. The letter C is used to mean the heat transfer through a wall made of different substances.

$$\frac{1}{C} = \frac{X_1}{K_1} + \frac{X_2}{K_2} + \frac{X_3}{K_3}$$

where X is the thickness of the material in inches.

$$C = \frac{1}{\dfrac{X_1}{K_1} + \dfrac{X_2}{K_2} + \dfrac{X_3}{K_3}}$$

3. The letter U is used to represent the heat leakage from the air on one side of the wall to the air on the other side of the wall. The meaning and values for U are explained in the next paragraph.

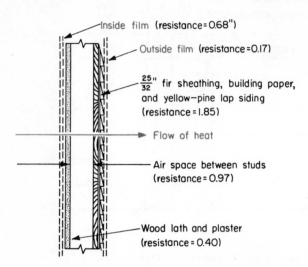

Inside film (resistance=0.68")

Outside film (resistance=0.17)

$\frac{25}{32}$" fir sheathing, building paper, and yellow–pine lap siding (resistance=1.85)

Flow of heat

Air space between studs (resistance=0.97)

Wood lath and plaster (resistance=0.40)

Fig. 24-4. Schematic of an outside wall section showing inside air film and outside air film. (Edison Electric Institute)

24-6 U Factor for Heat Leakage

The letter U is almost the same as C, but the value represents the additional insulating effect of an air film on each side of the surface, as shown in Fig. 24-4.

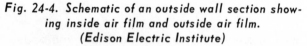

$$U = \frac{1}{\dfrac{1}{F_i} + \dfrac{X_1}{K_1} + \dfrac{X_2}{K_2} + \dfrac{X_3}{K_3} + \dfrac{1}{F_o}}$$

Where F_i is the heat transfer through the inside dead air film and F_o is the heat transfer through the outside air film.

The U value is a common term used to indicate the amount of heat transferred through a structure (a wall) and is expressed as: U = Btu/sq.ft./F./hour

This U value is based on a 15 mph wind on the outside and a 15 ft./min. (1/6 mph) draft on the inside wall surface.

The U value for almost every construction can be obtained from reference data books published by the American Society of Heating, Refrigerating and Air Conditioning Engineers. Fig. 24-5 is a simplified table for some of the more common constructions.

Therefore, if we know the U factor, that the design temperature conditions are

70 F. indoors and 0 F. outdoors, and the area, we may calculate the heat load as follows:

Heat Load = Area x Temp. Diff. x U factor

The total heat transfer (Q) = U x total surface x temperature difference. Therefore, if there is 400 sq. ft. of surface and the temperature difference is 70 F.:

Total heat transfer (Q) = .25 x 400 x (70 F. –0 F.)
= .25 x 400 x 70
= .25 x 28,000
Q = 7000 Btu/hr.

As another example, a brick veneer wall, no insulation, has a U of .25. This value means that .25 Btu will transfer through each sq. ft. of the wall for each 1 F. temperature difference in one hour. The total surface area is 1200 sq. ft. The heat transfer can now be determined as follows:

Q = .25 x 1200 x (70 F. –0 F.)
= .25 x 1200 x 70
= 300 x 70
Q = 21,000 Btu/hr.

The outdoor or ambient temperature is different for each locality. Fig. 24-6 shows the design conditions for calculating heat loads for heating and cooling for various regions.

24-7 R Factor for Heat Leakage

Another method used for calculating heat leakage is using the thermal resistance or R factor. R is known as the unit of thermal resistance. It is also called ru which means resistance unit. If U is the heat transfer, then R is the reciprocal of heat transfer. The symbol R is the reciprocal of C or $R = \dfrac{1}{C}$ and in case of overall heat transfer $R = \dfrac{1}{U}$. For a composite wall (a typical building) R total equals the sum of the individual reciprocals of the C or

HEAT LOADS

Constants For Heat Transmission

Expressed in Btu per hour per square foot per degree temperature difference, based on 15 mph wind velocity

MASONRY CONSTRUCTION

GENERAL WALL CLASSIFICATION	MASONRY THICKNESS				
	6″	8″	10″	12″	16″
BRICK—Plain		.50		.36	
Plaster (½″) Applied Directly to Brick		.46		.34	
¾″ Plaster on Metal Lath		.32		.25	
½″ Plaster on ½″ Rigid Insulation		.22		.19	
½″ Plaster on 1″ Rigid Insulation		.16		.14	
CONCRETE—Plain	.79		.62		.48
½″ Plaster Applied Directly to Concrete	.70		.57		.44
¾″ Plaster on Metal Lath	.42		.37		.31
½″ Plaster on ½″ Rigid Insulation	.26		.24		.21
½″ Plaster on 1″ Rigid Insulation	.19		.18		.16
½″ Plaster, Lath, 2″ Space with Rock Wool Fill	.13		.13		.12
HOLLOW TILE—Plain		.40	.39		.25
½″ Plaster Applied to One Side		.38	.37		.24
¾ Plaster on Metal Lath		.28	.27		.22
4″ Brick Veneer, Hollow Tile, Metal Lath and Plaster (Tile thickness given)	.25	.25	.24	.21	
4″ Brick Veneer, Hollow Tile, 2″ Rock Wool Fill, Lath and Plaster (Tile thickness given)	.11	.11	.11	.10	

FRAME CONSTRUCTION

Wood Siding on 1″ Wood Sheathing, Studs, Wood Lath and Plaster	.25
Wood Siding, Sheathing, Studs, ½″ Rigid Insulation and Plaster	.19
Wood Siding, Sheathing, Studs, ½″ Flexible Insulation, Lath and Plaster	.15
Wood Siding, Sheathing, Studs, Rock Wool Fill, Lath and Plaster	.072
Note: Frame Walls with Shingle Exterior Finish same as Walls with Wood Siding.	
Stucco, Wood Siding, Studs, Wood Lath and Plaster	.30
Stucco on 25/32″ Rigid Insulation, Studs, Wood Lath and Plaster	.27
Stucco on 25/32″ Rigid Insulation, Studs, ½″ Rigid Insulation and Plaster	.20
Stucco on ½″ Rigid Insulation, Studs, Rock Wool Fill, Lath and Plaster	.074

CONCRETE FLOORS AND CEILINGS

4″ Thick Concrete, No Finish	.65
6″ Thick Concrete, No Finish	.59
4″ Concrete, Suspended Plaster Ceiling	.37
6″ Concrete, Suspended Plaster Ceiling	.35
4″ Concrete, Metal Lath and Plaster Ceiling, Hardwood Floor on Pine Sub-flooring	.23
6″ Thick Concrete, Metal Lath and Plaster Ceiling, Hardwood Floor on Pine Sub-flooring	.21
4″ Concrete, Hardwood and Pine Floor, No Ceiling	.31
6″ Concrete, Hardwood and Pine Floor, No Ceiling	.30

PITCHED ROOFS

Wood Shingles on Wood Strips	.16
Asbestos Shingles on Wood Sheathing	.56
Tile or Slate Roofing on Wood Sheathing	.56
Wood Shingles, 1″ Flexible Insulation between Rafters	.13
Asbestos or Slate Shingles, 1″ Flexible Insulation	.13

WINDOWS AND SKYLIGHTS

Single glass	1.13
Double glass, intermediate air space	.45
Hollow glass tile wall, 6″ x 6″ x 4″ blocks	.60

BRICK VENEER ON FRAME CONSTRUCTION

Brick Veneer, 1″ Wood Siding, Studs, Lath and Plaster	.27
Brick Veneer, 25/32″ Rigid Insulation, Studs, Lath and Plaster	.25
Brick Veneer, 1″ Wood Siding, Studs, ½″ Flexible Insulation, Lath and Plaster	.16
Brick Veneer, 1″ Wood Siding, Studs, Rock Wool Fill, Lath and Plaster	.074

INTERIOR WALLS

Note: In general for Cooling Computations, base the calculations for Heat Gain from adjoining non-conditioned rooms on a differential equal to ½ the differential to outside.	
Wood Lath and Plaster on Studding (Both sides)	.34
Metal Lath and Plaster on Studding (Both sides)	.39
½″ Rigid Insulation and Plaster (Both sides)	.18
4″ Hollow Clay Tile	.45
4″ Gypsum Block	.30
4″ Gypsum Block, Plastered one side	.28
4″ Gypsum Block, Plastered both sides	.27

FLAT ROOFS WITH BUILT-UP ROOFING

Deck Material	No Ceiling	Metal Lath and Plaster Ceiling
Precast Cement Tile	.81	.43
Precast Cement Tile, 1″ Rigid Insulation	.24	.19
2″ Thick Concrete	.82	.42
2″ Thick Concrete, 1″ Rigid Insulation	.24	.19
4″ Thick Concrete	.72	.40
4″ Thick Concrete, 1″ Rigid Insulation	.23	.18
1″ Wood	.49	.32
2″ Wood	.32	.24
Flat Metal Roofs	.95	.46
Flat Metal Roofs, 1″ Rigid Insulation	.25	.19

FRAME FLOORS AND CEILINGS

Hardwood and Pine Flooring on Joists, no Ceiling	.34
Hardwood and Pine Flooring on Joists, Wood Lath and Plaster Ceiling	.24
Rough Pine Floor, Wood Lath and Plaster Ceiling	.28
No Floor, Lath and Plaster Ceiling	.62
No Floor, Lath and Plaster Ceiling, 3⅝″ Rock Wool Fill	.079
No Floor, Lath and Plaster Ceiling, 1″ Flexible Insulation	.17
Pine Floor, 3⅝″ Rock Wool Fill, Lath and Plaster	.063

Fig. 24-5. U values for walls, ceilings, floors and partitions for various types of construction and for various thicknesses. (ASHRAE Guide and Data Book)

HEAT LOADS

State	City	Extreme Temperatures		Mean Temperatures		Design Conditions		
						Winter	Summer	
		Low	High	January	July	Dry Bulb	Dry Bulb	Wet Bulb
Ala.	Mobile	— 1°	103°	52°	81°	15°	95°	79°
Ariz.	Phoenix	16	119	51	90	25	110	75
Ark.	Little Rock	—12	108	41	81	5	96	78
Calif.	San Francisco	27	101	50	58	30	90	65
Colo.	Denver	—29	105	30	72	—10	95	72
Conn.	New Haven	—14	101	28	72	0	95	75
D. C.	Washington	—15	106	33	77	0	96	78
Fla.	Jacksonville	10	104	55	82	30	95	79
Ga.	Atlanta	— 8	103	43	78	5	95	78
Idaho	Boise	—28	121	30	73	—10	100	70
Ill.	Chicago	—23	103	25	74	—10	95	75
Ind.	Indianapolis	—25	106	28	76	— 5	96	76
Iowa	Dubuque	—32	106	19	74	—15	96	75
Kan.	Wichita	—22	107	31	79	0	100	75
Ky.	Louisville	—20	107	34	79	0	98	77
La.	New Orleans	7	102	54	82	25	96	80
Maine	Portland	—21	103	22	68	—10	92	75
Md.	Baltimore	— 7	105	34	77	0	96	78
Mass.	Boston	—18	104	28	72	— 5	95	75
Mich.	Detroit	—24	104	24	72	—10	95	75
Minn.	St. Paul	—41	104	12	72	—20	95	75
Miss.	Vicksburg	— 1	104	48	81	15	96	80
Mo.	St. Louis	—22	108	31	79	0	98	79
Mont.	Helena	—42	103	20	66	—20	90	68
Neb.	Omaha	—32	111	22	77	—15	100	75
Nev.	Winnemucca	—28	104	29	71	—10	95	70
N. C.	Charlotte	— 5	103	41	78	10	96	79
N. D.	Bismarck	—45	108	8	70	—25	98	70
N. H.	Concord	—35	102	22	68	—15	95	75
N. J.	Atlantic City	— 7	104	32	72	0	95	75
N. M.	Santa Fe	—13	97	29	69	0	92	70
N. Y.	New York City	—14	102	31	74	0	95	77
Ohio	Cincinnati	—17	105	30	75	0	98	77
Okla.	Oklahoma City	—17	108	36	81	0	100	76
Ore.	Portland	— 2	104	39	67	10	95	70
Penna.	Philadelphia	— 6	106	33	76	0	95	78
R. I.	Providence	—12	101	29	72	0	95	75
S. C.	Charleston	7	104	50	81	15	96	80
S. D.	Pierre	—40	112	16	75	—20	100	72
Tenn.	Nashville	—13	106	39	79	5	98	79
Texas	Galveston	8	101	54	83	25	95	78
Utah	Salt Lake City	—20	105	29	76	— 5	95	70
Vt.	Burlington	—28	100	19	70	—15	92	73
Va.	Norfolk	2	105	41	79	10	98	78
Wash.	Seattle	3	98	40	63	10	90	67
W. Va.	Parkersburg	—27	106	32	75	— 5	96	77
Wis.	Milwaukee	—25	102	21	70	—15	94	75
Wyo.	Cheyenne	—38	100	26	67	—15	92	70

Fig. 24-6. Design conditions used for calculating heat loads for heating or cooling for various regions of the U.S. (ASHRAE Guide and Data Book)

$$R_T = \frac{1}{C_1} + \frac{1}{C_2} + \frac{1}{C_3} + \frac{1}{C_4} + \frac{1}{C_5} \quad or$$

$$R_T = R_1 + R_2 + R_3 + R_4 + R_5$$

This method is becoming popular because any composite wall can be easily calculated. By knowing the individual R values, they can be totaled and then U will equal the reciprocal of the total R. The R values can be found by taking reciprocals of the heat conductance or C values from tables or by using tables showing the R values. Fig. 24-7 shows some typical R values as recommended by the American

CONSTRUCTION	(R) RESISTANCE VALUE
1. Surface (still air)	.68
2. Air Space	.97
3. Gypsum Wallboard 3/8 in.	.32
4. Outside Surface (15 mph wind)	.17
5. Face Brick	.39
6. Concrete Block 4 in.	1.11
7. Plaster 1/2 in.	.09
8. Siding (wood) 1/2 in. x 8 in.	.85
9. Building Paper	.06
10. Wood Sheathing	.98
11. Wood Floor 1 in.	.98
12. Linoleum or Tile	.05
13. Asphalt Shingles or Plywood	.95

Fig. 24-7. Table of typical thermal resistance (R) values for various parts of a building. (ASHRAE Guide and Data Book)

Society of Heating, Refrigerating and Air Conditioning Engineers.

For example a typical brick veneer wall will be as follows:

	R
Outside Air Film	.17
Face Brick Veneer	.39
Wood Siding and Building Paper	.86
Air Space	.97
1/2 in. Plaster (.09) on Gypsum Lath (.32)	.41
Inside Air Film	.68
TOTAL R =	3.48

$$U = \frac{1}{R} = \frac{1}{3.48} = .287$$

24-8 Wall Heat Leakage Areas

In addition to finding the U factors for the building structure, the area of the walls will need to be calculated because:

Wall Heat Leakage = U x Wall Area x Temp. Diff.

Areas are usually measured based on the outside dimensions of the building. These measurements will result in slightly higher heat leakage loads than if inside dimensions are used but the values are on the safer side.

For rough estimates of the heat load, the complete building is measured as one unit. The areas measured are:

1. Walls.
2. Windows.
3. Ceilings.
4. Floors.

The walls are measured by taking the outside length and width of the house and the inside ceiling height. To determine the total surface area, first determine the distance around the house; this will be the length plus length, plus width, plus width (perimeter). When these values are added together and multiplied by the wall height, the total wall area is obtained. For example, a house 24 ft. x 32 ft. (outside), as

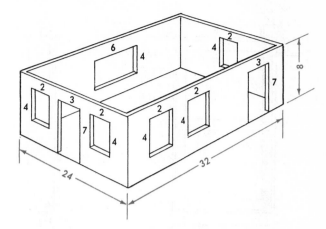

Fig. 24-8. Simplified one story home used to show wall areas and windows, plus door areas.

shown in Fig. 24-8, with an 8 ft. ceiling has a total area of 32 plus 32 plus 24 plus 24 = 64 plus 48 = 112 ft.

112 ft. x 8 ft. = 996 sq. ft.

This is the total wall area, and the window and door areas must be subtracted. If the window and door areas total 99 sq. ft., then the net wall area is:

996 sq. ft. – 99 sq. ft. = 897 sq. ft.

The ceiling area is the width times the length.

24 ft. x 32 ft. = 768 sq. ft.

The floor area will be computed the same as the ceiling. Note that wall closet areas, stairways, etc., are considered part of the heated space.

24-9 Windows and Doors

The area of the windows is measured by measuring the opening in the wall. In a brick veneer wall, this would be the distance to the brick edges, as shown in Fig. 24-9. The windows may be either single or double pane.

The single pane window is referred to as the "primary" window. The storm window which is not sealed to the primary but is movable is called the "storm" window or "secondary" pane. Many installations have an assembly whereby the primary and secondary panes are inserted in a single

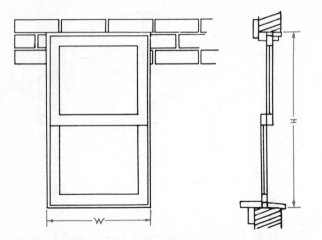

Fig. 24-9. Typical double hung window showing window openings.

frame with an air space between them. This air space usually contains nitrogen or some other dry gas to prevent sweating (condensation). Fig. 24-10 shows the "R" and "U" values of various window pane assemblies.

24-10 Ceilings

The ceilings are usually made with a plaster finish which adheres to rock lath which is in turn fastened to the joists. Another method of ceiling construction is the use of dry-wall. Variations in construction will not change this calculation to any great extent. If the joists do not have a floor over them, or if there is no insulation between the joists, the heat leakage will be considerable.

See Fig. 24-5 for U values for ceilings.

24-11 Design Temperatures

Design temperatures, shown in Fig. 24-6, are the result of considerable testing and the accumulation of much data. A study of the table reveals that for the areas listed, places requiring the largest heating plant would be Helena, Montana; and Pierre, South Dakota. Locals needing the least heat are San Francisco, California and Jackson-

ville, Florida. There are areas colder and warmer than these places, and the local weather bureau or the local chapter of the Society of Heating, Refrigerating and Air Conditioning Engineers may be contacted for local data.

It is always best to choose design ambient temperatures on the low side, because heating plants that are overworked cause excessive stack and chimney temperatures and may cause fires.

The design temperature is never as low as the lowest temperature recorded for the

TYPE WINDOW	U	R
Single Glass	1.13	.9
Double Glass 1/2 in. Space	.65	1.54
Triple Glass 1/2 in. Space	.36	2.79
Storm Windows	.56	1.79

Fig. 24-10. Thermal resistance (R) and overall heat leakage of various window pane assemblies. (ASHRAE Handbook of Fundamentals)

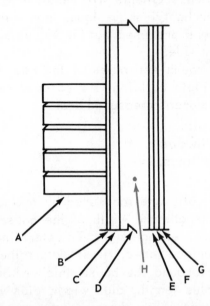

Fig. 24-11. Brick veneer wall construction. A—Brick. B—Outside vapor barrier. C—Sheathing. D—Stud and insulation. E—Inside vapor barrier. F—Rock lath. G—Plaster. H—Approximate dew point location.

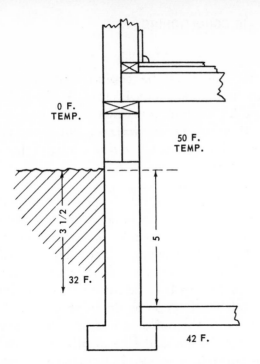

Fig. 24-12. *Temperature conditions and construction of building with basement.*

area, as these extreme lows are usually of short duration. The residual heat in the building enables the design temperature to handle the load.

24-12 Wall Construction

Building wall construction has been altered the past few years to reduce heat leakage and to reduce moisture passage through the wall structure. Fig. 24-11 shows a typical brick veneer outside wall construction. During the heating season, the inside vapor barrier (E) is necessary, while in summer the outside vapor barrier (B) is required. These barriers should be as tightly sealed as possible even to the extent of tarring the breaks in the seal. The barriers may be made of tarred paper, aluminum foil or plastic film. Aluminum foil has a reflection value as well as being a vapor tight seal.

24-13 Basement Heat Loss

Heat losses or gains for basements vary widely. Basements built approximately five feet into the ground have a varying

heat loss, as shown in Fig. 24-12. It is usually assumed that a basement is at 50 F. This means a floor loss and a basement wall loss. Leakage through the floor is usually not calculated. Buildings built on a concrete slab have heat losses of a different nature. See Fig. 24-13. In the former, the heat loss above ground is calculated in the typical manner.

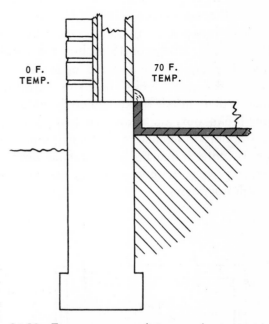

Fig. 24-13. *Temperature conditions and construction of building built on concrete slab.*

Heat losses for the slab design are usually calculated by determining the perimeter of the building and multiplying this total length by 18 Btu/hr. for each foot of length (0 F. design temperature). Refer to the recommendations of the American Society of Heating, Refrigerating and Air Conditioning Engineers for additional data for other conditions.

24-14 Unheated Spaces

In many buildings there are unheated areas, such as closets, hallways, attic storage, and the like. These spaces receive their heat from heat leakage through partitions, ceilings, and floors. These spaces are usually assumed to be at a temperature half the distance between the indoor temperature and the ambient temperature.

24-15 Infiltration

Since buildings are not airtight, air leaks into a building if there is any air pressure difference between the inside and the outside pressure. Air also leaks out under the same conditions. The air pressure difference is usually caused by wind. Those parts of the building that the wind is pressing against are those areas through which the air leaks in. The remaining areas are those areas through which the air leaks out, as shown in Fig. 24-14. It is important to insure that sufficient fresh air is entering a building during both the heating season and cooling season for health purposes.

filters in must be cooled, and the cooled air that filters out is lost. If the building can be sealed, this infiltration and exfiltration can be minimized, but we must be careful to always provide enough fresh air for ventilation purposes.

Another way to prevent unwanted infiltration is to maintain a positive air pressure within the building, and thus air will filter out at the cracks and openings in the building. This practice necessitates a special fresh air intake. This air can be conditioned before it is admitted to the building.

Infiltration can be calculated on the total volume of the building basis, or by measuring the length and size of all the cracks in the building. Fig. 24-15 lists the air changes in buildings. If a building has a volume of

TYPES OF SPACE	NO. OF AIR CHANGES/HR.
1 Side Exposed	1
2 Sides Exposed	1 1/2
3 Sides Exposed	2
4 Sides Exposed	2
Entrances	2–3

Fig. 24-15. Approximate number of air changes desirable per hour for various room exposures.

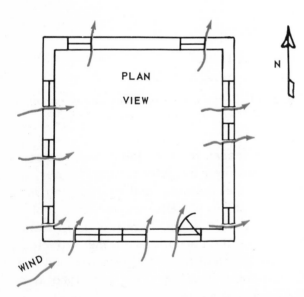

Fig. 24-14. Diagram illustrating how wind direction affects air leakage into and out of house.

SURFACE	AREA	U VALUE	TEMP. DIFF.	HEAT LEAKAGE
Wall, gross	996			
Window	116	1.13	70	23176
Wall, net	880	.25	70	15400
Ceiling	768	.62	35	16666
Floor	768	.34	25	6528
			Total	61770

Fig. 24-16. Typical heat load calculation for 24 x 32 ft. home having 8 ft. ceiling height.

During the heating season, the cold air that filters in must be heated, and the air that leaks out represents lost heat. During the cooling season, the warm air that

10,000 cu. ft., it will have at least 10,000 cu. ft. of fresh air filter in per hour. If six people occupy this space, there is 10,000 ÷6 or 1667 cu. ft. per hour for each person or 1667 ÷ 60 = 27.7 cu. ft. per minute, which is a good ventilating value. If this building is constructed with vapor barriers, and all doors and windows are fitted with weather stripping, the air change will be reduced considerably. It may even be reduced to the point of unsafe ventilation (too little oxygen in the air).

24-16 Total Heat Load for Heating

It is best to set up the total heat load calculations in tabular form. Fig. 24-16 illustrates a typical heat load calculation for a 24 by 32 ft. house. Note that the temperature difference for the ceiling is only 35 F. This is because the attic temperature is assumed to be 35 F., and the roof is an added insulation and keeps the attic temperature from equalling the outdoor temperature. The attic temperature can be accurately calculated by making the heat leaking into the attic equal the heat leaking out.

Ceiling area x (70 attic temp.) x U_c = Roof area x (attic temp. -0 F.) x U_r.

We should remember that many homes are now being constructed with 7 1/2 ft. ceilings.

The temperature in the basement is usually considered to be approximately 50 F. to be on the safe side when calculating the heat load.

It is also possible to calculate the total heat load by using the thermal resistance method and then take the total R and convert to a U factor by taking the reciprocal of the R ($U = \frac{1}{R}$).

It is sometimes desirable to calculate the total heat loss for one degree and then multiply this value by the design temperature difference to obtain the total heat loss.

24-17 Total Heat Gain for Cooling

The heat gain calculations for a building to determine the total cooling load are similar to the calculations for heat loss.

The temperature difference is based on the locality being considered. The indoor temperature is usually designed to be 75 F. at 50 percent relative humidity (RH). Therefore, if the summer design temperature is 100 F., the temperature difference we should use is 25 F. This temperature difference is for load calculations only. In practice, a 10 to 15 F. difference is recommended.

Miscellaneous heat sources must be considered. Such sources as sun load, electrical load, and occupants are large enough sources of heat that they must be in the calculations. The following paragraphs describe some of the specifics of these heat sources.

24-18 Conducted Heat, and Solar Heat Through Glass

Heat flow through ordinary window glass is approximately four times as great as that through ordinary residential roofs and ceilings. The U factor (see Par. 24-6) for ordinary glass is 1.13, whereas the U factor for residential roofs is .31. As can be seen from this comparison, air conditioning of areas containing a large amount of ordinary glass can become a problem. To overcome this problem of heat conductivity through glass and the reduction of solar heat through glass, it is often advisable to use special types of glass which have high heat absorbing qualities.

Special heat absorbing glass can reduce the solar heat load by as much as 30 percent. Another method is to use glass which is tinted a bluish gray, this reduces the solar glare and cooling load.

Double glazed windows may be used to reduce solar heat absorption approximately

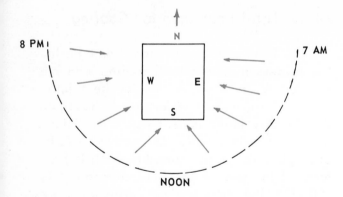

Fig. 24-17. Sun rays and their impact on walls of a building during 12 hour period.

EXPOSURE	HEAT ABSORPTION BTU/HR./SQ.FT.
Southwest	110
West	100
South	75
East	55
Single Skylights	110
Double Skylights	60

Fig. 24-18. Heat absorption from sun when sun is shining on windows.

15 percent. Awnings to shade glass windows exposed to the sun are recommended.

24-19 Sun Heat Load

The heat energy that comes from the sun adds considerable to the total heat load during the summer. The sun's rays in the northern hemisphere shine on the east wall, the south wall, the west wall, and on those roof sections that are open to its rays. Therefore, the heat from the sun must be considered on the east wall in the morning, on the south wall all day long, and on the west wall in the afternoon, as shown in Fig. 24-17.

The sun releases different amounts of heat to surfaces, depending upon the part of the world in which the building is located. The approximate maximum heat pickup or heat gain from the sun is 330 Btu per hr. per sq. ft. This condition exists for a black surface at right angles to the sun's rays near the equator (tropic). Any other color or any surface at an angle to the sun's rays will receive less than this amount of heat.

At the 42nd parallel, a line going through New York City, Cleveland, Salt Lake City, etc., the maximum heat from the rays is about 315 Btu per hr. per sq. ft. Much of the heat from the sun is reflected back into the atmosphere. That amount of heat gain

through windows that must be removed with air conditioning cooling is listed in Fig. 24-18.

If the windows are not protected with awnings, it is generally agreed that using an outside temperature of 15 F. higher than the outside ambient temperature will give correct results. The sun effect on walls may also be taken care of by adding 15 F. to the ambient temperature.

The approximate values obtained by using the 15 F. are generally usable. However, there are many special cases that require careful study. Of considerable interest is the changing position of the sun relative to the surfaces of the building and the time lag required for this heat to reach the interior of the building.

24-20 Heat Lag

When a substance is heated on one side, it takes time for the heat to travel through the substance. This time is called time lag. When the sun heats the outside wall of a building, several hours elapse before this heat reaches the inner surfaces of that wall. In normal buildings this time varies between 3 and 4 hours. If the wall is insulated well enough or is thick enough, the sun will be gone by the time the heat penetrates or "soaks" through. In the Southwest, adobe walls are so thick that the sun heat moves into the wall during the sunshine time and then reverses itself and travels out again during the evening, because the outdoor temperatures fall below the indoor temperatures during the night.

Except for windows, heat from the sun on an east wall actually reaches the rooms as follows:

Sun 8 to 9 a.m. heat goes into the rooms 11-12 a.m.

9 to 10 a.m. heat goes into the rooms 12-1 p.m.

10 to 11 a.m. heat goes into the rooms 1-2 p.m.

The south wall is affected from 8 a.m. to 7 p.m., but not as strongly as the east and west walls (rays from overhead).

Likewise, the west wall that receives sun rays from 4 to 7 p.m. acts as follows:

Sun 4 to 5 p.m. heat goes into the rooms 7-8 p.m.

5 to 6 p.m. heat goes into the rooms 8-9 p.m.

6 to 7 p.m. heat goes into the rooms 9-10 p.m.

It is also because of this heat lag that the rooms are being heated even after the sun goes below the horizon, and when the outdoor temperature drops, as shown in Fig. 24-19. Many people complain of the uncomfortable heat in their bedrooms, etc., up to as late as 12 midnight and even 1 and 2 a.m.

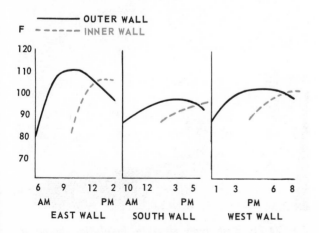

Fig. 24-19. Lag in noticeable interior wall temperature following exposure to sun.

24-21 Attic Fan

One inexpensive solution to this delayed heating is the attic fan. The attic fan exhausts the air out of the building allowing the cooled evening outside air to move into the house. This cooling effect partly overcomes the effect of the heated walls and ceiling. However, this exhaust fan system does have the disadvantage of bringing considerable outdoor dust into the building, because the windows or doors must be left open to allow for make up for the air exhausted by the attic fan.

24-22 Heat Sources in Buildings

During the heating season, the heating plant is aided by many other sources of heat. Practically all energy expended in the building finally becomes heat. These heat sources are usually ignored when figuring the heat load in the winter, because they are small compared to the total heat load in temperate zones and are an additional safety factor.

However, when figuring the summer heat load or the cooling heat load, all sources of heat energy must be carefully considered. Such items as the heat released by human beings, stoves, lights, electric motors, etc., must all be considered in the final heat load. Fig. 24-20 shows some of these heat sources. Notice that the two sources of heat are itemized, the sensible heat gain and the latent heat gain. Because of the efficiency of a small electric motor, the 1/2 hp motor releases 2100 Btu/hr.

24-23 Insulation

A large number of different insulating materials have been developed for buildings. It is essential that the insulation reduce heat loss by conduction, convection, and radiation. It is also important that vapor barriers be included in the insulation or in the walls to reduce moisture travel through the wall.

HEAT LOADS

Device	HP	Heat Btu/hr. Sensible	Latent
Electric			
Lights/kwhr		3415	
Motors, electric/hp in room	Up to 1/2 max.	4200	
	Up to 3 max.	3700	
	Up to 20 max.	2950	
Motors, electric/hp out of room	1/2	1700	
	3	1150	
	20	400	
Stoves, electric/kwhr		3415	
Gas			
Natural gas/cu.ft.		1100	300
Artificial gas/cu.ft.		550	675
General			
Heat from meals/meal		36	
Steam tables/sq.ft.		400	800
Humans			140
Sitting		370	
Working		700–1500	
Dancing		2000	

Fig. 24-20. Heat released by various energy sources within building in Btu per hour.

Insulation must have sufficient strength so that it can support itself and will not shrink or settle. It must not deteriorate in the presence of moisture, and it must not have any unpleasant odor. It should also be vermin proof.

The type of insulation to use depends, to some extent, on the method of application. For example, a bulk easy flowing insulation can be placed between the studs of a building already constructed. For new buildings rigid insulation can be used as a part of the building wall, such as the plaster base or as a substitute for the sheeting.

Flexible insulations are easily installed and conform to any irregularities in the construction. Batts of rock wool and blankets of pulverized wood are examples of this practice. Fig. 24-21 shows a batt type insulation being installed between studs. It is exceedingly important that all insulations that are hydroscopic (moisture absorbent) be hermetically sealed. Even those insulations not affected by moisture should be

Fig. 24-21. Batt type flexible insulation being installed between studs of residence.
(Owens-Corning Fiberglas Corp.)

vapor sealed, as the insulation will lose much of its insulating value as it fills up with moisture. This is particularly important in summer cooling applications.

24-24 Ponded Roof

An ordinary roof may be heated by the sun to a temperature of 100 F. to 150 F. Ceilings under such roofs will also become quite warm and will radiate this heat through the span below.

Many buildings are now provided with summer comfort cooling by having a shallow (2-3 in.) pond of water covering the roof surface. This type of cooling is particularly effective with one story factory and market buildings. To be effective, the roof area should be almost as large as the floor area.

The cooling effect comes from the evaporation of water from the roof. Naturally these systems are most effective in areas having high summer time temperature and bright sunshine. By ponding, the roof temperature may be kept at, or below, the temperature of the surrounding atmosphere.

Ponded roofs must be provided with a means of maintaining a constant level of water on the roof, drains to take away excess water due to rain and, if the roof is large, wave breakers to prevent waves forming under high winds which might result in a large quantity of water being blown off the edge of the roof.

Buildings having ponded roofs may also be fitted with complete air conditioning equipment. The use of a ponded roof may reduce the required air conditioning capacity by as much as 30 percent.

24-25 Unit Air Conditioner Heat Load Calculations

A relatively easy way to calculate the summer heat load per hour on a room is tabulated as follows:

Name _____

Address_____

Zone _____ Phone _____

Space used for _____

Interior room dimensions:

Length _____ Width _____ Height _____

Windows

No. ___ Facing ___ Size ___ x _____

No. ___ Facing ___ Size ___ x _____

No. ___ Facing ___ Size ___ x _____

Window Load

1. Sun exposed (interior shades only) west side ___ sq. ft. x 60 = _____
2. Sun exposed (interior shades) south side ___ sq. ft. x 40 = _____
3. Sun exposed (awnings)_____ sq. ft. x 35 = _____
4. East exposure, north exposure, or shaded _____ sq. ft. x 15 = _____

Wall Load

1. Sun exposed--south and west walls _____ sq. ft. x 8 = _____
2. East or North exposure _____ sq. ft. x 5 = _____
3. All exposures, thin walls _____ sq. ft. x 10 = _____
4. Interior walls _____ sq. ft. x 4 = _____
5. Interior glass partition _____ sq. ft. x 10 = _____ _____

Floor Load

_____ sq. ft. x 3 = _____

Ceiling Load

1. Occupied above _____ sq. ft. x 3 = _____
2. Insulated roof _____ sq. ft. x 8 = _____
3. Uninsulated roof _____ sq. ft. x 20 = _____ _____

Ventilation Load

_____ cu. ft. x .4 = _____

Occupancy Load

No. of people _____ x 400 = _____

Miscellaneous Load

Electrical watts _____ x 3.4 = _____

Other _____ x _____ = _____

Total Btu per hour_____

The average window type comfort cooling unit will adequately handle the following loads:

Up to 6000 Btu/hr. = 1/2 hp.
6000 - 9000   = 3/4 hp.
9000 - 11,000   = 1 hp.

The multipliers in the tabulation are obtained by multiplying a typical U factor by the temperature difference. For example, the windows (no sun) have a U factor of 1.25 and if the temperature difference is about 12 F., therefore the multiplier becomes 15.

$$12 \times 1.25 = 15$$

24-26 Building Insulation and Ventilation for Electric Heating

Electric heating of residences and commercial establishments is increasing rapidly. Problems in electric heating usually involve insulation, ventilation, humidity, and cost.

The matter of insulation is very important. It usually costs more to produce a unit of heat electrically than with most other types of fuels. If the heat loss through windows, walls, floors, and ceilings can be reduced, the cost of electric heating will then also be reduced.

The use of efficient insulating materials, and double glazed windows all help in reducing the heat load.

Electric space heating, as indicated in a preceding paragraph, requires a well insulated and tight structure. This sometimes increases the ventilation problem. If the building is a restaurant or other space occupied by a great number of people, provisions must be made for frequent air changes for ventilation purposes. Spaces which are comfort cooled as well as electrically heated usually have the electric heating elements in the plenum chamber or in the air duct system. Some systems also have electric elements located in each room to enable individual control of the spaces being heated.

Humidity control in electrically heated buildings is usually different than is experienced with fuel burning heating equipment. With fuel burning equipment, a fairly large quantity of air passes through the furnace and out the stack. This air is usually made up in the building by leakage around the doors, windows, cracks in the floor, and the like. With most electrically heated structures, the building construction is such that there is little infiltration of this nature. Consequently, there is a possibility of a too high humidity condition since the water vapor formed in the space cannot readily escape from the occupied space. This may require the use of dehumidifying equipment under certain weather and occupancy conditions. The cost of producing a unit of heat electrically is usually higher than the cost of producing the same amount of heat by using combustion fuels. However, with modern building and proper insulation, double glazing and weather stripping, costs can be kept to a minimum. There are other factors too, which help to make the cost of heating with electricity favorable. Since there is no dirt or smoke generated in connection with the heating, drapes, upholstery, woodwork, and the like remain clean longer and the cost of cleaning and redecorating may be reduced.

See Chapter 27 for more information concerning building construction for electric heating.

24-27 Degree-Day Method

The method commonly used to determine the fuel consumption and/or the cost of heating during a season is the degree-day method.

This method determines by previous weather records, the average temperature of each day during the season. It also keeps a record of the temperature each day during the season under study.

The method is as follows:

A 65 F. indoor temperature is used as a standard.

If the average temperature outside for a particular day was 15 F., the temperature difference was 50 F. that day, or that day had 50 degree days. Each degree-day requires a certain Btu load to keep the building at 65 F.

If we know the number of degree-days since a fuel oil tank was filled, we can accurately calculate how much fuel is left in the tank. If we know the degree-days for a certain season, we can quite accurately calculate the cost of heating for that season.

24-28 Review of Safety

It is essential to safety that a heating system have enough capacity to heat a structure without taxing or overheating the heating system. The heating system should be slightly oversize--never undersize.

All heating system and cooling system designs should be checked carefully to insure that enough fresh air enters the structure to provide adequate ventilation for the maximum number of occupants (and combustion air during the heating season).

In some modern homes which are well insulated, weather stripped and very tight, it may be necessary to open a basement window or provide some other air inlet in order that the fireplace flue may draw properly and not release smoke into the room.

24-29 Test Your Knowledge – Chapter 24

1. What are the two main portions of the heating load?
2. What are the main sources of heat that cause cooling load?
3. What are the variables for calculating heat leakage?
4. How are window size dimensions determined?
5. Is the heating design outdoor temperature the coldest temperature recorded?
6. How are storage closets handled when figuring the heating load?
7. How are unheated spaces accounted for when figuring heating loads?
8. Describe infiltration and exfiltration.
9. What is meant by having a positive air pressure in the building?
10. What building walls are affected by the sun (42nd parallel)?
11. How is the sun effect usually included in cooling load calculations?
12. Does sun load on the walls and windows effect the heat load at the same time?
13. What is heat lag in a building?
14. If the outside temperature is 20 F. for 24 hours, how many degree-days accumulate?
15. What is an air film?
16. What is the unit of thermal resistance?
17. If one knows the U factor, how is the R (RU) factor determined?
18. Do people release heat when sitting idle?
19. How much heat does it take to vaporize one pound of water in a humidifier?
20. What is the usual design wind velocity?
21. What is conductance?
22. Are outside or inside dimensions used when determining wall areas?
23. Which has the greatest heat flow resistance, inside air film or outside air film?
24. Describe perimeter heat loss for grade level slabs.
25. What is a vapor barrier?

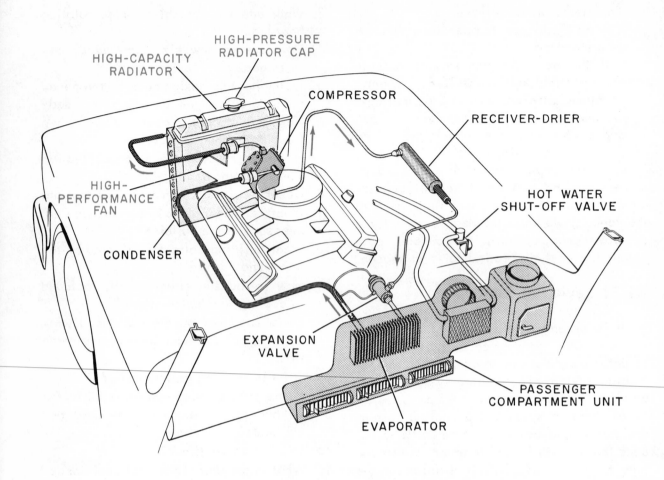

HIGH-CAPACITY
RADIATOR

HIGH-PRESSURE
RADIATOR CAP

COMPRESSOR

RECEIVER-DRIER

HIGH-
PERFORMANCE
FAN

HOT WATER
SHUT-OFF VALVE

CONDENSER

EXPANSION
VALVE

PASSENGER
COMPARTMENT UNIT

EVAPORATOR

AIR CONDITIONING SYSTEM INSTALLATION

Fig. 25-1. Simplified drawing of automotive air conditioning system. Note high pressure radiator cap, large fan, and radiator. Also, note independent heating system. (Dodge Div., Chrysler Corp.)

Chapter 25

AUTOMOBILE
AIR CONDITIONING

In preceding chapters, various refrigeration principles and applications have been discussed. Also, many principles and applications of heating have been shown and explained. In automobile air conditioning, few new principles are involved. However, there are many unique applications since air conditioning a moving automobile presents problems not found in most refrigeration or air conditioning applications.

Modern automobile air conditioning involves heating, cooling, and dehumidification. The heat needed to warm the automobile is usually provided by circulating warm water from the engine cooling system through a heater coil. When a cooling effect is required, a refrigerating system is brought into operation and an evaporator coil in the plenum chamber of the car cools the air that is to be circulated through the passenger compartment.

The automatic controls, temperature, pressure and vacuum, which control the flow of air, flow of warm water, and flow of refrigerant through the various passages, are discussed in this chapter.

You must thoroughly understand these control mechanisms as well as understand the refrigerating devices. It is recommended that you study Chapters 3, 4, 5, 6, 9, and 19 of this text, or have previous refrigeration and air conditioning experience as a preparation for this work.

As mentioned in a preceding paragraph, the principles of refrigeration and air conditioning required will not be covered in any detail in this chapter; rather, it is assumed that these fundamentals have been mastered. The refrigeration and air conditioning service engineer may also find reference to the above chapters helpful from time to time.

25-1 Automotive Air Conditioning Principles

An automobile, although it is relatively small, when traveling at high speed on a hot day in the summer will require a considerable amount of refrigerating capacity to keep the interior at a comfortable temperature level.

Likewise, the same car traveling on a cold day in winter will require considerable heating capacity to keep it warm.

The automobile air conditioner uses a refrigerating machine driven by the car engine to furnish the cooling desired and, in most cases, warm water from the engine cooling system is used for heating purposes. See Fig. 25-1.

The air conditioning mechanism and controls on the standard factory installation are arranged to make the task of selecting and controlling the required car temperature easy for the occupants of the car. Fig. 25-2 shows a schematic diagram of a typical automotive refrigerating system used for air conditioning.

In addition, in the summertime, with the air conditioner in operation, the humidity of the air inside the car is reduced.

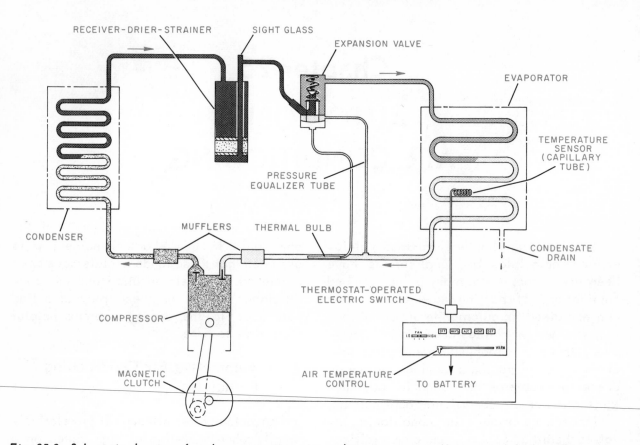

Fig. 25-2. Schematic drawing of modern automotive air conditioning system. Note use of dual mufflers on re-frigerant lines with enlarged chamber to slow down flow of gas and consequently amount of noise caused by unit. (Chrysler Corp.)

The moisture (condensate) formed on the evaporator surfaces collects much of the dust and pollen. These entrapped particles are carried away by the condensate as it drains from the evaporator to the ground. In this way, the air conditioner serves to clean the air as well as control its temperature.

25-2 Development

The purpose of the air conditioning system for automobiles and buses is identical to the general purpose of air conditioning as stated in Chapter 19.

During the late thirties, some passenger buses were air conditioned on an experimental basis. Since World War II, most automobile manufacturers have offered completely air conditioned automobiles.

There has been a rapid increase in the use of air conditioning in automobiles. A late model comfort cooling unit for automobiles is shown in Fig. 25-3.

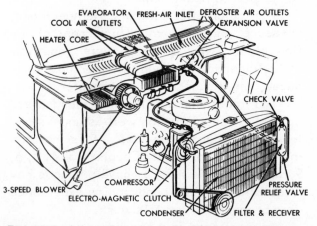

Fig. 25-3. All season air conditioning system which combines cooling, heating, ventilating and defrosting in one unit. (American Motors Corp.)

In this installation, the compressor is mounted above the engine and is driven by a belt from the front end of the engine. The condenser is mounted ahead of the car radiator. The liquid refrigerant flows from the condenser to the liquid receiver through a filter and a refrigerant control to the evaporator coil where it is vaporized and heat is absorbed. The vaporized refrigerant then flows back through the suction line to the compressor.

A blower forces air from the inside of the car through the evaporator and circulates it to the interior of the car by means of the grilles at each end of the instrument panel. A refrigeration system for an auto air conditioner is shown in Fig. 25-4.

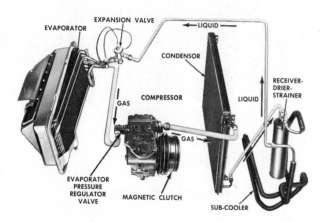

Fig. 25-4. System using evaporator pressure regulator valve to prevent frosting of evaporator.

The operation of the basic air conditioning system is similar to the domestic or commercial systems (Chapters 1, 3, and 4). On the air conditioning cycle, low pressure refrigerant vapor enters the compressor through the suction service valve (low side). The vapor is then drawn into the cylinder and compressed by the piston and discharged through the discharge service valve into the condenser (high side). The heat of compression and the latent heat of vaporization are given up to the air flowing past the condenser and the refrigerant is again liquefied. The liquid receiver stores the liquid refrigerant under high pressure. The liquid receiver is equipped with a fusible plug set to discharge at about 350 F. in the event of a fire.

The liquid refrigerant flows through a filter and through a sight glass. The sight glass provides a quick, easy way of checking the refrigerant charge in the system. The presence of bubbles or foam indicates a shortage of refrigerant. The liquid refrigerant flows to the thermostatic expansion valve which is the dividing point between the high and the low pressure side. The control bulb of the thermostatic expansion valve is clamped to the suction line as it leaves the evaporator coil.

During the "on" cycle, the expansion valve provides a throttling action which controls the quantity of refrigerant in the evaporator coil, and it prevents liquid refrigerant from reaching the compressor. The evaporator receives the liquid refrigerant at low pressure. The refrigerant evaporates and absorbs heat from the air passing over the surface of the evaporator coil. Fig. 25-5 is a phantom view of the system showing the condition of the refrigerant in each part of the cycle.

Electrically driven blowers circulate air over the evaporator coils and through the interior of the car. The evaporated refrigerant (vapor) is returned through the suction line to the suction service valve and the cycle is repeated.

If the cycle was repeated continuously, the temperature in the car would drop to an uncomfortable level and the evaporator coil would frost over. To prevent this condition most systems use a magnetic clutch mechanism to provide a condition known as "free wheeling." This is triggered by the thermostat which opens the electrical circuit to the electromagnetic clutch and allows the compressor pulley to rotate while the shaft remains stationary.

When the air conditioning system is not turned on, as in winter when the heater is used, the refrigerating mechanism is not in operation. The electromagnetic clutch on the compressor is not energized. This allows the compressor pulley to "free wheel" when the air conditioning is not

and condenser must have enough capacity to give sufficient cooling at idling speed on the hottest day, in the sun, and under side wind conditions. This capacity pro-

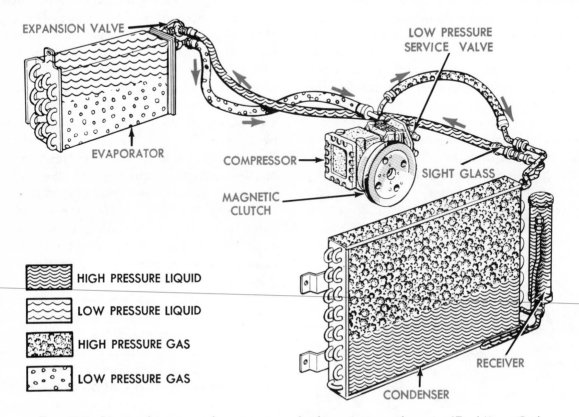

Fig. 25-5. System showing condition or state of refrigerant in each part. (Ford Motor Co.)

turned on. Instead, hot water is circulated through the heating coil and the same blower and ducts used for cooling are used for heating, as shown in Fig. 25-6.

25-3 Operating Conditions

The automobile air conditioner must provide comfort and control conditions in the car during mild or damp weather, hot weather, heating, defogging, deicing, and remove dust, smoke, and odor.

In automobile air conditioning, the compressor is belt driven from the engine, and the compressor speed will vary with the engine speed, which, of course, varies as the car speed changes. The compressor

vides considerable excess capacity for normal speed driving, particularly under cool weather conditions. Fig. 25-7 shows typical performance curves for an air conditioning system.

This condition brings in problems in both the matter of controlling the temperature and the control of refrigerant flow (both liquid and vapor) within the system. If the compressor is operating rapidly and little or no refrigeration is required, the the high side pressure will build up and the low side pressure may drop too low.

Dropping the low side pressure lowers the evaporator temperature. The evaporator temperature should not be allowed to drop below 32 F. If it should operate at a temperature of 32 F. or lower for any length of time, the evaporator surface will frost over and may become covered with ice and stop air circulation through it.

Also, operating the system under a low, low side pressure may cause oil pumping which may damage the compressor valves and which, if continued, may burn out the compressor.

Various cycle and mechanical systems have been devised to overcome these problems. It is important to remember the fresh air ducts must be closed during high heat loads in the cooling season to obtain maximum cooling. These ducts should also be closed when the car is being washed or is in a heavy rainstorm.

A typical automobile air conditioning system will cool an automobile which has been standing in the sun, and is at 110 F., down to 85 F. in about 10 minutes. The inside of the car may reach 150 F. when parked in the sun with the windows closed. The greatest heat load or heat gain is the

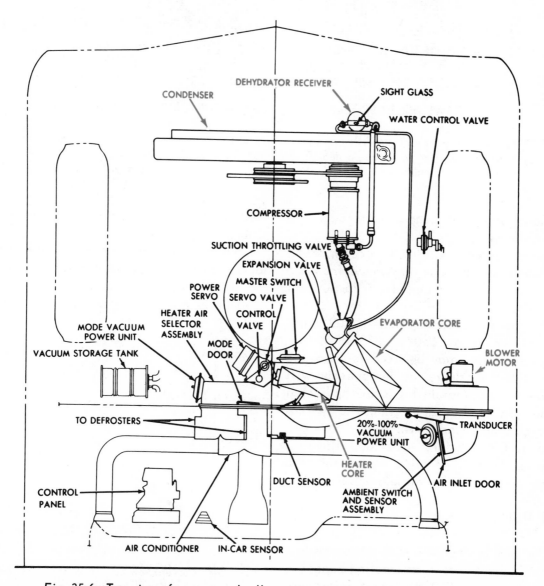

Fig. 25-6. Top view of year around, all season system showing main components. (Cadillac Motor Car Div., General Motors Corp.)

60, 62, SERIES

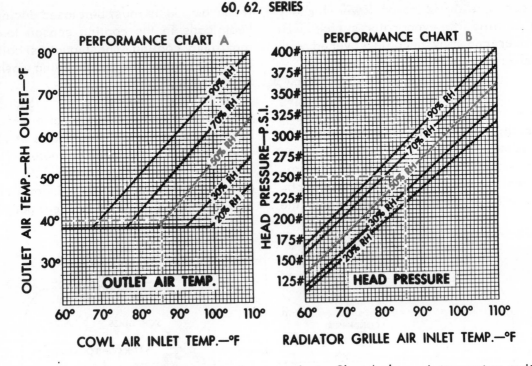

Fig. 25-7. Typical automobile air conditioning performance charts. Chart A shows air temperature as it leaves cooling system. The red line is for an 86 deg. F. air inlet. Chart B shows head pressure of system. The red line indicates a 250 psig if ambient air temperature is 86 deg. F.

sun load and heat conducted through the car windows.

Some systems use 100 percent fresh air, while others use anywhere from no fresh air (all recirculated) to 25 percent fresh air.

The fans use approximately 200 watts and deliver from 250 to 275 cfm. Air scoops or rams may be used to increase the airflow. To drive the compressor will require approximately 1 1/2 to 2 hp, which is supplied by the car engine. The system has a cooling capacity which may vary between 12,000 Btu/hr. to 24,000 Btu/hr., which is the refrigerating equivalent of a one to two ton refrigerating machine.

25-4 Performance

The unit is designed to be of a size that varies from 3/4 to 4 ton cooling capacity. A capacity of 12,000 Btu/hr. is minimum. This is equivalent to a one ton machine.

See Par. 1-31. Capacities up to 48,000 Btu/hr. are available. The capacity should match the car size. Undercapacity will reduce cooling, while overcapacity is uneconomical and causes too frequent cycling. The units are usually designed to keep the

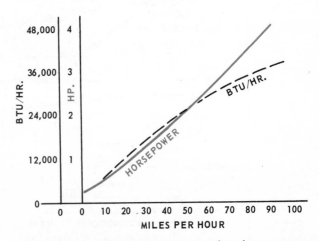

Fig. 25-8. Curve showing relationship between car speed, heat load and horsepower required to drive automobile cooling mechanism.

inside of the automobile 15 F. to 20 F. below the outside (ambient) temperature when the car is traveling about 30 mph. Fig. 25-8 shows how the horsepower required varies as the car speed changes. .

As the automobile slows down, the capacity will decrease, and as the automobile speeds up, the compressor capacity will increase. This variation in capacity is somewhat parallel to the changing heat load, except at one critical interval which is when the car is parked or is in slow moving traffic. At these critical times, the compressor capacity may be below its needed capacity. A partial solution is to idle the engine at a higher speed, and to travel in traffic in some intermediate gear to obtain higher engine speeds.

The refrigerating system can consume as much as 8 hp from the engine at high speeds, and at this high speed the unit capacity will be approximately 36,000 Btu/hr. or three (3) tons capacity. This means that about 1 1/2 to 2 1/2 hp are needed for each ton of refrigeration effect. This compares to the use of 1 hp for each ton of refrigeration in a motor driven constant speed compressor comparably built and with the evaporator coil and condenser more ideally located.

When heating is required, the typical hot water coil using engine heat is installed in the air duct. The same fans and also the same filters may be used during both the cooling and heating cycles. See Par. 25-24.

25-5 Typical Installation

Most automobile manufacturers provide, as an option, a factory installed air conditioner. There are certain accessory manufacturers who also manufacture and market an "add on" type of cooling mechanism which may be installed in any standard make of automobile. The instructions given in this chapter will deal with both of these types of automobile air conditioners. The chief characteristic of the factory in-

stallations is the fact that a small plenum or mixing chamber under the dash receives air from both the evaporator coil and the heater coil. The conditioned air travels from this chamber to the passenger compartment.

If the controls are set to heat the car, hot water from the engine block will circulate through the heater coils in the passenger compartment unit. Later in this chapter, this part of the system will be shown in some detail.

If the controls are set to provde air conditioning, cooling, the operation will be as follows:

Air is blown through the cold evaporator coils and circulated into the passenger compartment of the car. Some automatic systems operate both the evaporator and the heater coil. Air travels through the evaporator coil first and is cooled, then part or all of this air travels through the heater coil and is reheated to the desired temperature.

25-6 Types of Systems

There are four basic cycle and mechanical systems in common use. These systems vary in size and installation procedures. However, the function and operation of a unit which is classified as one of the four basic cycles will have the same operational and repair characteristics as other units in that classification.

1. Pressure operated low side pressure regulators.
2. Pressure operated bypass.
3. Solenoid operated bypass.
4. Electromagnetic clutch.
5. Combinations of the above.

27-7 Low Side Pressure Control

In the low side pressure control system, an evaporator pressure controlled regulator valve is installed in the suction line of the system. The purpose of this valve is to hold a constant pressure in the evaporator. The valve will close if the evaporator tends to go below a certain setting thereby holding the evaporator at a constant pressure and temperature, as shown in Fig. 25-9. The low side pressure control also prevents the compressor from producing a high vacuum at high speeds, which might cause the compressor to lose its oil.

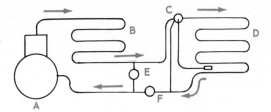

Fig. 25-10. Cycle diagram of pressure operated bypass and low side pressure refrigerator system. A—Compressor. B—Condenser. C—Thermostatic expansion valve. D—Evaporator. E—Low side pressure operated bypass. F—Evaporator pressure control.

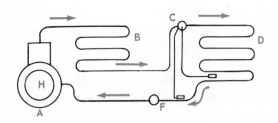

Fig. 25-9. System with evaporator pressure controlled suction line valve. A—Compressor. B—Condenser. C—Thermostatic expansion valve. D—Evaporator. F—Evaporator pressure control. H—Magnetic clutch.

To overcome this problem some manufacturers use a system with an automatic expansion valve bypass. This valve has a small bleeder hole in the orifice to allow a small amount of refrigerant to enter the suction line and prevent too high a vacuum

from forming. This type system is shown in Fig. 25-10. In this type system, the compressor may operate continuously as long as air conditioning is needed. A refinement of this system is the installation of an evaporator pressure controlled valve in the body of the compressor or next to it. To overcome the problem of the vacuum, the valve is designed not to close completely. It allows enough refrigerant to enter the compressor to maintain a positive pressure. There are other variations too which have been used.

Other low pressure control systems use an instrument panel Bowden cable attached to a low side pressure control, as shown in Fig. 25-11. In this case, pulling

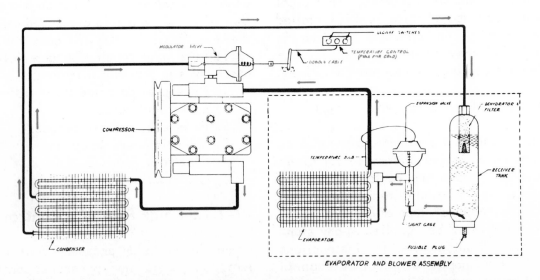

Fig. 25-11. Cycle diagram for pressure operated bypass. Modulator valve is pressure bypass in this system Note solid core type dehydrator and filter at entrance to liquid receiver.

the control knob out decreases the pressure in the evaporator, resulting in colder evaporator temperatures. The pressure reduction is produced by reducing the amount of vapor being bypassed into the low side from the condenser.

25-8 Pressure Operated "Hot Gas" Bypass Valve

A cycle diagram of a pressure operated bypass is shown in Fig. 25-12. In this system the pressure operated bypass valve (J) is connected between the compressor discharge (high side) and the compressor suction line (low side). It is set to open and

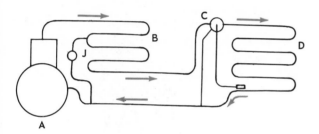

Fig. 25-12. Cycle diagram of pressure operated bypass. A—Compressor. B—Condenser. C—Thermostatic expansion valve. D—Evaporator coil. J—Pressure operated bypass valve.

bypass hot vapor from the high side to the low side when the pressure difference reaches the setting of the valve. This valve opens when there is a lowering of the suction line pressure and closes when there is an increase in the suction pressure. Hot gas (vapor) is fed into the low pressure side to maintain a certain pressure in the evaporator. A continuously operating compressor is usually used with this system.

25-9 Solenoid Operated "Hot Gas" Bypass

In a solenoid operated bypass system, a thermostat mounted on the evaporator operates to open a solenoid valve and by-

pass "hot gas" from the high side to the low side when the temperature of the evaporator drops to 32 F.

On this system a thermostat is mounted with the sensing bulb located in the return airflow. As the return air temperature is lowered, the thermostat is satisfied, 32 F., and in turn, opens the solenoid allowing hot gas from the condenser to bypass back into the suction line.

Since the solenoid valve is either closed or wide open, it does not give the throttling effect of a pressure operated valve. This basic system was used in the 50's. A continuous operating compressor was normally used on most of these systems. One system used a rotary compressor.

The solenoid is in a closed position when the current is on (closed circuit). The valve opens when the circuit is open. The thermostat therefore opens on temperature drop. The solenoid valve also opens when power is off and the pressures in the system balance to reduce the starting load.

25-10 Magnetic Clutch

Many automotive air conditioning compressors have a mechanism which permits the engine to run without the compressor

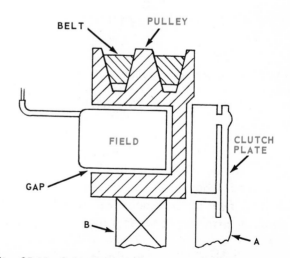

Fig. 25-13. Schematic of electromagnetic clutch. Note stationary magnetic field, cross section of clutch plate A, and cross section of drive pulley B.

running. A clutch is used to engage the compressor belt drive pulley to the compressor crankshaft or to disengage it. The clutch is operated by forcing a clutch disk against the pulley through the use of electromagnetism. The principle is shown in Fig. 25-13. The general construction showing the magnetic field circuit is shown in Fig. 25-14.

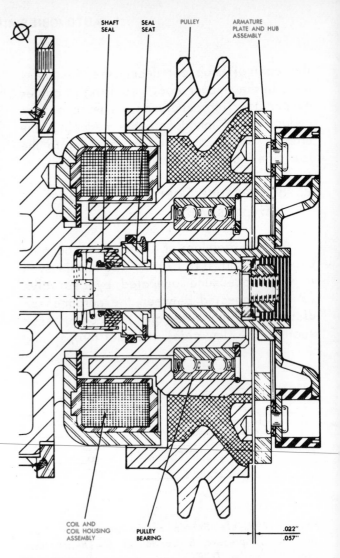

Fig. 25-15. Automotive air conditioning compressor magnetic clutch. When coil is energized armature revolves with pulley. Armature turns compressor shaft. (Pontiac Motor Div., General Motors Corp.)

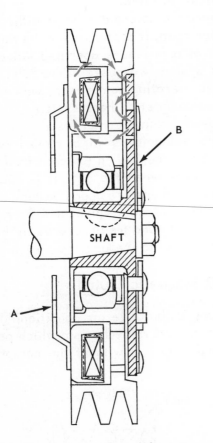

Fig. 25-14. Compressor pulley with stationary electromagnet showing magnetic field. A—Stationary coil bracket. B—Clutch disk.

Two basic designs have been used:

1. Revolving magnetic coil. This coil revolves when the compressor revolves. It has two carbon brushes, which are in contact with two copper rings mounted on the coil.

2. Stationary magnetic coil. This coil is mounted on the compressor body. It has two electrical leads, one from the controls and one to connect to ground. The electromagnetic type can be operated by a manual switch, thermostat, or by a time delay switch. Most systems use thermostatic control. Continuous operating systems have a time delay switch which delays the energizing of the magnetic clutch until the engine starts (to reduce the cranking motor load during starting). Fig. 25-15 shows the design of one type of stationary coil electromagnetic clutch.

When the temperature of the evaporator coil is brought down to a predetermined setting, the thermostat opens the electric circuit to the magnetic clutch on the com-

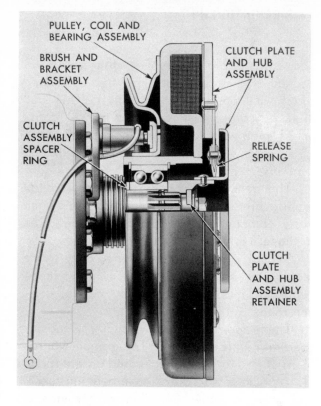

Fig. 25-16. Electromagnetic clutch assembly which has revolving magnetic coil.

pressor drive pulley and the pulley "free wheels" on its shaft and the compressor stops.

There are several makes of electromagnetic clutches on the market. The current draw to magnetize the various clutches is approximately the same.

1. Warner plate type.
   2.7 to 3.3 amperes at 12 volts and normal temperatures.
2. Warner Heli-Grip.
   2.7 to 3.1 amperes at 12 volts and normal temperatures.
3. Electro-lock plate type.
   2.9 to 3.3 amperes at 12 volts and normal temperatures.

Replacement clutches may be of the rotating type. These clutches use two stationary carbon brushes and slip rings to carry the current to the coil while the coil is revolving. A rotating coil type magnetic clutch is shown in Fig. 25-16.

The magnetic coil must be carefully mounted to prevent rubbing and to provide efficient operation.

An electromagnetic clutch designed for use with two drive belts is shown in Fig. 25-17.

25-11 Compressor

The compressors used at present are belt driven from the engine. They operate at slightly above engine rpm. Therefore, with the engine idling, the compressors will revolve at approximately 600 rpm and at maximum engine speeds, the compressors will revolve at near 5000 rpm.

There are two types of compressors in general use in automobile air conditioning. The conventional crankshaft, connecting rod, piston, cylinder, reciprocating type was first used and is still popular.

The General Motors Corp. has developed a compressor which uses a reciprocating piston and cylinder arrangement; however, the conventional crankshaft and connecting rod has been replaced by a

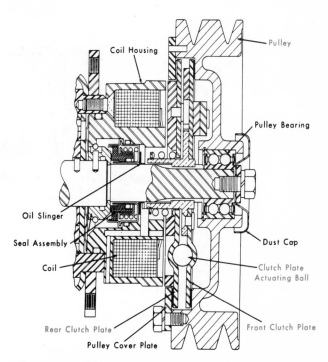

Fig. 25-17. Electromagnetic clutch which has two-belt pulley "free wheel" on compressor shaft until magnetism clamps shaft mounted clutch plate between front and rear clutch plates.

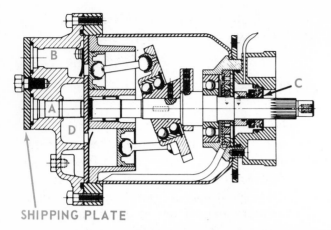

SHIPPING PLATE

Fig. 25-18. Section drawing of five-cylinder swash plate type compressor. Exhaust valve is shown at upper left. The suction port is shown at D, and crankshaft seal at C. Connecting rods are of the ball and socket type.
(Cadillac Motor Car Div., General Motors Corp.)

straight shaft and a "swash plate" which is mounted at an angle to the shaft, and the double acting pistons are fitted over the swash plate in such a way that, as the shaft

and swash plate revolve, the piston is caused to reciprocate in the cylinders which are parallel to the shaft. This design is sometimes called a barrel compressor or wobble plate compressor.

A rotary compressor was used at one time but is no longer used.

The general compressor used on automobile air conditioners (except the swash plate compressor) is similar in operation to those explained in Chapter 5.

Swash plate compressors are made mostly of steel, while two cylinder conventional models, cylinders, heads, etc., are made of aluminum alloy.

These compressors use 300 viscosity special refrigerant oil. The amount varies from 3 oz. to 7 oz., depending on the model. A lack of oil may cause bearing, seal, and valve trouble. Oil plugs on the side of the compressor crankcase may be used to check the oil level.

Crankshaft seals must be heavy-duty type; the moving parts must be balanced

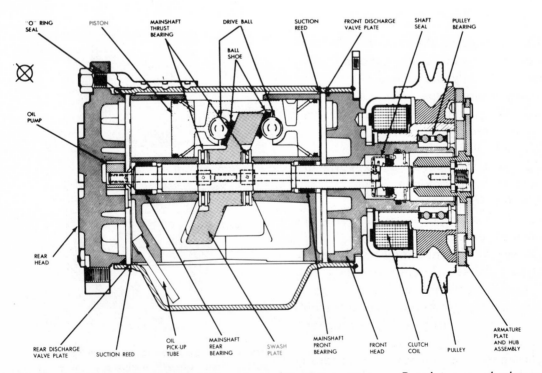

Fig. 25-19. Six-cylinder axial type automotive air conditioning compressor. Revolving swash plate set at an angle drives three double acting pistons.

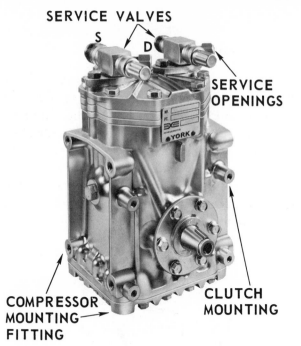

SERVICE VALVES

S   D

SERVICE OPENINGS

YORK

COMPRESSOR MOUNTING FITTING

CLUTCH MOUNTING

Fig. 25-20. Two-cylinder reciprocating compressor. Compressor body has variety of mounting holes to permit vertical, horizontal, or inclined mounting. S—Suction service valve. D—Discharge service valve. (York Corp., Sub. of Borg-Warner Corp.)

for all the varying speeds. The compressor volumetric efficiency must remain at a certain minimum regardless of the speed. Therefore, the valve and valve port design must be substantial.

Service valves or Schrader valves may be provided for mounting gauges in and/or servicing the low pressure side and the high pressure side of the system.

General Motors Corp. automobiles from 1956 through 1961 used a swash plate type compressor having five cylinders, as shown in Fig. 25-18. This compressor uses a swash plate mounted on a double row of ball bearings. These bearings run on an inclined race which is fastened to the rotating shaft.

The suction line connection is centered with the shaft. An oil pump is mounted between the single row ball bearings and the seal.

The six cylinder General Motors compressor is shown in Fig. 25-19. It con-

sists of three sets of opposing cylinders and three double end pistons. Two cylinder reciprocating type units are used by Ford and American Motors and by companies that manufacture "add on" units. Fig. 25-20 shows a two cylinder unit, while Fig. 25-21 shows the internal construc-

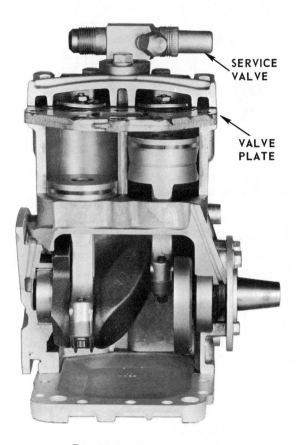

SERVICE VALVE

VALVE PLATE

Fig. 25-21. Cut-a-way view of two-cylinder compressor.

tion of a two cylinder compressor. Some compressors are of the two cylinder V-type, as shown in Fig. 25-22.

25-12 Compressor Seal

All automotive air conditioning compressors have a crankshaft seal. In some cases, sealing is sometimes done by using a carbon ring with a smooth surface rubbing against a flat, smooth cast iron surface which is bolted to and sealed on the body of the compressor. Some compressors use a rotating carbon ring rubbing against a stationary carbon ring. A synthetic rubber, usually Buna N, seals the

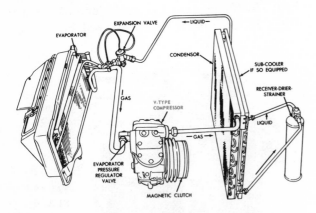

Fig. 25-22. V-type compressor mounted in air conditioning system. (Chrysler Corp.)

joint between the carbon ring and the shaft. Teflon seal surfaces are used on some late model compressors. Fig. 25-23 shows a typical crankshaft seal. This seal must hold refrigerant oil between -60 F. and 250 F., and from a micron vacuum to several hundreds of pounds of pressure.

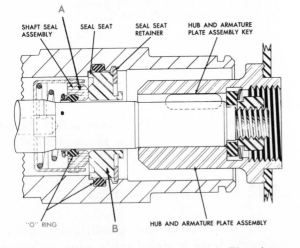

Fig. 25-23. Compressor crankshaft seal. This design has a rotating carbon ring (A) rubbing against cast iron seat (B). Rubbing surfaces should be smooth and flat (accurate to .000001 in.). Note use of O rings to seal two rings in place.

25-13 Belts

One or two belts may be used to drive the air conditioning compressor. The belt is mounted on the pulley of the electromagnetic clutch and is driven by a pulley on the engine crankshaft. An idler pulley may be used to maintain the correct belt tension. The idler pulley is adjusted to obtain the correct tautness. Fig. 25-24 shows a belt installation.

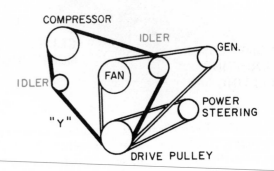

Fig. 25-24. Belt and pulley installation showing two idler pulleys. (Climatic Air Sales, Inc.)

The belt used must be designed and constructed for automotive type service. It must run true on the pulleys; the pulleys must be in line. The belt must have the correct tension for efficient use and long life.

For a new belt, the tension should be from 140 to 145 lbs. Use a belt tension gauge to measure the tension. A new belt should be rechecked for tension a day or two after installation.

A used belt (when overhauling a system that has been in use) should have a 55-75 lb. tension.

A way to roughly check belt tension, is to apply a firm hand pressure in the middle of the longest belt span. If the belt is correctly tensioned, you should be able to depress it about 1/2 in. out of line. Also, a correctly tensioned belt will twist 1/4 to 1/2 in. by using a firm grip and some firm twisting.

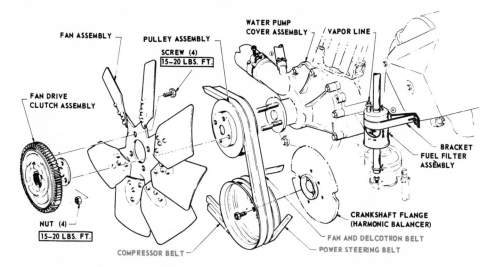

Fig. 25-25. *Belts driving the water pump, fan, power steering, Delcotron, and air conditioning compressor. (Buick Motor Div., General Motors Corp.)*

The belts usually also power the water pump and the fan, as shown in Fig. 25-25. Some fans have a clutch which connects the fan to engine only after the engine compartment has reached a correct temperature (for quieter engine warm-up). Details of one installation are shown in Fig. 25-26.

25-14 Condenser

The condenser is usually mounted in front of the car radiator. The discharge line from the compressor to the condenser may have a vibration absorber mounted in it, or the line may be flexible. Many systems also mount a muffler in this line, as shown in Fig. 25-27.

The condenser may be a one, two, or three pass finned tube type, made of copper or aluminum. Fig. 25-28 shows a typical automotive condenser. It is firmly fastened to the radiator shell using rubber grommets, washers, and screws. Air going through the radiator and into the engine compartment usually goes through the condenser first. On some independent units, the condenser is mounted back of the radiator. The condenser is of the standard construction air-cooled type.

Refrigerant lines are made of steel or copper, or the lines may be flexible. Double flare connections are sometimes used where units must be disconnected for servicing. Flexible lines using other types of fittings are shown in Fig. 25-29. It is important that the lines be prevented from rubbing against any part of the car. Wear and corrosion would quickly cause leaks at the contact points.

Fig. 25-30 shows one method of mounting the condenser on the front of the radiator. It is sometimes necessary to mount the condenser on the engine side of the radiator, because there is not enough space in front of the radiator. These units will operate satisfactorily, but a higher head pressure will be noted.

It is important to keep the outside of the condenser clean. A partially clogged airflow will affect the efficiency of the condenser, and also the efficiency of the car radiator.

25-15 Receiver-Drier

This system uses a receiver located between the condenser and evaporator. Its purpose is to store liquid refrigerant, and to allow for some changes in the refrig-

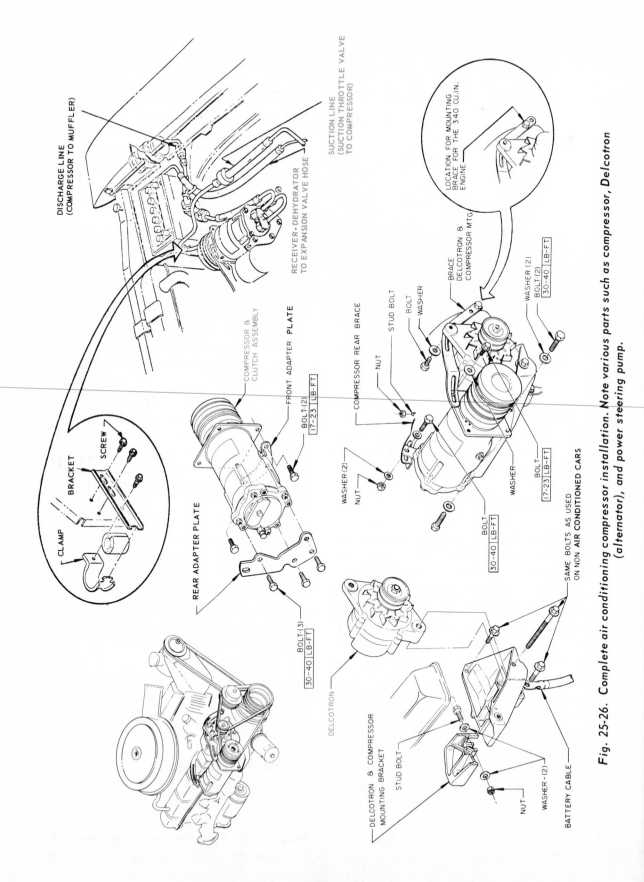

DISCHARGE LINE
(COMPRESSOR TO MUFFLER)

SUCTION LINE
(SUCTION THROTTLE VALVE
TO COMPRESSOR)

RECEIVER-DEHYDRATOR
TO EXPANSION VALVE HOSE

LOCATION FOR MOUNTING
BRACE FOR THE 340 CU.IN.
ENGINE

BRACE
DELCOTRON &
COMPRESSOR MTG.

WASHER (2)

BOLT (2)
30-40 LB-FT

COMPRESSOR &
CLUTCH ASSEMBLY

FRONT ADAPTER PLATE

BOLT (2)
17-23 LB-FT

COMPRESSOR REAR BRACE

NUT

STUD BOLT

BOLT

WASHER

WASHER (2)

NUT

WASHER

BOLT
17-23 LB-FT

BOLT
30-40 LB-FT

REAR ADAPTER PLATE

CLAMP

BRACKET

SCREW

BOLT (3)
30-40 LB-FT

DELCOTRON

SAME BOLTS AS USED
ON NON AIR CONDITIONED CARS

DELCOTRON & COMPRESSOR
MOUNTING BRACKET

STUD BOLT

NUT

WASHER (2)

BATTERY CABLE

Fig. 25-26. Complete air conditioning compressor installation. Note various parts such as compressor, Delcotron (alternator), and power steering pump.

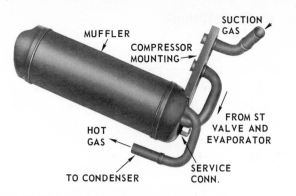

Fig. 25-27. *Muffler used on air conditioning system. Note the service connections; also, how muffler is connected into system.*

erant charge, or for changes in liquid volume caused by the expansion and contraction of the liquid refrigerant, as temperatures change. A receiver-drier is shown in Fig. 25-31. Such a receiver usually has a drier chemical placed inside. This drier

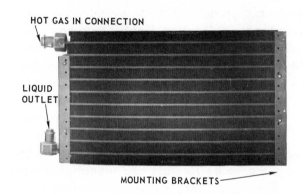

Fig. 25-28. *Automotive air conditioning condenser. The condenser is placed in front of car radiator.*

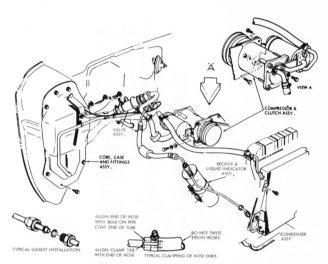

Fig. 25-29. *Typical condenser mounting and refrigerant lines connections.*

Fig. 25-30. *Assembly view of air conditioning system. Note car radiator, compressor, and other parts of air conditioning system.*

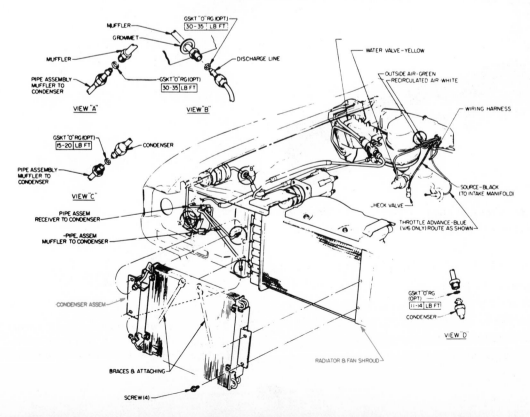

(desiccant) chemical will remove moisture from the liquid and hold the moisture unless the chemical is heated to a high temperature or unless the water is replaced by a more active chemical, such as alcohol.

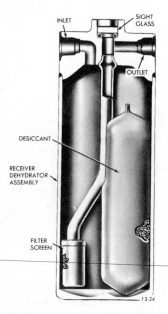

Fig. 25-31. Cut-a-way of liquid receiver-drier. The device holds about 10 cu. in. of desiccant. Note sight glass located in the liquid refrigerant outlet. (Buick Motor Div., General Motors Corp.)

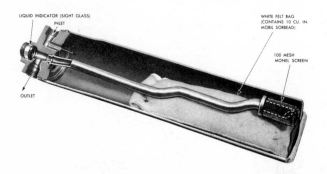

Fig. 25-32. Cross section of combination liquid receiver, filter, drier, and sight glass.

Some of these receivers also have a sight glass as part of the liquid line outlet, as shown in Fig. 25-32. If, after the system has been operating for a few minutes, bubbles appear in the window of the sight glass, the vapor bubbles indicate the sys-

tem is short of refrigerant (no reserve liquid in the receiver). The bubbles usually indicate the system has lost over half of its charge.

25-16 Refrigerant Lines

Special flexible refrigerant lines are used: (1) to carry liquid refrigerant from the receiver-drier to the evaporator expansion valve (liquid line); (2) to carry vapor refrigerant from the evaporator to the compressor (suction line); (3) to carry hot compressed vapor from the compressor to the condenser; (4) on some units to carry liquid refrigerant from the condenser to the liquid, receiver-drier. These lines are also called hoses. They are commonly covered with a braid to protect them against injury. They are designed and constructed to be flexible and vibration proof.

They are fastened to the system parts in various ways:

A. Flared fitting.
B. O ring fitting.
C. Hose clamp fitting.

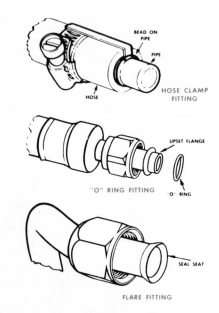

Fig. 25-33. Typical refrigerant lines connection fittings. Flare, O ring, and hose clamp. (Harrison Radiator Div., General Motors Corp.)

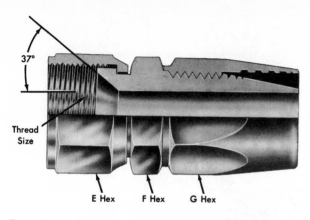

Fig. 25-34. Fitting used in connecting nylon flexible tubing. (Polymer Corp.)

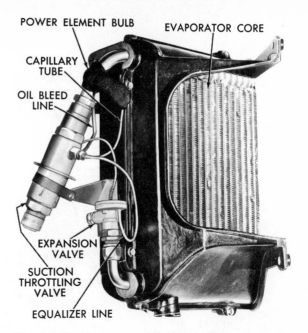

Fig. 25-35. Evaporator complete with housing, drain, TEV, and suction throttling valve. (Cadillac Motor Car Div., General Motors Corp.)

These fittings are shown in Fig. 25-33. The flexible lines or hoses vary in size from 3/8 to 5/8 in., depending on the capacity of the unit and on the state of the refrigerant. A fitting often used with nylon flexible tubing is shown in Fig. 25-34. Vapor carrying lines, (2) and (3) above, are the larger. The size of the lines must match the fittings supplied by manufacturer so the system capacity will not be changed.

These lines should have large bends, and they should be supported, grommeted, and clamped to prevent wear by chafing and to prevent them from touching hot en-

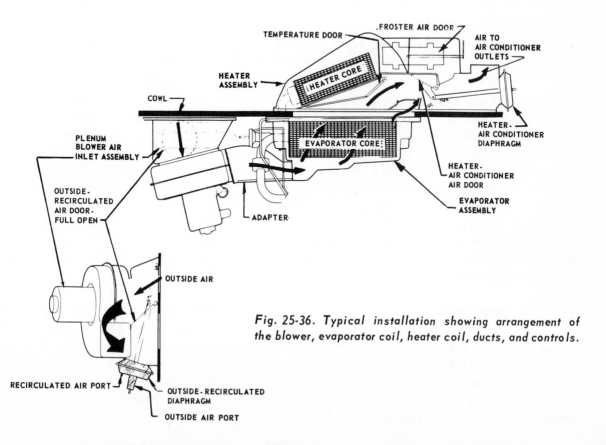

Fig. 25-36. Typical installation showing arrangement of the blower, evaporator coil, heater coil, ducts, and controls.

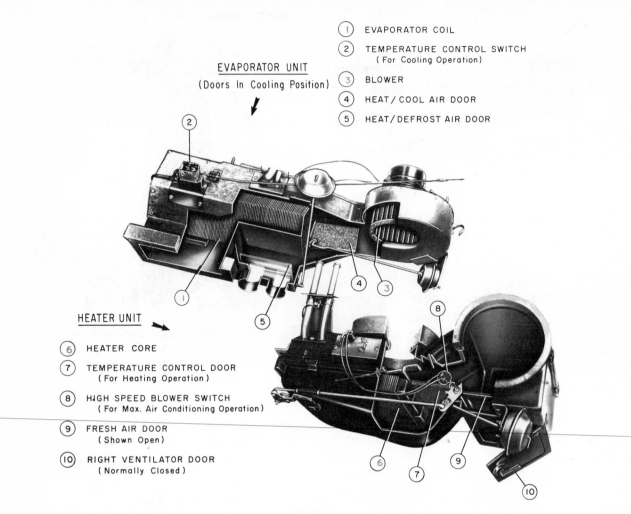

EVAPORATOR UNIT
(Doors In Cooling Position)

1. EVAPORATOR COIL
2. TEMPERATURE CONTROL SWITCH
   (For Cooling Operation)
3. BLOWER
4. HEAT/COOL AIR DOOR
5. HEAT/DEFROST AIR DOOR

HEATER UNIT

6. HEATER CORE
7. TEMPERATURE CONTROL DOOR
   (For Heating Operation)
8. HIGH SPEED BLOWER SWITCH
   (For Max. Air Conditioning Operation)
9. FRESH AIR DOOR
   (Shown Open)
10. RIGHT VENTILATOR DOOR
    (Normally Closed)

Fig. 25-37. Two views of combination heating, cooling, and duct system. 1—Evaporator coil. 3—Blower. 6— Heater core. (Dodge Div., Chrysler Corp.)

gine parts. Leave enough hose free at the compressor end of the lines to allow for movement of the engine on its vibration absorber mounts.

The lines come equipped with caps and plugs to keep the inside of the lines clean and dry. Do not remove these plugs and caps until just before installing. All assembly threads and fittings should have clean, fresh refrigerant oil put on them just before assembly.

25-17 Evaporators

Evaporating coils are usually mounted in a plenum chamber attached to the engine compartment, fire wall, or dashboard. The evaporating coil of the automotive air conditioner is of the finned, forced con-

vection type. It is enclosed in a metal or plastic housing that also serves as a duct for the conditioned air. A moisture drain pan and drainpipe must also be incorporated in the unit. See Fig. 25-35.

Some systems in the past have mounted the evaporating coil in the trunk of the car, while others have mounted the coils in front fender well. Most installations today have the system mounted on the engine side of the dash (fire wall) or on the passenger side of the dash (fire wall). An evaporating coil, blower, and duct installation mounted under the hood and under the instrument panel is shown in Fig. 25-36.

The heating coil is also mounted in the same duct system which fastens to the fire wall or dash. Another design is shown in Fig. 25-37.

The design and installation of an "add on" unit evaporator, evaporator housing, and blower unit is shown in Fig. 25-38. The evaporator can be inverted. The blower assembly can also be inverted as shown, to permit greater flexibility of installation.

Some independent units are mounted in the trunk of the vehicle because of lack of space under the hood or because of the style of the car (limousine).

A hose schematic and wiring diagram of a typical trunk unit are shown in Fig. 25-39.

25-18 Expansion Valves

The system must have a reducing device to throttle the high pressure liquid refrigerant to low pressure liquid refrigerant in the evaporator. The device used in automobile air conditioners is the thermostatic expansion valve. This control responds to the temperature of the evaporator outlet as well as the low side (suction) pressure. Chapter 6 explains the principle, design, construction, installation, and service of this type valve. Some of these valves are adjustable; some are preset for

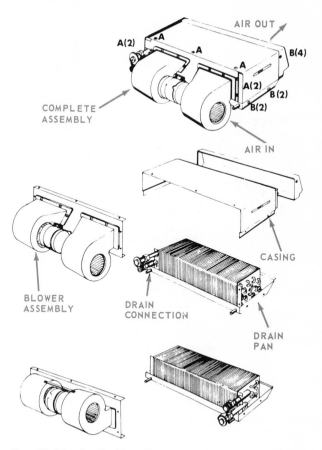

Fig. 25-38. An "add on" unit evaporator and blower assembly. Both evaporator and blower assembly may be inverted to facilitate installation.
(Climatic Air Sales, Inc.)

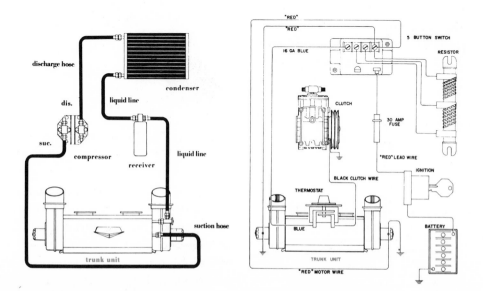

Fig. 25-39. Typical trunk unit installation. Left. Schematic diagram of refrigeration cycle. Right. Electrical circuits wiring diagram. Note use of a dual blower system.

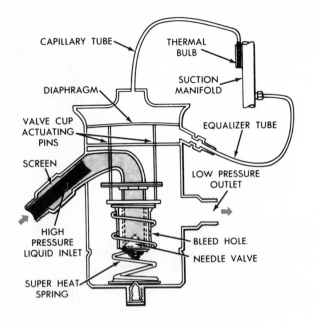

Fig. 25-40. Cross section showing operating principles of thermostatic expansion valve.
(Chrysler Corp.)

a 15 F. superheat and are not adjustable. Fig. 25-40 is a schematic of a typical valve.

The capacity of this valve (orifice size) must match the capacity of the unit. A valve that is too small will reduce the capacity, while a valve that is too large will "hunt" or alternately flood and starve the evaporator of liquid refrigerant.

Most of the automotive TEV's have a pressure equalizer connection from the valve body to the outlet of the evaporator.

The equalizer is needed because the evaporator coil has enough pressure drop to make it necessary to use the outlet evaporator pressure only to push against the low side facing of the diaphragm for accurate, consistent operation. A nonadjustable thermostatic expansion valve is shown in Fig. 25-41.

The valve is located on the evaporator. It is usually covered with tape insulation to permit it to operate without engine compartment heat affecting its operation. The sensitive bulb must be clean, the outlet tube to which it is clamped must be clean, and the clamps must be tight. After mounting the bulb, the assembly should be covered with insulation, which results in only the evaporator outlet temperature affecting the valve operation. Fig. 25-42 shows a recommended bulb mounting. The bulb should be mounted with the capillary tube connection at the top.

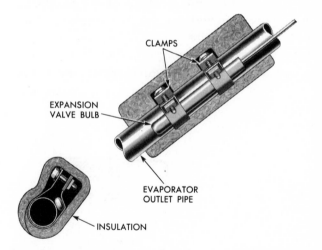

Fig. 25-42. Details of mounting thermostatic expansion valve thermal bulb on outlet of evaporator coil.

Some TEV's are equipped with a built-in sight glass on the inlet side to show the refrigerant flow. Ford Motor Co. has this arrangement on some of their cars. When the sight glass is part of the TEV, there is no need for a sight glass in the liquid receiver. Most TEV's with a built-in sight glass are of the nonadjustable type.

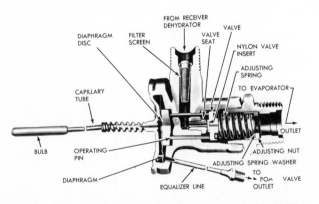

Fig. 25-41. Nonadjustable thermostatic valve. Note type of inlet connections and outlet connections.

25-19 Suction Pressure Control Valves

Some systems have suction pressure valves which are used to maintain a certain pressure in the evaporator independent of the compressor low side pressure and independent of the cooling demand. In most cases, a diaphragm or bellows responding only to the pressure in the evaporator opens this valve if the evaporator pressure is above 29 to 31 psig (R-12) and closes the valve if the pressure tends to go below these settings. Fig. 25-43 shows a cross section of such a valve with a manual pressure adjustment.

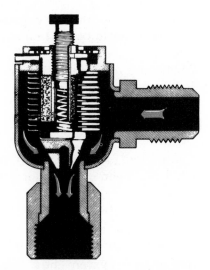

Fig. 25-43. A suction pressure regulator valve with a manual pressure adjustment.
(Frigiking Co., Div. of Cummins Engine Co.)

Several types have been used:
1. Suction throttling valves (STV).
2. Evaporator pressure regulators (EPR).
3. Pressure operated altitude valve (POA) (GMC).

Most of them are adjustable. Some have valve core access ports which are used to check the valve operating pressure.

The General Motors pilot operated absolute valve (POA) has a connection for the expansion valve equalizer line and another connection for the oil bleed (oil return from the evaporator), and a valve core access port.

The main purposes of these valves is to keep the evaporator above a freezing temperature to prevent the moisture which condenses on the evaporator, from freezing as the air flows through it. Some of the valves maintain a 28 psig pressure in the evaporator until the air temperature becomes too cold and then a manual (by the operator) or vacuum adjustment raises the pressure to about 31 psig. Fig. 25-44 shows a vacuum control unit. At 0 vacuum, the valve will operate at 3 psig higher evaporator pressure. These valves usually have a service attachment to permit a pressure check of the evaporator. Notice that the vacuum attachment body can be adjusted by threading into or out of the main body of the valve.

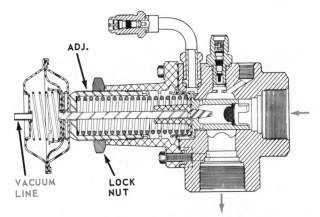

Fig. 25-44. Vacuum operated suction pressure regulator valve.

The POA as developed by General Motors Corp. uses a sealed pressure element which maintains a constant pressure independent of the altitude of the car. Fig. 25-45 shows the outer appearance of this valve. This valve is equipped with a Schrader service connection, an oil bleed connection (to remove oil from the evaporator), and a thermostatic expansion valve equalizer connection.

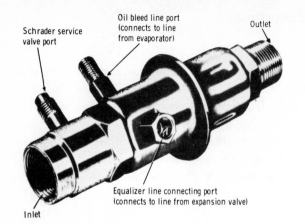

Fig. 25-45. Pressure operated altitude suction throttling valve.
(Buick Motor Div., General Motors Corp.)

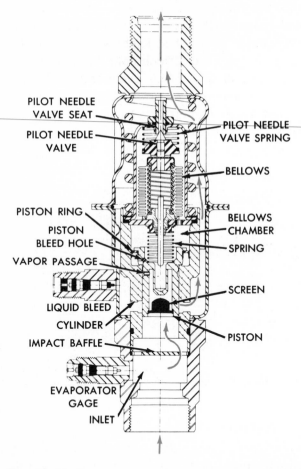

PILOT NEEDLE VALVE SEAT
PILOT NEEDLE VALVE
PILOT NEEDLE VALVE SPRING
BELLOWS
PISTON RING
PISTON BLEED HOLE
VAPOR PASSAGE
BELLOWS CHAMBER
SPRING
LIQUID BLEED
CYLINDER
IMPACT BAFFLE
SCREEN
PISTON
EVAPORATOR GAGE
INLET

Fig. 25-46. Cross section of pressure operated altitude valve (POA).
(Cadillac Motor Car Div., General Motors Corp.)

A cross section of this valve is shown in Fig. 25-46. The operating steps of this valve are shown in Fig. 25-47.

25-20 Bypass Valves

Some systems use a bypass control which automatically keeps the low pressure in the system at 23.5 to 24.5 psig by releasing vapor from the high pressure side to the low side, if the pressure tries to go below the preset pressure. Fig. 25-48 shows such a control.

25-21 Service Valves

A variety of service valves have been used on automotive systems, from standard front and back seat (one way and two way) service valves (see Chapter 15), to Schrader valves (see Chapter 12).

All the systems have some means to connect high and low pressure gauges to the system and also to permit charging or adding oil to the system.

Fig. 25-49 shows a compressor fitting with a Schrader valve connection.

25-22 Heating Systems

Three principal types of heating systems which have been used in automobiles are:

1. Hot water heating systems.
2. Hot air heating systems.
3. Gasoline burner heating systems.

The hot water system has been the most popular. It uses the 120 to 180 F. water in the engine cooling system. Some of this water is circulated through a finned coil on the driver side of the dash and a 2 or 3 speed fan blows air over this coil. The heated air is forced through the passenger compartment.

The hot air system is used when air-cooled engines are used. Heat from the exhaust manifold is used to heat this air which is then carried by ducts to the passenger compartment.

The gasoline burner system uses an electrically ignited gasoline burner. Heat from this flame is used to heat air circu-

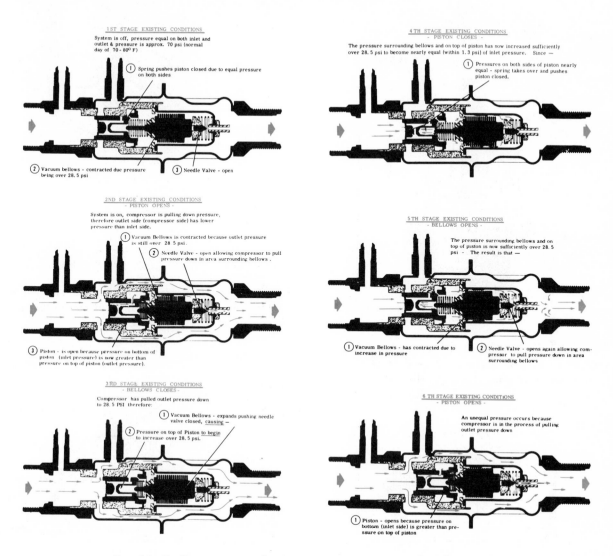

1ST STAGE EXISTING CONDITIONS

System is off, pressure equal on both inlet and outlet & pressure is approx. 70 psi (normal day of 70 - 80° F)

① Spring pushes piston closed due to equal pressure on both sides

② Vacuum bellows - contracted due pressure being over 28.5 psi

③ Needle Valve - open

2ND STAGE EXISTING CONDITIONS
- PISTON OPENS -

System is on, compressor is pulling down pressure, therefore outlet side (compressor side) has lower pressure than inlet side.

① Vacuum Bellows is contracted because outlet pressure is still over 28.5 psi.

② Needle Valve - open allowing compressor to pull pressure down in area surrounding bellows.

③ Piston - is open because pressure on bottom of piston (inlet pressure) is now greater than pressure on top of piston (outlet pressure).

3RD STAGE EXISTING CONDITIONS
- BELLOWS CLOSES -

Compressor has pulled outlet pressure down to 28.5 PSI therefore:

① Vacuum Bellows - expands pushing needle valve closed, _causing_ -

② Pressure on top of Piston _to begin_ to increase over 28.5 psi.

4TH STAGE EXISTING CONDITIONS
- PISTON CLOSES -

The pressure surrounding bellows and on top of piston has now increased sufficiently over 28.5 psi to become nearly equal (within 1.3 psi) of inlet pressure.   Since —

① Pressures on both sides of piston nearly equal - spring takes over and pushes piston closed.

5TH STAGE EXISTING CONDITIONS
- BELLOWS OPENS -

The pressure surrounding bellows and on top of piston is now sufficiently over 28.5 psi - The result is that —

① Vacuum Bellows - has contracted due to increase in pressure

② Needle Valve - opens again allowing compressor to pull pressure down in area surrounding bellows

6TH STAGE EXISTING CONDITIONS
- PISTON OPENS -

An unequal pressure occurs because compressor is in the process of pulling outlet pressure down

① Piston - opens because pressure on bottom (inlet side) is greater than pressure on top of piston

Fig. 25-47. Six operational stages of POA suction throttling valve. (Pontiac Motor Div., General Motors Corp.)

lated around the firepot and into the passenger compartment by a fan.

Cars which are comfort cooled have heating systems which are:

1. Independent of the comfort cooling system (usually for air conditioning a car after it has been made and sold--"add on" units).

2. Built-in part of the comfort cooling system (the heating coils and cooling coils operate at the same time in the same heat or plenum chamber system).

A year around air conditioning system also uses a heating system. Many summer air conditioners use a heating system to reheat some or all of the air which has been cooled by the evaporator.

Fig. 25-50 shows a typical heating system using the engine coolant.

Water in the system should contain antifreeze. The solution must be kept at 15 F. or lower, and the antifreeze is required to prevent freeze-up during summer operation of the air conditioner.

The coolant system must be kept in good condition. Hose connections must be kept tight; hose lines free of abrasions,

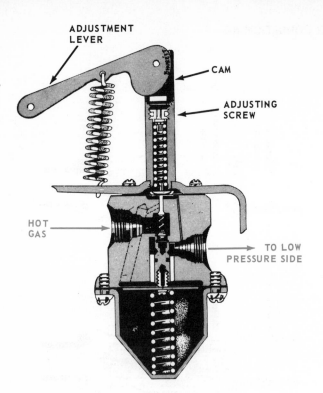

Fig. 25-48. Bypass valve used to keep low side pressure at 25 psig or higher, independent of the running conditions. (John E. Mitchell Co.)

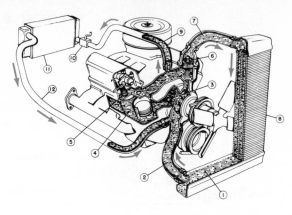

COOLANT CIRCUIT FOR ENGINE AND HEATER

1. COOLANT IN RADIATOR
2. COOLANT BEING DRAWN BY PUMP
3. WATER PUMP
4. COOLANT CIRCULATING AROUND CYLINDERS
5. COOLANT CIRCULATING AROUND VALVES
6. THERMOSTAT
7. HEATED COOLANT RETURNING TO RADIATOR
8. RADIATOR
9. HEATER COOLANT HOSE–TO HEATER
10. WATER SHUT-OFF VALVE
11. HEATER CORE
12. HEATER RETURN HOSE

Fig. 25-50. Coolant circuit for engine and heater. Note coolant return to the inlet of coolant pump. (Chrysler Corp.)

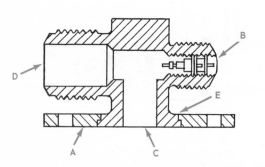

Fig. 25-49. A compressor mounting equipped with Schrader valve attachment. A–Flange. B–Refrigerant service connection. C–Opening to compressor. D–Refrigerant line opening. E–Swivel joint.

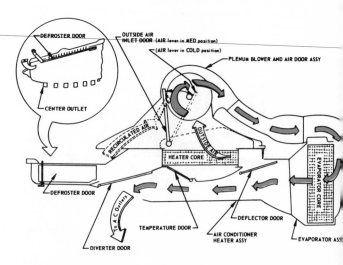

Fig. 25-51. Assembly of evaporator, a heater core, ducts, blower, and air flow control doors.

and the radiator pressure cap should be checked periodically.

Principal parts of the cooling system are:

1. Radiator.
2. Fan.
3. Water pump.
4. Belt.
5. Thermostat.
6. Heater core.

Whether a car has a heating system only, or a year around air conditioning system, the radiator should be kept clean both inside and outside. The radiator is usually tested for leaks by using a pressure pump which fastens to the radiator cap. The test should be at approximately 14 psig. If this pressure drops rapidly, there is a leak. Check the external parts of the system first. If no leak is observed, the leak will be internal and the coolant may be contaminating the engine oil. A fluctuating pressure with the engine running will indicate a combustion chamber coolant leak.

Fig. 25-51 shows how a heater core is installed in a year around air conditioning system. A different type installation is shown in Fig. 25-52.

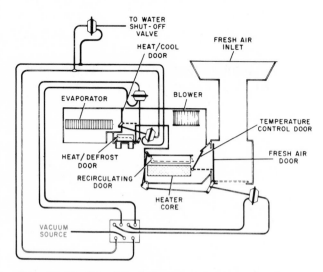

Fig. 25-52. Simplified drawing of year around automotive air conditioning system. Note vacuum system used to operate dampers and water valve.
(Dodge Div., Chrysler Corp.)

25-23 Heating Coils

The thermostat controls the water flow to maintain a temperature of approximately 160-180 F. This coolant averages about 140 F. as it circulates through the heater core. A water control valve is often installed in the coolant hose to the heater core.

The heating system usually starts to operate when coolant temperature reaches 120 F.

A common problem especially after assembling a heating system, is air in the heating coil or core. This entrapped air will prevent water circulating in the coil. The air is bled out by loosening the water outlet connection of the heating coil with

the engine running and allowing the air to be released. Reconnect only after coolant flows out of the connection. If no coolant flows, the heating coil is plugged and the coil must be removed and either replaced or repaired.

25-24 Heating Controls

There are two basic controls in the hot water heating system:

1. A thermostat which bypasses the water flow back into the engine block and prevents the water flow into the radiator until the coolant has reached 120, 140, 160, or 180 F. (there are different units depending on the temperature desired).

2. A thermostat which controls the flow of water into the heater coil. This control is usually operated by the temperature of the return air to the heater coil.

Year around air conditioners use controls which provide enough heat to reheat air coming from the evaporator to the desired temperature.

In many systems, vacuum valves are used together with electrical controls to operate water valves and air dampers.

25-25 Air Distribution

The distribution of air within the automobile body offers several unusual problems. The space is confined, the seats present a restriction to the airflow, and the low roof accelerates the possibility of drafts.

One method of air distribution is to provide two air duct openings back of the back seat which blow the conditioned air forward and along the ceiling of the body. This air mixes by turbulence with the air in the car and settles over the occupants. This system may produce noticeable drafts under certain conditions.

A popular system has the air conditioning system under the instrument panel and on the passenger side of the fire wall

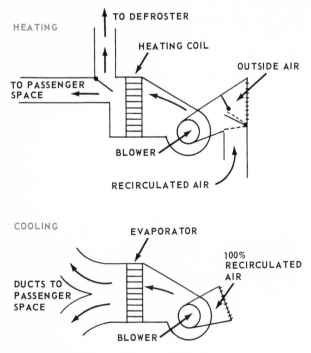

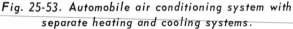

Fig. 25-53. *Automobile air conditioning system with separate heating and cooling systems.*

The main parts of the duct system are dependent on the type of system:

1. Separate cooling and heating system.
2. Combination cooling and heating system.

The separate cooling and heating system is shown diagrammatically in Fig. 25-53. This system is quite popular. It has separate blower motors, separate duct system, and separate damper controls. Note that only the heating system has a fresh air intake and a windshield defrost duct system.

The combination system has the heating coil and the evaporator in the same

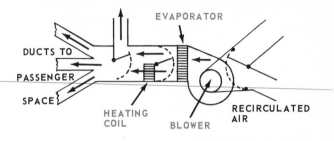

Fig. 25-54. *Combination cooling and heating system.*

(some are on the engine side of the fire wall). These systems have a duct system to control the airflow.

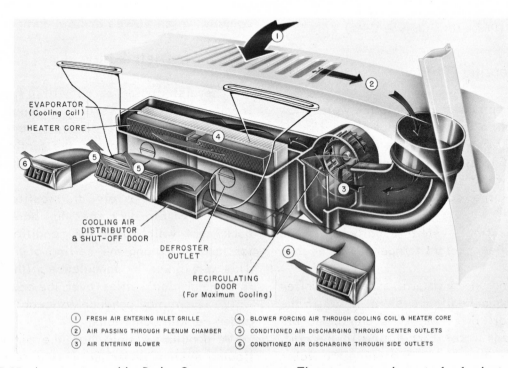

①	FRESH AIR ENTERING INLET GRILLE	④	BLOWER FORCING AIR THROUGH COOLING COIL & HEATER CORE
②	AIR PASSING THROUGH PLENUM CHAMBER	⑤	CONDITIONED AIR DISCHARGING THROUGH CENTER OUTLETS
③	AIR ENTERING BLOWER	⑥	CONDITIONED AIR DISCHARGING THROUGH SIDE OUTLETS

Fig. 25-55. *Air circuit used by Dodge Corp. on some cars. The air pattern shown is for fresh air cooling (1).*

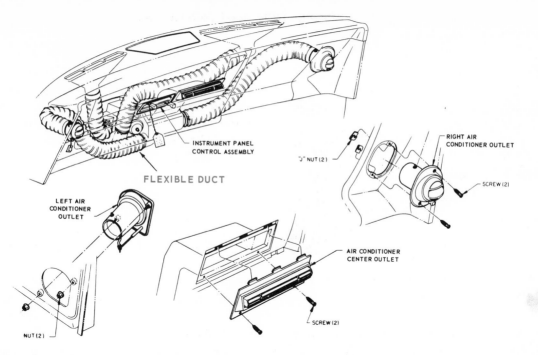

Fig. 25-56. Duct system which uses flexible distribution ducts and fresh air inlet ducts. Note assembly devices and grille construction and installation.

duct system and uses only one blower system. Fig. 25-54 shows the principle of operation.

25-26 Ducts

The ducts are made of metal or plastic. Fairly high air velocities are used as the air movement noise is not as critical as it is in an office or residence.

The duct system includes:
1. Fresh air inlet.
2. Return air inlet.
3. Evaporator housing.
4. Drain pan and drain connection.
5. Plenum chamber.
6. Conditioned air outlets.
   A. Defrost.
   B. Deice.
   C. Grilles.
7. Dampers to change airflow.
   A. Manual.
   B. Power operated.

Fig. 25-55 shows the main parts of a duct system. Note that the heater core and evaporator are in series (airflow) and that the same duct system is used for both systems. A system which uses flexible ducts

for distributing the conditioned air is shown in Fig. 25-56. It is common practice to control the air dampers by using a vacuum powered diaphragm to move the damper in one direction and to use a spring to

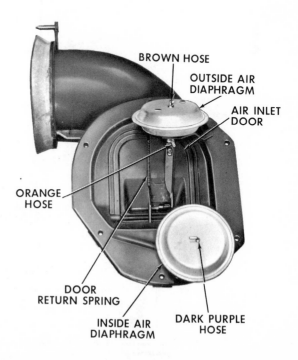

Fig. 25-57. Fresh air and inside air damper showing diaphragm power units and return spring.

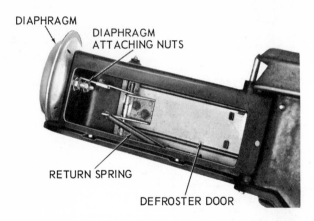

Fig. 25-58. The defroster control damper showing diaphragm power unit and return spring.

return the damper to a certain position (move the damper in the other direction). Figs. 25-57 and 25-58 show the application of vacuum powered dampers. A complete system showing the duct system and the vacuum powered controls is shown in Fig. 25-59. A view of heating airflow, de-

frost airflow and the damper positions for these actions is shown in Fig. 25-60. A dual air conditioning system for a station wagon style body with two evaporators and two TEV's, and auxiliary blower, is shown in Fig. 25-61.

25-27 Fans

Fans used to circulate air are of the radial flow type (squirrel cage or centrifugal type). They are driven by DC motors, either 6V or 12V. The motors are usually flexibly mounted to reduce noise. They are of several models, i.e., single speed, two speed, three speed, etc.

The motors are either single shaft or double shaft with sealed-in bearings which usually do not require oiling. If a motor develops bearing noise, the trouble may be worn bearings or too much end play. Worn bearings necessitate replacing the

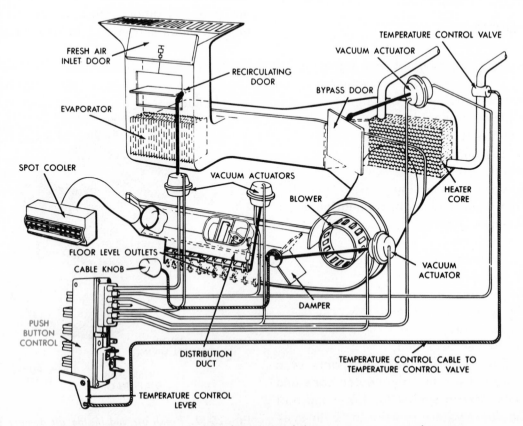

Fig. 25-59. Complete system showing push button vacuum control system.

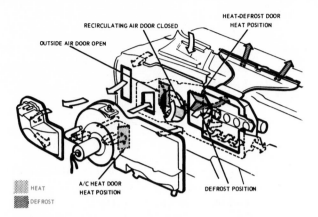

Fig. 25-60. Cut-a-way view of duct system which has blower and coils on engine side of fire wall. Various dampers and their positions are shown. (Ford Motor Co.)

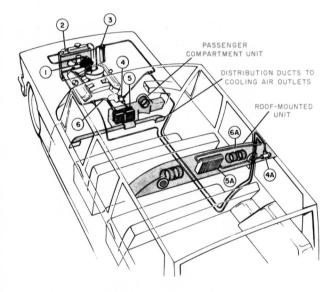

STATION WAGON AIR CONDITIONING SYSTEM
WITH REAR ROOF-MOUNTED UNIT

REFRIGERANT CIRCUIT COMPONENTS
AND FLOW DIRECTION

COMPRESSOR ① TO CONDENSER ②
CONDENSER TO RECEIVER DRIER ③
RECEIVER DRIER TO EXPANSION VALVES ④ AND ④A
EXPANSION VALVES TO EVAPORATORS ⑤ AND ⑤A
RETURN LINES ⑥ AND ⑥A FROM EVAPORATORS
TO COMPRESSOR

Fig. 25-61. Complete air conditioning system using a roof mounted duct and grille system. 1—Compressor. 2—Condenser. 3—Receiver-drier. 4 and 4A—Thermostatic expansion valves. 5 and 5A—Evaporators. (Dodge Div., Chrysler Corp.)

motor. Too much end play can sometimes be remedied by installing end play washers.

The electrical load of the motor can be checked by inserting an ammeter in the line to the blower motors. If the ammeter reading is higher than the specifications in the manufacturer's manual, and if the motor is overheated, the windings may be shorted. Remove the motor, check it again and replace if faulty. If the reading is lower than the specifications, there may be a loose or dirty connection. Check further, using a voltmeter (to check voltage drops). Correct cause of voltage drop when located.

25-28 Filters

Some systems use filters. Most of the filters are of the maze-oil impregnated type. See Chapter 22. Average size of the filters is 12 x 12 x 1/2 to 1 in. thick. Air velocity through the filter is fairly high. It is important that the filters be replaced frequently (every three months average).

The filters are located at the intake of the blower and are positioned to clean both the recirculated and the fresh air.

Many systems do not use filters. The air washing effect of the condensate on the evaporator removes dust and dirt particles from the air quite effectively. The dirt is removed with the condensate, by way of the drain tube.

25-29 Insulation

Most car bodies are insulated. Fiber glass, glass wool, and various low K value nonsettling flexible insulations are used.

The large amount of window area allows considerable heat leakage and also a high sun load. The use of tinted glass reduces the radiant heat load considerably. Light colored cars will absorb considerably less radiant heat than dark or black colored cars.

To avoid air conditioning the trunk space, insulation is usually placed over the back of the rear seat of the car. This insulation also reduces the noise level of the blower unit when a trunk mounted evaporator is used.

It is essential that the body of the car be tightly sealed at all joints. The door gaskets must be in good condition. In addition to the usual water tightness test of the car body, it should also be tested for air tightness. This testing may be done with a water column manometer and with the air blower on and the outside air inlet duct open.

25-30 Electrical Systems

The electrical system of the automobile air conditioner is unique in that a single wire system is used, as the frame of the car serves as the return wire or ground.

The electrical system varies as to the type of system:

1. Separate system.
2. Combination system.
3. Full automatic control (fixed dry bulb setting).

The main parts of the electrical system of the separate system are:

1. Blower or blowers.
2. Blower switch.
3. Thermostat.
4. Electromagnetic clutch.

A typical wiring diagram is shown in Fig. 25-62. The electrical connections must be kept in good condition, because the voltages are low (6 to 8V or 12 to 14V).

This system uses a fast idle solenoid to permit sufficient comfort cooling when parked or waiting for traffic conditions to clear. The solenoid valve usually opens a vacuum control that automatically adjusts the engine idle speed to about 750 rpm. It is wired into the system to function only when the car transmission is in neutral.

Since the refrigerating mechanism and its controls maintain evaporator coil temperature within certain limits, the amount and degree of cooling within the car are

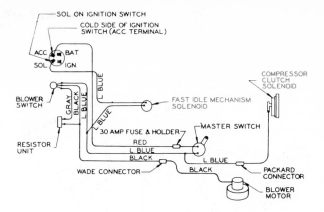

Fig. 25-62. Wiring diagram of automobile air conditioning unit that uses fast idle solenoid and compressor pulley solenoid clutch.

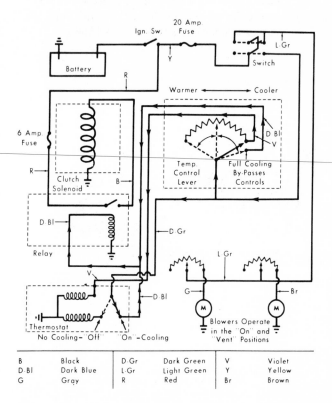

B	Black	D-Gr	Dark Green	V	Violet
D-Bl	Dark Blue	L-Gr	Light Green	Y	Yellow
G	Gray	R	Red	Br	Brown

Fig. 25-63. Wiring diagram of automobile air conditioning system. The unit has a solenoid clutch, two blower motors with variable speed rheostats, a thermostat, and a manually operated rheostat in the thermostat circuit.

controlled by the amount or rate of air circulation over the evaporating coils. The air speed is controlled by the speed of the blowers. Some blowers have two different speed steps, others are controlled by a variable rheostat and a great range of speeds may be provided. Fig. 25-63 shows

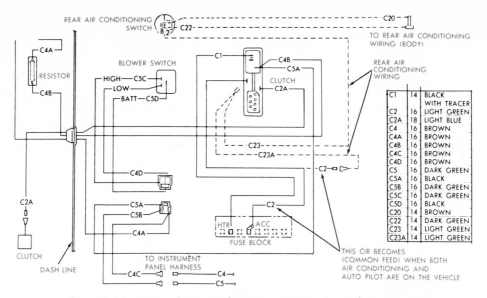

C1	14	BLACK WITH TRACER
C2	16	LIGHT GREEN
C2A	18	LIGHT BLUE
C4	16	BROWN
C4A	16	BROWN
C4B	16	BROWN
C4C	16	BROWN
C4D	16	BROWN
C5	16	DARK GREEN
C5A	16	BLACK
C5B	16	DARK GREEN
C5C	16	DARK GREEN
C5D	16	BLACK
C20	14	BROWN
C22	16	DARK GREEN
C23	14	LIGHT GREEN
C23A	14	LIGHT GREEN

Fig. 25-64. Wiring diagram of station wagon air conditioning system. (Chrysler Corp.)

Fig. 25-65. Complete wiring diagram of automotive air conditioning system. Note compressor clutch solenoid, relays, and switches. (Pontiac Motor Div., General Motors Corp.)

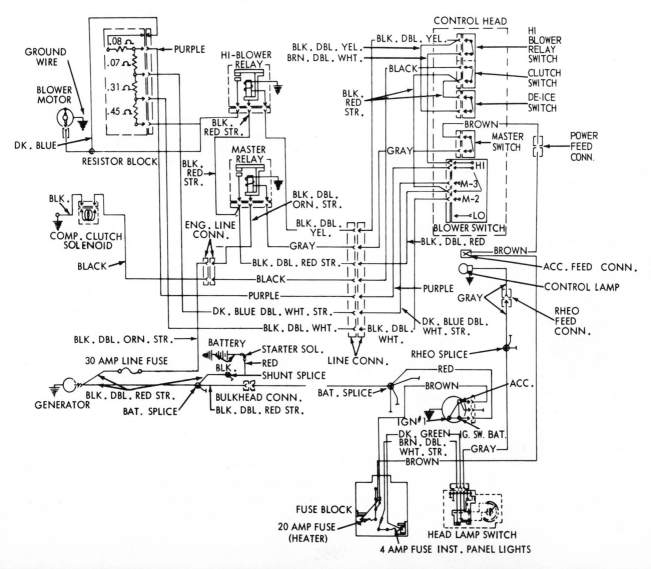

a wiring diagram for an automobile air conditioning system which uses a solenoid clutch, two blower motors with variable speed rheostats, a thermostat, and a manually operated rheostat in the thermostat circuit.

The combination systems have more elaborate electrical wiring systems and components. See Fig. 25-64.

A typical fully automatic system has an electrical system, as shown in Fig. 25-65. A wiring system using sensors, an

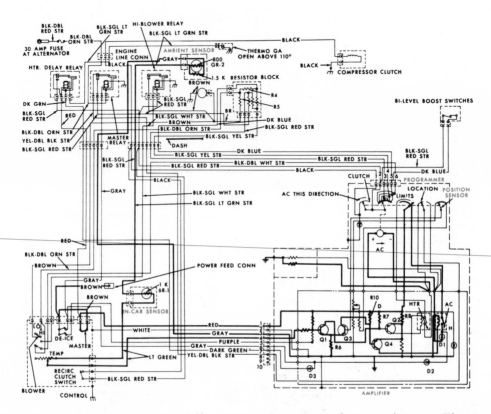

Fig. 25-66. *Electrical-electronic system for fully automatic year around air conditioner. This system uses temperature sensors, amplifier, and programmer to help obtain complete sequence of automatic operation.*

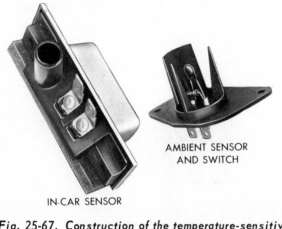

AMBIENT SENSOR AND SWITCH

IN-CAR SENSOR

Fig. 25-67. *Construction of the temperature-sensitive sensors.*

amplifier, and a programmer is shown in Fig. 25-66. The sensors are minute thermistors. There are three of them: (1) outside air, (2) car temperature, (3) position sensor. The amplifier uses four transistors. The appearance of the sensors is shown in Fig. 25-67.

25-31 Thermostats

The thermostat is usually operated by the air temperature leaving the evaporator. It is usually adjustable from 34 F. to 57 F.

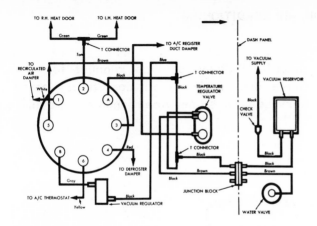

Fig. 25-68. *Vacuum piping and vacuum actuators of air conditioning system.* (Ford Motor Co.)

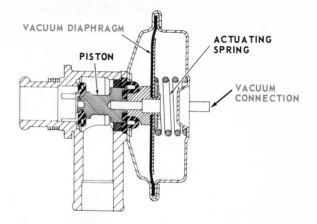

Fig. 25-69. *Vacuum operated water valve (heater). Note that engine vacuum operates valve and spring returns the valve to its original position when the vacuum is released.*

The design of the thermostat depends on the type of system. The "add on" systems use an adjustable thermostat with the sensitive bulb located at the air outlet of the evaporator. The thermostat controls the magnetic coil in the clutch pulley.

In the combined systems, the same thermostat may also be connected to the heater water flow control.

The completely automatic year around systems have sensors, amplifiers, and programmers in place of the thermostat.

25-32 Vacuum Control Systems

Many air conditioning systems use a vacuum power system (vacuum actuators) to operate dampers, water flow control valve, etc. A vacuum system is shown in Fig. 25-68. The manual controls or the automatic controls select what tubing will be subjected to the vacuum, and the diaphragms react to the vacuum and move against a spring pressure to move dampers or to open or close valves. The springs return the mechanism to its former position when the vacuum is released. The vacuum source is the engine intake manifold which operates at a varying vacuum from 5 to 20 in. The system is usually designed to operate at a 5 in. vacuum. Fig. 25-69 shows a vacuum actuated water valve.

To check for leaks in a vacuum system, connect a vacuum gauge into the system.

Run the engine until the system is at 16 in. vacuum. Stop the engine. If the vacuum gauge starts to creep back toward zero (atmospheric), there is a leak in the system or the check valve in the line to the intake manifold is leaking.

To check the operation of the actuators, install the vacuum gauge, run the engine until the vacuum is 16 in. vacuum, stop the engine, and watch the vacuum gauge as each actuator is operated. The vacuum should creep a little toward zero as each actuator is valved into operation. If the vacuum does not decrease, that actuator has a pinched tube, the line is plugged, or the damper is binding.

The dampers usually have an adjustment to enable the serviceman to adjust the dampers for full closing or opening.

Vacuum systems have a vacuum reservoir tank to enable operation of the dampers during engine shutoff intervals.

25-33 Specific Systems

In this chapter, air conditioning systems on cars manufactured by these well-known companies will be discussed in some detail:

1. Chrysler.
2. Ford.
3. General Motors.
4. American Motors.

Prior to servicing any automobile air conditioning system, the serviceman should have available for reference the manufac-turer's factory service manual for the make and model of air conditioner being serviced. These service manuals are avail-

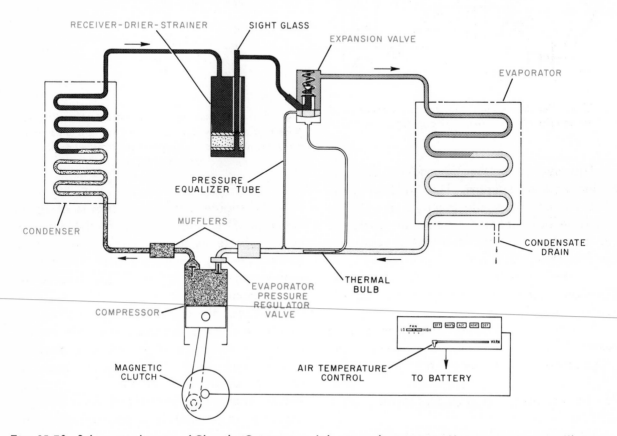

Fig. 25-70. *Schematic diagram of Chrysler Corp. automobile air cooling system. Note compressor, mufflers, con-denser, receiver-drier strainer, expansion valve, evaporator, and evaporator pressure (suction) regulator valve. (Chrysler Corp.)*

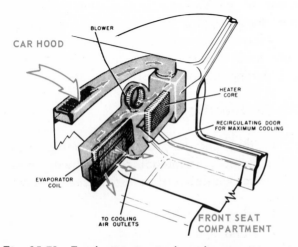

Fig. 25-71. *Fresh air circuit through automotive air conditioner.*

able, for a reasonable fee, from the Fac-tory Service Department of the various au-tomobile manufacturers.

Many independent manufacturers are making units to air condition automobiles, trucks, buses, etc. To service these units efficiently, it is recommended that the manufacturer's service manual and parts manual be used for reference.

25-34 Chrysler

Chrysler Corporation's air condition-ing systems have varied through the years. Their air cooling system uses an evaporator pressure (suction) regulator valve mounted on the compressor, as shown in Fig. 25-70. The airflow through one model is shown in Fig. 25-71. Typical outlet grille designs are shown in Fig. 25-72. The outlet grilles are both adjustable and have shutoff dampers.

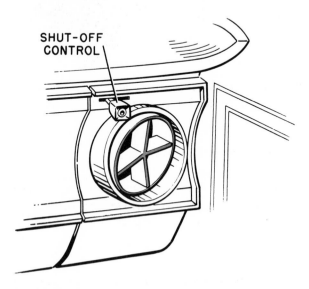

Fig. 25-72. An end grille. The core of grille will move in any direction to control the direction of air flow.

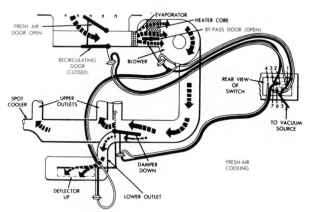

Fig. 25-73. Automobile air cooling circuit. Note that 100 percent fresh air is brought into car. Heater by-pass door is fully open and air flowing through evaporator coil receives maximum cooling.

A schematic of the airflow showing 100 percent fresh air use with maximum air cooling effect (bypass door open) is shown

in Fig. 25-73. Fig. 25-74 shows 100 percent recirculated air with maximum air cooling.

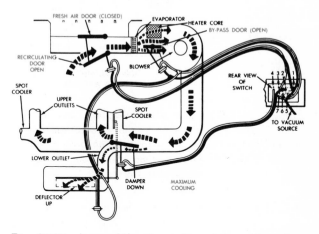

Fig. 25-74. Automobile air cooling circuit. Note that 100 percent recirculated air is passed through evaporator coil and receives maximum cooling.

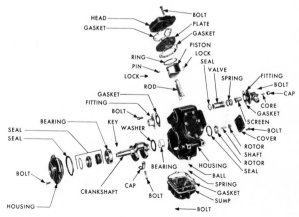

Fig. 25-75. An exploded view of the two cylinder V-type refrigeration compressor. (Chrysler Corp.)

The Chrysler system uses a V-type two cylinder compressor, as shown in Fig. 25-75. These compressors have had seal design changes and oil pump design changes, and the serviceman must be sure to obtain the correct replacement. The compressor has an approximate 9.5 cu. in. displacement and uses an 11 oz. oil charge. The electromagnetic clutch unit is shown in Fig. 25-76.

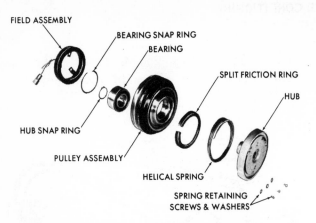

FIELD ASSEMBLY

BEARING SNAP RING

BEARING

SPLIT FRICTION RING

HUB

HUB SNAP RING

PULLEY ASSEMBLY

HELICAL SPRING

SPRING RETAINING
SCREWS & WASHERS

Fig. 25-76. Compressor electromagnetic clutch. Exploded view shows field assembly (electromagnets) and pulley assembly. Unit uses load absorbing helical spring to absorb shock at time coil is energized and compressor starts.

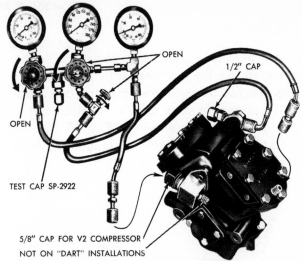

OPEN

1/2" CAP

OPEN

TEST CAP SP-2922

5/8" CAP FOR V2 COMPRESSOR
NOT ON "DART" INSTALLATIONS

Fig. 25-77. A service manifold mounted on a two cylinder V-type compressor.

The service procedures for the Chrysler Corporation units are similar to standard procedures. The use of a three gauge service manifold, as shown in Fig. 25-77, illustrates the installation used to check compressing ability of the V-type compressor.

25-35 Ford

Ford Motor Company factory installed units use a system similar to others in principle. A basic cycle is shown in Fig. 25-78.

Fig. 25-78. Basic cycle of Ford air cooling refrigerating system. Note compressor is in horizontal position. (Ford Motor Co.)

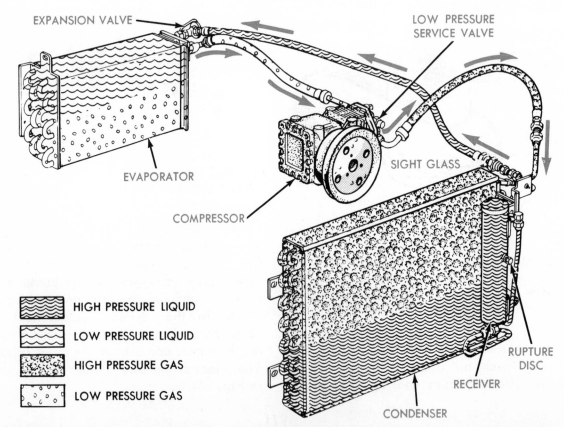

EXPANSION VALVE

LOW PRESSURE
SERVICE VALVE

EVAPORATOR

COMPRESSOR

SIGHT GLASS

HIGH PRESSURE LIQUID

LOW PRESSURE LIQUID

HIGH PRESSURE GAS

LOW PRESSURE GAS

RUPTURE
DISC

RECEIVER

CONDENSER

Many of the factory installed units have the blower, heat exchangers, and housing on the engine side of the fire wall. The systems use a thermostatic expansion valve with a built-in sight glass; and a two cylinder compressor, usually mounted horizontally. The compressor has two service valves mounted on the head of the compressor. The low side pressure ranges between 12 to 50 psig, while the head pressure varies between 80 to 300 psig, depending on the load and the ambient temperature.

The compressor magnetic clutch is operated by a thermostat which has its sensitive bulb clamped to the evaporator fins.

Fig. 25-79 shows the air circulation with the dampers positioned for 100 percent fresh air and also for recirculated air.

The duct dampers are operated by a vacuum actuating system.

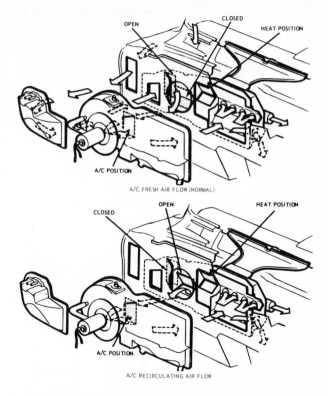

Fig. 25-79. Air flow through Ford Motor Co. air conditioner. Above. Normal fresh air flow. Below. Recirculated air.

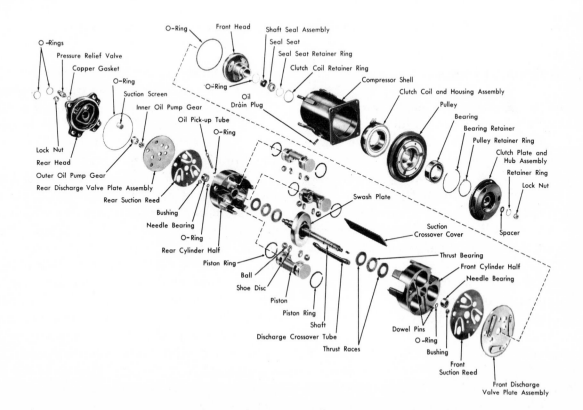

Fig. 25-80. Exploded view of a swash plate axial type six-cylinder automotive air conditioning compressor. (Cadillac Motor Car Div., General Motors Corp.)

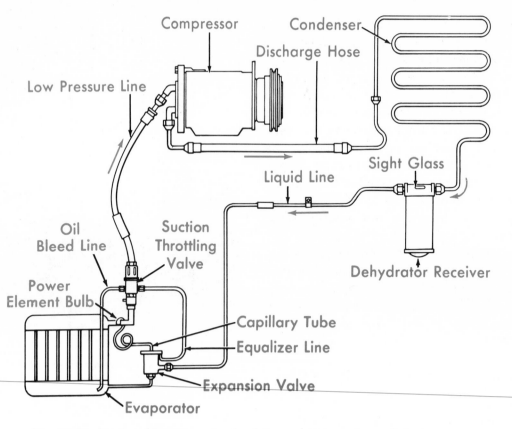

Fig. 25-81. Basic refrigeration circuit of General Motors air conditioning system.

25-36 General Motors

The General Motors swash plate compressor has been in use as follows:

1. 1955 – original model (valve core oil spline shaft).
2. 1956–57 – (cup screw oil check, smooth press fit shaft).
3. 1958 – (a three stage shaft––(1) Woodruff key, (2) smooth, (3) threaded, there is a ridge around coil housing).
4. 1959–60–61 – (three stage shaft––no ridge around coil housing).
5. 1962–67 – (four bolts welded to rear housing).

An exploded view of the 1962-67 model is shown in Fig. 25-80.

A model earlier than 1955, used mainly on Cadillacs, was a rotary compressor built by the Frigidaire Div., General Motors Corp.

The refrigeration cycle is shown in Fig. 25-81; the operation of the cycle is shown in Fig. 25-82. The system featured a POA valve (pressure operated altitude) to control the evaporator pressure and an exhaust muffler on the compressor.

The oil charge is usually 9 oz. When the system is operating normally, the oil is distributed as follows: about 4 oz. in the compressor, 3 oz. in the evaporator, 1 oz. in the condenser, and 1 oz. in the receiver-drier. When servicing the unit, this distribution must be remembered and the oil added to the parts as indicated. It is recommended that oil level be checked only after the compressor is removed from the system and oil drained and measured.

General Motors cars have used the hot gas bypass valve for several years. In this system, the evaporator pressure should be 23.5 to 24.5 psig. The adjusting screw is turned clockwise to raise the pressure,

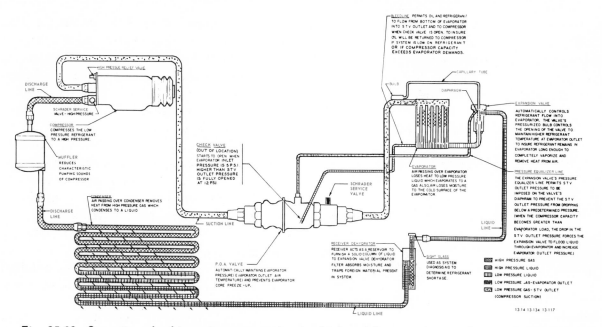

Fig. 25-82. *Operation of refrigerating system showing high and low pressures and state of refrigerant.* *(Buick Motor Div., General Motors Corp.)*

counterclockwise to lower the pressure.

Several types of suction pressure control valves have been used. Some were adjustable by the driver, some by the serviceman. The latest is nonadjustable. The suction line throttling valve has two service connections equipped valve cores. When servicing this valve, connect the gauge manifold to this valve. The normal valve adjustment is 29 to 30 psig. A lower pressure will result in frost forming on the evaporator. To check, disconnect vacuum line and run the engine at about 200 rpm. Adjustment increases the pressure if turned in and decreases the pressure if turned out (counterclockwise). It requires about three turns to change the pressure setting 1 psig.

The completely automatic General Motors air conditioning system consists of an electronically controlled heating system, air cooling system, and air duct flow which uses a vacuum actuator system to control the dampers and the valves. The system uses three temperature sensors (one outside the car, one inside the car, and one in the discharge duct) connected

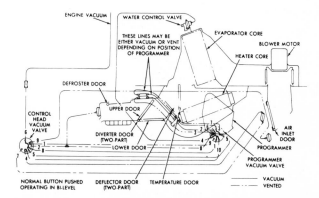

Fig. 25-83. *System adjusted to normal operation in bi-level. (Pontiac Motor Div., General Motors Corp.)*

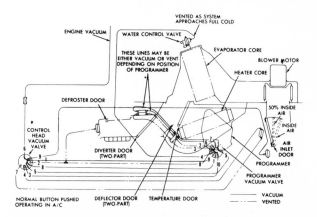

Fig. 25-84. *System adjusted to normal operation with air cooling at 100 percent.*

to an amplifier and a programmer. Figs. 25-83, 25-84, 25-85, 25-86, 25-87 show one system and the various positions of the four damper doors. Damper door A controls the flow of warmed air to the de-

froster; damper door B controls the flow of air through the heater core; damper door C controls the flow of air through the evaporator core; and damper door D controls the flow of outside air into the air conditioner. Fig. 25-83 shows the dampers positioned for normal operation; Fig. 25-84 shows the dampers positioned for cooling; Fig. 25-85 shows the dampers set for car heating; Fig. 25-86 shows the dampers in position for defrosting; and Fig. 25-87 shows the dampers set for deicing.

The blower moves 2000 cfm when in the high position. The system uses 100 percent fresh air except during original pull-down or when the heating load is extreme (when comfort cooling).

The electrical system for the year around automatic air conditioning system is shown in Fig. 25-88.

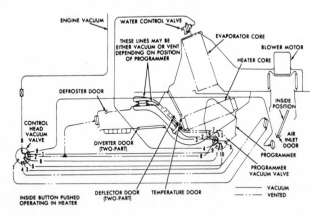

Fig. 25-85. *System adjusted to full heat condition and with some recirculated air.*

25-37 American Motors

The American Motors Corp. unit is called "The All Season Air Conditioning System." A three speed blower evaporator and a two cylinder compressor are used. The thermostat settings range from 34 to 57 F. evaporator surface temperature. R-12 refrigerant is used in all models. The installed system is shown in Fig. 25-89. The liquid receiver has a check valve on the inlet, and it has a pressure relief valve.

The unit should operate as follows: at 30 mph with an ambient temperature of 80 F., the evaporator outlet air should be 42 F. (low side pressure of 20 psig) and the head pressure should be 155 psig. At 30 mph with an ambient temperature of 90 F., the evaporator outlet air temperature should be 47 F. (low side pressure of 20 psig) and the head pressure should be 185 psig.

The instrument panel controls are shown in Fig. 25-90. There are four levers. The lever on the left is the air conditioning control; comfort cooling is provided when the lever is down; heating when

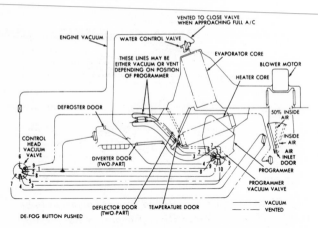

Fig. 25-86. *System adjusted to defog condition.*

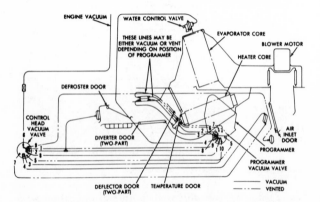

Fig. 25-87. *System adjusted to deice condition.*

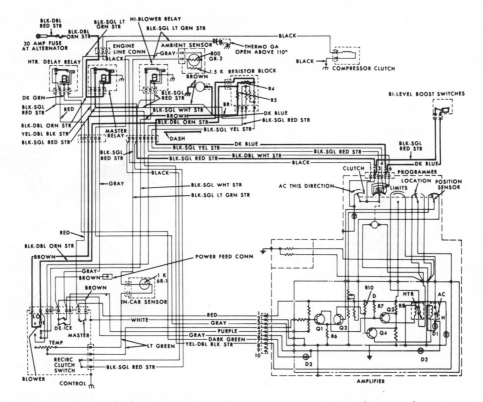

Fig. 25-88. Electrical-electronic system for automatic year around air conditioning system.
(Pontiac Motor Div., General Motors Corp.)

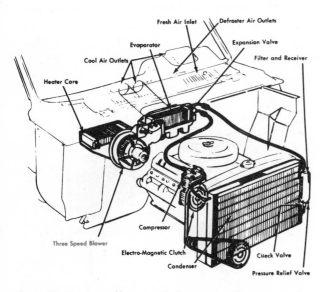

Fig. 25-89. Installation of American Motors comfort cooling system. Blower is mounted on engine side of fire wall. (American Motors Corp.)

it is up. Note that the blower is turned on as the lever is moved down. The second lever from the left is the "TEMP" control

for heater operation. The third lever from the left is the "AIR" control for heater operation. As this lever moves down, it turns on the blower in one of three speed posi-

Fig. 25-90. Controls used for all season air conditioning system. Note four levers: air cond., temp., air, and def. The controls are located on left end of instrument panel.

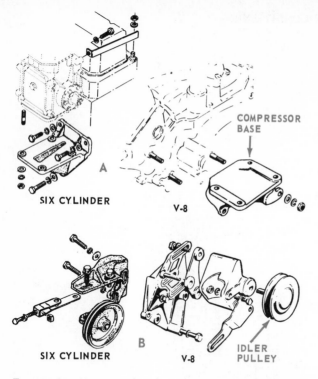

SIX CYLINDER

COMPRESSOR BASE

V-8

SIX CYLINDER

B

V-8

IDLER PULLEY

Fig. 25-91. Mounting brackets for compressor (A) and for the idler pulley (B). Brackets for both six-cylinder engine and eight-cylinder engine are shown. Note how the idler pulley brackets are adjustable to provide for belt tension adjustments.

and each should do a good air conditioning job if properly installed and maintained. The units have different capacities and the correct size unit must be used. Most of

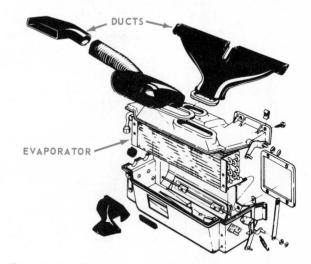

DUCTS

EVAPORATOR

Fig. 25-92. Exploded view of evaporator, evaporator housing, ducts, and air dampers. Note assembly cap screw used to mount the upper evaporator housing to fire wall.

tions. The defroster is actuated by moving the lever on the right down.

The compressor and idler pulley mounting brackets and assembly are shown in Fig. 25-91. These brackets must be securely mounted and accurately aligned for efficient and long life operation. The proper assembly of the flat washers, lock washers, cap screws and nuts is important to insure a permanent mounting.

The evaporator construction, evaporator housing construction, and air ducts are shown in Fig. 25-92. Note the grommet used to protect the refrigerant lines as they enter the evaporator housing between the upper and lower sections of the evaporator housing.

25-38 Special Systems – Add On – Not Factory Equipment

There are many automotive air conditioning systems on the market. Basically they are quite similar. Each has features

the units are designed and built to be installed in automobiles, trucks, and buses which have already been built. In the trade they are called "add on" units. Fig. 25-93

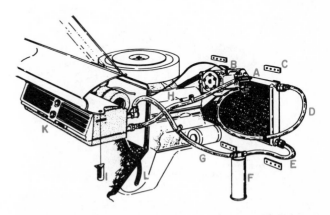

Fig. 25-93. Schematic of "add on" air conditioning unit installed in an automobile. Special brackets are furnished to fit the parts to the different model cars. A–Condenser. B–Compressor. C–Condenser mounting straps. D–Discharge hose. E and G–Liquid hose. F–Receiver-drier. H–Suction hose. I–Evaporator hanger bracket. K–Evaporator. L–Condensate drain hose.
(Climatic Air Sales, Inc.)

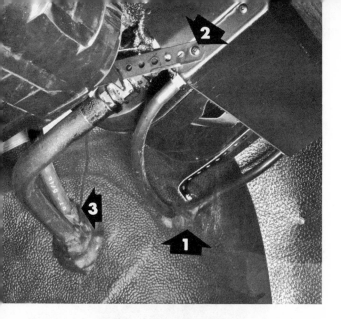

Fig. 25-94. Details of an evaporator installation. 1–
Sealing compound. 2–Strap brace. 3–Refrigerant lines.
(Climatic Air Sales, Inc.)

Fig. 25-95 shows the mounting brackets used to install an independent unit compressor.

These units generally use York or Tecumseh compressors.

The York compressors are available in several different capacities. Models are available with approximately 6, 9, and 10 cu. in. piston displacement. The oil charge is 6 to 10 oz., depending on the model. A metal dipstick can be used to measure oil level. This level varies between 7/8 and 1 3/16 in. The compressors have aluminum cylinders. Cap screws and bolts must be torqued as follows: 1/4 in.- 11 to 17 ft./lbs.; 5/16 in.-14 to 18 ft./lbs. These compressors will work satisfactori-

shows an independent or add on unit installed in an automobile.

All of these units have rather standard features. A compressor is driven by a belt from the crankshaft; a condenser is installed in front of the car radiator; a liquid receiver-drier filter is installed in the liquid line; a thermostatic expansion valve controls the flow of liquid refrigerant into the evaporator, although some systems use a capilliary tube refrigerant control; and a thermostatically controlled magnetic clutch controls the pressure operation. These systems do not usually use a suction pressure control valve. Consequently, some special means must be provided to keep frost and ice from forming on the evaporator coil. Some of these devices will be described along with the air conditioning systems.

It should be noted that since these systems are added on after the car is built, there will be no connection with the car heating system. This means that the car heating controls will be operated normally. The air conditioner or cooling controls, however, will be added.

Fig. 25-94 shows the details of the evaporator, evaporator housing, and drain lines for an "independent" unit.

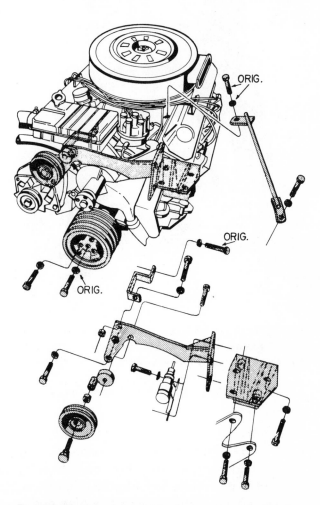

Fig. 25-95. Drawing which shows mounting brackets needed to install "add on" compressor.

979

ly in vertical position on either the left or right side of the engine or they may be mounted horizontally. Fig. 25-96 shows a York compressor with a swivel mounting for the service valve. The internal con-

inder compressors of cast iron cylinder material. Some are two cylinder units with aluminum cylinders. When mounted in certain positions, the oil system must be changed. Three of the models are HH, HA850, HG850. These have approximately 8 3/4 or 8 1/2 cu. in. piston displacement. These compressors use 280-300 viscosity

Fig. 25-97. Internal construction of the York compressor. Pistons have one piston ring.

Fig. 25-96. York compressor. There are special instructions on nameplate concerning mounting compressor in various positions. Note that service valve has swivel mounting.
(York Corp., Sub. of Borg-Warner Corp.)

struction of the compressor is shown in Fig. 25-97. The crankshaft is the 180 deg. two cylinder type with two ball bearing type main bearings. See Fig. 25-98.

Tecumseh compressors are also available in several models. Some are two cylinder

Fig. 25-98. Crankshaft and main bearings of the York compressor.

oil. Some models have a sight glass for checking oil level; others require a dip-stick. The oil level should be 1 1/8 to 1 9/16 in. The oil change requirement is approximately 11 oz.

The manufacturer and model names of several independent or "hang on" or "add on" automotive air conditioners are as follows:

COMPANY AND TRADE NAME

Ara Manufacturing Co.
  (Ara)
Capitol Refrigeration, Inc.
  (Artic-Kar)
Clardy Mfg. Co.
  (Cool Car; Customatic; Jet Star)
Climatic Air Sales, Inc.
  (Equip-Aire)
Delanair Engineering Co., Inc.
Eaton Mfg. Co., Heater Div.
  (Eaton)
Fleet-Air Mfg. Inc.
  (E 100)
Forston Mfg. Co.
  (Lincoln; Continental Voyager; Forston)
Frigiking Co., Div. Cummings Engine Co.
  (Frigikab; Frigibus; Frigiadairy; Coldmaster; Air Con; Thru-Wall)
Frigiquip Corp.
  (Frigette; Cool Queen)
Harrison Radiator Div. GMC
Kauffman Air Conditioning Co.
  (Kauffman)
Kool Engineering Corp.
  (Arctic Air; Kool King)
Kysor Industrial Div.
  (Kysor)
Lindustries, Inc.
  (Frostemp; Kab-Air)
McCord Corp.
Mitchell Co., John E.
  (Mark IV)
Montgomery Ward
  (Riverside)
Nordic International Co.
  (Nordic)
Parkomat Sales Co., Inc.
  (Parkomat)
Sears Roebuck and Co.
  (Allstate)
Thermo Equipment Corp.
  (TEC; Thermoquip)

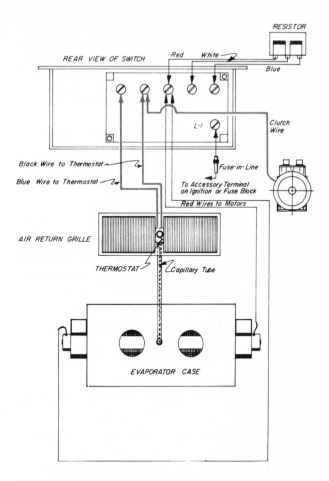

Fig. 25-99. Wiring diagram of independent or "add on" unit which has the evaporator mounted in the car trunk. Note thermostat and clutch circuit, shown in red. (Climatic Air Sales, Inc.)

Thermo King Corp.
  (Thermo King)
Vanguard Products, Inc.
Vornado Auto Air Conditioning Corp., Div. of Automatic Radio
  (Vornado)
York Division
  (Turbopak; Turbomaster; Yorkaire; Embassy; Flexomatic; Marinepak; Yorkpak; Hydraline; Coldnet; B-W Furnaces; Pathfinder; Twinline; Champion)

BUS

Carrier Air Conditioning Co.
  (Weathermaker; Weathermaster; Rotaspray)
McCord Corp. (listed above)
Ther-Air Mfg. Co., Inc.
  (Weathertrol)
Trane Co.
  (CenTra Vac; Une Trane; Torrivent; Climate Changer; Cold Generator; Sigma-Flo)

A wiring diagram of an independent unit with a trunk mounted evaporator is shown in Fig. 25-99.

25-39 Special Systems Controls

Most of the special "add on" systems use control devices which have been covered in previous paragraphs. Practically all of these systems use a thermostatically controlled magnetic clutch in the compressor drive pulley. Before attempting to service any "add on" system, the manufacturer's instruction manual should be studied carefully, because some of these systems use unique control mechanisms.

25-40 Bus Air Conditioning

The air conditioning of buses has progressed rapidly. Due to the size of the unit, most of the systems use a separate gasoline engine with an automatic starting device to drive the compressor. The system is of standard construction except the condensing unit is made as compact as possible, and it is generally installed in the bus in such a way it is readily accessible for servicing.

The condensing units are often mounted on rails with flexible suction and liquid lines to permit sliding the condensing unit out of the bus body to aid in servicing.

Air-cooled condensers are used. Thermostatic expansion valves refrigerant controls are standard. Finned blower evaporators are used.

The duct system usually runs between a false ceiling and the roof of the bus. The ducts, usually one on each side of the bus, have grilles at the passenger seats which are controllable by the passengers.

25-41 Truck Air Conditioning

The cabs of many truck tractors and long distance hauling trucks are air conditioned.

Most of this equipment is of the "hang on" type and is installed after the cab has been made.

Some of these units have two evaporators, one for the cab and one for the relief driver's quarters back of the driver. Some of the systems use a remote condenser mounted on the roof of the cab. This removes the condenser from in front of the radiator mainly to enable the radiator to operate at full efficiency especially for long pulls in low gear.

The components of the system are similar to the automobile air conditioner and are installed and serviced in the same general way.

25-42 Installing Automobile Air Conditioning

Before installing a unit, check to determine (1) if the unit is the correct capacity; (2) if the unit is designed to fit that model car. The installation manual should give these specifics. When installing the evaporator, wear goggles when drilling and be sure the drill does not drill into electrical wires, vacuum lines, fluid lines, etc. Careless drilling may damage car parts and even cause fires. Fig. 25-100 shows a hole saw suitable for making a large hole

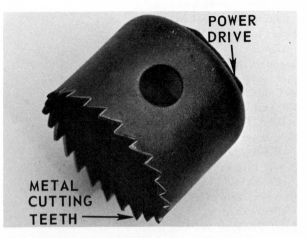

Fig. 25-100. Circular hole saw used to make necessary holes in fire wall and floor when installing add on types of car air conditioners.

in the fire wall or floorboard for the tubing to pass through. The refrigerant lines as furnished are clean and capped. Remove the caps and/or plugs just before installing them, to keep them as clean as possible. Put clean and dry refrigerant oil on the fittings before installing the lines. Line sizes usually are:

1. From compressor to condenser--1/2 in.
2. From condenser to receiver--3/8 in.
3. From receiver to evaporator--3/8 in.
4. From evaporator to compressor--5/8 in.

When mounting the lines and tightening the fittings, use two wrenches to prevent twisting the lines. The flexible lines must be loose enough to absorb vibration and engine movement. They must also be mounted to prevent chafing or touching hot parts of the engine (exhaust manifold). Always two (and sometimes three) wrenches should be used when tightening the screwed-on refrigerant lines, as shown in Fig. 25-101. Fig. 25-102 shows some installation details. The use of "O" rings and clamps is shown in detail in Fig. 25-103.

The electrical wiring must be carefully installed to insure against chafing the wire (this may cause a fire) and to insure clean and tight electrical connections.

Air in the system causes above normal condensing pressures as the air collects in the condenser (air is noncondensible). Air also contains oxygen which will oxidize the oil in the system and form other oxides.

Water must be kept out of the system as it will form a sludge with the oil and will also collect and freeze at the expansion valve orifice and may clog it.

Oil level in the compressor must be up to the correct level. A normal charge is 3 to 7 oz. Be sure to check the manufacturer's specifications for the correct oil charge.

Fig. 25-101. Correct method of line connections. One wrench is used to hold fitting while other wrench turns flare nut on fitting.

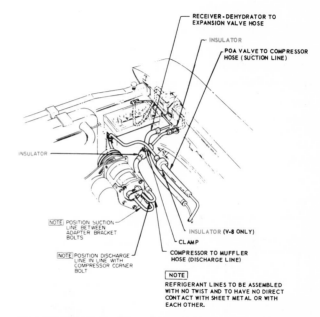

Fig. 25-102. Installing General Motors unit. Note insulation used to protect lines from chafing or rubbing.

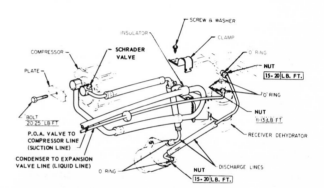

Fig. 25-103. Refrigerant lines must be protected from vibration and rubbing. Note use of O rings, clamps, and insulation to protect lines.

Installation of the compressor must be carefully done. The compressor must be firmly mounted. The compressor pulley must be carefully aligned with the idler and engine pulleys. Install the belt and adjust the belt tightener to 100 to 140 lbs. tension.

After the evaporator, evaporator housing, and the electrical lines and refrigerant lines have been installed, seal the body openings with caulking compound.

After installing an air conditioning system on a car, a separate vacuum pump should be used to pump the system down and to charge it. The system should be held under a high vacuum for 1 to 24 hours at room temperature before charging. A gauge manifold, vacuum pump and charging cylinder and connecting refrigerant lines are used. Fig. 25-104 shows a vacuum pump installation.

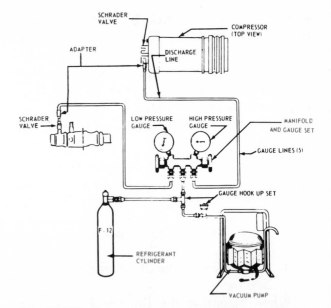

Fig. 25-105. *Gauge and service manifold installed in General Motors system. Both charging cylinder and vacuum pump are connected to middle opening of manifold.*

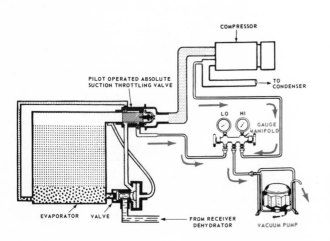

Fig. 25-104. *Vacuum pump installation. Both hand valves on gauge manifold are open to insure evacuating both high and low pressure sides of system.*

Always refer to the manufacturer's service manual for information concerning the amount of refrigerant to be used in charging a particular system. The correct charge varies from 1.25 to approximately 5 lbs. Use gauges to check the operating pressures. Low head pressures indicate lack of refrigerant in most cases.

The failure of the compressor shaft seal is probably the greatest cause of loss of refrigerant. A blown seal will usually be indicated by a leakage of oil around the shaft. Be sure to check for leaks each time the unit is serviced.

It is important to remember that obtaining good tools and using the tools properly are necessities. Because the refrigerant lines are easily twisted, two wrenches, and many times three wrenches, should be used when loosening or tightening connections.

The outside of the system should be clean. The condenser surfaces and evaporator surfaces should be clean. Use brushes, a vacuum cleaner, pressurized air, nitrogen or carbon dioxide (wear goggles) may be used. The fins should be clean and straight (use a fin comb).

25-43 Servicing Automobile Air Conditioners

Servicing the automobile air conditioner is similar to servicing standard air conditioning systems and commercial systems. Chapters 12 and 15 should be studied carefully before attempting any work on an automobile refrigerating system.

Servicing usually originates with a customer complaint or for an annual check of the system. Owners' complaints received most are: (1) no cooling, (2) noise, (3) cooling intermittently, (4) vibration. There may be several causes for each complaint. The serviceman must check the system thoroughly to find the correct cause.

use a cloth to protect your hands. The gauge manifold and lines must be clean and dry both inside and out.

For personal safety, always wear goggles when working on the refrigeration unit or with the cylinders. Avoid breathing any escaped refrigerant. Although the refrigerant is virtually harmless, the fact that it excludes oxygen makes it dangerous. Fig. 25-106 shows a set of tools used to service General Motors air conditioners.

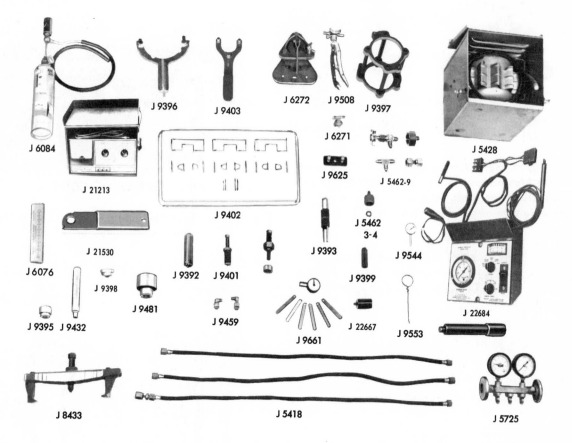

Fig. 25-106. Tools for servicing General Motors air conditioning units.

The method of installing the gauge manifold is similar to the procedure described in Chapters 12 and 15. Always clean the connections before removing any caps or plugs. Fig. 25-105 shows a gauge manifold installed. The service valve stems must be back seated to seal the gauge openings. When removing Schrader caps or lines,

Always attach a gauge manifold to the system before attempting to service it. Never use a manifold set that has been left open to the air until it has been cleaned and dried. Some compressors are fitted with gauge openings at both the suction service valve and the discharge service valve. Some use the valve core method.

These are Schrader or Dill valve cores. They have been in common use since about 1964. Internal construction of a gauge and service manifold is shown in Fig. 25-107.

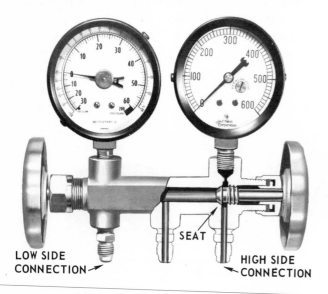

LOW SIDE CONNECTION →

SEAT

HIGH SIDE CONNECTION ←

Fig. 25-107. Construction of gauge and service manifold. Note high pressure gauge reads to 600 psig and low pressure gauge reads from 30 in. vacuum to 0 to 60 psig with retarded movement to 200 psig.

Most automobile air conditioning systems use flexible refrigerant lines. These lines are fastened to the compressor, condenser, and evaporator, by several types of joints:
1. Flare joint.
2. Clamp.
3. Special hose flare connection.
The flare joint can be of two types:
1. Single flare.
2. Double flare.

Both of the flare designs and the method used to make them are described in Chapter 2. A tool used to make a double flare is shown in Fig. 25-108. Fig. 25-109 shows the steps followed when making a double flare.

Before you can service an automobile air conditioning system, you must know what performance to expect from the unit. Fig. 25-110 is a table of operating conditions of a unit at various temperatures and

humidities. Abnormal low and/or high side pressures, noise, and many other evidences will indicate the need for service.

Altitude has an effect on the operation of a system. This changing pressure affects vaccum actuators and some suction pressure controls, particularly if any part of the bellows or diaphragm movement is exposed to the pressure of the atmosphere. Fig. 25-111 shows the steps necessary to check a system, to charge refrigerant, to purge the receiver, and to evacuate the system.

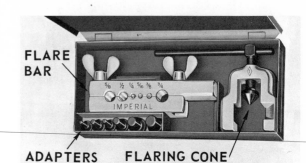

FLARE BAR

ADAPTERS   FLARING CONE

Fig. 25-108. Tool designed for making double flares. (Imperial-Eastman Corp.)

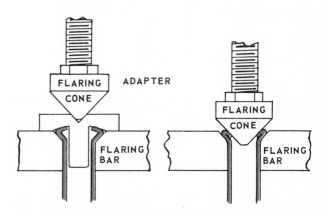

FLARING CONE   ADAPTER

FLARING BAR

FLARING CONE

FLARING BAR

Fig. 25-109. Tool used to make double flare which is the most common one used on automobile air conditioning refrigerant lines.

25-44 Adjusting and Replacing Belts

The belt system of an engine when several accessories are belt driven may total three to four belts, as shown in Fig. 25-112.

TEST #1				
Ambient Temperature (°F)	Evaporator Pressure (PSIG)	Compressor Pressure (PSIG)	Right A/C Outlet (TEMP)	Left A/C Outlet (TEMP)
70	28.5 - 30	150 - 225	39 - 42	39 - 42
80	28.5 - 30	200 - 245	40 - 43	40 - 43
90	28.5 - 30	240 - 290	42 - 45	43 - 45
100	28.5 - 30	270 - 330	44 - 47	45 - 48
110	28.5 - 30	310 - 345	47 - 52	47 - 52

TEST #2						
Ambient Temperature (°F)	Humidity	Engine RPM	Evaporator Pressure (PSIG)	Compressor Pressure (PSIG)	Right A/C Outlet (°F)	Left A/C Outlet (°F)
90	High	480	35	210	59	57
90	Low	400	35	190	54	52
100	High	570	35	235	60	58
100	Low	550	35	230	55	54
110	High	940	35	320	59	59
110	Low	615	35	270	58	58

Fig. 25-110. Two series of tests on completely automatic year around air conditioning system. In test No. 1, note head pressure at 90 F. ambient. In test No. 2, note head pressure at 90 F. ambient and low humidity. (Buick Motor Div., General Motors Corp.)

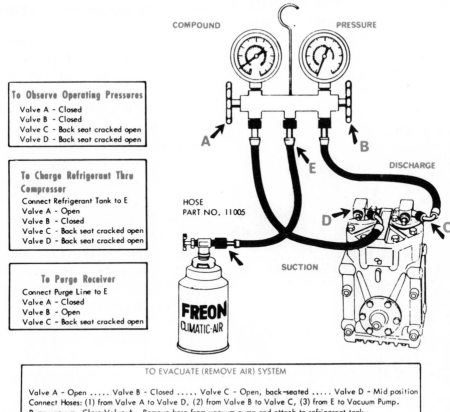

To Observe Operating Pressures
Valve A - Closed
Valve B - Closed
Valve C - Back seat cracked open
Valve D - Back seat cracked open

To Charge Refrigerant Thru Compressor
Connect Refrigerant Tank to E
Valve A - Open
Valve B - Closed
Valve C - Back seat cracked open
Valve D - Back seat cracked open

To Purge Receiver
Connect Purge Line to E
Valve A - Closed
Valve B - Open
Valve C - Back seat cracked open

COMPOUND   PRESSURE

HOSE
PART NO. 11005

FREON
CLIMATIC-AIR

DISCHARGE

SUCTION

TO EVACUATE (REMOVE AIR) SYSTEM
Valve A - Open ..... Valve B - Closed ..... Valve C - Open, back-seated ..... Valve D - Mid position
Connect Hoses: (1) from Valve A to Valve D, (2) from Valve B to Valve C, (3) from E to Vacuum Pump.
Pump vacuum, Close Valve A. Remove hose from vacuum pump and attach to refrigerant tank.
Open Valve A. Open refrigerant tank to break vacuum, and use Step 2 for charging system.

NOTE: CHECK EQUIPMENT MANUFACTURER'S CATALOG OR INSTRUCTION SHEET FOR SPECIFIC RECOMMENDATIONS ON REFRIGERANT CHARGE, OIL CHARGE AND SERVICE PROCEDURES FOR ANY PARTICULAR PIECE OF EQUIPMENT.

Fig. 25-111. Procedures to follow for observing operating pressures, method of charging a system, steps necessary to purge receiver, and procedure for evacuating air. (Climatic Air Sales, Inc.)

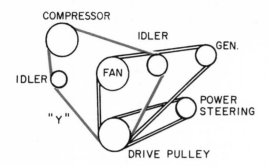

Fig. 25-112. Diagrammatic view of belts used in typical air conditioning installation which also has belt drive for power steering pump.

Belt tensions are adjusted by moving the generator, power steering pump, and the idler pulley. Belts stretch in use. They should be periodically checked for tightness and adjusted to approximately 75 lbs. tension. When a new belt is installed, a tension of from 140 to 145 lbs. is recommended. A loose belt will soon fail and the pulleys will soon fail due to the wear caused by slippage. The belt should be dry. Excessive oil should be removed from the belt and the pulleys. A shrill squeal when

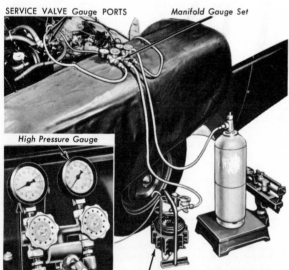

Fig. 25-113. Gauge and service manifold connected to system, vacuum pump, and to charging cylinder. Note how fender is protected with cover.
(Ford Motor Co.)

the engine speed is increased will indicate loose belts or glazed belt surfaces. A few drops of penetrating oil on a glazed belt may eliminate the squeal.

Belts with any sign of cracks or frayed edges should be replaced.

Always remember that a "short life" belt or a broken belt may be the result of an unusual overload (excessive pressures), pulley out of line, wrong type belt, wrong tension, etc. The cause of the failure should be determined and remedied.

Always loosen a belt before removing it. Forcing a belt may injure and weaken it.

If the system has two belts, always replace both if one fails (the lengths of a used belt and a new belt are different).

25-45 Charging the System

When the system is operating normally, there will be no bubbles in the sight glass after the system has run for a few minutes. If the system is short of refrigerant, bubbles will appear regularly in the sight glass. A system without any refrigerant or very little refrigerant may not have enough liquid to form bubble formations. An overcharged unit may be detected by excessive head pressure; it will not show in the sight glass. If a high head pressure is shown after installing the gauge manifold, the correct system pressure should be determined and excessive refrigerant purged. Fig. 25-113 shows a gauge manifold connected to a system.

The system is charged by using the service manifold. Connect the manifold to the system, connect the charging cylinder to the manifold, and purge the lines.

If only a small amount of refrigerant is to be added to the system, charge through the low side of the system with the cylinder upright. If the complete charge of the cylinder is to be put in the system and if the system is under a vacuum, charge the refrigerant into the high side of the sys-

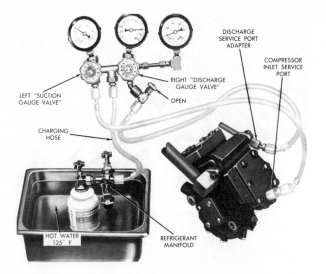

Fig. 25-114. Gauge and service manifold connected to a Chrysler compressor. Note use of third gauge on manifold. This is used when manifold is used for evacuating purposes. (Chrysler Corp.)

tem in the liquid form by inverting the cylinder and opening the service valves. Chapter 12 gives instructions on the operation of the gauge manifold.

Charging a system using a disposable refrigerant cylinder, Fig. 25-114. The cylinder is being warmed using hot water. The gauge manifold has three gauges. The two gauges back of the manifold handwheels

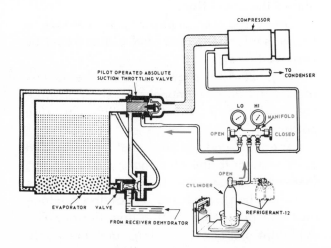

Fig. 25-115. Diagram showing how refrigerant cylinder is connected to air conditioning unit using gauge and service manifold.
(Pontiac Motor Div., General Motors Corp.)

are the suction gauge and the high pressure gauge. The gauge on the right is used during vacuum operations. The compressor is equipped with Schrader valve service connections.

Gauge manifold installation on a General Motors unit is shown in Fig. 25-115. A portable unit which has a gauge manifold, vacuum pump, charging tube, and a leak detector is shown in Fig. 25-116.

Because these systems have a receiver for holding some refrigerant, the charge can vary somewhat and the operation will still be efficient. If the charge is 4 lbs., the system may operate on as low as 2 1/2 lbs. refrigerant.

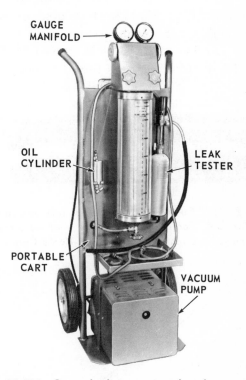

Fig. 25-116. Cart which is equipped with necessary devices to test unit for leaks and to charge it.

25-46 Replacing Compressor Seal

If the seal is leaking (as determined by leak test or observing a large amount of oil around the shaft), or if the seal is noisy (shrill squeak), the seal must be replaced.

It is best to discharge the refrigerant R-12 from the system and then turn both the discharge and suction service valves all the way in to isolate the compressor from the rest of the system to keep out air and moisture. Remove the compressor, plug the refrigerant openings in the compressor.

To remove the seal on the two cylinder compressors, the pulley and clutch plate must first be removed.

Remove the seal plate by first removing the cap screws and washers and carefully prying the plate from the compressor body. Pry or use a puller to remove the seal assembly from the shaft. A special tool used to remove one type of seal is shown in Fig. 25-117. It is also used to install this type seal. A tool used to remove another type seal is shown in Fig. 25-118. Install the new seal (carefully oil

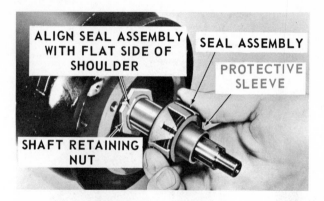

Fig. 25-119. Sleeve mounted on shaft. This is used to protect seal surfaces from being scratched as seal is being installed.

the seal and shaft with clean refrigerant oil). The carbon seal face must be carefully handled to avoid scratching its surface. Fig. 25-119 shows a seal being installed. A sleeve on the shaft protects the seal parts from sharp edges on the shaft.

The General Motors compressor is completely serviceable. It is best to remove it from the car for any service operation. The system is first purged of its refrigerant. The refrigerant openings on the rest of the system should be plugged. The seals are held in place with a retainer ring. Fig. 25-120 shows a tool to use in removing the retainer ring; Fig. 25-121 shows the operation.

On some compressors, to remove a faulty seal, the pulley and clutch must be removed first.

Fig. 25-122 shows a pulley being removed from a compressor shaft. Notice the puller adjustment for different size pulleys.

The seal and the seal seat are replaced as a unit. Both the stationary surface part, (generally cast iron but on some models it is carbon), and the revolving surface must be protected during installation. The synthetic rubber "O" rings and the parts must be protected from the sharp edges of the shaft and housing. Sleeves are available to protect the seal while it is being installed.

Fig. 25-117. Compressor shaft seal remover and installer tool. Tool engages tang of seal for easy removal and installation. (Kent-Moore Corp.)

Fig. 25-118. Tong and tong clamping sleeve used to remove one type of shaft seal seat.

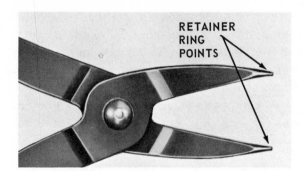

Fig. 25-120. *Special pliers used to contract retainer ring which holds shaft seal seat in place.*

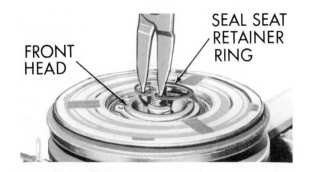

Fig. 25-121. *Retainer ring pliers. This tool will contract seal retainer ring clamped in external groove.*

25-47 Testing for Leaks

As described in Chapters 12 and 15, leaks may be checked using:

1. A trace chemical.
2. Halide leak torch.
3. Electronic leak detector.
4. Pressure rise method.
5. Foam leak detector (soap bubbles).

Some servicemen put reddish dye in the refrigerant in the system then, if a leak occurs, the red dye will show on the metal surfaces where the leak occurs.

Most frequently, leaks are detected by using the halide torch leak detector. This detector will locate a leak small enough to allow a leak of only 1 lb. in about 14 years. In using this detector, an exploring tube end is placed near the joint being checked. If there is a leak, some escaping refrigerant is drawn up the tube and passes over a propane or acetylene heated cop-

per element. If there is refrigerant gas in the air sample, the flame will turn green in color. Fig. 25-123 shows an alcohol fuel halide leak tester in use.

The electronic leak detector is a device which can locate a leak so small that it will take almost 40 years for the system to lose a pound of refrigerant.

A serviceman can check a system for leaks at the time a vacuum is being drawn on the system. With the vacuum pump running, shut off the vacuum valve on the manifold. If the vacuum gauge needle starts to creep back toward 0 (atmospheric pressure) there is a leak in the system. This leak must be located and corrected before completing the vacuum operation for drying out the system. This detection is done by pressuring the system with R-12 re-

Compressor Pulley

Fig. 25-122. *Compressor pulley puller in use.*

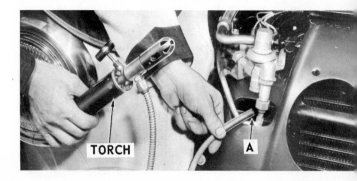

TORCH   A

Fig. 25-123. *Halide torch leak detector being used to search for leak in automotive air conditioning system.*

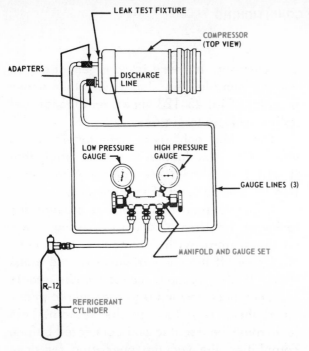

Fig. 25-124. Compressor removed from system, and connected to service and gauge manifold, and R-12 refrigerant cylinder.

frigerant and then using the torch type leak detector, electronic leak detector, or foam leak detector (soap bubbles).

25-48 Testing Compressor

The compressor must pump efficiently. If the capacity of the compressor decreases (worn valves, worn rings, etc.), maximum cooling effect will not be obtained.

A compressor should pump 15 in. vacuum quickly against a normal head pressure. If this cannot be done, the pistons, rings or intake valves are leaking (worn).

A compressor should quickly pump a 200 psig head pressure with the discharge service valve closed (turned in) and hold this pressure after compressor is stopped. Be careful. Do this pumping only with the cranking motor. DO NOT RUN THE ENGINE OR THE PRESSURE WILL RISE TO DANGEROUS LEVELS TOO QUICKLY. Another safer method is to allow the system to run; stop the engine, then turn the discharge service valve all the way in. If the head pressure drops, the exhaust valve in the compressor is leaking.

Fig. 25-124 shows a compressor being tested. R-12 refrigerant is used for testing for leaks and the gauges are used to test the pumping capacity and valve condition of the compressor.

A compressor should never be run unless it has the correct amount of clean refrigerant oil in it.

25-49 Overhauling Compressor

The overhaul procedures for two cylinder compressors and five and six cylinder General Motors compressors vary considerably. First, the compressors are checked for efficiency and they are repaired only if the compressor does not pump efficiently or if the compressor is noisy.

The two cylinder compressors are repaired in much the same way compressors are repaired as described in Chapter 15.

The General Motors compressors are of a different design and construction, and the two models developed are explained in more detail in the following paragraphs. Fig. 25-125 shows a late model compressor. This cross section shows the lubrication system. It also shows the compressor ready for dismantling.

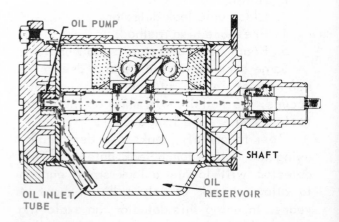

Fig. 25-125. Cross section of six cylinder General Motors compressor. Lubrication system is of forced type (pump). Oil pump is mounted on rear end of compressor crankshaft.

Before the compressor is dismantled, the hub and drive plate are removed using a special puller and two wrenches, as shown in Fig. 25-126.

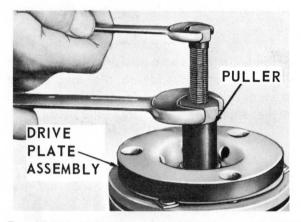

Fig. 25-126. *Using two end wrenches and special puller to remove hub and drive plate from General Motors swash plate type compressor.*

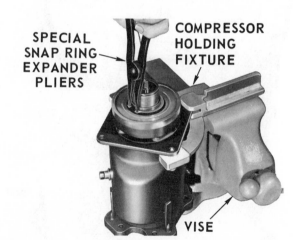

Fig. 25-127. *Removing the snap retaining ring which holds the electromagnetic coil housing on the compressor body.*

The coil housing retaining ring is removed, as shown in Fig. 25-127.

After the rear head is removed by removing the four nuts and carefully prying the head from the compressor body, the valve plates are removed.

The rear valve plate is removed by using two screwdrivers, as shown in Fig. 25-128. Only gentle lift action is used. Do

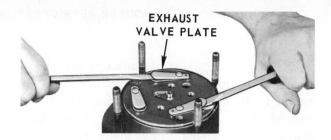

Fig. 25-128. *Proper way to remove the exhaust valve plate. Two screwdrivers are placed under two of exhaust valve retainers (not reeds).*
(Pontiac Motor Div., General Motors Corp.)

not force the plate. The suction reed plate is removed using the same technique.

The cylinders and shaft are then removed from the housing as one assembly. The suction gas (vapor) crossover covers are then removed, as shown in Fig. 25-129.

Fig. 25-129. *Use of screwdriver to remove suction gas (vapor) cross over. This passage carries suction gas from rear plate suction chamber to front three cylinders.*

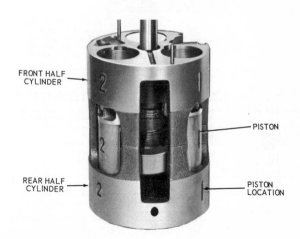

Fig. 25-130. *Pistons and cylinders are marked to insure pistons being placed in correct cylinders and not reversed.*

The cylinders and pistons are matched, and the pistons must be replaced in the same cylinders from which they were removed. Fig. 25-130 shows how to number the parts to make sure the correct assembly will take place. After the two sets of cylinders are separated, the crankshaft and the inclined drive plate are removed, as shown in Fig. 25-131.

The compressor shaft, service shoes, and thrust races must be carefully assembled. Fig. 25-132 shows the check points.

The oil pump must be assembled with the ends in the same position they were in when dismantled, facing the end of the compressor, and then carefully mounted on the shaft, as shown in Fig. 25-133.

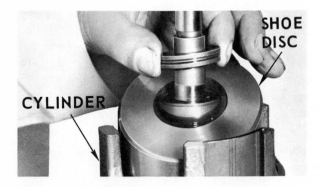

Fig. 25-131. Rear thrust bearing being removed from crankshaft.

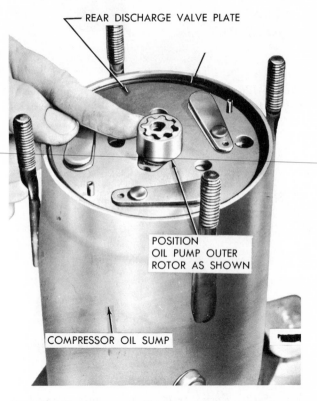

Fig. 25-133. Locating oil pump prior to installing rear cylinder head.

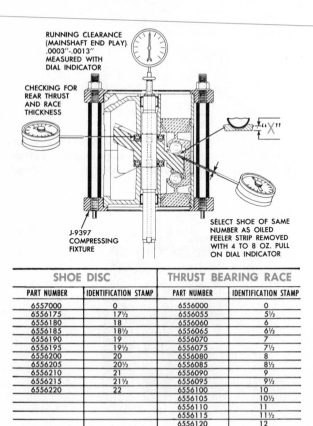

SHOE DISC		THRUST BEARING RACE	
PART NUMBER	IDENTIFICATION STAMP	PART NUMBER	IDENTIFICATION STAMP
6557000	0	6556000	0
6556175	17½	6556055	5½
6556180	18	6556060	6
6556185	18½	6556065	6½
6556190	19	6556070	7
6556195	19½	6556075	7½
6556200	20	6556080	8
6556205	20½	6556085	8½
6556210	21	6556090	9
6556215	21½	6556095	9½
6556220	22	6556100	10
		6556105	10½
		6556110	11
		6556115	11½
		6556120	12

Fig. 25-132. Crankshaft end play and clearance between shoe disk and piston drive ball are shown being measured as assembly is mounted in special fixture.

The rear head is then mounted on the compressor, as shown in Fig. 25-134. The Teflon sealing surfaces should first be coated with a thin film of clean, dry refrigerant oil (525 viscosity). These surfaces are shown on the rear head in Fig. 25-135. If dowel pins do not line up, rotate the cylinder head slightly, as shown in Fig. 25-134.

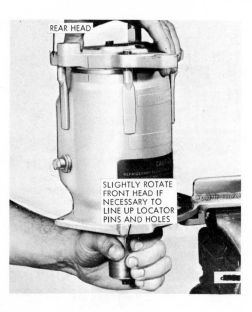

Fig. 25-134. Mounting rear cylinder head on compressor. Oil pump and dowel pins must be carefully aligned.

25-50 Adding Oil to System

The compressor must have the correct amount of the right specification oil. Usually, 525 viscosity oil with additive is used. It must be clean and dry. Too much oil will cause continuous oil pumping and will reduce the efficiency of the system plus possible injury to the compressor valves.

Too little oil will cause rapid wear of the compressor bearings, pistons, rings and valves, and will also cause the seal to be scored and ruin it.

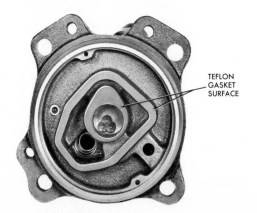

Fig. 25-135. Rear cylinder head of compressor showing Teflon gasket coated surfaces.

It is important to check the oil level each time a unit is serviced.

To do this, install the gauge manifold, purge the lines, turn the suction service valve all the way in, run the compressor until the compound (low side) gauge reads (0 psig), turn the discharge service valve all the way in, remove the oil level plug and check the oil level. If the oil is too high, it will drain out. If too low, add oil by syphoning it into the compressor with the compressor crankcase at a partial vacuum. Use either a vacuum pump or the compressor to create this vacuum.

Some compressors must be removed from the system to check the amount of oil.

25-51 Servicing Electromagnetic Clutch

The magnetizing coil is bolted to the compressor and is stationary. When this coil is energized, its magnetism pulls a clutch plate which is fastened to the compressor crankshaft against the pulley and locks the two together. The continuously turning pulley can then turn the compressor crankshaft.

Faulty coils (shorted, open circuit, etc.) should be replaced. A faulty clutch plate should also be replaced. A common reason for a slipping clutch is low voltage at the magnetic coil.

If the clutch does not operate when the thermostat is turned to the low position and the blower is operating, check for the cause as follows: be sure the engine is off. Remove the magnetic coil lead and connect this lead directly to the battery. If the coil operates, the trouble is in the wiring circuit (perhaps the thermostat) and should be traced using a voltmeter or a jumper wire. If the coil does not operate, the coil is faulty and should be replaced.

Another check on the electromagnetic coil is to put a 0 to 10 ampere scale ammeter in the circuit (series with the coil).

If it is operating correctly, the 12V coil should draw between 2.7 and 3.3 amps. while 6V systems use 4 amps. A greater flow indicates a short. A decreased reading indicates a loose connection or some other resistance in the circuit.

A noisy clutch may indicate loose mounts, worn or loose bearings, worn clutch faces (excessive use).

To remove the clutch plate or the coil, remove the belt by first loosening the idler pulley (if there is one) or loosen the belt adjustment. On some systems, the clutch assembly can be removed without removing the compressor. Other systems require removing the compressor.

Energize the coil to lock the pulley end and remove the shaft bolt and washer. Some clutch plates have a threaded hole. Thread a cap screw into this hole to remove the clutch plate. The clutch plate should not be pried loose from the shaft. A key is used to cause the clutch to drive the shaft. Fig. 25-136 shows a typical pulley and electromagnetic clutch assembly.

Fig. 25-137. Technique used to remove or replace clutch drive plate on General Motors six cylinder compressor. (Buick Motor Div., General Motors Corp.)

25-52 Noisy Units

Most noisy units are caused by faulty mounting, faulty drive (belt and pulley), excessive head pressure, etc. All units have some vibration and all units have certain harmonic speeds where vibration is more noticeable than at other speeds.

Check belt and pulley alignment and correct if necessary.

Check belt tension and correct if necessary. Sometimes a small change in belt tension will reduce vibration and noise.

Check all mounting bolts and correct torque settings if necessary.

Occasionally refrigerant flow noise is part of the problem. Suction line and discharge line mufflers will reduce this noise. Sometimes the suction line or discharge line are too taut (short). Install longer lines to reduce this source of noise.

Be sure the clutch is tight on the shaft and the coil mounting is tight (stationary coil clutch units).

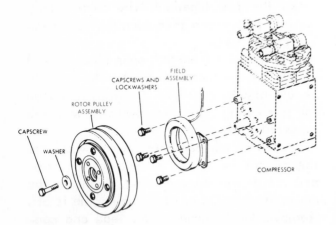

Fig. 25-136. Exploded view of electromagnetic pulley and clutch assembly. Note method of mounting field assembly (magnetic coil) and pulley. (Climatic Air Sales, Inc.)

General Motors compressors use a special wrench and a shaft nut socket to either remove or install the shaft nut. See Fig. 25-137.

NOTE: All General Motors illustrations in this chapter are copyrighted, and are used by special permission.

25-53 Periodic Maintenance

The owner should check the unit each spring and fall as follows:

1. Condenser (clean).
2. Refrigerant lines (should show no signs of chafing or wear).
3. Belt tension.
4. Run each month for a few minutes (fall, winter, spring) to keep compressor parts (especially the seal) lubricated.

The serviceman should check the unit each spring and fall or each 10,000 miles as follows:

1. All parts externally clean (condenser, evaporator, etc.).
   A. Fins on condenser and evaporator should be straight.
2. Check refrigerant charge.
   A. Sight glass or by
   B. Pressures in system.
3. Check oil level in compressor (very important).
4. Check for leaks using leak detector (or color trace).

25-54 Review of Safety

There are several very important safety precautions to be observed when working on automotive air conditioning units. The engine must be running to provide power for the air conditioner and air for the condenser. You must be careful to avoid touching the exhaust manifold (or serious burns may result). You must be cautious about putting tools, your hands, or clothing in contact with the revolving fan. Moving belts are also dangerous. One solution is to put a temporary shield over the fan. These shields are usually made of plastic and fasten to the radiator of the car.

Be careful about putting your hands or tools near the spark plugs, or you may receive an electrical shock which is not harmful but may cause you to jump against something, fall down, or jerk into moving parts of the engine. If it is at all possible, stop the engine before performing any work on those parts of the air conditioner that are under the hood. Always block the wheels of the car when running the engine.

Always wear goggles when charging or when working on parts which contain refrigerant. R-12 boils at -21.7 F. when spilled on the skin or in an eye and will freeze damage the skin or eyes.

Keep a protective cap on the refrigerant cylinder when it is not in use. Fasten the cylinder to a part of the vehicle or to some sturdy stand when using it, or it may fall and break the connections or the valve.

If necessary to heat a refrigerant cylinder, use warm water only. A torch, electric heat, steam heat, stove or radiator should never be used, as it may cause the cylinder to explode.

Avoid welding, brazing, or steam cleaning near the system unless the refrigerant has been removed, or the excessive pressures may injure the unit and the people near the unit.

Breathing quantities of any refrigerant is harmful to a human or an animal. Ventilate the area to keep the vapor concentration to a minimum.

Refrigerants tend to break down in an open flame and form toxic gases. When discharging a system near a flame, harmful gases are formed at the flame. These gases also tarnish metal and plated surfaces.

Most engine cooling systems are pressurized. If a pressure cap is removed when the engine is hot, hot water will erupt out of the radiator and you may be severely injured.

Blower fans can cause painful injuries to your hands. The sharp fins on the coils can easily make deep cuts.

Manifold service lines must be kept clear of pulleys, belts and fans.

25-55 Test Your Knowledge – Chapter 25

1. Does the heat load increase or decrease as the speed of the automobile increases?
2. How are the compressors driven?
3. Where is the condenser usually mounted?
4. What type of suction line connections are used in these units?
5. Are the systems provided with service connections?
6. What kind of a fan motor is usually used?
7. Why is air distribution an unusual problem in the automobile?
8. Do the automobile comfort cooling units have a fresh air intake?
9. How do most automobile air conditioners clean the air?
10. What is the proper belt tension?
11. What is the most popular refrigerant?
12. What refrigerant control is used on automobile comfort cooling units?
13. Where is the evaporator coil usually located?
14. Where is the plenum chamber located?
15. At what speeds do the engine mounted compressors operate compared to the engine speed?
16. How are these systems tested for leaks?
17. How does the serviceman determine if the system is low on refrigerant?
18. What is a popular type of electromagnetic clutch?
19. Of what materials are the compressor seal surfaces made?
20. How is the evaporator coil prevented from collecting frost or ice?
21. What is the purpose of the drier?
22. Name three compressor designs used in automobile air conditioning.
23. Of what materials are condensers usually made?
24. Why do some automotive air conditioners use mufflers?
25. What is the best method to use when adding refrigerant to the system?
26. Why are flexible refrigerant lines used in automotive air conditioning systems?
27. Which system uses an evaporator pressure regulator built into the compressor?
28. Where is the sensitive bulb of the thermostat usually located?
29. How are the duct dampers usually operated?
30. What type of termperature sensing device is used in conjunction with transistors and programmers?
31. What is the source of the vacuum or vacuum actuated dampers?
32. In what positions may a two cylinder compressor be mounted?
33. Why do the thermostatic expansion valves have pressure equalizer connections?
34. What is used to seal the openings in the fire wall after the refrigerant lines have been installed?
35. Where are "O" rings used in compressor seals?

Chapter 26

HEAT PUMP SYSTEMS
PRINCIPLES, APPLICATIONS

All refrigeration units are heat pumps. They all move heat from one place to another. They all pick up heat at a low temperature level and release it at high temperature level.

Evaporators and condensers are heat transfer devices which can be used for cooling (picking up heat) or heating (releasing heat).

The principle of using a refrigeration unit as a heating mechanism too was first proposed by Lord Kelvin over 100 years ago, but it has only been since World War II that there has been a serious effort to actually use the mechanism for heating.

The heat pump is sometimes called a reverse-cycle mechanism. However, the cycle is not actually reversed, only the evaporator coil and condenser are interchanged and therefore the name "reverse-cycle" is not technically correct.

The heat pump has been used for many purposes such as heating water, and heat recovery from industrial processes. Even the defrosting of evaporators using the hot gas defrosting method is a form of heat pump. Both the compression system and the absorption system can be adapted for use as heat pumps.

This chapter is devoted to the compression cycle heat pump as it is used in air conditioning.

26-1 Purpose

The heat pump is a mechanism that can either remove heat from the occupied space and discharge this heat to the outside, or it can be used to pick up heat from the outside and discharge it into the occupied space to heat it.

Large systems of 100 to 1000 ton capacity are in use. Self-contained systems of 2 to 25 tons are also in use, and window units of 1/2 to 2 tons are common.

26-2 Theory

The theory of the heat pump is based on the principle that heat will move from a high temperature to a lower temperature. This principle means that if a heat transfer coil can be maintained at a lower temperature than its surroundings, it will pick up heat from its surroundings.

Therefore, if the evaporator coil of a refrigerating system can be kept at a temperature below its surroundings, it will pick up heat. If an evaporator coil is mounted outdoors and operated at refrigerant temperature of 0 F., it will remove heat from the air even though the outside temperature is only 10 or 15 F. If this refrigerant, after it has evaporated, is compressed by a compressor to a temperature of 120 to 140 F., this hot refrigerant will release heat to the surroundings, i.e., the inside of the house.

Then, if by using a system of valves, the evaporator coil is changed into the condenser, and the condenser is changed into the evaporator coil during the summer months, heat can be removed from the occupied zone and discharged or moved outdoors, Fig. 26-1 shows the pressure heat diagram for a heat pump.

26-3 Operation, Compression System

The operation of the heat pump is identical to any other compression cycle. The principal parts of the system are:

1. Compressor.
2. Condenser
3. Receiver.
4. Liquid line.
5. Refrigerant control.
6. Evaporator coil.
7. Suction line.
8. Motor control.

However, there are two check valves, a reversing valve, and two refrigerant controls used in the simpler of the heat pumps in order to change from summer cooling to winter heating. Fig. 26-2 shows a heat pump operating as a comfort cooler.

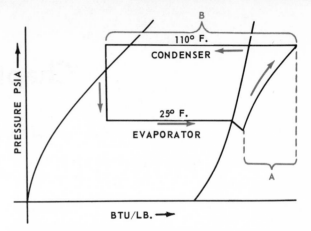

Fig. 26-1. Typical heat pump cycle used for heating with refrigerant evaporating outside at 25 F. (35 F. air) and same refrigerant condensing at 110 F. in condenser in air duct. A—Heat of compression. B—Heat released to house.

The liquid refrigerant bypasses the TEV at the lower left (it goes through the check valve bypass). The TEV at the lower right is the refrigerant control in use.

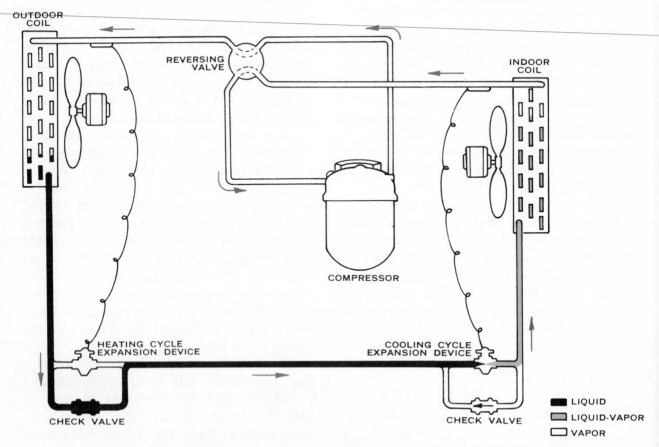

Fig. 26-2. Heat pump. Both heat transfer coils are blower coils. TEV refrigerant controls are used. Note four-way reversing valve. System is operating as comfort cooling unit.
(Westinghouse Electric Corp., Air Conditioning—Sturtevant Div.)

By turning reversing valve 90 deg., refrigerant flow is reversed in all lines except the two lines adjacent to compressor. These valves are often called four-way valves because of the number of openings (4).

Some of these valves are electrically operated to permit changing the system over by simply pushing a button.

Many systems use a compact self-contained system. The system has its heat transfer surfaces self-contained in this unit. The heat transfer units in this system cool or heat liquids. These liquids in turn are pumped through heat transfer surfaces either outdoors or indoors. This system requires two liquid pumps, but it enables the heat pump to operate more efficiently and confines the refrigerant to a relatively small space.

26-4 Cycles

The heat pump actually operates as two cycles:
1. Heating cycle.
2. Cooling cycle.

The same mechanism is used for both cycles, but the travel of refrigerant is re-

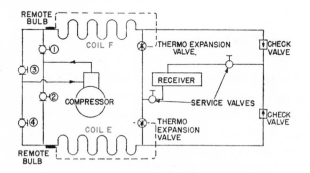

Fig. 26-3. *Heat pump equipped with hand valves to permit manual changing of system from heating system to cooling system. Coil F is outside coil and coil E is inside heat transfer surface.*
(Alco Valve Co.)

versed in order to change from cooling to heating. Fig. 26-3 shows a basic heat pump system. Hand valves are used to reverse the cycle.

Theoretically, it would take no energy to maintain correct conditions if the outside (ambient) conditions equaled inside conditions.

For example:
Outside (ambient)

Temperature F.	Humidity %
72	50

Inside

Temperature F.	Humidity %
72	50

If the ambient conditions are within 10 F. and 10 percent rh of these conditions, very little treatment is needed due to the heat lag and time lag in controlling the variables. But if the ambient temperatures were to increase over this amount, for example:

Outside (Ambient) Conditions		Inside Conditions	
Temp. 85 F.	Humidity 75%	Temp. 72 F.	Humidity 50%

The cycle needed to reduce the temperatures and humidity is shown in Fig. 26-4.

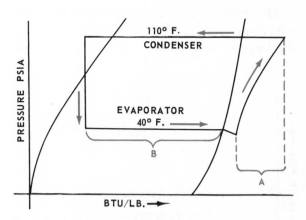

Fig. 26-4. *Cooling cycle for heat pump. A—Heat energy of compression. B—Heat energy removed from air (cooling and dehumidifying). Note that A is approximately one-third of B.*

On the psychrometric chart, the apparatus would affect the air conditions, as shown in Fig. 26-5. Point A is the condition of the ambient air and represents air

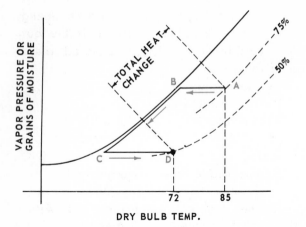

Fig. 26-5. Effect on air in house when using cooling cycle of heat pump.

at 85 F. and 75% rh. The line A to B shows how the air is cooled to 100% humidity. The line B to C shows how the air is further cooled and how moisture is removed from the air. If 100% fresh air is being conditioned, point C represents the air as it leaves the evaporator coil. Then as the air mixes with the air in the house, or as it mixes with air being brought into the duct system, (recirculated air) point D is reached.

The heating cycle consists of removing heat from the ambient air and releasing this heat in the house. It must be remem-

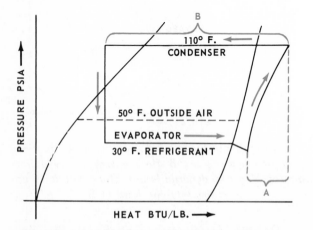

Fig. 26-6. Heat pump serving as heating system with outside temperature at 50 F. Refrigerant is evaporating at 30 F. and refrigerant is condensing at 110 F. The Btu ratio of A to B is coefficient of performance (cop).

bered that heating is not usually needed until the outdoor temperature is less than 65 F. Heat from appliances and from occupants usually makes up this small difference.

For example, if the following conditions prevail:

Outdoor Conditions   Inside Conditions
   50 F.   80%   72 F.   50%

the outdoor coil will operate as an evaporator coil and pick up heat from outdoors and discharge this heat into the house, as shown in Fig. 26-6.

The heating cycle of the heat pump becomes less efficient as the outdoor temperature lowers. This action, plus an increase in the load as the outside temperature lowers, offers considerable difficulties for those latitudes where temperatures drop to 20 F. or lower. Fig. 26-7 shows such a condition with the outside temperature at 20 F. requiring a refrigerant temperature of 0 F.

Note that A has increased with very little increase in B, which means that the coefficient of performance is less. Also, with the refrigerant boiling at 0 F., the evaporator coil will frost rapidly necessitating some means of frequent defrosting.

26-5 Performance

Heat pump units have been designed for single rooms, for complete houses, and for industrial uses. The unit takes the place of both the comfort cooling unit and the heating apparatus.

The source of energy is usually electricity. To furnish 50,000 Btu per hour directly from electrical resistance heating would require 50,000 Btu/hr. ÷ 3412 Btu/hr. = 14.6 kwhr. (1 kwhr. = 3412 Btu/hr.).

At one cent per kwhr., the heat load would cost 14.6 x .01 = .146/hr. For one day, cost would be .146 x 24 = $3.50/day.

For one 30-day month the cost would be $3.50 x 30 = $105/mo.

This cost appears high; however, the actual cost is much less than this, as the heat load for a house averages much less than this value. The average temperature is much higher than the design temperature. The 50,000 Btu/hr. is based on 70 F. indoor and 0 F. outdoor. If the average outdoor temperature is 35 F. (quite common), the heat load would be 25,000 Btu/hr. $(\frac{70}{35})$, and the cost would therefore be one half, or $52.50/mo.

The heat pump reduces this cost considerably.

The heat pump uses electricity only to drive the compressor. The refrigeration cycle, if the proper temperatures are used, permits the condenser to release three to four times as much heat as it takes in electrical energy to drive the compressor. This coefficient of performance (c.o.p.) means that one kwhr. of electrical energy driving the compressor can, by using the heat pump, release not 3412 Btu/hr., but 3412 x 3 or 10,236.0 Btu/hr.

This coefficient of performance can be further increased by using a heat source that is warmer than the outside air. For example, well water, lake water, and the ground itself, may be used to provide the heat for the heat pump.

If a well furnishing water at 60 deg. F. can be found, the coefficient of performance can be raised to as much as 4 or 5. This factor will make the cost of heating, using a heat pump, considerably less.

26-6 Heat Pump Systems

The use of heat pumps for residential heating and cooling is increasing. Hermetic units for heat pump use have been developed in many designs, and in a wide range of sizes.

The hermetic system is ideal for such installations, as it is simple to install. Some of these systems are equipped with service valves, suction and discharge muf-

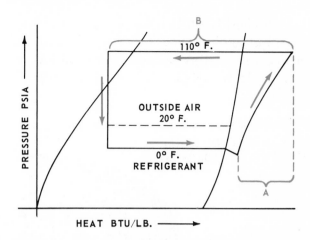

Fig. 26-7. *Heat pump heating cycle in operation when outside (ambient) temperature is 20 F. requiring a 0 F. refrigerant temperature. Note increase in heat of compression.*

flers and other special features which contribute to quiet, reliable operation and long life. Fig. 26-8 illustrates a hermetic compressor designed for residential heat pump installation.

26-7 Condensers and Evaporator Coils

The coil mounted inside the house is usually a standard finned coil with a blower.

The outside coil comes in a variety of designs. The coil design depends on what substance the coil is to release its heat to or pick up its heat from. Some types of coils classified as to the heat medium are:
1. Air coil.
2. Lake water coil.
3. Well water coil.
4. Ground coil.

26-8 Air Coil

The easiest to install and the least expensive of the outdoor coils for heat pump use is a coil used to release its heat to the outside air, or to pick up heat from the outside air. This type coil has a number of advantages in climates where the outdoor temperatures do not vary more than from 20 to 110 F.

The coil itself is a standard heat transfer coil with tubing for primary surface and extended fins bonded to the tubing. A blower is mounted in the housing that pro-

During the heating cycle there is a tendency for these units to frost and ice in certain weather conditions. To prevent this action, most heat pumps have a spe-

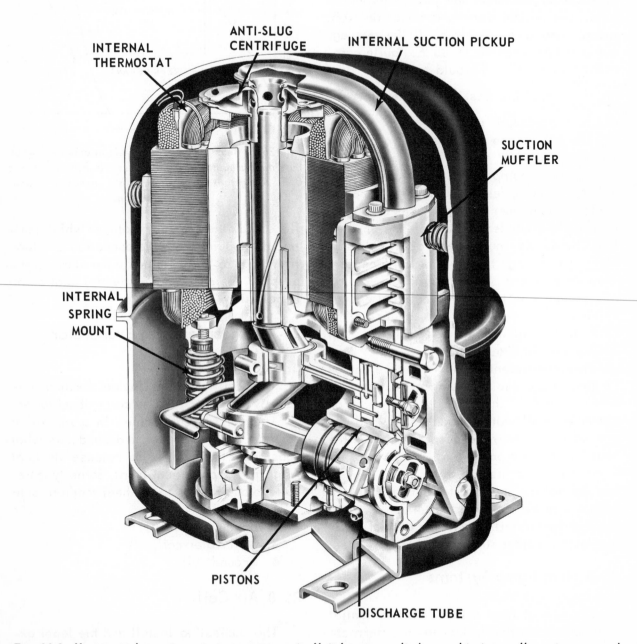

INTERNAL THERMOSTAT

ANTI-SLUG CENTRIFUGE

INTERNAL SUCTION PICKUP

SUCTION MUFFLER

INTERNAL SPRING MOUNT

PISTONS

DISCHARGE TUBE

Fig. 26-8. Heat pump hermetic motor-compressor unit. Unit has two cylinders and is internally spring mounted. (Tecumseh Products Co.)

tects the coil from the weather. The coils have been mounted on the outside wall of a building on the roof and in separate shelters adjacent to the building.

cial thermostat mounted on the coil. If frost or ice starts to accumulate, this control will shut off the system and start a defrost action (heating coils) or will re-

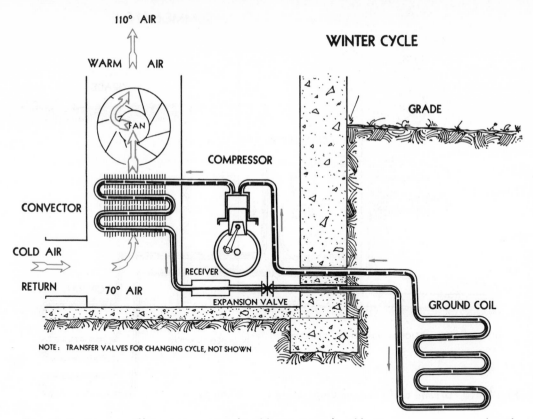

110° AIR

WARM AIR

FAN

COMPRESSOR

CONVECTOR

COLD AIR

RETURN

70° AIR

RECEIVER

EXPANSION VALVE

GRADE

GROUND COIL

NOTE: TRANSFER VALVES FOR CHANGING CYCLE, NOT SHOWN

Fig. 26-9. Diagram illustrating principle of heating cycle of heat pump using ground coil.
(American Brass Co.)

verse the cycle long enough to defrost the coil. Some systems use a timer to operate the system or defrost for a time to rid the outdoor coil of frost or ice.

26-9 Lake Water Coil

As has been explained, the performance of a heat pump increases in efficiency as the condensing and evaporator coil temperature approach each other. Therefore, during the heating cycle, if a warmer source can be found than the ambient air, an increase in performance can be expected.

Several installations have been tried where the outside coil is dropped on the bottom of a lake adjacent to the premises. The coil if installed at the bottom of the lake has a more consistent temperature than otherwise. During the cooling cycle, this coil readily releases its heat to the lake water. During the heating cycle the evaporator coil absorbs heat from the water at the bottom of the lake.

The temperature of maximum density of water is 39 F. (4 C.). This means that the temperature of the water at the bottom of a lake will be 39 F. or above. If the water is cooled below 39 F., it will expand and rise to the surface, and a temperature of 32 F. will cause it to freeze. This is the reason that ice forms on the surface of a lake. The lake would be frozen solid before the temperature of the water at the bottom could be lower than 39 F.

From this you can see that a lake, even one covered with ice, may be a reservoir of heat.

26-10 Well Water Coil

Well water may provide an efficient heat pickup unit for heating and a good heat dissipator during the cooling cycle.

The cost of the well is a disadvantage, but its cost will probably soon be offset by the lower cost of operation.

A popular method of using well water is to pump the water out of the well, then

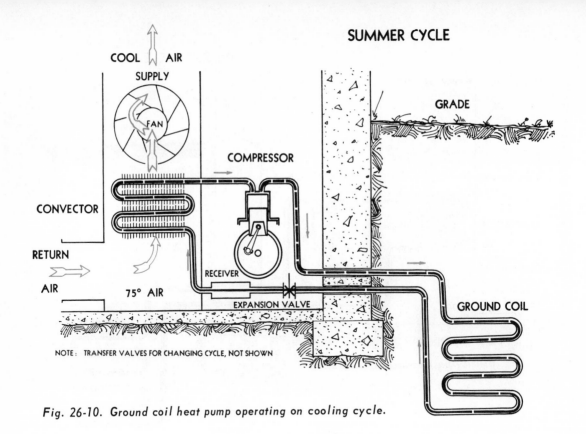

COOL AIR

SUPPLY

FAN

COMPRESSOR

CONVECTOR

GRADE

RETURN

AIR

75° AIR

RECEIVER

EXPANSION VALVE

GROUND COIL

NOTE: TRANSFER VALVES FOR CHANGING CYCLE, NOT SHOWN

Fig. 26-10. Ground coil heat pump operating on cooling cycle.

after heat has been removed from the water or released to it, the water is returned to the well using a tube-within-a-tube or a shell-and-tube heat exchanger.

When well water is 60 F., a condensing temperature of 80 F. can be used during cooling cycle. An evaporator temperature of 40 F. can be used during heating cycle.

Often flowing wells or springs are used to supply water for heat pump installations.

26-11 Ground Coil

A type of outside coil which is receiving considerable attention is a ground coil. It has been found that, regardless of the latitude and the air temperature changes, the temperature in the ground at a depth of 4 to 6 ft. changes very little. These temperatures average between 40 F. and 60 F.

If a coil is buried in the ground at a depth of 4 to 6 ft. and it has sufficient heat transfer surface, the coil can be used as an outdoor coil for both heating and cooling cycles. Fig. 26-9 illustrates a ground coil system as it operates during the winter. In actual construction, the ground coil

is installed in a flat position. Also, the air return is usually a split-air system with a fresh air makeup duct. Fig. 26-10 illustrates the same basic system used as a comfort cooling mechanism. In actual practice, valves would be used to flow the condensed refrigerant first, through the liquid receiver, and then through the expansion valve from left to right before the reduced pressure refrigerant enters the evaporating coil in the duct.

Installations have been made using a combination of air coils and either a lake coil, well coil, or ground coil. The air coil is used alone when the outdoor temperature permits efficient operation, but when the outside air becomes too cold or too warm the auxiliary coil may be connected into the system.

26-12 Compressors

Compressors used in heat pumps are of standard construction. Units up to 5 hp use compressors of constant capacity. The trend is to use hermetic systems.

Because the pumping load varies ex-

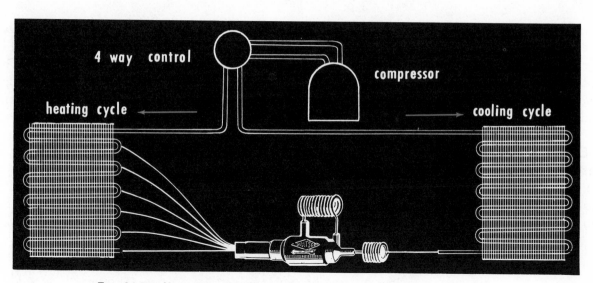

Fig. 26-11. Heat pump system using capillary tube refrigerant controls.
(Watsco, Inc.)

tensively during the day and also during the change of seasons, variable capacity compressors are being used. These compressors vary their capacity by operating valves which unload a compressor cylinder or cylinders into clearance pockets. See Chapter 13.

The mechanism used is hydraulically or electrically operated to hold open the intake valves, or to open a passage to a clearance pocket for that cylinder or cylinders, that are to be unloaded.

Compressors for heat pump use must be designed to operate during the unusual conditions of reversing the cycle. The motors should be protected with internal temperature thermostats. The compressor must be designed to handle liquid slugging without injury. Crankcase heaters are often used to protect the compressor from liquid refrigerant buildup during low temperature operating periods. Suction line accumulators are often used to protect the motor-compressor.

26-13 Motors

Heat pumps of 1/3 to 1 ton capacity use standard single-phase motors. They usually have a starting capacitor. Single-phase

motors should be operated at 240 volts if possible.

Three-phase motors are preferred in units over one ton capacity mainly for electrical economy.

Motors in hermetic systems are usually better insulated, can tolerate a wider voltage change, and have temperature sensor protectors built into the motor windings.

26-14 Refrigerant Controls and Motor Controls

Either thermostatic expansion valve or capillary tube refrigerant controls may be used with heat pumps. Fig. 26-11 illustrates a heat pump system using a capillary tube. Two thermostatic expansion valves or capillary tubes may be used on a heat pump system. The thermostatic expansion valve is usually the pressure limiting type. Two valves are used. Depending on whether the system is heating or cooling, one control will be operational and the other will be in the liquid line. If an air coil is used, the valve should be cross charged to provide more efficient operation at low air temperatures. The change-over valves are much simpler in units that use the capillary tube control, because the flow of refrigerant can be reversed through the tube for pressure reducing purposes. In this type of installation, a strainer must be installed at both ends of the tube.

Both the thermostatic expansion valve (TEV) and the capillary tube control are described in Chapter 6.

Fig. 26-12 illustrates a heat pump using a capillary tube and a solenoid reversing valve. It is shown operating on the cooling cycle. The wiring diagram showing the control contacts in position for this cooling cycle is shown in Fig. 26-13. The interlocking of the four-way solenoid operated reversing valve and the compressor is shown.

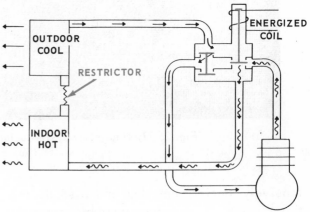

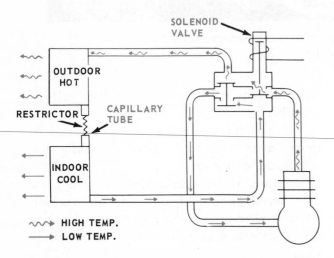

Fig. 26-12. *Heat pump with capillary tube refrigerant control operating on cooling cycle (indoor coil). Bent arrow lines mean high temperature. Straight arrow lines mean low temperature.   (Ranco, Inc.)*

Fig. 26-14. *Heat pump operating on heating cycle. The crooked arrows indicate high temperature. The straight arrows indicate low temperatures. Note use of 4-way valve.*

Fig. 26-14 illustrates a heat pump using a capillary tube and a solenoid operated reversing valve operating on a heating cycle. The wiring diagram showing the control contacts for the heating cycle is shown in Fig. 26-15. Note the change in contact position of the reversing lever.

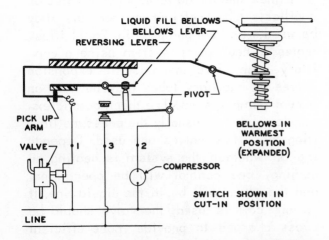

Fig. 26-13. *Wiring diagram of heat pump showing electrical connections for cooling cycle.*

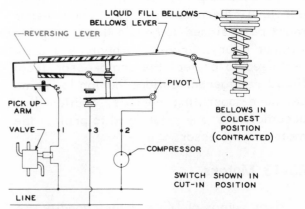

Fig. 26-15. *Electrical connections during heating cycle of heat pump.*

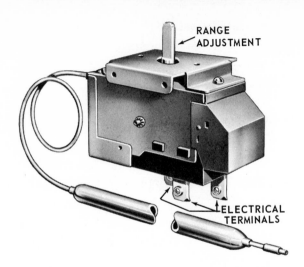

Fig. 26-16. *Thermostat for controlling a reverse cycle air conditioner heat pump.* (*Ranco, Inc.*)

The thermostat which operates the four-way valve and also controls the temperature is shown in Fig. 26-16.

some kind of starter (magnetic or transformer) is used, as shown in A, B, and C, Fig. 26-17.

A double set of automatic controls is usually required for the heat pump. A thermostat designed for heating is needed for cold weather conditions, and a thermostat designed for cooling conditions is needed for warm weather. In most cases these two controls are mounted in one casing or housing. Humidistats are not used on all models; however, they are needed for complete automatic control.

26-15 Refrigerant Lines

The suction lines and liquid lines of the heat pump are unusual in that both lines

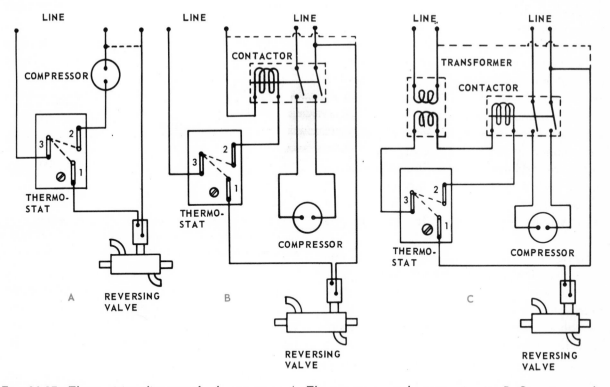

Fig. 26-17. *Three wiring diagrams for heat pumps: A—Thermostat controls motor circuit. B—Circuit uses line voltage coil magnetic starter. C—Circuit diagram using low voltage coil magnetic starter.*

The three terminals are used, as shown in Fig. 26-17. The wiring of heat pumps depends mainly on whether the motor is connected directly to the line, or whether

are constructed large enough to handle the refrigerant in a vapor form. This is because the use of the lines is reversed as the cycles are reversed. A line which is serving as a liquid line while on a cooling cycle may become a suction line when the unit is used for heating.

The lines are normally fitted with brazed or welded connections. Silver brazing is the most popular. Flexible connections are usually installed in the lines at the compressor to eliminate noise and to allow for some vibration of the compressor.

The systems usually have a receiver to hold the extra refrigerant needed when the system is on a cooling cycle. An accumulator is often used on the main suction line to minimize the chance of liquid refrigerant reaching the compressor.

26-16 Reversing Valves

Several different types of special reversing valves are used in heat pumps to reverse the refrigerant flow. If the system is reversed manually at least six one-way valves are needed. The reversing valves may be electrically operated (solenoids) or manually operated.

Some units use three-way valves, either manually or electrically operated. These valves have one opening to the compressor, one opening to the condenser, and one to the evaporator coil. Two of these valves are needed to operate the unit.

Some units use a four-way valve to reverse the flow of refrigerant. It is operated by the movement of one valve stem which closes and opens several ports in one valve body, either by moving the stem manually or electrically. The complete system is easily reversed with one of these valves. This type valve is popular in small tonnage units such as window units and other air-to-air units.

A four-way valve that is operated by pressure is shown in Fig. 26-18. A solenoid valve controls the pressure at the top portion of the reversing valve. When the solenoid pilot valve is energized, the

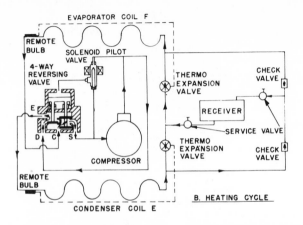

REVERSE CYCLE SYSTEM USING A 4-WAY REVERSING VALVE

Fig. 26-18. Heat pump schematic diagram which uses one four-way reversing valve. A solenoid pilot valve is used to operate four-way valve. As shown, it is operating on heating cycle. E—Indoor coil. F—Outdoor coil. (Alco Valve Co.)

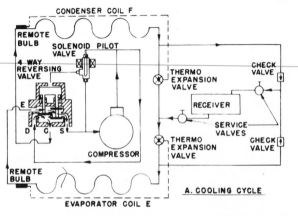

REVERSE CYCLE SYSTEM USING A 4-WAY REVERSING VALVE

Fig. 26-19. Heat pump schematic diagram which uses special four-way reversing valve. As shown, it is operating on cooling cycle. E—Indoor coil. F—Outdoor coil.

compressor low side pressure is imposed on the four-way valve, and all three internal valves are lifted, producing the heating cycle. Coil E is the indoor coil, while Coil F is the outdoor coil.

When the solenoid pilot valve circuit is opened, manually or by a thermostat, the solenoid valve closes and the three valves inside the four-way valve drop, and the refrigerant flow to the coils is reversed.

This heat pump uses a thermostatic expansion valve on each coil and a check

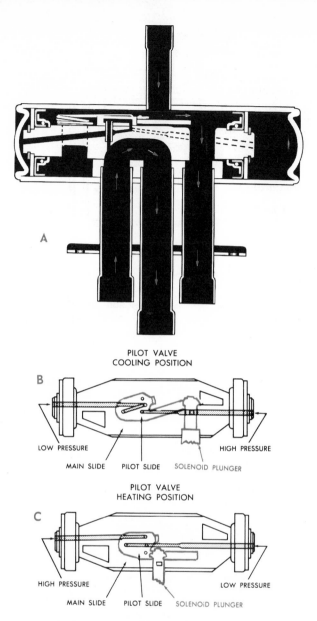

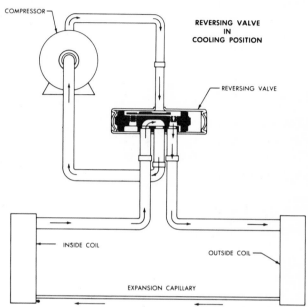

tem operating as a cooling unit. Coil F becomes the condenser and is releasing heat to the outdoors, while Coil E becomes the evaporator.

Fig. 26-21. Basic heat pump cycle using reversing valve. Note flow of refrigerant when valve is positioned for cooling cycle.

Fig. 26-20. Cut-away of pilot valve mechanism used to operate four-way reversing valve. Note position of solenoid plunger in heating position when solenoid is energized. A—Side view of four-way valve. B—Pilot mechanism and piston in cooling position. C—Pilot mechanism and piston in heating position. (Robertshaw Controls Co., Milford Div.)

valve on each coil to permit reversing the refrigerant flow around the thermostatic expansion valve of the coil serving as the condenser.

During the cooling cycle (F) the upper thermostatic expansion valve is used because the refrigerant cannot travel through the companion check valve.

Fig. 26-19 illustrates this same sys-

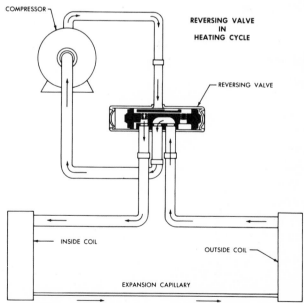

Fig. 26-22. Heat pump circuit when reversing valve is positioned for heating cycle.

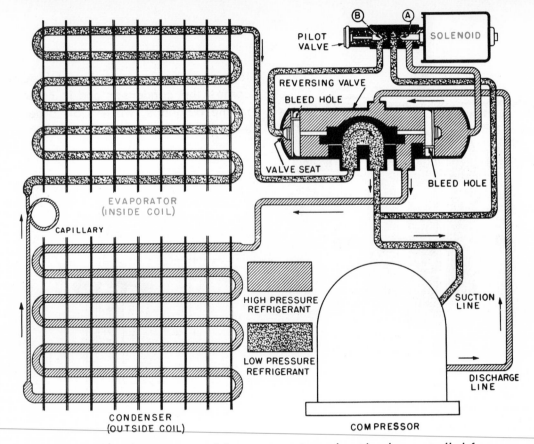

Fig. 26-23. Capillary tube refrigerant control heat pump using solenoid valve controlled four-way valve. Indoor coil is serving as an evaporator. (Kelvinator Div., American Motors Corp.)

Fig. 26-24. Capillary tube type heat pump using indoor coil as condenser.

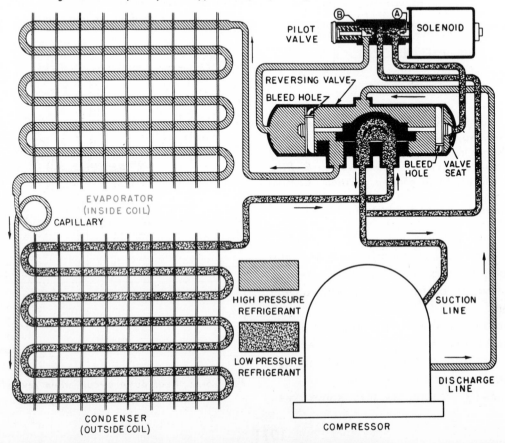

Another popular type of reversing valve is the solenoid pilot-operated sliding port type valve. Its operation is by a solenoid valve. The solenoid coil is energized on the heating cycle which causes the pilot slide to pivot and changes the flow of pressure which causes the main slide to move, as seen in Fig. 26-20. In the cooling cycle the solenoid is not energized. Fig. 26-21 shows the reversing valve installed in a heat pump system with the system on a cooling cycle. The system valved for a heating cycle is shown in Fig. 26-22. Figs. 26-23 and 26-24 show this sliding valve in more detail.

A diagrammatic sketch of a self-contained system is shown in Fig. 26-25. Notice that two separate circulating fans are used. The black coil is the warm coil and the white coil is the cooling coil in each illustration. These units are installed in a home, either in the basement or on the first floor. Fig. 26-26 shows a typical first floor utility room installation. Both of the coils and the motor-compressor are installed in a casing. The indoor air and the outdoor air are ducted to the self-contained unit.

26-17 Wall Mounted Heat Pumps

Fig. 26-27 shows a heat pump unit which can be installed in an exterior wall of an office or apartment. This type of unit extracts "natural heat" from the outside in the winter for heating the room or apartment and cools it in the summer by absorbing heat from the room and discharging it to the outside atmosphere. It should be noted that this heat pump is supplied with a supplementary electric resistance heating unit to increase its heating capacity in very cold weather. These compact heat pumps require little interior space and the blowers distribute the heated or cooled air evenly throughout a room.

Through the wall heat pumps also provide ease of maintenance, since the heat

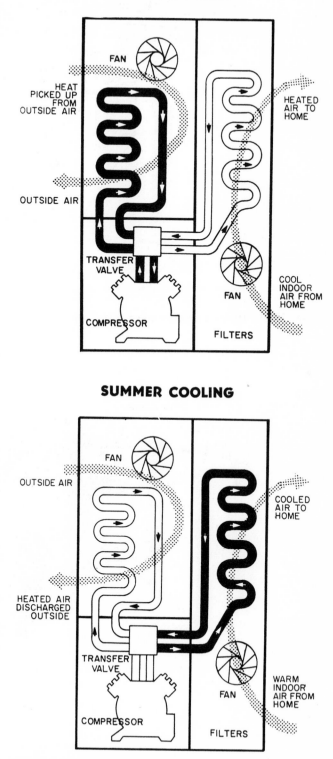

Fig. 26-25. Diagram illustrating the air and refrigerant circuits in heat pump during the heating and cooling operation. (Westinghouse Electric Corp., Air Conditioning-Sturtevant Div.)

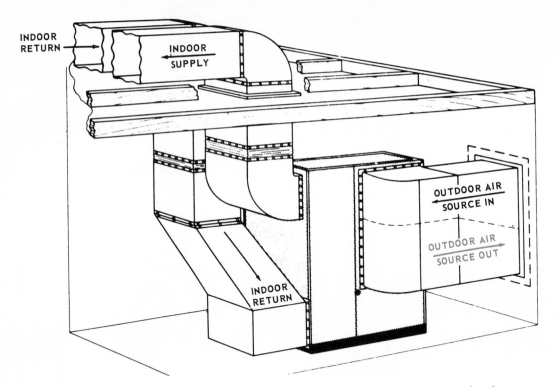

Fig. 26-26. Diagram of heat pump installation in a house. Note that outdoor air is ducted to heat pump mechanism which is located inside the house.

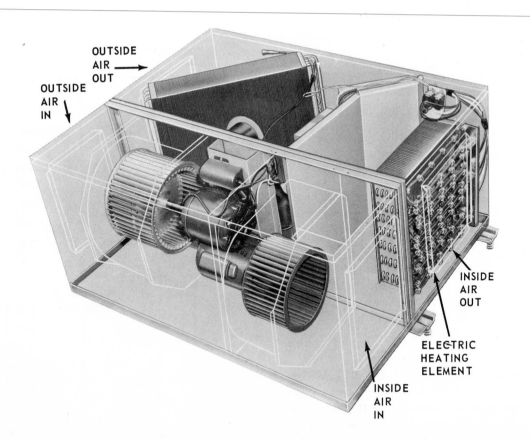

Fig. 26-27. A 3 hp Adoptomatic Heat Pump which can be installed through wall. Note supplementary electric resistance heating element uses to increase the amount of heating during unusual cold spells.
(Fedders Corp.)

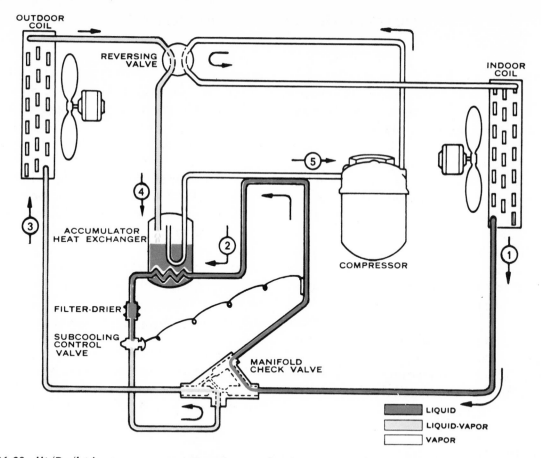

Fig. 26-28. Hi/Re/Li heat pump system operating as a heating system. Note: 1—Condenser surfaces are drained by liquid subcooling control—no refrigerant storage or liquid back-up that results in reduced coil efficiency and higher discharge temperature and pressures. 2—Subcooling of high pressure liquid at suction line and in accumulator-heat exchanger increases heat-absorbing capability of refrigerant—no flash gas accompanied by low head pressures that limit cooling operation or require head pressure control. 3—Excess liquid refrigerant is introduced to evaporator, over-feeding coil and wetting all surfaces for optimum heat transfer efficiency — no evaporator superheat to cause reduced evaporator effectiveness. Refrigerant distribution and oil return are not critical. 4—Accumulator-heat exchanger separates vapor and excess liquid refrigerant. The liquid is then evaporated in the subcooling process. Accumulator-heat exchanger also serves to store the refrigerant not in use. 5—Only dry, essentially saturated gas is returned to compressor. Even oil-refrigerant mixture aspirated into suction tube is dried of liquid before returning to compressor.
(Westinghouse Electric Corp., Air Conditioning-Sturtevant Div.)

pump chassis may be removed for servicing. The individual heat pump unit is desirable in many apartment units, since the owner of the multiple does not have to operate a central air conditioning system. Each tenant can set the thermostat to give the heating or cooling desired without affecting the other tenants in the building.

26-18 Unique Heat Pump (Hi/Re/Li) System

A recent innovation in heat pump cycles is the Hi/Re/Li system developed by the Westinghouse Corporation. The Hi/Re/Li system differs from the conventional heat pump system in many ways. Fig. 26-28 illustrates some of the main operational differences, which are as follows:

1. The location of the refrigerant control is not on the evaporator coil but is located on the condensing unit with the thermal bulb mounted on the liquid line, thereby keeping control over liquid leaving the condenser rather than entering the evaporator.

2. The heat exchanger-accumulator in the suction line allows a greater amount

of subcooling of the refrigerant. It separates liquid-vapor and allows dry vapor and oil to enter the compressor because the liquid is boiled off by the heat exchanger.

3. A suction line-heat exchanger subcools the condensed liquid refrigerant before entrance to the expansion valve. By subcooling the liquid, the amount of "flash gas" and pressure drop is lowered.

4. The evaporator is completely flooded and utilized for cooling, since it is not required to also superheat "suction gas" as in a normal system.

5. The condenser size can be reduced because of the lack of necessity to store refrigerant during periods of low load.

The Hi/Re/Li system uses a reversing valve to change the direction of flow of the refrigerant to correspond to the requirements of either heating or cooling. In addition, it uses a check valve to direct the flow of refrigerant in the proper direction dependent upon whether a heating or cooling cycle is desired. A complete diagram of this cycle is shown in Fig. 26-29.

When charging the system, it is best to remove all of the refrigerant, then charge with the correct amount as indicated in the manufacturer's manual. Install service valves on the suction lines and discharge lines fairly close to the compressor to obtain the correct operating pressures.

26-19 Installing Heat Pumps

Basically, a heat pump is a refrigerating system. Most of the installation instructions in Chapters 12 and 15 also apply to heat pumps. The units must be in-

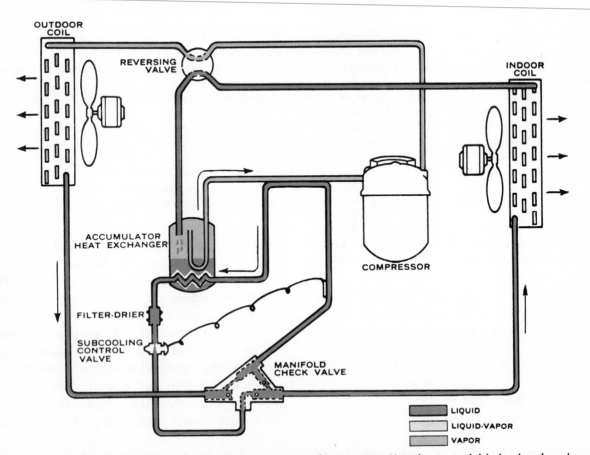

Fig. 26-29. Hi/Re/Li heat pump system operating as a cooling system. Note how manifold check valve changes or reverses refrigerant flow.

stalled level. The electrical service must be the correct voltage and phase. The wiring must be large enough to carry the load without a critical voltage drop.

Installing window and wall units utilize the same casing mounting techniques as the window and wall air conditioners described in Chapter 21.

When installing a heat pump, it is important to closely follow the manufacturer's instructions.

26-20 Servicing Heat Pumps

Because the heat pump system is a refrigerating unit, the service techniques of troubleshooting and repair are much the same as the service described in Chapters 12 and 15.

Routine maintenance requires that the refrigerant pressures be checked and the voltage and current at the unit be checked. The heat pump should be cleaned. Blow out the coils, clean the duct passages, oil the fan bearings and fan motor bearings. The unit should be operated on both cycles to check the operation of the reversing valve.

Service calls usually start with a customer complaint, such as:

1. Unit will not operate--on cooling or heating.
2. Unit runs too much.
3. System is noisy.

The diagnosis must not only find the cause of the complaint, but must also find the reason for the trouble. For example, a lack of refrigerant indicates a leak. The leak must be located and repaired.

A four-way valve that will not operate must be replaced.

26-21 Review of Safety

Working on a heat pump involves most of the dangers which exist in a refrigerating system.

Always wear goggles when working on the refrigerating mechanism. Be sure the electrical service is off and locked off before working on the electrical circuits, or on electrically powered parts such as the controls, fans, etc.

Always install pressure gauges when checking the system, charging it, adding oil, etc.

A heat pump used for heating a house must collect heat by evaporating refrigerant in some outside source of heat. An evaporator operating below 32 F. will frost and freeze over. Some means must be provided to defrost the evaporator quite often if it is used under these conditions.

26-22 Test Your Knowledge - Chapter 26

1. What part of the refrigerating unit releases heat?
2. Who first proposed the use of a refrigerating unit for heating?
3. How many heat transfer surfaces does a heat pump have?
4. How can heat be removed from 0 F. air?
5. What are the two operating cycles of a heat pump?
6. Under what conditions is a heat pump the most efficient?
7. What is coefficient of performance?
8. Is it less expensive to heat with electrical resistors or with a heat pump? Why?
9. How many Btu/hr. are generated by one kwhr. through direct electrical resistance?
10. List one disadvantage of each type of outside coil.
11. What are the various types of outdoor coils?
12. What type of coil is used indoors?
13. What outdoor coils are used when dual coils are used?
14. Why is the capillary tube especially advantageous to use in heat pumps?

15. Explain the operation of a three-way valve used to reverse the refrigerant flow.

16. How many refrigerant connections does a four-way reversing valve have?

17. Describe the two ways a solenoid is used to operate a reversing valve.

18. In a heat pump how many thermostatic expansion valves are used?

19. How many check valves are used in a heat pump system equipped with thermostatic expansion valves?

20. What does the TEV control in the Hi/Re/Li system?

21. What does the check valve do in the Hi/Re/Li system?

22. What is done to keep frost or ice from an air outdoor coil?

23. How does well water release heat to or pick up heat from the heat pump?

24. When is the operation of the motor-compressor most critical in a heat pump system?

25. What two electrical devices does a heat pump thermostat control?

Chapter 27

TECHNICAL CHARACTERISTICS

27-1 Weights and Specific Heats of Substances

MATERIAL	WEIGHT LBS./CU.FT.	SPECIFIC HEAT Btu/LB.
GASES		
Air	.075	.24
(normal temp.)		
METALS		
Aluminum	166.5	.214
Copper	552	.094
Iron	480·	.118
Lead	710	.030
Mercury	847	.033
Steel	492	.117
Zinc	446	.096
LIQUIDS		
Alcohol	49.6	.60
Glycerine	83.6	.576
Oil	57.5	.400
Water	62.4	1.000
OTHERS		
Concrete	147	.19
Cork	15	.48
Glass	164	.199
Ice	57.5	.504
Masonry	112	.200
Paper	58	.324
Rubber	59	.48
Sand	100	.195
Stone	138−200	.20
Tar	75	.35
Wood, Oak	48	.57
Wood, Pine	38	.47

27-2 Heat Transfer Coefficients

Unit of heat--pound centigrade or centigrade heat unit is the heat required to raise one pound of water 1 C. degree and equals 1.8 Btu.

1 Btu/hr./sq.ft./F. = 4.88 kg-ca./hr./sq.m./C.

1 kg-cal./hr./sq.m./C. = .205 Btu/hr./sq.ft./F.

27-3 Heat Coefficients

1 Btu	= 252 calories	
1 kilocalorie	= 1000 calories	
1 Btu/lb.	= .555 kcal/kg	
1 kcal/kg	= 1.8 Btu/lb.	

27-4 Energy Conversion Equivalents

1 Btu	= 778 ft. lbs.
1 Horsepower	= 33,000 ft.lb./min.
	= 550 ft.lb./sec.
	= 746 watts
	= 2545.6 Btu/hr.
	= 42.42 Btu/min.
1 Horsepower hour	= 1 horsepower for 1 hr.
	= 1,980,000 ft.lb.
	= 746 watt hours
	= .746 kilowatt hours
	= 2545.6 Btu
1 Kilowatt	= 1,000 watts
	= 1.34 horsepower
1 Kilowatt hour	= 1 kilowatt for 1 hr.
	= 1,000 watt hours

ICE MELTING EFFECT (IME)

1 ton of Refrigeration	= 288,000 Btu/day
	= 12,000 Btu/hr.
	= 200 Btu/min.
	= 83.3 lbs. of ice/hr.

ENERGY

1 dyne cm = 1 erg = .001 g.cm = 7.38×10.8 ft.lb.

1 g.cm = 980.6 ergs = 7.233×10.5 ft.lb.

1 ft.lb. = 13,557,300 ergs = 13,825.5 g.cm

1 therm = 100,000 Btu

RATE OF ENERGY

1 erg/sec. = 1 dyne cm = 7.38×10^{-8} ft.lb./sec.

1 gram.cm = 980.6 ergs/sec. = 7.24×10.5 ft.lb./sec.

1 ft.lb./sec.= 13,557,300 ergs/sec. = 13,800 grams cm/sec.

27-5 Velocity Equivalents

1 mi./hr.	= 1.47 ft./sec.	= 1.61 km./hr.
	= .87 knots	= .45 meters/sec.
1 ft./sec.	= .68 mi./hr.	= 1.1 km./hr.
	= 60 ft./min.	= .305 meters/sec.
	= .59 knots	
1 meter/sec.	= 3.28 ft./sec.	= 3.6 km./hr.
	= 2.24 mi./hr.	
	= 1.94 knots	
1 km./hr.	= .91 ft./sec.	= .28 meters/sec.
	= .62 mi./hr.	
	= .54 knots	

27-6 Volume Equivalents

1 cu. in.		= .016 liters
		= 16.39 cu. centimeters
1 cu. ft.	= 1728 cu. in.	= 28.317 liters
	= 7.481 gallons	= 28,317.00 cu. centimeters
1 cu. yd.	= 27 cu. ft.	
	= 46,656 cu. in.	
1 gallon	= .1337 cu. ft.	= 3.79 liters
	= 231 cu. in.	= 3785 cu. centimeters
1 cu. centimeter	= .155 cu. in.	
1 liter	= 61.03 cu. in.	= 1000 cu. centimeters
	= .2642 gallons	

27-7 Linear Measure Equivalents

1 inch		= 2.54 centimeters
		= 25.4 millimeters
		= 25,400 microns
1 foot	= 12 inches	= .304 meters
		= 30.48 centimeters
1 yard	= 3 feet	= .914 meters
		= 91.44 centimeters
1 micron		= .000394 inches
1 millimeter	= 1000 microns	= .0394 inches
1 centimeter	= 10 millimeters	= .3937 inches
1 meter	= 100 centimeters	= 39.37 inches
1 kilometer	= 1000 meters	= .62137 miles

27-8 Area Equivalents

1 sq. in.		= .0065 sq. meters
1 sq. ft.	= 144 sq. in.	= .093 sq. meters
1 sq. yd.	= 9 sq. ft.	= .836 sq. meters
1 sq. yd.	= 1296 sq. in.	

27-9 Pressure Equivalents

	ENGLISH	METRIC
1 psi	= 0.068 atmosphere	= .07031 kg/cm^2
	= 144 lbs./sq.ft.	= .703 meters water
	= 2.036 in. of mercury	= 70.3 cm water
	= 2.307 ft. of water	= 51.7 mm. hg.
	= 27.7 in. of water	
1 oz./sq. in.	= .128 in. of mercury	
	= 1.73 in. of water	
1 in. of mercury	= .0334 atmosphere	= .0345 kg/cm^2
	= .491 psi	= 25.4 mm. hg.
	= 1.13 ft. of water	= .3453 m. water
	= 13.6 in. of water	
	= 70.73 psf	
1 ft. of water	= .0295 atmosphere	= .03 kg/cm^2
	= .434 psi	= 22.42 mm. hg.
	= 62.43 lb./sq.ft.	= .305 m. water
	= .03 atmosphere	
	= .883 in. of mercury	
1 atmosphere	= 29.92 in. of mercury	= 1.03 kg/cm^2
	= 33.94 ft. of water	= 760 mm./hg.
	= 14.696 psi	= 10.33 m. water
	= 2116.35 psf	
1 psf	= .007 psi	= 4.88 x 10^4 g/cm
	= 4.725 x 10.4 atmosphere	= .359 mm. hg.
	= .01414 in. hg.	= .0049 m. water
	= .016 ft. water	
1 kilogram/sq.cm	= 14.22 psi	= 10 meters of water
	= 2048.17 psf	
	= .967 atmosphere	
	= 28.96 in. hg.	
	= 32.8083 inches water	
1 meter of water	= 1.42 psi	= 73.55 mm. hg.
	= 204.8 psf	= .10 kg/cm^2
	= .097 atmosphere	
	= 2.896 in. hg.	
	= 3.28 ft. water	
1 mm. hg.	= .019 psi	= .00136 kg/cm^2
	= 2.78 psf	= .0136 m. water
	= .001316 atmosphere	
	= .039 in. hg.	
	= .0446 ft. water	

27-10 Liquid Measure Equivalents

Liquid Measure		U. S.	Metric
1 pint	=	16 ounces	= .473 liters
1 quart	=	2 pints	= .946 liters
1 quart	=	32 ounces	
1 gallon	=	4 quarts	= 3.785 liters
1 gallon	=	8 pints	
1 gallon	=	231 cubic inches	
1 cu. ft.	=	7.84 gallons	
1 gallon	=	8.34 pounds of water	

27-11 Weight Equivalents

AVOIRDUPOIS

1 ounce	= 473 grains	= 28.35 grams
		= .028 kg.
1 pound	= 7000 grains	= .4536 kg.
		= 453.6 grams
1 pound	= 16 ounces	= 453.6 grams
1 grain	= .00043 pounds	= .06480 grams
1 ton	= 2000 pounds	= 909.09 kilograms
1 gram	= 15.43 grains	= .001 kg.
	= .03527 ounces	
	= .002205 pounds	
1 kilogram	= 2.2 pounds	

SPECIFIC WEIGHTS (DENSITY)

1 lb./cu.in.= 1728 lb./cu.ft. = 27.68 gms./cu.m.

1 lb./cu.ft. = 5.787 x 10.4 lb./cu.in. =.016 g./cu.cm.

27-12 Flow Equivalents

1 cu. ft. per min. = 7.481 gal./min. = 28,317 cu.cm./min.
= 449 gal./hr. = 28.32 liters/min.
= 1700.00 liters/hr.

1 cu. ft. per hour = .0167 cu.ft./min. = .472 liters/min.
= .1247 gal./min. = 28.317 liters/hr.
= 7.481 gal./hr. = 472 cu.cm./min.

1 gallon per min. = .1337 cu.ft./min. = 3.79 liters/min.
= 8.022 cu.ft./hr. = 227.1 liters/hr.
= 3785 cu.cm./min.

1 liter per min. = .0353 cu.ft./min. = 1000 cu.cm./min.
= 2.118 cu.ft./hr.
= .2642 gal./min.
= 15.852 gal./hr.

27-13 Laws of Thermodynamics

FIRST LAW OF THERMODYNAMICS

Simply stated, the first law of thermodynamics is a formula for the conversion of heat into work or work into heat. It is as follows:

778 foot pounds of work is equivalent to the heat energy of 1 Btu.

SECOND LAW OF THERMODYNAMICS

The second law of thermodynamics is a statement to the effect that heat will only flow from a body at a certain temperature to another body which is at a lower temperature.

27-14 Numbered Twist Drill Sizes

No.	Size of Drill In Inches	No.	Size of Drill In Inches	No.	Size of Drill In Inches	No.	Size of Drill In Inches
1	.2280	21	.1590	41	.0960	61	.0390
2	.2210	22	.1570	42	.0935	62	.0380
3	.2130	23	.1540	43	.0890	63	.0370
4	.2090	24	.1520	44	.0860	64	.0360
5	.2055	25	.1495	45	.0820	65	.0350
6	.2040	26	.1470	46	.0810	66	.0330
7	.2010	27	.1440	47	.0785	67	.0320
8	.1990	28	.1405	48	.0760	68	.0310
9	.1960	29	.1360	49	.0730	69	.0292
10	.1935	30	.1285	50	.0700	70	.0280
11	.1910	31	.1200	51	.0670	71	.0260
12	.1890	32	.1160	52	.0635	72	.0250
13	.1850	33	.1130	53	.0595	73	.0240
14	.1820	34	.1110	54	.0550	74	.0225
15	.1800	35	.1100	55	.0520	75	.0210
16	.1770	36	.1065	56	.0465	76	.0200
17	.1730	37	.1040	57	.0430	77	.0180
18	.1695	38	.1015	58	.0420	78	.0160
19	.1660	39	.0995	59	.0410	79	.0145
20	.1610	40	.0980	60	.0400	80	.0135

27-15 Lettered Twist Drill Sizes

Letter	Dia. In.	Letter	Dia. In.	Letter	Dia. In.
A	0.234	J	0.277	S	0.348
B	0.238	K	0.281	T	0.358
C	0.242	L	0.290	U	0.368
D	0.246	M	0.295	V	0.377
E	0.250	N	0.302	W	0.386
F	0.257	O	0.316	X	0.397
G	0.261	P	0.323	Y	0.404
H	0.266	Q	0.332	Z	0.413
I	0.272	R	0.339		

27-16 Desiccants

Desiccants are used in driers installed in refrigerator liquid and/or suction lines

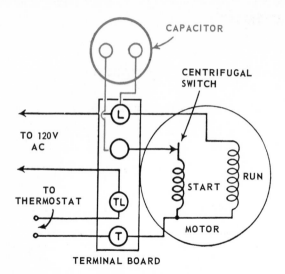

Fig. 27-1. Wiring diagram of capacitor-start motor.
(Aerovox Corp.)

CAPACITOR

CENTRIFUGAL
SWITCH

TO 120V
AC

TO
THERMOSTAT

L

TL

T

START

RUN

MOTOR

TERMINAL BOARD

to collect and remove moisture (water) from the system.

Some common desiccants are:

Activated alumina.

Calcium sulfate.

Silica gel.

Alumina gel.

Molecular sieve.

Most driers will remove moisture, sediment, and acids from the refrigerant in circulation.

Driers are usually placed in the liquid line close to the refrigerant control valve. They must always be placed in a cool place because heat may cause moisture to leave the desiccant and continue to circulate.

The drier on a liquid line should be mounted in a vertical position with the liquid inlet at the bottom. Liquid line driers are usually installed permanently and are only replaced when they lose their effectiveness.

Following a "burnout" a large capacity drier is usually placed in the suction line. Suction line driers should be mounted in a vertical position with the inlet at the top and the outlet at the bottom to allow the oil to flow through easily. Suction line driers should be removed as soon as the clean-up is completed.

Driers which have been used in a refrigerator system should not be reactivated by heating.

27-17 Capacitors and Power Factor

Electric motor driven equipment is usually powered by single-phase fractional horsepower alternating current motors. The development and perfection of economical high capacity electrolytic AC capacitors has made possible the practical use of electrically efficient high starting torque capacitor motors.

The circuit diagram of a typical capacitor-start single-phase induction motor is shown in Fig. 27-1. The purpose of the capacitor is to develop a current in the starting winding that produces a magnetic field which combines with the main winding to produce a high starting torque. The current that flows in the starting winding is determined by the voltage of the line and the design of the starting winding.

If various size capacitors are used on a motor and the starting torque and voltages across the capacitor are measured, a curve similar to that of Fig. 27-2 is obtained. The torque rises rapidly, and, after reaching its maximum value, slowly decreases. In the vicinity of the maximum value a fairly large change in capacity produces a relatively small change in torque. This is advantageous, as the relatively wide tolerance in the capacity of the capacitor keeps the cost of the unit down. The voltage across the capacitor reaches its maximum value before the torque and then starts to decrease. Since the voltage across the capacitor is determined by the design of the starting winding and the line voltage, the voltage across the capacitor is a good indication of the proper size capacitor.

Standard practice today calls for a maximum capacitor voltage of 138 volts during the starting period for a 120V motor. This voltage lasts for a short period of time, usually less than one second. Higher voltages, such as occur with undersize capacitors, will decrease the life of the capacitor. The use of undersize capac-

1022

itors will not prevent the motor from starting, but it will increase the starting time and the voltage across the capacitor.

Since electrolytic motor-starting units are not continuous-duty units, the excessive voltages and starting period that occur with improper capacitors decrease the life of the unit. If the capacitor is too small, the torque produced may be insufficient to bring the motor speed up to the point at which the centrifugal switch disconnects the capacitor from the line. Under such conditions the capacitor soon fails by drying out. The starting period should not exceed three seconds in a properly functioning motor.

Capacitors are made for intermittent duty only, and are usually damaged by the failure of the associated equipment. IT IS IMPORTANT, THEREFORE, TO DETERMINE AND ELIMINATE THE CAUSE OF CAPACITOR FAILURE BEFORE REPLACEMENT. In addition, the replacement capacitor should be of proper capacity and voltage rating. The use of a wrong capacitor will usually result in rapid failure. For that reason, AC electrolytic capacitors are guaranteed as follows:

1. 120V capacitors.

A. Starts-heavy-duty capacitors (standard foil and papers), not more than 20 starts per hour, each start not over 1 second duration (except that not over 100 times per year the capacitor may be on the line for periods not exceeding 10 seconds maximum). Ultra-compact capacitors (etched foil and reduced papers) not more than 20 starts per hour, each start not over 1 second duration (except that not over 50 times per year the capacitor may be on line for periods not exceeding 10 seconds maximum).

B. Voltage not in excess of 125 percent of the rated voltage during any service period.

C. Ambient temperature not to exceed 130 F.

D. Damage - capacitor shall not have been damaged after shipment by manufacturer.

E. Motor defects - capacitor shall not have been subjected to abnormal operating conditions resulting from motor and associated defects such as: (1) defective or dry bearings; (2) sticky compressor; (3) tight belt; (4) defective centrifugal switch or relay; (5) improper adjustment of thermostat or refrigerator valves. Before applying capacitor, always check (a) centrifugal switch or relay; (b) easy turning of motor and compressor; (c) thermostat and valves, as a prerequisite of the guarantee.

2. All other voltages. Same as for 120V capacitors except that the voltage applied to the units during any service period may not exceed 10 percent of the rating. It is recommended that the serviceman check the following points before leaving the job:

A. Measure the voltage across the capacitor during the starting period. It should not exceed 138 volts for 120V capacitors. For other voltage ratings, it should not exceed 110 percent of the nominal rating. If the voltage across the capacitor is higher than the limiting value given, a capacitor of too low capacity is usually indicated.

B. Time the duration and frequency of the starting period. These should not

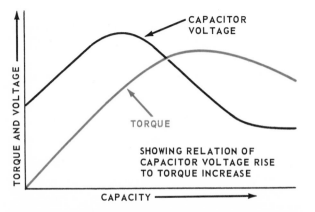

Fig. 27-2. Graph which shows relationship between the capacitor voltage rise and the increase in starting torque.

exceed the limits given in the guarantee. If the start takes too long, either the capacity of the unit is incorrect--too high or too low--or the associated equipment is defective. Too frequent starts (over 20 per hour) should not be allowed. This usually indicates some defect in the control equipment.

C. Measure the temperature of the capacitor motor compartment. It should not exceed 130 F.

D. The container of the capacitor should be insulated from ground.

Attention to these factors will generally result in a satisfactory job.

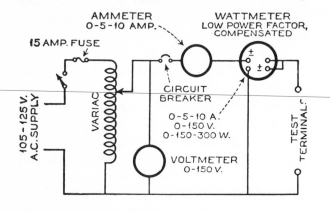

Fig. 27-3. Circuit diagram which may be used with ammeter-voltmeter-wattmeter method of measuring capacity and power factor.

Electrolytic motor-starting capacitors may be tested for their capacity and power factor by connecting them to AC of proper voltage, and reading the current and wattage of the unit, as shown in Fig. 27-3. The capacity of the unit is then approximately

$$C \text{ MFD} = \frac{159,300 \; I}{f \; E}$$

$$= \frac{amperes}{cycles \; p. \; sec. \times v.}$$

Fig. 27-4 shows a table which has been compiled to facilitate computation of capacities at various voltages and frequencies.

The power factor of the capacitor is the measure of the loss of power in it. Ca-

pacitors of high power factor do not give as high starting torque for a given capacity as those with a low power factor. For the same torque, higher capacity should be used for units with high power factor. Capacitors with a low power factor may be readily made at a sacrifice of stability and life. As a result, a compromise between all the factors involved produces the best overall performance.

The value of power factor is given by the expression:

$$\text{Power Factor \%} = \frac{W}{E \, I} \times 100$$

For the usual requirements in service, the wattmeter used should be capable of carrying about 10 amperes with a full scale of 150 watts. Such wattmeters are known as low power factor wattmeters and are generally made to order.

Since the capacity of the unit is by far more critical than its power factor for satisfactory service, for most purposes the use of a voltmeter and an ammeter is sufficient.

If a circuit breaker is not available, the capacitor should first be tested for a short. This can be done in several ways. The easiest method is to test the unit on DC if a source is available. The capacitor is connected in series with a 100-watt lamp across a 120V DC line. The lamp will light to full brilliancy when a shorted unit is

	Any voltage E	120 volts	240 volts
Any freq.	$159,300 \dfrac{I}{f \, E}$	$144.8 \dfrac{I}{f}$	$72.4 \dfrac{I}{f}$
25 cycles	$6368 \dfrac{I}{E}$	$57.9 \; I$	$28.9 \; I$
60 cycles	$2653 \dfrac{I}{E}$	$24.1 \; I$	$12.06 \; I$

Fig. 27-4. Table which may be used in computing capacities of motor starting capacitors. Units are in microfarads.

connected across the line. A capacitor having high leakage will cause the lamp to glow. This test for leakage has very little meaning, as any leakage that will cause a 100-watt lamp to glow is much too great to be tolerated. The 100-watt lamp can be replaced with a 20-watt lamp to give a better indication of leakage. A short can be determined on AC with the circuit shown in Fig. 27-5. The neon lamp will light up when a shorted capacitor is tested.

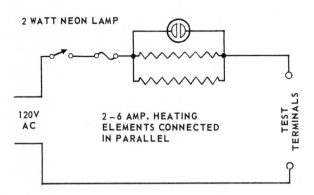

Fig. 27-5. An AC circuit which may be used in testing for capacitor shorts.
(Aerovox Corp.)

Another method of testing a capacitor for power factor which requires more calculation is as follows: the capacitance is found, as before, from the current and voltage readings. Then, to find the power factor, the effective or equivalent series resistance of the capacitor is found by this method: the capacitor is connected in the circuit, Fig. 27-6, and readings of the current and voltage are taken with the knife switch open (E_1 and I_1). If the capacitor is not shorted, the knife switch is closed and another reading of the current and voltage is taken (E_2 and I_2).

The capacitance is found from the second set of readings. To find the equivalent series resistance, use is made of the following equation:

$$R_e = \frac{\dfrac{E_1}{I_1} - \dfrac{E_2}{I_2} - R^2}{2R}$$

E_1 and I_1 are readings with the switch open, and E_2 and I_2 are readings with the switch closed. The power factor of the capacitor is then given by the equation:

$$\text{Percent P.F.} = \frac{R_e}{\dfrac{E_2}{I_2}} \times 100$$

No simple graph or chart can be made for the calculation of the first equation. If R is fixed, a family of curves can be computed and used for a more rapid calculation of the resistance, but this does not save much time.

For the average size motor-starting capacitor, a resistance of 20 ohms is a satisfactory value. The exact value of the resistance is not necessary as the voltage drop across it can be found. The circuit, as shown in Fig. 27-6, can be so arranged that by pressing a series of three buttons, the voltmeter can be connected across the resistor, the capacitor, and the line in any order desired. The current will be read on the ammeter as before.

The equivalent series resistance is

$$R_e = \frac{\dfrac{E_1{}^2 - E_R{}^2}{I_1{}^2} - \dfrac{E_2{}^2}{I_2}}{2\dfrac{E_R}{I_1}}$$

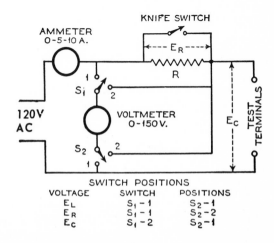

VOLTAGE	SWITCH	POSITIONS
E_L	S_1-1	S_2-1
E_R	S_1-1	S_2-2
E_C	S_1-2	S_2-1

Fig. 27-6. Circuit which may be used to determine capacitor sizes.

E_1 and I_1 are taken with switch open.
E_2 and I_2 are taken with switch closed.
E_R is voltage across R.

With this sequence of measurements it is not necessary to make a separate short circuit test, as the first reading with the knife switch open, will be sufficient to indicate a shorted capacitor. When a 20-ohm series resistor is used, the current will be equal to the voltage divided by the 20 ohms if the capacitor is short circuited. Thus, if a 150-mfd. capacitor is being tested on a 120V line, the ammeter will read 4.5 amperes for a good unit and 6 amperes for a shorted unit. If the unit is found to be good, the readings of current and voltage are recorded and the knife switch closed. The readings of current and voltage are again recorded and the computations performed. A sample computation is:

$$E_1 = 120 \text{ volts} \quad I_1 = 4.0 \text{ amperes}$$
$$E_R = 80 \text{ volts} \quad E_2 = 120 \text{ volts}$$
$$E_C = 85.6 \text{ volts} \quad I_2 = 5.6 \text{ amperes}$$

To find the power factor, the first and second sets of readings are used.

$$R_e = \frac{\dfrac{(120)^2 - (80)^2}{4^2} - \dfrac{(120)^2}{(5.6)}}{2 \dfrac{(80)}{(4)}}$$

$$= \frac{\dfrac{14400-6400}{16} - \dfrac{14400}{31.6}}{2 \times 20}$$

$$= \frac{\dfrac{8000}{16} - \dfrac{14400}{31.6}}{40}$$

$$= \frac{500 - 460}{40}$$

$$R_e = \frac{40}{40} = 1.0 \text{ ohm}$$

The power factor of this capacitor is then found from equation

$$\text{Percent P.F.} = \frac{R_e \times 100}{\dfrac{E_2}{I_2}} = \frac{1 \times 100}{\dfrac{120}{5.6}}$$

$$= \frac{1}{21.4} \times 100 = 4.7 \text{ percent}$$

Two methods are in use to designate the capacity of capacitors; either their nominal value is given, or the limits of capacity are listed. For the first case, the usual tolerance employed by most motor manufacturers is minus 10 plus 20 percent. The second method fixes the lower limit by the value given. The upper limit, however, is generally 15 percent greater than the figure listed for the range. Frequently, superior performance is obtained in such cases with capacitors of somewhat higher capacity.

Fig. 27-7 lists capacitors generally used for several sizes and types of capacitor-start motors.

MOTOR RATING HP	MOTOR SPEED RPM	CAPACITORS RATINGS MFD
1/8	3450 1725 1140	75–84
1/6	3450 1725 1140	89–96
1/4	3450 1725 1140	108–120 124–138
1/3	3450 1325 1140	161–180
1/2	3450 1725 1140	216–240
3/4 & 1	3450 1725 1140	378–420

Fig. 27-7. Typical capacitor ratings for capacitor-start motors.

Some capacitor-start motors may require capacitors other than those listed. If there is any question as to the correct rating of the capacitor, the exact value can be determined by using a capacitor selector (one type is Aerovox Model 85).

Because of the wide diversity in capacitance and voltage ratings for motor starting and running oil capacitors, it is not practical to list in these columns capacitors for all possible motor ratings.

Power Factor Control

In many cases it is possible to increase the power factor of a line by connecting power factor correction capacitors across the motors on the line. For this purpose oil-impregnated paper capacitors should be used. Fig. 27-8 gives the approximate total capacity required for various size motors operating at 230-240V 60 cycles 3-phase. These values can be used for single-phase 230V 60 cycle motors. When used for 3-phase motors, one-third of the capacity required is connected across each pair of lines. For single-phase operation, the total capacity given is connected across the line.

In addition to the increase in line capacity, the uses of the power factor capacitors will improve the voltage regulation of the line especially on long feeders.

The use of capacitors across lines supplying neon signs or fluorescent tube lighting equipment will decrease the voltage fluctuations and flicker, due to sudden changes in load. In addition, use of capacitors will decrease to a certain extent the radio interference produced by these devices.

HP	SPEED IN RPM					
	3600	1800	1200	900	720	600
1/2			20	39		
3/4		15	24	36		
1	15	21	24	30		
1 1/2	15	21	36	54		
2	24	21	36	60		
3	24	24	51	75		
5	30	36	75	99	99	165
7 1/2	39	51	75	165	201	222
10	39	60	84	165	175	250

Fig. 27-8. Approximate total capacity in mfds. required for power factor correction of standard 240V 3-phase induction motors. Approximately one-third of the values given should be used across each phase.

Capacity - Current - Power Factor Chart

Instructions for the use of capacity - current - power factor chart for electrolytic motor-starting capacitors: (See Fig. 27-9).

1. To find the capacity of a capacitor from the current readings when the capacitor is connected across a 110V circuit, draw a line vertically from the current scale to the line marked MFDS-scale A and read the capacity on the right-hand scale marked A. If the current drawn by the capacitor is greater than 4 amperes, use scale marked MFDS-scale B and read the corresponding capacity on the right-hand scale marked B, in the lower right-hand corner of the chart. The capacity can also be found by reading the capacity on the scale marked C-C in the center of the chart.

Example: To find the capacity of a capacitor which draws 2 amperes from a 120V line--from the point marked 2 amperes on the current scale, draw a perpendicular line to the scale marked MFDS-scale A. From the point of intersection, X, draw a horizontal line to the right and read the capacity, 48 microfarads on scale A. The capacity may also be read at the point Y where the vertical line crosses the scale marked C-C.

2. To find the power factor from the current and wattmeter readings, draw a horizontal line from the power scale on the left of the chart, and a vertical line from the current scale on the bottom of the chart. Read the power factor at the point of intersection of the two lines. The capacity may be determined by extending the vertical line until it intersects the scale marked C-C or the scale marked MFDS-scale A or B.

Example: To find the power factor of a capacitor which draws 2 amperes and 16.5 watts from a 120V line--draw a horizontal line from the point marked 16.5

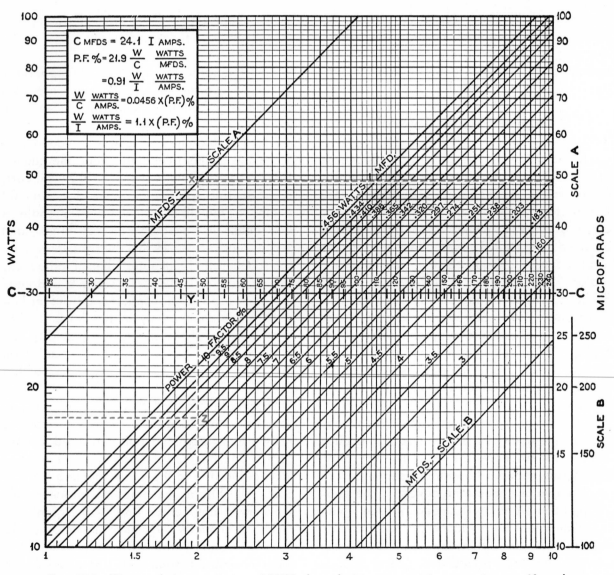

Fig. 27-9. Electrical characteristics of 120V electrolytic motor starting capacitors at 60 cycles. (Aerovox Corp.)

watts on the power scale at the left of the chart, and a vertical line from the point marked 2 amperes on the current scale, and read the power factor at the point of intersection Z. The power factor will be 8 percent.

3. To find the current that will flow when a given capacitor is connected across a 120V line, draw a horizontal line from the microfarad scale A or B, on the left of the chart, to the corresponding MFDS line, and drop a perpendicular line to the current scale at the bottom of the chart.

The current can also be found by dropping a perpendicular line from the desired capacity value in microfarads on scale C-C to the current scale.

Example: To find the current taken by a 48-microfarad capacitor when connected to a 120V line--draw a horizontal line from 48 microfarads scale A to the MFDS-scale A, and drop a perpendicular line from the point of intersection X to the current scale on the bottom of the chart, and read 2 amperes.

4. To find the power in watts for a ca-

pacitor of known capacity and power factor--draw a vertical line from the value of capacity in microfarads on scale C-C to the power factor line given and then draw a horizontal line from the point of intersection to the power scale on the left of the chart.

Example: To find the power of a 48-microfarad capacitor, 8 percent power factor when connected to a 120V line--from the point Y, 48 microfarads, on scale C-C, drop a perpendicular line until it intersects the 8 percent power factor line at the point Z. From that point draw a horizontal line to the power scale on the left of the chart and read 16.5 watts.

27-18 Cleaning Metal

During the course of use and during repair operations, metal parts may become coated with lubricating oils, greases, oxides, dirt, metallic particles or abrasives.

There are a variety of methods which may be successfully used to clean these metal parts. Lubricants or greases made from animal or vegetable oils or fats such as tallow, lard oil, palm oil, olive oil, can usually be removed by saponification (making a soap of the oil or fat). This is done by treating the parts in an alkaline solution where the oils react with the alkali to form water soluble soap compounds.

Unsaponifiable mineral oils such as kerosene, machine oil, cylinder oil and general lubricating oils are usually cleaned by an emulsification process using soaps, wetting agents and dispersing agents.

Dirt, abrasives, metal dust and inert materials are generally removed by one or both of these processes.

SOLVENT CLEANING is used for removing most of the oils from coated pieces, by immersing them in a solvent such as mineral spirits. The tanks used should have safety lids and should be hooded and vented.

DEGREASING or vapor cleaning is also used to remove oils. By holding the parts in a container where solvent vapors can condense on the parts to be cleaned, the condensed solvent washes away the oily coating, leaving the work dry and nearly clean. Production degreasing machines have two or three compartments. The work is immersed in the first compartment containing a boiling solution of the solvent. It is then dipped into the second section, which contains clean cold solvent. Finally, it is hung in the third section where only clean vapors condense on and wash over the work. The degreasing unit is self-purifying--oils and waste accumulating at bottom of third section. Job shop cleaning uses the third section only. The solvents used are generally chlorinated hydrocarbons such as carbon tetrachloride and trichlorethylene. Venting is of extreme importance for safety to the operator.

ALKALINE SCOURING. Alkaline cleaning baths are used primarily for the removal of oils, greases, solid particles of dirt, and metal particles, by immersing pieces in hot alkaline solutions. The chemicals saponify or make soap of vegetable and animal oils and fats, emulsifying mineral oils and greases and suspend the solid material. The combination of heat, active chemicals and agitations are important factors. Soap is used either as a direct addition or is formed by the saponification of vegetable or animal fats present. Caustic soda, soda ash and causticized soda form the cheapest and most direct methods of producing alkalinity in the bath. However, such materials, as a general rule, have less surface activity than more complex materials. Sodium metasilicate trisodium phosphate, and similar salts are often used to obtain alkalinity in a solution.

EMULSION SCRUBBING. A number of proprietary preparations are used for this purpose. They comprise an emulsification agent which acts to disperse organic solvents in water solutions. Emulsifiable cleaners are miscible with oils and can be washed off with water, although a film of oil may remain on the work and necessitate a subsequent alkali cleaning treatment. Dragout costs are high.

ELECTROLYTIC CLEANING. Alkaline materials are used in electrolytic cleaning. The bath is maintained at as near boiling as permissible without excessive tarnishing. The gas evolved tends to lift off the soil, presenting a clean surface for subsequent operations. The work to be cleaned is usually made the cathode. There are many formulas available for this work, but the one used depends upon the nature of the material to be used and the degree of tarnish permissible. In many cases, particularly with carbon steel or cast iron, unusual results can be obtained by switching the polarity several times during cleaning.

TARNISH REMOVAL. Brass and copper articles often become discolored or tarnished on standing or during the course of alkaline cleaning. This tarnish can be removed when work is free from oil or grease by immersion in a water solution containing 4 to 8 oz. of sodium cyanide per gallon. After discoloration has been removed--usually a matter of seconds-- pieces should be thoroughly rinsed. SODIUM CYANIDE IS VERY POISONOUS AND EXTREME CARE MUST BE OBSERVED DURING HANDLING. WHEN WORK IS CLEANED IN ALKALI, THE ALKALI SHOULD BE COMPLETELY REMOVED BECAUSE IF ALKALI AND CYANIDE ARE MIXED AND ALLOWED TO STAND, AMMONIA MAY BE DEVELOPED. CARE MUST BE TAKEN NOT TO ALLOW ANY CYANIDE TO COME IN CONTACT WITH ACIDS BECAUSE OF LIBERATION OF LETHAL HYDROCYANIC ACID GAS.

PICKLING. The pickling operation is used to remove oxides or films which usually develop on the surface of the metals from annealing. Inorganic acids are generally used for this purpose; sulphuric acid and hydrochloric acid being the more common ones. Either sodium bichromate or ferric sulphate are used in combination with an acid to remove red stains on brass or to produce a special surface effect. After pickling, it is important that metals be rinsed well and, where conditions permit, immersed in a neutralizer to remove the last traces of acid.

SULPHURIC ACID PICKLE

Sulphuric Acid	1/4 to 1 gal.
Water	4 gal.
Temperature	100 to 160 F.

Used frequently after an annealing operation where scale and tarnish has been developed. Usually the heavier the scale, the more concentrated and hotter is the pickle which is used.

SODIUM BICHROMATE PICKLE

Sulphuric Acid	1/4 gal.
Water	4 1/2 gal.
Sodium Bichromate	2 to 5 oz. per gal.
Temperature	80 to 120 F.

The lowest concentrate of chemicals that will do the required brightening is recommended. If pieces remain too long in this solution or solution is too concentrated, some pitting or etching of the surface may result. When properly employed it will give a clear yellow surface finish which is not glossy. Sodium bichromate pickle is used for removing red stains which remain after sulphuric acid pickling.

BRIGHT DIP

Sulphuric Acid	2 gal.
Nitric Acid	1 gal.
Water	1 qt.
Hydrochloric Acid	1 oz. to every 5 gal.
Operate	Cold, room temperature

To obtain a gloss, a bright dip solution is required. There are many possible combinations which will give the desired results. Increasing the nitric acid makes the solution more active. Increasing the sulphuric acid slows down the action of the solution. Add salt carefully and in small quantities if work is sooty.

SCALE DIP. Sometimes a preliminary preparation of the surface is necessary before immersing the pieces in the bright dip, especially when a very bright, smooth surface is desired.

(a) Where very heavy cutting of the surface is desired, use concentrated nitric acid as received from the carboy.

(b) For milder treatment, use the formula:

Nitric Acid	1 gal.
Sulphuric Acid	1 to 2 gal.
Water	1 to 5 gal.

These solutions are quite active and must be used with care to prevent too deeply attacking the brass. After the bright dipping, either preceded by scale or bichromate dipping, the work should be thoroughly rinsed in water, immersed in 2 to 4 oz. solution of sodium cyanide followed by thorough rinsing. Then immerse in 1 oz. solution of neutral soap, and thoroughly rinse. Omit the soap solution if pieces are to be soldered. Ferric sulphate can be used in place of sodium bichromate, and for certain purposes it is preferred, particularly where attack of base metal is to be kept to the minimum.

27-19 Food Preservation by Radiation Treatment

Experiments have been conducted using atomic energy radiations to preserve food. Fresh foods have been put in sealed containers. These containers were exposed to a form of atomic energy radiation. It was found, upon inspection, that the food remains in its fresh state with no change in appearance, flavor or food value, as a result of being treated in this manner.

27-20 Capillary Tube Refrigerant Controls

Today practically all domestic refrigerators being built, and many of the smaller size package-type hermetic commercial refrigerating systems built by mass production methods, employ a capillary tube.

ADVANTAGES OF CAPILLARY TUBE. A capillary tube is simply a small diameter liquid line connecting the high side to the low side. It is usually soldered to the suction line for heat exchange purposes. Because of the pressure drop caused by the length and the small bore of the tube, it controls the flow of refrigerant to the low side. There are no moving parts and the capillary is merely substituted for the conventional liquid line. In addition, the unloading characteristic of the capillary tube (1) reduces the amount of refrigerant charge required, and (2) permits the use of a split-phase hermetic motor compressor. Split-phase motor-compressors are recommended for use only with devices such as a capillary that allows the low side and high side pressures to equalize during the off cycle, thereby reducing

COND. UNIT	HIGH (30 DEG. F.)	MEDIUM (10 DEG. F.)	LOW (−10 DEG. F.)
	−	5 ft. of 0.031 in., or	10 ft. of 0.031 in., or
1/8 hp	5 ft. of 0.036 in., or	9 ft. of 0.036 in., or	20 ft. of 0.036 in.
	8 ft. of 0.042 in., or	18 ft. of 0.042 in.	−
	16 ft. of 0.049 in.	−	−
	−	−	8 ft. of 0.031 in., or
1/5 hp	−	6 ft. of 0.036 in., or	16 ft. of 0.036 in.
	5 ft. of 0.042 in., or	12 ft. of 0.042 in.	−
	10 ft. of 0.049 in.	−	−

Fig. 27-10. Approximate capillary tube sizes for R-12 refrigerant.

the starting torque requirements of the motor.

PRECAUTIONS NEEDED IN APPLYING CAPILLARY TUBE. The serviceman may wish to replace some of the components of a system that already uses a capillary. In order to do this successfully in the field or service shop, extreme caution is necessary. In spite of the apparent simplicity of the capillary, careful balancing of the system is required to insure satisfactory performance. Improper balance of the system will be evidenced by excessive running time, abnormal operating pressures, or by extreme difficulty in adjusting the refrigerant charge properly.

Both the high side and low side must be suitable for use with a capillary tube. The capillary must be properly matched to the capacity of the condensing unit. High standards of cleanliness and dehydration during processing are essential. Failure to take these factors into account will inevitably result in unsatisfactory performance.

FIRST STEP - DESIGN OF HIGH SIDE AND LOW SIDE. During certain portions of the operating cycle, the compressor may pump more than a capillary can pass. This will result in liquid refrigerant backing up in the high side. If a conventional receiver is used, most of the refrigerant will accumulate there. Therefore, to prevent possible short charging of the low side during portions of the operating cycle, the conventional liquid receiver should be omitted. For this reason, capacitor-type units employing a receiver are not recommended for use with a capillary tube.

In the event that a hermetic condensing unit is being reworked for capillary tube application, not only should the receiver be omitted, but also all liquid traps in the high side should be avoided to insure rapid unloading of the high side during the off cycle of the compressor.

Design of the lowside is equally important. The lowside should be of the type that will satisfactorily operate on a comparatively small amount of refrigerant, preferrably less than one pound, in order not to impose excessive loads on the condensing unit during pulldown. This is especially important because of the necessity of operating without a receiver. If the evaporator is of the dry type, a liquid accumulator will usually be required to allow for some variation in refrigerant charge.

SECOND STEP - CAPILLARY SELECTION. Although good engineering practice demands that the proper capillary be determined by laboratory tests for each piece of equipment at standard operating conditions, this procedure is not practical on the job from a serviceman's standpoint. However, as a result of numerous tests, it is possible to recommend the approximate capillary tube to be used with 1/8 hp and 1/5 hp split-phase condensing units and compressors for the particular low side application. Fig. 27-10 gives capillary recommendations in tabular form which will enable you to choose a capillary tube best suited to the application at hand. Approximately four feet of the capillary tube should be soldered to the suction line to provide good heat exchange and to stabilize the metering action of the capillary tube. The remaining capillary should be coiled in the unit compartment.

These recommended lengths and bores are based on the assumption that a four foot section of the capillary will be soldered to the suction line, as shown in Fig. 27-11. Recommended lengths will not apply if this is not done, or if certain patented prefabricated assemblies of equivalent flow resistance are used.

Insufficient capillary will give poor overall efficiency due to the blowing of some uncondensed gas through the capillary; on the other hand, too much capillary will result in liquid refrigerant backing up in the high side, thus increasing the discharge pressure and short charging the low side. Thus, proper matching of the capillary to the compressor is essential to insure satisfactory performance of the system.

THIRD STEP – CAREFUL PROCESSING. It is obvious that extreme care must be taken to insure a dry, clean system. The hermetic condensing unit is dry and clean when it leaves the factory; however, it will be necessary to make sure that no moisture or dirt enters during the installation and that the rest of the refrigerating system is dry and clean before final assembly to the unit. As an additional precaution an approved high side drier incorporating a strainer should be located ahead of the capillary.

All air must be exhausted from the system before the final refrigerant charge is introduced. Before final charging, the system should be evacuated through the charging valve. If evacuating equipment is not available, the suction line flare connection at the valve should be left loose and the discharge service valve opened to allow the R-12 gas charge in the high side to sweep through the lines and low side, purging any remaining air from the system.

Finally, the system must be charged with the proper amount of refrigerant. Unlike the float valve or expansion valve system, which provides for continuous storage of surplus refrigerant in the high side, the capillary system refrigerant charge is especially critical. The best method is to charge refrigerant slowly into the system with the unit running until frost forms on the suction line to a point just beyond the outlet of the evaporator. To avoid overcharging of the system, it is important that there be no refrigerant backed up in the high side during the final adjustment of the refrigerant charge.

This condition can be determined by noting the temperature difference between the first few and the last few rows of the condenser. If the last few rows are noticeably cooler to the touch, you can feel sure that liquid refrigerant is backed up in the condenser, indicating either a restriction or poor selection of the capillary. The charge should then be checked later on after the system has cycled to be sure this frost line is being maintained. If the system is overcharged, frost or heavy sweat will form on the suction line beyond this point. If the system is undercharged, frosting of the suction line or evaporator will cease somewhat ahead of that point. Another test to check the charge is to shut off the compressor for a few moments until the liquid refrigerant has drained from the high side, and has passed out through the capillary to the low side. If the system is properly charged, there will be no indications of severe overcharge when the unit is restarted.

To summarize, although the proper application of a capillary requires considerable design and test in the laboratory to achieve the best balanced system with maximum operating efficiency, it is possible for the service shop to make successful conversion to a capillary providing the serviceman is willing to follow the preceding instructions, viz:

1. Be sure that both the high side and the low side are properly designed for capillary application.
2. Make the proper capillary selection.
3. Process carefully to insure a clean, dry job properly charged with refrigerant.

27-21 System for Determining Dryness of Refrigerants

The DFN Moisture Indicator shown in Chapter 12 (McIntire Connector Co.) is a laboratory test instrument for use as a production and service tool. In a matter of minutes it shows the moisture vapor concentration in the refrigerant and the LOWEST TEMPERATURE at which the SYSTEM can be SAFELY OPERATED.

The indicator cartridge contains Drierite, specially treated with coloring agent.

This is green when dry, purple when wet. The time required for the indicating crystals to change color determines the point at which the refrigerant or any gas will release water.

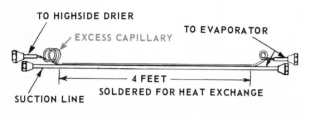

TO HIGHSIDE DRIER
EXCESS CAPILLARY
TO EVAPORATOR
4 FEET
SOLDERED FOR HEAT EXCHANGE
SUCTION LINE

Fig. 27-11. *Typical replacement capillary tube and suction line.*

Any gas holding water in the vapor state, when cooled, will reach a temperature at which free moisture (liquid water) will appear. The greater the concentration of water vapor in a gas, the higher the temperature at which water will be released. This freeing of moisture is readily shown by frost on cold lines, beads of water on glasses of cold liquids, and in the refrigeration system by frozen expansion valves. Free water must be present before ice can be formed. The highest temperature at which free water is liberated, on cooling, is called the DEW POINT. For a given moisture concentration in a gas there is only one dew point temperature. Knowing the dew point of a refrigerant determines the lowest temperature at which the expansion valve will operate satisfactorily.

HOW DRY SHOULD THE SYSTEM BE?

A. To prevent the formation of sludges and plating, the dew point should be -10 F. or lower.

B. To prevent valve freeze-up, it should have a dew point 5 F. lower than the suction temperature.

C. For safe operation the dew point must be -10 F. or lower for all systems operating at a suction temperature of -5 F. or above.

Where suction temperature is below -5 F., the dew point must be 5 F. lower than the suction temperature.

Instructions for Assembly and Operation

ASSEMBLY. Assemble unit without cartridge, using nondrying pipe compound on 1/4 in. male pipe threads. Remove gauge port plug and purge out free oil lodged in port. Attach assembly to suction gauge if system is operating above 10 lb. back pressure. If operating below 10 lb., attach to discharge gauge port. Crack metering valve and allow gas to purge slowly through the unit for at least 20 seconds. Close metering valve. Put top felt in place, using tweezers, as moisture from the hands may contaminate it. Remove caps from indicator cartridge and install as shown. Hold wet fingertip 1/2 in. above indicator cartridge and crack metering valve. If cold vapor can be felt, sufficient gas is passing through cartridge. CAUTION--Do not open metering valve further, as liquid oil and/ or refrigerant may be passed into the indicator cartridge and spoil it beyond use.

TEST. For checking systems operating at -10 F. and above, watch crystals change to purple, shut metering valve and check time of test. Refer to Fig. 27-12 to find condition of the refrigerant. Leaving metering valve open to show added color just uses up the cartridge and does not prove anything. It is the time taken to start color change that counts.

CONDITION	TIME MINUTES	REFRIGERANT DRY TO F. DEW POINT
If green cartridge starts to show purple in the following time	1	20
	2	0
	4	-10
If purple in cartridge starts to fade in the following time	1/2	-60
	1	-50
	2	-40
	3	-30
No color changes either way	5	-15

Fig. 27-12. *Table of time intervals for color indication. (McIntire Co., Sub. of Superior Valve and Fittings Co.)*

FOR CHECKING SYSTEMS OPERAT-ING BELOW -10 F. Blow into cartridge to give purple indication or take a partly used cartridge and install in indicator unit with purple coloring at the bottom. Crack valve, as stated above, and watch for the crystals to fade or pale out. When this starts, close metering valve and check time.

The table is for new cartridges and varies slightly for cartridges that have been used.

Color change of the small particles in cotton should not be considered a true test. These minute particles are almost pure, indicating chemical--and its color change does not provide an accurate indication of the moisture condition of the system. Moisture indicator can be used in a like manner to check refrigerant in service drums, low sides and dry air for purging.

CAUTION--Mount indicator assembly vertical with outlet at the top. Keep all parts as clean and dry as possible. Do not run test with cap on top, as glass will not stand high pressure. By limiting test to a few grains indication, cartridge may be used several times if recapped and kept in a dry place.

Take assembly apart after test and flush out any oil which may have accumulated during test.

Indicator is effective on halogen refrigerants. Do not use on sulphur dioxide or ammonia.

27-22 Refrigerant and Air Changes in Evaporative Condenser

An evaporative condenser is described in Chapter 13. Such condensers are used because they provide lower head pressures than air-cooled condensers and use less water than water-cooled condensers. As mentioned previously, they are popular where localities restrict the use of water for cooling purposes.

The evaporative condenser is based on the principle that one pound of water ab-sorbs approximately 1000 Btu per pound as it evaporates. This value compared to the specific heat of water of 1 Btu per pound per F. gives some indication of the water saving. Furthermore, the water evaporates into the air and the water cools to its wet bulb temperature, as shown in Fig. 27-13.

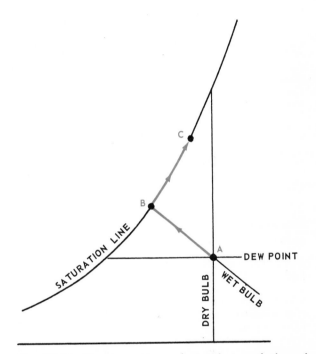

Fig. 27-13. Psychrometic analysis of air path through an evaporative condenser.

Air enters the evaporative condenser at (A), is cooled to temperature (B), but becomes saturated with moisture in the interval. The saturated air then travels over the condenser tubes against the water spray and exits at the blower at temperature (C). Note that (B) has a lower dry bulb than (A) and therefore the condenser temperatures and pressures are lower than if air at (A) were used for cooling only.

Fig. 27-14 shows the path of the refrigerant in the condenser tubes of the evaporative condenser. The gas enters the condenser at (A) in a superheated condition. The gas cools to the saturated vapor line and then condenses along line (B) to (C). The final cooling to the room or ambient temperature takes place (C) to (D). The line (B) to (C) would be at a higher temperature if the condenser were air-cooled.

27-23 Heat Conductivity

CONDUCTIVITY OF MISCELLANEOUS SUBSTANCES

Material	k
Air	.175
Concrete wall	8.00
Glass	5.0
Lead	243.0
Vacuum, High	.004

CONDUCTIVITY OF MISCELLANEOUS INSULATING MATERIALS

Material	Density #/cu.ft.	k conductivity
Asbestos, loose	29.3	.94
Cork, granulated	8.1	.34
Cork, granulated, impregnated with pitch	17.79	0.428
Balsa	7.05	0.32
Felt	16.9	.25
Glass wool (curled pyrex)	4.0	0.29
Kapok	.87	.24
Mineral (slag) wool, loose packed	12.0	0.26
Rock wool (fibrous rock, also felted)	6.0	0.26
Rubber, cellular	5.0	.37
Sawdust, pine	18.76	0.57
Straw fibres, pressed	8.67	0.32
Wood fibres (kingia australis)	8.4	0.33
Wool, pure	4.99	0.26

Note: k = Btu/hr./sq.ft./in. thickness/degree F.

CONDUCTIVITY OF PROPRIETARY MATERIALS

Trade Name	Density #/cu.ft.	k conductivity
Armstrong's corkboard	7.3	0.285
Celotex	13.2	0.31
Dry-Zero	1.0	0.24
Nu Wood	15.0	0.32
United's 100% pure corkboard	9.0	0.27
U. S. mineral wool	12.0	0.26
Ferro Therm metal sheet (4 sheets)	4 oz./□1/ sheet	0.226

(American Society of Refrigerating Engineers)

27-24 Brine Freezing Temperatures

Brines are water mixed with a substance which will go into solution with the water and provide a fluid which can readily flow at temperatures below 32 F.

There are several types of brines: (1) alcohol; (2) salt; (3) glycol.

1. Alcohol brines are usually made of ethyl alcohol.
2. Salt brines are usually made of sodium chloride and calcium chloride. Eutectic point for sodium chloride solution is -6 F., and for calcium chloride is -60 F.
3. The glycol brines with noncorrosive properties are usually made of glycerine, ethylene glycol, and propylene glycol.

ALCOHOL (Formula No. 1)

Temperature F. (Freezing)	20	10	0	−10	−20	−30	−40
Specific Gravity at 60 F.		.9691	.9592	.9486	.9345		

GLYCERINE

Temperature F. (Freezing)	20	10	0	−10	−20	−30	−40
Specific Gravity at 60 F.	1.056	1.082	1.105	1.123	1.137	1.151	

CALCIUM CHLORIDE

Temperature F. (Freezing)	20	10	0	−10	−20	−30	−40
Specific Gravity at 60 F.	1.090	1.140	1.175	1.201	1.227	1.254	1.265
Percent of Chemical	10	17	20.5	23	25	27	28

* SODIUM CHLORIDE

Temperature F. (Freezing)	20	10	0	−10	−20	−30	−40
Specific Gravity of 60 F.	1.072	1.118	1.158				
Percent of Chemical	10	16	21				

(*Usable only down to 0 F.)

ETHYLENE GLYCOL

Temperature F. (Freezing)	20	10	0	−10	−20	−30	−40
Specific Gravity at 60 F.	1.05	1.07	1.075	1.08	1.09	1.096	1.105
Percent of Chemical	32	40	43	45	50	53	57

PROPYLENE GLYCOL

Temperature F. (Freezing)	20	10	0	−10	−20	−30	−40
Specific Gravity at 60 F.	1.037	1.045	1.051				
Percent of Chemical	30	35	39				

27-25 Sealing Insulations

A serious problem with any insulation is to keep the insulation dry. The moisture that can collect in insulation is always present in the air. When the air on one side of a structure is more moist than on the other, the pressure difference (vapor pressure) is quite high. The moisture will then seek its way through the smallest opening and then condense in the colder area if the temperature is at or below the dew point temperature.

It is most important, therefore, to install a vapor seal on the warm side of the wall and also to allow any moisture that does get into the insulation to easily reach the evaporator coil.

27-26 Gas and Vapor

A true gas exists as a gas at standard temperatures and pressures.

A vapor is a saturated gas.

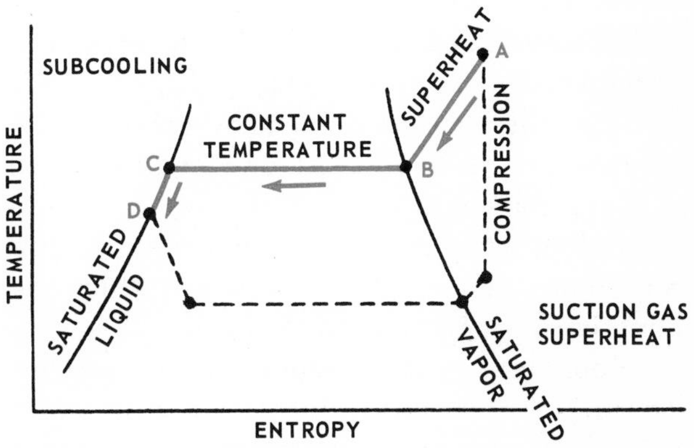

Fig. 27-14. Temperature-entropy diagram showing theoretical refrigeration cycle (solid line shows path of refrigerant through condenser).

Vapor is the gas state of a substance which is a liquid at standard atmospheric pressures and temperatures (such as water). However, vapor is also the term applied to refrigerants in the gaseous state inside the refrigerating system.

27-27 Refrigerant Oils

REFRIGERANTS	VISCOSITY SUV* AT 100 F.	SPECIFIC GRAVITY	FLOC TEST F. **	POUR TEST ASTM F.
RECIPROCATING COMPRESSORS				
R–12	150–300	.90	−80	−40
R–22	150–300			
R–40	280–300	.92		
R–717 NH$_3$	150–300			
R–744 CO$_2$	280–300			
ROTARY COMPRESSORS				
R–30	150–300		−80	−40
R–12	280–300			
CENTRIFUGAL COMPRESSORS				
R–30	280–300	.92	−80	−40
R–11	280–300			
R–12	280–300			
AUTOMOTIVE COMPRESSORS	300 600	.92	−25	−10

* Viscosity SUV at 100 F. means Saybolt Universal Viscosity. This is the time in seconds which is required for 60 cubic centimeters of the oil at 100 deg. F. to flow through the standard Saybolt orifice.

** Floc test F. This applies to oils which are used with completely miscible refrigerants, such as R-11, R-12, or R-22.

The test is conducted by mixing 10% refrigerant with 90% oil and sealing it in a glass tube and cooling it slowly until a flocculent precipitate of wax appears. The maximum temperature at which this occurs is recorded as the floc point.

Pour test ASTM (American Society for Testing Materials) – Petroleum oils when cooled to very low temperatures become plastic solids. The temperature at which oil will just flow is called the pour point and is indicated in F.

Refrigerant oils are sometimes given a very small amount of antifoam inhibitor to reduce foaming. Compressor parts are sometimes given a phosphating treatment to improve lubrication. Tricresyl phosphate has also been added to refrigerant oils to improve lubrication.

Refrigerant oil must be free of moisture. Moisture in oil is measured by its ability to resist the flow of electricity through it. This is known as its dielectric property. Refrigerant oil should have a dielectric value of 25,000 volts minimum.

There are two types of oils in use, the the paraffin base and the naphthene base. The paraffin base oil has a dominance of paraffin hydrocarbons in the refined oil and likewise for the naphthene base oils.

27-28 Refrigerant Charging Apparatus (Vacuum Pump and Refrigerant)

A refrigerant charging apparatus using a vacuum pump and an evaporator is shown in Fig. 27-15.

This popular method of transferring refrigerants cools the refrigerant to maintain a good pressure differential between the storage cylinder and the service cylinder. The principle of operation is simple. Because the refrigerants are volatile, which means they evaporate and condense readily and their pressures quickly react to temperature changes, the flow of the refrigerant from the warm storage cylinder can be greatly speeded if the refrigerant going into the service cylinder can be kept cool. This cooling may be done by inserting an evaporator into the charging line (B). If this evaporator is kept at 40 F. and as the cooled refrigerant flows into the service cylinder (D), the pressure in this cylinder is constantly kept at a lower pressure than the pressure in cylinder A. To operate this system, proceed as follows:

1. Connect the flexible charging line to the service cylinder D.
2. Purge the cylinder by opening valves 3 and 4.
3. If a vacuum is desired in the service cylinder, close valve 3 and open valves 1, 2, and 5, and operate the vacuum pump until the desired vacuum has been reached, stop the vacuum pump 4.
4. Close valves 1 and 2 and then open valve 4 and start the refrigerating mechanism. Open valve 4 and the pressure in the storage cylinder A will now push the cooled refrigerant in the evaporator C into the service cylinder D. As this cooled refrigerant passes into cylinder D, it keeps the cylinder cool and therefore the pressure is low.
5. By watching the scale E, the amount of refrigerant charged into cylinder D can be easily determined.

CAUTION: NEVER FILL THE CYLINDER COMPLETELY FULL OF REFRIGERANT. A COMPLETELY FILLED CYLINDER MAY BURST AS IT WARMS TO ROOM TEMPERATURE.

Another charging method is more complicated, but is very convenient when large

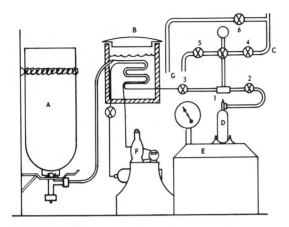

Fig. 27-15. Refrigerant charging apparatus using vacuum pump and cooling coil. A—Storage cylinder. B—Evaporator. C—Purging line. D—Service cylinder. E—Weighing scale. F—Refrigeration pump. G—Vacuum pump connections. 1—Cylinder valve. 2—Charging panel main valve. 3—Evaporator coil shutoff valve. 4—Purging valve. 5—Vacuum pump valve. 6—Vacuum pump discharge hand valve.

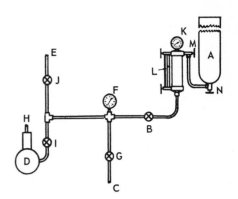

Fig. 27-16. Method of transferring refrigerant from storage cylinder to service cylinder by means of charging board. A—Storage cylinder. B—Charging control valve. C—Connection to unit or cylinder to be charged. D—Evacuating pump. E—Purging line. F—Compound gauge. G—Disconnecting valve. H—Pump discharge. I—Pump control valve. J—Purge control valve. K—High pressure gauge. L—Liquid level sight gauge. M—Charging cylinder control valve. N—Storage cylinder valve.

quantities of refrigerant are to be handled. It eliminates the necessity of weighing the cylinders when charging. The device is called a charging board. It uses an intermediate drum, having a reinforced glass liquid-level indicator built into it, as shown in Fig. 27-16. The intermediate drum is permanently connected to the 150 pound storage cylinder (A) by means of a copper line and a shutoff valve; it is then filled with the refrigerant. The level of the refrigerant is indicated in the glass sight level gauge (L) which is calibrated in

pounds of refrigerant. When a small cylinder is to be charged, the cylinder is attached to the intermediate drum at C and the connecting line is purged. After the cylinder is cooled, the opening of the necessary valves will allow the refrigerant to flow from the intermediate drum to the service cylinder. The amount being charged into the cylinder is indicated by the weight scale mounted on the liquid-level gauge.

27-29 Air and Its Moisture Holding Properties

DEW POINT TEMPERATURE F.	POUNDS OF MOISTURE PER POUND OF DRY AIR	GRAINS OF MOISTURE PER POUND OF DRY AIR	PPM (WT.)
120	.08	570	80,000
110	.06	400	60,000
100	.044	300	42,000
90	.03	210	30,000
80	.022	150	22,000
70	.015	110	15,000
60	.011	76	11,000
50	.0075	53	7,500
40	.005	36	5,000
30	.0033	24	3,300
20	.002	15	2,000
10	.0014	9	1,400
0	.0008	5.5	800

(ASHRAE Handbook of Fundamentals)

27-30 Motor Size--Mean Effective Pressure Method

The mep, (mean effective pressure), of the gas is the median (average) pressure bearing down upon the piston head, and it is the pressure to be overcome by the electric motor when driving the compressor. The mep is determined by a formula which uses as the basic variables the low side pressure, the high side pressure, and the ratio of the specific heat of constant pressure to the specific heat of constant volume $\frac{C_p}{C_v} = K$ for the kind of refrigerant. This formula is as follows:

$$mep = P_1 \times \frac{K}{K-1} \left[\left(\frac{P_2}{P_1} \right) \frac{K}{K-1} \right]$$

P_1 = suction pressure, psia

P_2 = condenser pressure, psia

$K = \frac{C_p}{C_v}$

This value, when multiplied by the area of the piston, by the length of the stroke, and by the rpm, will give the foot-pounds per minute needed to drive the compressor.

$$\text{Ft. lb. per min.} = mep \times \frac{\pi D^2}{4} \times S \times N \times R$$

D = Piston diameter

S = Stroke

N = Number of cylinders

R = Rpm

Convert the foot-pound per min. into hp by dividing by 33,000.

$$hp = \frac{\text{ft. lb./min.}}{33,000}$$

The mep may be determined from the above or may be determined by obtaining the indicator card of the compressor being studied. Engineers' handbooks set forth the methods of using and obtaining indicator cards.

For example: If the indicator card shows a mep of 30 lbs. per sq. in., the indicated hp necessary to drive a 1 cylinder compressor with a 2 in. bore and a 2 in. stroke and running at 200 rpm would be as follows:

$$hp = \frac{30 \text{ psi} \times \text{area} \times \text{stroke} \times \text{rpm}}{33,000}$$

The dimensions have to be in foot-pounds = pressure x area. The resistance is the number of compression strokes x rpm =

$$\frac{30 \text{ psi} \times \frac{\pi d^2}{4} \times \frac{2}{12} \times 200}{33,000} =$$

$$\frac{30 \times \pi d^2 \times 2 \times 200}{4 \times 33,000 \times 12} = \frac{r \times 8 \times \pi}{3700 \times 4} =$$

$$\frac{10 \times \pi}{330} = \frac{31.416}{330} = .0952 \text{ or}$$

approximately .10 hp or $\frac{1}{10}$ hp.

This is the theoretical hp and neglects friction, oil pumping, starting load, drive losses, etc. Up to a 1 ton machine, one should double this hp, i.e., 1/4 hp calculated will need a 1/2 hp motor. Up to 5 tons, this ratio gradually tapers off until adding 30 percent at 5 tons capacity will take into consideration the above losses. The reason for the decrease is that some of the losses remain constant, while others do not increase as rapidly in proportion to the increase in the size of the unit.

27-31 Solders

Some common solder alloys used in refrigeration work:

SOLDER	MELTING PT. F.	FLOW PT. F.	SHEAR STRENGTH psi
50-50 Tin-Lead	358	414	83.4
95-5 Tin-Antimony	450	465	327.0
Silver Solder			
45 Ag., 15 Cu, 24 Cd, 16 Zn	1120	1145	8340
Phos.-Copper	1310	1650	8340

27-32 Galvanic Action Sequence

Least Noble (easiest to corrode) (anode-positive)

Magnesium
Magnesium alloys
Zinc
Aluminum 2S
Cadmium
Aluminum 17ST
Steel or iron
Cast iron
18-8 Stainless steel
Lead-tin solders
Lead
Tin
Nickel
Brass
Copper
Bronze
Silver solder
Silver
Graphite
Gold
Platinum

Most Noble (hardest to corrode) (cathode-negative)

27-33 Electrical Constants and Unit Prefixes

ELECTRICAL ENGINEERING UNITS AND CONSTANTS

As adopted by NBS

Symbols and Units

Quantity	Symbol	Unit	Symbol
charge	Q	coulomb	C
current	I	ampere	A
voltage, potential difference	V	volt	V
electromotive force	$\mathscr{E}$	volt	V
resistance	R	ohm	Ω
conductance	G	mho (siemens)	A/V, or mho (S)
reactance	X	ohm	Ω
susceptance	B	mho	A/V, or mho

impedance	Z	ohm	Ω
admittance	Y	mho	A/V, or mho
capacitance	C	farad	F
inductance	L	henry	H
energy, work	W	joule	J
power	P	watt	W
resistivity	ρ	ohm-meter	Ωm
conductivity	σ	mho per meter	mho/m
electric displacement	D	coulomb per sq. meter	C/m²
electric field strength	E	volt per meter	V/m
permittivity (absolute)	ϵ	farad per meter	F/m
relative permittivity	ϵ_r	(numeric)	
magnetic flux	Φ	weber	Wb
magnetomotive force	$\mathscr{F}$	ampere (ampere-turn)	A
reluctance	$\mathscr{R}$	ampere per weber	A/Wb
permeance	$\mathscr{P}$	weber per ampere	Wb/A
magnetic flux density	B	tesla	T
magnetic field strength	H	ampere per meter	A/m
permeability (absolute)	μ	henry per meter	H/m
relative permeability	μ_r	(numeric)	
length	l	meter	m
mass	m	kilogram	kg
time	t	second	s
frequency	f	hertz	Hz
angular frequency	ω	radian per second	rad/s
force	F	newton	N
pressure	p	newton per sq. meter	N/m²
temperature (absolute)	T	degree Kelvin	°K
temperature (International)	t	degree Celsius	°C

RECOMMENDED UNIT PREFIXES

Multiples and submultiples	Prefixes	Symbols	Pronunciation
10^{12}	tera	T	tĕr′ á
10^9	giga	G	jī′gá
10^6	mega	M	mĕg′ á
10^3	kilo	k	kĭl′ ŏ
10^2	hecto	h	hĕk′ tŏ
10	deka	da	dĕk′ á
10^{-1}	deci	d	dĕs′ ĭ
10^{-2}	centi	c	sĕn′ tĭ
10^{-3}	milli	m	mĭl′ ĭ
10^{-6}	micro	μ	mī′ krŏ
10^{-9}	nano	n	năn′ ŏ
10^{-12}	pico	p	pē′ kŏ
10^{-15}	femto	f	fĕm′ tŏ
10^{-18}	atto	a	ăt′ tŏ

DEFINED VALUES AND CONVERSION FACTORS

Meter	1 650 763.73 wavelengths of the transition $2p_{10} - 5d_5$ in ^{86}Kr
Kilogram	mass of the international kilogram
Second	1/31 556 925.974 7 of the tropical year 1900
Degree Kelvin	In the thermodynamic scale, 273.16 °K = triple point of water (fp, 273.15 °K=0 °C)
Unified atomic mass unit, u	1/12 the mass of an atom of the ^{12}C nuclide
Standard acceleration of free fall	9.806 65 m s⁻², 980.665 cm s⁻²
Normal atmosphere	101 325 N m⁻², 1 013 250 dyn cm⁻²
Thermochemical calorie	4.1840 J, 4.1840×10⁷ erg
Int. Steam Table calorie	4.1868 J, 4.1868×10⁷ erg
Liter	0.001 000 028 m³, 1 000.028 cm³ (recommended by CIPM, 1950)
Inch	0.0254 m, 2.54 cm
Pound (avdp.)	0.453 592 37 kg, 453.592 37 g

PHYSICAL CONSTANTS

Constant	Symbol	Value	Est.* error limit	Unit Système Intern. (MKSA)		Unit Centimeter-gram-second (CGS)	
Speed of light in vacuum	c	2.997925	3	×10⁸	m s⁻¹	×10¹⁰	cm s⁻¹
Elementary charge	e	1.60210	7	10⁻¹⁹	C	10⁻²⁰	cm$^{1/2}$g$^{1/2}$†
		4.80298	20			10⁻¹⁰	cm$^{3/2}$g$^{1/2}$s⁻¹‡
Avogadro constant	N_A	6.02252	28	10²³	mol⁻¹	10²³	mol⁻¹
Electron rest mass	m_e	9.1091	4	10⁻³¹	kg	10⁻²⁸	g
Proton rest mass	m_p	1.67252	8	10⁻²⁷	kg	10⁻²⁴	g
Faraday constant	F	9.64870	16	10⁴	C mol⁻¹	10³	cm$^{1/2}$g$^{1/2}$mol⁻¹†
Planck constant	h	6.6256	5	10⁻³⁴	J s	10⁻²⁷	erg s
Fine structure constant	α	7.29720	10	10⁻³		10⁻³	
Charge to mass ratio for electron	e/m_e	1.758796	19	10¹¹	C kg⁻¹	10⁷	cm$^{1/2}$g⁻$^{1/2}$†
		5.27274	6			10¹⁷	cm$^{3/2}$g⁻$^{1/2}$s⁻¹‡
Rydberg constant	R_∞	1.0973731	3	10⁷	m⁻¹	10⁵	cm⁻¹
Gyromagnetic ratio of proton	γ	2.67519	2	10⁸	rad s⁻¹T⁻¹	10⁴	rad s⁻¹G⁻¹†
(Uncorrected for diamagnetism, H₂O)	γ'	2.67512	2	10⁸	rad s⁻¹T⁻¹	10⁴	rad s⁻¹G⁻¹†
Bohr magneton	μ_B	9.2732	6	10⁻²⁴	J T⁻¹	10⁻²¹	erg G⁻¹†
Gas constant	R	8.3143	12	10⁰	J°K⁻¹mol⁻¹	10⁷	erg°K⁻¹mol⁻¹
Boltzmann constant	k	1.38054	18	10⁻²³	J°K⁻¹	10⁻¹⁶	erg°K⁻¹
First radiation constant ($2\pi hc^2$)	c_1	3.7405	3	10⁻¹⁶	W m²	10⁻⁵	erg cm²s⁻¹
Second radiation constant	c_2	1.43879	19	10⁻²	m°K	10⁰	cm°K
Stefan-Boltzmann constant	σ	5.6697	29	10⁻⁸	W m⁻²°K⁻⁴	10⁻⁵	erg cm⁻²s⁻¹°K⁻⁴
Gravitational constant	G	6.670	15	10⁻¹¹	N m²kg⁻²	10⁻⁸	dyn cm²g⁻²

*Based on 3 std. dev., applies to last digits in preceding col.   †Electromagnetic syst.
‡Electrostatic syst.

27-34 Moisture Evaporation Sources

METHOD	POUNDS OF MOISTURE
Bathing	.1 to .5
Clothes	
Drying (average family)	26.0
Washing (average family)	4.0
Cooking	
Breakfast	.9
Lunch	1.2
Dinner	2.7
Dishwashing	
Breakfast and Lunch	.2
Dinner	.7
Humans	
Average	.4
Mopping per 100 sq. ft.	3.0

27-35 Refrigerator Storage Air Velocities

ITEM	VELOCITY fpm
Beer	150
Candy	60
Cheese	90
Flowers	60
Fruits	60–150
Furs	150
Meats	60–150
Nuts	150
Vegetables	60–150

27-36 Decibel

The decibel is a measurement of sound. Sound has two variables: (1) magnitude, and (2) frequency (audible to the ear 20 to 10,000 cycles/second). The decibel is a ratio only between the sound power and a reference value.

Decibel level is the combination of magnitude and frequency over a reference level (acceptable surrounding sound).

A change of 2 decibels (db) is the smallest change a human ear can detect. There are two levels which must be considered: (1) sound pressure level, and (2) sound power level. Sound pressure level is measured in microbars and sound power level in watts.

75 db noise to 43 db, but background is 30 db, therefore noisy.

75 db noise level to 27 db, which is below 30 db background level, therefore it is considered a quiet condition.

The attenuation of sound means the reduction of sound.

Sound levels identified with various localities are as follows:

PLACE	DECIBEL RANGE
Auditorium	25–35
Churches	25–35
Hospitals	30–40
Hotels	35–45
Offices	35–45
Public Buildings	35–45
Residences	25–35
Restaurants	40–50
Schools	35–45
Stores	40–50
Transportation Depots	35–45

27-37 Noise Distribution

Complaints of unpleasant noise connected with air conditioning and refrigeration equipment are often directed to equipment venders and servicemen.

Sound or noise is produced by the movement or vibration of an object. This movement may be caused by vibration of two objects, from the movement of air against an object, as in air conditioning ducts. An example of how sound is generated is to visualize the movement of the wing of a bee. As the wing moves up and down, it causes the gas molecules (air) toward the top of the wing to be compressed, thus transferring energy to the molecules in an upward direction. At the same time the gas molecules under the wing expand into the space left behind as the wing moves upward, and become rarefied, thereby creating less pressure under the wing. This procedure, compression and rarefication, alternates from one side of the wing to another; first the top compresses and then the bottom. This compression and rarefication of the atmosphere causes waves of pressure to be transmitted through the air or adjacent material.

One of the most common complaints connected with domestic refrigeration is "a high pitch whine on a new unit." Frequently this is caused by the use of a high speed sealed compressor and is difficult to remedy.

27-38 Noise Levels

Noise associated with air conditioning is often caused by air traveling through ducts at high speed causing air turbulence.

This is often the result of using an under-size unit and speeding up the blower in an attempt to compensate for the inadequacy of the cooling unit.

The air velocity (feet/minute) is determined by the type of building being air conditioned; church, hall, residential. If the noise is a factor, as in hospitals and churches, the velocity should be kept to a minimum. If the velocity cannot be decreased, noise may be reduced by using acoustical discharge chambers or lining the ducts with sound absorbing material such as fiberglas.

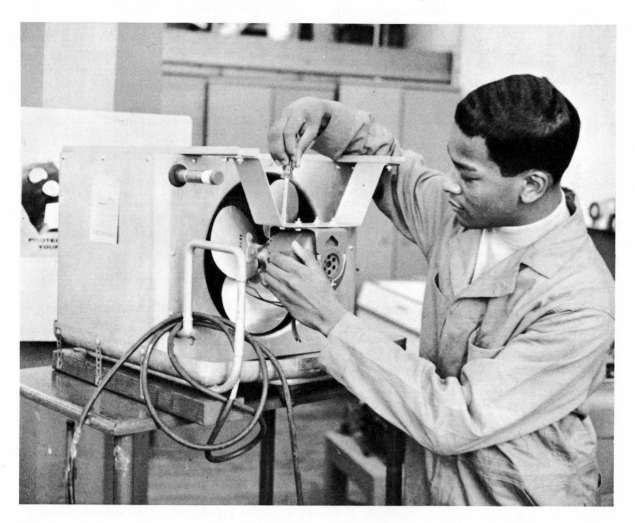

Mounting a motor fan on a commercial evaporator.
(Detroit Public Schools)

27-39 The Ringelmann Scale (Smoke Test)

The Ringelmann scale consists of four charts with various degrees of blackness. The scale is numbered 1 to 4. The chart is observed at a 50 foot distance and the blackness of the smoke in question is compared to the blackness scale of the chart.

27-40 Kata Thermometer

A Kata thermometer is an instrument used to measure air currents in open spaces. It is an alcohol thermometer with F. scales etched in the glass. There are two types; one reads from 95 to 100 F., the other from 125 to 130 F.

The thermometer is heated to the high-er value in a hot water bath. It is then thoroughly dried and suspended in the air currents. The time, in seconds, it takes it to cool to the lower reading is recorded. A table is then referred to, to determine the air movement in feet per minute.

27-41 Color Code for Piping

USE	COLOR
Fire Protection Equipment	Red
Safe Material	Green (or, if needed, white, black, gray, or aluminum)
Protective Material	Bright Blue
Extra Valuable Material	Deep Purple
Dangerous Material	Yellow or Orange

27-42 Safety Code for Mechanical Refrigeration

This Safety Code for Mechanical Refrigeration is sponsored by The American Society of Heating, Refrigerating and Air Conditioning Engineers under the rules and regulations of the American Standards Association Inc. as Project B9.

Complete administrative details are not provided as they will necessarily vary in different states and municipalities.

Most of the refrigeration-producing equipment, household, commercial, or industrial, is manufactured by companies whose business is nation-wide. It is, therefore, desirable that this Code be universally adopted so that safety provisions for refrigerating installations will be standardized, thereby permitting quantity production of refrigerating equipment with minimum cost to the user.

A standing Sectional Committee is provided to keep the provisions of this Code abreast of the advancements in the art of refrigeration.

Words *italicized* in the text have been specifically defined in Section 2 and are used in accordance with those definitions.

Section 1. SCOPE AND PURPOSE

1.1 Scope. The application of this Code is intended to insure the safe design, construction, installation, operation, and inspection of every *refrigerating system* employing a fluid which is vaporized and is normally liquefied in its refrigerating cycle, when employed under the occupancy classifications listed in Section 3. The provisions of this Code are not intended to apply to the use of water or air as a *refrigerant* nor to *refrigerating systems* installed on railroad cars, motor vehicles, motor drawn vehicles or on shipboard. (For shipboard installations see ASA B59.1-1964).

1.2 Purpose. This Code is intended to provide reasonable safeguards to life, limb, health, and property; to correct certain practices which are inconsistent with safety; and to prescribe standards of safety which will properly influence future progress and developments in *refrigerating systems*. Equipment listed by an approved, nationally recognized testing laboratory, as defined in 2.3.1, is deemed to meet the design, manufacture, and factory test requirements of this Code or equivalent, for the *refrigerant* or *refrigerants* for which such equipment is designed.

1.3 Application. This Code *shall* apply to *refrigerating systems* installed subsequent to its adoption and to parts replaced or added to systems installed prior or subsequent to its adoption. In cases of practical difficulty or unnecessary hardship, the authority having jurisdiction may grant exceptions from the literal requirements of this Code or permit the use of other devices or methods, but only when it is clearly evident that equivalent protection is thereby secured.

NOTE: To secure the uniform application of this Code, authorities having jurisdiction are urged, before rendering decisions on disputed points, to consult the committee which formulated it — the Committee on Safety Code for Mechanical Refrigeration, B9, in care of the American Standards Association, Incorporated, 10 East 40th Street, New York, N.Y. 10016, or the American Society of Heating, Refrigerating and Air-Conditioning Engineers, Inc., 345 East 47th Street, New York, N.Y. 10017.

Section 2. DEFINITIONS

2.1 *Absorber (Adsorber)* is that part of the *low side* of an *absorption system* used for absorbing (adsorbing) vapor refrigerant.

2.2 *Absorption System* — see 2.52.1.

2.3 *Approved* means acceptable to the authorities having jurisdiction.

2.3.1 *An Approved Nationally Recognized Testing Laboratory* is one acceptable to the authorities having jurisdiction, that provides uniform testing and examination procedures under established standards, is properly organized,

equipped, and qualified for testing, and has a follow-up inspection service of the current production of the listed products.

2.4 *Brazed Joint*, for the purpose of this Code, is a gastight joint obtained by the joining of metal parts with alloys which melt at temperatures higher than 1000 F but less than the melting temperatures of the joined parts.

2.5 *Brine* is any liquid, used for the transmission of heat without a change in its state, having no flash point or a flash point above 150 F determined by American Society for Testing and Materials method D93.62 (see 16.1).

2.6 *Companion or Block Valves* are pairs of mating stop valves, valving off sections of systems and arranged so that these sections may be joined before opening these valves or separated after closing them.

2.7 *Compressor* is a specific machine, with or without accessories, for compressing a given *refrigerant* vapor.

2.8 *Compressor Unit* is a *condensing unit* less the *condenser* and *liquid receiver*.

2.9 *Condenser* is a vessel or arrangement of pipe or tubing in which vaporized *refrigerant* is liquefied by the removal of heat.

2.10 *Condensing Unit* is a specific refrigerating machine combination for a given *refrigerant*, consisting of one or more power-driven *compressors*, *condensers*, *liquid receivers* (when required), and the regularly furnished accessories.

2.11 *Container* is a cylinder for the transportation of *refrigerant* (see 16.2).

2.12 *Department Store* is the entire space occupied by one *tenant* or more than one *tenant* in an individual store where more than 100 persons commonly assemble on other than the street-level floor for the purpose of buying personal wearables and other merchandise.

2.13 *Design Working Pressure* is the maximum allowable working pressure for which a specific part of a system is designed.

2.14 *Direct System* — see 4.2.

2.15 *Double Indirect Vented Open-Spray System* — see 4.3.4.

2.16 *Double (or Secondary) Refrigerant System* — see 4.4.

2.17 *Duct* is a tube or conduit used for conveying or encasing purposes as specifically defined below:

  a) *Air duct* is a tube or conduit used for conveying air. (The air passages of *self-contained systems* are not to be construed as *air ducts*.)
  b) *Pipe duct* is a tube or conduit used for encasing pipe.
  c) *Wire duct* is a tube or conduit used for encasing either moving or stationary wire, rope, etc.

2.18 *Entrance* is a confined passageway immediately adjacent to the door through which people enter a building.

2.19 *Evaporator* is that part of the system in which liquid *refrigerant* is vaporized to produce refrigeration.

2.20 *Exit* is a confined passageway immediately adjacent to the door through which people leave a building.

2.21 *Expansion Coil* is an *evaporator* constructed of pipe or tubing.

2.22 *Fusible Plug* is a device having a predetermined-temperature fusible member for the relief of pressure.

2.23 *Generator* is any device equipped with a heating element used in the *refrigerating system* to increase the pressure of *refrigerant* in its gas or vapor state for the purpose of liquefying the *refrigerant*.

2.24 *Hallway* is a corridor for the passage of people.

2.25 *High Side* means the parts of a *refrigerating system* under *condenser* pressure.

2.26 *Humanly Occupied Space* is a space normally frequented or occupied by people but excluding *machinery rooms* and walk-in coolers used primarily for refrigerated storage.

2.27 *Indirect Closed-Surface System* — see 4.3.2.

2.28 *Indirect Open-Spray System* — see 4.3.1.

2.29 *Indirect System* — see 4.3.

2.30 *Indirect Vented Closed-Surface System* — see 4.3.3.

2.31 *Internal Gross Volume* is the volume as determined from internal dimensions of the container with no allowance for volume of internal parts.

2.32 *Limited Charged System* is a system in which, with the compressor idle, the internal volume and total refrigerant charge are such that the design working pressure will not be exceeded by complete evaporation of the refrigerant charge.

2.33 *Liquid Receiver* is a vessel permanently connected to a system by inlet and outlet pipes for storage of a liquid *refrigerant*.

2.34 *Lobby* is a waiting room, or large *hallway* serving as a waiting room.

2.35 *Low Side* means the parts of a *refrigerating system* under *evaporator* pressure.

2.36 *Machinery* is the refrigerating equipment forming a part of the *refrigerating system* including any or all of the following: *compressor, condenser, generator, absorber (adsorber), liquid receiver*, connecting pipe, or *evaporator*.

2.37 *Machinery Room* as required by Section 6, is a room in which a *refrigerating system* is permanently installed and operated but not including *evaporators* located in a cold storage room, refrigerator box, air cooled space, or other enclosed space. Closets solely contained within, and opening only into, a room *shall not* be considered *machinery rooms* but *shall* be considered a part of the *machinery room* in which they are contained or open into. It is not the intent of this definition to cause the space in which a *self-contained system* is located to be classified as a *machinery room*. (See 8.11).

2.38 *Machinery Room, Class T* as required by Section 6, is a room having *machinery* but no flame-producing apparatus permanently installed and operated and also conforming to the following:

  a) Any doors, communicating with the building, *shall* be *approved* self-closing, tight-fitting fire doors.
  b) Walls, floor, and ceiling *shall* be tight and of not less than one-hour fire-resistive construction.
  c) It *shall* have an *exit* door which opens directly to the outer air or through a vestibule-type *exit* equipped with self-closing, tight-fitting doors.
  d) Exterior openings, if present, *shall not* be under any fire escape or any open stairway.
  e) All pipes piercing the interior walls, ceiling, or floor of such room *shall* be tightly sealed to the walls, ceiling, or floor through which they pass.
  f) Emergency remote controls to stop the action of the *refrigerant compressor shall* be provided and located immediately outside the *machinery room*.
  g) An independent mechanical ventilation system *shall* be provided.
  h) Emergency remote controls for the mechanical means of ventilation *shall* be provided and located outside the *machinery room*.

2.39 *Manufacturer* is, for the purpose of this Code, the company or organization which evidences its responsibility by affixing its name or nationally registered trade-mark or trade name to the refrigeration equipment concerned.

2.40 *Mechanical Joint*, for the purpose of this Code, is a gastight joint, obtained by the joining of metal parts through a positive-holding mechanical construction.

2.41 *Nonpositive Displacement Compressor* is a *compressor* in which increase in vapor pressure is attained without changing the internal volume of the compression chamber.

2.42 *Piping* means the pipe or tube mains for inter-connecting the various parts of a *refrigerating system.*

2.43 *Positive Displacement Compressor* is a *compressor* in which increase in vapor pressure is attained by changing the internal volume of the compression chamber.

2.44 *Premises* are the buildings and that part of the grounds of one property, where an installation would affect the the safety of those buildings or adjacent property.

2.45 *Pressure-Imposing Element* is any device or portion of the equipment used for the purpose of increasing the *refrigerant* vapor pressure.

2.46 *Pressure-Limiting Device* is a pressure-responsive mechanism designed to automatically stop the operation of the *pressure-imposing element* at a predetermined pressure.

2.47 *Pressure-Relief Device* is a pressure-actuated valve or *rupture member* designed to automatically relieve excessive pressure.

2.48 *Pressure-Relief Valve* is a pressure-actuated valve held closed by a spring or other means and designed to automatically relieve pressure in excess of its setting.

2.49 *Pressure Vessel* is any refrigerant-containing receptacle of a *refrigerating system*, other than *evaporators* (each separate section of which does not exceed ½ cubic foot of refrigerant-containing volume), *expansion coils, compressors,* controls, headers, pipe, and pipe fittings.

2.50 *Receiver* — see 2.33.

2.51 *Refrigerant* is a substance used to produce refrigeration by its expansion or vaporization.

2.52 *Refrigerating System* is a combination of inter-connected refrigerant-containing parts constituting one closed *refrigerant* circuit in which a *refrigerant* is circulated for the purpose of extracting heat. (See Section 4 for classification of *refrigerating systems* by type.)

2.52.1 *Absorption System* is a *refrigerating system* in which the gas evolved in the *evaporator* is taken up by an *absorber* or *adsorber.*

2.52.2 *Sealed Absorption System* is a *unit system* for Group 2 *refrigerants* only in which all refrigerant-containing parts are made permanently tight by welding or brazing against *refrigerant* loss. (This is a restrictive definition for the purposes of this Code as used in 6.1.2 and 6.3.1). (See 2.52.1).

2.52.3 *Self-Contained System* is a complete factory-made and factory-tested system in a suitable frame or enclosure which is fabricated and shipped in one or more sections and in which no refrigerant-containing parts are connected in the field other than by *companion* or *block valves.*

2.52.4 *Unit System* is a *self-contained system* which has been assembled and tested prior to its installation and which is installed without connecting any refrigerant-containing parts. A *unit system* may include factory-assembled *companion* or *block valves.*

2.53 *Rupture Member* is a device that will rupture at a predetermined pressure.

2.54 *Shall.* Where "shall" or "shall not" is used for a provision specified, that provision is intended to be mandatory.

2.55 *Should.* "Should" or "it is recommended" is used to indicate provisions which are not mandatory but which are pointed out here as recommended good practice.

2.56 *Sealed Absorption System* — see 2.52.2.

2.57 *Self-Contained System* — see 2.52.3.

2.58 *Soldered Joint,* for the purpose of this Code, is a gas-tight joint obtained by the joining of metal parts with metallic mixtures or alloys which melt at temperatures below 1000 F and above 400 F.

2.59 *Stop Valve* is a shut-off for controlling the flow of *refrigerant.*

2.60 *Tenant,* as herein used, shall be construed as a person, firm, or corporation possessed with the legal right to occupy premises.

2.61 *Unit System* — see 2.52.4.

2.62 *Welded Joint,* for the purpose of this code, is a gas-tight joint, obtained by the joining of metal parts in the plastic or molten state.

Section 3. OCCUPANCY CLASSIFICATION

3.1 Locations governed by this Code in which *refrigerating systems* may be placed are grouped by occupancy as follows:

3.1.1 Institutional Occupancy *shall* apply to that portion of *the premises* in which persons are confined to receive medical, charitable, educational, or other care or treatment, or in which persons are held or detained by reason of public or civic duty, including among others, hospitals, asylums, sanitariums, police stations, jails, court houses with cells, and similar occupancies.

3.1.2 Public Assembly Occupancy *shall* apply to that portion of the *premises* in which persons congregate for civic, political, educational, religious, social, or recreational purposes; including among others, armories, assembly rooms, auditoriums, ballrooms, bath houses, bus terminals, broadcasting studios, churches, colleges, court houses without cells, dance halls, *department stores,* exhibition halls, fraternity halls, libraries, lodge rooms, mortuary chapels, museums, passenger depots, schools, skating rinks, subway stations, theaters, and similar occupancies.

3.1.3 Residential Occupancy *shall* apply to that portion of *the premises* in which sleeping accommodations are provided, including among others, club houses, convents, dormitories, hotels, lodging houses, multiple story apartments, residences, studios, tenements, and similar occupancies.

3.1.4 Commercial Occupancy *shall* apply to that portion of *the premises* used for the transaction of business; for the rendering of professional services; for the supplying of food, drink, or other bodily needs and comforts; for manufacturing purposes or for the performance of work or labor (except as included under 3.1.5 Industrial Occupancy) including among others, bake shops, fur storage, laboratories, loft buildings, markets, office buildings, professional buildings, restaurants, stores other than *department stores,* and similar occupancies.

3.1.5 Industrial Occupancy *shall* apply to an entire building or *premises* or to that portion of a building used for manufacturing, processing, or storage of materials or products, including among others, chemical, food, candy and ice cream factories, ice making plants, meat packing plants, refineries, perishable food warehouses and similar occupancies, provided the entire building is occupied by a single *tenant.*

3.1.6 Mixed Occupancy *shall* apply to a building occupied or used for different purposes in different parts. When the occupancies are cut off from the rest of the building by tight partitions, floors, and ceilings and protected by self-closing doors, the requirements for each type of occupancy *shall* apply for its portion of the building or *premises.* For example, the cold storage spaces in retail frozen food lockers, hotels, and *department stores* in buildings occupied by a single *tenant* might be classified under Industrial Occupancy, whereas other portions of the building would be classified under other occupancies. When the occupancies are not so separated, the occupancy carrying the more stringent requirements *shall* govern.

3.2 Adjacent Locations. Equipment installed in locations adjacent to areas outlined in 3.1.1 through 3.1.6, including outdoor installations, shall be governed by the applicable requirements of this Code.

Section 4. REFRIGERATING SYSTEM CLASSIFICATION BY TYPE

4.1 Refrigerating Systems (see 2.52) *shall* be divided into classes, descriptive of the method employed for extracting heat as follows in 4.2 to 4.4, inclusive. The *direct, indirect* and *double refrigerant systems* are illustrated in Figures 1 and 1A.

4.2 Direct System is one in which the *evaporator* is in direct contact with the material or space refrigerated or is located in air-circulating passages communicating with such spaces.

4.3 Indirect System is one in which a liquid, such as *brine* or water, cooled by the *refrigerant*, is circulated to the material or space refrigerated or is used to cool air so circulated. *Indirect systems* which are distinguished by the type or method of application are as given in the following paragraphs:

4.3.1 Indirect Open-Spray System is one in which a liquid, such as *brine* or water, cooled by an *evaporator* located in an enclosure external to a cooling chamber, is circulated to such cooling chamber and is sprayed therein.

4.3.2 Indirect Closed-Surface System is one in which a liquid such as *brine* or water, cooled by an *evaporator* located in an enclosure external to a cooling chamber, is circulated to and through such a cooling chamber in pipes or other closed circuits.

4.3.3 Indirect Vented Closed-Surface System is one in which a liquid, such as *brine* or water, cooled by an *evaporator* located in a vented enclosure external to a cooling chamber, is circulated to and through such cooling chamber in pipes or other closed circuits.

4.3.4 Double Indirect Vented Open-Spray System is one in which a liquid, such as *brine* or water, cooled by an *evaporator* located in a vented enclosure, is circulated through a closed circuit to a second enclosure where it cools another supply of a liquid, such as *brine* or water, and this liquid in turn is circulated to a cooling chamber and is sprayed therein.

4.4 Double (or Secondary) Refrigerant System is one in which an evaporative *refrigerant* is used in a secondary circuit. For the purpose of this Code, each system enclosing a separate body of an evaporative *refrigerant shall* be considered as a separate *direct system.*

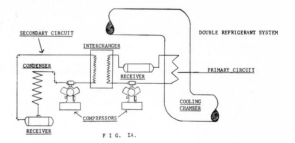

F I G. IA.

Section 5. REFRIGERANT CLASSIFICATION*

*Numerical Refrigerant Designation from ASHRAE Standard 34-57 (American Standard B79.1-1960) (See 16.19)

5.1 General. *Refrigerants* are, for the purposes of this Code, divided into groups as follows:

5.1.1 Group 1

Carbon dioxide (Refrigerant 744)	CO_2
Dichlorodifluoromethane (Refrigerant 12)	CCl_2F_2
Dichlorodifluoromethane, 73.8%	CCl_2F_2
and Ethylidene Fluoride, 26.2%	CH_3-CHF_2
(Refrigerant 500)	
Dichloromethane (Methylene chloride)	
(Refrigerant 30)	CH_2Cl_2
Dichloromonofluoromethane (Refrigerant 21)	$CHCl_2F$
Dichlorotetrafluoroethane (Refrigerant 114)	$C_2Cl_2F_4$
Monobromotrifluoromethane (Refrigerant 13B1)	$CBrF_3$
Monochlorodifluoromethane (Refrigerant 22)	$CHClF_2$
Monochlorodifluoromethane, 48.8%	$CHClF_2$
and Monochloropenta-fluoroethane, 51.2%	
(Refrigerant 502)	$CClF_2CF_3$
Monochlorotrifluoromethane (Refrigerant 13)	$CClF_3$
Octafluorocyclobutane (Refrigerant C318)	C_4F_8
Trichloromonofluoromethane (Refrigerant 11)	CCl_3F
Trichlorotrifluoroethane (Refrigerant 113)	$C_2Cl_3F_3$

5.1.2 Group 2

Ammonia	NH_3
Dichloroethylene	$C_2H_2Cl_2$
Ethyl chloride	C_2H_5Cl
Methyl chloride	CH_3Cl
Methyl formate	$HCOOCH_3$
Sulphur dioxide	SO_2

5.1.3 Group 3

Butane	C_4H_{10}
Ethane	C_2H_6
Ethylene	C_2H_4
Isobutane	$(CH_3)_3CH$
Propane	C_3H_8

Section 6. REQUIREMENTS FOR INSTITUTIONAL, PUBLIC ASSEMBLY, RESIDENTIAL, AND COMMERCIAL OCCUPANCIES

6.1 General.

6.1.1 *Public Stairway, Stair Landing, Entrance, or Exit.* No *refrigerating system shall be installed* in or on a public stairway, stair landing, *entrance,* or *exit.*

6.1.2 *Public Hallway or Lobby.* No *refrigerating system shall* interfere with free passage. No Group 2 *refrigerant shall* be permitted in public *hallways* or *lobbies* of Institutional or Public Assembly Occupancies. *Refrigerating systems* installed in a public *hallway* or *lobby shall* be limited to:

a) *Unit Systems* containing not more than the quantities of a Group 1 *refrigerant* specified in Table 1, or

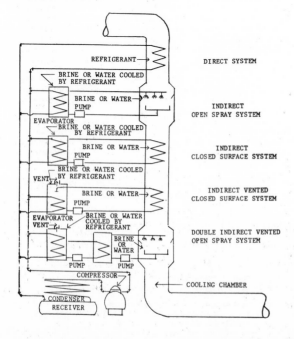

b) *Sealed Absorption Systems* containing not more than 3 pounds of Group 2 *refrigerant* when in Residential and Commercial Occupancies.

6.1.3 Refrigerant Piping Through Floors. *Refrigerant piping shall not* be carried through floors except as follows:

a) It may be carried from the basement to the first floor or from the top floor to a *machinery* penthouse or to the roof.

b) For the purpose of connecting to a *condenser* on the roof, it may be carried through an *approved*, rigid and tight continuous fire-resisting *pipe duct* or shaft having no openings on intermediate floors, or it may be carried on the outer wall of the building provided it is not located in an air shaft, closed court, or in other similar open spaces enclosed within the outer walls of the building.

c) In systems containing Group 1 *refrigerants*, the *refrigerant piping* may also be carried through floors, intermediate between the first floor and the top floor, provided it is enclosed in an *approved*, rigid and tight continuous fire-resisting *pipe duct* or shaft where it passes through intermediate spaces not served by the system. *Piping* of *direct systems*, as governed by 6.2.1, need not be enclosed where it passes through space served by that system. The *pipe duct* or shaft *shall* be vented to the outside or to a space served by the system.

TABLE 1. Maximum Permissible Quantities of Group 1 Refrigerants for Direct Systems

Refrigerant name and number**	Chemical formula	Maximum quantity in lb per 1000 cu ft of humanly occupied space*
Carbon dioxide (Refrigerant 744)	CO_2	11
Dichlorodifluoromethane (Refrigerant 12)	CCl_2F_2	31
Dichlorodifluoromethane, 73.8% and Ethylidene Fluoride, 26.2% (Refrigerant 500)	CCl_2F_2 $CH_3 \cdot CHF_2$ }	26
Dichloromethane (Methylene chloride) (Refrigerant 30)	CH_2Cl_2	6
Dichloromonofluoromethane (Refrigerant 21)	$CHCl_2F$	13
Dichlorotetrafluoromethane (Refrigerant 114)	$C_2Cl_2F_4$	44
Monobromotrifluoromethane (Refrigerant 13B1)	$CBrF_3$	38
Monochlorodifluoromethane (Refrigerant 22)	$CHClF_2$	22
Monochlorodifluoromethane, 48.8% and Monochloropentafluoroethane, 51.2% (Refrigerant 502)	$CHClF_2$ $CClF_2CF_3$	30
Monochlorotrifluoromethane (Refrigerant 13)	$CClF_3$	27
Octafluorocyclobutane (Refrigerant C318)	C_4F_8	50
Trichloromonofluoromethane (Refrigerant 11)	CCl_3F	35
Trichlorotrifluoroethane (Refrigerant 113)	$C_2Cl_3F_3$	24

* Volatile charge in a control *shall not* be considered as *refrigerant*.

** ASHRAE Designation (see Section 5).

6.2 Group 1 Refrigerants

6.2.1 Direct Systems. The maximum permissible quantity of a Group 1 *refrigerant* in a *direct system* as specified in Table 1 except Institutional Occupancies where further limited by 6.2.1.1.

6.2.1.1 *Direct Systems* in Institutional Occupancies *shall* be limited to *unit systems* each containing not more than 20 pounds of Group 1 *refrigerants*, except in kitchens, laboratories, and mortuaries. (See 6.2.4.)

6.2.1.2 When the refrigerant-containing parts of a system are located in one or more enclosed spaces, the cubical content of the smallest enclosed *humanly occupied space* other than the *machinery room, shall* be used to determine the permissible quantity of *refrigerant* in the system. Where a *refrigerating system* has *evaporator* coils serving individual stories of a building, the story having the smallest volume shall be used to determine the maximum quantity of *refrigerant* in the entire system.

6.2.1.3 When the *evaporator* is located in an *air duct* system, cubical content of the smallest *humanly occupied enclosed space* served by the *air duct* system *shall* be used to determine the permissible quantity of *refrigerant* in the system; however, if the air flow to any enclosed space served by the *air duct* system cannot be shut off or reduced below one-quarter of its maximum, the cubical contents of the entire space served by the *air duct* system may be used to determine the permissible quantity of *refrigerant* in the system.

6.2.1.4 In Institutional and Public Assembly Occupancies, direct *expansion coils* or *evaporators* used for air conditioning and located downstream from, and in proximity to, a *heating coil*, or located upstream within 18 inches of a heating coil, *shall* be fitted with a *pressure relief device* discharging to the outside of the building in an *approved* manner; except that such a relief device *shall not* be required on *unit* or *self-contained systems* if the internal volume of the *low side* of the system which may be shut off by valves, divided by the total weight of *refrigerant* in the system less the weight of *refrigerant* vapor contained in the other parts of the system at 110 F, exceeds the specific volume of the *refrigerant* at critical conditions of temperature and pressure.

(NOTE: The above exemption is also stated in formula form below.)

$$\frac{V_1}{W_1 - W_2} \text{ shall be more than } V_{sp}$$

where V_1 = *low side* volume, cu ft

V_{sp} = specific volume at critical conditions of temperature and pressure, cu ft per lb

W_1 = total weight of *refrigerant* in system, lb

W_2 = weight of *refrigerant* vapor (lb) at 110 F in V_2,

$$= \frac{V_2}{}$$

specific volume of *refrigerant*, in cu ft per lb, at 110 F, where V_2 = total volume of system less V_1 cu ft

6.2.2 Indirect Systems. A system containing more than the quantity of a Group 1 *refrigerant* allowed in Table 1 *shall* be of the *indirect* type with all refrigerant-containing parts, excepting parts mounted outside the building and *piping* installed in accordance with Paragraph 6.1.3, installed in a *machinery room* used for no other purpose than for mechanical equipment.

6.2.3 Open Flames in Machinery Rooms. No open flame or apparatus to produce an open flame *shall* be installed in a *machinery room* where any *refrigerant* other than carbon dioxide is used unless the flame is enclosed and vented to the open air. The use of matches, cigarette lighters, halide leak detectors, and similar devices *shall not* be considered a violation of this paragraph or of 6.2.4.

6.2.4 Open Flames in Institutional Occupancies. In Institutional Occupancies, where more than 1 pound of a Group 1 *refrigerant*, other than carbon dioxide, is used in a system, any portion of which is in a room where there is an apparatus for producing an open flame, then such *refrigerant shall* be classed in Group 2, unless the flame-producing apparatus is provided with a hood and flue capable of removing the products of combustion to the open air.

6.3 Group 2 Refrigerants

6.3.1 Direct Systems. *Direct systems* containing Group 2 *refrigerants shall not* be used for air conditioning for human comfort. For other applications, the maximum permissible quantity of Group 2 *refrigerants* in a direct system is shown in Table 2.

6.3.2 Indirect Systems. The maximum permissible quantity of Group 2 *refrigerent* in any *indirect system* is shown in Table 3. Such systems *shall* be of the following type:

a) Institutional and Public Assembly Occupancies —*Indirect vented closed-surface, or double indirect vented open-spray.*

TABLE 2. Maximum Permissible Quantities of Group 2 Refrigerants for Direct Systems

Type of refrigerating system	Maximum pounds for various occupancies			
	Institutional	Public assembly	Residential	Commercial
Sealed Absorption Systems·				
a) In public *hallways* or *lobbies*	0	0	3	3
b) In other than public *hallways of lobbies*	0*	6	6	20
Self-Contained or Unit Systems:				
a) In public *hallways* or *lobbies*	0	0	0	0
b) In other than public *hallways or lobbies*	0	0*	6	20

* Six pounds allowed when installed in kitchens, laboratories, and mortuaries.

b) Residential and Commercial Occupancies — *Indirect vented closed-surface,* or *double indirect vented open-spray,* or *primary circuit of double-refrigerant* type.

6.3.2.1 Machinery Rooms for Indirect Systems, Group 2 Refrigerants

6.3.2.1.1 *Indirect* systems using Group 2 *refrigerants* not in excess of the quantities shown in Column 1 of Table 3 *shall* have all refrigerant-containing parts, excepting parts mounted outside the building and *piping* installed in accordance with Paragraph 6.1.3, installed in a *machinery room* used for no other purpose than for mechanical equipment.

TABLE 3. Maximum Permissible Quantities of Group 2 Refrigerants for Indirect Systems

Occupancy	Column 1 Machinery Rooms (see 2.37), max lb ·	Column 2 Class T Machinery Rooms (see 2.38), max lb
Institutional	0	Not more than 500 lb
Public Assembly	0	Not more than 1000 lb
Residential	Not more than 300 lb	No limit
Commercial	Not more than 600 lb	No limit

6.3.2.1.2 *Indirect systems* using Group 2 *refrigerants* not in excess of the quantities shown in Column 2 of Table 3 *shall* have all refrigerant-containing parts installed in a *Class T machinery room.*

6.3.2.1.3 *Flame-Producing Devices, Hot Surfaces, and Electrical Equipment in Machinery Rooms.* Where a *machinery room* is required by this Code to house a *refrigerating system* containing any Group 2 *refrigerant* other than sulphur dioxide, no flame-producing device or hot surface above 800 F *shall* be permitted in such room and all electrical equipment in the room *shall* conform to the requirements of Hazardous Locations Class I of the latest edition of the National Electrical Code (see 16.6). The use of matches, cigarette lighters, halide leak detectors, and similar devices *shall not* be considered a violation of this paragraph.

6.4 Group 3 Refrigerants

6.4.1 Group 3 *refrigerants shall not* be used in Institutional, Public Assembly, Residential, or Commercial Occupancies except in laboratories for Commercial Occupancies. In such laboratory installations only *unit systems* containing not more than 6 pounds *shall* be used unless the number of persons does not exceed one person per 100 square feet of laboratory floor area, in which case the requirements for Industrial Occupancy *shall* apply.

Section 7. REQUIREMENTS FOR INDUSTRIAL OCCUPANCIES

7.1 General. There *shall* be no restrictions on the quantity or kind of *refrigerant* used in an Industrial Occupancy, except as specified in 7.2 and 8.10.

7.2 Number of Persons. When the number of persons in a refrigerated space, served by a *direct system,* on any floor above the first floor (ground level or deck level) exceeds one person per 100 square feet of floor area, the requirements of Commercial Occupancy *shall* apply unless that refrigerated space containing more than one person per 100 square feet of floor area above the first floor is provided with the required number of doors opening directly into approved building exits. Such refrigerated space shall be cut off from the rest of the building by tight construction with tight-fitting doors. (See 16.17)

NOTE: The above does not prohibit openings for the passage of products from one refrigerated space to another refrigerated space.

Section 8. INSTALLATION REQUIREMENTS

8.1 Foundations and Supports for *condensing units* or *compressor units shall* be of substantial and non-combustible construction when more than 6 inches high. (See 8.3).

8.2 Moving Machinery *should* be guarded in accordance with accepted safety standards. (See 16.3).

8.3 Clear Space adequate for inspection and servicing of *condensing units* or *compressor units shall* be provided.

8.4 Condensing Units or Compressor Units with Enclosures *shall* be readily accessible for servicing and inspection.

8.5 Water Supply and Discharge Connections *should* be made in accordance with accepted safety and health standards. (See 16.4).

8.5.1 Discharge water lines *shall not* be directly connected to the waste or sewer system. The waste or discharge from such equipment *shall* be over and above a trapped and vented plumbing fixture.

8.6 Illumination adequate for inspection and servicing of *condensing units* or *compressor units should* be provided. (See 16.5).

8.7 Electrical Equipment and Wiring *shall* be installed in accordance with accepted safety standards. (See 16.6).

8.8 Gas Fuel Devices and Equipment used with *refrigerating systems shall* be installed in accordance with accepted safety standards. (See 16.7).

8.9 Open Flames. When the quantity of flammable *refrigerant* in any one *refrigerating system* exceeds the amount given in Table 4 for each 1000 cubic feet of room volume in which the system or any part thereof is installed, then no flame-producing device or hot surface above 800 F *shall* be permitted in such room and all electrical equipment in the room *shall* conform to the requirements of Hazardous Locations Class I of the latest edition of the National Electrical Code. (See 16.6).

TABLE 4. Maximum Permissible Quantities of Flammable Refrigerants

Name	Chemical formula	Maximum quantity in lb per 1000 cu ft of room volume
Butane	C_4H_{10}	2½
Ethane	C_2H_6	2½
Ethyl chloride	C_2H_5Cl	6
Ethylene	C_2H_4	2
Isobutane	$(CH_3)_3CH$	2½
Methyl chloride	CH_3Cl	10
Methyl formate	$HCOOCH_3$	7
Propane	C_3H_8	2½

8.10 Flammable Refrigerants as listed in Table 4 *shall not* be used in a *refrigerating system* in excess of 1000 pounds unless *approved* by the authority having jurisdiction.

8.11 Machinery Room Requirements (see Definitions 2.37 and 2.38).

8.11.1 Each refrigerating *machinery room shall* be provided with tight-fitting door or doors and have no partitions or openings that will permit the passage of escaping *refrigerant* to other parts of the building.

8.11.2 Each refrigerating *machinery room shall* be provided with means for ventilation to the outer air. The ventilation *shall* consist of windows or doors opening to the outer air, of the size shown in Table 5, or of mechanical means capable of removing the air from the room in accordance with Table 5. The amount of ventilation for *refrigerant* removal purposes *shall* be determined by the *refrigerant* content of the largest system in the *machinery room*.

8.11.3 *Mechanical Ventilation*, when used, *shall* consist of one or more power-driven exhaust fans, which *shall* be capable of removing from the refrigerating *machinery room* the amount of air specified in Table 5. The inlet to the fan, or fans, or *air duct* connection *shall* be located near the refrigerating equipment. The outlet from the fan, or fans, or *air duct* connections *shall* terminate outside of the building in an *approved* manner. When *air ducts* are used either on the inlet or discharge side of the fan, or fans, they *shall* have an area not less than specified in Table 5. Provision *should* be made for the inlet of air to replace that being exhausted.

8.11.4 *Class T Machinery Rooms* in basements or subbasements (see Definition 2.38) *shall* have, as specified in Table 5, mechanical ventilation operating continuously.

8.12 Air Duct Systems of air-conditioning equipment for human comfort using mechanical refrigeration *should* be installed in accordance with accepted safety standards. (See 16.8 and 16.9).

TABLE 5. Minimum Air Duct Areas and Openings

	Weight of refrigerant in system, lb	Mechanical discharge of air, cfm	Duct area, sq ft	Open areas of windows and doors sq ft
up to	20	150	1/4	4
	50	250	1/3	6
	100	400	1/2	10
	150	550	2/3	12 1/2
	200	680	2/3	14
	250	800	1	15
	300	900	1	17
	400	1,100	1 1/4	20
	500	1,275	1 1/4	22
	600	1,450	1 1/2	24
	700	1,630	1 1/2	26
	800	1,800	2	28
	900	1,950	2	30
	1,000	2,050	2	31
	1,250	2,250	2 1/4	33
	1,500	2,500	2 1/4	37
	1,750	2,700	2 1/4	38
	2,000	2,900	2 1/4	40
	2,500	3,300	2 1/2	43
	3,000	3,700	3	48
	4,000	4,600	3 3/4	55
	5,000	5,500	4 1/2	62
	6,000	6,300	5	68
	7,000	7,200	5 1/2	74
	8,000	8,000	5 3/4	80
	9,000	8,700	6 1/4	85
	10,000	9,500	6 1/2	90
	12,000	10,900	7	100
	14,000	12,200	7 1/2	109
	16,000	13,300	7 3/4	118
	18,000	14,300	8	125
	20,000	15,200	8 1/4	130
	25,000	17,000	8 3/4	140
	30,000	18,200	9	145
	35,000	19,400	9 1/4	150
	40,000	20,500	9 1/2	155
	45,000	21,500	9 3/4	160

Section 9. REFRIGERANT PIPING, VALVES, FITTINGS, AND RELATED PARTS

9.1 General. *Refrigerating piping*, valves, fittings, and related parts used in the construction and installation of *refrigerating systems shall* conform to the American Standard Code for Pressure Piping. (See 16.10).

9.2 Metal Enclosures or Pipe Ducts for Soft Copper Tubing. Rigid or flexible metal enclosures *shall* be provided for soft, annealed copper tubing used for *refrigerant piping* erected on the premises and containing other than Group 1 *refrigerants*. No enclosures *shall* be required for connections between *condensing unit* and the nearest riser box, provided such connections do not exceed 6 feet in length.

9.3 Specific Minimum Requirements for Refrigerant Pipe and Tubing

9.3.1 No less than Schedule 80 wall thickness carbon steel or wrought iron pipe (See 16.10) *shall* be used for

Group II and Group III *refrigerant* liquid lines for sizes 1½ inches and smaller.

No less than Schedule 40 wall thickness carbon steel or wrought iron pipe (See 16.10) *shall* be used for Group I *refrigerant* liquid lines sizes 6 inches and smaller, Group II and Group III *refrigerant* liquid lines sizes 2 inches through 6 inches, and Group I, Group II, and Group III *refrigerant* vapor lines 6 inches and smaller.

Butt-Welded carbon steel and butt-welded wrought iron pipe *shall not* be used for *refrigerant* liquid lines.

Cast iron pipe *shall not* be used for Group I, Group II, or Group III *refrigerant* lines.

9.3.2 Standard iron pipe size copper and red brass (not less than 80 per cent copper) pipe may be used and *shall* conform to ASTM Specification B-42 (See 16.11) for copper pipe and ASTM Specification B-43 (See 16.18) for red brass pipe.

9.3.3 Watertube size hard copper tubing used for *refrigerant piping* erected on the premises *shall* conform to ASTM Specifications B88-62 Types K or L (See 16.13), for dimensions and specifications, except that copper tubing with outside diameters of 1/4 inch and 3/8 inch *shall* have a minimum nominal wall thickness of not less than 0.030 inch and 0.032 inch, respectively.

9.3.4 Soft annealed copper tubing used for *refrigerant piping* erected on the premises *shall not* be used in sizes larger than 1-3/8 inch Standard Size (1.375 outside diameter). Mechanical Joints *shall not* be used on soft annealed copper tubing on sizes larger than 7/8 inch Standard Size (0.875 outside diameter). It *shall* conform to ASTM Specifications B280-62. (See 16.14.) Minimum nominal wall thickness of soft annealed copper tubing *shall* be as follows:

Standard Size In.	Outside Diameter In.	Wall Thickness In.
1/4	0.250	0.030
3/8	0.375	0.032
1/2	0.500	0.032
5/8	0.625	0.035
3/4	0.750	0.042
7/8	0.875	0.045
*1	1.000	0.050
1 1/8	1.125	0.050
*1 1/4	1.250	0.055
1 3/8	1.375	0.055

* Not included as standard size in ASTM B280-62.

9.3.5 Sweat joints on copper tubing used in *refrigerating systems* containing Group 2 or Group 3 *refrigerants shall* be brazed joints. *Soldered joints shall not* be used in such refrigerating systems.

9.4 Joints and Refrigerant-Containing Parts in Air Ducts. Joints and all refrigerant-containing parts of a *refrigerating system* located in an *air duct* of an air-conditioning system carrying conditioned air to and from a *humanly occupied space* shall be constructed to withstand, without leakage, a temperature of 1000 F.

9.5 Exposure of Refrigerant Pipe Joints. *Refrigerant* pipe joints erected on the premises *shall* be exposed to view for visual inspection prior to being covered or enclosed.

9.6 Stop Valves

9.6.1 *General Requirements.* All systems containing more than 50 pounds of a Group 1 *refrigerant* or 6 pounds of a Group 2 or 3 *refrigerant*, other than systems utilizing *nonpositive displacement compressors*, shall have *stop valves* installed as follows:

   a) Each inlet of each *compressor, compressor unit,* or *condensing unit;*

   b) Each discharge outlet of each *compressor, compressor unit,* or *condensing unit,* and of each *liquid receiver.*

9.6.2 *Systems Containing 100 Pounds or More of Refrigerant.* All systems containing 100 pounds or more of a *refrigerant,* other than systems utilizing *nonpositive displacement compressors, shall* have *stop valves,* in addition to those in 9.6.1, on each inlet of each *liquid receiver* except that none *shall* be required on the inlet of a *receiver* in a *condensing unit* nor on the inlet of a *receiver* which is an integral part of a *condenser.*

9.6.3 *Stop valves* used with soft annealed copper tubing or hard drawn copper tubing 7/8 inch standard size (0.875 outside diameter) or smaller *shall* be securely mounted, independent of tubing fastenings or supports.

9.6.4 *Stop valves shall* be suitably labelled if it is not obvious what they control. Numbers may be used to label the valves provided a key to the numbers is located near the valves.

9.7 Location of Refrigerant Piping

9.7.1 *Refrigerant piping* crossing an open space which affords passageway in any building *shall* be not less than 7½ feet above the floor unless against the ceiling of such space.

9.7.2 Free passageway *shall not* be obstructed by *refrigerant piping*. *Refrigerant piping shall not* be placed in any elevator, dumbwaiter, or other shaft containing a moving object, or in any shaft which has openings to living quarters or to main *exit hallways*. *Refrigerant piping shall not* be placed in public *hallways*, *lobbies*, or stairways, except that such *refrigerant piping* may pass across a public *hallway* if there are no joints in the section in the public *hallway*, and provided nonferrous tubing of 1 inch nominal diameter (1-1/8 inch outside diameter) and smaller be contained in a rigid metal pipe.

Section 10. DESIGN AND CONSTRUCTION OF EQUIPMENT
(Also see Section 11 for pressure vessels)

10.1 General

10.1.1 Every part of a *refrigerating system*, with the exception of pressure gages, control mechanisms and limited charged systems, *shall* be designed, constructed, and assembled to be capable of withstanding a test pressure not less than the minimum *refrigerant* leak field test pressure specified in Table 6 without being stressed beyond one-third of its ultimate strength. (See 10.2.) Limited charged systems equipped with a pressure-relief device, shall be designed, constructed, and assembled to be capable of withstanding a test pressure not less than 1.5 times the setting of the pressure relief device without being stressed beyond 1/3 of its ultimate strength.

NOTE: This paragraph establishes a minimum *design working pressure* in terms of the field test pressure so that the minimum *refrigerant leak field test pressure*, specified in Table 6, can be safely applied. Rules governing *pressure-relief devices, pressure-limiting devices*, etc., *shall* be based on the *design working pressure* selected.

10.1.2 All materials used in the construction and installation of *refrigerating systems shall* be suitable for conveying the *refrigerant* used. No material *shall* be used that will deteriorate because of the *refrigerant*, or the oil, or the combination of both.

NOTE: Many *refrigerants* are corrosive to the usual materials when moisture or air, or both, are present and it is assumed in approving these materials that the system will be charged and operated in accordance with accepted practice, to prevent or minimize this corrosion.

10.1.3 *Aluminum, Zinc, or Magnesium shall* not be used in contact with methyl chloride in a *refrigerating system*. Magnesium alloys *shall not* be used in contact with any halogenated refrigerant.

10.2 Minimum Test Pressures. Every refrigerant-containing part of every system, including pressure gages and control mechanisms, *shall* be tested and proved tight by the *manufacturer* at not less than the minimum *refrigerant* leak field test pressure specified in Table 6 except limited charged systems. (See 10.3 and 14.1.2.)

10.2.1 The test pressure applied to either the *high* or *low* side of each *refrigerating system shall* be at least equal to the *design working pressure* of the *pressure vessels* in the *high* or *low side* of the system, respectively, or to the setting of the *pressure-relief device* protecting the respective pressure vessels, whichever is lower, but not less than the minimum *refrigerant* leak field test pressures specified in Table 6. Any components connected to said *pressure vessels shall* be of sufficient strength to conform to the design requirements of Paragraph 10.1.1.

10.2.2 Limited Charged *Unit Systems shall* be tested in accordance with Paragraph 10.2 except that limited charged

unit systems equipped with a pressure-relief device may be tested and proved tight at a pressure not less than 1½ times the setting of the pressure-relief device.

10.3 Equipment Listed by an Approved Nationally Recognized Testing Laboratory having a follow-up inspection service *shall* be deemed as meeting the intent of the requirements of 10.1 and 10.2. (See 1.2 and 2.3.1.)

10.4 Pressure-Limiting Devices

10.4.1 *Pressure-limiting devices shall* be provided on all systems containing more than 20 pounds of *refrigerant* and operating above atmospheric pressure, and on all water cooled systems so constructed that the *compressor* or *generator* is capable of producing a pressure in excess of the test pressure; except water cooled *unit systems* containing not more than 3 pounds of a Group 1 *refrigerant* providing the operating pressure developed in the system with the water supply shut off does not exceed one-fifth the ultimate strength of the system, or providing an overload device will stop the action of the *compressor* before the pressure exceeds one-fifth the ultimate strength of the system.

10.4.2 The maximum setting to which a *pressure limiting device* may readily be set by use of the adjusting means provided *shall not* exceed 90 percent of the setting of the *pressure-relief device* installed on the *high side* of a system, 90 percent of the *refrigerant* leak field test pressure actually applied, or 90 percent of the design working pressure of the *high side* of the system, whichever is smallest. The *pressure-limiting device shall* stop the action of the *pressure-imposing element* at a pressure no higher than this maximum setting. In determining this maximum setting for systems erected on the *premises* and field leak tested in accordance with 14.1.1, 90 percent of the leak test pressures in Table 6 may be utilized in lieu of the field test pressure actually applied. (See 14.1 and 14.1.1 for minimum *refrigerant* leak field test pressures.)

10.4.2.1 On systems using nonpositive displacement *compressors*, the *pressure-limiting device* may be set at the *pressure setting of* the relief device, the *refrigerant* leak field test pressure actually applied or the design working pressure of the *high side* of the system, whichever is smallest, provided the *pressure-relief device* is subject to *low side* pressure and there are no *stop valves* on the system as as exempted by Paragraph 9.6 for nonpositive displacement *compressors*.

10.4.3 *Pressure-limiting devices shall* be connected, with no intervening *stop valves*, between the *pressure-imposing element* and any *stop valve* on the discharge side.

10.5 Liquid Level Gage Glasses, except those of the bull's-eye or reflex type, *shall* have automatic closing shut-off valves, and such glasses *shall* be adequately protected against injury.

10.6 Dial of a Pressure Gage, when the gage is permanently installed on the *high side* of a *refrigerating system, shall* be graduated up to approximately double the operating pressure, but in no case less than 1.2 times the *design working pressure*.

10.7 Nameplate. Each separately sold *condensing unit* and each *compressor* or *compressor unit* sold for field assembly in a *refrigerating system shall* carry a nameplate marked with the manufacturer's name, nationally registered trademark or trade name, identification number, the test pressure applied by the manufacturer, and the *refrigerant* for which it is designed. The *refrigerant shall* be designated according to American Standard B79.1-1960, Number Designation of Refrigerants.

Section 11. REFRIGERANT-CONTAINING PRESSURE VESSELS

11.1 Refrigerant-Containing Pressure Vessels Exceeding 6 inches Inside Diameter, except those having a maximum allowable internal or external working pressure 15 psig or less, shall comply with the rules of Section VIII of the 1962 Edition of the ASME Boiler and Pressure Vessel Code (see 16.15) covering the requirements for the design, fabrication, and inspection during construction of unfired *pressure vessels*.

11.1.1 *Certification for ASME "UM" Stamped Pressure Vessels.* Certification requirements on *pressure vessels* which are built in accordance with Section VIII of the 1962 Edition of the ASME Boiler and Pressure Vessel Code under Paragraph U-1(g) and stamped with the "UM" symbol (see Paragraph UG-116) can be met by keeping a production series record of material used and tests made. Certification for individual vessels, where required, may be made by abstracting data from the series record on Data Report Form U-3.

11.2 Refrigerant-Containing Pressure Vessels Not Exceeding an Inside Diameter of 6 Inches, irrespective of pressure, *shall* be listed either individually or as part of refrigeration equipment, by *an approved nationally recognized testing laboratory* having a follow-up inspection service. Vessels not so listed *shall* be constructed according to Paragraph 11.1 and 11.1.1. (See 1.2 and 2.3.1.)

11.3 Relief Devices. All *pressure vessels,* irrespective of size or pressure, shall be equipped with relief devices in accordance with the requirements of Section 13 of this Code.

11.4 Standard Hydrostatic Tests. Fusion welded *pressure vessels shall* be tested in accordance with Paragraph UG-99, Section VIII of the 1962 Edition of the ASME Boiler and Pressure Vessel Code. (See also 11.4.1.)

11.4.1 *Pneumatic Tests.* Vessels for use in services which cannot tolerate the presence of a testing liquid and which cannot be readily dried, and the parts of which have been previously tested by hydrostatic pressure to not less than 1½ times the *design working pressure* of the vessel, may be given a pneumatic test as prescribed in Paragraph UG-100, Section VIII of the 1962 Edition of the ASME Boiler and Pressure Vessel Code.

Section 12. RELIEF DEVICES IN GENERAL

12.1 General. Every *refrigerating system shall* be protected by a *pressure-relief device* unless so constructed that pressure due to fire conditions will be safely relieved by some part of the system.

12.1.1 No *stop valve shall* be located between any automatic *pressure-relief device* or *fusible plug* and the part or parts of the system protected thereby, except when the parallel relief devices mentioned in 13.2 are so arranged that only one can be rendered inoperative at a time for testing or repair purposes.

12.1.2 All *pressure-relief devices shall* be connected as nearly as practicable directly to the *pressure vessel* or other parts of the system protected thereby, above the liquid *refrigerant* level, and installed so that they are readily accessible for inspection and repair and so that they cannot be readily rendered inoperative. *Fusible plugs* may be located above or below the liquid *refrigerant* level.

12.1.3 The seats and discs of *pressure-relief devices shall* be constructed of suitable material to resist *refrigerant* corrosion or other chemical action caused by the *refrigerant.* Seats or discs of cast iron *shall not* be used.

12.1.4 The rated discharge capacity of a *pressure-relief valve* for a refrigerant-containing vessel, expressed in pounds of air per minute, *shall* be determined at a pressure at the inlet of the relief valve equal to 110 percent of the valve setting in accordance with Paragraph UG-131, Section VIII of the 1962 Edition of the ASME Boiler and Pressure Vessel Code. (See 16.15.)

12.1.5 The rated discharge capacity of a *rupture member* or *fusible plug* discharging to atmosphere under critical flow conditions in pounds of air per minute *shall* be determined by the following formulas:

$$C = 0.8\, P_1 d^2 \qquad (1)$$

$$d = 1.12 \sqrt{\frac{C}{P_1}}$$

where C = minimum required discharge capacity, in lb of air per min

d = minimum diameter of bore of *fusible plug* or internal diameter of inlet pipe to *rupture member* in inches

Where for *rupture members:*
P_1 = (set pressure $\times$ 1.10) + 14.7

For *fusible plugs:*
P_1 = absolute saturation pressure, corresponding to the stamped temperature melting point of the *fusible plug* or the critical pressure of the *refrigerant* used, whichever is smaller, psia

12.1.6 All *pressure-relief devices (not fusible plugs) shall* be directly pressure-actuated.

12.1.7 The size of the discharge pipe from the *pressure-relief device shall* be not less than the size of the relief device outlet. The discharge from more than one relief device may be run into a common header, the area of which *shall* be not less than the sum of the areas of the pipes connected thereto.

12.1.8 The length of discharge *piping* permitted to be installed on the outlet of a relief valve, *rupture member,* or *fusible plug shall* be determined as follows:

$$C = \frac{3\,P\,d^{5/2}}{L^{\frac{1}{2}}} \qquad (2)$$

or

$$d = \sqrt[5]{\frac{C^2 L}{9 P^2}}$$

where C = minimum required discharge capacity, in lb of air per min

d = internal diameter of pipe in in.

L = length of discharge pipe in ft

$P = 0.25 P_1$ (P_1 is defined under Equation 1.)

(See Table 7 for computations derived from the preceding formula.)

12.2 Pressure-Relief Devices for Positive Displacement Compressors. *Positive displacement compressors* operating above 15 pounds per square inch gage and having a displacement exceeding 50 cubic feet per minute, *shall* be equipped by the *manufacturer* with a *pressure-relief device* of adequate size and pressure setting to prevent rupture of the *compressor,* located between the *compressor* and *stop valve* on the discharge side. The discharge from such relief device may be vented to the atmosphere or into the low pressure side of the system.

12.3 Discharge of Pressure-Relief Devices and Fusible Plugs on all systems containing more than 6 pounds of Group 2 or Group 3 *refrigerants shall* be to the outside of the building in an approved manner. Discharge of *pressure-relief devices* and *fusible plugs* on all systems containing more than 100 pounds of Group 1 *refrigerants,* unless installed in a *Machinery Room* used for no purpose other than to house mechanical equipment and complying with the provisions as specified in Paragraph 8.11, *shall* be to the outside of the building in an *approved* manner.

12.3.1 *Pressure-relief devices* may discharge into the *low side* of the system, provided the *pressure-relief devices* are of a type not appreciably affected by back pressures and provided the *low side* of the system is equipped with *pressure-relief devices.* The relief devices on the *low side* of the system *shall* have sufficient capacity to protect the *pressure vessels* that are relieved into the *low side* of the system, or to protect all *pressure vessels* on the *low side* of the system, whichever relieving capacity is the largest, as computed by the formula in Paragraph 13.5. Such *low side pressure-relief devices shall* be set in accordance with Paragraph 13.6 and vented to the outside of the building in an *approved* manner.

12.4 Ammonia Discharge. Where ammonia is used, the discharge may be into a tank of water which *shall* be used for no purpose except ammonia absorption. At least 1 gallon of fresh water *shall* be provided for each pound of ammonia in the system. The water used *shall* be prevented from freezing without the use of salt or chemicals. The tank *shall* be substantially constructed of not less than 1/8 inch or No. 11 U.S. gage iron or steel. No horizontal dimension of the tank *shall* be greater than one-half the height. The tank *shall* have hinged cover, or, if of the enclosed type, *shall* have a vent hole at the top. All pipe connections *shall* be through the top of the tank only. The discharge pipe from the *pressure-relief valves shall* discharge the ammonia in the center of the tank near the bottom.

12.5 Sulphur Dioxide Discharge. Where sulphur dioxide is used, the discharge may be into a tank of absorptive *brine* which *shall* be used for no purpose except sulphur dioxide absorption. There *shall* be 1 gallon of standard dichromate *brine* (2½ pounds sodium dichromate per gallon of water) for each pound of sulphur dioxide in the system. *Brines* made with caustic soda or soda ash may be used in place of sodium dichromate, provided the quantity and strength give the equivalent sulphur dioxide absorbing power. The tank *shall* be substantially constructed of not less than 1/8 inch or No. 11 U.S. gage iron or steel. The tank *shall* have a hinged cover, or, if of the enclosed type, *shall* have a vent hole at the top. All pipe connections *shall* be through the top of the tank only. The discharge pipe from the *pressure-relief valve shall* discharge the sulphur dioxide in the center of the tank near the bottom.

Section 13. RELIEF DEVICES FOR PRESSURE VESSELS

13.1 General. The rules of this section are based upon the rules given in Paragraphs UG-125 to UG-134 inclusive, of Section VIII of the 1962 Edition of the ASME Boiler and Pressure Vessel Code, with such additional modifications as are necessary for control of *refrigerants*.

13.2 Pressure Vessels Over 3 Cubic Feet. Each *pressure vessel* containing liquid *refrigerant* with internal gross volume exceeding 3 cubic feet, except as specified in 13.4, and which may be shut off by valves from all other parts of a *refrigerating system, shall* be protected by a *pressure-relief device,* having sufficient capacity to prevent the pressure in the *pressure vessel* from rising more than 10 percent above the setting of the *pressure-relief device.* (See 13.5.)

13.2.1 Pressure Vessels over 3 Cubic Feet, but Less Than 10 Cubic Feet. Under conditions specified in 13.2, a single relief device *(relief valve* or *rupture member)* may be used on *pressure vessels* having less than 10 cubic feet internal gross volume.

13.2.2 Pressure Vessels of 10 Cubic Feet Internal Gross Volume or Over. Under conditions specified in 13.2, a relief device system consisting of a pressure-relief device in parallel with a second pressure-relief device as described in Paragraph 12.1.1 *shall* be provided on *pressure vessels* having *internal gross volume* of 10 cu ft or over. Each relief valve or rupture member shall have sufficient capacity to prevent the pressure in the *pressure vessel* from rising more than ten percent above the setting of the *pressure-relief device.* (See Paragraph 13.8.)

13.2.2.1 Relief Valves Discharging into Low Side of the System. Under conditions permitted in 12.3.1 a single *relief valve* (not *rupture member)* of the required relieving capacity may be used on vessels of 10 cubic feet or over.

13.2.3 Relief Devices in Parallel on Large Vessels. In cases where large *pressure vessels* containing liquid *refrigerant* except as specified in 13.4, require the use of two or more *pressure-relief devices* in parallel to obtain the capacity required by 13.5, the battery of *pressure-relief devices shall* be considered as a unit, and therefore as one *pressure-relief device.*

13.3 Pressure Vessels with Internal Gross Volume of 3 Cubic Feet or Less. Each *pressure vessel* having an internal gross volume of 3 cubic feet or less, containing liquid *refrigerant,* except as specified in 13.4, and which may be shut off by valves from all other parts of a *refrigerating system,* shall be protected by a *pressure-relief device,* or *fusible plug.* A *fusible plug* is permitted only on the *high side* of a *refrigerating system. Pressure vessels* of less than 3 inch I D are exempt from these requirements.

13.3.1 Relief Valves on Pressure Vessels with Gross Volume of 3 Cubic Feet or Less. If a *relief valve* or *rupture member* is used to protect a *pressure vessel,* the ultimate bursting pressure of the *pressure vessel* so protected *shall* be at least 2½ times the pressure setting of the *pressure-relief valve* or *rupture member.*

13.3.2 Fusible Plugs and Pressure Vessels with Gross Volume of 3 Cubic Feet or Less. If a *fusible plug* is used, the ultimate bursting pressure of the *pressure vessel* so protected *shall* be at least 2½ times the *refrigerant* saturation pressure, psia, corresponding to the stamped temperature on the *fusible plug,* or at least 2½ times the critical pressure of the *refrigerant* used, whichever is smaller.

13.4 Relief Device for Pressure Vessels Used As, or As Part of Evaporator. *Pressure vessels* having internal diameters greater than 6 inches used as, or as part of, *evaporators* insulated or installed in insulated space, and which may be shut off by valves from all other parts of a *refrigerating system shall* be protected by a *pressure-relief device* in accordance with the provisions of Paragraph 13.2 and 13.3 except

that the provisions of Paragraph 13.2.2, requiring a second parallel *relief device, shall not* apply. *Pressure vessels* used as *evaporators,* having internal diameters of 6 inches or less, are exempt from *pressure-relief valve* requirements.

13.5 Required Capacity. The minimum required rated discharge capacity of the *pressure-relief device* or *fusible plug* for a refrigerant-containing vessel *shall* be determined by the following:

$$C = fDL \qquad (3)$$

where C = minimum required discharge capacity of the relief device in lb of air per min

D = outside diameter of the vessel in ft

L = length of the vessel in ft

f = factor dependent upon kind of *refrigerant,* as follows:

Kind of refrigerant	*Value of f*
Ammonia (Refrigerant 717)	0.5
Refrigerants 12, 22 and 500	1.6
Refrigerant 502 and	
Refrigerants 13, 13B1, and	
14 when on cascaded systems	2.5
All other *refrigerants*	1.0

13.6 Pressure-Relief Device Setting. Except as permitted in 13.3.1 all *pressure-relief devices shall* be set to start to function at a pressure not to exceed the *design working pressure* of the *pressure vessel* as determined by the *manufacturer* and stamped on the *pressure vessel* or system.

13.7 Rupture Member Setting. All *rupture members* used in lieu of, or in series with, a relief valve *shall* function at a pressure not to exceed the *design working pressure* of the vessel and the conditions of application *shall* conform to the requirements of Section VIII of the 1962 Edition of the ASME Boiler and Pressure Vessel Code.

Rupture members installed ahead of relief valves need not be larger, but *shall not* be smaller, than the relief valve inlet. (See Paragraph 12.1.5.)

13.8 Marking of Relief Devices.

13.8.1 All *pressure-relief valves* for refrigerant-containing vessels *shall* be set and sealed by the *manufacturer.* Each relief valve *shall* be marked by the *manufacturer* with the data required in Paragraph UG-129 (a) of Section VIII of the 1962 Edition of the ASME Boiler and Pressure Vessel Code.

13.8.2 Each *rupture member* for refrigerant-containing *pressure vessels shall* be marked with the information required in Paragraph UG-129 (d) of Section VIII of the 1962 Edition of the ASME Boiler and Pressure Vessel Code.

Section 14. FIELD TESTS

14.1 General. Every refrigerant-containing part of every system that is erected on the premises, except *compressors, condensers, evaporators,* safety devices, pressure gages, and control mechanisms, that are factory tested, *shall* be tested and proved tight after complete installation, and before operation, at not less than the minimum *refrigerant* leak field test pressures shown in Table 6, or in accordance with 14.1.1 and 14.1.2.

14.1.1 Systems erected on the *premises* using Group 1 *refrigerant* and with copper tubing not exceeding 5/8 inch O D, with wall thickness as required by Paragraphs 9.3.3 and 9.3.4 may be tested by means of the *refrigerant* charged into the system at the saturated vapor pressure of the *refrigerant* at 70 F or higher.

14.1.2 Limited charged systems equipped with a *pressure-relief device,* erected on the premises, *shall* be tested at a pressure not less than 1½ times the pressure setting of the relief device.

14.2 Test Medium. No oxygen or any combustible gas or combustible mixture of gases *shall* be used within the system for testing.

TABLE 6. Minimum Refrigerant Leak Field Test Pressures

Refrigerant name and number *	Chemical formula	Minimum field refrigerant leak test pressures, psig High side	Low side
Ammonia (717)	NH_3	300	150
Butane (600)	C_4H_{10}	95	50
Carbon dioxide (744)	CO_2	1500	1000
Dichlorodifluoromethane (12)	CCl_2F_2	235	140
Dichlorodifluoromethane 73.8% } (500) Ethylidene fluoride 26.2% }	CCl_2F_2 } $CH_3\text{-}CHF_2$ }	285	150
Dichloroethylene (1130)	$C_2H_2Cl_2$	30	30
Dichloromethane (Methylene chloride) (30)	CH_2Cl_2	30	30
Dichloromonofluoromethane (21)	$CHCl_2F$	70	40
Dichlorotetrafluoroethane (114)	$C_2Cl_2F_4$	50	50
Ethane (170)	C_2H_6	1200	700
Ethyl chloride (160)	C_2H_5Cl	60	50
Ethylene (1150)	C_2H_4	1600	1200
Isobutane (601)	$(CH_3)_3CH$	130	70
Methyl chloride (40)	CH_3Cl	210	120
Methyl formate (611)	$HCOOCH_3$	50	50
Monobromotrifluoromethane (13B1)	$CBrF_3$	435	245
Monochlorodifluoromethane (22)	$CHClF_2$	300	150
Monochlorodifluoromethane 48.8%, and Monochloropentafluoroethane } 51.2% (502)	$CHClF_2$ } $CClF_2CF_3$ }	300	150
Monochlorotrifluoromethane (13)	$CClF_3$	685**	685**
Octafluorocyclobutane (C318)	C_4F_8	130	70
Propane (290)	C_3H_8	300	150
Sulphur dioxide (764)	SO_2	170	85
Trichloromonofluoromethane (11)	CCl_3F	20	20
Trichlorotrifluoroethane (113)	$C_2Cl_3F_3$	20	20

NOTES:

a) For *refrigerants* not listed in Table 6 the test pressure for the high pressure side *shall* be not less than the saturated vapor pressure of the *refrigerant* at 150 F. The test pressure for the low pressure side *shall* be not less than the saturated vapor pressure of the *refrigerant* at 110 F. However, the test pressure for either the *high* or *low side* need not exceed 125 percent of the critical pressure of the *refrigerant*. In no case *shall* the test pressure be less than 30 psig.

b) When a *compressor* is used as a booster to obtain a low pressure and discharges into the suction line of another system, the booster *compressor* is considered a part of the *low side*, and values listed under the *low side* column in Table 6 *shall* be used for both *high* and *low side* of the booster *compressor* provided that a low pressure stage *compressor* of the *positive displacement* type *shall* have a *pressure-relief valve*.

c) In field testing systems using *nonpositive displacement compressors*, the entire system *shall* be considered for field test purposes as the *low side* pressure.

* ASHRAE Designation

** Critical pressure is 561 psia at critical temp of 83.9 F (See Note (a) above).

14.2.1 The means used to build up the test pressure *shall* have either a *pressure-limiting device* or a pressure reducing device and a gage on the outlet side.

14.3 **Posting of Tests.** A dated declaration of test *should* be provided for all systems containing 50 lb or more of *refrigerant*, where required by 14.1. The declaration *should* be mounted in a frame, protected by glass, and posted in the *machinery room* and *should* give the name of the *refrigerant* and the field *refrigerant* leak test pressures applied to the *high side* and the *low side* of the system. The declaration of test *should* be signed by the installer and, if an inspector is present at the tests, he *should* also sign the declaration. When requested, copies of this declaration *shall* be furnished to the enforcing authority

The leak test pressure requirements of Table 6 are not

intended to apply to gas bulk storage tanks that are not permanently connected to a *refrigeration system*.

Section 15. INSTRUCTIONS

15.1 **Signs.** Each *refrigerating system* erected on the premises *shall* be provided with an easily legible permanent sign securely attached and easily accessible, indicating thereon the name and address of the installer, the kind and total number of pounds of *refrigerant* required in the system for normal operations, and the *refrigerant* leak field test pressure applied.

15.2 **Metal Signs for Systems Containing More than 100 Pounds of Refrigerant.** Systems containing more than 100 pounds of *refrigerant shall* be provided with metal signs having letters not less than ½ inch in height designating the main shutoff valves to each vessel, main steam or electrical control, remote control switch, and *pressure-limiting device*. On all exposed high pressure and low pressure *piping* in each room where installed outside the *machinery room*, *shall* be signs, as specified above, with the name of the *refrigerant* and the letters "HP" of "LP."

15.3 **New Sign for Changed Refrigerant.** When the kind of *refrigerant* is changed as provided in 15.7 (Substitution of Refrigerant), there *shall* be a new sign, of the same type as specified in 15.2, indicating clearly that a substitution has been made, and stating the same information for the new *refrigerant* as was stated in the original.

15.4 **Charging and Discharging Refrigerants.** When *refrigerant* is added to a system, except a *unit system* requiring less than 6 pounds of *refrigerant* it *shall* be charged into the low pressure side of the system. Any point on the downstream side of the main liquid line *stop valve shall* be considered as part of the low pressure side when operating with said *stop valve* in the closed position. No service *container shall* be left connected to a system except while charging or withdrawing *refrigerant*.

15.5 **Refrigerants Withdrawn from Refrigerating Systems** *shall* be transferred to *approved containers* only. (See 16.2.) No *refrigerant shall* be discharged to a sewer.

15.6 **Containers Used for Refrigerants Withdrawn from a Refrigerating System** *shall* be carefully weighed each time they are used for this purpose, and the *containers shall* not be filled in excess of the permissible filling weight for such *containers* and such *refrigerants* as are prescribed in the pertinent regulations of the Interstate Commerce Commission. (See 16.2.)

15.7 **Substitution of Kind of Refrigerant** in a system *shall* not be made without the permission of the approving authority, the user, and the makers of the original equipment, and due observance of safety requirements, including:

a) The effects of the substituted *refrigerant* on materials in the system;

b) The possibility of overloading the *liquid receiver* which *should not* be more than 80 percent full of liquid;

c) The liability of exceeding motor horsepower, *design working pressure*, or any other element that would violate any of the provisions of this *Code*;

d) The proper size of *refrigerant* controls;

e) The effect on the operation and setting of safety devices;

f) The possible hazards created by mixture of the original and the substituted *refrigerant*;

g) Effect of the classification of the *refrigerant* as provided in this standard.

15.8 **Refrigerant Stored in a Machinery Room** *shall* be not more than 20 percent of the normal *refrigerant* charged nor more than 300 pounds of the *refrigerant*, in addition to the charge in the system and the *refrigerant* stored in a permanently attached *receiver*, and then only in *approved* storage *containers*. (See 16.2.)

15.9 **Masks or Helmets.** One mask or helmet *shall* be provided at a location convenient to the *machinery room* when an amount of a Group 2 *refrigerant* between 100 and 1000 pounds, inclusive, is employed. If more than 1000 pounds of a Group 2 *refrigerant* are employed, at least two masks or helmets *shall* be provided.

15.9.1 Only complete helmets or masks marked as *approved* by the Bureau of Mines of the United States Department of the Interior and suitable for the *refrigerant* employed *shall* be used and they *shall* be kept in a suitable cabinet immediately outside the *machinery room* or other *approved* accessible location.

15.9.2 Canisters or cartridges of helmets or masks *shall* be renewed immediately after having been used or the seal broken and, if unused, the canisters shall be renewed not later than the date noted on the canister labels.

15.10 Maintenance. All *refrigerating systems shall* be maintained by the user in a clean condition, free from accumulations of oily dirt, waste, and other debris, and *shall* be kept readily accessible at all times.

15.11 Responsibility as to Operation of the System. It *shall* be the duty of the person in charge of the premises on which a *refrigerating system* containing more than 50 pounds of *refrigerant* is installed, to place a card conspicuously as near as practicable to the *refrigerant compressor* giving directions for the operation of the system, including precautions to be observed in case of a breakdown or leak as follows:

a) Instruction for shutting down the system in case of emergency;

b) The name, address, and day and night telephone numbers for obtaining service;

c) The name, address, and telephone number of the municipal inspection department having jurisdiction, and instructions to notify said department immediately in case of emergency.

15.12 Pressure Gages *should* be checked for accuracy prior to test and immediately after every occasion of unusually high pressure, equal to full scale reading either by comparison with master gages or by setting the pointer as determined by a dead weight pressure gage tester.

TABLE 7. Length of Discharge Piping for Relief Valves or Rupture Members of Various Discharge Capacities

Equiv. length of discharge pipe, ft (L)	Discharge capacity in lb of air per min (C) Standard wall iron pipe sizes, in.							
	½	¾	1	1¼	1½	2	2½	3
RELIEF DEVICE SET AT 25 PSIA (P₁)								
50	0.81	1.6	2.9	5.9	8.7	16.3	25.3	43.8
75	0.67	1.4	2.4	4.9	7.2	13.3	20.9	35.8
100	0.58	1.2	2.1	4.2	6.2	11.5	18.0	30.9
150	0.47	0.95	1.7	3.4	5.0	9.4	14.6	25.3
200	0.41	0.8	1.5	2.9	4.4	8.1	12.6	21.8
300	0.33	0.67	1.2	2.4	3.6	6.6	10.5	17.9
RELIEF DEVICE SET AT 50 PSIA (P₁)								
50	1.6	3.3	5.9	11.9	17.4	32.5	50.6	87.6
75	1.3	2.7	4.9	9.7	14.3	26.5	41.8	71.5
100	1.2	2.3	4.2	8.4	12.3	23.0	36.0	61.7
150	0.94	1.9	3.5	6.9	10.0	18.7	29.2	50.6
200	0.81	1.6	2.9	5.9	8.7	16.3	25.3	43.7
300	0.66	1.3	2.5	4.9	7.1	13.3	21.0	35.7
RELIEF DEVICE SET AT 75 PSIA (P₁)								
50	2.4	4.9	8.9	17.9	26.1	48.7	75.9	131.5
75	2.0	4.1	7.3	14.6	21.4	39.8	62.6	107.0
100	1.7	3.5	6.4	12.6	18.5	34.4	54.0	92.6
150	1.4	2.8	5.2	10.3	15.0	28.0	43.8	75.9
200	1.2	2.5	4.4	8.9	13.1	24.4	37.9	65.6
300	0.9	2.0	3.7	7.3	10.7	19.9	31.5	53.5
RELIEF DEVICE SET AT 100 PSIA (P₁)								
50	3.2	6.6	11.9	23.8	34.8	65.0	101.2	175.2
75	2.7	5.4	9.7	19.4	28.6	53.0	83.6	143.0
100	2.3	4.6	8.5	16.8	24.6	45.9	72.0	123.6
150	1.9	3.8	6.9	13.7	20.0	37.4	58.4	101.2
200	1.6	3.3	5.9	11.9	17.5	32.5	50.6	87.6
300	1.3	2.7	4.9	9.7	14.2	26.5	42.0	71.4
RELIEF DEVICE SET AT 150 PSIA (P₁)								
50	4.9	9.9	17.9	35.7	52.3	97.5	151.8	262.8
75	4.0	8.1	14.6	29.2	42.9	79.5	125.4	214.5
100	3.5	6.9	12.7	25.2	36.9	68.9	108.0	185.4
150	2.8	5.7	10.4	20.6	30.0	56.1	87.6	151.8
200	2.4	4.9	8.9	17.8	26.2	48.7	75.9	131.4
300	1.9	4.0	7.4	14.6	21.1	39.7	63.0	107.1
RELIEF DEVICE SET AT 200 PSIA (P₁)								
50	6.5	13.2	23.8	47.6	69.7	130.0	202.4	350.4
75	5.3	10.8	19.4	38.9	57.2	106.0	167.2	286.0
100	4.6	9.2	16.9	33.6	49.2	91.8	144.0	247.2
150	3.8	7.6	13.8	27.4	40.0	74.8	116.8	202.4
200	3.2	6.5	11.8	23.8	34.9	64.9	101.2	175.2
300	2.6	5.3	9.8	19.4	28.4	52.9	84.0	142.8
RELIEF DEVICE SET AT 250 PSIA (P₁)								
50	8.1	16.5	29.8	59.5	87.1	162.5	253.0	437.0
75	6.7	13.5	24.3	48.6	71.5	132.5	209.0	357.5
100	5.8	11.6	21.2	42.0	61.6	114.8	180.0	309.0
150	4.7	9.5	17.3	34.3	50.0	93.5	146.0	253.0
200	4.1	8.2	14.8	29.7	43.7	81.2	126.5	219.0
300	3.3	6.7	12.3	24.3	35.5	66.2	105.0	178.5
RELIEF DEVICE SET AT 300 PSIA (P₁)								
50	9.7	19.8	35.7	71.4	104.5	195.0	303.6	525.6
75	7.9	16.2	29.1	58.3	85.8	159.0	250.8	429.0
100	6.9	13.9	25.4	50.4	73.9	137.7	216.0	370.8
150	5.6	11.3	20.7	41.1	60.0	112.2	175.2	303.6
200	4.9	9.8	17.8	35.6	52.4	97.4	151.8	262.8
300	3.9	7.9	14.7	29.1	42.6	79.4	126.0	214.2

SECTION 16

Titles and Sources of Reference Standards

16.1 American Standard, Z11.7-1962, Method of Test for Flash Point by Means of the Pensky-Martens Closed Tester. (ASTM D93-62) (1) (4)

16.2 Interstate Commerce Commission's Regulations for Transportation of Explosive and other Dangerous Articles by Land and Water in Rail Freight Service and by Motor Vehicle (Highway) and Water, Including Specifications for Shipping Containers; Agent T.C. George's Tariff No. 15, Effective Sept. 25, 1963 prescribed under the Act of June 25, 1948. (5)

16.3 American Standard, B15.1-1958, Safety Code for Mechanical Power-Transmission Apparatus. (1)

16.4 American Standard, A40.8-1955, National Plumbing Code. (1)

16.5 American Standard, A11.1-1952, for Industrial Lighting. (1)

16.6 National Fire Protection Association Standard 70, National ·Electrical Code, American Standard C1-1962. (1) (6)

16.7 National Fire Protection Association Standard 54-1959 Installation of Gas Appliances and Gas Piping, American Standard Z21.30-1959 (1) (6)

16.8 National Fire Protection Association Standard 90A, 1963 Air Conditioning and Ventilating Systems of Other Than Residence Type. (6)

16.9 National Fire Protection Association Standard 90B, 1963 Residence Type Warm Air Heating and Air Conditioning Systems. (6)

16.10 American Standard, B31.5-1962, Code for Pressure Piping: Refrigerant Piping. (1)

16.11 American Standard, B36.10-1959, Wrought-Steel and Wrought-Iron Pipe. (1)

16.12 American Standard, H26.1-1963, Specifications for Seamless Copper Pipe, Standard Sizes. (ASTM B42-62) (1) (4)

16.13 American Standard, H23.1-1963, Specifications for Seamless Copper Water Tube. (ASTM B88-62) (1) (4)

16.14 American Standard, H23.5-1963, Specifications for Seamless Copper Tube for Refrigeration Field Service. (ASTM B280-62) (1) (4)

16.15 ASME Boiler and Pressure Vessel Code, Section VIII 1962 Edition, known as ASME Unfired Pressure Vessel Code. (3)

16.16 For reference to items not found in the body of the Code, the ASHRAE GUIDE AND DATA BOOKS, current editions are recommended. (2)

16.17 National Fire Protection Association Standard 101-1963, Building Exits Code for Life Safety from Fire. (6)

16.18 American Standard, H27.1-1963, Specification for Seamless Red Brass Pipe, Standard Sizes. (ASTM B43-62) (1) (4)

16.19 American Standard, B79.1-1960, Number Designation of Refrigerants. (ASHRAE 34-57) (1) (2)

Reference Sources

(1) American Standards Association Inc., 10 East 40th Street, New York, N.Y., 10016

(2) American Society of Heating, Refrigerating and Air-Conditioning Engineers, Inc., United Engineering Center, 345 East 47th Street, New York, N.Y., 10017

(3) American Society of Mechanical Engineers, United Engineering Center, 345 East 47th Street, New York, N.Y., 10017

(4) American Society for Testing and Materials, 1916 Race Street, Philadelphia 3, Pa.

(5) Interstate Commerce Commission, 12th Street and Constitution Avenue, Washington, D.C.

(6) National Fire Protection Association, 60 Batterymarch Street, Boston 10, Mass.

APPENDIX

Extract from ASA B 79. 1-1960 Number Designation of Refrigerants

ASHRAE Standard Refrigerant Designation	Chemical Name	Chemical Formula
Halocarbon Compounds		
10	Carbontetrachloride	CCl_4
11	Trichloromonofluoromethane	CCl_3F
12	Dichlorodifluoromethane	CCl_2F_2
13	Monochlorotrifluoromethane	$CClF_3$
13B1	Monobromotrifluoromethane	$CBrF_3$
14	Carbontetrafluoride	CF_4
20	Chloroform	$CHCl_3$
21	Dichloromonofluoromethane	$CHCl_2F$
22	Monochlorodifluoromethane	$CHClF_2$
23	Trifluoromethane	CHF_3
30	Methylene Chloride	CH_2Cl_2
31	Monochloromonofluoromethane	CH_2ClF
32	Methylene fluoride	CH_2F_2
40	Methyl chloride	CH_3Cl
41	Methyl fluoride	CH_3F
50	Methane	CH_4
110	Hexachloroethane	CCl_3CCl_3
111	Pentachloromonofluoroethane	CCl_3CCl_2F
112	Tetrachlorodifluoroethane	CCl_2FCCl_2F
112a	Tetrachlorodifluoroethane	CCl_3CClF_2
113	Trichlorotrifluoroethane	CCl_2FCClF_2
113a	Trichlorotrifluoroethane	CCl_3CF_3
114	Dichlorotetrafluoroethane	$CClF_2CClF_2$
114a	Dichlorotetrafluoroethane	CCl_2FCF_3
114B2	Dibromotetrafluoroethane	$CBrF_2CBrF_2$
115	Monochloropentafluoroethane	$CClF_2CF_3$
116	Hexafluoroethane	CF_3CF_3
120	Pentachloroethane	$CHCl_2CCl_3$
123	Dichlorotrifluoroethane	$CHCl_2CF_3$
124	Monochlorotetrafluoroethane	$CHClFCF_3$
124a	Monochlorotetrafluoroethane	CHF_2CClF_2
125	Pentafluoroethane	CHF_2CF_3
133a	Monochlorotrifluoroethane	CH_2ClCF_3
140a	Trichloroethane	CH_3CCl_3
142b	Monochlorodifluoroethane	CH_3CClF_2
143a	Trifluoroethane	CH_3CF_3
150a	Dichloroethane	CH_3CHCl_2
152a	Difluoroethane	CH_3CHF_2
160	Ethyl chloride	CH_3CH_2Cl
170	Ethane	CH_3CH_3
218	Octafluoropropane	$CF_3CF_2CF_3$
290	Propane	$CH_3CH_2CH_3$
Cyclic Organic Compounds		
C316	Dichlorohexafluorocyclobutane	$C_4Cl_2F_6$
C317	Monochloroheptafluorocyclobutane	C_4ClF_7
C318	Octafluorocyclobutane	C_4F_8

ASHRAE Standard Refrigerant Designation	Chemical Name	Chemical Formula
Azeotropes		
500	Refrigerants 12/152a 73.8/26.2 wt %†	CCl_2F_2/CH_3CHF_2
501	Refrigerants 22/12 75/25 wt %	$CHClF_2/CCl_2F_2$
502	Refrigerants 22/115 48.8/51.2 wt %	$CHClF_2/CClF_2CF_3$
Miscellaneous Organic Compounds		
Hydrocarbons		
50	Methane	CH_4
170	Ethane	CH_3CH_3
290	Propane	$CH_3CH_2CH_3$
600	Butane	$CH_3CH_2CH_2CH_3$
601	Isobutane	$CH(CH_3)_3$
(1150	Ethylene	$CH_2=CH_2$
(1270	Propylene	$CH_3CH=CH_2$
Oxygen Compounds		
610	Ethyl ether	$C_2H_5OC_2H_5$
611	Methyl formate	$HCOOCH_3$
Sulfur Compounds		
620		
Nitrogen Compounds		
630	Methyl amine	CH_3NH_2
631	Ethyl amine	$C_2H_5NH_2$
Inorganic Compounds		
717	Ammonia	NH_3
718	Water	H_2O
729	Air	
744	Carbon dioxide	CO_2
744A	Nitrous oxide	N_2O
764	Sulfur dioxide	SO_2
Unsaturated Organic Compounds		
112a	Dichlorodifluoroethylene	$CCl_2=CF_2$
1113	Monochlorotrifluoroethylene	$CClF=CF_2$
1114	Tetrafluoroethylene	$CF_2=CF_2$
1120	Trichloroethylene	$CHCl=CCl_2$
1130	Dichloroethylene	$CHCl=CHCl$
1132a	Vinylidene fluoride	$CH_2=CF_2$
1140	Vinyl chloride	$CH_2=CHCl$
1141	Vinyl fluoride	$CH_2=CHF$
1150	Ethylene	$CH_2=CH_2$
1270	Propylene	$CH_3CH=CH_2$

27-43 Building Construction for Electric Heating

Included in the following paragraphs are some suggestions concerning building construction which are recommended when using electric heating. While the recommendations are made for electric heating application, they would also be effective with other types of heating.

SILL SEALER. It is desirable to install a moisture resisting sill sealer between the foundation and the wooden sill which acts as a gasket to minimize infiltration. With slab-on-grade construction, this sealer should be applied between the sole plate and the concrete slab. A sill sealer should be used in all applications except for floors over well vented crawl spaces.

PERIMETER INSULATION. Frequently, heat escapes from concrete floor slabs around the outside edges, or perimeters. This heat loss may be reduced by using perimeter insulation.

A ground moisture seal (vapor barrier) laid under the slabs is required to protect the finished flooring on top of the slab. Perimeter insulation may be used around the interior face of foundation walls in place of batts or blankets between the floor joists.

Note that weep holes are required at the base of the cavity in brick veneer walls, to allow wind driven moisture to escape from the cavity.

CEILING INSULATION, GENERAL. Begin at the outside wall plate. Peel back one or two inches of the vapor barrier at the end of the insulation. Using this as a stapling flange, staple the vapor barrier to the outside of the plate.

Make sure insulation on top of the plate does not block eave ventilation.

With the end of the insulation attached to the plate, staple the insulation to the under face of the ceiling joists, or inset along the sides of the joists. Pay close attention to the manufacturer's application instructions.

In studio or "cathedral" type ceilings, insulation should be installed between the rafters or on top of decking, using face staplings. Be sure to maintain a ventilation space between the top of the insulation and the underside of the roof sheathing.

If the finished ceiling is in place, batts or blankets may be laid in from above. Be sure to keep the vapor barrier side down. Tightly butt batts or blankets where they meet. Lay insulation over as close to the outside plate as possible without blocking the eave vents. This is particularly important with low-pitched roofs.

CEILING INSULATION-BRIDGING. If there is sufficient clearance, compress the ceiling insulation under the bridging, OR:

Cut away the insulation and carry the vapor barrier under the bridging, and staple it in place. Stuff insulation in and around the bridging, or add a separate piece of vapor barrier under the bridging, overlapping the barriers of adjoining batts. Then fill space in and around bridging with insulation.

Regardless of the method used, vapor barrier protection must be continuous.

ATTIC INSULATION, GENERAL. To insulate the whole attic space, staple insulation across the collar beams and down the rafters to the wall plate.

To insulate just the living space within an attic, staple insulation across the collar beams, down the rafters and knee wall studs and along the ceiling joists to the wall plate.

Do not try to run a continuous blanket across the collar beam and down the rafters and knee wall. Use separate sections of insulation for collar beams and knee walls to avoid buckling and gaps. Lap and seal vapor barriers at these junction points.

In either application, ventilation above the collar beams is mandatory. In addition, be sure to leave space for ventilation between the insulation and roof sheathing when attaching insulation to rafters.

Use staples no more than 6 in. apart to avoid gaps along the stapling flange.

WALL INSULATION, GENERAL. When stapling to plates, sills, and other horizontal framing members, cut away the insulation to allow an extra inch of vapor barrier as a stapling flange.

Facings on insulation must be face stapled. Masonry walls and walls of heated basements should be furred to the depth required to accommodate the particular insulation chosen for the job.

Use staples no more than 6 in. apart to avoid gaps.

WALL INSULATION, NONSTANDARD SPACES. Cut the batt or blanket a bit wider than the space to be filled, leaving an extra inch of vapor barrier as a stapling flange; or apply a series of batts or blanket sections horizontally across the space. Cut the sections a little wider than the space, and use the extra length of the vapor barrier as a stapling flange. Fit each successive piece similarly, lapping the flanges.

WALL INSULATION, OBSTRUCTIONS- Piping, Conduit and Ducts. Wherever possible, batts and blankets should be compressed and tucked behind conduit, piping and ducts. Install vapor barrier between cold water pipes and inside warm surface (wall, floor, ceiling).

Where this is not possible, the insulation may be easily split, placing as much insulation as possible behind the obstruction, and omitting insulation in front on the warm side.

Wall projections - Where outlet boxes, electrical receptacles, and wall projections such as faucets are encountered, place the insulation behind the obstruction, carefully cutting and fitting the vapor barrier to insure maximum vapor protection.

Window and Door Framing - Where accessible, stuff the small spaces between the rough framing and the heads, jambs,

and sills of windows and doors with insulation. Cover these stuffed spaces with small, separate vapor barrier.

FLOOR INSULATION, GENERAL. Warm side vapor protection is required. Place the insulation with the vapor barrier facing up in all applications except where a vapor barrier paper is used in place of the building paper over the sub floor. Only in this application may the barrier on the insulation be omitted.

1. Use a thin, rigid, vapor-permeable board supported on ledger strips nailed to floor joists.
2. Galvanized wire mesh stapled to the under face of the joists.
3. Galvanized wire mesh supported on ledger strips.

Other systems of support include baling wire lacing, arched wire supports, wood slats, and prefabricated form boards.

Reversed flange material may be used as floor insulation and may be stapled from below. Additional support may be required.

Always install insulation flush against floor. Never leave an air space between the insulation and the floor.

INSTALLATION OF WOOL, BLOWN AND POURED. Blown wool should be installed only by an experienced applicator who can assure that proper density, coverage, and thickness will be provided. An applicator must have a considerable knowledge of building construction to be sure of filling all hollow spaces.

Pouring may be readily applied in unfinished attic areas by simply emptying the bags evenly between ceiling joists, paying particular attention to the manufacturer's recommendations as to the proper thickness and coverage per bag. The insulation may be leveled with a wood slat or garden rake.

Be sure that the eave ventilation openings are not blocked when blowing ceiling areas.

Small openings, such as around the

chimney, should be hand packed with insulation.

Cover cavities, drops, and scuttles with suitable retaining material before insulating.

In floored attics, floorboards must be removed as required for access to all areas to be insulated. Check for obstructions, such as bridging and conduit, between openings.

BLOWING FINISHED ATTIC AREAS. When insulation is applied in attics containing enclosed areas, the horizontal ceiling and collar beam surfaces are blown in the normal manner. The knee walls and rafters of the enclosed area should be insulated with batts or blankets.

BLOWING INSULATION IN WALLS. All accessible exterior wall areas should be insulated.

Whenever the vertical space to be insulated is more than four feet high, the "double blow" method, with two access holes to each stud space, should be used.

Check each space with a plumb bob for possible obstructions below the holes. Insert a flexible steel rule to check for obstructions above the holes.

After the wall has been insulated, the access holes should be covered with a breather-type retainer.

In existing construction, the number of shingles or bricks to be removed may be minimized by cutting access holes as close together as possible on either side of the stud.

If spaces at joists between floors are to be blown, sufficient wool should be applied to fill the space the full depth of the joists.

TYPES OF VENTS. There are many different types of vents that will do a highly satisfactory job and blend in with any type of architecture.

The ridge vent is particularly useful with studio or "cathedral" type ceilings.

The main thing to be remembered with any of them is that they should be large enough and they should be kept open.

VENTILATION OF CRAWL SPACES. Note that the addition of a ground moisture seal over the bare earth is necessary to keep the crawl space humidity at a minimum level.

Fifty-five-pound roll roofing or 4 mil or thicker polyethylene sheeting, lapped at least 3 inches, are satisfactory materials. As with attic vents, crawl space ventilation is as necessary in winter as it is in summer. Do not close the vents in winter.

Always provide at least two vent openings. If possible, place them so air can flow in one, over the crawl space earth, and out the other.

These recommended vent sizes are based on a completely open vent with no screen or louvers in front of it. Where vents are protected by screens or rain louvers, the crawl space vent should be increased as follows:

TYPE OF COVERING	SIZE OF OPENING
1/4 in. hardware cloth	1 times net vent area
1/4 in. hardware cloth and rain louvers	2 times net vent area
8-mesh screen	1 1/4 times net vent area
8-mesh screen and rain louvers	2 1/4 times net vent area
16-mesh screen	2 times net vent area
16-mesh screen and rain louvers	3 times net vent area

VAPOR BARRIERS. Vapor barriers should be placed on the warm or heated-in-winter side of walls, ceilings, and floors.

Suitable vapor barriers are usually provided on batt and blanket insulation. Where no vapor barrier is attached to the insulation, separate vapor barriers are necessary. The following typical materials have been found satisfactory:

1. Waterproof laminated asphalt-coated paper.
2. Polyethylene sheeting: 2 mil or thicker in walls and ceiling, and 4 mil or thicker as ground moisture seals under slabs or over earth space.
3. Foil-backed gypsum board. Tape joists with vapor proof tape.

4. Similar films, sheets, or materials with comparable vapor resistant qualities.

Any vapor barrier damage during installation or construction should be repaired by either replacing the damaged barrier or mending the damage with tape.

When blown insulation is to be used in new work, continuous vapor barriers should be applied to the underside of ceiling joists where specified, and to the inside of wall studs. The barrier should be brought up tight against electrical outlets, registers, door and window frames, and other similar openings.

In existing houses, vapor protection may be obtained by painting the areas needing protection with two coats of good vapor resistant paint.

SPECIFICATIONS FOR BASEMENTS (when area is to be heated and used continuously):

Basements should only be constructed in those areas where the water table is below the proposed basement floor.

The exterior basement wall should be waterproofed and insulation installed. You can cement foamed plastic insulation to the wall. Batts, blankets, or blown insulation can be installed between furring strips with a vapor barrier installed on the warm side. If the batt, blanket, or blown insulation is installed in an enclosed vapor barrier, see that the warm side vapor barrier has a lower vapor rating than the cold side surface.

WINDOWS AND DOORS. Storm windows and storm doors form dead air spaces. The relatively immobile air contained, slows down heat losses through these openings. "Storms" are therefore a good investment for all single pane windows and exterior doors.

The prime, or innermost, windows should be weather stripped to reduce airflow to a minimum. Storm sash, though tight fitting, should permit controlled air movement to and from the enclosed air space. It can be achieved by means of weep holes in the storm sash; weep holes that are not subsequently blocked by caulking compound or paint.

Heat loss through the sash and frames of storm windows is another factor for serious consideration. Other things being equal, wood is superior to metal in its insulating qualities. Window frames that are better heat conductors than glass panes should not be used in residential construction.

In addition to costly heat losses, the high thermal conductivity of metal window frames can cause moisture condensation on their interior surfaces. This is true of both prime and storm windows. Changing the inside temperature of a house, changing the degree of its relative humidity, or the nature of the heating system, will not mend this condition if it exists.

Even with the best combination of storm and prime windows, heat losses through them are eight to ten times as great as through a well-insulated wall. Obviously, every effort to slow down these heat losses should be made in the interest of economy and comfort. Finally, it is wise to weather strip all exterior doors. Cracks and openings around window and exterior door frames should also be kept tightly caulked.

27-44 Refrigerant Characteristics

Several refrigerant tables and pressure-heat enthalpy diagrams are given in this section. Most of the physical properties of refrigerants may be ascertained from these tables and charts.

Chapter 9 describes the characteristics and uses of the more popular refrigerants in more detail.

Fig. 27-17 is a table showing the comparable properties of many of the refrigerants. The comparison of the pressure-temperature curves of several of the refrigerants is shown in Fig. 27-18.

Fig. 27-17. Table of properties of refrigerants.

Refrigerant Number	Name	Chemical Symbol	Trade Name	Molecular Weight	Odor	Toxity	Flammability	Pressure psia at 5 F.	Pressure psia at 86 F.	Latent Heat at 5 F.	Sp. Heat of Liquid at 5 F.	Critical Temperature of	Critical Pressure psia	Sp. Volume of Gas at 5 F.	Density of Liquid in a 5 F. #/cu. ft.	CP/CV Ratio	Sp. Heat of Vapor at 86 F.
R-764	Sulphur Dioxide	SO₂		64.06	Pungent	High	Non	11.81	66.45	172.3	.34	314.8	1141.5	6.421	92	1.256*	.34
R-40	Methyl Chloride	CH₃Cl		50.489	Sweet	Med.	Slight	20.89	95.53	180.6	.45	289.6	969.2	4.530	61	1.20	.4
R-717	Ammonia	NH₃		17.031	Pungent	High	Slight	34.27	169.2	565	1.10	271.4	1651	8.150	41.11	1.247	1.10
R-160	Ethyl Chloride	C₂H₅Cl	Alcozol	64.51	Etheral	Med.	Yes	4.65	27.10	177	.47	369	764	17.55	59.00	1.13	.42
R-12	R-12	CCl₂F₂		120.9	Sweet	Low	Non	26.61	107.9	68.2	.215	232.6	582.0	1.485	90	. . .	.243
R-13	R-13	CClF₃		104.46	Sweet	Low	Non	. . .	. . .	63.85 (-115 F.)	.247 (-22 F.)	84	561	.431	77 (0 F.)	1.172	. . .
R-744	Carbon Dioxide	CO₂		44.005	Non	Med.	Non	334.4	1039.0	116 (-115 F.)	.5	87.8	1066.2	.2673	61.22 (-115 F.)	1.30**	1.95
R-611	Methyl Formate	C₂H₃O₂		60.04	Slight	. . .	Slight	1.96	13.69	236	.515	417	870	46.7	. . .	. . .	.515
R-30	Methylene Chloride	CH₂Cl₂	Carrene No. 1	84.9	Sweet	. . .	Yes	1.17	10.6	162.1	.34	421	670	50.58	. . .	. . .	.34
R-114	R-114	C₂Cl₂F₄		170.93	Sweet	Low	Non	6.76	36.2	55#	.15#	294.3	474.0	. . .	99.1#	. . .	.20#
R-21	R-21	CHCl₂F	Thermon	102.92	Sweet	Low	Non	5.5	30.5	105.5	.26	353.3	750.0	8.83	90.1	. . .	.26
R-22	R-22	CHClF₂		86.48	Sweet	Low	Non	43.02	174.5	93.43	11.97	204.8	716	1.246	83.34	. . .	.34
R-11	R-11	CCl₃F	Carrene No. 2	137.38	Sweet	Low	Non	29.31	18.28	84.0	.197	388.4	635.0	12.3	97.8	. . .	.20
R-114	R-114	CClF₂CClF₂		170.93	Sweet	Low	Non	. . .	. . .	58.9	.238	294	474	.488	73.1	1.088	.160
R-113	R-113	C₂Cl₃F₃		187.4	Sweet	Low	Non	.98	7.86	70.62	.199	417.4	495	27.04	103	. . .	.26
R-500	R-500	CCl₂F₂/CH₃CHF₂		-99.29	Sweet	Low	Non	31.07	128.14	85.03	11.83	221.1	631	1.5227	80.10	4.61	. . .
R-502	R-502	CHClF₂ + CClF₂CF₃		111.64	Sweet	Low	Non	50.68	175.1	68.86	.027	194.1	618.7	.825	87.24	4.37	.07
R-290	Propane	C₃H₈		44.06	Sweet	Low	Yes	41.9	155	170.2	.56	302	661.5	2.48	34.33	. . .	.55
R-171	Ethane	C₂H₆		30.04	Sweet	Low	Yes	236.0	675.0	150.5	.66	90.1	730	.533	26.96	. . .	.83
R-600	Butane	C₄H₁₀		58.12	Sweet	Low	Yes	8.2	41.6	170.7	.51	308	529	9.98	38.41	. . .	.51
R-13B1	Kulene 131	CF₃Br		. . .	Etheral	Low	Non	77.93	261.8	44.88	.182	1535	587	.3854	112	. . .	.10
R-115	Monochloropenta-fluoroethane	CClF₂CF₃		154.48	Sweet	Low	Non	38	148.9	. . .	. . .	175.9	. . .	.82	. . .	3.76	. . .

* at 70 F.   ** at 32 F.   # at 70 F.

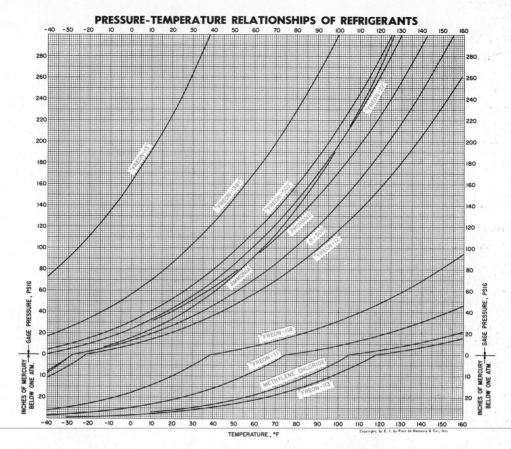

Fig. 27-18. Comparison of pressure-temperature relationships for some of the common refrigerants.

Fig. 27-19. Pressure-enthalpy diagram for R–11.

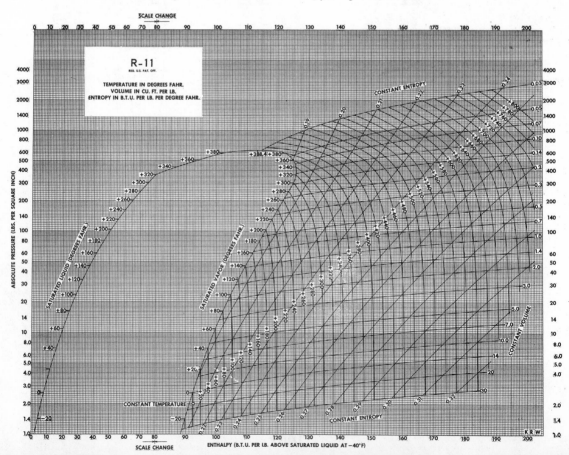

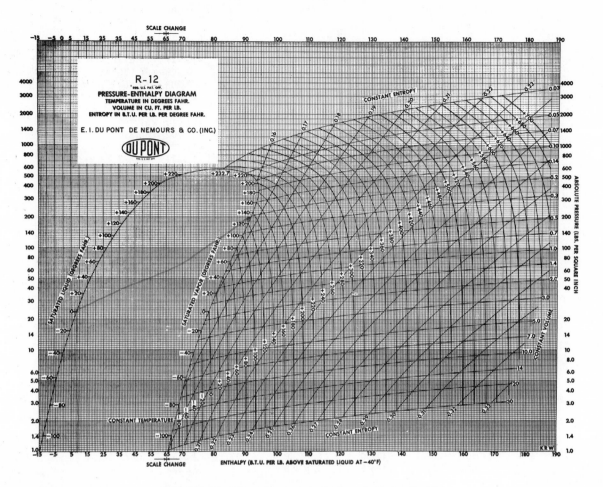

Fig. 27-20. The pressure-enthalpy chart for R-12.

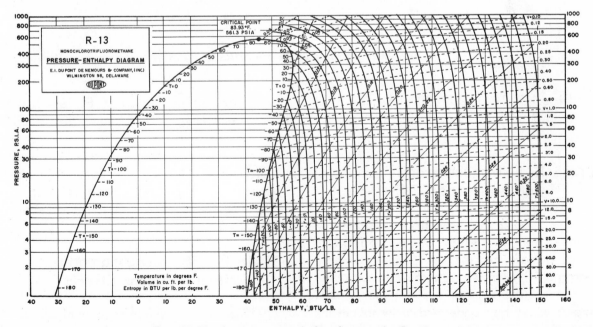

Fig. 27-21. A pressure-enthalpy diagram for R-13.

Temp. F.	Pressure		Volume cu.ft./lb.	Density lb./cu.ft.	Heat Content Btu/lb.	
t	psig	psia	Vapor	Liquid	Liquid hf	Latent h
−200	*29.04"	0.4329	61.33	105.6	−34.551	73.096
−190	*28.40"	0.7490	36.74	104.4	−32.429	72.029
−180	*27.40"	1.238	22.99	103.2	−30.298	70.970
−170	*25.92"	1.967	14.942	102.0	−28.208	69.904
−160	*23.60"	3.104	9.750	100.8	−26.083	68.808
−150	*20.83"	4.464	6.976	99.60	−24.010	67.783
−140	*16.78"	6.455	4.950	98.33	−21.902	66.696
−130	*11.43"	9.080	3.605	96.99	−19.792	65.596
−120	* 4.51"	12.48	2.681	95.69	−17.671	64.473
−110	2.11	16.81	2.031	94.34	−15.527	63.316
−100	7.53	22.23	1.5642	93.02	−13.387	62.138
−90	14.19	28.89	1.2232	91.66	−11.241	60.941
−80	22.28	36.98	0.9689	90.17	−9.052	59.672
−70	31.98	46.68	0.7766	88.73	−6.843	58.362
−60	43.49	58.19	0.6289	87.26	−4.604	56.993
−50	57.01	71.71	0.5139	85.69	−2.320	55.546
−40	72.73	87.43	0.4234	84.10	0.000	54.023
−30	90.90	105.6	0.3512	82.44	2.363	52.416
−20	111.7	126.4	0.2930	80.71	4.809	50.668
−10	135.4	150.1	0.2454	78.86	7.484	48.630
0	162.1	176.8	0.2066	76.98	10.052	46.638
10	192.1	206.8	0.17443	74.91	12.696	44.479
20	225.7	240.4	0.14732	72.73	15.443	42.100
30	263.2	277.9	0.12437	70.32	18.247	39.472
40	304.9	319.6	0.10455	67.70	21.370	36.450
45	327.5	342.2	0.09565	66.27	22.979	34.769
50	351.2	365.9	0.08734	64.68	24.651	32.958
55	376.1	390.8	0.07945	62.97	26.418	30.946
60	402.3	417.0	0.07189	61.09	28.310	28.677
65	429.8	444.5	0.06468	58.96	30.322	26.137
70	458.7	473.4	0.05767	56.46	32.515	23.193
75	489.0	503.7	0.05027	53.36	35.110	19.382
80	520.8	535.5	0.04131	48.85	38.527	13.565
83.93	546.6	561.3	0.02772	36.08	45.271	....

Fig. 27-22. A table of the properties of R–13.

Figs. 27-19 and 27-20 show the pressure enthalpy diagram for R-11 and R-12 respectively.

27-45 R-13 Monochlorotri-fluoromethane CClF$_3$

R-13 is a refrigerant especially developed for low temperature applications. It is a safe refrigerant to use both on a flammability basis and a toxic basis.

Its boiling pressure at 5 F. is 177 psig and it must be condensed at temperatures less than 83.93 F., its critical tempera-

ture. Its latent heat at 5 F. is 45.56 Btu per pound. Fig. 27-21 shows the graph for R-13.

The development of this refrigerant indicates the steady increase in low temperature refrigeration applications. A table of the properties of R-13 is shown in Fig. 27-22.

27-46 R-13B1 Monobromotri-fluoromethane CBrF$_3$

This refrigerant was especially developed for low temperature systems. It has a boiling temperature of –73.6 F. at atmospheric pressure. Its condensing pressure at 86 F. is 247.1 psi. It has a gas volume of .3854 cubic feet per pound at 5 F. and a latent heat of 44.88 Btu per pound at 5 F.

pressure is 48 F., as shown in Fig. 27-23. It is practically nonexplosive and nonflammable. Its odor is similar to chloroform, and it is not irritating in any way. It mixes in practically all proportions with oil and may be tested for leaks by using a halide

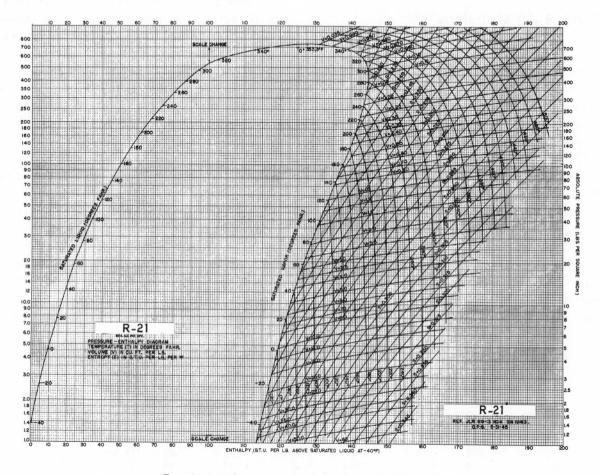

Fig. 27-23. A pressure-enthalpy graph for R–21.

This refrigerant is nontoxic and nonflammable, which would put it in the Group 1, Class 5 or 6. It is usable with all common metals.

27-47 R-21 Dichloromonofluoromethane CHCl₂F

R-21 is a refrigerant similar to R-114, having many of its characteristics. Its operating pressures are almost the same. Its boiling temperature under atmospheric

torch or an electronic leak detector. It is a noncorrosive and nonpoisonous refrigerant. It operates at 18.8 inches of vacuum at 5 F. and at 15.8 psi at 86 F. Its liquid has a density at 5 F. of 0.0111 cubic feet per pound and at 86 F. of 0.119 cubic feet per pound. Its saturated vapor has a density at 5 F. of .883 cubic feet per pound, and at 86 F. of 1.87 cubic feet per pound. The specific heat of the liquid is approximately .26 Btu per pound per degree F. The latent heat of the refrigerant at 5 F.

is 105.5 Btu per pound. R-21 is used primarily in centrifugal machines. Fig. 27-24 shows a table of the properties of R-21.

Approximately 13 pounds of this refrigerant can be safely used per 1000 cubic feet of air conditioned space.

27-48 R-30 Methylene Chloride CH$_2$Cl$_2$

R-30 is a good low pressure refrigerant having operating pressures of 27.5 inches vacuum at 5 F. and an 8.8-inch vacuum at 86 F. Its chemical formula is CH$_2$Cl$_2$, and its freezing temperature is -142 F. The gas has a slight odor which is not distasteful. It may be carried or stored in tins, although the refrigerant evaporates under room conditions fast enough to warrant sealing the cans in which it is stored. The refrigerant may be poured into a system through a funnel when charging. The specific heat of the liquid is .34, and its boiling point at atmospheric pressure is 103.6 F.

27-49 R-40 Methyl Chloride CH$_3$Cl

R-40 (methyl chloride) is classed as noncorrosive in a dry state. It is a poisonous refrigerant and should be used carefully. Carbon tetrachloride is closely related and carries the same hazard. Breathing of sufficient quantities of these chlorinated materials may cause one to stop breathing, and may damage the liver, kidneys, and central nervous system. The effects are cumulative, building up on one exposure on top of another. Many deaths have resulted from its careless use. Fig. 27-25 shows the graph for R-40.

The boiling point of R-40 at atmospheric pressure is -11.36 F., and its melting point is -136.7 F.

Leaks may be detected in R-40 by using the soap bubble method or by using the electronic leak detector.

Much copper plating has been experienced in R-40 machines. This has been caused by excessive moisture in the system. Copper plating is the result of these

Temp. F.	Pressure		Volume Gas cu.ft./lb.	Density Liquid lb./cu.ft.	Heat Content Btu/lb.	
	psig	psia			Liquid	Latent
-40	27.16"	1.358	32.09	94.52	0	114.56
-30	26.08"	1.888	23.61	93.79	2.36	113.40
-20	24.67"	2.578	17.66	93.04	4.71	112.25
-10	22.87"	3.463	13.43	92.28	7.07	111.10
0	20.59"	4.582	10.35	91.52	9.44	109.93
5	19.25"	5.243	9.13	91.13	10.63	109.34
10	17.75"	5.978	8.09	90.74	11.81	108.76
20	14.25"	7.699	6.39	89.96	14.21	107.57
30	9.98"	9.793	5.11	89.16	16.61	106.37
40	4.84"	12.32	4.13	88.35	19.04	105.15
50	0.63	15.33	3.37	87.54	21.49	103.90
60	4.20	18.90	2.77	86.71	23.98	102.62
70	8.38	23.08	2.30	85.87	26.49	101.30
80	13.26	27.96	1.92	85.03	29.03	99.95
86	16.53	31.23	1.73	84.52	30.56	99.12
90	18.88	33.58	1.62	84.17	31.59	98.55
100	25.34	40.04	1.37	83.31	34.18	97.11
110	32.70	47.40	1.17	82.43	36.79	95.63
120	41.05	55.75	1.00	81.54	39.46	94.07
130	50.45	65.15	.86	80.65	42.13	92.48
140	61.02	75.72	.76	79.74	44.86	90.80
150	72.81	87.51	.65	78.82	47.62	89.06
160	85.91	100.6	.56	77.90	50.43	87.26

Fig. 27-24. A table of the properties of R-21.

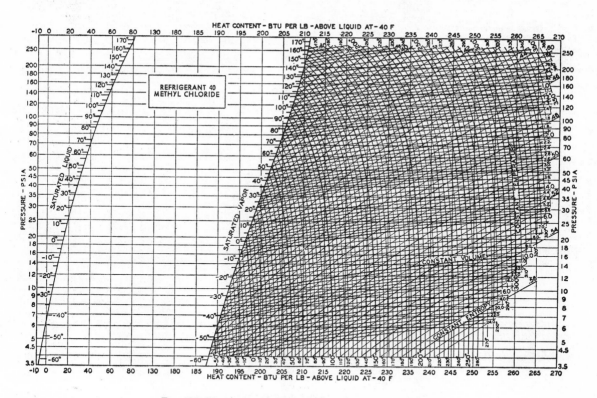

Fig. 27-25. A pressure-enthalpy diagram for R–40.

Temp F	Pressure psia	Pressure psig	Volume cu ft/lb Vapor v_g	Density lb/cu ft Liquid $1/v_f$	Enthalpy Btu/lb Liquid h_f	Enthalpy Btu/lb Vapor h_g	Entropy Btu/(lb)(°R) Liquid s_f	Entropy Btu/(lb)(°R) Vapor s_g
−80	1.953	25.94*	41.08	66.98	−13.988	184.75	−0.0351	0.4882
−70	2.751	24.32*	29.84	66.31	−10.521	186.25	−.0261	.4790
−60	3.799	22.19*	22.09	65.66	− 7.039	187.74.	− .0172	.4703
−50	5.155	19.43*	16.64	65.02	− 3.532	189.21	− .0085	.4620
−40	6.878	15.92*	12.72	64.39	0.000	190.66	0.0000	.4544
−30	9.036	11.52*	9.873	63.78	3.562	192.08	0.0084	.4472
−20	11.71	6.090*	7.761	63.17	7.146	193.49	.0166	.4405
−10	14.96	0.266	6.176	62.58	10.75	194.87	.0247	.4343
0	18.90	4.201	4.969	62.00	14.39	196.23	.0327	.4284
2	19.77	5.077	4.763	61.88	15.12	196.51	0.0343	0.4273
4	20.68	5.985	4.568	61.77	15.85	196.78	.0359	.4262
5	21.15	6.455	4.471	61.65	16.21	196.92	.0367	.4257
6	21.62	6.924	4.379	61.54	16.58	197.05	.0375	.4251
8	22.59	7.896	4.206	61.43	17.31	197.31	.0390	.4240
10	23.60	8.903	4.038	61.31	18.04	197.58	0.0406	0.4229
12	24.64	9.943	3.878	61.20	18.77	197.83	.0442	.4218
14	25.72	11.02	3.726	61.09	19.51	198.09	.0437	.4208
16	26.83	12.13	3.581	60.98	20.25	198.34	.0453	.4198
18	27.97	13.28	3.443	60.83	20.98	198.59	.0468	.4187
20	29.16	14.46	3.312	60.72	21.73	198.84	0.0484	0.4177
22	30.38	15.69	3.186	60.61	22.47	199.08	.0499	.4166
24	31.64	16.95	3.067	60.46	22.21	199.32	.0514	.4156
26	32.95	18.25	2.952	60.31	23.95	199.56	.0530	.4146
28	34.29	19.60	2.843	60.17	24.70	199.79	.0545	.4136
30	35.68	20.98	2.739	60.06	25.44	200.03	0.0560	0.4126
32	37.11	22.41	2.640	59.92	26.18	200.24	.0575	.4117
34	38.58	23.88	2.546	59.77	26.93	200.49	.0590	.4107
36	40.09	25.39	2.455	59.63	27.67	200.72	.0605	.4098
38	41.65	26.95	2.369	59.49	28.42	200.95	.0621	.4088
40	43.25	28.56	2.286	59.38	29.17	201.17	0.0636	0.4079
42	44.91	30.21	2.206	59.24	29.92	201.40	.0651	.4070
44	46.61	31.91	2.130	59.10	30.67	201.62	.0665	.4061
46	48.35	33.66	2.057	58.96	31.42	201.84	.0680	.4052
48	50.15	35.45	1.987	58.82	32.17	202.06	.0695	.4043

Temp F	Pressure psia	Pressure psig	Volume cu ft/lb Vapor v_g	Density lb/cu ft Liquid $1/v_f$	Enthalpy Btu/lb Liquid h_f	Enthalpy Btu/lb Vapor h_g	Entropy Btu/(lb)(°R) Liquid s_f	Entropy Btu/(lb)(°R) Vapor s_g
50	51.99	37.29	1.920	58.69	32.93	202.28	0.0710	0.4034
52	53.88	39.18	1.856	58.55	33.68	202.49	.0725	.4025
54	55.83	41.13	1.794	58.41	34.44	202.71	.0740	.4017
56	57.83	43.13	1.735	58.28	35.19	202.91	.0754	.4008
58	59.88	45.19	1.679	58.14	35.95	203.13	.0769	.3999
60	62.00	47.30	1.624	58.00	36.71	203.33	0.0784	0.3991
62	64.17	49.47	1.572	57.87	37.47	203.54	.0798	.3983
64	66.39	51.70	1.522	57.74	38.23	203.74	.0813	.3974
66	68.67	53.98	1.473	57.60	39.00	203.95	.0827	.3966
68	71.01	56.32	1.427	57.47	39.76	204.15	.0842	.3958
70	73.41	58.71	1.382	57.34	40.52	204.34	0.0856	0.3950
72	75.86	61.17	1.339	57.21	41.29	204.53	.0870	.3941
74	78.37	63.68	1.298	57.08	42.06	204.72	.0885	.3933
76	80.94	66.25	1.258	56.95	42.82	204.90	.0899	.3925
78	83.57	68.87	1.220	56.82	43.59	205.09	.0913	.3918
80	86.26	71.56	1.183	56.69	44.36	205.27	0.0928	0.3910
82	89.01	74.31	1.148	56.56	45.13	205.45	.0942	.3902
84	91.82	77.13	1.114	56.40	45.90	205.62	.0956	.3894
86	94.70	80.00	1.081	56.24	46.67	205.80	.0970	.3887
88	97.64	82.94	1.049	56.12	47.44	205.96	.0984	.3879
90	100.6	85.95	1.018	55.99	48.21	206.13	0.0998	0.3872
92	103.7	89.02	0.9889	55.83	48.99	206.30	.1012	.3867
94	106.9	92.16	0.9603	55.68	49.77	206.46	.1026	.3857
96	110.1	95.37	0.9333	55.56	50.54	206.62	.1041	.3850
98	113.4	98.65	0.9069	55.43	51.32	206.78	.1055	.3843
100	116.7	102.0	0.8814	55.31	52.09	206.94	0.1069	0.3836
120	154.2	139.5	.6710	53.79	59.93	208.39	.1206	.3768
140	199.6	184.9	.5189	52.22	67.87	209.58	.1341	.3705
160	253.5	238.8	.4070	50.56	75.90	210.56	.1473	.3646

[a] From published data of E. I. du Pont de Nemours & Co., Inc.

* Inches of mercury below one standard atmosphere.   ** Based on 0 for the saturated liquid at −40 F.

Fig. 27-26. A table of the properties of R–40.

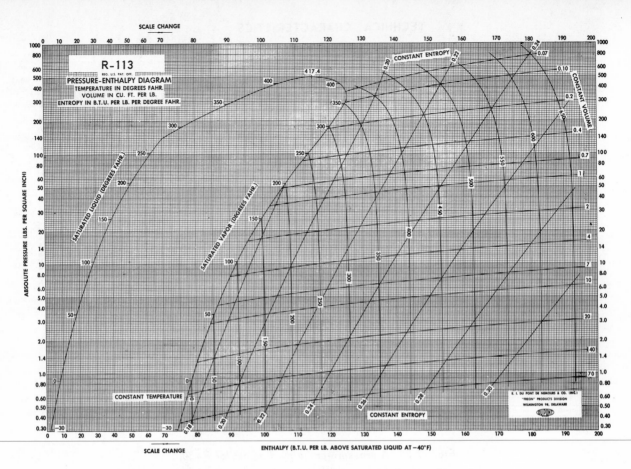

Fig. 27-27. A pressure-enthalpy graph for R-113.

conditions. Copper plating does not take place in dry systems. A drier eight times as large as for the same poundage of R-12 should be used. The properties of R-40 are shown in Fig. 27-26.

27-50 R-113 Trichlorotri-fluoroethane CCl₂FCClF₂

R-113 is a low pressure refrigerant that is used chiefly with centrifugal compressors in air conditioning systems of large tonnage capacity. At 5 F. it evaporates at 27.92 inches vacuum, and the gas occupied 27.04 cubic feet per pound, and the latent heat is 70.62 Btu per pound. At 86 F. the refrigerant condenses at a 13.93 inch vacuum, as shown in Fig. 27-27. R-113 can be tested for leaks by warming the refrigerant to 200 F., which will produce a pressure of 39.96 psi. A halide torch or an electronic leak detector is then used. At room temperature and pressure the re-

frigerant is a liquid and it can therefore be carried in sealed tins rather than in cylinders. It is classed as a Group 1 refrigerant as to fire safety, and as a Class 4 refrigerant as to toxicity. The properties of R-113 are shown in Fig. 27-28.

27-51 R-114 Dichlorotetra-fluoroethane CClF₂CClF₂

R-114 has a boiling point at atmospheric pressure of 38 F. The refrigerant has properties similar to that of R-12 in relation to its combination with water and oil. It is of the same family as R-12, but its operating pressures are considerably lower. At 86 F. it has a pressure of 21.5 psi, while at 5 F. its pressure is 16.1 inches of mercury vacuum, as shown in Fig. 27-29. It is a colorless liquid having a slight odor. The properties of R-114 are shown in Fig. 27-30.

In addition to being nonexplosive, it is

Temp. F.	Pressure		Volume Gas cu.ft./lb.	Density Liquid lb./cu.ft.	Heat Content Btu/lb.	
	psig	psia			Liquid	Latent
−40					0	
−30	29.31"	.2987	82.26	105.7	1.97	72.68
−20	29.05"	.4288	58.61	104.8	3.96	72.09
−10	28.69"	.6046	42.48	104.2	5.96	71.51
0	28.21"	.8377	31.31	103.5	7.98	70.91
5	27.92"	.9802	27.04	103.1	8.98	70.62
10	27.60"	1.142	23.45	102.8	10.00	70.32
20	26.80"	1.534	17.81	102.1	12.03	69.72
30	25.79"	2.031	13.71	101.3	14.08	69.12
40	24.52"	2.655	10.68	100.5	16.16	68.49
50	22.94"	3.427	8.426	99.7	18.24	67.87
60	21.02"	4.374	6.713	99.0	20.35	67.57
70	18.68"	5.523	5.404	98.2	22.48	66.56
80	15.87"	6.902	4.392	97.5	24.63	65.88
86	13.93"	7.856	3.893	97.0	25.93	65.46
90	12.53"	8.545	3.600	96.6	26.80	65.18
100	8.59"	10.48	2.976	95.7	28.99	64.46
120	0.70	15.40	2.078	94.0	33.48	62.93
140	7.23	21.93	1.491	92.2	38.05	60.31
160	15.74	30.44	1.094	90.4	42.74	59.55
180	26.52	41.22	.819	88.7	47.53	57.66
200	39.96	54.66	.624	86.8	52.45	55.62

Fig. 27-28. A table of the properties of R−113.

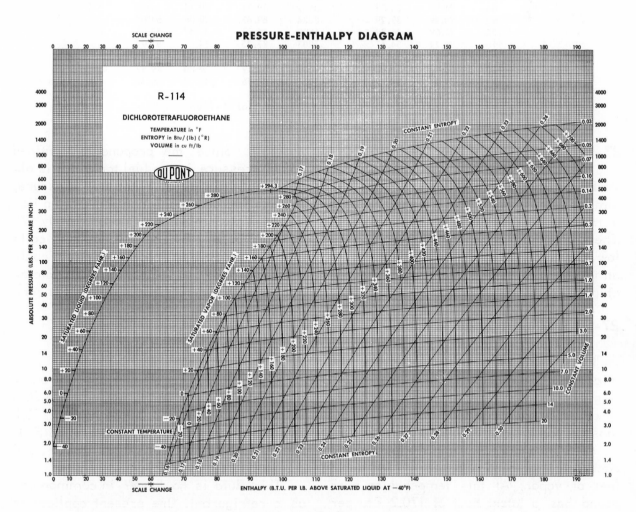

Fig. 27-29. A pressure-enthalpy graph for R−114.

a noncorrosive liquid which will not corrode even in the presence of water. The halide torch or electronic leak detector may be used to test it for leaks.

R-290 is a common fuel for many heating and power applications. It is a product of refining crude oil. Some refrigerated trucks use propane as a fuel in place of

Temp. F.	Pressure		Volume Gas cu.ft./lb.	Density Liquid lb./cu.ft.	Heat Content Btu/lb.	
	psig	psia			Liquid	Latent
−40	26.12''	1.866	14.02	102.25	0	65.91
−30	24.72''	2.557	10.45	101.37	2.27	65.03
−20	22.91''	3.444	7.921	100.47	4.54	64.16
−10	20.63''	4.564	6.095	99.56	6.81	63.29
0	17.79''	5.958	4.756	98.62	9.09	62.41
5	16.14''	6.772	4.221	98.15	10.23	61.98
10	14.31''	7.671	3.758	97.68	11.37	61.54
20	10.07''	9.753	3.005	96.71	13.66	60.66
30	4.99''	12.25	2.429	95.73	15.97	59.16
40	0.52	15.22	1.982	94.73	18.28	58.86
50	4.03	18.73	1.632	93.71	20.61	57.94
60	8.13	22.83	1.354	92.68	22.95	57.00
70	12.87	27.57	1.133	91.63	25.30	56.05
80	18.34	33.04	0.9541	90.56	27.68	55.05
86	21.99	36.69	.8632	89.91	29.11	54.45
90	24.59	39.29	.8084	89.47	30.06	54.05
100	31.69	46.39	.6890	88.37	32.47	53.01
110	39.71	54.41	.5901	87.25	34.89	51.94
120	48.74	63.44	.5077	86.08	37.33	50.83
130	58.84	73.54	.4387	84.89	39.80	49.67
140	70.09	84.79	.3803	83.66	42.29	48.47

Fig. 27-30. A table of the properties of R−114.

27-52 R-160 Ethyl Chloride C$_2$H$_5$Cl

R-160 is a little used refrigerant. It is similar in many respects to R-40, being a member of the same chemical family. The outstanding difference is found in the low pressure at which it evaporates. At atmospheric pressure, the boiling temperature of R-160 is 55.6 F.

27-53 R-290 Propane (C$_3$H$_8$)

R-290 is a medium high pressure refrigerant. One must operate the evaporating unit temperature at -14 F. or below in order to operate at pressures below atmospheric.

At 5 F. and 27.2 psi in the evaporator each pound of refrigerant forms 248 cubic feet of vapor. At this temperature each pound has a latent heat of 170.2 Btu per pound.

gasoline. Since the propane is confined under pressure in the fuel tank, if it is allowed to vaporize at a reduced pressure, the heat absorbed in changing from a liquid to a gas amounts to approximately 170 Btu per pound. By using vaporizing coils in the refrigerated truck space this cooling effect may be used to aid in maintaining necessary refrigeration within the cargo space.

27-54 R-600 Butane C$_4$H$_{10}$

R-600 has a pressure-temperature relationship of 13.2 in Hg at 5 F. and 30.5 psi at 86 F. It has a latent heat of 170.7 Btu at 5 F. and of 154.0 Btu at 86 F. It forms 9.98 cubic feet of gas at 0 F. and 2.24 cubic feet at 86 F.

This fluid is no longer in common use as a refrigerant. One present application is its use in expendable refrigerant (chem-

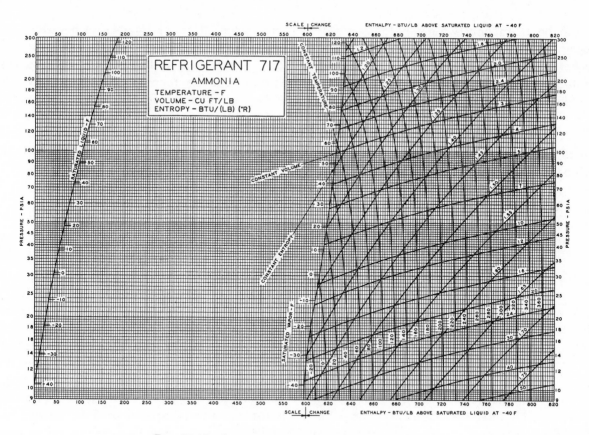

Fig. 27-31. A pressure-enthalpy diagram for R-717.
(ASHRAE Guide and Data Book)

ical) refrigeration applications where the discharge gas is used for combustion purposes.

27-55 R-611 Methyl Formate C₂H₄O₂

The General Electric Corp. has produced some refrigerators using R-20 as the refrigerant. This is a relatively rare refrigerant. The chemical formula is $C_2H_4O_2$ and its operating pressure at 5 F. is 25.9 inches vacuum while at 86 F. its pressure is 2 inches of vacuum. The gas is slightly flammable.

27-56 R-717 Ammonia NH₃

The characteristics of R-717 are discussed in some detail in Par. 9-14. The pressure enthalpy diagram for R-717 is shown in Fig. 27-31.

27-57 R-744 Carbon Dioxide CO₂

R-744 was first used in 1881. It differs considerably in its characteristics from many of the other refrigerants. The difference is especially noticeable in regard to pressures encountered within the machine. The operating pressures in the R-744 machine are many times higher than those encountered in most others.

At ordinary temperatures and pressures, R-744 is a colorless and odorless gas considerably heavier than air. It is nonexplosive, nonflammable and nontoxic. The boiling point of carbon dioxide is so extremely low that even at 5 F. a pressure of over 300 psi is required to prevent its evaporation, while with a temperature of 80 F. in the condenser, a pressure of almost 1000 psi is required to liquefy it. Its critical temperature is 87.8 F., so it can be used only where relatively cold water is available for condenser cooling, and it cannot be used at all with the air-cooled type condenser. It is not used in local domestic machines, but has been used in Europe.

As a result of the high operating pressures, the compressor of the R-744 machine is quite small for relatively large refrigerating capacity, and the machine is therefore particularly good for use on shipboard where space is at a premium and safety is a prime necessity. The latent heat of evaporation of R-744 at 5 F. is 116 Btu per pound. Leaks may be located by an oil film or soap solution. A large leak will be easily detected from the cloud of condensation or vapor produced at the leak. This refrigerant is sometimes used in large installations where an operator is in charge.

As much as 12 pounds of this refrigerant can be used for each 1000 cubic feet of air conditioned space (a room 10 ft. x 12.5 ft. x 8 ft.).

Fig. 27-32 is a table of the more com-mon properties of R-744. As mentioned in Par. 1-44, R-744 can be formed into dry ice. That is, solidified carbon dioxide, R-744, can be formed starting at -69.9 F. under pressure of 60.4 psig. This solid exists at atmospheric pressure at -109.4 F. As it vaporizes at this low pressure, it changes from a solid to a gas (sublimes) and does not go through a liquid state.

27-58 R-764 Sulphur Dioxide SO$_2$

R-764 was used in many of the early automatic refrigeration units. R-764 was first produced in 1775 and, in addition to its use as a refrigerant, it has consider-able use in refining sugar, bleaching wool, preserving food, and fumigating. It is usu-ally produced by the burning of sulphur. It is a colorless gas with a pronounced ir-ritating odor. Its boiling point at atmo-spheric pressure is 14 F. It has a boiling point of 5 in. vacuum at 5 F. and 65 psi at 86 F. Leaks are detected using an am-monia saturated swab. White fumes indi-cate a sulphur dioxide leak.

R-744 Carbon Dioxide

Temp. F.	Pressure		Volume Vapor cu.ft./lb.	Density Liquid lb./cu.ft.	Heat Content Btu/lb.	
	psi	psia			Liquid	Latent
-40	131.2	145.9	.6113	69.6	0	137.9
-30	163.3	178.0	.5025	68.2	4.7	133.6
-20	200.4	215.0	.4165	66.7	9.2	129.5
-10	242.8	257.5	.3465	65.2	13.9	125.0
0	291.1	305.8	.2905	63.7	18.8	120.1
5	317.6	332.3	.2659	62.8	21.3	117.6
10	345.7	360.4	.2435	61.9	24.0	114.8
20	407.1	421.8	.2048	60.2	29.6	108.9
30	475.9	490.6	.1720	58.2	35.6	102.2
40	552.6	567.3	.1442	56.0	41.8	95.0
50	638.0	652.7	.1204	53.6	48.5	86.6
60	732.7	747.4	.0995	50.75	55.7	76.5
70	837.8	852.5	.0800	47.4	63.7	64.1
80	954.6	969.3	.0600	42.2	74.0	45.0
86	1031.0	1045.7	.0479	37.2	83.4	27.1
87.8	1057.4	1072.1	.0345	29.1	97.1	0

Fig. 27-32. Table of properties of R-744. Note this is a high pressure refrigerant. At -20 F. the refrigerant boils under pressure of 200 psi.

Chapter 28

GLOSSARY OF TECHNICAL TERMS

ABSOLUTE HUMIDITY: Amount of moisture in the air, indicated in grains per cubic foot.

ABSOLUTE PRESSURE: Gauge pressure plus atmospheric pressure (14.7 lbs. per sq. in.).

ABSOLUTE TEMPERATURE: Temperature measured from absolute zero.

ABSOLUTE ZERO TEMPERATURE: Temperature at which all molecular motion ceases. (-460 F. and -275 C.)

ABSORBENT: Substance which has the ability to take up or absorb another substance.

ABSORPTION REFRIGERATOR: Refrigerator which creates low temperatures by using the cooling effect formed when a refrigerant is absorbed by chemical substance.

ACCELERATE: To add to speed; hasten progress of development.

ACCUMULATOR: Storage tank which receives liquid refrigerant from evaporator and prevents it from flowing into suction line.

ACID CONDITION IN SYSTEM: Condition in which refrigerant or oil in system is mixed with fluids which are acid in nature.

ACR TUBING: Tubing used in refrigeration which has ends sealed to keep tubing clean and dry.

ACTIVATED ALUMINA: Chemical used as a drier or desiccant.

ACTIVATED CARBON: Specially processed carbon used as a filter-drier; commonly used to clean air.

ADIABATIC COMPRESSION: Compressing refrigerant gas without removing or adding heat.

ADSORBENT: Substance which has property to hold molecules of fluids without causing a chemical or physical change.

AGITATOR: Device used to cause motion in confined fluid.

AIR CLEANER: Device used for removal of airborne impurities.

AIR COIL: Coil used with some types of heat pumps which may be used either as an evaporator or as a condenser.

AIR CONDITIONER: Device used to control temperature, humidity, cleanliness, and movement of air in conditioned space.

AIR-COOLED CONDENSER: Heat of compression is transferred from condensing coils to surrounding air. This may be done either by convection or by a fan or blower.

AIR COOLER: Mechanism designed to lower temperature of air passing through it.

AIR CYCLE, AIR CONDITIONING: System which removes heat from air and transfers this heat to air.

AIR DIFFUSER: Air distribution outlet designed to direct airflow into desired patterns.

AIR SENSING THERMOSTAT: Thermostat unit in which sensing element is located in refrigerated space.

AIR SPILL-OVER: Refrigerating effect formed by cold air from freezing compartment in refrigerator spilling over, or flowing into normal storage area of refrigerator.

AIR WASHER: Device used to clean air, which may increase or decrease humidity.

ALCOHOL BRINE: Water and alcohol solution which remains a liquid at below 32 F.

ALLEN-TYPE SCREW: Screw with recessed head designed to be turned with hex shaped wrench.

ALTERNATING CURRENT (AC): Electric current in which direction of flow alternates or changes. In 60 cycle current direction of flow reverses every 120th second.

ALTITUDE ADJUSTMENT: Adjusting refrigerator controls so unit will operate efficiently at altitude in which it is to be used.

AMBIENT TEMPERATURE: Temperature of fluid (usually air) which surrounds object on all sides.

AMMETER: An electric meter used to measure current, calibrated in amperes.

AMMONIA: Chemical combination of nitrogen and hydrogen (NH_3). Ammonia refrigerant is identified by R-117.

AMPERAGE: Electron or current flow of one coulomb per second past given point in circuit.

AMPERE: Unit of electric current equivalent to flow of one coulomb per second.

AMPERE TURNS: Term used to measure magnetic force. Represents product of amperes times number of turns in coil of electromagnet.

AMPLIFIER: Electrical device which increases electron flow in a circuit.

ANEMOMETER: Instrument for measuring the rate of flow of air.

ANHYDROUS CALCIUM SULPHATE: Dry chemical made of calcium, sulphur and oxygen ($CaSO_4$).

ANNEALING: Process of heat treating metal to obtain desired properties of softness and ductility (easy to form into new shape).

ANODE: Positive terminal of electrolytic cell.

ARMATURE: Revolving part in electric motor or generator.

A.S.A.: Formerly, abbreviation for American Standards Association. Now known as United States of America Standards Institute.

ASPECT RATIO: Ratio of length to width of rectangular air grille or duct.

ASPIRATING PSYCHOMETER: A device which draws sample of air through it for humidity measurement purposes.

ASPIRATION: Movement produced in a fluid by suction.

ATMOSPHERIC PRESSURE: Pressure that gases in air exert upon the earth; measured in pounds per square inch.

ATOM: Smallest particle of element that can exist alone or in combination.

ATOMIZE: Process of changing a liquid to minute particles, or a fine spray.

ATTENUATE: Decrease or lessen in intensity.

AUTOMATIC DEFROST: System of removing ice and frost from evaporators automatically.

AUTOMATIC EXPANSION VALVE (AEV): Pressure controlled valve which reduces high pressure liquid refrigerant to low pressure liquid refrigerant.

AUTOMATIC ICE CUBE MAKER: Refrigerating mechanism designed to produce ice cubes in quantity automatically.

AUTOTRANSFORMER: A transformer in which both primary and secondary coils have turns in common. Step-up or step-down of voltage is accomplished by taps on common winding.

AZEOTROPIC MIXTURE: Example of azeotropic mixture--refrigerant R-502 is mixture consisting of 48.8% refrigerant R-22, and 51.2% R-115. The refrigerants do not combine chemically, yet azeotropic mixture provides refrigerant characteristics desired.

BACK PRESSURE: Pressure in low side of refrigerating system; also called suction pressure or low side pressure.

BAFFLE: Plate or vane used to direct or control movement of fluid or air within confined area.

BALL CHECK VALVE: Valve assembly (ball) which permits flow of fluid in one direction only.

BALLOON TYPE GASKET: Flexible refrigerator door gasket having a large cross section.

BAROMETER: Instrument for measuring atmospheric pressure. It may be calibrated in pounds per square inch or in inches of mercury in column.

BATH: A liquid solution used for cleaning, plating, or maintaining a specified temperature.

BATTERY: Electricity producing cells which use interaction of metals and chemicals to create electrical current flow.

BAUDELOT COOLER: Heat exchanger in which water flows by gravity over the outside of the tubes or plates.

BEARING: Low friction device for supporting and aligning a moving part.

BELLOWS: Corrugated cylindrical container which moves as pressures change, or provides a seal during movement of parts.

BENDING SPRING: Coil spring which is mounted on inside or outside to keep tube from collapsing while bending it.

BERNOULLI'S THEOREM: In stream of liquid, sum of elevation head, pressure head and velocity remains constant along any line of flow provided no work is done by or upon liquid in course of its flow, and decreases in proportion to energy lost in flow.

BIMETAL STRIP: Temperature regulating or indicating device which works on principle that two dissimilar metals with unequal expansion rates, welded together, will bend as temperatures change.

BLEED-VALVE: Valve with small opening inside which permits a minimum fluid flow when valve is closed.

BOILER: Closed container in which a liquid may be heated and vaporized.

BOILING TEMPERATURE: Temperature at which a fluid changes from a liquid to a gas.

BORE: Inside diameter of a cylindrical hole.

BOURDON TUBE: As used in pressure gauges. Thin walled tube of elastic metal flattened and bent into circular shape, which tends to straighten as pressure inside is increased.

BOWDEN CABLE: Tube containing a wire used to regulate a valve or control from a remote point.

BOYLE'S LAW: Law of physics--volume of a gas varies as pressure varies, if temperature remains the same. Examples: If pressure is doubled on quantity of gas, volume becomes one half. If volume becomes doubled, gas has its pressure reduced by one half.

BRAZING: Method of joining metals with nonferrous filler (without iron) using heat between 800 deg. F. and melting point of base metals.

BREAKER STRIP: Strip of wood or plastic used to cover joint between outside case and inside liner of refrigerator.

BRINE: Water saturated with chemical such as salt.

BRITISH THERMAL UNIT (BTU): Quantity of heat required to raise temperature of one pound of water one degree F.

BULB, SENSITIVE: Part of sealed fluid device which reacts to temperature to be measured, or which will control a mechanism.

BUNKER: In commercial installations, space in which ice or cooling element is installed.

BURNER: Device in which combustion of fuel takes place.

BUTANE: Liquid hydrocarbon (C_4H_{10})commonly used as fuel for heating purposes.

BYPASS: Passage at one side of, or around regular passage.

CADMIUM PLATED: Parts coated with thin corrosion-resistant covering of cadmium metal.

CALCIUM SULFATE: Chemical compound ($CaSO_4$) which is used as a drying agent or desiccant in liquid line driers.

CALIBRATE: To determine; position indicators as required to obtain accurate measurements.

CALORIE: Heat required to raise temperature of one gram of water one degree centigrade.

CALORIMETER: Device used to measure quantities of heat or determine specific heats.

CAPACITANCE (C): Property of nonconductor (condenser or capacitor) that permits storage of electrical energy in an electrostatic field.

CAPACITOR: Type of electrical storage device used in starting and/or running circuits on many electric motors.

CAPACITOR-START MOTOR: Motor which has a capacitor in the starting circuit.

CAPILLARY TUBE: A type of refrigerant control. Usually consists of several feet of tubing having small inside diameter. Friction of liquid refrigerant and bubbles of vaporized refrigerant within tube serve to restrict flow so that correct high side and low side pressures are maintained while the compressor is operating. A capillary tube refrigerant control allows high side and low side pressures to balance during off cycle. Also; a small diameter tubing used to connect temperature control bulbs to control mechanisms.

CARBON DIOXIDE (CO_2): Compound of carbon and oxygen which is sometimes used as a refrigerant. Refrigerant number is R-744.

CARBON FILTER: Air filter using activated carbon as air cleansing agent.

CARBON TETRACHLORIDE: A colorless nonflammable liquid used as solvent and in fire extinguishers. Very toxic. Should never be allowed to touch skin, or fumes inhaled.

CARRENE: A refrigerant in group 1 (R-11). Chemical combination of carbon, chlorine and fluorine.

CASCADE SYSTEMS: Arrangement in which two or more refrigerating systems are used in series; uses cooling coil of one machine to cool condenser of other machine. Produces ultra-low temperatures.

CASEHARDENED: Heat treating ferrous metals (iron) so surface layer is harder than interior.

CATHODE: Negative terminal of an electrical device. Electrons leave the device at this terminal.

CELSIUS: German language word for centigrade, the metric system temperature scale

CENTIGRADE SCALE: Temperature scale used in metric system. Freezing point of water is 0; boiling point 100.

CENTIMETER: Metric unit of linear measurement which equals .3937 inches.

CENTRIFUGAL COMPRESSOR: Compressor which compresses gaseous refrigerants by centrifugal force.

CHARGING BOARD: Specially designed panel or cabinet fitted with gauges, valves and refrigerant cylinders used for charging refrigerant and oil into refrigerating mechanisms.

CHARLES' LAW: The volume of a given mass of gas at a constant pressure varies according to its temperature.

CHECK VALVE: A device which permits fluid flow only in one direction.

CHEMICAL REFRIGERATION: A system of cooling using a disposable refrigerant.

CHIMNEY EFFECT: Tendency of air or gas to rise when heated.

CHOKE TUBE: Throttling device used to maintain correct pressure difference between high side and low side in refrigerating mechanism. Capillary tubes are sometimes called choke tubes.

CIRCUIT: A tubing, piping or electrical wire installation which permits flow from the energy source back to energy source.

CIRCUIT BREAKERS: Safety device which automatically opens an electrical circuit if overloaded.

CIRCUIT, PARALLEL: Arrangement of

electrical devices in which all positive terminals are joined to one conductor and all negative terminals to other conductor.

CIRCUIT, SERIES: Electrical wiring: electrical path (circuit) in which electricity to operate second lamp or device must pass through first, and so on; current flow travels through all devices connected together.

CLEARANCE POCKET COMPRESSOR: A small space in cylinder from which compressed gas is not completely expelled. This space is called the compressor clearance space or pocket. For effective operation, compressors are designed to have as small clearance space as possible.

CLOSED CIRCUIT: An electrical circuit in which electrons are flowing.

CLUTCH, ARMATURE: The part of the automotive compressor magnetic clutch which is attracted by the magnetic field and causes the compressor to be turned by a belt drive when the magnetic field is energized.

CLUTCH, FIELD: The coils of wire through which the current flows to create the magnetic force which engages the magnetic clutch.

CLUTCH, MAGNETIC: Clutch built into automobile compressor flywheel, operated magnetically, which allows pulley to revolve without driving compressor when refrigerating effect is not required.

CODE INSTALLATION: A refrigeration or air conditioning installation which conforms to the local code and/or the national code for safe and efficient installations.

COEFFICIENT OF CONDUCTIVITY: The measure of the relative rate at which different materials conduct heat. Copper is a good conductor of heat and therefore, has a high coefficient of conductivity.

COEFFICIENT OF PERFORMANCE (COP): The ratio of work or energy applied as compared to the energy used.

CO_2 INDICATOR: An instrument used to indicate the percent of carbon dioxide in stack gases.

COLD: Cold is the absence of heat; a temperature considerably below normal.

COLD JUNCTION: That part of a thermo-electric system which absorbs heat as the system operates.

COLD WALL: Refrigerator construction which has the inner lining of refrigerator serving as the cooling surface.

COLLOIDS: Miniature cells in meat, fish and poultry.

COMFORT CHART: Chart used in air conditioning to show the dry bulb temperature and humidity for human comfort conditions.

COMFORT COOLER: A system used to reduce the temperature in the living space in homes. These systems are not complete air conditioners as they do not provide complete control of heating, humidifying, dehumidification, and air circulation.

COMFORT ZONE: Area on psychrometric chart which shows conditions of temperature, humidity, and sometimes air movement, in which most people are comfortable.

COMMUTATOR: Part of electric motor rotor which conveys electric current to rotor windings.

COMPOUND GAUGE: Instrument for measuring pressures both above and below atmospheric pressure.

COMPOUND REFRIGERATING SYSTEMS: System which has several compressors or compressor cylinders in series. The system is used to pump low pressure vapors to condensing pressures.

COMPRESSION: Term used to denote increase of pressure on a fluid by using mechanical energy.

COMPRESSION GAUGE: Instrument used to measure positive pressures (pressures above atmospheric pressures) only. These gauges are usually calibrated from 0 to 300 pounds per square inch of pressure, gauge, (psig).

COMPRESSOR: The pump of a refrigerating mechanism which draws a vacuum or low pressure on cooling side of refrigerant cycle and squeezes or compresses the gas into the high pressure or condensing side of the cycle.

COMPRESSOR, HERMETIC: Compressor in which driving motor is sealed in the same dome or housing that contains the compressor.

COMPRESSOR, OPEN-TYPE: Compressor in which the crankshaft extends through the crankcase and is driven by an outside motor.

COMPRESSOR, RECIPROCATING: Compressor which uses a piston and cylinder mechanism to provide pumping action.

COMPRESSOR, ROTARY: A compressor which uses vanes, eccentric mechanisms, or other rotating devices to provide pumping action.

COMPRESSOR SEAL: Leakproof seal between crankshaft and compressor body.

CONDENSATE: Fluid which forms on an evaporator.

CONDENSATE PUMP: Device used to remove fluid condensate that collects beneath an evaporator.

CONDENSATION: Liquid or droplets which form when a gas or vapor is cooled below its dew point.

CONDENSE: Action of changing a gas or vapor to a liquid.

CONDENSER: The part of refrigeration mechanism which receives hot, high pressure refrigerant gas from compressor and cools gaseous refrigerant until it returns to liquid state.

CONDENSER, AIR-COOLED: A heat exchanger which transfers heat to surrounding air.

CONDENSER COMB: Comb-like device, metal or plastic, which is used to straighten the metal fins on condensers or evaporators.

CONDENSER FAN: Forced air device used to move air through air-cooled condenser.

CONDENSER, WATER-COOLED: Heat exchanger which is designed to transfer heat from hot gaseous refrigerant to water.

CONDENSER WATER PUMP: Forced water moving device used to move water through condenser.

CONDENSING UNIT: That part of refrigerating mechanism which pumps vaporized refrigerant from evaporator, compresses it, liquefies it in the condenser and returns the liquid refrigerant to refrigerant control.

CONDENSING UNIT SERVICE VALVES: Shutoff hand valves mounted on condensing unit to enable serviceman to install and/or service unit.

CONDUCTIVITY: Ability of a metal or a substance to conduct or transmit heat and/or electricity.

CONDUCTOR: Substance or body capable of transmitting electricity, heat, etc.

CONNECTING ROD: That part of compressor mechanism which connects piston to crankshaft.

CONSTRICTOR: Tube or orifice used to restrict flow of a gas or a liquid.

CONTAMINANT: A substance (dirt, moisture, or other substance) foreign to refrigerant or refrigerant oil in system.

CONTINUOUS CYCLE ABSORPTION SYSTEM: System which has a continuous flow of energy input.

CONTROL: Automatic or manual device used to stop, start and/or regulate flow of gas, liquid, and/or electricity.

CONTROL, COMPRESSOR: See Motor Control.

CONTROL, DEFROSTING: Device to automatically defrost evaporator. It may operate by means of a clock, door cycling mechanism, or during "off" portion of refrigerating cycle.

CONTROL, LOW PRESSURE: Cycling device connected to low pressure side of system.

CONTROL, MOTOR: A temperature or pressure operated device used to control running of motor.

CONTROL, PRESSURE MOTOR: A high

or low pressure control which is connected into the electrical circuit and used to start and stop motor when there is need for refrigeration or for safety purposes.

CONTROL, REFRIGERANT: Device used to regulate flow of liquid refrigerant into evaporator; such as capillary tube, expansion valves, high and low side float valves, etc.

CONTROL, TEMPERATURE: A thermostatic device which automatically stops and starts motor, operation of which is based on temperature changes.

CONTROLLED EVAPORATOR PRESSURE: Controlled system which maintains definite pressure or range of pressures in evaporator.

CONVECTION: Transfer of heat by means of movement or flow of a fluid or gas.

CONVECTION, FORCED: Transfer of heat resulting from forced movement of liquid or gas by means of fan or pump.

CONVECTION, NATURAL: Circulation of a gas or liquid due to difference in density resulting from temperature differences.

CONVERSION FACTORS: Force and power may be expressed in more than one way. A horsepower is equivalent to 33,000 foot pounds of work per minute, 746 watts, or 2,546 Btu per hour. These values can be used for changing horsepower into foot pounds, Btu or watts.

COOLING TOWER: Device which cools water by water evaporation in air. Water is cooled to wet bulb temperature of air.

COPPER PLATING: Condition developing in some units in which copper is electrolytically deposited on compressor part surfaces.

CORE, MAGNETIC: Magnetic center of a magnetic field.

COULOMB: Quantity of electricity transferred by electric current of one ampere in one second.

COUNTER EMF: Tendency for reverse electrical flow as magnetic field changes in an induction coil.

COUNTERFLOW: Flow in opposite direction.

"CRACKING" A VALVE: Opening valve a small amount.

CRANKSHAFT SEAL: Leakproof joint between crankshaft and compressor body.

CRANK THROW: Distance between center line of main bearing journal and center line of the crankpin or eccentric.

CRISPER: Drawer or compartment in refrigerator designed to provide high humidity along with low temperature to keep vegetables, especially leafy vegetables, cold and crisp.

CRITICAL PRESSURE: Condition of refrigerant at which liquid and gas have same properties.

CRITICAL TEMPERATURE: Temperature at which vapor and liquid have same properties.

CRITICAL VIBRATION: Vibration which is noticeable and harmful to structure.

CROSS CHARGED: Sealed container containing two fluids which together create a desired pressure-temperature curve.

CRYOGENIC FLUID: Substance which exists as a liquid or gas at ultra-low temperatures (-250 F. or lower).

CRYOGENICS: Refrigeration which deals with producing temperatures of 250 F. below zero and lower.

CURRENT (I): Transfer of electrical energy in conductor by means of electrons changing position.

CURRENT RELAY: Device which opens or closes a circuit based on change of current flow.

CUT-IN: Temperature or pressure valve which closes control circuit.

CUT-OUT: Temperature or pressure valve which opens control circuit.

CYCLE: Series of events which have tendency to repeat same events in same order.

CYLINDER HEAD: Part which encloses compression end of compressor cylinder.

CYLINDER, REFRIGERANT: Cylinder in which refrigerant is purchased and dispensed. Color code painted on cylinder indicates kind of refrigerant cylinder contains.

CYLINDRICAL COMMUTATOR: Commutator with contact surfaces parallel to the rotor shaft.

DALTON'S LAW: Vapor pressure exerted on container by a mixture of gases is equal to sum of individual vapor pressures of gases contained in mixture.

DAMPER: Valve for controlling airflow.

DECIBEL: Unit used for measuring relative loudness of sounds. One decibel is equal to approximate difference of loudness ordinarily detectable by human ear, the range of which is about 130 decibals on scale beginning with one for faintest audible sound.

DEFROST CYCLE: Refrigerating cycle in which evaporator frost and ice accumulation is melted.

DEFROST TIMER: Device connected into electrical circuit which shuts unit off long enough to permit ice and frost accumulation on evaporator to melt.

DEFROSTING: Process of removing frost accumulation from evaporators.

DEFROSTING TYPE EVAPORATOR: An evaporator operating at such temperatures that ice and frost on surface melts during off part of operating cycle.

DEGREASING: Solution or solvent used to remove oil or grease from refrigerator parts.

DEGREE-DAY: Unit that represents one degree of difference from given point in average outdoor temperature of one day and is often used in estimating fuel requirements for a building. Degree-days are based on average temperature over a 24 hour period. As an example; if an average temperature for a day is 50 F., the number of degree-days for that day would be equal to 65 F. minus 50 F. or 15 degree-days (65 -50 = 15). Degree-days are useful when calculating requirements for heating purposes.

DEHUMIDIFIER: Device used to remove moisture from air in enclosed space.

DEHYDRATED OIL: Lubricant which has had most of water content removed (a dry oil).

DEHYDRATOR: (See Drier.)

DEHYDRATOR-RECEIVER: A small tank which serves as liquid refrigerant reservoir and which also contains a desiccant to remove moisture. Used on most automobile air conditioning installations.

DEICE CONTROL: Device used to operate refrigerating system in such a way as to provide melting of the accumulated ice and frost.

DELTA TRANSFORMER: A three-phase electrical transformer which has ends of each of three windings electrically connected.

DEMAND METER: An instrument used to measure kilowatt-hour consumption of a particular circuit or group of circuits.

DENSITY: Closeness of texture or consistency.

DEODORIZER: Device which absorbs various odors, usually by principle of absorption. Activated charcoal is a common substance used.

DESICCANT: Substance used to collect and hold moisture in refrigerating system. A drying agent. Common desiccants are activated alumina, silica gel.

DETECTOR, LEAK: Device used to detect and locate refrigerant leaks.

DEW POINT: Temperature at which vapor (at 100 percent humidity) begins to condense and deposit as liquid.

DIALECTRIC FLUID: Fluid with high electrical resistance.

DIAPHRAGM: Flexible membrane usually made of thin metal, rubber, or plastic.

DICHLORODIFLUROMETHANE: Refrigerant commonly known as R-12. Chemical formula is CCl_2F_2. Cylinder color code is white. Boiling point at atmospheric pressure is -21.62 F.

DIE CAST: A process of moulding low melting temperature metals in accurately shaped metal moulds.

DIE STOCK: Tool used to hold dies with external threads.

DIES (THREAD): Tool used to cut external threads.

DIFFERENTIAL: As applied to refrigeration and heating: difference between "cut-in" and "cut-out" temperature or pressure of a control.

DIODE: A two-element electron tube which will allow more electron flow in one direction in a circuit than in the other direction; tube which serves a rectifier.

DIRECT CURRENT: Electron flow which moves continuously in one direction in circuit.

DIRECT EXPANSION EVAPORATOR: An evaporator coil using either an automatic expansion valve (AEV) or a thermostatic expansion valve (TEV) refrigerant control.

DISPLACEMENT, PISTON: Volume obtained by multiplying area of cylinder bore by length of piston stroke.

DISTILLING APPARATUS: Fluid reclaiming device used to reclaim used refrigerants. Reclaiming is usually done by vaporizing and then recondensing refrigerant.

DOME-HAT: Sealed metal container for the motor-compressor of a refrigerating unit.

DOUBLE DUTY CASE: Commercial refrigerator which has part of it for refrigerated storage and part equipped with glass windows for display purposes.

DOUBLE THICKNESS FLARE: Copper, aluminum or steel tubing end which has been formed into two-wall thickness, 37 to 45 deg. bell mouth or flare.

DOWEL PIN: Accurately dimensioned pin pressed into one assembly part and slipped into another assembly part to insure accurate alignment.

DRAFT GAUGE: Instrument used to measure air movement.

DRAFT INDICATOR: An instrument used to indicate or measure chimney draft or combustion gas movement. Draft is measured in units of .1 inch of water column.

DRIER: A substance or device used to remove moisture from a refrigeration system.

DRIP PAN: Pan-shaped panel or trough used to collect condensate from evaporator coil.

DRY BULB: An instrument with sensitive element which measures ambient (moving) air temperature.

DRY BULB TEMPERATURE: Air temperature as indicated by ordinary thermometer.

DRY CAPACITOR CONDENSER: An electrical device made of dry metal and dry insulation, used to store electrons.

DRY CELL BATTERY: Electrical device used to provide DC electricity, having no liquids in the cells.

DRY ICE: A refrigerating substance made of solid carbon dioxide which changes directly from a solid to a gas (sublimates). Its subliming temperature is 109 F. below zero.

DRY SYSTEM: A refrigeration system which has the evaporator liquid refrigerant mainly in the atomized or droplet condition.

DUCT: Heating and air conditioning. A tube or channel through which air is conveyed or moved.

DYNAMOMETER: Device for measuring power output or power input of a mechanism.

EBULATOR: A pointed or sharp edged solid substance inserted in flooded type evaporators to improve evaporation (boiling) of refrigerant in coil.

ECCENTRIC: A circle or disk mounted off center. Eccentrics are used to adjust controls and connect compressor driveshafts to pistons.

EFFECTIVE AREA: Actual flow area of an air inlet or outlet. Gross area minus area of vanes or grille bars.

EFFECTIVE TEMPERATURE: Overall effect on a human of air temperature, humidity and air movement.

EJECTOR: Device which uses high fluid velocity such as a venturi, to create low pressure or vacuum at its throat to draw in fluid from another source.

ELECTRIC DEFROSTING: Use of electric resistance heating coils to melt ice and frost off evaporators during defrosting.

ELECTRIC HEATING: House heating system in which heat from electrical resistance units is used to heat rooms.

ELECTRIC WATER VALVE: Solenoid type (electrically operated) valve used to turn water flow on and off.

ELECTROLUX SYSTEM: Trade name for a continuously operating absorption type of refrigerating system.

ELECTROLYTIC CONDENSER-CAPACITOR: Plate or surface capable of storing small electrical charges. Common electrolytic condensers are formed by rolling thin sheets of foil between insulating materials. Condenser capacity is expressed in microfarads.

ELECTROMAGNET: Made by winding coil of wire around soft iron core. When electric current is run through wire, coil becomes a magnet.

ELECTROMOTIVE FORCE (EMF) VOLTAGE: Electrical force which causes current (free electrons) to flow or move in an electrical circuit. Unit of measurement is the volt.

ELECTRON: Elementary particle or portion of an atom which carries a negative charge.

ELECTRONICS: Field of science dealing with electron devices and their uses.

ELECTRONIC LEAK DETECTOR: Electronic instrument which measures electronic flow across gas gap. Electronic flow changes indicates presence of refrigerant gas molecules.

ELECTRONIC SOUND TRACER: Instru-ment used to detect leaks by locating source of high frequency sound caused by leak.

ELECTROSTATIC FILTER: Type of filter which gives particles of dust electric charge. This causes particles to be attracted to plate so they can be removed from airstream or atmosphere.

END BELL: End structure of electric motor which usually holds motor bearings.

END PLAY: Slight movement of shaft along center line.

ENTHALPY: Total amount of heat in one pound of a substance calculated from accepted temperature base. Temperature of 32 deg. F. is accepted base for water vapor calculation. For refrigerator calculations, accepted base is -40 deg. F.

ENTROPY: Mathematical factor used in engineering calculations. Energy in a system.

ENZYME: A complex organic substance originating from living cells that speeds up chemical changes in foods. Enzyme action is slowed by cooling.

EPOXY (RESINS): A synthetic plastic adhesive.

EQUALIZER TUBE: Device used to maintain equal pressure or equal liquid levels between two containers.

EVAPORATION: A term applied to the changing of a liquid to a gas. Heat is absorbed in this process.

EVAPORATIVE CONDENSER: A device which uses open spray or spill water to cool a condenser. Evaporation of some of the water cools the condenser water and reduces water consumption.

EVAPORATOR: Part of a refrigerating mechanism in which the refrigerant vaporizes and absorbs heat.

EVAPORATOR COIL: Device made of a coil of tubing which functions as a refrigerant evaporator.

EVAPORATOR, DRY TYPE: An evaporator into which refrigerant is fed from a pressure reducing device. Little or no liquid refrigerant collects in the evaporator

EVAPORATOR FAN: Fan which cools extended heat exchange surface of evaporator.

EVAPORATOR, FLOODED: An evaporator containing liquid refrigerant at all times.

EXPANSION VALVE: A device in refrigerating system which maintains a pressure difference between the high side and low side and is operated by pressure.

EXPENDABLE REFRIGERANT SYSTEM: System which discards the refrigerant after it has evaporated.

EXTERNAL EQUALIZER: Tube connected to low pressure side of an expansion valve diaphragm and to exit of evaporator.

FAHRENHEIT SCALE: On a Fahrenheit thermometer, under standard atmospheric pressure, boiling point of water is 212 deg. and freezing point is 32 deg. above zero on its scale.

FAIL SAFE CONTROL: Device which opens circuit when sensing element fails to operate.

FAN: A radial or axial flow device used for moving or producing artificial currents of air.

FARAD: Unit of electrical capacity; capacity of a condenser which, when charged with one coulomb of electricity, gives difference of potential of one volt.

FARADAY EXPERIMENT: Silver chloride absorbs ammonia when cool and releases ammonia when heated. This is basis on which some absorption refrigerators operate.

FIELD POLE: Part of stator of motor which concentrates magnetic field of field winding.

FILE CARD: Tool used to clean metal files.

FILTER: Device for removing small particles from a fluid.

FLAME TEST FOR LEAKS: Tool which is principally a torch and when an air-refrigerant mixture is fed to flame, this flame will change color in presence of heated copper.

FLAPPER VALVE: The type of valve used in refrigeration compressors which allows gaseous refrigerants to flow in only one direction.

FLARE: Copper tubing is often connected to parts of refrigerating system by use of flared fittings. These fittings require that the end of tube be expanded at about 45 deg. angle. This flare is firmly gripped by fittings to make a strong leakproof seal.

FLARE NUT: Fitting used to clamp tubing flare against another fitting.

FLARED SINGLE THICKNESS CONNECTION: Tube ending formed into 37 1/2 deg. or 45 deg. bell mouth or flare.

FLASH GAS: This is the instantaneous evaporation of some liquid refrigerant in evaporator which cools remaining liquid refrigerant to desired evaporation temperature.

FLASH POINT: Temperature at which an oil will give off sufficient vapor to support a flash flame but will not support continuous combustion.

FLASH WELD: A resistance type weld in which mating parts are brought together under considerable pressure and a heavy electrical current is passed through the joint to be welded.

FLOAT VALVE: Type of valve which is operated by sphere or pan which floats on liquid surface and controls level of liquid.

FLOODED SYSTEM: Type of refrigerating system in which liquid refrigerant fills evaporator.

FLOODED SYSTEM, LOW SIDE FLOAT: Refrigerating system which has a low side float refrigerant control.

FLOODING: Act of filling a space with a liquid.

FLOW METER: Instrument used to measure velocity or volume of fluid movement.

FLUE: Gas or air passage which usually depends on natural convection to cause the combustion gases to flow through it. Forced convection may sometimes be used.

FLUID: Substance in a liquid or gaseous state; substance containing particles which move and change position without separation of the mass.

FLUID COUPLING: Device which transmits drive energy to energy absorber through a fluid.

FLUSH: An operation to remove any material or fluids from refrigeration system parts by purging them to the atmosphere using refrigerant or other fluids.

FLUX - BRAZING, SOLDERING: Substance applied to surfaces to be joined by brazing or soldering to free them from oxides and facilitate good joint.

FLUX, MAGNETIC: Lines of force of a magnet.

FOAM LEAK DETECTOR: A system of soap bubbles or special foaming liquids brushed over joints and connections to locate leaks.

FOAMING: Formation of a foam in an oil-refrigerant mixture due to rapid evaporation of refrigerant dissolved in the oil. This is most likely to occur when the compressor starts and the pressure is suddenly reduced.

FOOT POUND: A unit of work. A foot pound is the amount of work done in lifting one pound one foot.

FORCE: Force is accumulated pressure and is expressed in pounds. If the pressure is 10 psi on a plate of 10 sq. in. area, the force is 100 pounds.

FORCED CONVECTION: Movement of fluid by mechanical force such as fans or pumps.

FORCE-FEED OILING: A lubrication system which uses a pump to force oil to surfaces of moving parts.

FREEZER ALARM: Device used in many freezers which sounds an alarm (bell or buzzer) when freezer temperature rises above safe limit.

FREEZER BURN: A condition applied to food which has not been properly wrapped and that has become hard, dry, and discolored.

FREEZE-UP: 1-The formation of ice in the refrigerant control device which may stop the flow of refrigerant into the evaporator. 2-Frost formation on a coil may stop the airflow through the coil.

FREEZING: Change of state from liquid to solid.

FREEZING POINT: The temperature at which a liquid will solidify upon removal of heat. The freezing temperature for water is 32 F. at atmospheric pressure.

FREON: Trade name for a family of synthetic chemical refrigerants manufactured by DuPont De Nemours Inc.

FROST BACK: Condition in which liquid refrigerant flows from evaporator into suction line; indicated by frost formation on suction line.

FROST CONTROL, AUTOMATIC: A control which automatically cycles refrigerating system based on frost formation on evaporator.

FROST CONTROL, MANUAL: A manual control used to change refrigerating system to produce defrosting conditions.

FROST CONTROL, SEMIAUTOMATIC: A control which starts defrost part of a cycle manually and then returns system to normal operation automatically.

FROST FREE REFRIGERATOR: A refrigerated cabinet which operates with an automatic defrost during each cycle.

FROSTING TYPE EVAPORATOR: A refrigerating system which maintains the evaporator at frosting temperatures during all phases of cycle.

FULL FLOATING: A mechanism construction in which a shaft is free to turn in all the parts in which it is inserted.

FUSE: Electrical safety device consisting of strip of fusible metal in circuit which melts when current is overloaded.

FUSIBLE PLUG: A plug or fitting made with a metal of a known low melting temperature, used as safety device to release pressures in case of fire.

GALVANIC ACTION: Corrosion action between two metals of different electronic activity. The action is increased in the presence of moisture.

GAS: Vapor phase or state of a substance.

GASKET: A resilient or flexible material used between mating surfaces of refrigerating unit parts or of refrigerator doors to provide a leakproof seal.

GASKET, FOAM: A joint sealing device made of rubber or plastic foam strips.

GAS - NONCONDENSIBLE: A gas which will not form into a liquid under pressure-temperature conditions.

GAS VALVE: Device for controlling flow of gas.

GAUGE, COMPOUND: Instrument for measuring pressures both below and above atmospheric pressure.

GAUGE, HIGH PRESSURE: Instrument for measuring pressures in range of 0 psig to 500 psig.

GAUGE, LOW PRESSURE: Instrument for measuring pressures in range of 0 psig and 50 psig.

GAUGE MANIFOLD: A device constructed to hold compound and high pressure gauges and valved to control flow of fluids through it.

GAUGE, VACUUM: Instrument used to measure pressures below atmospheric pressure.

GRAIN: A unit of weight and equal to one 7000th of a pound. It is used to indicate the amount of moisture in the air.

GRILLE: An ornamental or louvered opening placed at the end of an air passageway.

GROMMET: A plastic metal or rubber doughnut-shaped protector for wires or tubing as they pass through hole in object.

GROUND COIL: A heat exchanger buried in the ground which may be used either as an evaporator or as a condenser.

GROUND, SHORT CIRCUIT: A fault in an electrical circuit allowing electricity to flow into the metal parts of the structure.

GROUND WIRE: An electrical wire which will safely conduct electricity from a structure into the ground.

HALIDE REFRIGERANTS: Family of refrigerants containing halogen chemicals.

HALIDE TORCH: Type of torch used to detect halogen refrigerant leaks.

HASTELLOY: Trade name for a hard, non-corroding metal alloy.

HEAD PRESSURE: Pressure which exists in condensing side of refrigerating system.

HEAD PRESSURE CONTROL: Pressure operated control which opens electrical circuit if high side pressure becomes excessive.

HEAD, STATIC: Pressure of fluid expressed in terms of height of column of the fluid, such as water or mercury.

HEAD, VELOCITY: In flowing fluid, height of fluid equivalent to its velocity pressure.

HEAT: Form of energy the addition of which causes substances to rise in temperature; energy associated with random motion of molecules.

HEAT EXCHANGER: Device used to transfer heat from a warm or hot surface to a cold or cooler surface. Evaporators and condensers are heat exchangers.

HEAT LAG: When a substance is heated on one side, it takes time for the heat to travel through the substance. This time is called heat lag.

HEAT LEAKAGE: Flow of heat through a substance is called heat leakage.

HEAT LOAD: Amount of heat, measured in Btu, which is removed during a period of 24 hours.

HEAT OF COMPRESSION: Mechanical energy of pressure transformed into energy of heat.

HEAT OF FUSION: The heat released in changing a substance from a liquid state to a solid state. The heat of fusion of ice is 144 Btu per pound.

HEAT OF RESPIRATION: The process by which oxygen and carbohydrates are assimilated by a substance; also when carbon dioxide and water are given off by a substance.

HEAT PUMP: A compression cycle system used to supply heat to a temperature controlled space, which can also remove heat from the same space.

HEAT TRANSFER: Movement of heat from one body or substance to another. Heat may be transferred by radiation, conduction, convection or a combination of these three methods.

HEATING COIL: A heat transfer device which releases heat.

HEATING CONTROL: Device which controls temperature of heat transfer unit which releases heat.

HEATING VALUE: Amount of heat which may be obtained by burning a fuel. It is usually expressed in Btu per pound or Btu per gallon.

HEAVY ENDS, HYDROCARBON OILS: The heavy molecules or larger molecules of hydrocarbon oils.

HERMETIC MOTOR: Compressor drive motor sealed within same casing which contains compressor.

HERMETIC SYSTEM: Refrigeration system which has a compressor driven by a motor contained in compressor dome or housing.

HG - (MERCURY): Heavy silver-white metallic element; only metal that is liquid at ordinary room temperature. Symbol, Hg.

HIGH PRESSURE CUT-OUT: Electrical control switch operated by the high side pressure which automatically opens electrical circuit if too high head pressure or condensing pressure is reached.

HIGH SIDE: Parts of a refrigerating system which are under condensing or high side pressure.

HIGH SIDE FLOAT: Refrigerant control mechanism which controls the level of the liquid refrigerant in the high pressure side of mechanism.

HIGH VACUUM PUMP: Mechanism which can create vacuum in 1000 to 1 micron range.

HI-RE-LI SYSTEM: A patented heat pump cycle developed by Westinghouse Corp.

HOLLOW TUBE GASKET: Sealing device made of rubber or plastic with tubular cross section.

HONE: Fine-grit stone used for precision sharpening.

HORSEPOWER: A unit of power equal to 33,000 foot pounds of work per minute. One electrical horsepower equals 746 watts.

HOT GAS BYPASS: Piping system in refrigerating unit which moves hot refrigerant gas from condenser into low pressure side.

HOT GAS DEFROST: A defrosting system in which hot refrigerant gas from the high side is directed through evaporator for short period of time and at predetermined intervals in order to remove frost from evaporator.

HOT JUNCTION: That part of thermoelectric circuit which releases heat.

HOT WIRE: A resistance wire in an electrical relay which expands when heated and contracts when cooled.

HUMIDIFIERS: Device used to add to and control the humidity in a confined space.

HUMIDISTAT: An electrical control which is operated by changing humidity.

HUMIDITY: Moisture; dampness. Relative humidity is ratio of quantity of vapor present in air to greatest amount possible at given temperature.

HYDROLEN - TAR: A hydrocarbon by-product of oil industry. Used as a low melting temperature, waterproof sealing compound.

HYDROMETER: Floating instrument used to measure specific gravity of a liquid. Specific gravity is ratio of weight of any volume of a substance to weight of equal volume of substance used as a standard.

HYDRONIC: Type of heating system which circulates a heated fluid, usually water, through baseboard coils. Circulating pump is usually controlled by a thermostat.

HYGROMETER: An instrument used to measure degree of moisture in the atmosphere.

HYGROSCOPIC: Ability of a substance to absorb and retain moisture and change physical dimensions as its moisture content changes.

ICC - INTERSTATE COMMERCE COMMISSION: A government body which controls the design and construction of pressure containers.

ICE CREAM CABINET: Commercial refrigerator which operates at approximately 0 F. and is used for storage of ice cream.

ICE MELTING EQUIVALENT (I.M.E.) (ICE MELTING EFFECT): Amount of heat absorbed by melting ice at 32 F. is 144 Btu per pound of ice or 288,000 Btu per ton.

IDLER: A pulley used on some belt drives to provide the proper belt tension and to eliminate belt vibration.

IGNITION TRANSFORMER: A transformer designed to provide a high voltage current. Used in many heating systems to ignite fuel.

IMPELLER: Rotating part of a centrifugal pump.

INDUCED MAGNETISM: Ability of a magnetic field to produce magnetism in a metal.

INDUCTION MOTOR: An AC motor which operates on principle of rotating magnetic field. Rotor has no electrical connection, but receives electrical energy by transformer action from field windings.

INFRARED LAMP: An electrical device which emits infrared rays; invisible rays just beyond red in the visible spectrum.

INSULATION, THERMAL: Substance used to retard or slow flow of heat through wall or partition.

INTERMITTENT CYCLE: A cycle which repeats itself at different intervals.

IR DROP: An electrical term indicating the loss in a circuit expressed in amperes x resistance (I x R) or voltage drop.

ISOTHERMAL: Changes of volume or pressure under conditions of constant temperature.

ISOTHERMAL EXPANSION AND CONTRACTION: An action which takes place without a temperature change.

JOULE-THOMSON EFFECT: Change in temperature of a gas on expansion through a porous plug from a high pressure to a lower pressure.

JOURNAL, CRANKSHAFT: Part of shaft which contacts the bearing.

JUNCTION BOX: Group of electrical terminals housed in protective box or container.

KATA THERMOMETER: Large bulb alcohol thermometer used to measure air velocities or atmospheric conditions by means of cooling effect.

KELVIN SCALE (K): Thermometer scale on which unit of measurement equals the centigrade degree and according to which absolute zero is 0 deg., the equivalent of -273.16 deg. C. Water freezes at 273.16 deg. and boils at 373.16 deg.

KILOMETER: A metric unit of linear measurement = 1000 meters.

KILOWATT: Unit of electrical power, equal to 1000 watts.

LACQUER: A protective coating or finish which dries to form a film by evaporation of a volatile constituent.

LAMPS, STERI: A lamp which gives forth a high intensity ultraviolet ray and is used to kill bacteria. It is often used in food storage cabinets.

LAPPING: Smoothing a metal surface to high degree of refinement or accuracy using a fine abrasive.

LATENT HEAT: Heat energy absorbed in process of changing form of substance (melting, vaporization, fusion) without change in temperature or pressure.

LEAK DETECTOR: Device or instrument such as a halide torch, an electronic sniffer; or soap solution used to detect leaks.

LIMIT CONTROL: Control used to open or

close electrical circuits as temperature or pressure limits are reached.

LIQUID ABSORBENT: A chemical in liquid form which has the property to "take on" or absorb moisture.

LIQUID INDICATOR: Device located in liquid line which provides a glass window through which liquid flow may be observed.

LIQUID LINE: The tube which carries liquid refrigerant from the condenser or liquid receiver to the refrigerant control mechanism.

LIQUID NITROGEN: Nitrogen in liquid form which is used as a low temperature refrigerant in chemical (or expendable) refrigerating systems.

LIQUID RECEIVER: Cylinder connected to condenser outlet for storage of liquid refrigerant in a system.

LIQUID-VAPOR VALVE REFRIGERANT CYLINDER: A dual hand valve on refrigerant cylinders which is used to release either gas or liquid refrigerant from the cylinder.

LITHARGE: Lead powder mixed with glycerine to seal pipe thread joints.

LIQUOR: Solution used in absorption refrigeration.

LITER: Metric unit of volume which equals 61.03 cubic inches.

LOW SIDE: That portion of a refrigerating system which is under the lowest evaporating pressure.

LOW SIDE FLOAT VALVE: Refrigerant control valve operated by level of liquid refrigerant in low pressure side of system.

LOW SIDE PRESSURE: Pressure in cooling side of refrigerating cycle.

LOW SIDE PRESSURE CONTROL: Device used to keep low side evaporating pressure from dropping below certain pressure.

LP FUEL: Liquefied petroleum which is used as a fuel gas.

MAGNETIC CLUTCH: A device operated by magnetism to connect or disconnect a power drive.

MAGNETIC FIELD: Space in which magnetic lines of force exist.

MAGNETIC GASKET: A sealing material which adheres due to small magnets inserted in gasket.

MAGNETISM: An electronic force which causes a magnet to attract items made of steel.

MANIFOLD, SERVICE: A device equipped with gauges and manual valves, used by serviceman to service refrigerating systems.

MANOMETER: Instrument for measuring pressure of gases and vapors. Gas pressure is balanced against column of liquid such as mercury, in U-shaped tube.

MASS: A quantity of matter cohering together to make one body which is usually of indefinite shape.

MEAN EFFECTIVE PRESSURE (M.E.P.): Average pressure on a surface when a changing pressure condition exists.

MECHANICAL CYCLE: Cycle which is a repetitive series of mechanical events.

MEGOHM: One megohm is equal to a million ohms.

MEGOHMMETER: An instrument for measuring extremely high resistances (in the millions of ohms ranges).

MELTING POINT: Temperature at atmospheric pressure, at which a substance will melt.

MERCOID BULB: An electrical circuit switch which uses a small quantity of mercury in a sealed glass tube to make or break electrical contact with terminals within the tube.

METER: Metric unit of linear measurement equal to 39.37 inches.

METHANOL DRIER: Alcohol type chemical used to change water in refrigerating system into a nonfreezing solution.

METHYL CHLORIDE (R-40): A chemical once commonly used as a refrigerant. The chemical formula is CH_3Cl. Cylinder color code is orange. The boiling point at atmospheric pressure is -10.4 F.

METRIC SYSTEM: A decimal system of measures and weights, based on the meter and gram. Length of one meter, 39.37 in.

MICRO: One millionth part of unit specified.

MICROFARAD: Unit of condenser electrical capacity equal to one millionth of a farad.

MICROMETER: A precision measuring instrument used for making measurements accurate to .001 to .0001 in.

MICRON: Unit of length in metric system; a thousandth part of one millimeter.

MICRON GAUGE: Instrument for measuring vacuums very close to a perfect vacuum.

MILLI: A combining form denoting one thousandth; example, millivolt, one thousandth of a volt.

MODULATING: A type of device or control which tends to adjust by increments (minute changes) rather than by either full on or full off operation.

MODULATING REFRIGERATION CYCLE: Refrigerating system of variable capacity.

MOISTURE DETERMINATION: An action using instruments and calculations to measure the relative or absolute moisture in an air conditioned space.

MOISTURE INDICATOR: Instrument used to measure moisture content of a refrigerant.

MOLECULE: Smallest portion of an element or compound that retains chemical identity with the substance in mass.

MOLLIERS DIAGRAM: Graph of refrigerant pressure, heat and temperature properties.

MONEL: A trademark name for metal alloy consisting chiefly of copper and nickel.

MONITOR TOP: Unit built by General Electric which had a cylindrical condenser surrounding the motor-compressor, mounted on top of the cabinet.

MONOCHLORODIFLUOROMETHANE: A refrigerant better known as Freon 12 or R-22. Chemical formula is $CHClF_2$. Cylinder color code is green.

MOTOR - 2-POLE: A 3600 rpm electric motor (synchronous speed).

MOTOR - 4-POLE: A 1800 rpm electric motor (synchronous speed).

MOTOR, CAPACITOR: A single-phase induction motor with an auxiliary starting winding connected in series with a condenser (capacitor) for better starting characteristics.

MOTOR BURNOUT: Condition in which the insulation of electric motor has deteriorated by overheating.

MOTOR CONTROL: Device to start and/or stop a motor at certain temperature or pressure conditions.

MOTOR STARTER: High capacity electric switches usually operated by electromagnets.

MUFFLER, COMPRESSOR: Sound absorber chamber in refrigeration system used to reduce sound of gas pulsations.

MULLION: Stationary part of a structure between two doors.

MULLION HEATER: An electrical heating element mounted in the mullion and used to keep mullion from sweating or frosting.

MULTIPLE EVAPORATOR SYSTEM: Refrigerating system with two or more evaporators connected in parallel.

MULTIPLE SYSTEM: Refrigerating mechanism in which several evaporators are connected to one condensing unit.

NATURAL CONVECTION: Movement of a fluid caused by temperature differences (density changes).

NEOPRENE: A synthetic rubber which is resistant to hydrocarbon oil and gas.

NEUTRALIZER: Substance used to counteract acids, in refrigeration system.

NEUTRON: That part of an atom core which has no electrical potential; electrically neutral.

NO-FROST FREEZER: A low temperature refrigerator-cabinet in which no frost or ice collects on produce stored in cabinet.

NOMINAL SIZE TUBING: Tubing measurement which has an inside diameter the same as iron pipe of the same stated size.

NON-CODE INSTALLATION: A functional refrigerating system installed where there are no local, state, or national refrigeration codes in force.

NONCONDENSABLE GAS: Gas which does not change into a liquid at operating temperatures and pressures.

NONFERROUS: Group of metals and metal alloys which contain no iron.

NONFROSTING EVAPORATOR: An evaporator which never collects frost or ice on its surface.

NORMAL CHARGE: The thermal element charge which is part liquid and part gas under all operating conditions.

NORTH POLE, MAGNETIC: End of magnet from which magnetic lines of force flow.

OFF CYCLE: That part of a refrigeration cycle when the system is not operating.

OHM (R): Unit of measurement of electrical resistance. One ohm exists when one volt causes a flow of one ampere.

OHMMETER: An instrument for measuring resistance in ohms.

OHMS LAW: Mathematical relationship between voltage, current and resistance in an electric circuit, discovered by George Simon Ohm. It is stated as follows: voltage (E = Amperes (I) x Ohms (R); or E = I x R.

OIL BINDING: Physical condition when an oil layer on top of refrigerant liquid hinders it from evaporating at its normal pressure-temperature condition.

OIL, REFRIGERATION: Specially prepared oil used in refrigerator mechanism circulates to some extent with refrigerant. The oil must be dry (entirely free of moisture), otherwise, moisture will condense out and freeze in the refrigerant control and may cause refrigerant mechanism to fail. An oil classified as a refrigerant oil must be free of moisture and other contaminants.

OIL RINGS: Expanding rings mounted in grooves and piston; designed to prevent oil from moving into compression chamber.

OIL SEPARATOR: Device used to remove oil from gaseous refrigerant.

OPEN CIRCUIT: An interrupted electrical circuit which stops flow of electricity.

OPEN DISPLAY CASE: Commercial refrigerator designed to maintain its contents at refrigerating temperatures even though the contents are in an open case.

OPEN TYPE SYSTEM: A refrigerating system which uses a belt-driven compressor or a coupling-driven compressor.

ORIFICE: Accurate size opening for controlling fluid flow.

OSCILLOSCOPE: A flourescent coated tube which visually shows an electrical wave.

OVERLOAD: Load greater than load for which system or mechanism was intended.

OVERLOAD PROTECTOR: A device, either temperature, pressure, or current operated, which will stop operation of unit if dangerous conditions arise.

OZONE: A gaseous form of oxygen usually obtained by silent discharge of electricity in oxygen or air.

PARTIAL PRESSURES: Condition where two or more gases occupy a space and each one creates part of the total pressure.

PASCAL'S LAW: A pressure imposed upon a fluid is transmitted equally in all directions.

PELETIER EFFECT: When direct current is passed through two adjacent metals one junction will become cooler and the other will become warmer. This principle is the basis of thermoelectric refrigeration.

PERMANENT MAGNET: A material which has its molecules aligned and has its own magnetic field; bar of metal which has been permanently magnetized.

PHOTOELECTRICITY: A physical action wherein an electrical flow is generated by light waves.

PINCH-OFF TOOL: Device used to press walls of a tubing together until fluid flow ceases.

PISTON: Close fitting part which moves up and down in a cylinder.

PISTON DISPLACEMENT: Volume displaced by piston as it travels length of stroke.

PITOT TUBE: Tube used to measure air velocities.

PLENUM CHAMBER: Chamber or container for moving air or other gas under a slight positive pressure.

POLYPHASE MOTOR: Electrical motor designed to be used with three-phase electrical circuit.

POLYSTYRENE: Plastic used as an insulation in some refrigerator cabinet structures.

PONDED ROOF: Flat roof designed to hold quantity of water which acts as a cooling device.

PORCELAIN: Ceramic china-like coating applied to steel surfaces.

POTENTIAL, ELECTRICAL: The electrical force which moves, or attempts to move, electrons along a conductor or resistance.

POTENTIAL RELAY VOLTAGE: Electrical switch which is operated by voltage changes in electromagnet.

POTENTIOMETER: Instrument for measuring or controlling electrical potential.

POUR POINT (OIL): Lowest temperature at which oil will pour or flow.

POWER: Time rate at which work is done or energy emitted; source or means of supplying energy.

POWER ELEMENT: Sensitive element of a temperature operated control.

POWER FACTOR: Correction coefficient for AC power necessary because of changing current and voltage values.

PRESSURE: An energy impact on a unit area; force or thrust exerted on a surface.

PRESSURE DROP: The pressure difference at two ends of a circuit, or part of a circuit, the two sides of a filter, or the pressure difference between the high side and low side in a refrigerator mechanism.

PRESSURE LIMITER: Device which remains closed until a certain pressure is reached and then opens and releases fluid to another part of system.

PRESSURE-HEAT DIAGRAM: Graph of refrigerant pressure, heat and temperature properties. (Mollier's diagram.)

PRESSURE MOTOR CONTROL: A device which opens and closes an electrical circuit as pressures change to desired pressures.

PRESSURE OPERATED ALTITUDE (POA) VALVE: Device which maintains a constant low side pressure independent of altitude of operation.

PRESSURE REGULATOR, EVAPORATOR: An automatic pressure regulating valve. Mounted in suction line between evaporator outlet and compressor inlet. Its purpose is to maintain a predetermined pressure and temperature in the evaporator.

PRESSURE SUCTION: Pressure in low pressure side of a refrigerating system.

PRESSURE WATER VALVE: Device used to control water flow which is responsive to head pressure of refrigerating system.

PRIMARY CONTROL: Device which directly controls operation of heating system.

PROCESS TUBE: Length of tubing fastened to hermetic unit dome, used for servicing unit.

PROPANE: Volatile hydrocarbon used as a fuel, also as a refrigerant.

PROTECTOR, CIRCUIT: An electrical device which will open an electrical circuit if excessive electrical conditions occur.

PROTON: Positive charged particle of an atom.

PSI: A symbol or initials used to indicate pressure measured in pounds per square inch.

PSIA: A symbol or initials used to indicate pressure measured in pounds per square inch absolute. Absolute pressure equals gauge pressure plus atmospheric pressure.

PSIG: A symbol or initials used to indicate pressure in pounds per square inch gauge. The "g" indicates that it is gauge pressure and not absolute pressure.

PSYCHROMETER OR WET BULB HYGROMETER: An instrument for measuring the relative humidity of atmospheric air.

PSYCHROMETRIC CHART: A chart that shows relationship between the temperature, pressure and moisture content of the air.

PSYCHROMETRIC MEASUREMENT: Measurement of temperature pressure, and humidity using a psychrometric chart.

PULL DOWN: An expression indicating action of removing refrigerant from all or a part of refrigerating system.

PUMP DOWN: The act of using a compressor or a pump to reduce the pressure in a container or a system.

PURGING: Releasing compressed gas to atmosphere through some part or parts for the purpose of removing contaminants from that part or parts.

PYROMETER: Instrument for measuring high temperatures.

QUENCHING: Submerging hot solid object in cooling fluid.

QUICK CONNECT COUPLING: A device which permits easy, fast, connecting of two fluid lines.

R-11, TRICHLOROMONOFLUOROMETHANE: Low pressure, synthetic chemical refrigerant which is also used as a cleaning fluid.

R-12, DICHLORODIFLUOROMETHANE: A popular refrigerant known as Freon 12.

R-22, MONOCHLORODIFLUOROMETHANE: Synthetic chemical refrigerant.

R-40, Methyl Chloride: Refrigerant which was used extensively in the 1920's and 1930's.

R-113, TRICHLOROTRIFLUOROETHANE: Synthetic chemical refrigerant.

R-160, ETHYL CHLORIDE: Refrigerant which is seldom used at present time.

R-170, ETHANE: Low temperature application refrigerant.

R-290, PROPANE: Low temperature application refrigerant.

R-500: Refrigerant which is azeotropic mixture of R-12 and R-152a.

R-502: Refrigerant which is azeotropic mixture of R-22 and R-115.

R-503: Refrigerant which is azeotropic mixture of R-23 and R-13.

R-504: Refrigerant which is azeotropic mixture of R-32 and R-115.

R-600, BUTANE: Low temperature application refrigerant; also used as a fuel.

R-611, METHYL FORMATE: Low pressure refrigerant.

R-717, AMMONIA: Popular refrigerant for industrial refrigerating systems; also a popular absorption system refrigerant.

R-764, SULPHUR DIOXIDE: Low pressure refrigerant used extensively in 1920's and 1930's. Not in use at present; chemical is often used as an industrial bleaching agent.

RADIAL COMMUTATOR: Electrical contact surface on a rotor which is perpendicular or at right angles to the shaft center line.

RADIANT HEATING: Heating system in which warm or hot surfaces are used to radiate heat into the space to be conditioned.

RADIATION: Transfer of heat by heat rays.

RANGE: Pressure or temperature settings of a control; change within limits.

RANKIN SCALE: Name given the absolute (Fahrenheit) scale. Zero on this scale is -460 F.

RECEIVER-DRIER: A cylinder in a refrigerating system for storing liquid refrigerant and which also holds a quantity of desiccant.

RECEIVER HEATING ELEMENT: Electrical resistance mounted in or around liquid receiver, used to maintain head pressures when ambient temperature is at freezing or below freezing.

RECIPROCATING: Action in which the motion is back and forth in a straight line.

RECORDING AMMETER: Electrical instrument which uses a pen to record amount of current flow on a moving paper chart.

RECORDING THERMOMETER: Temperature measuring instrument which has a pen marking a moving chart.

RECTIFIER, ELECTRIC: An electrical device for converting AC into DC.

REED VALVE: Thin flat tempered steel plate fastened at one end.

REFRIGERANT: Substance used in refrigerating mechanism to absorb heat in evaporator coil by change of state from a liquid to a gas, and to release its heat in a condenser as the substance returns from the gaseous state back to a liquid state.

REFRIGERANT CHARGE: Quantity of refrigerant in a system.

REFRIGERANT CONTROL: Device which meters refrigerant and maintains pressure difference between high pressure and low pressure side of mechanical refrigerating system while unit is running.

REGISTER: Combination grille and damper assembly covering on an air opening or end of an air duct.

RELATIVE HUMIDITY: Ratio of amount of water vapor present in air to greatest amount possible at same temperature.

RELAY: Electrical mechanism which uses small current in control circuit to operate a valve switch in operating circuit.

RELIEF VALVE: Safety device designed to open before dangerous pressure is reached.

REMOTE POWER ELEMENT CONTROL: Device with sensing element located apart from operating mechanism.

REMOTE SYSTEM: Refrigerating system which has condensing unit located outside and separate from refrigerator cabinet.

REPULSION-START INDUCTION MOTOR: Type of motor which has an electrical winding on the rotor for starting purposes.

RESISTANCE, (R) ELECTRICAL: The difficulty electrons encounter moving through a conductor or substance.

REVERSE CYCLE DEFROST: Method of heating evaporator for defrosting purposes by using valves to move hot gas from compressor into evaporator.

REVERSING VALVE: Device used to reverse direction of the refrigerant flow depending upon whether heating or cooling is desired.

RINGELMANN SCALE: Measuring device for determing smoke density.

RISER VALVE: Device used to manually control flow of refrigerant in vertical piping.

ROTARY BLADE COMPRESSOR: Mechanism for pumping fluid by revolving blades inside cylindrical housing.

ROTARY COMPRESSOR: Mechanism which pumps fluid by using rotating motion.

ROTOR: Rotating part of a mechanism.

RUNNING WINDING: Electrical winding of motor which has current flowing through it during normal operation of motor.

SADDLE VALVE (TAP-A-LINE): Valve body shaped so it may be silver brazed to refrigerant tubing surface.

SAFETY CONTROL: Device which will stop the refrigerating unit if unsafe pressures and/or temperatures are reached.

SAFETY MOTOR CONTROL: Electrical device used to open circuit if the temperature, pressure, and/or the current flow exceed safe conditions.

SAFETY PLUG: Device which will release the contents of a container above normal pressure conditions and before rupture pressures are reached.

SATURATION: Condition existing when substance contains maximum of another substance for that temperature and pressure.

SCAVENGER PUMP: Mechanism used to remove fluid from sump or container.

SCHRADER VALVE: Spring loaded device which permits fluid flow in one direction when a center pin is depressed; in other direction when a pressure difference exists.

SCOTCH YOKE: Mechanism used to change reciprocating motion into rotary motion or vice-versa. Used to connect crankshaft to piston in refrigeration compressor.

SEALED UNIT: (See Hermetic System.) A motor-compressor assembly in which motor and compressor operate inside sealed dome or housing.

SEAL LEAK: Escape of oil and/or refrigerant at the junction where shaft enters housing.

SEAL, SHAFT: A device used to prevent leakage between shaft and housing.

SECONDARY REFRIGERATING SYSTEM: Refrigerating system in which condenser is cooled by evaporator of another or primary refrigerating system.

SECOND LAW OF THERMODYNAMICS: Heat will flow only from material at certain temperature to material at lower temperature.

SEEBECK EFFECT: When two different adjacent metals are heated, an electric current is generated.

SELF-INDUCTANCE: Magnetic field induced in conductor carrying the current.

SEMICONDUCTOR: A material that has electrical properties of current flow, between a conductor and an insulator.

SENSIBLE HEAT: Heat which causes a change in temperature of a substance.

SENSOR: A material or device which goes through a physical change or an electronic characteristic change as the conditions change.

SEPARATOR, OIL: A device used to separate refrigerant oil from refrigerant gas and return the oil to crankcase of compressor.

SEQUENCE CONTROLS: Group of devices which act in series or in time order.

SERVEL SYSTEM: One type of continuous operation absorption refrigerating system.

SERVICEABLE HERMETIC: Hermetic unit housing containing motor and compressor assembled by use of bolts or threads.

SERVICE VALVE: A device to be attached to system which provides opening for gauges and/or charging lines. Also provides means of shutting off or opening gauge and charging ports, and controlling refrigerant flow in system.

SHADED POLE MOTOR: A small AC motor used for light start loads. Has no brushes or commutator.

SHARP FREEZING: Refrigeration at temperature slightly below freezing, with moderate air circulation.

SHELL-AND-TUBE FLOODED EVAPORATOR: Device which flows water through tubes built into cylindrical evaporator or vice-versa.

SHELL TYPE CONDENSER: Cylinder or receiver which contains condensing water coils or tubes.

SHORT CIRCUIT: An electrical condition where part of circuit touches another part of circuit and causes all or part of current to take wrong path.

SHORT CYCLING: Refrigerating system that starts and stops more frequently than it should.

SHROUD: Housing over condenser or evaporator.

SIGHT GLASS: Glass tube or glass window in refrigerating mechanism which shows amount of refrigerant, or oil in system; or, pressure of gas bubbles in liquid line.

SILICA GEL: Chemical compound used as a drier, which has ability to absorb moisture when heated, moisture is released and compound may be reused.

SILICON CONTROLLED RECTIFIER (SCR): Electronic semiconductor which contains silicon.

SILVER BRAZING: Brazing process in which brazing alloy contains some silver as part of joining alloy.

SINE WAVE, AC CURRENT: Wave form of single frequency alternating current; wave whose displacement is sine of angle proportional to time or distance.

SINGLE-PHASE MOTOR: Electric motor which operates on single-phase alternating current.

SINGLE-POLE, DOUBLE-THROW SWITCH, SPDT: Electric switch with one blade and two contact points.

SINGLE-POLE, SINGLE-THROW SWITCH, SPST: Electric switch with one blade and one contact point.

SINTERED OIL BEARING: Porous bearing metal, usually bronze, and which has oil in pores of bearing metal.

SLING PSYCHROMETER: Humidity measuring device with wet and dry bulb thermometers, which is moved rapidly through air when measuring humidity.

SLUG: A unit of mass equal to the weight (English units) of object divided by 32.2 (acceleration due to the force of gravity).

SMOKE TEST: Test made to determine completeness of combustion.

SOLAR HEAT: Heat from visible and invisible energy waves from the sun.

SOLDERING: Joining two metals by adhesion of a low melting temperature metal (less than 800 F.).

SOLENOID VALVE: Electromagnet with a moving core which serves as a valve, or operates a valve.

SOLID ABSORBENT REFRIGERATION: Refrigerating system which uses solid substance as absorber of the refrigerant during cooling part of cycle and releases refrigerant when heated during generating part of cycle.

SOUTH POLE, MAGNETIC: That part of magnet into which magnetic flux lines flow.

SPECIFIC GRAVITY: Weight of a liquid compared to water which is assigned value of 1.0.

SPECIFIC HEAT: Ratio of quantity of heat required to raise temperature of a body one-degree to that required to raise temperature of equal mass of water one degree.

SPECIFIC VOLUME: Volume per unit mass of a substance.

SPLASH SYSTEM, OILING: Method of lubricating moving parts by agitating or splashing oil.

SPLIT-PHASE MOTOR: Motor with two stator windings. Winding in use while starting is disconnected by centrifugal switch after motor attains speed, then motor operates on other winding.

SPLIT SYSTEM: Refrigeration or air conditioning installation which places condensing unit outside or remote from evaporator. Also applicable to heat pump installations.

SPRAY COOLING: Method of refrigerating by spraying refrigerant inside of evaporator or by spraying refrigerated water.

SQUIRREL CAGE: Fan which has blades parallel to fan axis and moves air at right angles or perpendicular to fan axis.

STANDARD ATMOSPHERE: Condition when air is at 14.7 psia pressure, at 68 F. temperature.

STANDARD CONDITIONS: Used as a basis for air conditioning calculations. Temperature of 68 degrees F., pressure of 29.92 inches of Hg and relative humidity of 30 percent.

STARTING RELAY: An electrical device which connects and/or disconnects starting winding of electric motor.

STARTING WINDING: Winding in electric motor used only during brief period when motor is starting.

STATIONARY BLADE COMPRESSOR: A rotary pump which uses blade inside pump to separate intake chamber from exhaust chamber.

STATOR, MOTOR: Stationary part of electric motor.

STEAM: Water in vapor state.

STEAM HEATING: Heating system in which steam from a boiler is conducted to radiators in space to be heated.

STEAM JET REFRIGERATION: Refrigerating system which uses a steam venturi to create high vacuum (low pressure) on a water container causing water to evaporate at low temperature.

STELLITE: Trade name for metal alloy which is very hard.

STETHOSCOPE: Instrument used to detect sounds.

STOKER: Machine used to supply a furnace with coal.

STRAINER: Device such as a screen or filter used to retain solid particles while liquid passes through.

STRATIFICATION OF AIR: Condition in which there is little or no air movement in room; air lies in temperature layers.

STRIKE: Door part of a door latch.

SUBCOOLING: Cooling of liquid refrigerant below its condensing temperature.

SUBLIMATION: Condition where a substance changes from a solid to a gas without becoming a liquid.

SUCTION LINE: Tube or pipe used to carry refrigerant gas from evaporator to compressor.

SUCTION PRESSURE CONTROL VALVE: Device located in the suction line which maintains constant pressure in evaporator during running portion of cycle.

SUCTION SERVICE VALVE: A two-way manual-operated valve located at the inlet to compressor, which controls suction gas flow and is used to service unit.

SULFUR DIOXIDE: Gas once commonly used as a refrigerant. Refrigerant number is R-764; chemical formula is SO_2. Cylinder color code, black; boiling point at atmospheric pressure 14 F.

SUPERHEAT: Temperature of vapor above boiling temperature of its liquid at that pressure.

SUPERHEATER: Heat exchanger arranged to cool liquid going to evaporator using this heat to superheat vapor leaving evaporator.

SURFACE PLATE: Tool with a very accurate flat surface, used for measuring purposes, and for lapping flat surfaces.

SURGE: Modulating action of temperature or pressure before it reaches its final value or setting.

SURGE TANK: Container connected to a refrigerating system which increases gas volume and reduces rate of pressure change.

SWAGING: Enlarging one tube end so end of other tube of same size will fit within.

SWASH PLATE-WOBBLE PLATE: Device used to change rotary motion to reciprocating motion, used in some refrigeration compressors.

SWEATING: This term is used two different ways in refrigeration work: 1-Condensation of moisture from air on cold surface. 2-Method of soldering in which the parts to be joined are first coated with a thin layer of solder.

SWEET WATER: Term sometimes used to describe tap water.

SYLPHON SEAL: Corrugated metal tubing used to hold seal ring and provide leakproof connection between seal ring and compressor body or shaft.

SYNTHETIC RUBBER, NEOPRENE: Soft resilient material made of a synthetic chemical compound.

TAP-A-LINE: Device used to puncture or tap a line where there are no service valves available; sometimes called a saddle valve.

TAP DRILL: Drill used to form hole prior to placing threads in hole. The drill is the size of the root diameter of tap threads.

TAP (SCREW THREAD): Tool used to cut internal threads.

TEFLON: Synthetic rubber material often used for O rings.

TEMPERATURE: Degree of hotness or coldness as measured by a thermometer; measurement of speed of motion of molecules.

TEMPERATURE HUMIDITY INDEX: Actual temperature and humidity of sample of air, compared to air at standard conditions.

TEST LIGHT: Light provided with test leads, used to test or probe electrical circuits to determine if they are alive.

THERM: Quantity of heat equivalent to 100,000 Btu.

THERMAL RELAY (HOT WIRE RELAY): Electrical control used to actuate a refrigeration system. This system uses a wire to convert electrical energy into heat energy.

THERMISTOR: Material called a semiconductor, which is between a conductor and an insulator, which has electrical resistance that varies with temperature.

THERMOCOUPLE: Device which generates electricity, using principle that if two dissimilar metals are welded together and junction is heated, a voltage will develop across open ends.

THERMOCOUPLE THERMOMETER: Electrical instrument using thermocouple as source of electrical flow, connected to milliammeter calibrated in temperature degrees.

THERMODISK DEFROST CONTROL: Electrical switch with bimetal disk which is controlled by electrical energy.

THERMODYNAMICS: Science which deals with mechanical action or relations of heat.

THERMOELECTRIC REFRIGERATION: A refrigerator mechanism which depends on Peletier effect. Direct current flowing through electrical junction between dissimilar metals provides heating or cooling effect depending on direction of flow of current.

THERMOMETER: Device for measuring temperatures.

THERMOMODULE: Number of thermocouples used in parallel to achieve low temperatures.

THERMOSTAT: Device responsive to ambient temperature conditions.

THERMOSTATIC CONTROL: Device which operates system or part of system based on temperature changes.

THERMOSTATIC EXPANSION VALVE: A control valve operated by temperature and pressure within evaporator coil, which controls flow of refrigerant. Control bulb is attached to outlet of coil.

THERMOSTATIC MOTOR CONTROL: Device used to control cycling of unit through use of control bulb attached to evaporator.

THERMOSTATIC VALVE: Valve controlled by thermostatic elements.

THERMOSTATIC WATER VALVE: Valve used to control flow of water through system, actuated by temperature difference. Used in units such as water-cooled compressor or condenser.

THREE-PHASE: Operating by means of combination of three alternating current circuits which differ in phase by one third of a cycle.

THROTTLING: Expansion of gas through orifice or controlled opening without gas performing any work in expansion process.

TIMERS: Mechanism used to control on and off times of an electrical circuit.

TIMER-THERMOSTAT: Thermostat control which includes a clock mechanism. Unit automatically controls room temperature and changes it according to time of day.

TON OF REFRIGERATION: Refrigerating effect equal to the melting of one ton of ice in 24 hours. This may be expressed as follows:

$$288,000 \text{ Btu/24 hours}$$
$$12,000 \text{ Btu/1 hour}$$
$$200 \text{ Btu/minute}$$

TON REFRIGERATION UNIT: Unit which removes same amount of heat in 24 hours as melting of one ton of ice.

TORQUE: Turning or twisting force.

TORQUE WRENCHES: Wrench which may be used to measure torque or pressure applied to a nut or bolt.

TRANSDUCER: Device actuated by power from one system and supplies power in another form to second system.

TRANSFORMER: Device which transfers electrical energy from primary circuit, into variations of voltage in secondary circuit, by electromagnetic induction.

TRANSFORMER-RECTIFIER: Combination transformer and rectifier in which input in AC may be varied and then rectified into DC.

TRANSISTOR: Electronic device commonly used for amplification, similar in use to electron tube. Depends on conducting properties of semiconductors in which electrons moving in one direction are considered as leaving holes that serve as carriers of positive electricity in opposite direction.

TRICHLOROTRIFLUOROETHANE: Complete name of refrigerant R-113. Group I refrigerant in rather common use. Chemical compounds which make up this refrigerant are chlorine, fluorine, and ethane.

TUBE, CONSTRICTED: Tubing that is reduced in diameter.

TUBE-WITHIN-A-TUBE: A water-cooled condensing unit in which a small tube is placed inside large unit. Refrigerant passes through one tube; water through the other.

TUBING: Fluid carrying pipe which has a thin wall.

TRIPLE POINT: Pressure temperature condition in which a substance is in equilibrium in solid, liquid and vapor states.

TRUCK, REFRIGERATED: Commercial vehicle equipped to maintain below atmospheric temperatures.

TWO-TEMPERATURE VALVE: Pressure opened valve used in suction line, on multiple refrigerator installations which maintains evaporators in system at different temperatures.

ULTRAVIOLET: Invisible radiation waves with frequencies shorter than wave lengths of visible light and longer than X-Ray.

UNIVERSAL MOTOR: Electric motor which will operate on both AC and DC.

URETHANE FOAM: Type of insulation which is foamed in between inner and outer walls of display case.

VACUUM: Reduction in pressure below atmospheric pressure.

VACUUM CONTROL SYSTEMS: In many automobile air conditioning systems, intake manifold vacuum is used to operate dampers and controls in system.

VACUUM PUMP: Special high efficiency compressor used for creating high vacuums for testing or drying purposes.

VALVE: Device used for controlling fluid flow.

VALVE, EXPANSION: Type of refrigerant control which maintains pressure difference between high side and low side pressure in refrigerating mechanism. Valve is caused to operate by pressure in low or suction side. Often referred to as an automatic expansion valve or AEV.

VALVE PLATE: Part of compressor located between top of compressor body and head which contains compressor valves.

VALVE, SERVICE: Device used by service technicians to check pressures and charge refrigerating units.

VALVE, SOLENOID: Valve actuated by magnetic action by means of an electrically energized coil.

VALVE, SUCTION: Valve in refrigeration compressor which allows vaporized refrigerant to enter cylinder from suction line and prevents its return.

VALVES, WATER: Most water cooling units are supplied with water valves. These valves provide a flow of water to cool the system while it is running. Most water valves are controlled by solenoids.

VAPOR: Word usually used to denote vaporized refrigerant rather than the word gas.

VAPOR BARRIER: Thin plastic or metal foil sheet used in air conditioned structures to prevent water vapor from penetrating insulating material.

VAPOR CHARGED: Lines and component parts of system which are charged at the factory.

VAPOR LOCK: Condition where liquid is trapped in line because of bend or improper installation which prevents the vapor from flowing.

VAPOR PRESSURE: Pressure impassed by either a vapor or gas.

VAPOR PRESSURE CURVE: Graphic presentation of various pressures produced by refrigerant under various temperatures.

VAPOR, SATURATED: A vapor condition which will result in condensation into droplets of liquid as vapor temperature is reduced.

VARIABLE PITCH PULLEY: Pulley which can be adjusted to provide different pulley ratios.

V-BELT: Type of belt that is commonly used in refrigeration work. It has a contact surface which is in the shape of letter V.

V-BLOCK: V-shaped groove in metal block used to hold shaft.

VELOCIMETER: Instrument used to measure air velocities using a direct reading air speed indicating dial.

VISCOSITY: Term used to describe resistance of flow of fluids.

VOLATILE LIQUID: Liquid which evaporates at low temperature and pressure.

VOLTAGE: Term used to indicate the electrical potential or electromotive force in an electrical circuit. It is voltage or electrical pressure which causes current to flow.

VOLTAGE CONTROL: It is necessary to provide some electrical circuits with uniform or constant voltage. Electronic devices used for this purpose are called voltage controls.

VOLTMETER: Instrument for measuring voltage action in electrical circuit.

VOLUMETRIC EFFICIENCY: Term used to express the relationship between the actual performance of a compressor or of a vacuum pump and calculated performance of the pump based on its displacement versus its actual pumping ability.

VORTEX TUBE: Mechanism for cooling or refrigerating which accomplishes cooling effect by releasing compressed air through specially designed opening. Air expands in rapidly spiraling column of air which separates slow moving molecules (cool) from fast moving molecules (hot).

VORTEX TUBE REFRIGERATION: Refrigerating or cooling devices using principle of vortex tube, as in mining suits.

WALK-IN COOLER: Large commercial refrigerated space kept below room temperature. Often found in large supermarkets or wholesale meat distribution centers.

WATER-COOLED CONDENSER: Condensing unit which is cooled through use of water.

WATER DEFROSTING: Use of water to melt ice and frost from evaporator during off-cycle.

WATT: Unit of electrical power.

WAX: Ingredient in many lubricating oils which may separate out if cooled sufficiently.

WET BULB: Device used in measurement of relative humidity. Evaporation of moisture lowers temperature of wet bulb compared to dry bulb temperature in same area.

WET CELL BATTERY: Cell or connected group of cells that converts chemical energy into electrical energy by reversible chemical reactions.

WINDOW UNIT: Commonly used when referring to air conditioners which are placed in a window. Normally a domestic application.

WOBBLE PLATE-SWASH PLATE: Type of compressor designed by General Motors to compress gas, having pistons with piston motion parallel to crankshaft.

WOODRUFF KEY: Device used to align and hold a flywheel, pulley or other rotating mechanism on a shaft, often half-moon in shape.

ZERO IZE: Trade name for dry ice. See Dry Ice.

INDEX